Arlene M Barr

STRONG AND ELWYN'S

HUMAN NEUROANATOMY

Strong and Elwyn's

HUMAN NEUROANATOMY

by RAYMOND C. TRUEX

Professor of Anatomy, Hahnemann Medical College

FOURTH EDITION

THE WILLIAMS & WILKINS COMPANY

Baltimore • 1959

Published May, 1943
Reprinted December, 1943
Reprinted December, 1945
Reprinted December, 1946
Second Edition, 1948
Reprinted June, 1951
Third Edition, 1953
Fourth Edition, 1959
Reprinted August, 1960

Made in the United States of America

Library of Congress
Catalog Card Number
59-6568

COMPOSED AND PRINTED AT THE
WAVERLY PRESS, INC.
BALTIMORE 2, MD., U.S.A.

PREFACE TO FOURTH EDITION

The First Edition of Strong and Elwyn's Human Neuroanatomy was published in 1943. Professor Adolph Elwyn, with the able assistance of his wife, Frances H. Elwyn, made further changes in both the text and illustrative materials of the Second and Third Editions which appeared in 1948 and 1953 respectively. The text material in the present revision was similarly rearranged, grafted, and pruned. Much of the text material in the third edition remains. Major changes were incorporated in Chapters I and XIII, while minor revisions were made in each of the remaining chapters. It is imperative that the student acquire an appreciation of the gross aspects of the brain and spinal cord, as well as knowledge of their blood supply, early in the course of study. Such information has been assembled in two new chapters (IV and V). The rhinencephalon and olfactory pathways were elevated to chapter status. Editorial surgery was undertaken optimistically in what appears to have been a futile effort to shorten the text material. Alterations were dictated largely by student use and comprehension of the text, in the lecture hall, laboratory, and subsequent clinical courses. Thus, a conscientious effort was made throughout this revision to maintain Professor Elwyn's original objective, namely, to keep this volume a "student textbook".

Neither space nor student time will permit the inclusion of all the many excellent contributions to neuroanatomy since the publication of the third edition. The field of neuroanatomy has continued to attract research interests of many disciplines. Investigators in neurohistology, neurophysiology, neurosurgery, neuropathology, neurochemistry, and neuropharmacology alone have made innumerable contributions in recent years. Each specialist has centered his disciplinary technics and often highly complex instruments upon the innermost secrets of the nerve cell. In the course of these ingenious studies the nerve cell has been probed, stimulated, irritated, injured, destroyed, cultured, irradiated, centrifuged, stained, homogenized and extracted. Neither the fetal nor the aged neuron has escaped scientific scrutiny. Increments in our knowledge of nerve cell structure and function is tremendously increased each year. Even a brief appraisal of such literature is beyond the scope of the present book. Recent information on some of the neural pathways of man and higher mammals have been placed in appropriate chapters of the present edition. References to the pertinent clinical literature have also been included.

The new student can be overwhelmed by the maze of nerve cells, nuclei, pathways and levels he is required to study. In an attempt to help him visualize this neuroanatomic material, 37 new illustrations have been added. Twenty-three are in color. The highly schematic, and often greatly enlarged, diagrams of major nervous pathways were designed to provide visual continuity through different levels of the central and peripheral nervous system. Schematic lesions at the end of Chapter XIII provide a means for the student to correlate the nerve pathways with their clinical significance. The beautifully stained Weigert preparations, through crucial levels of the spinal cord and brain stem, have been retained as text figures rather than incorporated in an Atlas at the end of the book.

All of the illustrations used for the first time in this revision were prepared by

Marjorie Stodgell, head of the Medical Art Department, Hahnemann Medical College and Hospital. Her skill, patience and artistic contributions are deeply appreciated. I am indebted to all my colleagues in the Department of Anatomy for their hearty cooperation and encouragement; to Martha Q. Smythe for valuable editorial help; to Irene Gamerman for her capable technical assistance with the manuscript; to Drs. E. H. Polley and G. S. Crouse who read some of the chapters; to Dr. Ray S. Snider of Northwestern University and Dr. Malcolm Carpenter of Columbia University who offered many constructive suggestions; to Dr. Clement Fox of Marquette University and Dr. Charles Noback of Columbia University for their generous loan of neurologic materials. Many colleagues of other teaching institutions have offered invaluable suggestions and their interest is gratefully acknowledged. Time imposed severe limitations upon the present edition. Many of the recommendations were omitted due to this factor alone.

It is a pleasure to express my personal appreciation to the Williams and Wilkins Company for their confidence, encouragement, and innumerable courtesies.

Raymond C. Truex

PREFACE TO FIRST EDITION

Neurology, more perhaps than any other branch of medicine, is dependent on an accurate knowledge of anatomy as a basis for the intelligent diagnosis and localization of neural disturbances. This book, the result of many years of neuroanatomical teaching, is intended to supply this basic anatomical need, to give the student and physician a thorough and clear presentation of the structural mechanisms of the human nervous system together with some understanding of their functional and clinical significance. It is an attempt to link structure and function into a dynamic pattern without sacrificing anatomical detail.

The book is a human neuroanatomy sufficiently rich in content to obviate the necessity of constantly consulting larger anatomical texts. It may be conveniently divided into two parts. The first part (Chapters I–VIII) is concerned with the general organization and meaning of the nervous system, its embryology and histological structure, and with some fundamental neurological problems as they apply to man. This is followed by a discussion of the organization and segmental distribution of the peripheral nerve elements, including an analysis of the functional components of the spinal nerves and of the various receptors and effectors. If these earlier chapters are perhaps more extensive than in most other texts, it is due to the conviction that the book should be complete in itself, and also that a knowledge of these preliminaries is essential for an understanding of the complex machinery of the spinal cord and brain.

The second and larger part (Chapter IX–XX) is devoted to the architectonics of the central nervous system and may be regarded as "applied neuroanatomy." Special features of this part are the many fine photographs, both gross and microscopic, of the human brain and spinal cord, the great wealth of anatomical detail, and the discussion of the structural mechanisms in the light of clinical experience. While the individual portions of the nervous system are treated separately, an attempt has been made to achieve organic structural continuity by judicious repetition and overlapping and by constant reference to related topics already familiar to the student from previous chapters. The plan of exposition is substantially the same for each topic. The gross structure and relationships are concisely but thoroughly reviewed with the aid of clear and graphic illustrations. The internal structure is then presented in detail, usually based on a carefully graded series of fine and clearly labeled microphotographs of human material. At each level the student is familiarized with the exact location, extent and relationships of the various structures seen in the section. Finally the anatomical features of each part are reviewed more comprehensively as three-dimensional structural mechanisms, with a full discussion of their connections and clinical significance. We believe that this treatment will make the complicated structural details alive and interesting to the student. The illustrations are not segregated in the back of the book in the form of an atlas but are scattered in the text, in proper relation to the levels studied.

Besides the many original illustrations, a number of others selected from various and duly acknowledged sources have been completely redrawn and relabeled for the sake of clarity and simplicity. All the illustrations, whether original or borrowed, have been executed by Frances H. Elwyn to whose skill and patience the authors are deeply indebted. We are also indebted to Dr. H. Alsop Riley for the use of several microphotographs; to Drs. R. C. Truex and Benjamin Salzer for the reading of several chapters; and especially to Dr. Otto Marburg for his many stimulating discussions and suggestions and for his critical reading of the chapters on the mesencephalon, diencephalon, and cerebral hemispheres. Thanks are also due to Rosette Spoerri for her competent help in preparing the manuscript and bibliography.

The authors cannot express too strongly their obligation to the publishers for their continuous courtesy and coöperation in all matters, and for their infinite patience in waiting for a manuscript long overdue.

Adolph Elwyn
Oliver S. Strong

CONTENTS

CHAPTER VI

CHAPTER VII

CHAPTER VIII

CHAPTER IX

CHAPTER X

CHAPTER XI

CHAPTER XII

CHAPTER XIII

CHAPTER XIV

CHAPTER XV

CHAPTER XVI

CHAPTER XX

CHAPTER XXI

1

Origin and Composition of the Nervous System

In the never ending history of life, the human nervous system represents man's greatest heritage from the ancient past, the culmination of innumerable evolutionary changes. Through a continuous series of adaptations to environment and increasing functional needs, organisms developed more efficient nervous systems, capable of interpreting and responding to a variety of sensations. Man, possessing the ability to reason, has evolved the most elaborate neural mechanism of any living creature. The human system consists of a *central nervous system*, the brain and spinal cord; a *peripheral nervous system*, which includes the cranial and spinal nerves, and the *autonomic* or involuntary system. A brief survey of some representatives from the lower animals will emphasize their kinship to the mammals and provide a keener appreciation of this extraordinary system in man.

Microscopic unicellular animals are unique in that the protoplasm performs all the necessary life activities including irritability, motility and an adaptive behavior to the surrounding environment. It is well known that Paramecium can avoid mechanical obstacles, excessive temperatures and irritating chemicals by virtue of the rhythmic movement of surface cilia. The control center for the coordinated beating of the cilia is located near the gullet, and if this region is destroyed the animal loses control of all movements. Although the protozoa manifest the basic properties of the higher forms, they possess no specialized sensory or locomotor cells.

It is in the aquatic coelenterates that a primitive neural mechanism is first observed. As examples, the hydra, jelly fish and sea anemone have a layer of modified external cells (ectoderm) and an internal layer (endoderm) that lines a hollow digestive cavity (Fig. 1A). Slender sensory cells are found between the columnar epithelial cells, and the latter have fine contractile fibrils in their bases. In the jelly-like stratum between the two cell layers of the hydra are nerve cells whose processes communicate with the surface sensory cells, and also send fibrils to the contractile bases of the epithelial cells. Thus a network of nerve cells extends throughout the entire animal. The *nerve net* (Fig. 1B) is thought to consist of separate neural units so that a nerve impulse must pass across definite breaks at the junction of two nerve cells. Such junctions or *synapses* between two nerve cells are characteristic of more highly developed nervous systems. Synapses of higher forms are said to be polarized, or so constituted that a nerve impulse can pass across them in only one direction, and thus form specialized pathways. However, in the nerve net of the hydra it is possible for impulses to cross the synapses in either direction and there are no discrete pathways. Impulses travel slowly and in a diffuse manner over this primitive nervous agency, for there is little evidence of a "control center" or ganglionic brain.

Representing further development, the flat worms are characterized by body symmetry, a head with photosensitive spots and

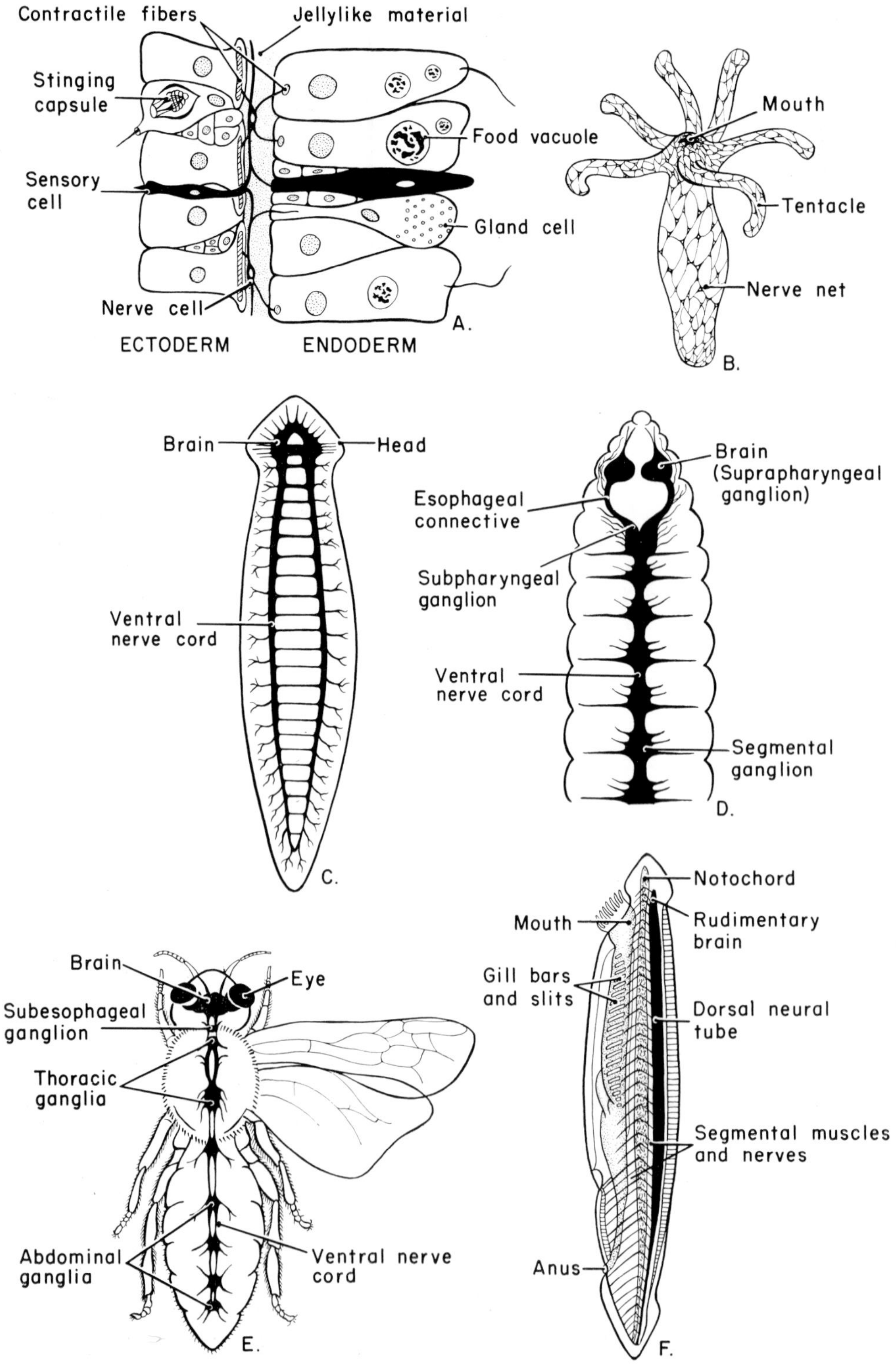

FIG. 1. Primitive nervous systems. A and B, hydra; C, planaria; D, earthworm; E, bee; F, amphioxus (modified from Buschsbaum, Courtesy University of Chicago Press).

other sense organs, the appearance of mesoderm with true muscle cells, and a more refined organization of tissues into organ systems. Planaria is an ideal example of this lowly phylum, for in the head the nervous tissue is concentrated into a bilobed mass called the brain, or head ganglion (Fig. 1C). Two strands or cords of nerve cells and fibers extend backward from the brain beneath the gastrovascular cavity, near the ventral surface of the animal. The brain and ladder-type nerve cords mark the first appearance of a central nervous system, although the nerve net of lower forms still persists. The brain is chiefly a sensory relay center that transmits impulses from the eyes and sense organs of the head region. The brain is not necessary for coordinated muscular activity, for a planaria deprived of its brain can still move along in a coordinated fashion. Because of its eyes, numerous sense organs, and centralized nervous system, this little animal manifests more rapid responses, independent locomotion, and a more varied behavior than does the hydra.

In adaptation to its subterranean life, the common earthworm has lost the prominent sense organs and eyes of the head region. At the same time the body segments have become streamlined as in other burrowing animals (Fig. 1D). The brain, or suprapharyngeal ganglion, remains essentially a sensory relay center for microscopic surface cells that are sensitive to light, touch, and probably chemicals. A worm deprived of this head ganglion shows little change in behavior and movement. A smaller subpharyngeal ganglion is interposed between the brain above, and a ventrally placed double nerve cord that extends to the posterior end of the animal. If the lower subpharyngeal ganglion is removed, a worm no longer eats and fails to burrow in a normal fashion. In the earthworm, each segmental ganglion of the nerve cord serves as a center which receives afferent impulses from sensory cells in the skin. Each ganglion also sends efferent impulses that coordinate the alternate contractions of well developed circular and longitudinal muscle layers. The intricate segmental neural apparatus of the earthworm presumably possesses all the components of a *simple reflex arc*, namely, the ability to respond segmentally and *involuntarily* to an appropriate stimulus. Larger nerve fibers within the ventral nerve cord extend over many segments and provide collateral branches to each of the segmental ganglia. Such giant fibers permit the longitudinal layers of muscle in all segments of the worm to contract simultaneously. This sudden contraction of the whole body is a stereotyped response that can be elicited by strong stimulation of any region. In such emergencies the simple reflexes of each segment becomes incorporated into a *mass response*, so that *intersegmental reflexes* take precedence over the local *segmental reflexes*. The coordination between anterior and posterior body segments is also evident to all who have observed the locomotion of an earthworm. The appearance and interplay of segmental and intersegmental reflexes in a centralized nervous system is of the utmost importance, for such simple reflexes form the neural basis of spinal cord activity in man. Of special significance is the nervous control of definitive muscle layers. Once this intimate relationship is established it becomes more elaborate and refined in higher forms.

The honey bee is included here as an illustrious example of the arthropod body plan (Fig. 1E). The individual body segments of lower forms are here incorporated into body regions—a head, thorax, and abdomen. The head now has movable mouth parts; simple and compound eyes capable of discerning light and movement; a pair of jointed antennae sensitive to touch and chemical odors. The thorax provides attachment for two pair of wings and three pair of jointed legs. The appearance of the head and thorax necessitated alterations in both muscular and nervous systems, namely, splitting of muscle layers into discrete muscle bundles, and a consolidation of neural elements into larger nerve ganglia adjacent to the major muscle masses (Fig. 1E). Synchronous wing movements and locomotion of jointed appendages are both attained by many of the insects through this refined *neuromuscular mechanism*. The brain has ceased to be a mere sensory relay center. Now a greater number of response patterns have been added and the bee has a measure of social and adaptive behavior as an integral part of instinctive behavior. All of the "specializations" in the organ systems attain their highest invertebrate development in the lowly arthropods, and they represent the peak of invertebrate evolution.

At this point it is desirable to recall the morphology of the primitive chordates. These unusual animals occupy a unique position midway between the invertebrates and the vertebrates. They all have, at some time in their life history, a cartilage-like bar, the *notochord*; a *tubular nervous system* located dorsal to the digestive tract; and pharyngeal gill bars and gill slits. Of the three sub-groups (amphioxus, tunicates, and acorn worms) amphioxus is perhaps the best known and the most like higher vertebrates (Fig. 1F). Although of questionable ancestry this animal is included because it illustrates advanced (vertebrate) and regressive (invertebrate) structural changes simultaneously. Hence it possesses a hollow, dorsally-placed neural tube with segmented musculature, but no definitive brain, eyes or special sense organs, and a very primitive digestive tract. Amphioxus also has more gill slits and gill bars than fish of higher forms, yet it has no cranial nerves or paired fins.

By a gradual process of centralization a spinal cord was thus fashioned from the primitive nerve net. This spinal cord in higher animals constitutes the primitive and most caudal portion of the central nervous system. The fact that the spinal cord developed anatomically in conjunction with, and assumed functional control over, the segmental muscles of the trunk is again emphasized.

In the lower vertebrates (e.g., lamprey eel) the sensory fibers are collected into separate bundles that course between the myotomes to enter the dorsal surface of the spinal cord (Fig. 2A). Motor nerve cells located in the gray matter of the spinal cord send their processes (*axons*) out through the ventral surface of the spinal cord as a ventral motor nerve. Each motor nerve enters the medial surface of the corresponding myotome and immediately breaks up into smaller branches. In this way the *dorsal sensory* and *ventral motor* nerves alternate with each other as they enter and leave the spinal cord. In all higher vertebrates the sensory and motor fibers are consolidated into a single nerve trunk, serving each segment of the cord.

The bipolar sensory nerve cells of the invertebrate are scattered in the periphery near the receptor endings (Figs. 1A; 3A, C). This arrangement still persists in some cranial nerves of the vertebrates (Fig. 3B, D). However, the *sensory* cells of all spinal nerves have migrated toward the spinal cord in most vertebrates and man (Fig. 3E). The bipolar sensory cells have become unipolar neurons (Figs. 80, 129) and these assembled masses of nerve cells outside the central nervous system form the dorsal root ganglia of the spinal nerves (Fig. 2B).

The simple relationship between myotome and ventral motor nerve is continued in the vertebrates. Each spinal nerve divides into a *dorsal primary ramus* to provide sensory and motor fibers to the integument and muscles of the back, and a larger *ventral primary ramus* to provide like fibers to the skin and muscles of the ventrolateral trunk (Fig. 2B). The "cord segment-spinal nerve-myotome" distribution is repeated bilaterally for each segment of the body, proceeding from the cranial to the caudal end of the spinal cord. Some animals have only

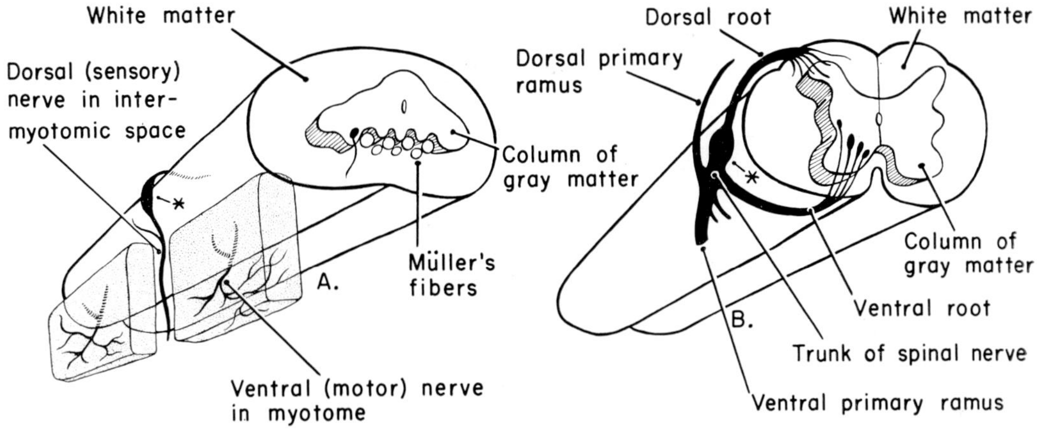

FIG. 2. Diagram of spinal nerves and spinal cord. In Amphioxus and the lamprey eel (A) separate dorsal and ventral roots alternate as they arise from the spinal cord. In most higher vertebrates (B) and in all mammals, the dorsal (sensory) and ventral (motor) roots are combined to form a single trunk. An asterisk (*) indicates the dorsal root ganglion in both diagrams.

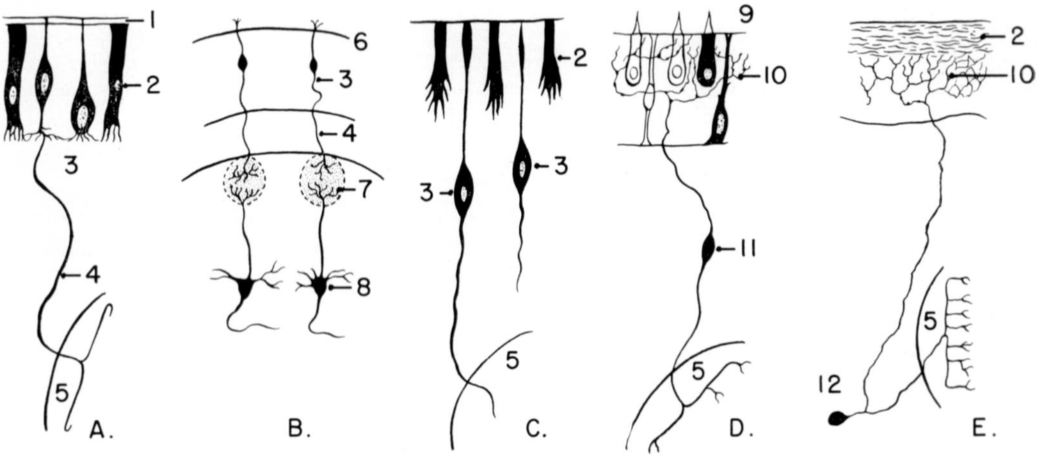

FIG. 3. Location and shape of sensory neurons in different animals (modified from Retzius) A. Earthworm (Lumbricus); B, man; C, mollusks (Limax); D, man; E, vertebrates

The neurosensory cells of lower forms (A and C) are compared with similar neural structures of man (B, D and E). 1, cuticula; 2, surface epithelial cells; 3, neurosensory cell; 4, axon or central process of sensory cell; 5, central nervous system; 6, olfactory mucous membrane; 7, glomerulus near periphery of olfactory bulb; 8, mitral cell; 9, hair cells in macula; 10, peripheral nerve terminals of sensory neuron; 11, bipolar sensory neuron in vestibular ganglion (of Scarpa); 12, unipolar sensory neuron of dorsal root ganglion.

a few paired spinal nerves and body segments; others have many (e.g., frog-10; man-31; dog-36; cat-38; horse-42).

In vertebrates with fins or appendages the ventral primary ramus becomes more complex in the regions where the limb buds develop. Muscles and connective tissue derived from each myotome retain nerve fibers from the original segmental spinal nerve. In a similar manner the skin overlying the appendage also keeps its segmental sensory nerve fibers (Figs. 157, 158). As a result the ventral primary rami of several spinal nerves unite with each other to form a "plexus" in the region of a limb bud or appendage (e.g., Figs. 161, 165, 166). The large muscle mass in an appendage attracted a greater number of sensory and motor nerves. As a result, both the spinal nerves and the segments of the spinal cord are considerably enlarged in the regions of the limb plexuses (e.g., cervical and lumbar enlargements in man; Fig. 30).

The branches of each plexus (*peripheral nerves*) then distribute sensory fibers to the original segment of skin (*dermatome*), and motor fibers to the original segment of muscle mesoderm (*myotome*). Two, three, or more myotomes usually contribute mesoderm to a single muscle in mammals. This fusion of segmental mesoderm explains why most limb muscles in man receive motor nerve fibers from two, three, or even more segmental nerves.

Soon after the spinal cord was evolved, a large number of nerve cells accumulated on its cephalic end. Hypothetically, this diffuse network of cells and fibers might be considered analagous to the *"reticular formation"*. These nerve cells regulated the activity of spinal motor neurons, which in turn controlled groups of segmental muscles. A modified reticular substrate is present in the nervous system of all higher vertebrates. In man this diffuse system exists throughout all levels of the *brain stem*, and functionally it is capable of modifying the reflex activity of the spinal motor neurons. Additional groups of nerve cells evolved within the reticular formation very early in vertebrate evolution. Some of the new clusters of cells functioned either as relay *nuclei*, or end-stations for incoming sensory fibers of taste, touch, vision, hearing, and equilibrium. Other central nerve cells related to cranial nerves were concerned with reflex control of visceral motor activity in the circulatory, digestive, and respiratory systems. Another new group of larger motor neurons appeared in the brain stem to assume control of the skeletal muscles, of the eyes and the tongue. Other motor neurons supplied the striated muscles derived from the mesoderm of the branchial arches.

All of these nerve cell and fiber additions to the cephalic end of the spinal cord contributed to the formation of a brain stem, which in mammals is subdivided for purposes of description, into four parts. The *Myelencephalon* or *medulla oblongata* is the most caudal segment of the brain stem and is continuous with the spinal cord. A second portion, the *Metencephalon*, is composed of the *pons* and *cerebellum*. The third segment is designated as the *Mesencephalon* or midbrain, while the fourth and most cranial portion of the brain stem is the *Diencephalon*. The *Telencephalon*, which is *not* a part of the brain stem, expands to cover most of the brain stem structures. The telencephalon is composed of the cerebral hemispheres and the basal ganglia. Each of these units of the brain have special anatomic features, subdivisions and neural functions.

The action of each portion of the brain stem is integrated with the functional activity of the more cranial brain segments by *ascending fiber pathways*. Through these pathways each of the brain segments contribute information to all higher levels. In a similar manner, higher regions of the brain stem are connected to more caudally placed segments by means of *descending fiber pathways*. Such descending tracts subject each of the lower segments to a measure of modified activity (inhibition and facilitation). For example, the cerebral cortex represents the highest level of sensory and motor integration. Normally it regulates neural activities within the brain stem and spinal cord. The pons and medulla, acting alone, exercise some control over neural activity in the more caudal spinal cord. If isolated from all higher portions of the brain stem, the spinal cord can maintain a measure of segmental reflex activity.

Generally speaking, there is a correlation between the size of a particular part of an animal's brain and its importance in the life of that animal. Six representative brains are illustrated in Fig. 4. When examined as a series, they demonstrate clearly that the vertebrate brain has evolved by a gradual "cephalic shift" of function from the lower brain stem (fish) to the higher cerebral cortex (man). It is also evident that certain neural structures attain considerable size and obvious functional importance in lower forms, then become proportionately smaller and therefore less conspicuous in higher forms (e.g., olfactory bulb, optic lobe). However, once a neural structure becomes incorporated into the vertebrate brain, it usually remains in higher animals even though reduced in size and functional significance (e.g., olfactory mechanism and epiphysis of man).

The primitive cerebellum developed in conjunction with the lateral-line system, semicircular canals, and maculae of the vestibular system. It assumed significance as a center for the reflex regulation of muscle tonus and muscular coordination. One can better appreciate the need for a highly developed cerebellar apparatus in fish and birds if one recalls these animals move in three dimensions and must balance their bodies in a fluid or gaseous environment. Reptiles and most land dwelling mammals, on the other hand, move primarily in two dimensions, but they still require a cerebellum for muscular coordination (synergy).

The size of the optic nerve and lobe (Fig. 4) show that visual stimuli play an important role in the life of most vertebrates, particularly birds and mammals. In man the optic relay centers and visual cortex cannot be seen in a lateral view of the brain.

Smell is probably the most important sense in some lower vertebrates (fish, frog, alligator), whereas in birds and man the sense of smell is poorly developed and this area of the brain is very small. Some mammals, however, still have a very acute sense of smell (rat, cat, dog, ungulates) and in these animals the olfactory areas of the brain are more prominent.

Masses of nerve cells buried deep in the cerebral hemispheres comprise the basal ganglia. Since they are adjacent to the diencephalon, they likewise become overlayed by the expanding cerebral hemispheres in the brains of higher vertebrates. Both the diencephalon and the basal ganglia are therefore hidden in higher forms and cannot be identified in surface views of the brain. However, the basal ganglia are quite prominent internal features in brains of lower vertebrates (fish, birds). Most of the bird cerebrum (goose, Fig. 4) is composed of these basal ganglia covered by thin layers of white matter and cortex. The thalamus (part of the diencephalon) of fish and birds serves as a center for sensory integration, whereas part of the basal ganglia (*globus pallidus*) comprises a diffuse descending motor pathway. This diffuse motor system dominates and varies the level of responses of the more caudal motor centers in the brain stem and spinal cord. Through such circuits the globus pallidus is able to initiate and maintain the automatic, stereotyped basic movements of swimming and flying so essential to the fish and bird. This old motor system still functions in man and participates in the smooth blending of muscle patterns, particularly the semi-automatic, synchronized group actions of muscles.

As the olfactory areas of the cerebral cortex (*archipallium*) diminished in reptiles, birds and man (Fig. 4), an extensive new cortex was elaborated (*neocortex, neopallium*). As the cerebrum increased in size it became necessary to enlarge the surface area, yet keep the brain volume within reasonable limits. This was accomplished by the formation of folds or convolutions. In the lower mammals there are only a few convolutions, while in man they reach maximum number.

This elaborate convoluted mantle of layered gray matter assumed control over the more caudal sensory and motor systems of

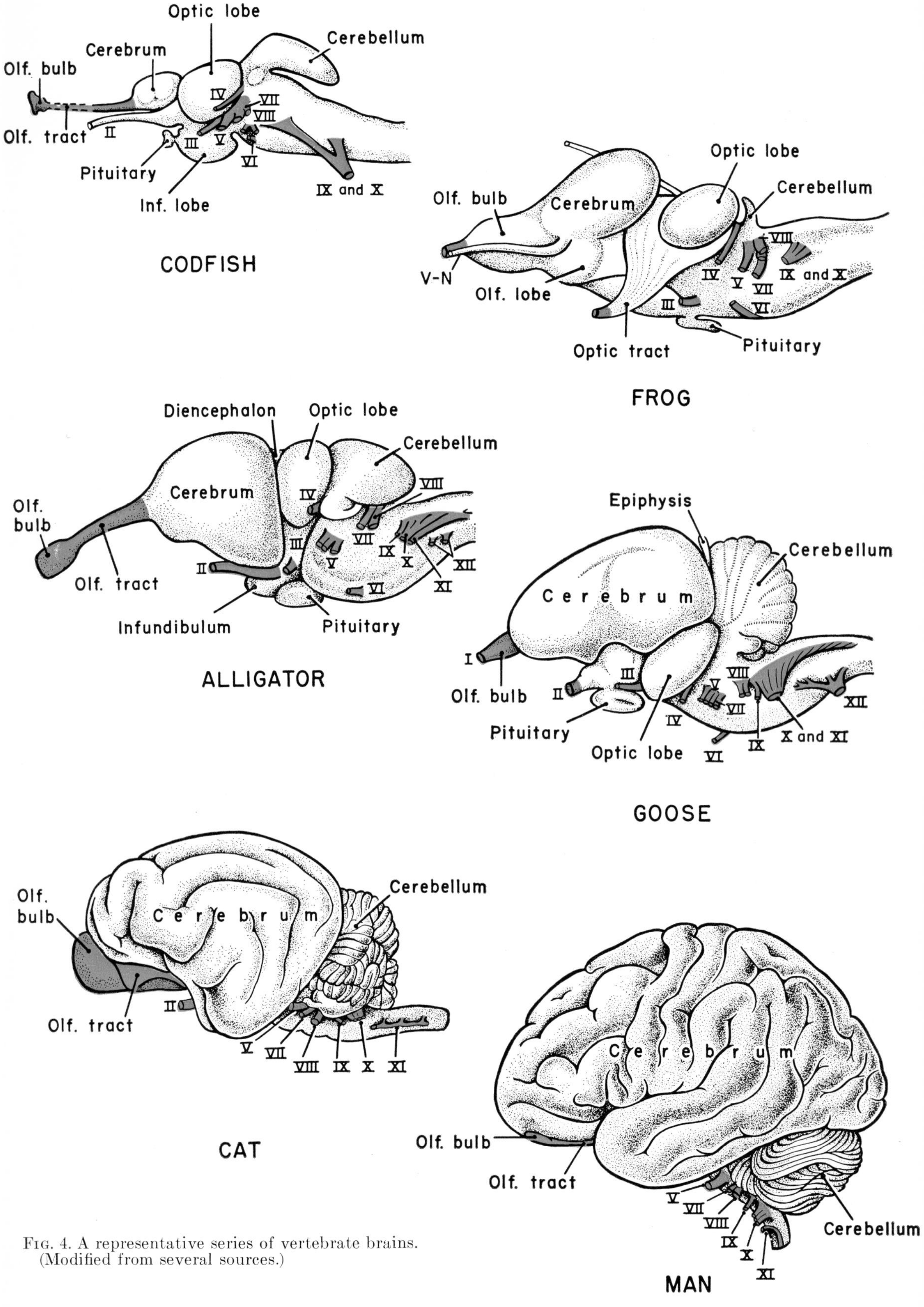

Fig. 4. A representative series of vertebrate brains. (Modified from several sources.)

the thalamus and basal ganglia. Specialized areas were promptly differentiated within the neocortex, and the thalamus then projected its sensory messages (nerve impulses) from lower levels to a new sensory (*somesthetic*) area of the cortex. In a similar manner other thalamic fibers relayed visual and auditory impulses to special areas of the cerebral cortex. Ascending fibers within the diffuse reticular formation of the brain stem also send impulses to the overlying cortex.

Of necessity, a new motor area developed in the cerebral cortex. The new motor pathway (*corticobulbar* and *corticospinal tracts*) established intimate neural connections with the older pallidal motor system, and sent descending fibers to all the cranial and spinal motor nerve cells. By the integration, control and use of preexisting neural mechanisms of the basal ganglia, cerebellum, and reticular formation, this new motor system provided for smooth voluntary muscle movements. Both individual muscles and groups of muscles could thus be controlled to produce fine isolated movement, as well as the more complicated muscle actions so common in the daily life of man. Although these intricate muscle actions are initiated and controlled by the motor neurons of the new motor system, one must remember that each of the older motor systems is contributing an essential component that is often hidden or masked.

In addition to the specialized projection and reception areas, the neocortex of higher mammals has perfected neural mechanisms for the more complex correlation and discrimination of sensory impulses. There is also greater storage and utilization of previous sensory and motor reactions. This sensory neural agency may be termed *associative memory* and the motor responses *mnemonic* (memory) *reactions*.

The receptors of the nose, eye, and ear were of primary importance in the development of mnemonic reactions. The centers for these three great senses are already indicated by the three primary expansions of the developing brain: the forebrain expansion for the nose; a midbrain expansion for the eye; and the hindbrain enlargement or cerebellum for the vestibular part of the ear. These three cephalic segments continue to enlarge and become highly differentiated in man. They receive stimuli from other parts of the body, and become important coordinating areas within the brain. Cortex, midbrain, and cerebellum, like the thalamus, corpus striatum and globus pallidus (parts of basal ganglia) are often called *suprasegmental* in contrast to the segmental (spinal cord) part of the central nervous system. The spinal segments are more intimately related to the peripheral nerves and contain the simpler and more fundamental coordinating neural mechanisms.

Each of the old and new sensory and motor units were thus blended into the remarkable nervous system found in man. The primate nervous system is a composite of ascending *integrated levels,* with vital nerve pathways connecting them together (e.g., spinal cord level; reticular-vestibular-cerebellum level; mesencephalon; diencephalon-basal ganglia level; cortical level). The normal interplay between these neural levels may be disrupted by injury to one or more parts, resulting in abnormal function and behavior. These symptoms may represent *deficits* due to loss of essential nerve cells and fibers at a higher level, or they may be *release phenomena.* The latter represent a return of less controlled nervous activity in the older motor systems, due to complete or partial destruction of higher motor centers.

Visceral motor centers are present in the spinal cord, brain stem and higher levels of most vertebrates. Such nerve cells within the central nervous system and in outlying ganglia form a two neuron visceral motor pathway for the reflex control of all smooth muscle, cardiac muscle, and glandular epithelium of the body. This diffuse involuntary neural mechanism is designated the *autonomic nervous system.* The cranial and spinal nerves, including the elements of the autonomic, comprise the *peripheral nervous system.* Through peripheral nerves the brain and spinal cord must receive all incoming sensory information and transmit all outgoing motor commands. Special attention is focused on those motor cells of the brain stem and spinal cord whose *axons* travel in either the cranial or spinal nerves. These efferent nerve cells and their axons constitute the last neural link or *final common pathway* between the central nervous system and the skeletal muscles and visceral structures of the body.

Although we are primarily concerned here with the nervous system of man, we should be ever mindful that this system came to us through a series of increasingly complex modifications imposed upon the simpler nervous systems of our remote forebears. During embryonic development the human nervous system repeats many of these ancestral stages. Indeed, the older systems appear first, and many of the more recent neural acquisitions are not functionally mature in man and other mammals even at the time of birth (Kaes, 1907; Truex, 1955).

In studying Neuroanatomy, one of the major objectives is to provide a clear understanding of the major pathways between these integrated levels of the human nervous system. The anatomic approach will afford a firm foundation for the comprehension of both normal and abnormal function of this intricate and fascinating system in man.

2

Development of the Nervous System

The entire nervous system except the olfactory epithelium and parts of certain ganglia, is derived ontogenetically from an elongated plate of thickened ectoderm, *the neural plate,* which extends longitudinally in the axis of the developing embryo. At first the thickened plate passes laterally without sharp demarcation into the thinner non-neural ectoderm. A more distinct boundary is formed in embryos of about 2 mm. when the lateral edges of the plate curve dorsally to form the *neural folds,* enclosing between them a median longitudinal groove, the *neural groove.* Already at this stage the cephalic portion of the plate is broader, the folds higher and the groove deeper, foreshadowing the future differentiation into brain and spinal cord (Figs. 5, 6, 7). The neural folds become more and more elevated, approaching the median line, and finally meet and fuse to form the *neural tube.* The fusion of the folds begins in the middle region of the plate at the boundary zone of spinal cord and brain and progresses both forward and backward (Fig. 7). The last portions to close are situated at the cephalic and caudal ends and the openings there are known as the anterior and posterior neuropore respectively. The former which marks the rostral wall of the neural tube (the future lamina terminalis) closes in embryos of about 18–20 somites. The posterior neuropore disappears somewhat later in embryos of 25–30 somites. When the latter occurs, the neural folds have become completely transformed into the closed neural tube detached from the overlying ectoderm which now covers it continuously. The tube thus formed shows an anterior enlarged portion, the *brain,* and posterior narrower portion, the *spinal cord.*

In the epithelial wall of the closed neural tube four plates or zones may be distinguished: a ventral median *floor plate,* a dorsal median *roof plate* where the fusion occurred, and two *lateral plates.* The roof and floor plates remain relatively thin, but the lateral plates become tremendously thickened and differentiated, expressive of the bilateral character of the neural tube. As the walls thicken, a longitudinal furrow, the *sulcus limitans,* appears on the internal surface of each lateral plate about midway between the roof and floor, dividing it into a dorsal and a ventral portion, the *alar* and *basal* plate respectively. In the course of further neural differentiation the motor cell groups develop in the basal plate, the receptive or sensory ones in the alar plate. The central autonomic cell groups related to visceral innervation are formed in the intermediate area, i.e., in the region of the sulcus limitans. Thus in the adult spinal cord and certain portions of the brain there is found a general territorial organization of functional significance, the dorsal half being primarily afferent or receptive in character, the ventral efferent or motor, each having its somatic and visceral divisions (Figs. 127, 13). The sulcus limitans is well marked in the hindbrain where it persists in the adult, but is difficult to distinguish in the midbrain even in developmental stages. There is evidence that the basal

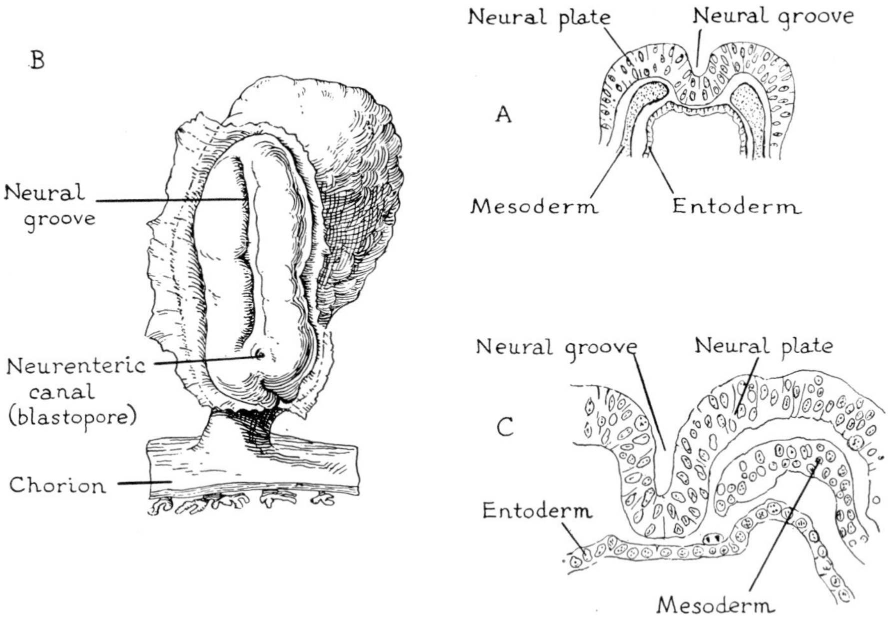

FIG. 5. *A*, transverse section through human embryo before appearance of somites. (After Keibel.) *B*, dorsal view, and *C*, transverse section of 2 mm. human embryo. (After Graf Spee.)

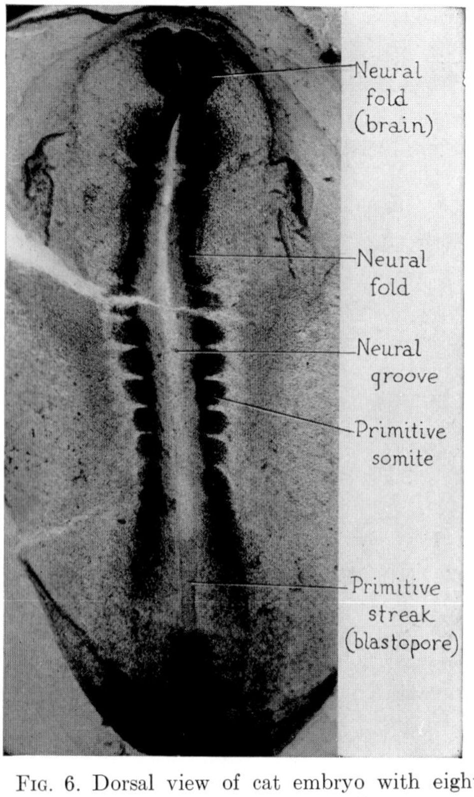

FIG. 6. Dorsal view of cat embryo with eight mesodermal somites. Microphotograph.

plate does not extend beyond the midbrain and that hence the whole forebrain wall is derived from the alar plate (Kingsbury, 1922; Johnston, 1923).

While the neural plate is closing there occurs a differentiation of cells along each lateral edge, forming an intermediate zone between the neural plate and skin ectoderm. When the plate is converted into a tube, these zones are naturally brought together at the point of fusion of the neural folds. They also fuse and become detached from the overlying ectoderm. They are not, however, included in the wall of the neural tube proper but form an unpaired ridge of small, pale staining cells, the *neural* or *ganglionic* crest, lying along its dorsal surface wedged in between the fusing neural folds (Fig. 9). The beginnings of the crest are already visible in embryos of seven somites. Somewhat later, in embryos of about 3 mm., the crest detaches itself from the neural tube, and splits longitudinally into a right and left half. The cells of each half migrate from the dorsal to the lateral surface of the

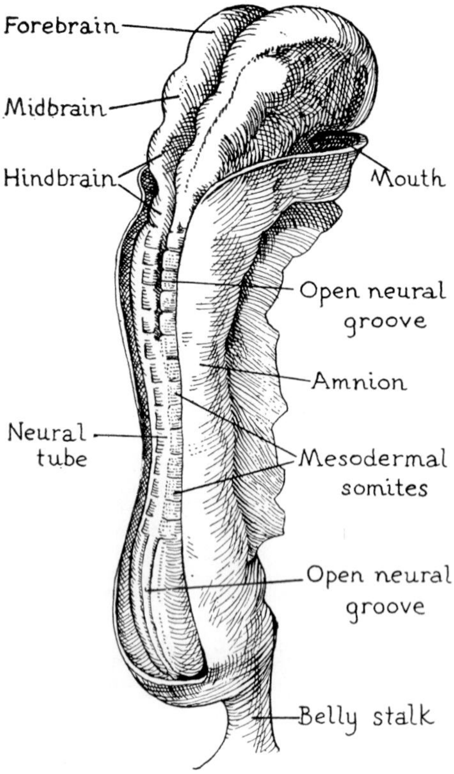

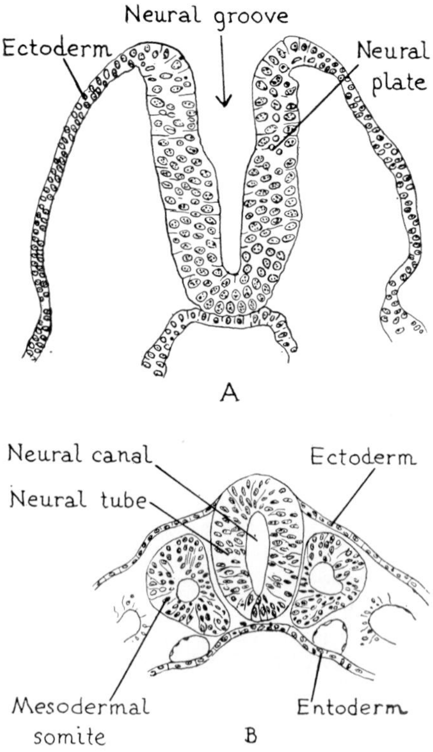

FIG. 7 FIG. 8

FIG. 7. Lateral view of human embryo about 2.2 mm. in length, showing partially closed neural tube. (After Kollmann.)

FIG. 8. Transverse sections through neural tube of 2.7 mm. human embryo. *A*, through brain; *B*, through upper portion of spinal cord. (After Kollmann.)

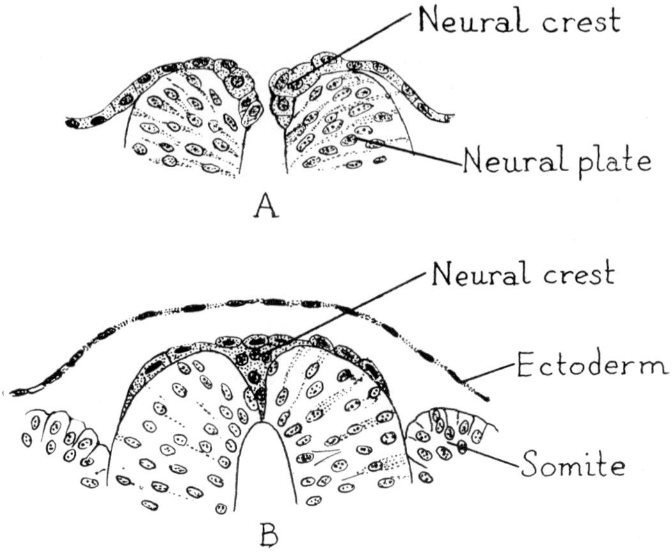

FIG. 9. Two stages in the closure of the neural tube and formation of the neural crest. From transverse sections of a 2.5 mm. human embryo. (After Lenhossék.)

tube. In this way two ridges are formed. Soon, as the result of unequal cellular proliferation, the originally unsegmented ridges break up into a series of cellular blocks or aggregations situated on either side of the neural tube, the aggregations corresponding to the metamerism of the primitive somites. These are the rudiments of the cerebrospinal ganglia which give rise to the afferent peripheral neurons, in part at least to efferent sympathetic neurons, and to certain other structures (capsule cells, sheath cells).

All afferent neurons are not formed from the neural crest. The olfactory cells whose fibers constitute the olfactory nerve are derived from the epithelium of the nasal mucous membrane. It is certain also that some of the sensory cells in the ganglia of the fifth, seventh, eighth, ninth, and tenth cranial nerves are derived from thickened patches of skin ectoderm, called *placodes*, which are in close contact with those ganglia during early development (Landacre, 1910). The formation of these placodes, like that of the neural tube itself, is the embryological expression of the tendency of highly specialized neural tissue to concentrate and withdraw from the surface. The neural tube itself is likewise derived from a plate of thickened ectoderm, the neural plate, which thus may be regarded as the oldest and most extensive placode.

The sensory cells of the retina, the rods and cones, are differentiated from the wall of the neural tube. As will be seen below, the retina represents a migrated portion of the brain and contains not only photoreceptors but several categories of neurons as well. Hence the "optic nerve" is in reality a fiber tract connecting two portions of the brain.

The neural crest is formed along the whole extent of the spinal cord and extends also into the region of the brain, thus furnishing a spinal and cerebral portion. The latter is well formed only in the region of the hindbrain where it detaches itself from the neural tube and forms typical ganglia. Yntema and Hammond (1954) extirpated the vagal area of the neural crest and adjacent neural fold in chick embryos at the 6–9 somite stage. Complete removal of neural crest material in the region of the hindbrain and cervical somites resulted in an absence of intrinsic ganglia within the heart, lungs, esophagus, stomach, and intestine. In front of the hindbrain a similar type of cell proliferation occurs at the line of fusion of the tube but apparently remains abortive and does not become detached. Traces of such crest formation are even visible in the still open fundament of the forebrain. Schulte and Tilney (1915) have suggested that the optic vesicles and mesencephalic nucleus of the trigeminal nerve are derived from portions of the cerebral crest which have failed to separate from the neural tube.

Development of the brain. When closure of the tube is completed the wider cephalic portion or brain already shows three imperfectly separated expansions. These are the primary brain "vesicles", known as the *forebrain* (prosencephalon), *midbrain* (mesencephalon) and *hindbrain* (rhombencephalon). These three vesicles are shown in Figs. 7, 10. The forebrain and midbrain vesicles are still small and difficult to delimit and in the forebrain are visible two large ventrolateral evaginations, the optic pouches. A more marked constriction separates the midbrain from the much larger rhombencephalon which passes without any definite demarcation into the spinal cord. The whole wall of the neural tube is still epithelial. The brain shows two ventrally directed flexures. The rostral of these, the *cephalic flexure,* is in the region of the midbrain and is bent almost at right angles. The *cervical flexure* at the junction of hindbrain and spinal cord is less marked. The rhombencephalon shows an indistinct division into six or seven segments or "neuromeres" separated by shallow furrows. The ganglion of the trigeminal nerve (V) is already associated with the first neuromere, the acusticofacial ganglion (VII and VIII) with the third.

In embryos of about 5 mm. (Fig. 11) the forebrain is more definitely marked off from the midbrain by the appearance ventrally of the mammillary protuberance. The optic

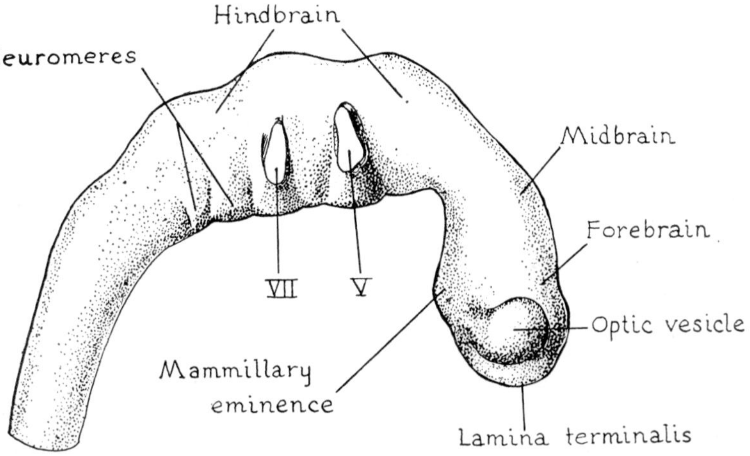

FIG. 10. Brain of 3.4 mm. human embryo, lateral view. *V*, trigeminal ganglion; *VII*, acustico-facial ganglion. (After Hochstetter.)

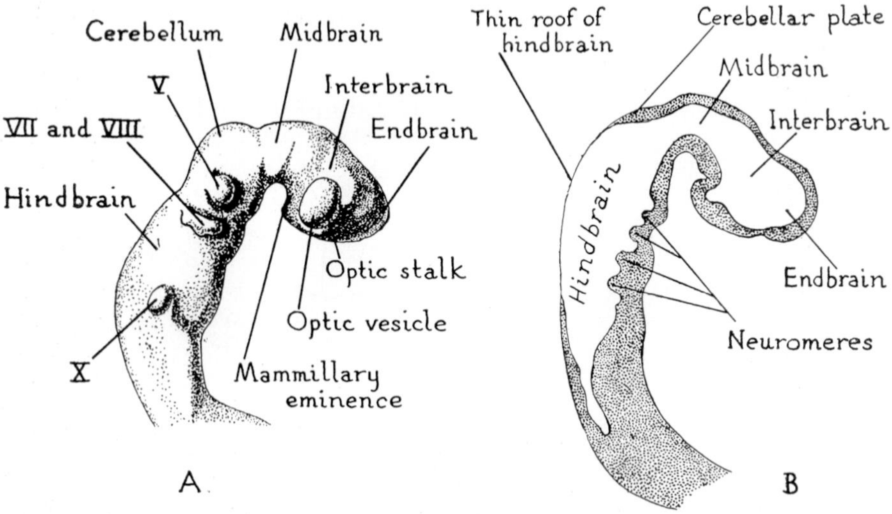

FIG. 11. *A*, brain of human embryo with 28 somites, lateral view. *B*, median sagittal section through brain of 5 mm. human embryo. (After Fischel.)

pouches are moving laterally, their now constricted attachments to the forebrain forming the optic stalks. In front, above the optic pouches, a dorsal protrusion of the anterior brain wall marks the appearance of the future hemisphere. The primary forebrain vesicle now exhibits two as yet indistinctly separable regions. The anterior region represented by the hemispheric bulge and soon to reach massive proportions, is known as the *endbrain* or *telencephalon*, the rest of the forebrain is called *interbrain* or *diencephalon*. The midbrain is still simple and little changed, and is separated dorsally and caudally from the large rhombencephalon by a definite furrow. The constricted portion of the hindbrain where it joins the midbrain is known as the *isthmus rhombencephali*.

The primary hindbrain or rhombencephalon is different from the other brain regions in that its dorsal wall becomes thickened only in its most cephalic and most caudal portions (Figs. 11, 12). Throughout the largest extent the roof remains exceedingly thin, expands laterally and assumes a diamond-shaped appearance. Beginning with a pointed extremity in the region of the isthmus, it gradually widens to about the middle of the hindbrain (region of future lateral recesses) and then gradually narrows again to end in a caudal point. Corresponding to this the floor plate likewise assumes a rhomboid shape. When the thin roof is removed, the cavity of the hindbrain or fourth ventricle appears as a shallow diamond-shaped depression and hence is known as the *fossa rhomboidea*. In early stages the rhomboid fossa can be seen externally shining through the ectoderm and thin epithelial roof of the hindbrain.

In the rhombencephalon two main regions may already be distinguished. In front, above the widest portion of the rhomboid fossa the roof plate becomes narrower and the dorsal parts of the lateral wall thicken to form the rudiments of the cerebellum. This part is known as the secondary hindbrain or *metencephalon* which later forms the pons and cerebellum. The rest of the rhombic brain forms the *myelencephalon* or *medulla oblongata*. On the dorsal surface the boundary zone between metencephalon and myelencephalon is marked by a transverse groove, the *transverse rhombencephalic sulcus* (Figs. 12, 14).

Thus at this stage five secondary cerebral expansions or vesicles have been formed from the three primary ones, due to the respective differentiation of the forebrain and hindbrain into two main regions, the midbrain alone remaining undivided. The five brain vesicles now present are the telencephalon, diencephalon, mesencephalon, metencephalon, and myelencephalon. The neuromeres of the hindbrain are still dis-

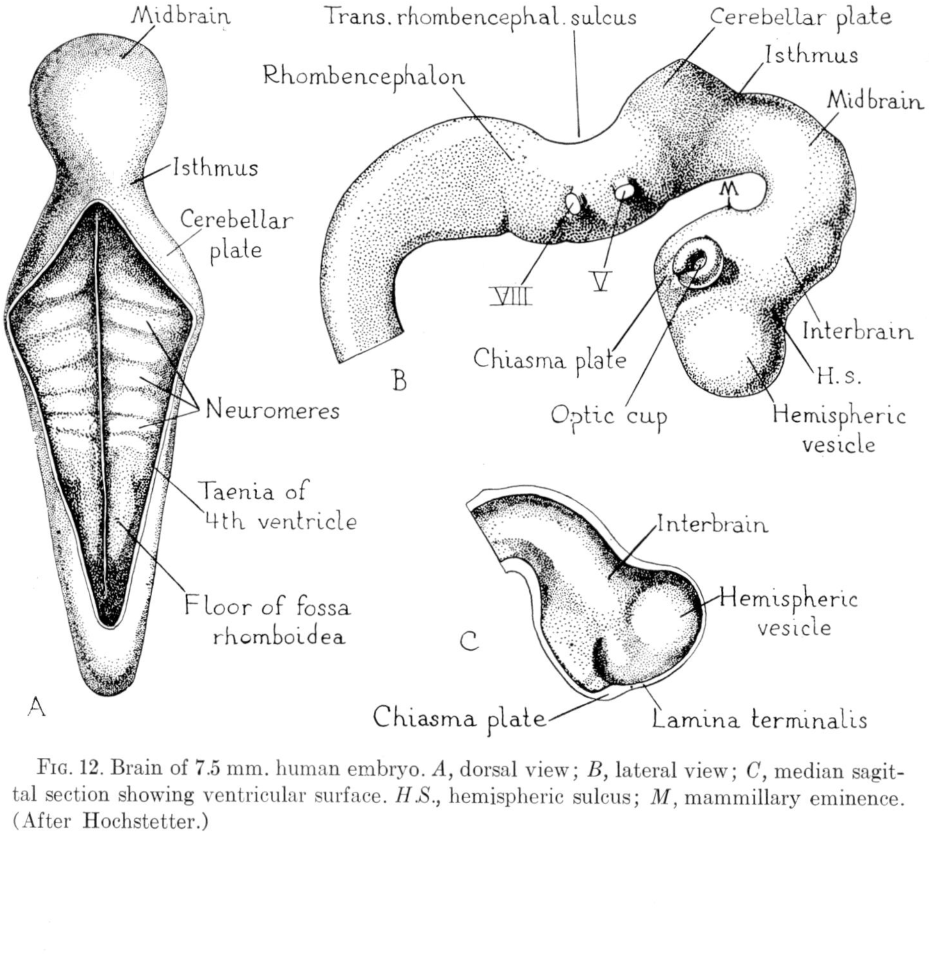

FIG. 12. Brain of 7.5 mm. human embryo. *A*, dorsal view; *B*, lateral view; *C*, median sagittal section showing ventricular surface. *H.S.*, hemispheric sulcus; *M*, mammillary eminence. (After Hochstetter.)

tinct, and associated with the last pair are the ganglionic rudiments of the *vagus* (X) and *glossopharyngeal* (IX) nerves.

In a 7.5 mm. embryo the five divisions of the brain are more easily distinguishable (Fig. 12). The telencephalon arising as a median structure has grown laterally to form a conspicuous bulge on each side, separated from the diencephalon by a shallow circular furrow, the *hemispheric sulcus.* The relatively large diencephalon has absorbed the terminal portions of the optic stalks, thus forming the chiasmatic plate. The optic vesicles have become invaginated into optic cups, due to the formation of the lens which as an ectodermal thickening presses against the lateral surface of the vesicle. The midbrain is practically unchanged. The cephalic and cervical flexures have deepened considerably and the ventral wall of the rhombencephalon has become convex indicating the beginning of another dorsally bending *pontine* flexure. This produces on the dorsal surface a transverse kink or fold in the thin roof in the region of the greatest width of the fourth ventricle. The transverse rhombencephalic sulcus thus formed, as already stated, constitutes the boundary between the more cranially placed metencephalon and the more caudal myelencephalon. The rhomboid fossa still shows indications of neuromeres, and the roof and dorsolateral walls of the metencephalon have thickened to form the cerebellar plate.

The ventricular surface of an embryo of the same age is seen in Fig. 12C. The anterior median wall of the brain is formed by a thin membrane, the *lamina terminalis,* which passes ventrally into the thickening of the chiasmatic plate. Dorsally the median wall thickens to form the so-called *commissural plate* (Fig. 18) in which later develop the various telencephalic commissures (anterior, corpus callosum, commissure of fornix). A ridge corresponding externally to the hemispheric sulcus separates endbrain from interbrain.

From the five secondary vesicles all parts of the definitive brain are ultimately derived. The further development is characterized by the tremendous increase in size of the endbrain which soon overshadows in mass all the other portions. The various flexures become more and more marked for a while, but in later stages the reverse occurs. The cephalic flexure gradually flattens out and is greatly reduced in the fully formed brain. The cervical and pontine flexures disappear altogether. The further development of the individual parts may be briefly summarized.

Rhombencephalon. As already stated, the rhombencephalon differentiates into an anterior metencephalic and a posterior myelencephalic portion, the boundary between the two being the transverse sulcus which marks the widest part of the fourth ventricle and is later continued into its lateral recesses. The rhombencephalon shows the following conditions (Fig. 12A). In its caudal portion it has the same form as the cervical spinal cord with which it is continuous. The lumen is small and completely surrounded by thickened walls. Proceeding forward, the dorsally placed thickened alar plates begin to diverge laterally, corresponding to the widening of the thin roof of the ventricle until in the widest portion the alar and basal plates come to lie more nearly in the same plane and form the ventral wall or floor of the fossa rhomboidea. The wide roof remains very thin, consisting of a single-layered epithelial membrane, the *lamina chorioidea epithelialis* (Figs. 11, 13). The dorsal border of the alar plate to which the thin roof is attached forms a thickened ridge known as the *rhombic lip.* In the myelencephalon, caudal to the lateral recess, this develops into the taenia of the fourth ventricle. Above the lateral recess the rhombic lip becomes considerably enlarged and contributes to the formation of the cerebellum. A median longitudinal sulcus appears in the floor of the fossa rhomboidea dividing it into two lateral halves, and another longitudinal furrow, the

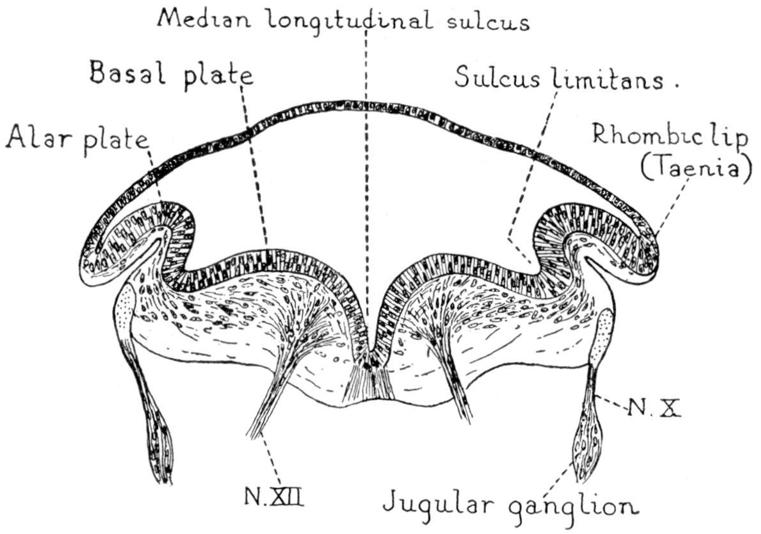

FIG. 13. Section through medulla of a 9.1 mm. human embryo. (After His.)

sulcus limitans, divides each half into a broader medial or basal plate and a narrower alar plate. All these sulci extend the whole length of the rhombencephalon. In the median portion are formed the motor cell groups or nuclei, comprising the somatic motor nuclei of the VIth and XIIth nerves and the general and special visceral motor nuclei of the Vth, VIIth, IXth, Xth, and XIth nerves (Figs. 13 and 222). Of these, the VIth and XIIth nuclei are more mesially placed and correspond to ventral horn cells of the spinal cord. In the alar plates, lateral to the sulcus limitans, are formed the receptive areas for nerves V, VII, VIII, IX, and X. The floor of the rhomboid fossa above the lateral recess gives rise to the pons, the part below becomes the medulla oblongata.

The thin epithelial roof fuses with the investing pial connective tissue to form the *tela chorioidea.* In embryos of about 20 mm. a fold of the tela dips into the ventricle, and by proliferation of the epithelium and richly vascular connective tissue is ultimately transformed into the chorioid plexus of the fourth ventricle (Fig. 18).

In front of the lateral recess, the thin roof of the fourth ventricle becomes progressively narrower. Consequently the alar plates, situated laterally in the medulla, assume a more dorsal position and gradually approach each other until in the most anterior portion they are separated only by a narrower zone of the roof plate which is thicker in this region (Fig. 12). From this portion of the alar lamina the cerebellum is formed. The rhombic lip and adjacent region become considerably thickened to form the *cerebellar swellings* or *plates* which bulge into the ventricle (Figs. 14, 15). As the swellings increase in size, they approach each other, finally invade the roof and fuse to form a transverse structure above the fourth ventricle (Figs. 15, 17). In further growth the lateral ends of this structure expand to form the cerebellar hemispheres; the narrower middle portion gives rise to the vermis. The first transverse furrows appear in the vermis at the end of the third month, somewhat later in the hemispheres. At the end of the seventh month all the main folia and sulci are already laid down.

The floor of the metencephalon is constituted by the upper portion of the fossa rhomboidea which thickens to form the *tegmentum* of the pons. As already mentioned, it contains the motor and sensory cell groups associated with the fifth, sixth,

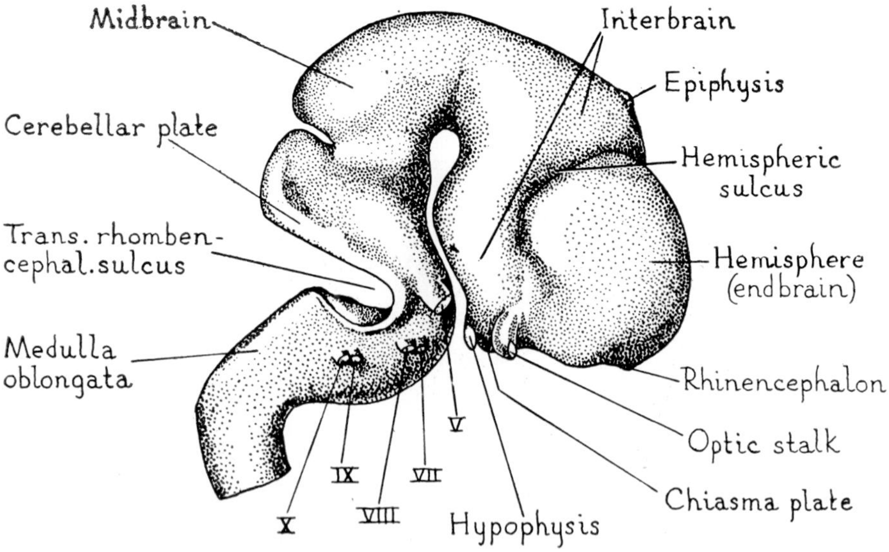

FIG. 14. Brain of 13.8 mm. human embryo, lateral view. Roman numbers indicate cranial nerves. (After Hochstetter.)

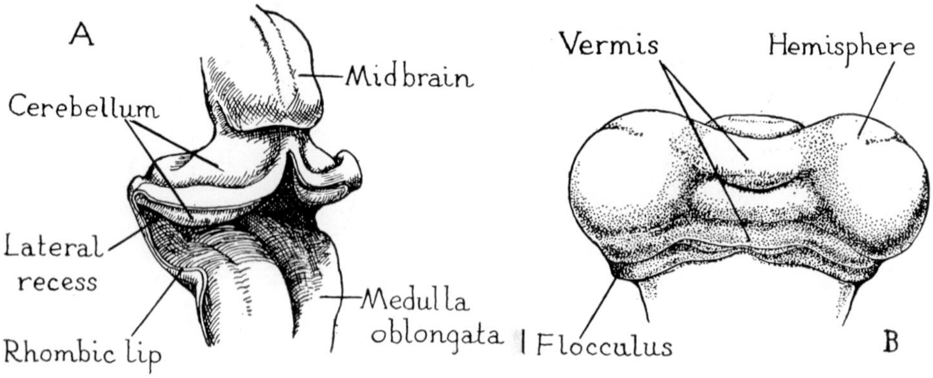

FIG. 15. Two stages in the development of the human cerebellum. *A*, embryo of six weeks (13.6 mm.); *B*, four months fetus (110 mm.). (*A*, after His; *B*, after Prentiss and Arey.)

seventh, and eighth nerves. Ventral to the tegmentum the *basilar* portion of the pons, or pons proper, is formed by massive cell groups and fiber tracts primarily related to the cerebellum (Fig. 18).

The uppermost narrowed portion of the hindbrain, lying in front of the cerebellum, is known as the *isthmus rhombencephali.* Its junction with the midbrain is marked by the emergence of the fourth nerve. Its thin roof, the *superior medullary velum,* is formed from the middle portion of the cerebellar plate.

Mesencephalon. The midbrain undergoes the least changes of any of the cerebral vesicles. Towards the end of the third month, the wall begins to thicken tremendously, gradually reducing the lumen to a narrow channel, the *iter* or *cerebral aqueduct* (Fig. 18). The roof or tectum forms the quadrigeminal plate, at first undivided but later differentiating into the paired nuclear masses of the superior and inferior colliculi. The ventral portion becomes the massive tegmentum. Some of the nerve cells group themselves on each side of the midline of the

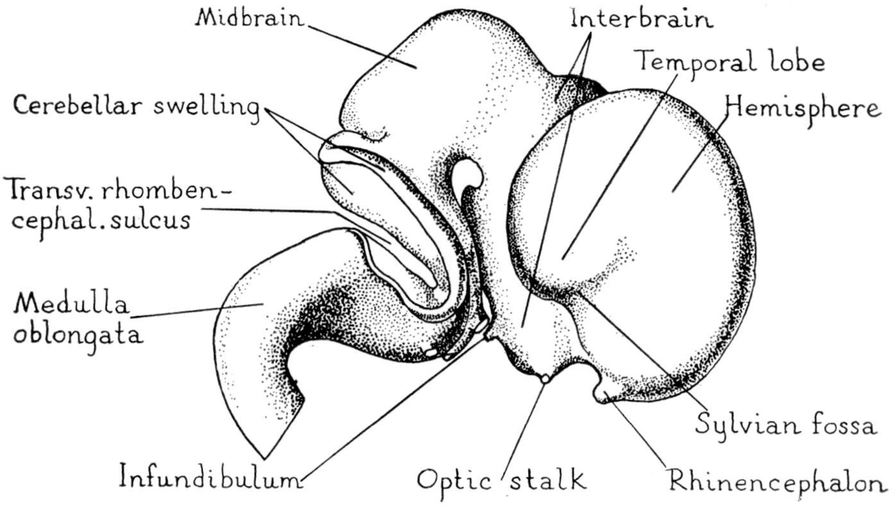

FIG. 16. Brain of 27 mm. human embryo, lateral view. (After Hochstetter.)

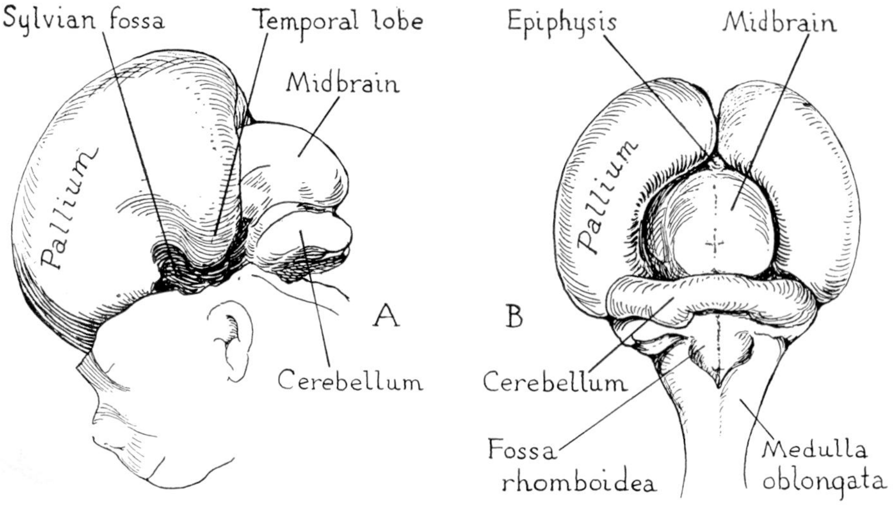

FIG. 17. Human embryo of the third month. *A*, viewed from the side; *B*, from behind.

floor of the iter into the motor nuclei of the third and fourth nerves. Others by migration give rise to the nucleus ruber, substantia nigra and other tegmental nuclei. Ventral to the tegmentum are the massive fiber tracts descending mainly from the cerebral cortex which constitute the *pes* or *basis peduncli* (crus cerebri). Tegmentum and basis together are often known as the cerebral peduncles or crura cerebri. It is usually stated that the quadrigeminal plate is derived from the "alar", the tegmentum from the "basal" lamina, but a real sulcus limitans is difficult to make out in the midbrain.

Diencephalon. Like the other portions of the brain, the embryonic diencephalon consists of a roof plate, a floor plate, and two lateral walls. During growth the latter become greatly thickened, finally reducing the lumen to a vertical cleft-like space, the *third ventricle.* In most brains actual fusion of the walls may occur at one place to form a narrow bridge of gray extending across

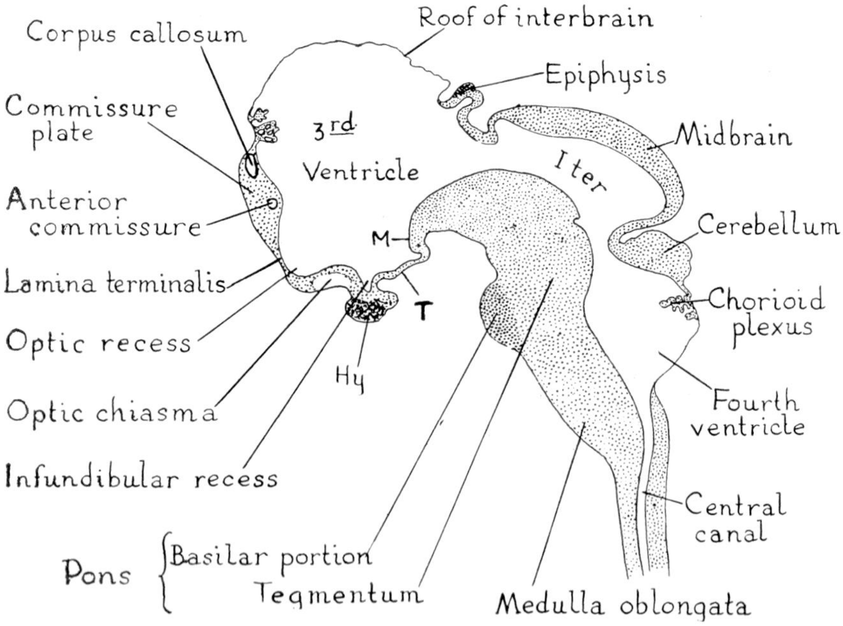

FIG. 18. Median longitudinal section through brain of 68 mm. human embryo. *Hy*, hypophysis; *M*, mammillary body; *T*, tuber cinereum. (After Hochstetter.)

the ventricle, the *massa intermedia*. The thickening of the walls is not uniform, being relatively less in a narrow longitudinal zone about the middle of the diencephalon. As a result, there is formed on the medial surface a shallow longitudinal groove, the *hypothalamic sulcus*, which demarcates a dorsal from a ventral plate in each lateral wall (Fig. 19A). From the dorsal portion which becomes the most massive part of the diencephalon, are formed the large gray masses of the *thalamus* and *metathalamus*. According to some, this part also furnishes the globus pallidus of the lenticular nucleus (Spatz). The ventral portion together with the floor plate gives rise to the various structures of the *hypothalamus* including the subthalamus laterally, and the tuber cinereum, neurohypophysis and mammillary bodies in the floor of the third ventricle (Fig. 18). Immediately anterior to the tuber cinereum is the thickening of the optic chiasma containing an extension of the ventricular cavity, the *optic recess*. The chiasma marks the junction of the interbrain and endbrain and is considered by many as the telencephalic portion of the hypothalamus. In front of the chiasma the medial anterior wall of the third ventricle turns upward and ascends as a thin membrane, the *lamina terminalis*, to the dorsal anterior margin of the thalamus. This membrane constitutes the cephalic median wall of the primary forebrain and belongs to the telencephalon, since the latter is formed by a secondary evagination from this portion of the brain. A line passing from the anterior margin of the thalamus (or from the interventricular foramen) to the optic recess may be considered the boundary zone between diencephalon and telencephalon.

The roof of the diencephalon remains thin. From the caudal end a median diverticulum gives rise to the *pineal body* or *epiphysis* which retains an extension of the third ventricle, the *pineal* recess. On either side of the pineal body along the line of attachment of the thin roof to the thalamus, a longitudinal thickening develops into the *habenula*, a ganglionic mass associated with olfactory pathways. As in the case of the hindbrain, the thin roof forms the epithelial chorioid lamina which together with the richly vascular connective tissue of the investing pia, constitutes the tela chorioidea. Two vertical longitudinal folds extend from the tela into the ventricle and develop into the chorioid plexus. At the rostral margin (region of the interventricular foramen) the tela becomes directly continuous with that of the lateral ventricles. Laterally the slightly thickened margin of attachment of the thin roof to the thalamus is known as the *taenia thalami*. Tela chorioidea, epiphysis and habenula collectively constitute the *epithalamus*.

Telencephalon. Arising as a hollow unpaired bud from the dorsal anterior wall of the primary forebrain, the telencephalon begins to bulge laterally and expands into the two *hemispheric vesicles* which begin to overlap the diencephalon and are separated from the latter by the hemispheric sulcus (Figs. 12, 14, 20). These vesicles are now connected to each other by the median portion of the endbrain (*telencephalon me-*

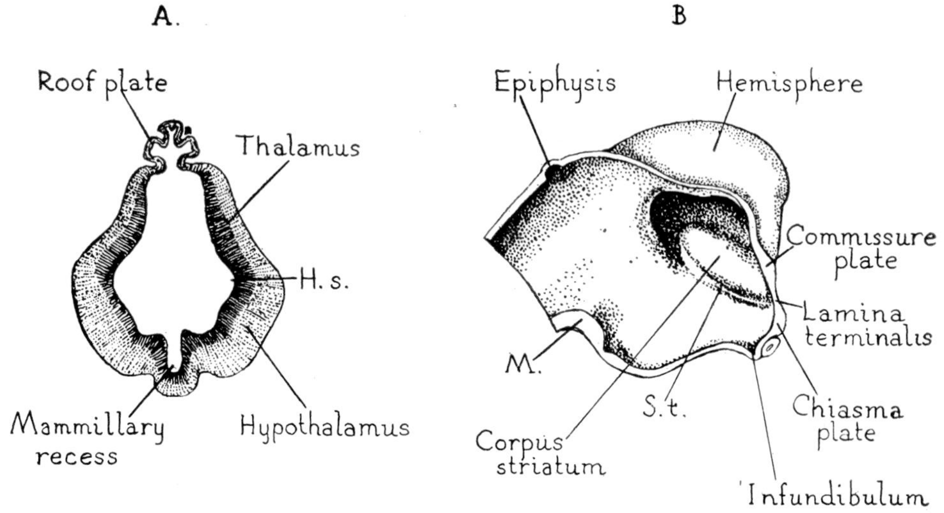

FIG. 19. *A*, section through diencephalon of a five weeks human embryo. (After His.) *H.s.*, hypothalamic sulcus. *B*, ventricular surface of brain of 13.8 mm. human embryo. (After Hochstetter.) *M*, mammillary swelling; *S.t.*, sulcus terminalis (semicircularis).

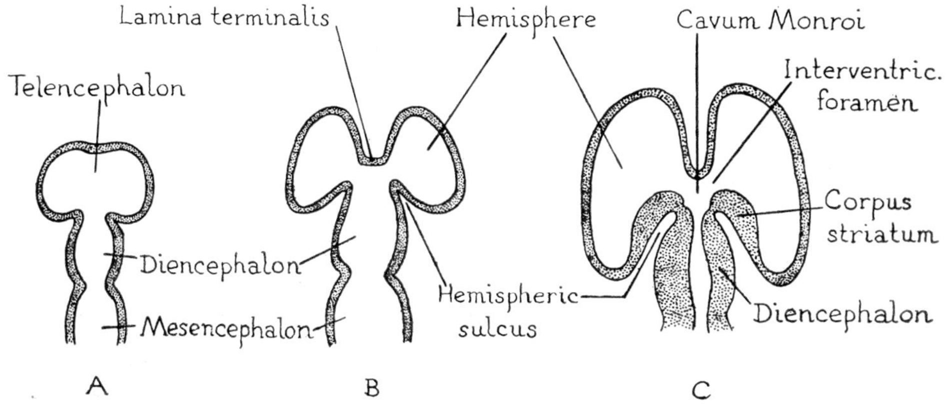

FIG. 20. Schematic representation of the development of the telencephalon.

dium) which undergoes relatively little growth and is composed of the lamina terminalis and the most rostral portion of the third ventricle, known as the *cavum Monroi*. The lateral extensions of the cavity into the hemispheric vesicles constitute the future lateral ventricles which at this stage communicate with the cavum Monroi by wide interventricular foramina (Figs. 20, 21).

The hemispheric vesicles rapidly expand in all directions. Their medial surfaces at first extend backward along the lateral surfaces of the diencephalon, producing a progressive deepening of the hemispheric sulcus whose fundus marks the place of attachment between endbrain and hindbrain (Figs. 12, 14, 20). Soon they expand dorsally to cover the roof of the diencephalon as well. In this manner the two hemispheric vesicles tower dorsally above the interbrain, their medial surfaces being separated from each other by a deep sagittal cleft, the *longitudinal* or *interhemispheric* fissure. As expansion continues, the midbrain and ultimately the cerebellum become likewise covered by the cerebral hemispheres.

From the hemispheric vesicles develop the three main structures of the endbrain—*olfactory lobe* (*rhinencephalon*), *corpus striatum* and *pallium*. The rhinencephalon arises as an evagination in the ventral wall of each hemisphere and is already visible in embryos of about 13 mm. (Figs. 14, 16). That part of the ventromedial wall adjacent to the diencephalon, i.e., the fundus region of the hemispheric sulcus, becomes greatly thickened to form a ganglionic mass, the *corpus striatum*, projecting into the lateral ventricle (Fig. 19B). The rest of the hemispheric wall, remaining relatively thin at first, develops into the *pallium* or cerebral cortex which becomes tremendously expanded in later development.

The chorioid plexus of the lateral ventricles is formed from the medial wall of the hemisphere, and the early stages are shown in Fig. 21. A little distance from the dorsal margin each hemispheric wall shows a longitudinal thickening, the hippocampal ridge, which is the forerunner of the future hippocampal formation. Below this the medial wall remains very thin and sends a longitudinal fold, the *plica chorioidea*, into the lateral ventricle. This fold, composed of the thin epithelial lamina and richly vascular connective tissue from the investing pia, is comparable to the tela chorioidea described in other portions of the brain, and by cellular proliferation gives rise to the chorioid plexus of the lateral ventricle. At the interventricular foramen this becomes continuous with the tela chorioidea of the third ventricle.

The hemispheres expand anteriorly to form the frontal lobe, posteriorly and ventrally to form the occipital and temporal lobes respectively. The middle portion in close relation to the diencephalon becomes the parietal lobe. During the second month, a shallow depression, the *lateral* or *Sylvian fossa*, appears in the region overlying the corpus striatum (Figs. 16, 17). The fossa is not produced by invagination but is due to the more rapid expansion and thickening of the adjacent portions of the frontal, parietal, and temporal walls. Gradually these portions overgrow the depression whose external opening becomes reduced to a deep cleft, the *lateral* or *Sylvian* fissure. The now hidden floor of the Sylvian fissure develops into the *insula* or *island of Reil* (Fig. 22).

In the fifth month, sulci begin to appear on the lateral surface of the hemisphere, though several have already been formed before on the medial surface. At the end of the seventh month, all the main sulci and convolutions are definitely indicated (Fig. 22). The lateral ventricles enlarge corresponding to the growth of the hemispheres, sending frontal, occipital, and temporal extensions or horns into the respective parts of the brain. The relatively wide interventricular foramina become smaller and smaller and are finally reduced to slit-like openings communicating with the cavum

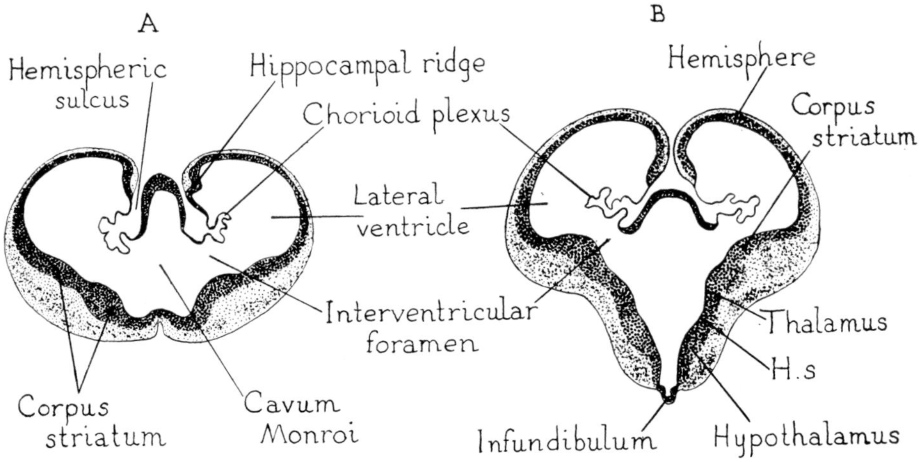

FIG. 21. Transverse sections through forebrain of human embryos. *A*, 17 mm.; *B*, 19.4 mm. *H.s.*, hypothalamic sulcus. (After Hochstetter.)

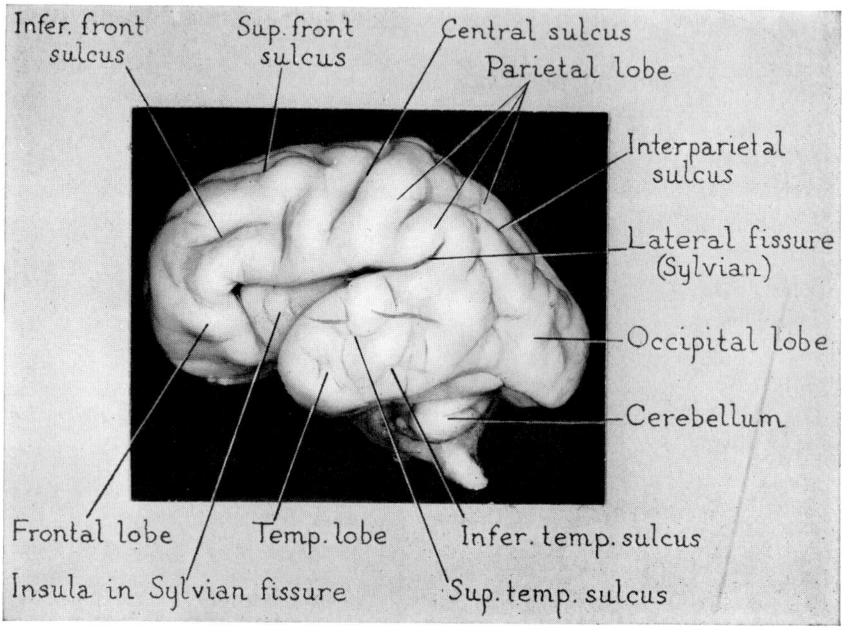

FIG. 22. Brain of six and one-half months human fetus, lateral view. Photograph.

Monroi which now forms the most rostral portion of the cleft-like third ventricle.

The first two chapters have provided background information on the comparative organization and embryonic development of the central nervous system. This material has afforded the student an opportunity to grasp and become familiar with many new anatomical terms.

After the neural tube has been formed, it lies deep to the overlying ectoderm and is surrounded on all sides by primitive mesoderm (mesenchyme). This embryonic relationship is shown in Fig. 132. Here the more darkly stained mesenchyme is seen to the left of the spinal nerve and neural tube. From the surrounding mesoderm is derived the muscles, blood vessels, cartilage, bone, and connective tissue of the body. The mesoderm thus gives rise to several supporting structures of the nervous system (e.g., skull, vertebrae, meninges, intervertebral discs, ligaments, sheaths of peripheral nerves, blood vessels, and microglia). These mesodermal structures are of paramount importance for they provide not only support, but protection and nourishment to the nervous system. It is paradoxical that the supporting tissues are, under some circumstances, responsible for serious damage to the nervous system. For example, an artery may rupture with extensive hemorrhage, or the lumen of a vessel may be occluded suddenly and produce anoxia in the area of its neural distribution. Tumors commonly arise from the meninges, or from the connective tissue sheaths along peripheral nerves. An intervertebral disc may rupture dorsally into the vertebral canal and compress the spinal cord or departing spinal nerve; also fractures of the skull and vertebrae often compress the underlying brain or spinal cord. To gain a better appreciation of these important adnexa, let us now examine the meninges of the central nervous system.

3

The Meninges of the Central Nervous System

The brain and spinal cord are enclosed by two connective tissue sheaths, the *dura mater* and *pia-arachnoid*, the latter being usually described as two separate membranes: the *pia mater* and *arachnoid* (Fig. 23). These membranes are collectively known as the meninges, the dura mater constituting the *pachymeninx* and the pia-arachnoid the *leptomeninx* or *leptomeninges*.

Dura mater. The dura mater is the outer sheath and consists of dense fibrous tissue. The *cerebral dura* serves both as an investing sheath for the brain and as periosteum for the inner surface of the cranium (Fig. 25). It consists of two layers: (a) an inner layer of dense fibrous tissue lined on its brain surface with a single layer of flat cells; and (b) an outer layer much richer in blood vessels and nerves, which forms the periosteum. Between the two layers are situated the large venous sinuses of the brain. The *spinal dura* corresponds to the inner layer of the cerebral dura, the vertebrae having their own separate periosteum. Both inner and outer surfaces of the spinal dura are covered by a single layer of flat cells, and it is separated from the periosteum by the narrow *epidural space* in which are found anastomosing venous channels lying in areolar tissue rich in fat. It is maintained by some that the spinal dura contains lymphatics which open on both of its surfaces. Between the dura and the arachnoid is the capillary *subdural space* filled with fluid and believed to communicate by clefts with the tissue spaces in the sheaths of nerves and through them with the deep lymphatic vessels of the neck and groin. It has no direct communication with the subarachnoid space. The spinal dura is attached to the outer surface of the arachnoid by thread-like subdural trabeculae.

As the nerve roots penetrate the dura mater, they receive a dural investment which is continuous with the epineurium of the peripheral nerve.

The spinal dura extends as a closed, tough sac from the margins of the foramen magnum above, to the second sacral vertebra below. Opposite the second sacral vertebra, the dura forms an investment about the filum terminale to form a thin fibrous cord, the *coccygeal ligament*. The latter extends caudally to the dorsal surface of the coccyx, where it blends with the periosteum and posterior longitudinal ligament of the vertebral column (Fig. 24). Since the spinal cord usually terminates at the lower border of the first lumbar vertebra, the lower portion of the dural cul-de-sac is occupied by the filum terminale and cauda equina (Fig. 30).

The cerebral dura gives off several reduplications or septa which tend to divide the cranial cavity into incomplete compartments (Fig. 29). The *falx cerebri* is a sickle-shaped, median septum extending from the crista galli to the internal occipital protuberance and separating the two hemispheres. The *tentorium cerebelli* is a transverse, dorsally arched septum placed between the occipital lobes and the cerebellum. Its free anterior border forms the tentorial incisure through which the brain stem passes. From the midline of its under surface, a small sagittal septum, the *falx cerebelli,* incompletely separates the hemispheres of the cerebellum. The *diaphragma sellae* forms the fibrous roof of the pituitary fossa (sella turcica) and is perforated by the infundibulum (Fig. 29).

Pia mater. The pia mater closely invests the brain and spinal cord, extending in all the sulci and fissures, and protrudes into the ventricles in the chorioid plexuses where it is lined on its inner surface by a layer of neural chorioideal cells (Fig. 123). The pia consists of fibrous connective tissue, rather rich in elastic fibers, which contains many fine nerve fibers, scattered pigment cells and numerous blood vessels which send perpendicular branches into the spinal cord and brain. These branches, in addition to their adventitial coats, may be accompanied for some distance by prolongations of pial tissue (Fig. 27).

The spinal cord is anchored to the dura by two lateral septa which extend the whole length of the cord and are collectively known as the *ligamentum denticulatum* (Figs. 23, 24). Mesially each septum is continuously attached to the pia, but laterally it is broken up into 19–21 flat denticulate processes which are inserted in the dura (Fig. 30). The first process is given off above the first cervical nerve root, the last one just below the first lumbar. Below this each ligament continues as a narrow seam to the tip of the conus medullaris where it fuses with its mate of the opposite side to continue as the covering of the *filum terminale.*

Arachnoid. The arachnoid or outer portion of the pia-arachnoid is a delicate nonvascular membrane which passes over the sulci without dipping into them and extends for a short distance along the roots of the cerebrospinal nerves and along the optic nerve. It is partly separated from the pia by numerous spaces traversed by trabeculae which pass from pia to arachnoid. These are the *subarachnoid spaces* or *space* and may be regarded as dilations of pial spaces by which the embryologically single leptomeninx is transformed into the double incompletely separated pia-arachnoid. They are thus intraleptomeningeal spaces. The subarachnoid spaces dip into the sulci of the brain and spinal cord. In the cerebral pia-arachnoid the subarachnoid spaces are traversed by numerous trabeculae and there is no clear distinction between pia and arachnoid (Figs. 26, 27). In the spinal pia-arachnoid the trabeculae are few and usually concentrated into several subarachnoid septa, hence the subarachnoid space is a more continuous cavity and the arachnoid a more distinct membrane. The arachnoid, trabeculae and outer pial surface are all covered with a single layer of flattened cells with large pale oval nuclei. When certain substances are injected in the subarachnoid space, these cells may swell and assume a phagocytic activity, ingesting particles of the foreign material. They may even become detached and form free macrophages.

In certain places the cerebral arachnoid sends prolongations into the dura, which protrude into a venous sinus or venous lacuna. These prolongations, into which extend the subarachnoid spaces and trabeculae, are likewise covered with a mesothelial lining and form the *arachnoid villi* which when hypertrophied are known as *Pacchionian bodies* or *Pacchionian granulations* (Fig. 26). They are most numerous along the interhemispheric fissure, in relation to the superior longitudinal sinus, but are also found along the other venous sinuses within the skull. Rudimentary arachnoid villi have been described in the spinal arachnoid, but their function is probably not the same (Hassin). In both the spinal and cerebral arachnoid, cell clusters are sometimes formed which become attached to the dura. These growths may become calcified or under abnormal conditions form the sites of neoplastic tumors. They are more frequent with advancing age.

The subarachnoid space is filled with cerebrospinal fluid and is in direct communication with the fourth ventricle of the

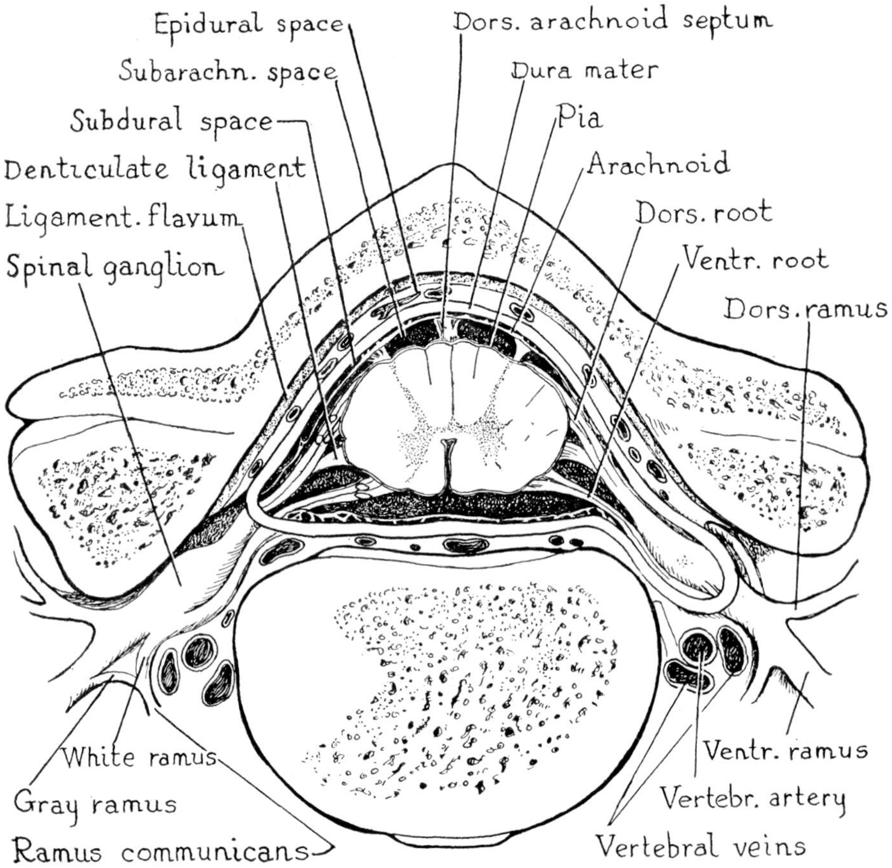

FIG. 23. Transverse section through first thoracic vertebra, showing spinal cord and its coverings. (After Rauber-Kopsch.)

brain by means of three apertures, one median and two lateral ones. The median aperture or *foramen of Magendie* is placed in the caudal part of the thin roof, the lateral apertures or *foramina of Luschka* open into the lateral recesses of the ventricle (Fig. 37). The subarachnoid space also communicates with the tissue spaces within or around the blood vessels which penetrate the central nervous system from the pia. In the larger vessels these *perivascular spaces* or *spaces of Virchow-Robin* lie within the adventitia, being covered externally by prolongations of pial connective tissue. When the smaller vessels are reached, the pial prolongations come to an end, and the perivascular spaces now lie between the vessel wall and the glial membrane. The spaces continue along the finer ramifications of the blood vessels, ultimately communicating with the perineuronal clefts which surround the bodies of nerve cells (Weed), (Fig. 27). Through these channels waste substances produced by the nerve cells may pass out to the subarachnoid space.

In the spinal canal there is always a relatively wide subarachnoid space between pia and arachnoid. Below the caudal tip of the spinal cord the space extends to the depth of the dural sac and here contains the filum terminale and descending lumbosacral nerve roots (cauda equina). This region is therefore most suitable for tapping the cerebrospinal fluid (lumbar puncture) since there is no likelihood of injury to the

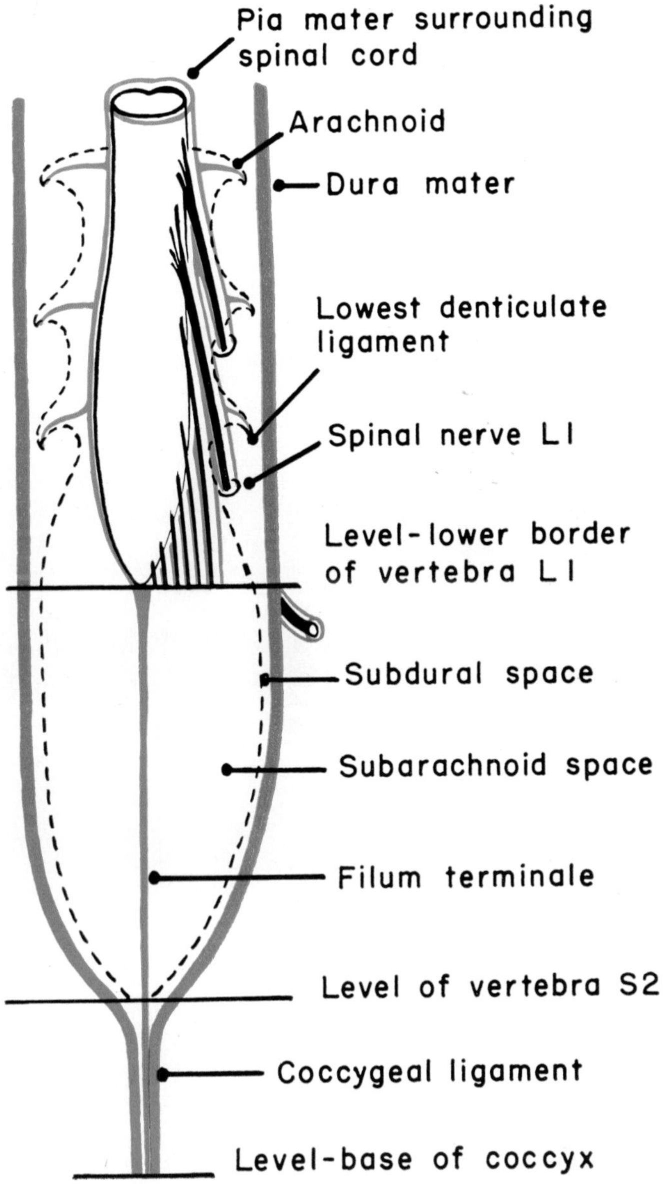

FIG. 24. Diagram of spinal cord and meninges in lumbar and sacral regions.

spinal cord (Fig. 24). In the cranial cavity the extent of the subarachnoid space shows many local variations, owing to the irregular contour of the brain surface. Over the convex surfaces of the convolutions, the pia and arachnoid are close to each other with only a narrow space between them. When passing over sulci the pia dips in while the arachnoid bridges over, hence the subarachnoid spaces are deeper. At the base of the brain and its transition to the spinal cord the arachnoid becomes widely separated from the pia in certain places, giving rise to large cavities, the *subarachnoid cisterns* (Fig. 28). The whole medulla has a rather wide subarachnoid space, but this is most extensive dorsally where the arachnoid passes from the dorsal surface of the

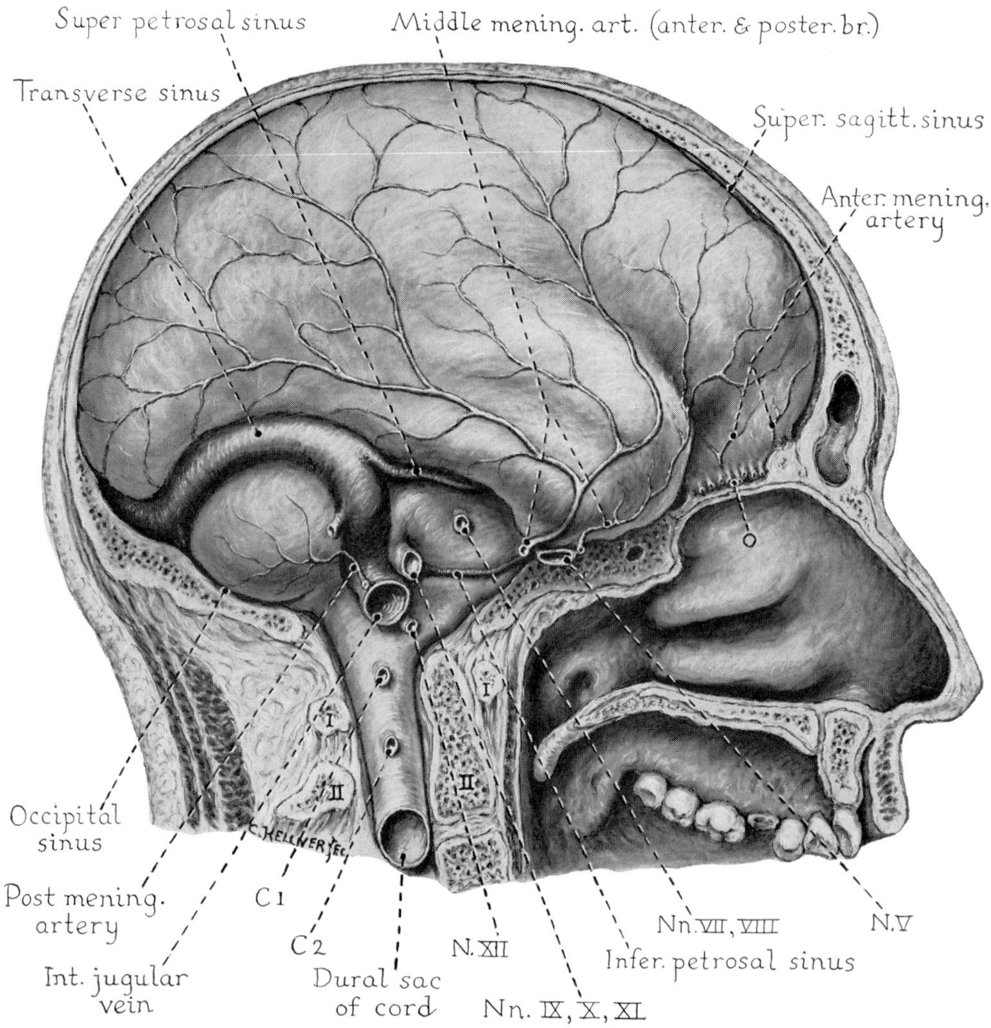

FIG. 25. External view of dural sac of brain and upper cervical cord. I, atlas; II, axis; C1, C2, dural sheaths of first and second cervical nerves; Nn. V-XII, dural sheaths of corresponding cranial nerves; O, dural sheaths of fila olfactoria.

medulla to the inferior surface of the cerebellum, forming the large *cisterna magna* (*cerebello-medullaris*) into which open the foramina of Magendie and Luschka. Ventrally the medullary subarachnoid space widens into the *cisterna pontis.* The midbrain is completely surrounded by cisterns, dorsally by the *cisterna superior,* laterally by the *cisterna ambiens,* and ventrally by the *cisterna interpeduncularis* which extends laterally over the stem of the Sylvian fissure. In front of the interpeduncular cistern is the *cisterna chiasmatica,* followed anteriorly and dorsally by cisterns along the lamina terminalis and the dorsal convex surface of the corpus callosum.

Cerebrospinal fluid. The cerebrospinal fluid is a clear colorless fluid apparently identical with the aqueous humor of the eye and other tissue fluids. Its specific gravity is about 1.004–1.007. It contains small amounts of protein and glucose, larger amounts of potassium and sodium chloride, and traces of sulfate, phosphate, calcium,

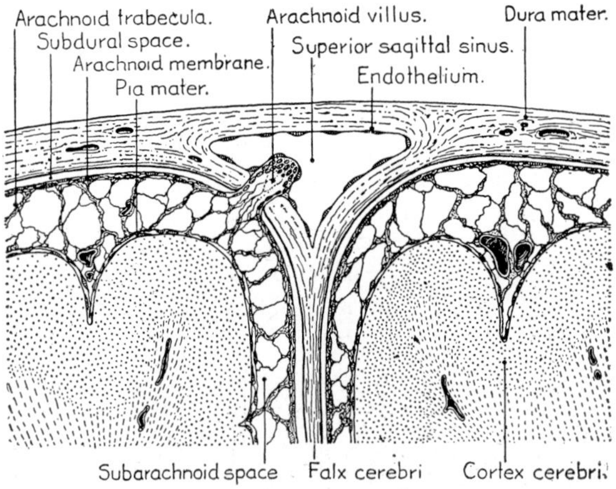

FIG. 26. Diagram of meninges surrounding cerebral cortex, showing relation of arachnoid villus to dural venous sinus. (Weed.)

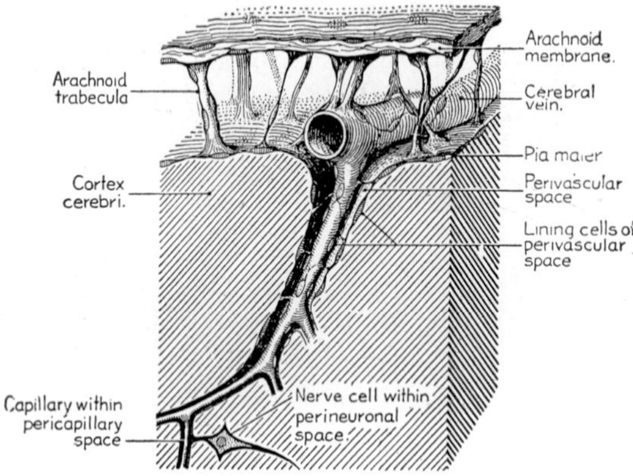

FIG. 27. Diagram of cerebral pia-arachnoid, showing relations of subarachnoid space, perivascular channels and nerve cells. (Weed.)

and uric acid. Normally a few lymphocytes, about 3–8 per cubic millimeter, are also found. The quantity of the fluid in the adult is around 80–200 cc., but there may be more extreme individual variations. The bulk of the fluid is formed by the activity of the chorioidal cells of the chorioid plexuses and telae and is poured into the ventricles of the brain from which it passes through the foramina of Magendie and Luschka to the cisterns and other subarachnoid spaces. A smaller amount is probably contributed by the nerve cells, the waste products of their metabolic activity reaching the subarachnoid space by way of the perineuronal and perivascular spaces. Whether ependyma and other neuroglia cells also contribute to its formation is not certain. The drainage of the fluid is principally by filtration through the wall of the arachnoid villi into the cerebral venous sinuses. The venous blood is hypertonic to the fluid and its pressure somewhat lower hence the direction of the drainage is from subarachnoid space to venous channel. Some of the fluid also escapes by way of the perineuronal spaces into the sheaths of the spinal and cranial nerves, ultimately reaching lymphatics and lymph nodes.

The cerebrospinal fluid probably has a

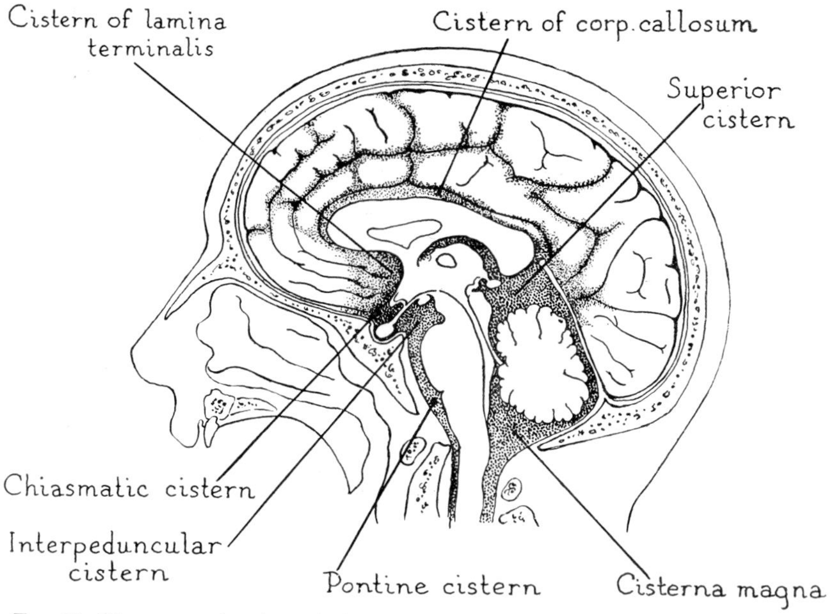

FIG. 28. Diagrammatic view of the main subarachnoid cisterns. (After Bailey.)

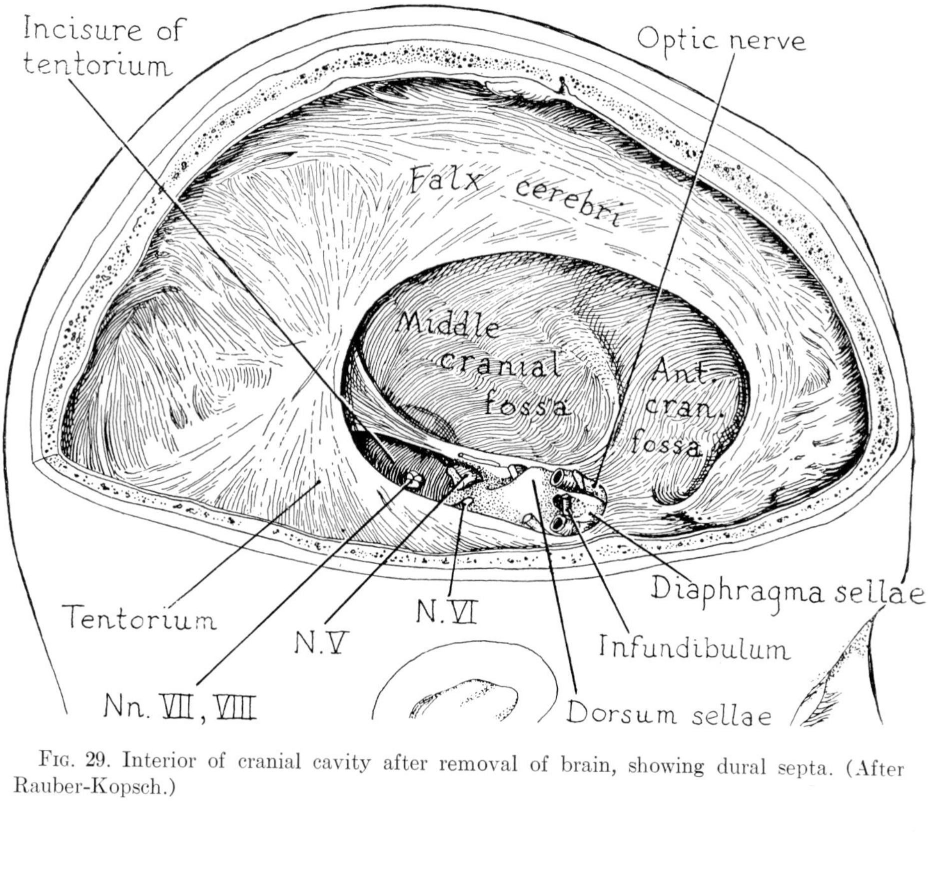

FIG. 29. Interior of cranial cavity after removal of brain, showing dural septa. (After Rauber-Kopsch.)

mechanical function, serving as a water cushion for the central nervous system and aiding in the maintenance of a relatively constant intracranial pressure. It also plays an important part in removing waste substances from the brain and spinal cord. Changes of the fluid in pathological states, both as to increase and nature of the cells found in it and its altered chemical composition, are of great importance in the diagnosis of many diseases of the nervous system. It is usually withdrawn by a lumbar puncture which taps the subarachnoid space below the level of the spinal cord in the region of the cauda equina. The same puncture is also used for the introduction of therapeutic agents. A block in the free passage of the cerebrospinal fluid from ventricles to subarachnoid space causes internal hydrocephalus.

According to Hassin (1948) the cerebrospinal fluid represents the lymph or tissue fluid of the nervous system serving for the removal of waste substances. It is formed by transudation from the brain and spinal cord into the perineuronal and perivascular spaces of Virchow-Robin, whence it is discharged into the ventricles and subarachnoid spaces. The main absorption of the fluid is not through the arachnoid villi and granulations but through the perineurial spaces of the cranial and spinal roots.

4

Gross Consideration of the Central Nervous System

The examination of the spinal cord and brain *in situ* is a prerequisite for a student beginning a course in Neuroanatomy. It will clarify many of the meningeal relationships discussed in the preceding chapter, and will also permit a lasting visual impression of the bones, ligaments, and meninges that house, support, and protect the central nervous system and attached nerves. Although the brain and spinal cord observed in the laboratory has been hardened by fixatives or embalming, it should be remembered that during life these structures are quite soft and in a semi-gelatinous state.

A familiarity with the gross appearance of the fixed brain and spinal cord is an equally valuable experience, for one can form clearer concepts of internal microscopic structure if he possesses a thorough knowledge of macroscopic surface appearance. For this reason the gross topography of the spinal cord, brain stem, and cerebral hemisphere is now presented.

THE SPINAL CORD

The spinal cord surrounded by its coverings lies loosely in the vertebral canal, extending from the foramen magnum where it is continuous with the medulla oblongata, to the lower border of the first lumbar vertebra (Figs. 23, 30). During early development the spinal cord extends to the lower end of the sacrum, but from the fourth month on the vertebral column elongates more rapidly than the cord. The latter, anchored above to the medulla oblongata, is pulled upward in the spinal canal, its caudal tip reaching the third lumbar vertebra at birth and the lower border of the first lumbar in the adult. Variations have been found, the spinal cord terminating as high as the twelfth thoracic or as low as the third lumbar vertebra. It is said to be slightly lower in woman.

The spinal cord is cylindrical in shape, somewhat flattened dorsoventrally, especially in the cervical portion, and shows two spindle-shaped swellings, the *cervical* and *lumbar* enlargements, comprising those portions of the cord which innervate respectively the upper and lower extremities. In animals without typical limbs there are no enlargements, the spinal cord having a uniform diameter which gradually narrows in its caudal portions. Below the lumbar enlargement the cord rapidly narrows to a cone shaped termination, the *conus medullaris.* From the conus a slender non-nervous filament, the *filum terminale,* extends downward to the fundus of the dural sac, at about the level of the second sacral vertebra (Fig. 30). There it penetrates the dura and, invested by a dural process, continues as the coccygeal ligament to the posterior surface of the coccyx to pass into the periosteum of the latter. A prolongation of the central canal of the spinal cord continues into the upper portion of the filum terminale which is otherwise composed mainly of pial connective tissue.

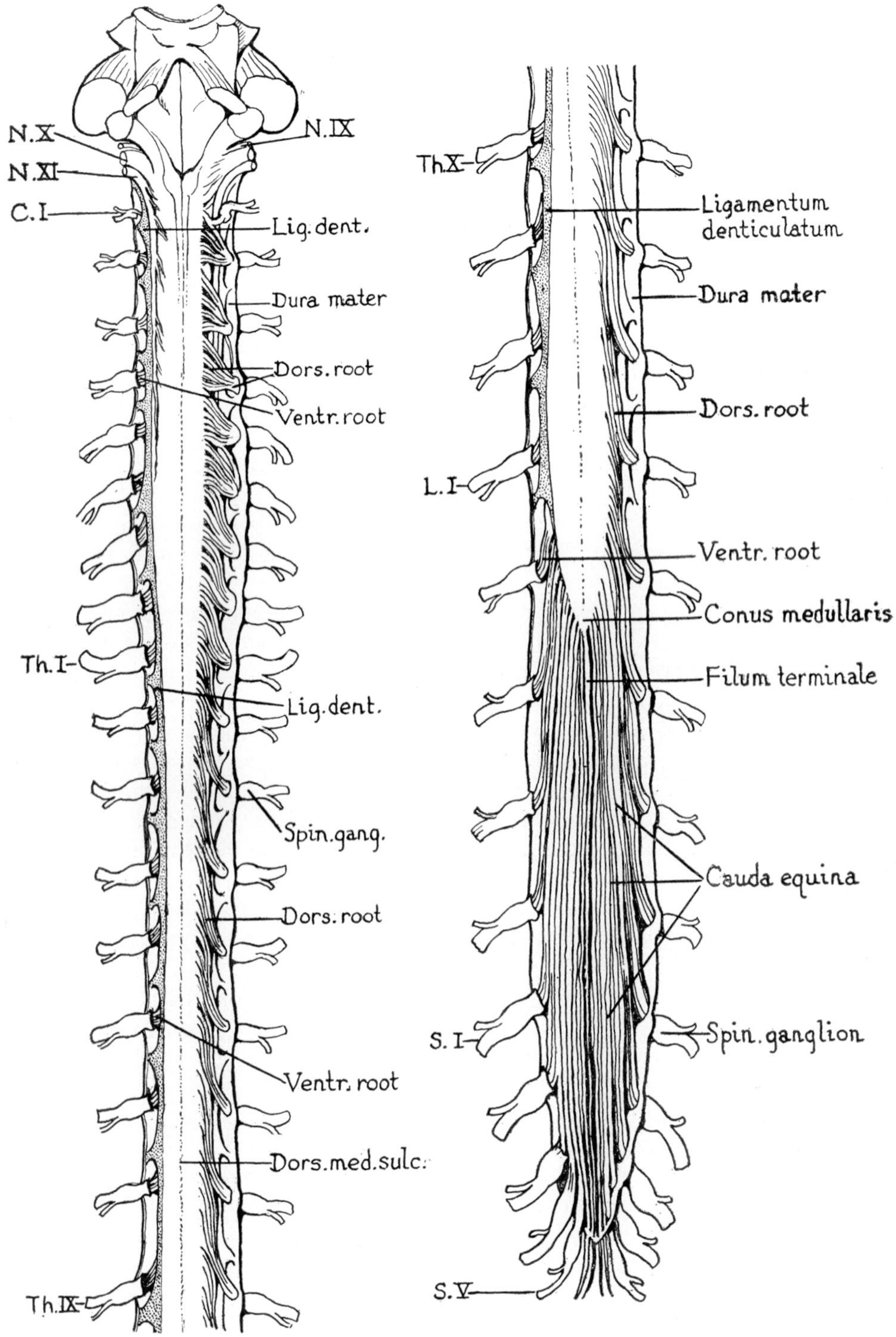

Fig. 30. Dorsal view of spinal cord with ganglia and nerve roots. The dorsal portion of the dura mater has been removed to show the contents of the dural sac. On the left side the dorsal roots have been cut to expose the denticulate ligament (*Lig. dent.*) and the ventral roots. The spinal nerves are indicated by Roman numerals. *C*, cervical; *Th*, thoracic; *L*, lumbar; *S*, sacral. (After Leveillé, from Hirschfeld's "Système Nerveux".)

Though the spinal cord is intrinsically a continuous and unsegmented structure, the thirty-one pairs of nerves which arise from it produce an appearance of external segmentation. Each segment is that portion of the cord which furnishes dorsal and ventral root filaments to a single pair of nerves. On this basis there are thirty-one segments corresponding to the nerve pairs; eight cervical, twelve thoracic, five lumbar, five sacral, and usually one coccygeal (Figs. 30, 31). The first cervical nerve emerges between the atlas and the occipital bone.

During early development, the "segments" of the spinal cord correspond closely to the respective embryonal vertebrae, and the spinal nerves pass laterally to their intervertebral foramina. Later, when the vertebral column grows more rapidly than the cord, the latter is pulled upward, and the interval between the spinal origin of a nerve and its vertebral exit gradually increases in length. The result is that in the adult where the cord terminates at the lower border of the first lumbar vertebra, the lumbar and sacral nerves have long roots which descend in the dural sac to reach their respective intervertebral foramina (Figs. 30, 31). This bundle of descending roots surrounding the filum terminale resembles a horse's tail and hence is known as the *cauda equina*. The exact relations of the spinal cord segments to the vertebral bodies and processes are shown in Fig. 31.

The length of the spinal cord from its upper limit to the tip of the conus medullaris is about 45 cm. in the male and 43 cm. in the female, contrasted to a length of about 70 cm. for the vertebral column. Its weight is about 35 grams. In the mid-thoracic region the transverse and sagittal diameters are about 10 mm. and 8 mm. respectively; in the cervical enlargement (sixth cervical) 13–14 mm. and 9 mm.; in the lumbar enlargement (third lumbar) about 12 mm. and 8.5 mm.

General topography. When freed from its meninges, the surface of the cord shows a number of longitudinal furrows (Figs. 32, 33). On the ventral side is the deep *ventral median fissure* which penetrates into the cord for a depth of some 3 mm. and into which extends a fold of the pia containing blood vessels. On the dorsal surface is the shallow *dorsal median sulcus*. This sulcus is continuous with a delicate glial partition, the *dorsal median septum*, which extends into the cord to a depth of 5 mm. and reaches the deep lying gray. More laterally are the *dorsolateral* and *ventrolateral sulci*. The former is a fairly distinct furrow into which the filaments of the dorsal roots enter in a rectilinear manner. The ventrolateral sulcus marks the exit of the ventral root fibers and is hardly distinguishable, since the ventral roots do not emerge rectilinearly but in groups of irregular filaments occupying an area of about 2 mm. in transverse diameter. In the cervical and upper thoracic cord another furrow, the *dorsal intermediate sulcus*, extends between the medial and lateral sulci. The ventral median fissure and dorsal median septum divide the cord into two incompletely separated halves connected by a narrow median bridge or commissure.

In a transverse section the cord is seen to consist of a centrally placed gray substance surrounded everywhere by a mantle of white (Fig. 33). The latter is composed mainly of closely packed myelinated fibers and hence appears glistening white in the fresh condition. The central substance appears pinkish-gray for it contains numerous unmyelinated nerve fibers, cell bodies, dendrites and terminal arborizations, and has a much richer blood supply. The gray substance forms a continuous deeply notched column extending the entire length of the cord (Fig. 32), which in section shows the form of a butterfly or of the letter H. The odd-shaped vertical bars form the gray columns of the lateral halves of the cord, the cross bar constitutes the gray commissure containing the central canal. In each half

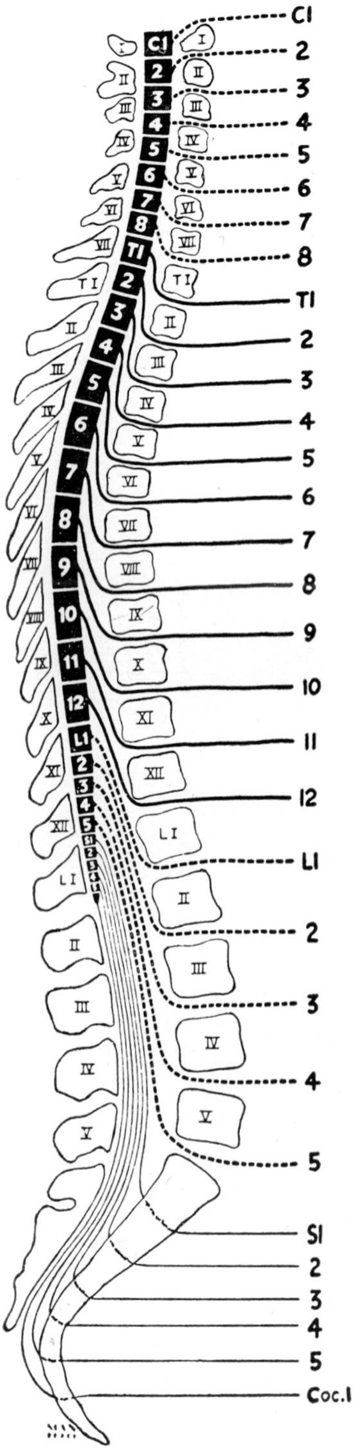

FIG. 31. Diagram of the position of the spinal cord segments with reference to the bodies and spinous processes of the vertebrae. Note also the place of origin of the nerve roots from the spinal cord and their emergence from the corresponding intervertebral foramina. (Haymaker and Woodhall.)

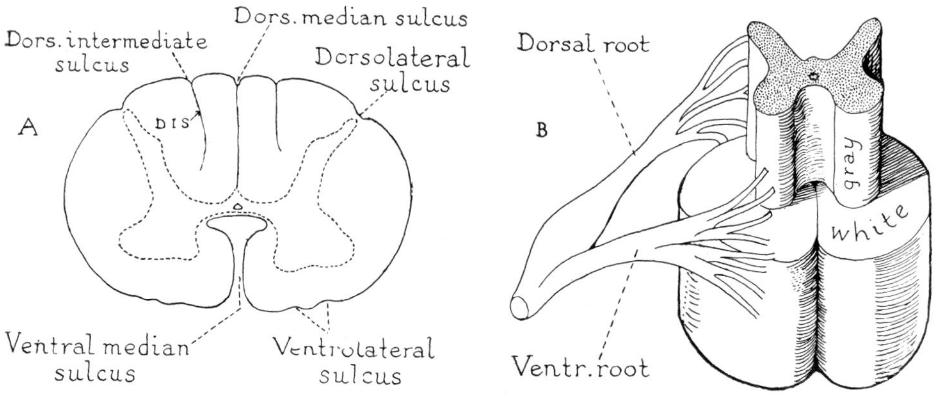

FIG. 32. *A*, section through cervical portion of spinal cord, schematic; *B*, diagram of the gray columns of the cord. *Dis*, dorsal intermediate septum.

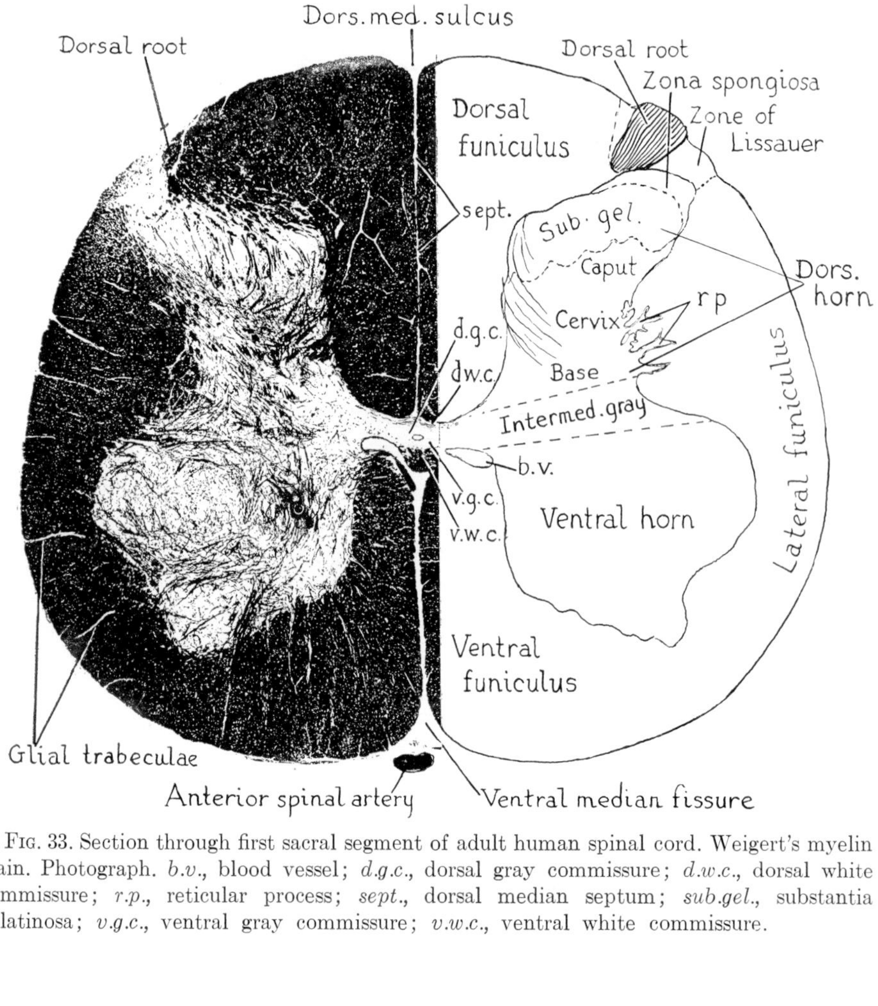

FIG. 33. Section through first sacral segment of adult human spinal cord. Weigert's myelin stain. Photograph. *b.v.*, blood vessel; *d.g.c.*, dorsal gray commissure; *d.w.c.*, dorsal white commissure; *r.p.*, reticular process; *sept.*, dorsal median septum; *sub.gel.*, substantia gelatinosa; *v.g.c.*, ventral gray commissure; *v.w.c.*, ventral white commissure.

the gray substance extending dorsal to the gray commissure is called the *dorsal column* or *horn,* that extending ventrally is the *ventral column* or horn. The portion connecting the two and from which the gray commissure extends is known as the intermediate gray. In the thoracic cord a slender lateral protrusion constitutes the *lateral* or *intermediolateral column* or horn (Figs. 170, 173). In the concavity between dorsal and ventral horn, small processes of gray extend into the white where they become intimately interlaced with longitudinally running fibers, forming the *reticular process* or *reticular formation,* most extensively developed in the cervical portion of the cord.

The gray commissure is divided by the central canal into a dorsal and ventral gray commissure. Immediately surrounding the central canal is a light granular area composed mainly of neuroglia and known as the central gelatinous substance (substantia gliosa). The dorsal horn extends nearly to the surface of the cord, being separated from the periphery by a narrow zone of white matter, the *zone of Lissauer* or *dorsolateral fasciculus,* composed of delicate longitudinally coursing myelinated and unmyelinated fibers. In most levels the dorsal horn shows a division into an expanded head or *caput* separated by a constricted neck or *cervix* from the *basal* portion which is continuous with the intermediate gray. The head is capped by a light staining area (in Weigert preparations) known as the *gelatinous substance of Rolando,* external to which is a thin zone, the *zona spongiosa,* containing scattered large nerve cells and a delicate plexus of fine myelinated fibers.

The mantle of white is divided by the entering dorsal and the emerging ventral roots into three main regions: a *dorsal funiculus* lying between the dorsal median septum and dorsal roots; a *lateral funiculus* between the dorsal and ventral roots; and a *ventral funiculus* between the ventral median fissure and the ventral roots. Since the dorsal gray horn extends almost to the periphery of the cord, the dorsal funiculus is quite definitely delimited from the rest of the white. There is, however, no clear boundary between the other two funiculi, the two together really constituting a single U-shaped ventrolateral funiculus. Just ventral to the ventral gray commissure is a bundle of transverse fibers, the *ventral white commissure,* composed of crossing fibers from various nerve cells to be described later. In the dorsal part of the dorsal gray commissure, fine decussating myelinated fibers constitute the *dorsal white commissure.*

Before the gross topography of the brain is undertaken, the student should examine the course of the vertebral and internal carotid arteries and their intracranial branches. A familiarity with the vascular pattern and its branches (Figs. 63, 64, 66, 67, 68) is essential at this stage, for many of the arteries and veins are destroyed when the pia-arachnoid layers are removed to expose the surface of the brain.

THE BRAIN STEM

When the cerebral hemispheres are dissected away, the remaining bulbous portion constitutes the so-called "brain-stem" (Figs. 34, 35, 36). In such specimens the cut surfaces of the fiber bundles, which connect the brain stem with the detached portions, can be seen. The massive fiber bundle at the rostral end is the *internal capsule.* It is literally a "turnpike" of fibers connecting the cerebral hemispheres above with all the segments of the brain stem and spinal cord below (Figs. 35, 327). The three smaller bundles are the cerebellar peduncles; the inferior cerebellar peduncle, or *restiform body*; the middle cerebellar peduncle, or *brachium pontis*; and the superior cerebellar peduncle, or *brachium conjunctivum* (Figs. 35, 36). The inferior connects the medulla with the cerebellum, while the middle is a large bridge between the pons and the cerebellum. The smaller superior peduncle extends upward to connect the cerebellum and midbrain.

Further examination of the isolated brain stem will reveal several striking changes when it is compared to the spinal cord. It becomes progressively larger, proceeding from the medulla to the diencephalon. The increase in size is the result of two factors, chiefly: first, the need for visceral and somatic nuclei to receive information from, and extend motor control over, all the structures supplied by the cranial nerves; secondly, the development of extensive coordinating mechanisms as each higher segment of the brain stem becomes integrated with existing lower levels. The pons and medulla are further distorted by the expansion of the central canal of the spinal cord to form the broad, but shallow, fourth ventricle.

The cranial nerves. The origin and arrangement of the twelve pairs of cranial nerves stand out in sharp contrast to the serial attachments of the dorsal and ventral roots of the spinal nerves. It will be recalled that each segmental spinal nerve had four functional types of nerve fibers (Fig. 180), and each type occupies a localized region in both the embryonic and adult spinal cord (Fig. 127). The same four functional types of nerve fibers are present in some of the cranial nerves, but in addition, three new "special" types of fibers are added. Two new sensory categories transmit specialized nerve impulses: those from the taste-buds are designated *special visceral afferent*; the nerve fibers conveying visual impulses from the retina and auditory impulses from the cochlea are designated *special somatic afferent*. The olfactory nerve fibers are considered by some as special visceral afferent. A third functional category, *special visceral efferent*, is used to designate the motor fibers that supply skeletal muscles of the head and neck which were derived from mesoderm of the embryonic branchial arches. Such muscles are often spoken of as "branchiomeric muscles", and receive their special motor fibers via cranial nerves V, VII, IX, X, and XI.

The addition of special nuclei, larger visceral nuclei, expansion of the fourth ventricle, development of the cerebellum, and formation of new pathways, all played a part in altering the location of these functional neurons within the brain stem. (Compare Figs. 127, 180, and 222.) The location of the functional components observed in the spinal cord has been shifted within the medulla to a dorsomedial position, and the nuclei of the special neurons lie in a dorsolateral position (Fig. 222). New cell groups and large fiber pathways are also added to the ventral and lateral surfaces of the medulla (e.g., pyramid and olive). As a result of these internal changes, the older ascending sensory and descending motor systems come to lie in a more dorsal position in the brain stem, while the newer descending tracts and integrating pathways occupy the ventral and lateral areas.

This internal rearrangement of cell groups and fiber pathways accounts for the size, surface topography of the brain stem, and altered arrangement of the cranial nerves. The individual cranial nerves vary widely in the composition of their functional components. Some are entirely sensory, some are mainly motor, while others resemble the mixed spinal nerves in having both afferent and efferent fibers.

In the following paragraphs, only the gross aspects of the brain are presented briefly. Special emphasis is given to those structures that will help the student orient and better interpret microscopic sections made from different levels. Each major subdivision of the brain will be presented in more detail in subsequent chapters.

The medulla (Myelencephalon). This conically expanded continuation of the cervical spinal cord extends from the foramen magnum to the caudal border of the pons. It has a transverse diameter of 9–12 mm. at the foramen magnum, attains a diameter of

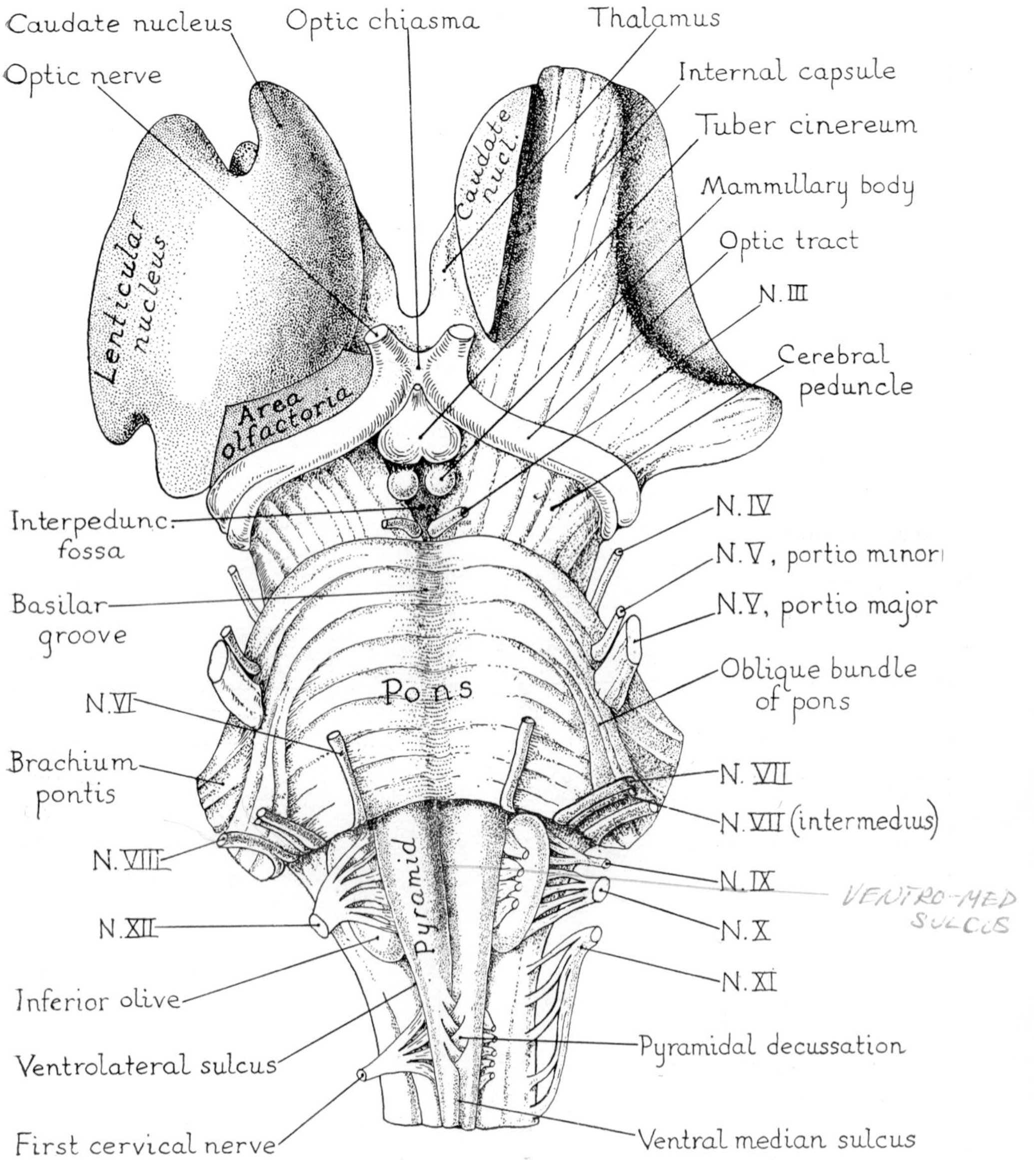

FIG. 34. Ventral view of the brain stem.

24 mm. near the pons, and is approximately 28 mm. in length.

The sulci observed on the surfaces of the spinal cord (Fig. 32) continue upward into the medulla (Figs. 34, 35). Above the medulla, only the dorsal median sulcus and sulcus limitans are present and of use in orientation. The *ventral median sulcus* is partially obliterated in the lower medulla by the obliquely crossing fiber bundles of the pyramidal decussation. Above the decussation the sulcus deepens as it ascends, and on either side it is flanked by a tapering longitudinal prominence, the *pyramid* (Fig. 34). The *ventrolateral* (*preolivary*) *sulcus* extends upward as a prominent furrow to separate the pyramid and *inferior olive* on each side. The hypoglossal (XII) nerve,

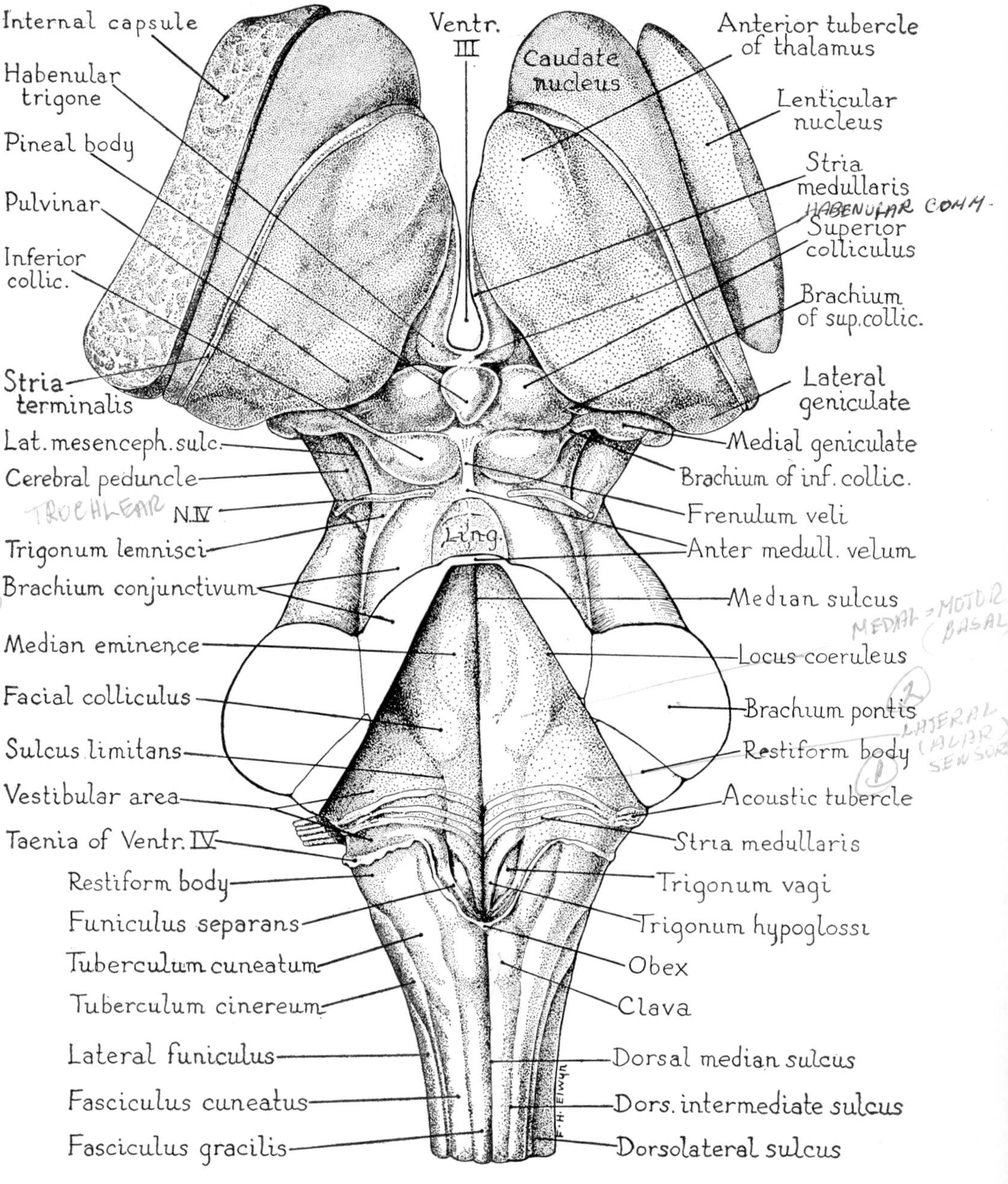

FIG. 35. Dorsal view of the brain stem. *Ling.*, lingula.

and lower down, the first cervical nerve emerge through this sulcus. At the junction of pons and medulla, the abducens (VI) nerve also emerges from this sulcus. A more lateral and deeper *postolivary sulcus* separates the inferior olive from the *tuberculum cinereum* (trigeminal eminence) and *restiform body*. Emerging from this sulcus are the roots of the facial (VII), glossopharyngeal (IX), and vagus (X) nerves. Below the level of the olive, but in line with the above nerves are the rootlets of the accessory (XI) nerve, which arise in part from the lower medulla and in part from the

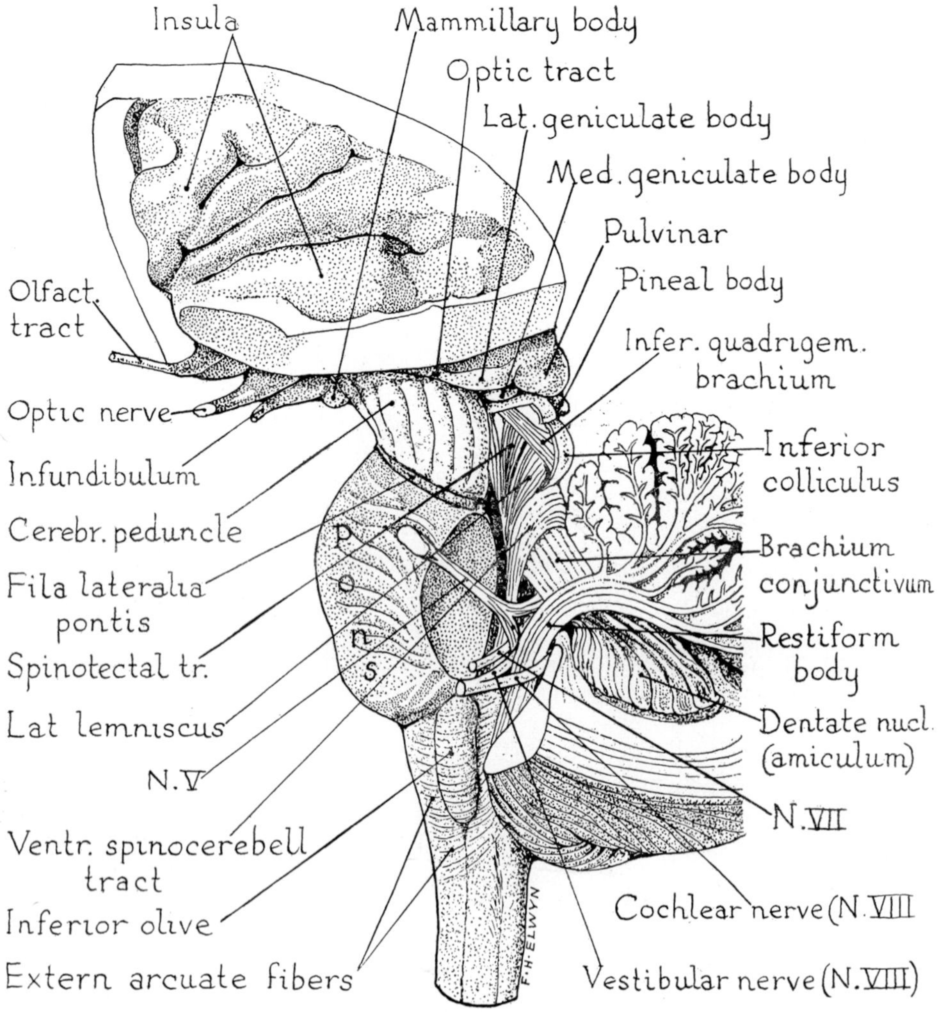

FIG. 36. Lateral view of the brain stem, partially dissected to show some of the fiber tracts. (Modified from Büttner, after Elze.)

upper four or five segments of the cervical spinal cord. The auditory nerve (VIII) enters the caudal border of the pons, immediately lateral to the roots of the facial nerve (Fig. 34). The vestibular nerve (VIII) enters the medulla-pons junction by passing ventral to the restiform body (Fig. 36).

On the lateral and dorsal surfaces of the medulla, one can easily identify the restiform body, tuberculum cuneatum, and clava. The latter two eminences are formed by the *nucleus cuneatus* and *nucleus gracilis* respectively.

The fourth ventricle. The fourth ventricle is the broad but shallow cavity of the hindbrain, extending from the middle of the medulla, where it is continuous with the central canal, to the cerebral aqueduct of the midbrain. Its floor is formed by the dorsal surface of the medulla and pontile tegmentum; its roof by the anterior medullary velum, a portion of the cerebellum, the posterior medullary velum and the tela chorioidea (Fig. 220). At its widest portion just behind the brachium pontis, it is continued on each side into a tubular *lateral*

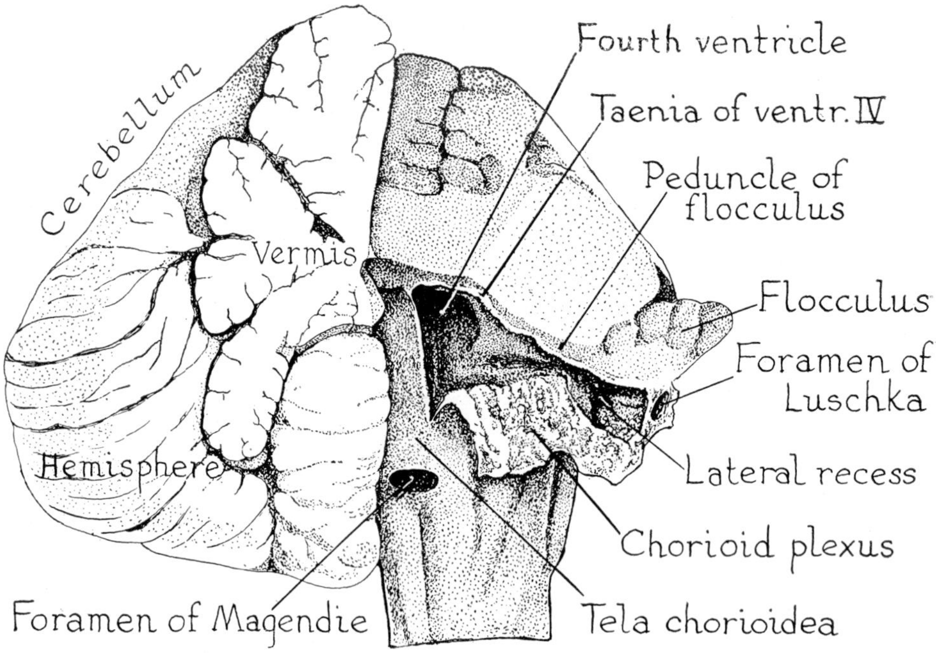

FIG. 37. The fourth ventricle partially opened, viewed from the right. The right half of the cerebellum has in large part been removed. (After Spalteholz.)

recess which curves laterally over the restiform body and extends along a portion of the cerebellum known as the peduncle of the flocculus, to the basal surface of the brain (Fig. 37).

The white substance of the cerebellum, which forms part of the roof, splits at an acute angle into two thin white lamina, enclosing between them a peak-like recess, the *fastigium* or roof recess of the fourth ventricle (Fig. 39). One lamina, the *anterior medullary velum,* extends rostrally to the midbrain and forms the roof of the superior or pontile portion of the ventricle. The other layer, the *posterior medullary velum,* passes caudally for a short distance and then becomes continuous with the *tela chorioidea* which forms the roof of the lower or medullary portion of the ventricle. From the tela the *chorioid plexus* projects into the ventricle. This is composed of irregular nodular evaginations of the tela chorioidea containing vascular loops covered by a modified glandular ependymal epithelium. These vascular tufts are evaginated in the form of two longitudinal ridges placed near the midline and extending from the most caudal portion of the ventricle to the inferior medullary velum to which the tela is attached. From each of these ridges another strip of chorioid plexus extends practically at right angles through the whole length of the lateral recess (Fig. 37). At its distal end each recess opens into the subarachnoid space by a small lateral aperture or *foramen of Luschka* through which protrudes a portion of the chorioid plexus which elsewhere is always limited to the ventricular cavities of the brain. A similar but medially placed aperture, the *foramen of Magendie,* is found in the most caudal part of the ventricular roof (Fig. 37). Through these three openings the cerebrospinal fluid produced by the various chorioid plexuses of the brain ventricles escapes into the subarachnoid spaces.

The rhomboid or diamond-shaped floor of the fourth ventricle is known as the *rhomboid fossa* (Fig. 35). It is widest at its lateral angles where the fossa is continued into the lateral recesses. The apex of its rostral angle is directed toward the midbrain, that of the caudal angle toward the central canal. The pointed caudal end of the fossa, because of its resemblance to a pen, is called the *calamus scriptorius.* The upper, larger triangular area belongs to the pons, and the lateral walls and lateral portions of the roof of the rhomboid fossa are formed by the *superior cerebellar peduncles,* or *brachium conjunctiva.* These two fiber bundles emerge from the cerebellum above the lateral recess and extend to the midbrain approaching each other as they proceed rostrally. The roof of this part of the ventricle, as already stated, is completed by the anterior medullary velum which is attached to the medial borders of the two superior cerebellar peduncles (Fig. 35). The lower triangular area belongs to the medulla and is bounded laterally by the clava, cuneate tubercle and restiform body.

The rhomboid fossa is divided into two symmetrical halves by the *median sulcus* which extends the whole length of the ventricular floor. Another groove, the *sulcus limitans* divides each half into a medial longitudinal ridge, the *median eminence,* and a lateral triangular region, the *area vestibularis,* beneath which lie the terminal nuclei of the vestibular nerve. The apex of this area extends into the lateral angle of the floor and there swells into a small eminence, the *tuberculum acusticum,* caused by a subjacent terminal nucleus of the cochlear nerve (Fig. 35). From the region of the acoustic tubercle a varying number of whitish strands may be seen running transversely or obliquely toward the midline where they disappear in the median sulcus of the fossa. These are the *striae medullares* or *striae cerebellares* whose significance will be discussed later. The region traversed by the striae medullares in the floor of the fossa is some times called the intermediate portion of the rhomboid fossa and is continuous on each side with the lateral recess.

The median eminence, produced largely by subjacent motor nuclei of the cranial nerves, is narrow in the lower part of the fossa but widens in a rostral direction. The tapering caudal portion is called the *trigonum hypoglossi* because of the underlying nucleus of the hypoglossal nerve. Above the striae medullares it expands into a rounded eminence, the *colliculus facialis* (*eminentia teres*), caused by the underlying nucleus of the sixth nerve and the root of the seventh nerve which here passes dorsally over the abducens nucleus. The deepened portion of the sulcus limitans lateral to the facial colliculus is the *superior fovea.* Extending from this fovea to the midbrain along the lateral border of the floor is a somewhat depressed narrow field of bluish color, the *locus caeruleus,* subjacent to which is a column of pigmented cells.

Lateral to the hypoglossal trigone is another triangular or oval area, the *ala cinerea* or *trigonum vagi,* beneath which lie the dorsal nuclei of the vagus nerve. The deepening of the sulcus limitans in this region is often known as the *inferior fovea.* A white strip, the *funiculus separans,* composed of neuroglial tissue, separates the ala cinerea from the *area postrema,* a narrow zone bordering on the lateral wall of the ventricle. The significance of this area is not known.

With these large ventral and dorsal landmarks of the medulla in mind, it is not too difficult to recognize them when they appear in stained microscopic sections. For example, Fig. 226 is a transverse section cut at the level of the pyramidal decussation, while Fig. 230 is a section through a slightly higher level. Can you recognize the prominent features in Fig. 230 of the pyramid, cuneate tubercle, and clava? A stained section of the medulla cut higher in the region of the lateral recess of the fourth ventricle, restiform body, and inferior olive would be similar to Fig. 243.

The pons (Metencephalon). This segment of the brain stem appears ventrally as a bulging mass of transverse fibers, and it is separated from the cerebellum dorsally by the fourth ventricle (Figs. 34, 36). The pons is delimited from the cerebral peduncles of the midbrain by the superior pontine sulcus, and from the ventral surface of the medulla by the inferior pontine sulcus. The distance between these two sulci is 20–30 mm., and the width of the pons varies from 30–36 mm.

The most prominent external feature of the pons ventrally is the broad band of predominantly transverse fibers. Laterally the fibers are collected into a stout bundle, the *brachium pontis,* or *middle cerebellar peduncle.* This bridge of fibers passes dorsally and somewhat caudally to fan out and end within the cerebellar hemispheres. A ventral median depression, the *basilar sulcus,* indicates the position of the basilar artery, while laterally the trigeminal (V) nerve emerges midway between the superior and inferior pontile sulci.

The structure of the pons can be better appreciated when viewed in transverse section, for then one can visualize its two main portions (Figs. 248, 265). The dorsal or *tegmental portion* represents the cranial continuation of the reticular formation of the medulla. Within this tegmental portion are the motor and sensory nuclei of cranial nerves (i.e., V, VI, VII, VIII), ascending sensory and older descending motor pathways, and several integrating pathways. Within the larger ventral, or *basilar portion,* of the pons are the transverse pontine fibers, pontine nuclei and the descending fiber bundles of the corticobulbar and corticospinal tracts. The latter are assembled into a compact bundle on each side at the lower end of the pons and form the pyramid of the medulla.

The cerebellum. The cerebellum lies above the medulla oblongata beyond which it extends laterally for a considerable distance and is covered dorsally by the cerebral hemispheres. Two surfaces may be distinguished: a superior somewhat flattened surface covered by the tentorium, and a strongly convex inferior surface which fills the cerebellar fossae of the occipital bone. The frontal margin of the cerebellum is notched by the shallow *anterior cerebellar incisure* (Fig. 40), the caudal margin by the deeper and narrower *posterior cerebellar incisure* which contains a fold of the dura mater, the falx cerebelli.

The human cerebellum consists of a median portion, the *vermis,* connecting two lateral lobes or *hemispheres.* The superior portion of the vermis is only poorly delimited from the hemispheres, but on the inferior surface two deep sulci separate the vermis from the lateral portions. The convex inferior surface is divided into two halves by a deep median fossa continuous with the posterior incisure. This is the *vallecula cerebelli* whose floor is formed by the inferior vermis and in which is lodged the medulla oblongata.

Structurally the cerebellum consists of a superficial mantle of gray matter, the cerebellar cortex, enclosing an internal mass of white, the corpus medullare. Within the latter are found four pairs of nuclear masses: the fastigial, globose, emboliform, and dentate nuclei (Fig. 303). The surface of the cerebellum receives its characteristic appearance from numerous transversely running sulci and fissures of varying depth, which separate a large number of narrow leaf-like lamina, the cerebellar *folia* or *gyri.* These lamina are in turn folded into secondary and tertiary folia, each composed of a medullary core capped by a superficial layer of cortex. In sagittal sections this complex branching of the corpus medullare and its cortical covering presents a tree-like appearance to which the name *arbor vitae* has been given (Fig. 38).

The more prominent transverse fissures,

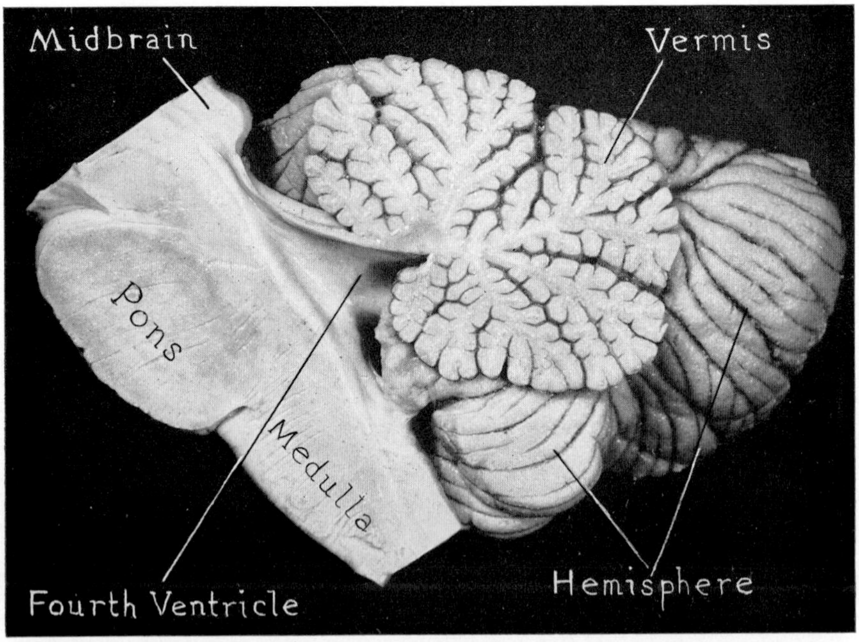

FIG. 38. Median longitudinal section through cerebellum. Photograph.

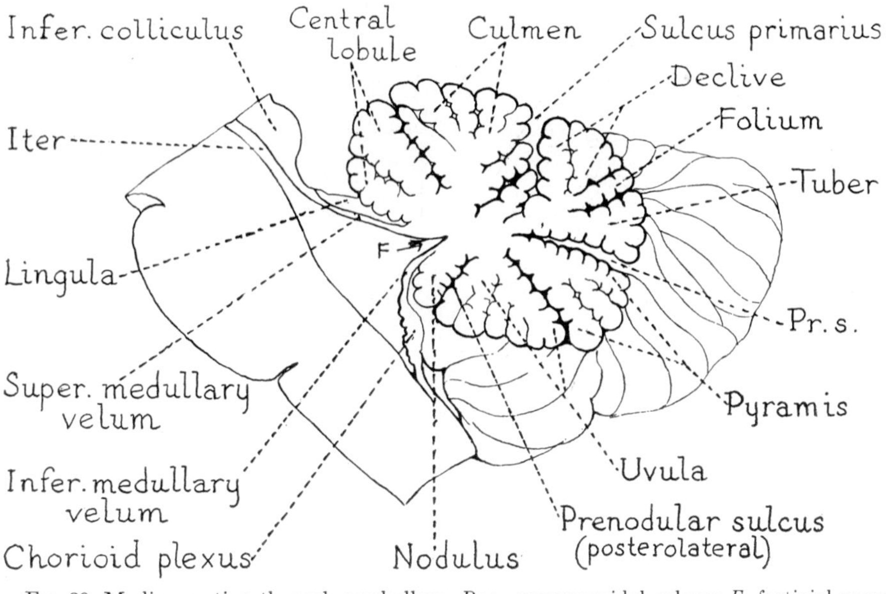

FIG. 39. Median section through cerebellum. *Pr.s.*, prepyramidal sulcus; *F*, fastigial recess of fourth ventricle.

some of which nearly reach the roof of the fourth ventricle, divide the cerebellum into a number of lobules, each with a medial portion belonging to the vermis and two wing-like extensions belonging to the hemispheres (Figs. 39, 40, 41). These lobules are still cumbered with peculiar and morphologically meaningless names given to

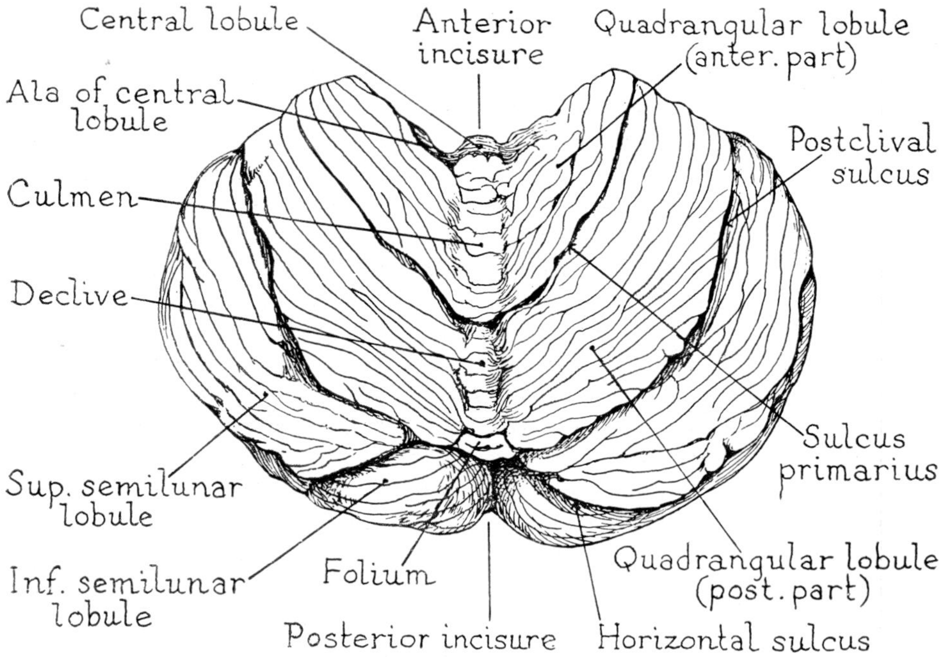

FIG. 40. Superior surface of human cerebellum. (After Jakob.)

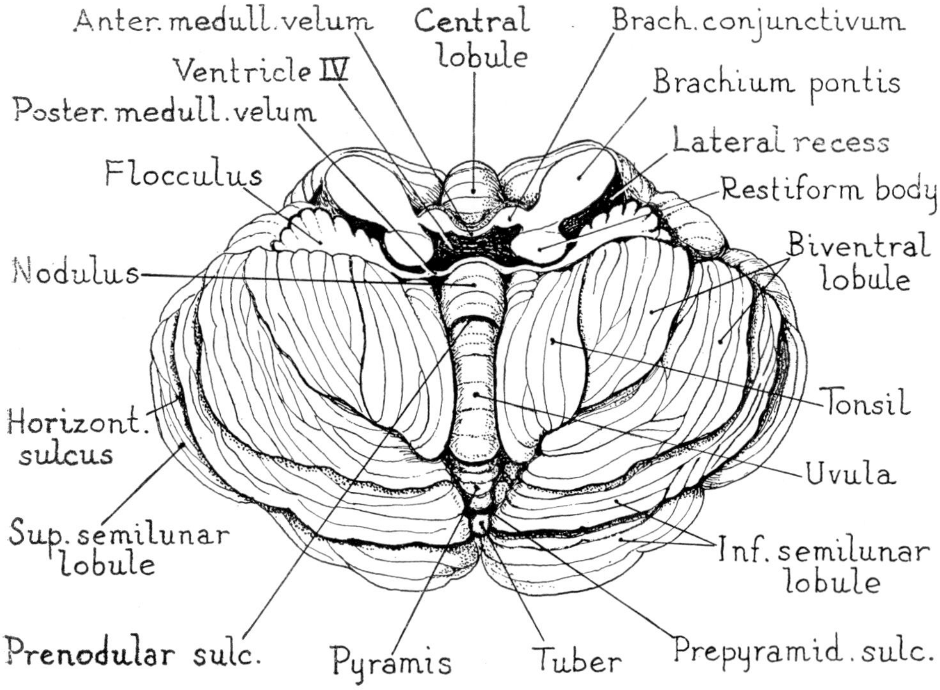

FIG. 41. Inferior surface of human cerebellum. (After Jakob.)

them by the older anatomists. Thus the superior vermis consists of the *lingula, lobulus centralis, monticulus* divided into *culmen* and *declive,* and *folium vermis.* On the under surface the inferior vermis includes the *tuber, pyramis, uvula,* and *nodulus.* Each of these lobules has corresponding lateral continuations in the hemispheres. The central lobule is continued into the *alae lobuli centralis*; the monticulus into the *quadrangular lobule* whose anterior portion belongs to the culmen, the posterior portion to the declive. The folium vermis extends laterally into the *superior semilunar lobule* separated from the *inferior semilunar lobule* which belongs to the tuber by the horizontal cerebellar fissure which roughly marks the boundary between the superior and inferior surfaces. The remaining hemispheral portions are the *biventral lobules* for the pyramis, the *tonsils* for the uvula, and the *flocculi* for the nodulus. The flocculi lie on the under surface of the middle cerebellar peduncle and are connected with the nodule by the peduncles of the flocculi and the posterior medullary velum (Fig. 41).

A simpler and more fundamental plan of mammalian cerebellar organization has been made possible by the comparative and ontogenetic investigations of Bolk, Ingvar, Jakob, Larsell, and others. According to Ingvar, the cerebellum may be divided into three lobes: anterior, middle, and posterior (Fig. 42). The middle lobe, phylogenetically the youngest, is bounded anteriorly by the sulcus primarius, posteriorly by the prepyramidal sulcus, two fundamental sulci appearing in early stages of development (Figs. 39, 43). The anterior lobe lies in front of the sulcus primarius and in man is composed of three or four lobules comprising the lingula, central lobule and culmen and their lateral extensions. It is an unpaired structure with transverse folia running continuously through vermis and lateral portions. A distinction between vermis and hemispheres is difficult.

In the middle lobe the anterior portion, known as the simple lobule, resembles the anterior lobe in showing continuous transverse folia and in the lack of distinction between vermis and hemispheres. It includes the declive and the posterior portion of the quadrangular lobe. The rest of the middle lobe consists of a median and two lateral portions. The former, the lobulus medius

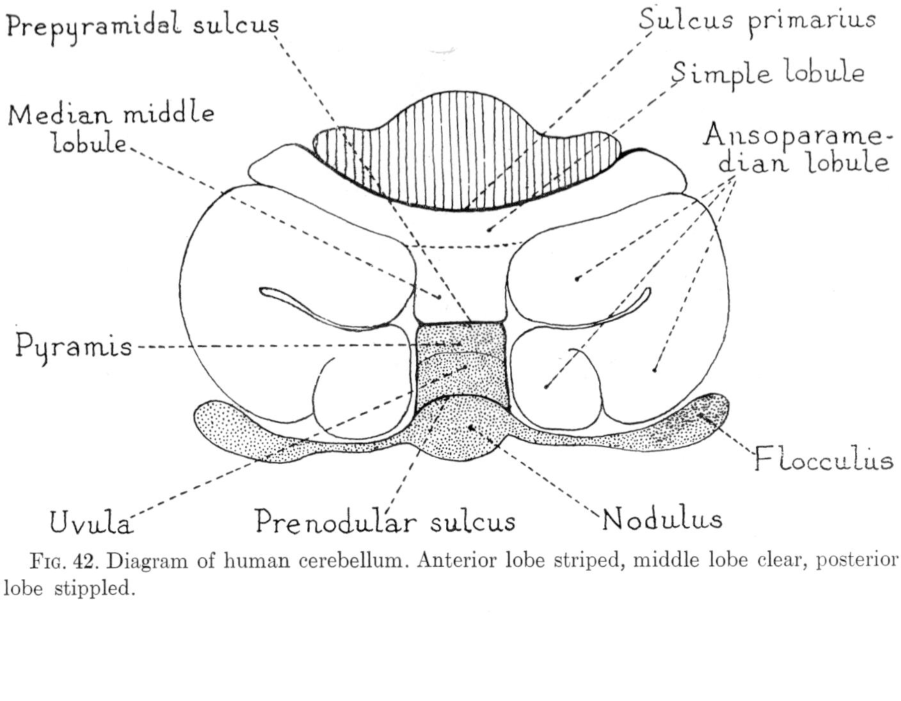

FIG. 42. Diagram of human cerebellum. Anterior lobe striped, middle lobe clear, posterior lobe stippled.

medianus, is relatively small and comprises the folium and tuber of the vermis. The lateral portions are, however, tremendously enlarged to form the folded ansoparamedian lobules which practically constitute the whole of the cerebellar hemispheres except the flocculi. They are phylogenetically newer structures found only in mammals. The ansiform portion of each lobule includes the semilunar and biventral lobules, the paramedian portion comprises the tonsil. In most mammals, the tonsil is of considerable size and is seen on the lateral surface of the cerebellum. In man, however, the tonsils have been pushed ventrally by the enormously developed ansiform lobules and lie closely apposed to the uvula (Fig. 41).

The posterior lobe consists of a median portion composed of the pyramis, uvula, and nodule and the paired flocculi which are connected to the nodulus by the peduncles of the flocculi and the posterior medullary velum (Fig. 41). In most mammals lateral extensions known as the paraflocculi are connected by narrow stalks with the uvula and pyramis, but in man these are rudimentary or entirely absent.

According to Larsell, the flocculonodular lobe (flocculi, nodule, and their connections) should be distinguished as a separate entity from the rest of the cerebellum (corpus cerebelli). The paired flocculi (auricles of lower vertebrates) are the first cerebellar structures to appear phylogenetically as expansions of the vestibular portion of the rhombencephalon. Their function and that of the nodulus which appears much later in phylogeny is entirely vestibular. The corpus cerebelli arises somewhat later and primarily receives general proprioceptive impulses and probably also exteroceptive ones through the spinocerebellar and other afferent cerebellar fibers. It is divided into an anterior and a posterior lobe, separated from each other by the sulcus primarius (fissura prima). Under this classification, the more complex posterior lobe would include the declive, folium, tuber, pyramis, and uvula and their lateral hemispheral portions. The corpus cerebelli is separated from the flocculi and nodulus by the posterolateral (prenodular) sulcus which, according to Larsell, is the first sulcus to appear both phylogenetically and in individual development (Fig. 43).

The middle lobe, especially the large ansoparamedian lobule, represents the newer portion of the cerebellum (neocerebellum)

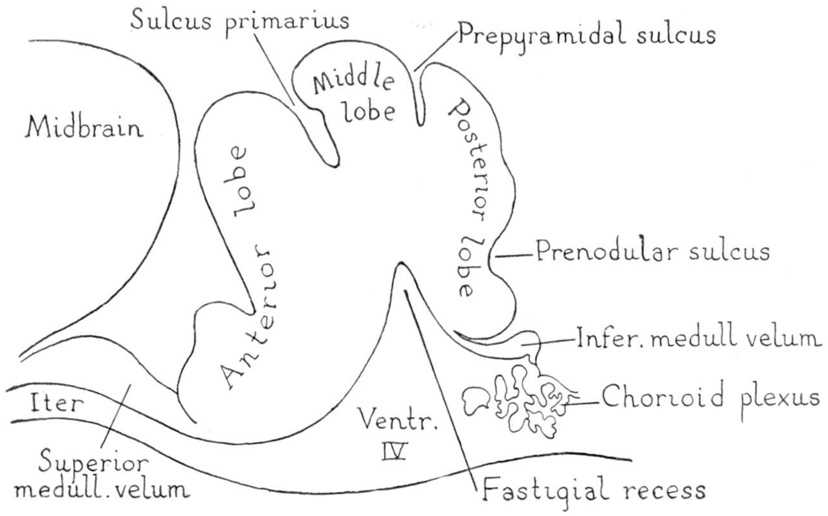

FIG. 43. Median longitudinal section through cerebellum of three months fetus, diagrammatic. (After Jakob.)

and has extensive afferent and efferent connections with the cerebral cortex. The rest of the vermis and the flocculi which primarily receive vestibular and general proprioceptive impulses constitute the older portion or paleocerebellum. Myelinization begins first in the floccular formation and in the basal portions of the superior and inferior vermis, to be continued soon in the rest of the vermis except the middle lobe which matures later. The process then spreads into the hemispheres, the caudal portion of the ansoparamedian lobules myelinating last. The topographical cellular differentiation of the cerebellar cortex is temporally similar to the myelinating areas.

The midbrain (Mesencephalon). The midbrain is the smallest and least differentiated of the five brain divisions, having a length of about 15–20 mm. Its caudal part is overlapped ventrally by the cephalic portion of the pons. Externally the dorsal surface extends from about the exit of the fourth cranial nerve to the root of the pineal body; the ventral surface from the rostral border of the pons to the mammillary bodies (Figs. 34, 35).

The midbrain consists of a dorsal part, the *quadrigeminal plate* or *tectum,* and a more massive ventral portion known as the *cerebral peduncles* or *crura cerebri.* Its narrow channel or cavity extending from the fourth to the third ventricle, is the *Sylvian aqueduct* or *iter.* In section each cerebral peduncle or crus shows a division into a dorsal part, the *tegmentum,* continuous with that of the pons, and a ventral part, the pes *pedunculi,* separated from each other by a broad pigmented plate of gray matter, the *substantia nigra* (Fig. 279). Pes pedunculi and substantia nigra together constitute the basis of the peduncle as distinguished from the tegmentum. Externally the tegmentum and basis are separated by two furrows, medially by the *oculomotor sulcus* from which the third nerve emerges, laterally by the *lateral mesencephalic sulcus.* The portion of the tegmentum which comes to the surface between the lateral mesencephalic sulcus and the inferior colliculi is occupied mainly by the fibers of the lateral lemniscus. These form a slight superficial bulge known as the *trigonum lemnisci,* (Fig. 35).

Viewed from the ventral surface the cerebral peduncles appear as two massive fiber bundles extending from the rostral border of the pons to the optic tracts where they disappear into the deep substance of the forebrain. On emerging from the pons the peduncles diverge laterally enclosing between them a deep triangular groove, the *interpeduncular* or *intercrural fossa,* bounded rostrally by the mammillary bodies. When freed from the pia the floor of this fossa shows a number of fine perforations serving for the passage of blood vessels and is hence known as the *posterior perforated substance.*

On the dorsal surface the quadrigeminal plate or roof shows two pairs of eminences, the *superior* and *inferior colliculi* (*corpora quadrigemina*), the latter somewhat smaller and more rounded than the former. The colliculi of the two sides are separated by a median longitudinal groove in the rostral portion of which lies the pineal body, tucked in between the superior colliculi. A narrow band extending from the anterior medullary velum and known as the *frenulum veli* is attached to the caudal part of the sulcus.

Each colliculus is connected with the thalamus by a superficially placed fiber strand which arises from the lateral margin of the colliculus and constitutes its arm or *brachium.* The *inferior quadrigeminal brachium* is a short flat band which runs from the inferior colliculus to the medial geniculate body, one of the caudal thalamic nuclei lying closely apposed to the lateral surface of the midbrain (Figs. 36, 44). The *superior quadrigeminal brachium* is a longer, narrower strand extending from the superior colliculus to the lateral geniculate body of the thalamus. A portion of this strand con-

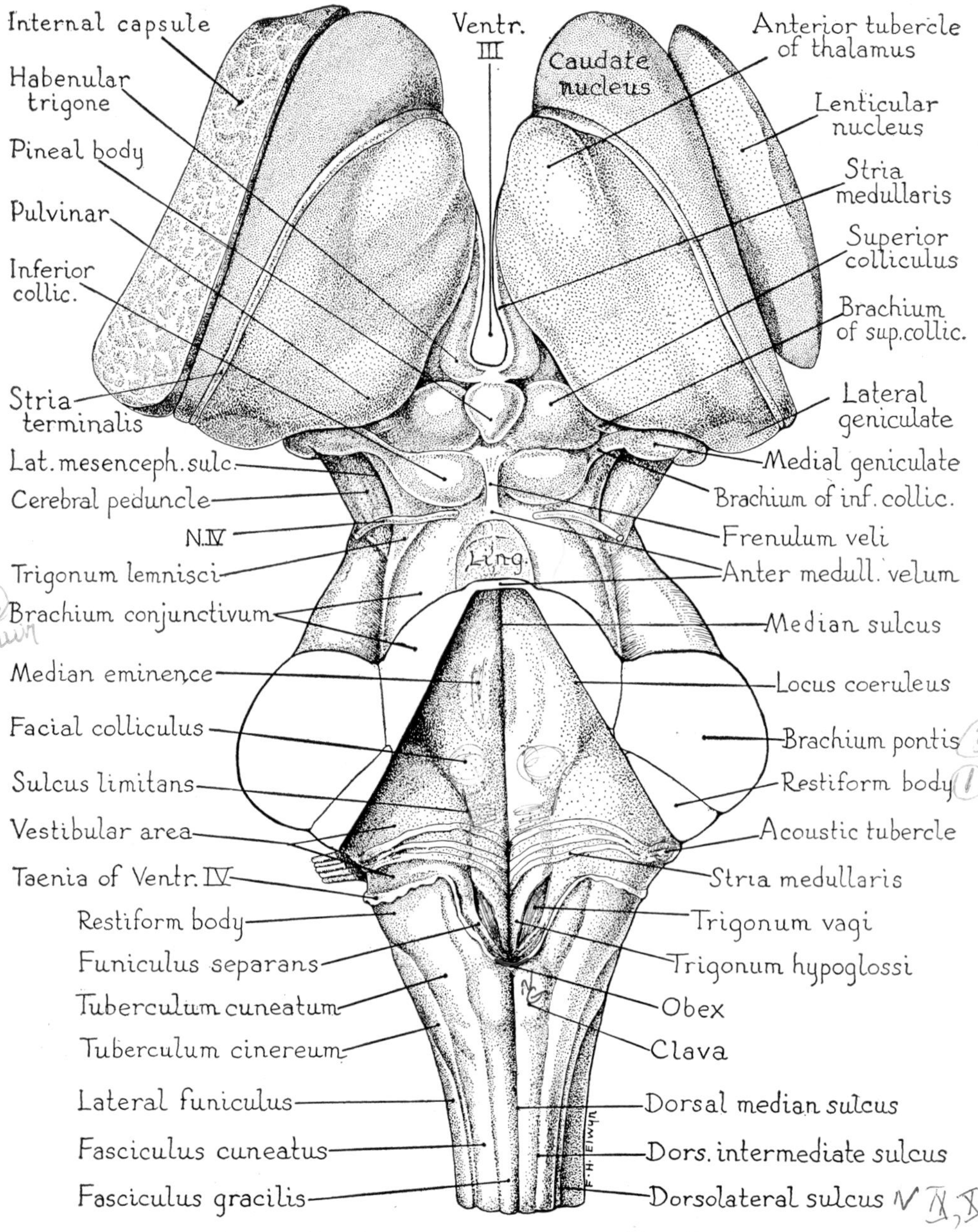

FIG. 44. Dorsal view of the brain stem. *Ling.*, lingula.

tinues beyond the geniculate body and merges with the optic tract.

The midbrain contains the principal segmental mechanisms for the various ocular reflexes and other eye movements, and higher postural reflex centers related especially to the "righting reactions" from abnormal to normal positions. Besides this it contains various paths to and from the cerebellum, pallium, striatum, and other forebrain structures, including certain gray masses forming their relay stations. The most conspicuous of these are the nucleus ruber and substantia nigra.

The diencephalon and corpus striatum. It has been noted in an earlier chapter that the primordial forebrain differentiates into a rostral portion, the endbrain or telencephalon, and a caudal portion, the interbrain or diencephalon. The endbrain arises as a hollow unpaired bud from the dorsal anterior wall of the forebrain, which then begins to bulge laterally and expands into the two hemispheric vesicles. These are connected to each other by the lamina terminalis and the most rostral portion of the third ventricle which here communicates with the hemispheric cavities or lateral ventricles by the large interventricular foramina (Fig. 20). These two structures, lamina terminalis and the most rostral portion of the third ventricle, therefore belong to the endbrain and constitute the median telencephalon as distinguished from the lateral telencephalon or cerebral hemispheres. All the forebrain structures caudal to the interventricular foramina belong to the diencephalon.

The hemispheric vesicles expand rapidly in all directions. Their medial surfaces at first extend backward along the lateral surfaces of the diencephalon (Figs. 20, 14), separated from the latter on each side by the hemispheric sulcus which progressively deepens with the growth of the hemisphere. Soon they expand dorsally and cover the roof of the diencephalon as well, so that the dorsal surface of the latter is now hidden from view and is separated from the overlying hemisphere by the *transverse cerebral fissure* formed by the folding back of the telencephalon. Into this fissure extends a double fold of pia mater, the *velum interpositum,* the dorsal layer of which is closely applied to the basal surface of the hemisphere, the ventral layer forming the pial investment of the diencephalic roof. The walls of the diencephalon become tremendously thickened while the floor and especially the roof plate remain relatively thin. The dorsal portion especially of each wall through the development of numerous nuclear masses constituting the thalamus, becomes so massive that it now furnishes most of the dorsal surface of the diencephalon (Figs. 44, 48). The originally large cavity of the diencephalon becomes reduced to the cleft-like third ventricle whose thin roof is formed by a layer of ependymal cells invested by richly vascular pial tissue from the velum interpositum, the two together constituting the *tela chorioidea* of the third ventricle. From the tela a double row of vascular tufts, invaginated along the median plane, projects into the ventricle forming its *chorioid plexus.* The plexus extends from the most caudal portion of the roof to the interventricular foramen where it becomes continuous with the chorioid plexuses of the lateral ventricles.

The hemispheric vesicles give rise to all the main parts of the telencephalon: the *olfactory lobes* or *rhinencephalon,* the large *pallium* or *cerebral cortex,* and a number of deep lying gray masses or *basal ganglia* comprising the *corpus striatum, amygdaloid nucleus* and *claustrum* (Fig. 342). These ganglia, especially the corpus striatum, are structurally so closely related to the diencephalon that it seems desirable to discuss them at this point, though actually they are parts of the endbrain. The corpus striatum develops as a thickening in that part of the hemispheric wall which lies adjacent to the lateral surface of the diencephalon, i.e., the fundus region of the hemispheric sulcus where the endbrain originally evaginated from the primitive forebrain (Fig. 20). As the corpus striatum and diencephalic wall increase in thickness they gradually approach each other and finally fuse, the zone of junction marked by a longitudinal groove, the *terminal* or *semicircular sulcus,* in which there is later found a fiber bundle known as the *stria terminalis* or *stria semicircularis* (Figs. 44, 19). At first the corpus striatum appears as an undivided cellular mass, but during further development it becomes perforated by fibers which pass to and from the cerebral cortex. These fibers increase in number and finally form a mas-

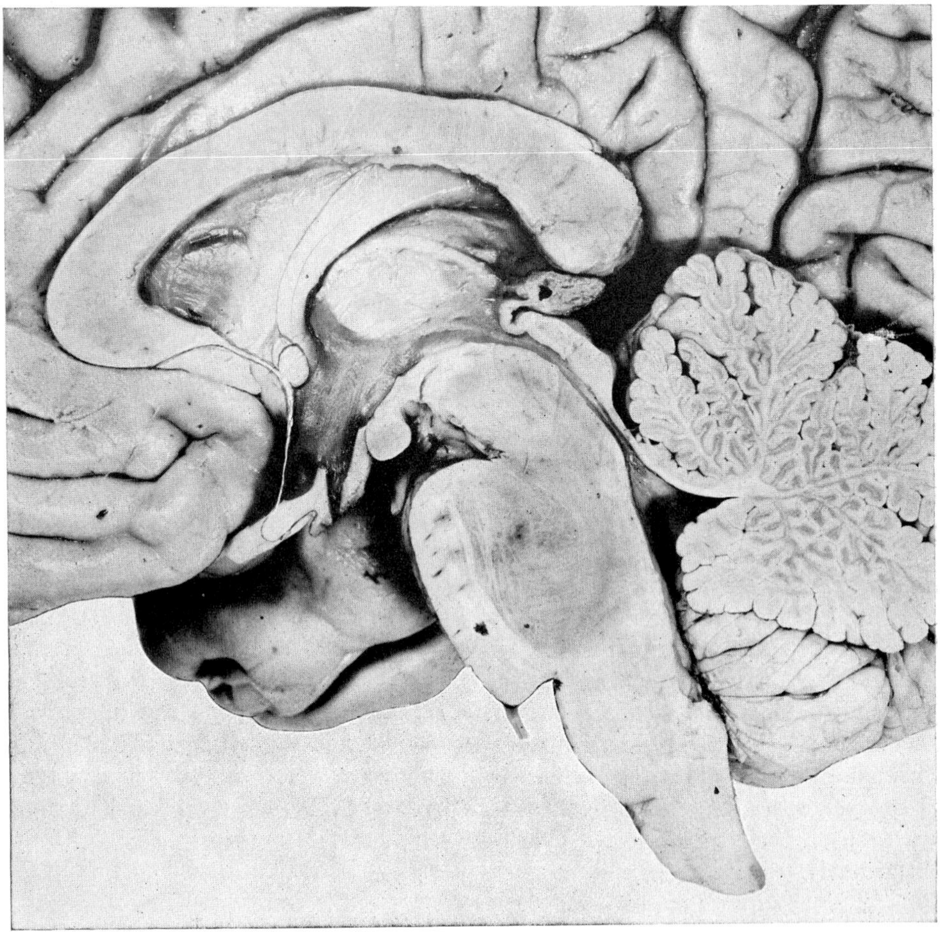

FIG. 45. Median sagittal section of human brain stem. Photograph. For identification of structures see Fig. 46.

sive bundle, the *internal capsule,* containing all the projection fibers connecting the pallium with the brain stem and spinal cord. This capsule divides the corpus striatum into two nuclear masses, a medial *caudate nucleus* and a lateral *lenticular* nucleus (Fig. 44). The division is incomplete since ventrally and anteriorly the caudate and lenticular nuclei retain their continuity (Fig. 343). The caudate nucleus is closely apposed to the thalamus, its expanded cephalic portion or *head* projecting rostrally beyond the latter, its attenuated caudal portion or tail extending along the entire dorsolateral border of the thalamus (Fig. 44). Throughout its length the caudate nucleus projects into the lateral ventricle forming part of its lateral wall. Thus the internal capsule is flanked laterally by the lenticular nucleus, medially by the diencephalon and the caudate nucleus (Figs. 47, 48).

General structure of the diencephalon. The diencephalon is composed of a larger dorsal and a smaller ventral portion, marked off from each other on the ventricular surface by a shallow longitudinal groove, the *hypothalamic sulcus,* extending from the interventricular foramen to the iter (Fig. 46). The dorsal portion comprises the massive *thalamus* and certain roof structures collectively known as the *epithalamus.* The ventral portion is composed of the medial

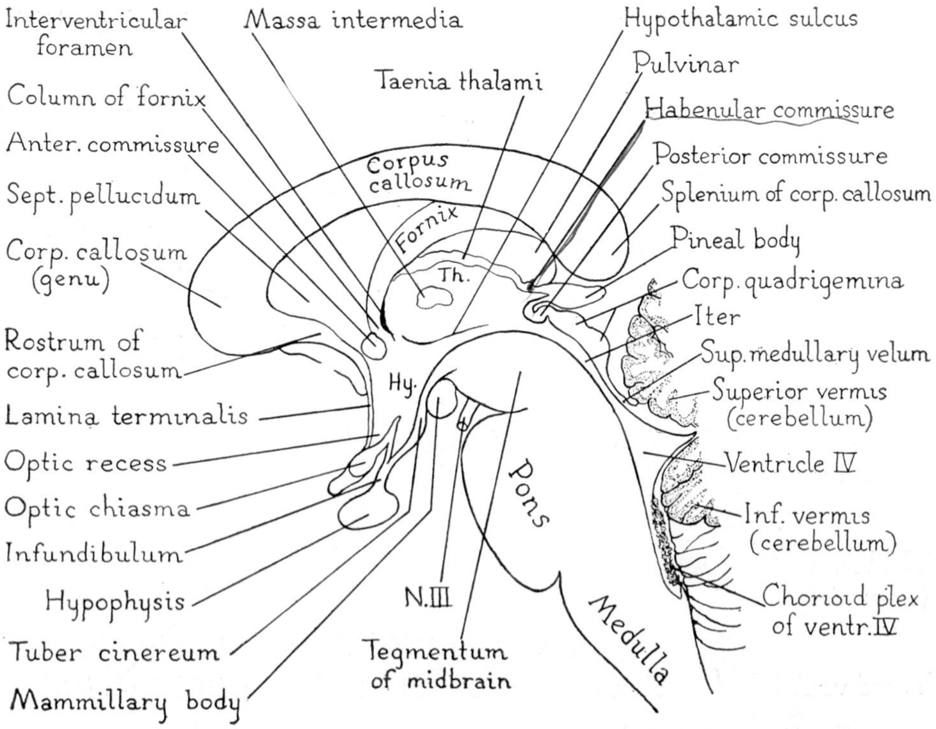

FIG. 46. Median sagittal section of brain stem. *Hy*, hypothalamus; *Th*, thalamus.

hypothalamus lying close to the ventricle and a deeper lateral part, the *subthalamus* or *ventral thalamus*, which can only be seen in sections of the diencephalon (Fig. 48).

The thalamus which forms the great bulk of the interbrain is an elongated somewhat egg-shaped ganglionic mass set obliquely above the midbrain. The narrower cephalic portions of the two thalami lie close together near the midline, the stouter caudal portions lie laterally and are separated by a wide space containing the superior colliculi. Rostrally each thalamus shows an ovoid swelling, the *anterior tubercle*, caused by the subjacent anterior thalamic nucleus. Caudally a larger prominence, the *pulvinar*, projects over the dorsolateral surface of the midbrain. Springing from the ventral surface of the pulvinar is the *medial geniculate body* connected to the inferior quadrigeminal brachium, and lateral to this the shallower elongated swelling of the *lateral geniculate* body, also largely hidden by the overhanging pulvinar (Fig. 44). Medial and lateral geniculate bodies are often spoken of as the *metathalamus*.

The dorsal and medial surfaces of the thalamus are free, but ventrally and laterally it fuses with adjacent structures, ventrally with the subthalamus, laterally with the internal capsule and caudate nucleus (Fig. 48). The free dorsal surface is everywhere covered by a thin plate of fibers, the *stratum zonale*, which gives it a whitish appearance, and is laterally marked off from the caudate nucleus by the *terminal* or *semicircular* sulcus in which is lodged the terminal (thalamostriate) vein and a slender fiber bundle, the *stria terminalis* (*stria semicircularis*). A shallow diagonal groove, the chorioid sulcus, divides the surface into a medial and a lateral zone (Fig. 47). The larger medial area forms the floor of the transverse cerebral fissure, separated by a pial fold from the overlying corpus callosum and fornix of the hemispheres. The narrower

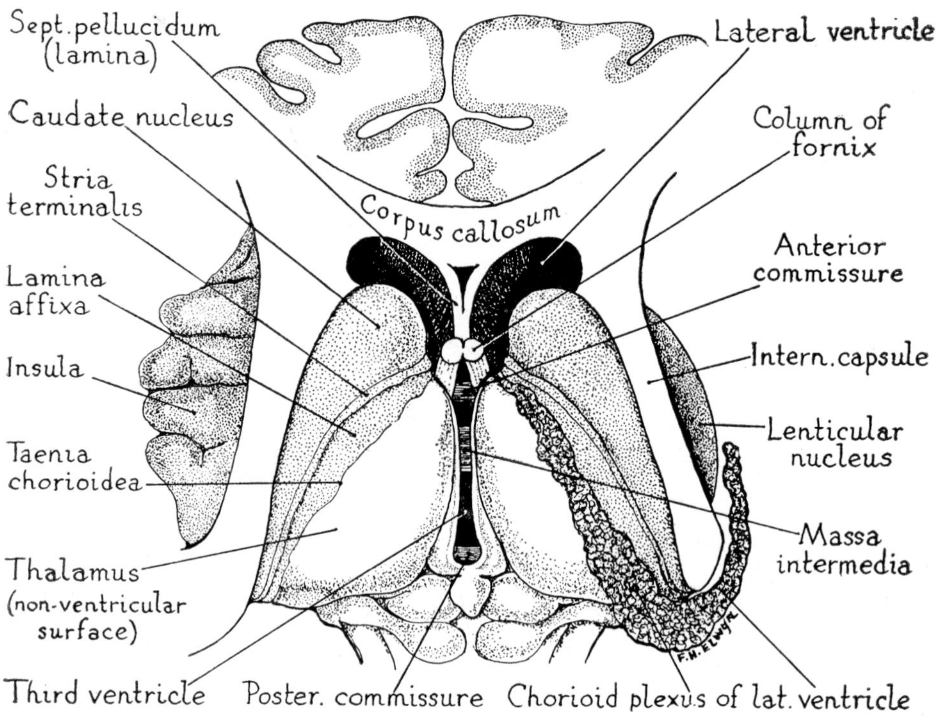

FIG. 47. Dorsal view of diencephalon, caudate nucleus and related structures.

lateral strip forms part of the floor of the lateral ventricle which has secondarily infringed on the dorsal surface of the thalamus. The ependymal epithelium covering this lateral portion is known as the *lamina affixa,* to the medial border of which is attached the chorioid plexus of the lateral ventricle (Figs. 47, 48).

The medial or ventricular surfaces of the thalami extend ventrally to the hypothalamic sulcus. In their middle regions the two surfaces approach each other closely and in most cases fuse to form a gray bridge of variable extent, the *massa intermedia* (Fig. 47). At the junction of the medial and dorsal surfaces a whitish fiber stripe, the *stria medullaris,* extends along the edge of the ventricular roof, and broadens caudally into a triangular field, the *trigonum habenulae,* beneath which lies the habenular ganglion. The two trigones are connected by a white band, the habenular commissure, to the caudal border of which is attached the cone-shaped *pineal body* or *epiphysis* tucked in between the superior colliculi. Stretched out between the two striae medullares is the thin roof of the third ventricle from which vascular tufts covered by ependymal epithelium project into the ventricle as its chorioid plexus (Fig. 48). When the thin roof is removed the torn edge of attachment to the stout thalamic wall appears as a narrow seam, the *taenia thalami,* which in its lateral portion contains the stria medullaris. Caudally the taenia of each side continues over the habenular trigone and fuses with its mate on the dorsal surface of the pineal gland.

The cavity of the interbrain is the cleft-like third ventricle whose most cephalic portion extends into the endbrain. Caudally it empties into the cerebral aqueduct, rostrally it communicates on each side with the lateral ventricle of the hemisphere by a narrow oval opening, the *interventricular foramen.* The relations of the ventricle are best seen in a medial sagittal section (Figs. 45, 46). Laterally it is bounded by the

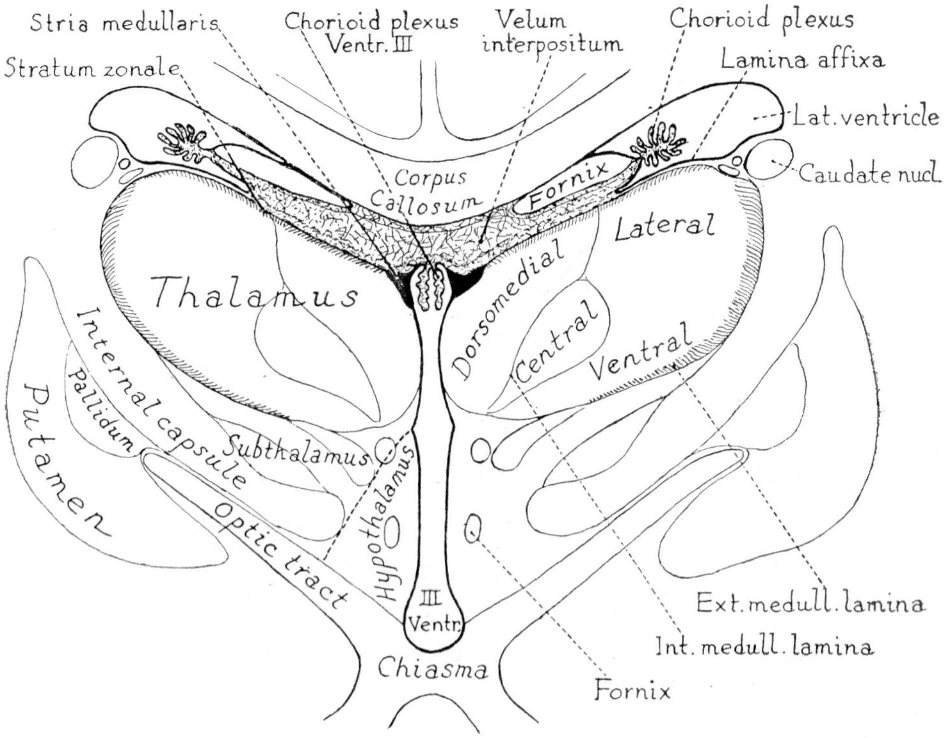

FIG. 48. Transverse section through diencephalon and adjacent structures, semischematic.

thick diencephalic walls, divided into a dorsal thalamic and a ventral hypothalamic portion by the hypothalamic sulcus which extends from the interventricular foramen to the iter. Rostrally it is bounded by the thin *lamina terminalis* which ascends dorsally to the *anterior commissure* where it becomes continuous with the rostral lamina of the corpus callosum. The anterior commissure is an ancient fiber bundle connecting the older olfactory regions of the two hemispheres. The corpus callosum is the massive commissure connecting the more extensive phylogenetically newer parts of the pallium. A small portion of the rostral wall is also formed by the fornix, a large fiber bundle which curves ventrally over the anterior border of the thalamus and perforates the hypothalamic region (Fig. 311). It lies immediately in front of the interventricular foramen.

The thin roof, formed by the chorioid tela and plexus, extends to the dorsal surface of the pineal body into which projects a spur of the ventricle, the *pineal recess.* Below this recess the posterior commissure marks the junction of the third ventricle and cerebral aqueduct. The floor of the ventricle is formed by the basal structures of the hypothalamus, including the *optic chiasma* separated from the lamina terminalis by the *optic recess,* the *tuber cinereum* and the *mammillary bodies.* The most caudal part of the floor is bounded by the cephalic portion of the midbrain tegmentum. From the tuber cinereum a funnel-shaped stalk, the *infundibulum* extends to the posterior lobe of the *hypophysis* or *pituitary body* (Fig. 65). Into it extends a spur of the third ventricle, the *infundibular recess.*

THE CEREBRAL HEMISPHERES

External Topography

By means of the sulci and fissures the brain is subdivided into a number of main territories or lobes, named in accordance with their topographical relations to the skull. This subdivision is largely a convenient one, and some of the lobar boundaries have to be arbitrarily determined. Furthermore each lobe consists of several histologically and functionally distinct cortical areas, some of which may overlap the anatomical boundaries of the lobe. In general, five lobes are usually recognized: *frontal, parietal, occipital, temporal,* and *insular* or *central.* The olfactory portions are not included in the above named lobes, but are regarded as constituting a separate anatomical entity, the *rhinencephalon.*

Each hemisphere consists of the pallium and the deep-lying basal ganglia whose structure and connections will be discussed in chapter XIX. The pallium or cerebral mantle is composed of an internal fibrous mass, the white or medullary substance, everywhere covered superficially by a layer of gray matter, the cerebral cortex. The paired cavities of the hemispheres are known as the lateral ventricles. The cerebral hemispheres are separated from each other by the deep vertical *interhemispheric* or *longitudinal fissure* containing the falx cerebri. In front and behind, the separation is complete, but in the middle portion the fissure extends only to the corpus callosum, a broad band of commissural fibers uniting the two hemispheres. Posteriorly the hemispheres overlap the thalamus, midbrain, and cerebellum, separated from these structures by the transverse fissure which is occupied posteriorly by the tentorium cerebelli, anteriorly by the tela chorioidea of the third ventricle. In each hemisphere three surfaces may be distinguished: dorsolateral, medial, and basal. A rounded dorsal border intervenes between the convex dorsolateral and the flat vertical medial surface, and similarly a lateral border separates the convex from the basal surface. The latter surface is more complex in shape, closely modeled in front to the base of the skull. Its anterior portion occupies the anterior and middle cranial fossa, its posterior portion rests on the tentorium cerebelli. A basal border separates the medial and basal surfaces.

The dorsolateral surface (Figs. 49, 50). The most striking furrows on the convex surface are the *lateral cerebral fissure* (Sylvian fissure) and the *central sulcus.* The *lateral fissure* starts on the basal surface as a deep cleft, the Sylvian fossa, separating the frontal and temporal lobes, then extends as the trunk of the fissure to the dorsolateral surface where it divides into three branches. The short anterior horizontal and anterior ascending branches incise the ventral surface of the frontal lobe. The long posterior branch which appears as a direct continuation of the trunk, passes backward almost horizontally and then curves upward to terminate in the parietal lobe (Fig. 50).

The central sulcus of Rolando is a deep and usually continuous furrow running downward and slightly forward from about the middle of the dorsal border to the Sylvian fissure without quite reaching the latter. The sulcus shows two knee-like bends and usually incises the dorsal border to reach the medial surface.

The **frontal lobe** which comprises about one third of the hemispheric surface extends from the frontal pole to the central sulcus and is limited below by the lateral fissure. On the convex surface four main convolutions may be distinguished. The vertical *precentral gyrus* runs parallel to the central sulcus, bounded in front by the *precentral sulcus* which is sometimes broken up into a superior and inferior segment. This gyrus comprises the motor and a considerable part of the premotor area, and is the site of origin of the corticospinal and corticobulbar tracts. The rest of the frontal lobe is composed of three horizontal convolutions, the *superior, middle* and *inferior frontal gyri,* separated from each other by the *superior* and *inferior frontal sulci.* Often a shallower middle frontal sulcus divides

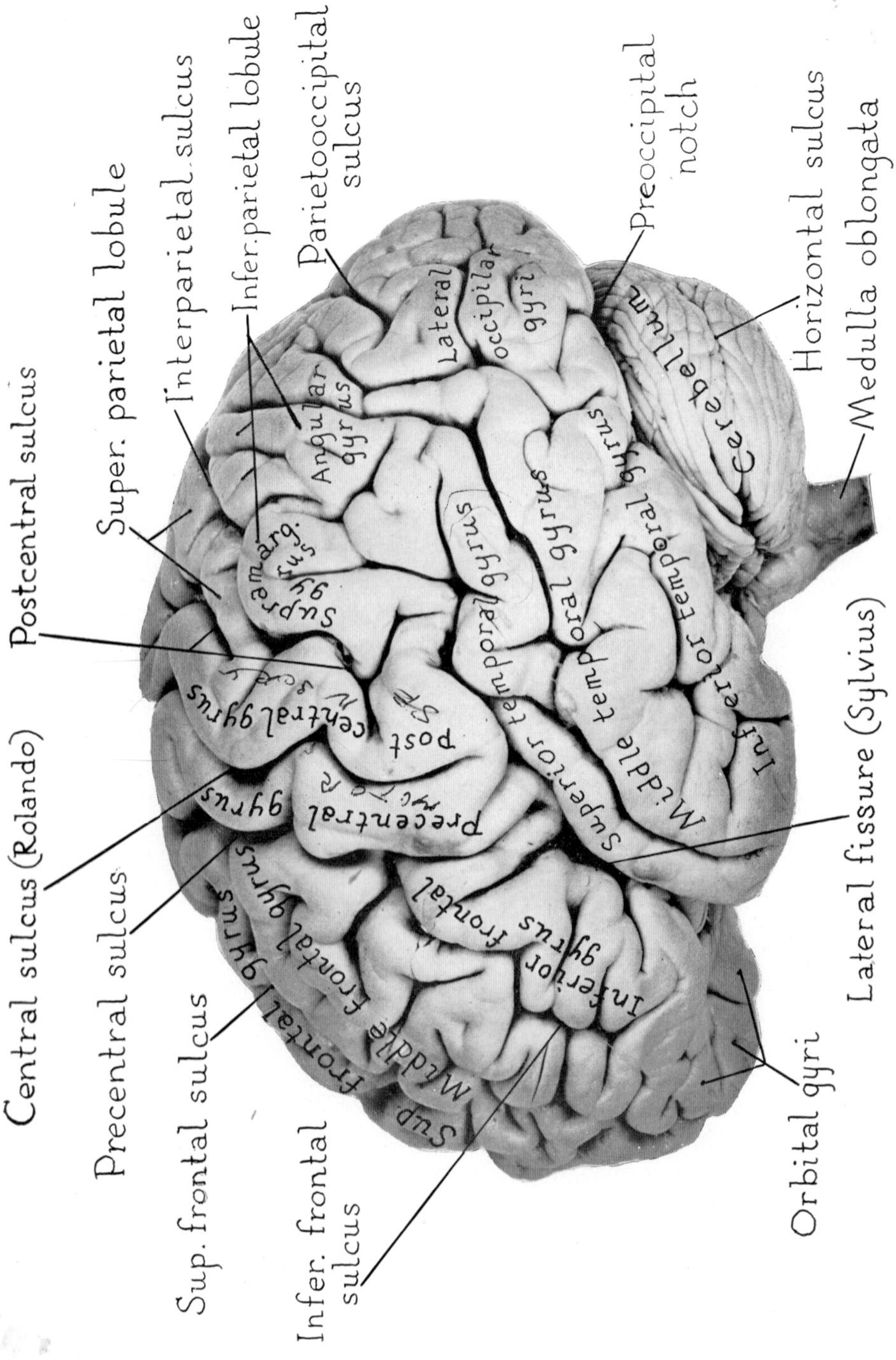

Central sulcus (Rolando)
Precentral sulcus
Sup. frontal sulcus
Infer. frontal sulcus
Postcentral sulcus
Super. parietal lobule
Interparietal sulcus
Infer. parietal lobule
Parietooccipital sulcus
Preoccipital notch
Horizontal sulcus
Medulla oblongata
Lateral fissure (Sylvius)
Orbital gyri
Sup. frontal gyrus
Middle frontal gyrus
Inferior frontal gyrus
Precentral gyrus
Post central gyrus
Supramarg. gyrus
Angular gyrus
Lateral occipital gyri
Superior temporal gyrus
Middle temporal gyrus
Inferior temporal gyrus
Cerebellum

FIG. 49. Lateral view of human brain. Photograph.

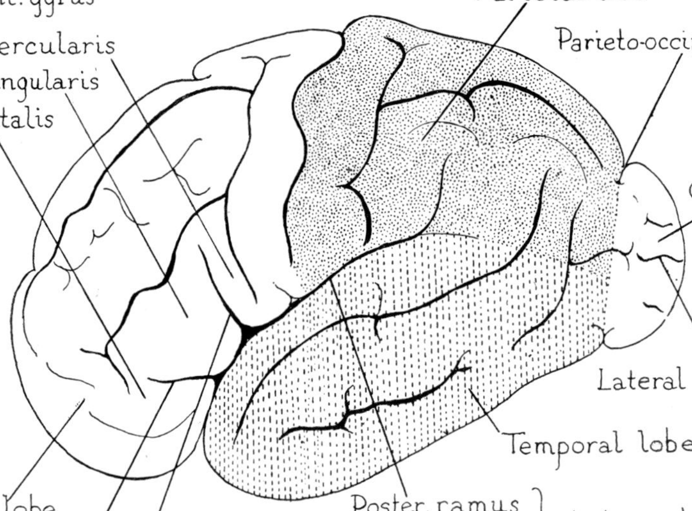

FIG. 50. Diagram of lobes on lateral surface of cerebral hemisphere.

the stout middle gyrus into an upper and lower tier. The inferior frontal gyrus which forms the frontal operculum of the insula, is subdivided by the anterior branches of the lateral fissure into an orbital, a triangular, and an opercular portion (Fig. 50). In the left or dominant hemisphere the triangular and opercular portions are known as Broca's area, regarded as the cortical center for the motor formulation of speech.

The smaller **parietal lobe** is more difficult to delimit on the convex surface. Bounded sharply in front by the central sulcus, its posterior part merges imperceptibly with the occipital lobe behind and the temporal lobe below. Its occipital boundary is arbitrarily established by a vertical line drawn from the upper end of the parieto-occipital sulcus to a shallow depression on the ventral hemispheric surface about 4 cm. from the occipital pole, and hence known as the preoccipital notch. Its temporal boundary is similarly established by an imaginary line extending the horizontal portion of the lateral fissure to the occipito-parietal line determined above (Fig. 50).

The sulci on the convex surface of the parietal lobe vary considerably in different individuals. As a rule two main sulci are distinguished though these may be continuous with each other and form a single sulcus of complicated form. The *postcentral sulcus,* usually broken up into a superior and inferior segment, runs parallel with the central sulcus and forms the caudal boundary of the vertical *postcentral gyrus* which represents the somesthetic sensory area of the cerebral cortex. The *intraparietal* or *interparietal sulcus* which is usually a direct continuation of the inferior postcentral, arches backward to the occipital lobe where it often ends as the transverse occipital sulcus beneath the dorsal margin of the parietooccipital sulcus. The sulcus divides the rest of the parietal lobe into a *superior parietal lobule* lying above it and an *inferior parietal lobule* below. The inferior lobule is primarily represented by the *supramarginal gyrus* which curves around the terminal ascending portion of the lateral fissure, and the *angular gyrus* which similarly surrounds the ascending

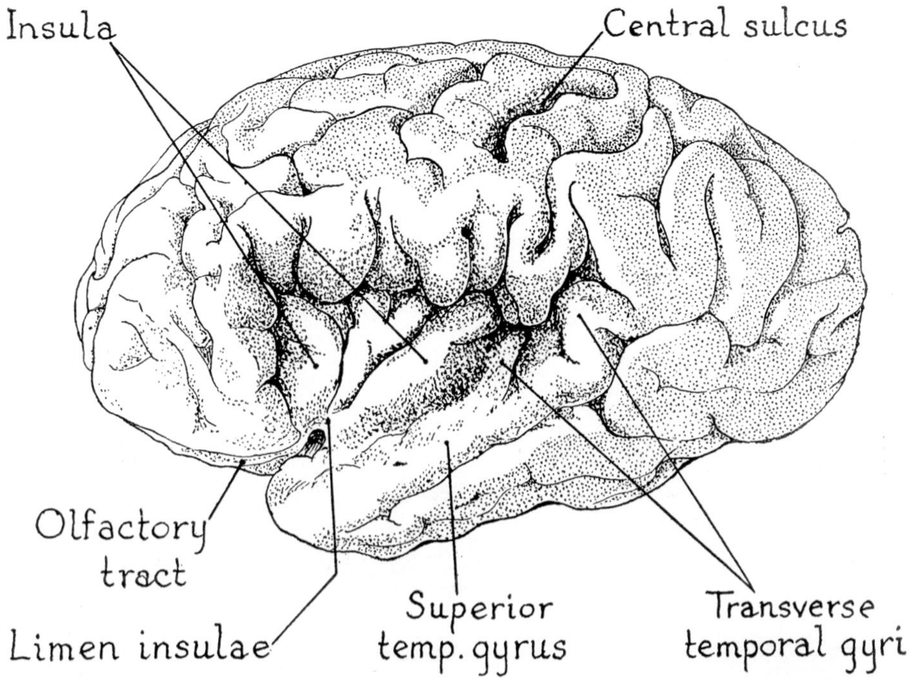

FIG. 51. Lateral surface of hemisphere. The lips (opercula) of the lateral fissure have been drawn apart to expose the insula. (After Henle.)

terminal part of the superior temporal sulcus. The most caudal part of the inferior lobule which receives the terminal extension of the middle temporal sulcus is the poorly defined *posterior parietal gyrus.* The ventral portions of the precentral, postcentral, and supramarginal gyri constitute the centroparietal operculum of the insula.

The large **temporal lobe** whose anterior tip is known as the temporal pole, shows three horizontal convolutions, the *superior, middle* and *inferior temporal gyri,* separated by similarly named sulci. The deep and constant superior temporal sulcus begins at the temporal pole and runs parallel to the Sylvian fissure, its ascending terminal portion ending in the angular gyrus. The posterior portions of the irregular and segmented middle temporal sulcus is related to the posterior parietal gyrus. The inferior temporal sulcus can only be seen on the basal surface. The superior temporal gyrus forms the temporal operculum, and its broad dorsal surface which faces the lateral fissure is marked in its caudal portion by several short obliquely running convolutions, the *transverse gyri of Heschl,* the most anterior of which represents the auditory projection area of the cortex (Fig. 51).

The small **occipital lobe** whose rounded apex constitutes the occipital pole, occupies only a restricted portion on the convex surface of the hemisphere. It is composed of a number of irregular and variable *lateral occipital gyri,* usually separated into a superior and an inferior group by the more definite and constant *lateral occipital sulcus* (Figs. 49, 50).

The **insula** or **island of Reil** lies buried in the lateral fissure and can only be seen when the lips of that fissure are drawn apart or the opercular portions removed (Fig. 51). It then appears as a large conical or triangular elevation, the apex of the triangle directed forward and downward to the floor of the Sylvian fossa. At this point, known as the *limen* or threshold of

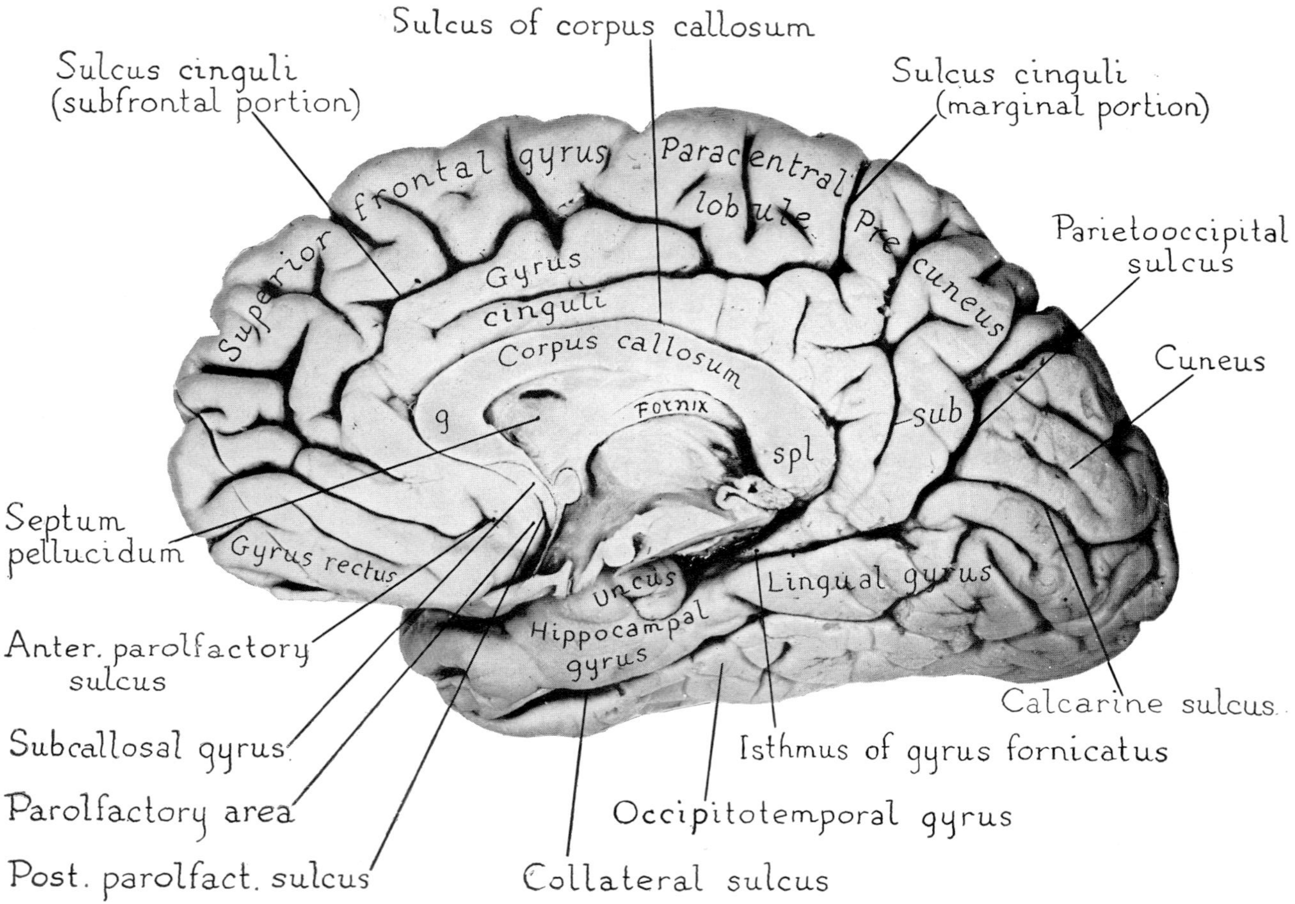

FIG. 52. Medial surface of right hemisphere. Hindbrain and larger part of midbrain have been removed. Photograph. *g*, *spl*, genu and splenium of corpus callosum; *sub*, subparietal sulcus.

the insula, the surface of the island curves over to the basal surface of the hemisphere and comes into relation with the olfactory area. The base of the insula is surrounded by the *circular* sulcus, really triangular in shape, which separates it from the frontal, parietal, and temporal opercula. Except for the limen, the surface of the insula is covered by sulci and gyri. A deep oblique furrow, the *central* or *longitudinal* sulcus, running parallel to the central sulcus of Rolando, divides the insula into a larger anterior and a smaller posterior part. The former is composed of a number of short convolutions, the *gyri breves.* The posterior part consists of a single long convolution, the *gyrus longus,* which often shows an incomplete bifurcation.

The medial and basal surfaces. These surfaces are exposed in their entirety only after the brain has been divided in the midsagittal plane and the brain stem removed posterior to the thalamus (Fig. 52). The cut surface of the corpus callosum appears as a white broad arched band whose thickened caudal end or *splenium* overhangs the pineal body and midbrain. The rostral margin turns abruptly downward to form the *genu* or bend and then tapers downward and backward as the *rostrum* of the corpus callosum. The rostrum becomes attenuated into a thin membrane, the *rostral lamina,* which extends to the anterior commissure and there becomes continuous with the lamina terminalis (Figs. 52, 46). Another white band, the *fornix,* emerges from the under side of the splenium, arches forward over the thalamus and enters the substance of the hypothalamus immediately in front of the interventricular foramen (Fig. 46). The triangular area between fornix and corpus callosum is occupied by the membranous *septum pellucidum.*

The convolutions on the medial and basal surfaces are somewhat flatter than on the convex surface, and here it is even more difficult to determine the boundaries of individual lobes. Many convolutions continue uninterruptedly from one lobe to another. Only the dorsal half of the occipital lobe is sharply separated from the parietal by the deep parietooccipital sulcus. A survey of the principal sulci will facilitate an

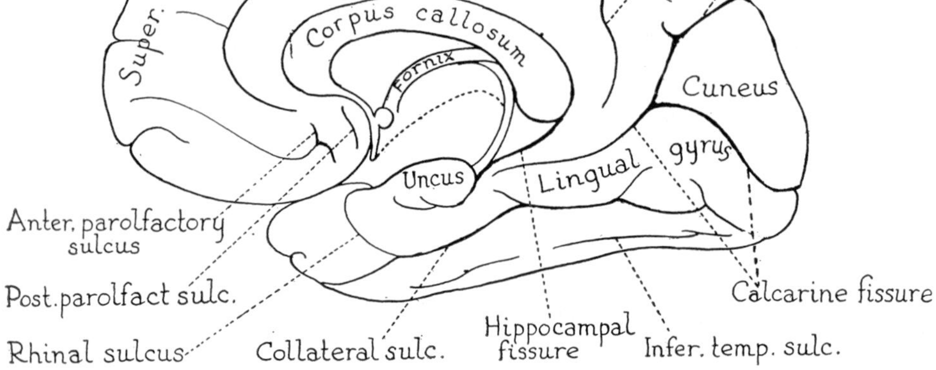

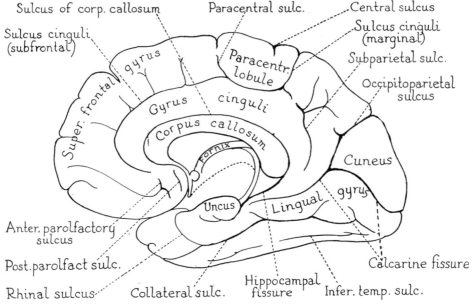

FIG. 53. Diagram showing sulci and gyri on medial surface of brain.

understanding of the convolutional pattern and the allocation of the various parts to the respective lobes.

The corpus callosum is separated from the gyrus overlying it by the *callosal sulcus.* Beginning at the rostrum the sulcus follows the dorsal surface of the corpus callosum and curving ventrally around the splenium is continued as the *hippocampal fissure* which extends to the anterior portion of the temporal lobe (Figs. 52, 53). The *sulcus cinguli* or *callosomarginal sulcus* likewise starts some distance ventral to the rostrum and runs parallel with the callosal sulcus to about the region of the splenium where it turns upward as the *marginal sulcus* and reaches the dorsal border a short distance behind the central sulcus. Another furrow, the *subparietal suclus,* which is usually regarded as a direct prolongation of the sulcus cinguli though often discontinuous with the latter, passes backward around the splenium. The sulcus cinguli gives off a number of dorsal branches, one of which, the *paracentral sulcus,* may reach the dorsal border at a point corresponding roughly to the position of the precentral sulcus. Thus the whole medial surface in front of and above the corpus callosum is divided by the cingular (and subparietal) sulcus into two tiers, an outer or marginal tier and an inner one, the *gyrus cinguli,* encircling the corpus callosum. The whole anterior portion of the outer tier up to the paracentral sulcus belongs to the frontal lobe and is the medial extension of the superior frontal gyrus, also known as the *marginal gyrus.* The paracentral lobule between the paracentral and marginal sulci is notched by the central sulcus, hence represents the medial continuation of both precentral and postcentral gyri which here become continuous. The larger anterior portion belongs to the frontal, the small posterior portion to the parietal lobe. Behind the marginal sulcus is the *precuneus* or *quadrate lobule* belonging entirely to the parietal lobe and sharply marked off behind from the occipital lobe by the deep parietooccipital sulcus. In close relation with the rostrum of the corpus callosum are two small cortical fields belonging to the rhinencephalon. The *subcallosal gyrus* is closely applied to the rostral lamina and is limited in front by the *posterior parolfactory sulcus,* anterior to which is the *parolfactory area* (Broca). The latter is continuous in front with the superior frontal gyrus and above with the gyrus cinguli, from both of which it is separated incompletely by the *anterior parolfactory sulcus* (Figs. 52, 53). Subcallosal gyrus and parolfactory area collectively constitute the *paraterminal body* also known as the *septal* or *precommissural area.*

The *calcarine fissure* is a deep arched cleft extending from the mid-temporal region to the occipital pole, its anterior portion producing an elevation the *calcar avis,* in the wall of the lateral ventricle (Fig. 348). Beginning near the hippocampal fissure it runs horizontally backward and near its middle course is joined at acute angles by the *parietooccipital sulcus* which extends obliquely downward and forward from the dorsal border. Then the calcarine fissure arches ventrally and usually terminates near the occipital pole, occasionally rounding the pole and extending a short distance on the lateral surface. Ventral to the calcarine fissure is the deep horizontal *collateral fissure* which likewise produces an impression in the ventricular wall known as the *collateral eminence* (Fig. 58). It runs forward from the region of the occipital pole and in the anterior portion of the temporal lobe usually becomes continuous with the shallow *rhinal fissure,* a phylogenetically old furrow separating the terminal archipallial portion of the hippocampal gyrus from the rest of the temporal lobe (Rh, Figs. 54, 55). Below and parallel to the collateral fissure is the inferior temporal sulcus, practically at the margin of transition between the basal and lateral surfaces.

The above named sulci enclose the following convolutions of the occipital and tem-

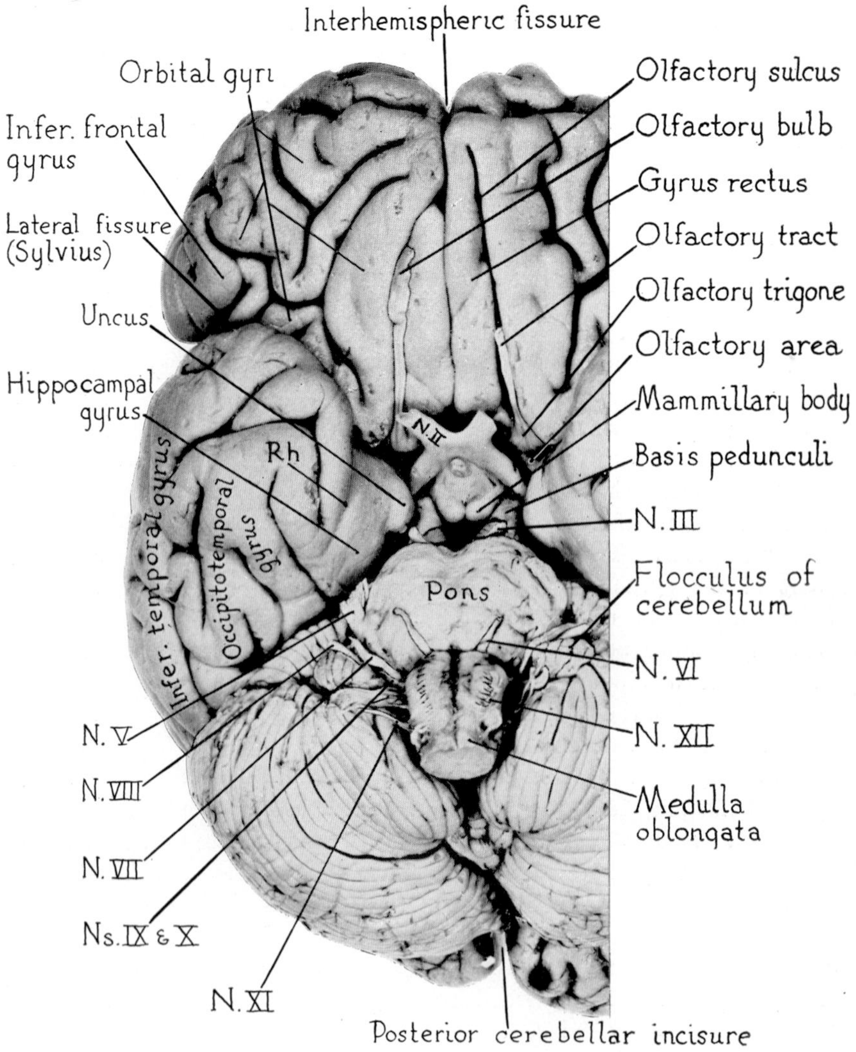

FIG. 54. Basal surface of human brain. Photograph. *Rh*, rhinal sulcus.

poral lobes. The occipital lobe is divided by the calcarine fissure into the dorsal wedge-shaped *cuneus* limited above by the parieto-occipital sulcus, and the ventral tongue-shaped *lingual gyrus* bounded below by the collateral fissure. The cuneus belongs entirely to the occipital lobe, but the lingual gyrus extends into the temporal lobe. The lips of the calcarine fissure and immediately adjacent regions constitute the visual projection area of the cortex. Anteriorly the lingual gyrus overlaps the caudal part of the *hippocampal gyrus,* the most medial convolution of the temporal lobe, bounded ventrally by the rhinal and collateral fissures, and dorsally by the hippocampal fissure. The rostral portion of the hippocampal gyrus hooks around the front end of the hippocampal fissure to form a short recurrent convolution, the *uncus* or *uncinate gyrus.* The hippocampal gyrus is directly continuous with the gyrus cinguli by a narrow strip of cortex known as the *isthmus of the gyrus fornicatus.* Ventral to the hippocampal and lingual gyri and forming part of the basal surface is the long *occipitotem-*

poral or *fusiform* gyrus, bounded dorsally by the collateral fissure and ventrally by the inferior temporal sulcus.

The gyrus cinguli, isthmus, hippocampal gyrus and uncus together form a continuous ring-like convolution which has been designated as the *gyrus fornicatus* or *limbic lobe* (Broca) in the belief that all these structures were related to the rhinencephalon. It seems certain, however, that the larger portion of the gyrus cinguli and a considerable part of the hippocampal gyrus have other than olfactory functions, and moreover they are neopallial formations of isocortical structure. There has been a tendency therefore to allocate the various parts of the fornicate gyrus to the lobes in which these parts are situated. Thus the larger anterior part of the gyrus cinguli to the region of the central sulcus belongs to the frontal lobe, the smaller posterior portion to the parietal, while the hippocampal gyrus and uncus are included in the temporal lobe.

The **basal** surface is divided by the Sylvian fossa into two parts. The larger posterior portion belonging to the temporal and occipital lobes rests on the tentorium cerebelli and middle cranial fossa. Its gyri and sulci, visible on the medial surface have been described in the preceding paragraphs. The smaller anterior part forms the orbital surface of the frontal lobe. It is divided by the deep straight *olfactory sulcus* into a narrow medial convolution, the *gyrus rectus,* and a larger lateral area composed of a number of irregular and variable *orbital gyri* (Figs. 54, 55). The straight gyrus is continuous on the medial surface with the marginal convolution, of which it forms the most ventral part. The irregular sulci which separate the orbital convolutions, form patterns of various shapes. Sometimes they have the form of a Maltese cross or an H, dividing the orbital area into four portions: lateral, medial, anterior, and posterior. Laterally the orbital area is continuous with the inferior frontal gyrus.

On the orbital surface are seen also a number of structures belonging to the olfactory lobe. The *olfactory bulb,* resting on the cribriform plate of the ethmoid bone, is a flattened ovoid body, continuous caudally with a slender band, the *olfactory tract.* Both these structures are lodged in the olfactory sulcus. Posteriorly the olfactory tract bifurcates into the *lateral* and *medial olfactory gyri* or *striae,* the bifurcation enclosing a triangular area, the *olfactory trigone.* Immediately behind the trigone is an irregular rhomboid area, the *olfactory area,* bounded caudally by the optic tract. This area especially in its anterior portion is studded with numerous apertures which serve for the passage of blood vessels, hence it is also known as *anterior perforated substance.* As already stated all these structures belong to the olfactory lobe and will be discussed more fully with the rhinencephalon.

The Medullary Substance

The white substance, especially in man, forms a volumetrically large portion of the hemisphere, filling in all the space between cortex, ventricle and basal ganglia, and furnishing medullary cores to the various convolutions. It is composed of three types of fibers: (1) *projection fibers* connecting the cortex with other parts of the nervous system; (2) *association fibers* connecting the various cortical areas of the same hemisphere; and (3) *commissural fibers,* which establish connections between the two hemispheres.

Projection fibers. Afferent and efferent projection fibers arise from the whole extent of the cortex and enter the white substance where they form a radiating mass of fibers, the *corona radiata,* converging toward the brain stem (Fig. 56). On reaching the latter they form a broad compact fiber band, the internal capsule, flanked medially by the thalamus and caudate nucleus, and laterally by the lenticular nucleus. The afferent fibers

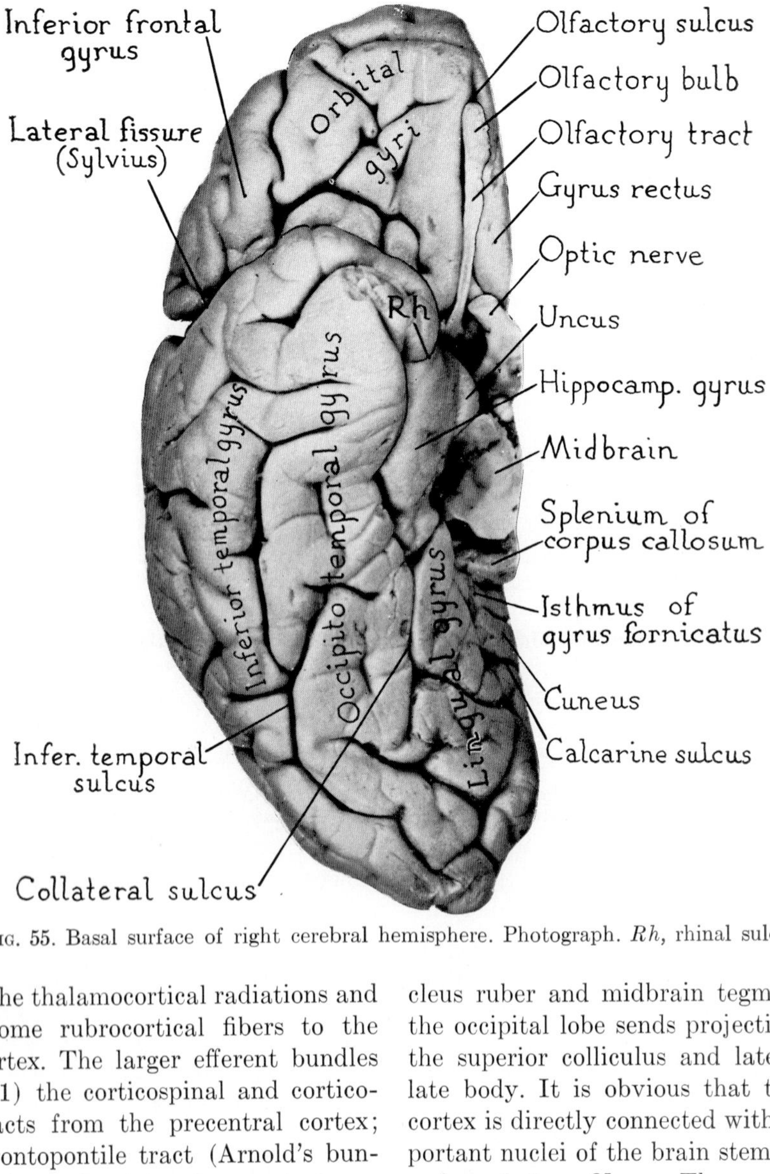

FIG. 55. Basal surface of right cerebral hemisphere. Photograph. *Rh*, rhinal sulcus.

comprise the thalamocortical radiations and perhaps some rubrocortical fibers to the frontal cortex. The larger efferent bundles include: (1) the corticospinal and corticobulbar tracts from the precentral cortex; (2) the frontopontile tract (Arnold's bundle) from the prefrontal and precentral cortex; (3) the temporo-parietopontile tract (Türck's bundle) from the temporal and parietal lobes; (4) corticothalamic fibers from most parts of the cortex, usually distributed with the corresponding thalamocortical fibers. Smaller efferent bundles arising especially from the premotor cortex go to the corpus striatum, hypothalamus, subthalamic nucleus, substantia nigra, nucleus ruber and midbrain tegmentum, and the occipital lobe sends projection fibers to the superior colliculus and lateral geniculate body. It is obvious that the cerebral cortex is directly connected with all the important nuclei of the brain stem (Fig. 327).

Association fibers. The association fibers which are tremendously developed in man, may either run within the cortex itself or in the medullary substance, and are hence designated as *intracortical* and *subcortical.* The latter, which are discussed here, may be grouped into short and long association fibers. The short ones known as arcuate fibers curve around the floor of each sulcus, thus connecting adjacent convolu-

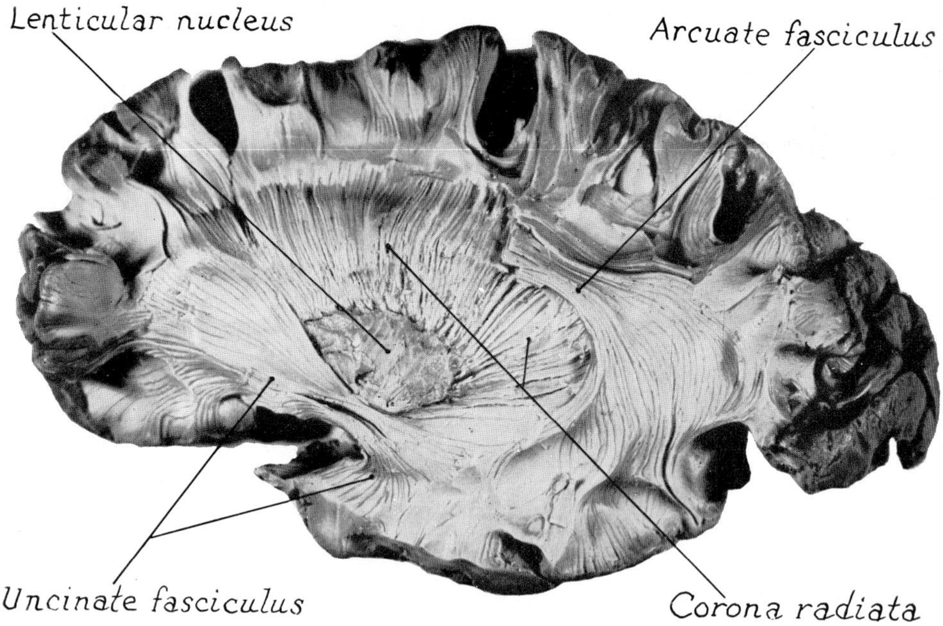

FIG. 56. Dissection of the lateral wall of the hemisphere to show the corona radiata and some of the long association bundles. Photograph. The anterior portion of the arcuate fasciculus has been removed.

tions (Fig. 330). Such fibers are found in every part of the neopallium and always run transversely to the long axis of the sulcus. Short subcortical fibers which run lengthwise are unknown, hence diffusion of neural impulses along a single convolution must be mediated entirely by intracortical fibers. Besides the short arcuate fibers there are longer ones which may bridge two or even three sulci.

The long association fibers which interconnect parts of different lobes lie more deeply in the medullary substance. The majority are organized into more or less distinct longitudinally running bundles which have an arched course conforming to the shape of the hemisphere. The most prominent of these are the uncinate fasciculus, arcuate fasciculus and cingulum. The *uncinate fasciculus* lying immediately below the limen insulae is a compact bundle in its middle portion but spreads out fanlike at either end (Fig. 56). The most basal fibers loop sharply around the Sylvian fossa, connecting the posterior orbital gyri with the tip of the hippocampal gyrus. Proceeding dorsally the looping fibers gradually flatten out and finally become straight or even slightly concave, running obliquely downward from the frontal to the temporal lobe. The bundle connects the orbital gyri and rostral portions of the middle and inferior frontal convolutions with the anterior portion of the temporal lobe. The most dorsal part of the fascicle is designated by some as the *inferior occipitofrontal fasciculus,* believed to connect the frontal and occipital lobes.

Lying more dorsally is a similar bundle, the *arcuate fasciculus,* which sweeps around the insula parallel to the circular sulcus. It likewise has a compact middle portion with radiating fan-shaped ends (Fig. 56). In its ventral portion the fibers are strongly arched and connect the superior and middle frontal convolutions with the temporal lobe, some fibers reaching the temporal pole. The dorsal part, also known as the *superior longitudinal fasciculus* connects the upper and caudal portions of the frontal lobe in-

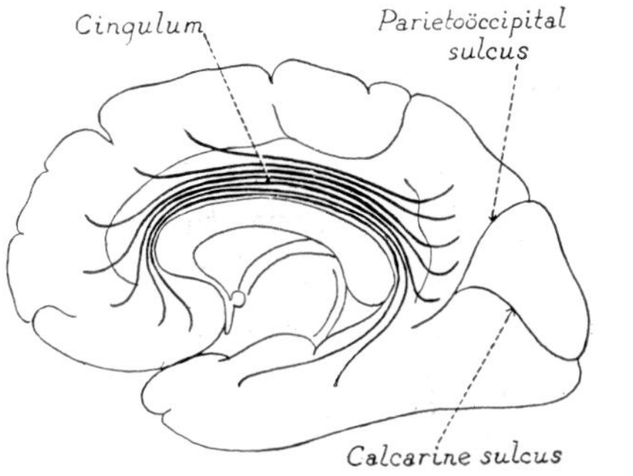

FIG. 57. Diagram showing some of the association fibers on the medial surface of the hemisphere.

cluding the precentral gyrus with the occipital, parietal, and adjacent portions of the temporal lobe.

The medial surfaces of the frontal, parietal, and temporal lobes are likewise interconnected by a system of long association fibers which run longitudinally in the underlying medullary substance. Many of these fibers are diffusely organized, but the basal portion of this system forms a well-marked arched bundle, the *cingulum,* placed in the medullary substance of the gyrus cinguli, immediately above the corpus callosum (Fig. 57). The bundle follows the contour of the gyrus cinguli, extending from beneath the rostrum of the corpus callosum (parolfactory area) to the splenium where it is continued as a greatly diminished strand into the hippocampal gyrus and uncus. The cingulum contains fibers of varying length, the longest and most curved ones connecting the frontal lobe with the hippocampal and adjacent temporal regions.

Running along the lateral walls of the posterior and inferior horns of the lateral ventricle is a longitudinal band of fibers which extends from the occipital to the temporal pole and was formerly thought to be an occipitotemporal association tract. It has been designated by some as the *inferior longitudinal fasciculus,* by others as the *external sagittal stratum* (Sachs). When, however, the bundle is exposed from the medial surface, it becomes obvious that it consists mainly of fibers from the geniculocalcarine tract (optic radiation), which run forward into the temporal lobe and then loop backward to go to the calcarine region (Fig. 330). Afferent projection fibers from the pulvinar to the occipital cortex and efferent temporopontile fibers likewise contribute to the bundle, and it seems certain that the external sagittal stratum constitutes primarily a mixed projection system of which the geniculocalcarine tract forms by far the largest component. It is probable that the most externally placed fibers may be associative in character and connect the occipital with the temporal lobe.

Vertical association fibers running in the medullary substance of the convex surface are also found, but in relatively few numbers. The *vertical occipital fasciculus* runs in the front part of the occipital lobe and apparently connects the inferior parietal lobule with the more caudal portions of the inferior temporal and fusiform gyri. Other vertical fibers have been described as connecting the dorsal regions of the frontal lobe with the orbital gyri.

Commissural fibers. The crossed commissural fibers are primarily represented by the massive *corpus callosum* which reciprocally interconnects the neopallial cortex of the two hemispheres. In its middle portions the commissure is a broad thick plate of densely packed transverse fibers placed in the floor of the interhemispheric fissure and forming most of the roof of the lateral ventricles (Fig. 59). Laterally it spreads out on either side into a mass of radiating fibers, the callosal radiations, which are distributed to practically all parts of the cortex. Since the rostral and caudal ends of the corpus callosum are placed at a considerable distance from the frontal and occipital poles respectively, the fibers distributed to these regions of the two hemispheres form U-shaped bundles known as the *anterior* and the *posterior forceps.* The former loops forward from the genu toward the frontal pole, the larger posterior forceps loops backward toward the occipital pole. The genu supplies the larger anterior part of the frontal lobe; the whole parietal and caudal portion of the frontal lobe receive fibers from the body or trunk of the commissure. The fibers which supply the temporal and occipital lobes come from the splenium and posterior part of the trunk, and are split into a dorsal and a ventral component by the external sagittal stratum (optic radiations) which runs its longitudinal course through this portion of the medullary substance (Fig. 58). The dorsal fibers sweep over and lateral to the stratum and supply the dorsal and lateral portions of the temporal and occipital lobes. The ventral fibers pass medially to the stratum and form a thin medullary plate, the *tapetum,* which sweeps around the ependymal lining of the roof and lateral walls of the inferior and posterior horns (Fig. 58). The tapetum is distributed to the medial and basal surfaces of the temporal and occipital lobes.

The exact distribution of the callosal fibers has not been fully ascertained. For the most part they connect identical portions of the two hemispheres, but fibers connecting morphologically dissimilar areas are also present (Déjérine). The fibers are difficult to follow beyond the lateral ventricles where they become intermingled with association and projection fibers.

The *anterior* and *hippocampal* commissures are primarily olfactory commissures and will be discussed with the rhinencephalon.

The Lateral Ventricles

The lateral ventricles are ependyma-lined cavities of irregular arched shape corresponding to the arched form of the hemispheres, and communicate with the rostral part of the third ventricle by two narrow and short channels, the *interventricular foramina.* They vary considerably in extent especially as regards their width, in some cases being narrow and cleft-like, in other cases constituting relatively wide spaces. Normally they are always filled with cerebrospinal fluid. When the ventricles become pathologically enlarged with a corresponding increase in fluid, the condition is known as internal hydrocephalus.

Each ventricle consists of a *central portion* or *body* from which three prolongations or horns extend respectively into the frontal, temporal, and occipital lobes (Figs. 59, 60). The **anterior** or **frontal horn** extends forward from the interventricular foramen

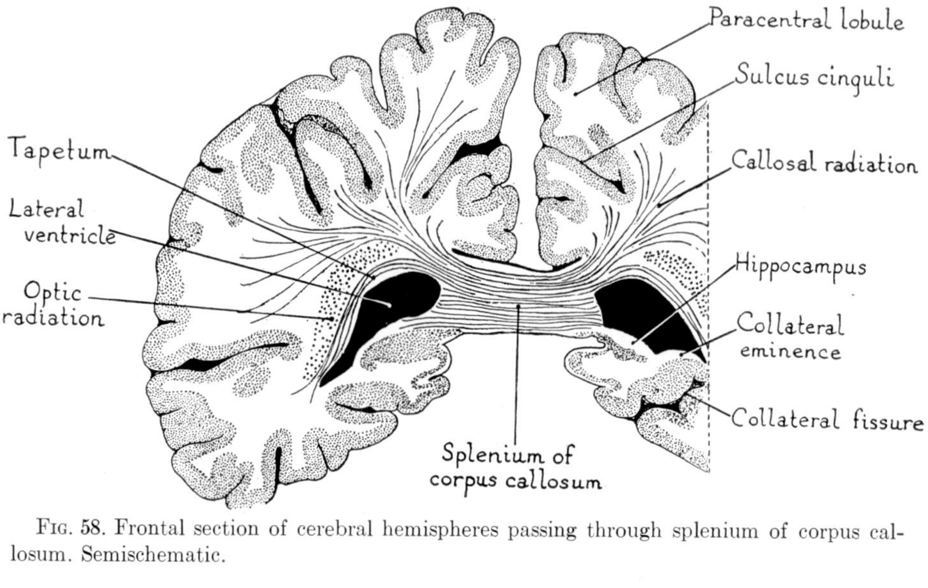

FIG. 58. Frontal section of cerebral hemispheres passing through splenium of corpus callosum. Semischematic.

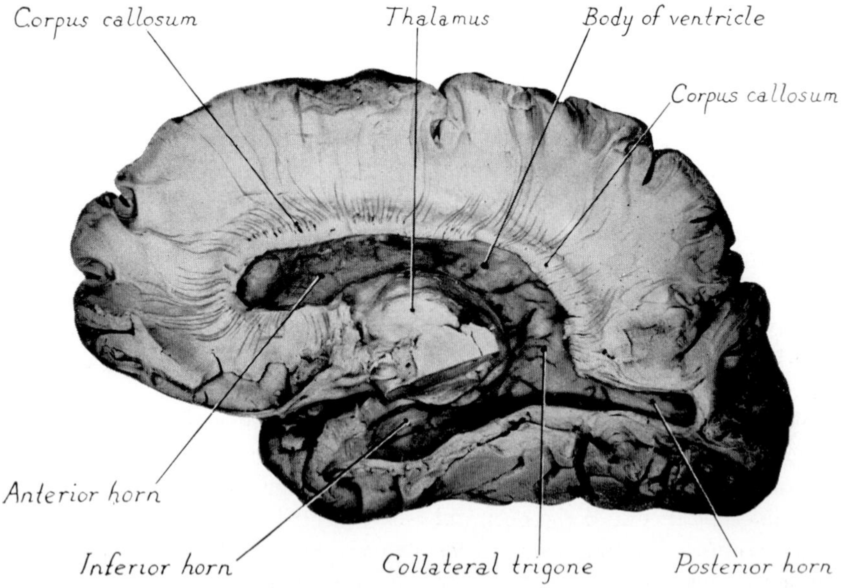

FIG. 59. Dissection of medial surface of cerebral hemisphere, showing lateral ventricle and callosal radiations. The usually shallow body of the ventricle is here abnormally enlarged. Photograph.

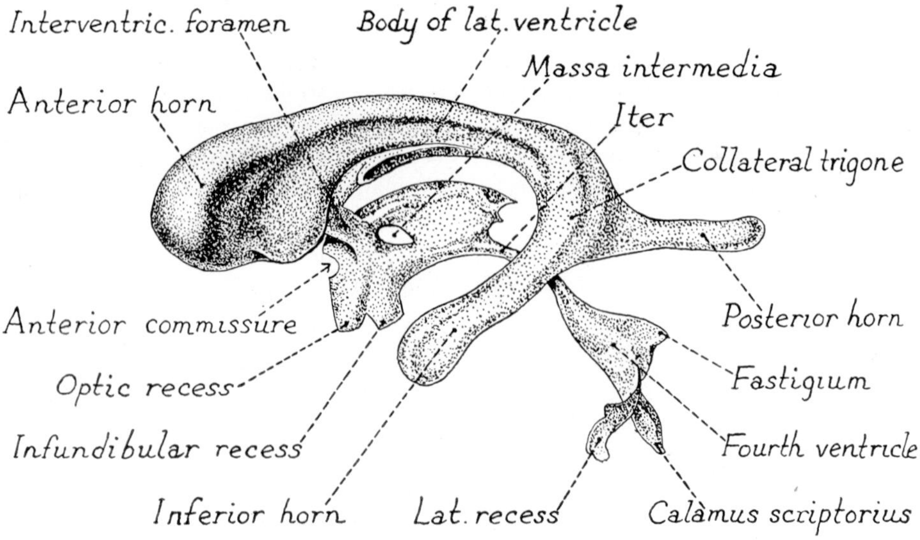

FIG. 60. Cast of the brain ventricles, viewed from the side. Only the left lateral ventricle is represented. (After Rauber-Kopsch.)

and in transverse section has a triangular shape (Fig. 341). Its roof and rostral wall are formed by the corpus callosum, while medially it is separated from the horn of the opposite side by the thin vertical laminae of the septum pellucidum. Floor and lateral wall are combined into the sloping hypotenuse of the triangle, formed by the head of the caudate nucleus whose surface bulges convexly into the cavity of the horn (Fig. 341).

The **central portion** is a relatively shallow cavity extending from the interventricular foramen to the splenium where it enlarges into the *collateral trigone* formed by the junction of posterior and inferior horns. Its roof is formed by the corpus callosum which curves ventrally at either end and becomes continuous with the dorsally slanting floor, so that a true medial and lateral wall are not present. The floor is formed by a number of structures (Figs. 47, 48). Most laterally is the caudate nucleus forming a bulge in the ventricular cavity. Proceeding medially are the stria terminalis, a part of the dorsal thalamic surface (lamina affixa), the choroid plexus, and the fornix.

The **posterior** or **occipital horn** extends a variable distance into the occipital lobe. It may be quite short and taper rapidly to a point, or it may form a longer more tubular prolongation. Its dorsal and lateral walls are formed by the tapetal fibers of the corpus callosum, its floor by the medullary substance of the occipital lobe. The medial wall shows a longitudinal prominence, the *calcar avis,* produced by the deep penetration of the calcarine fissure (Fig. 348).

The **inferior** or **temporal horn** begins at the collateral trigone, curves ventrally around the posterior portion of the thalamus and extends rostrally into the medial part of the temporal lobe, ending about one inch from the temporal pole (Fig. 59). Its floor, directly continuous with that of the posterior horn, is marked by a more or less distinct prominence, the *collateral eminence,* caused by the deep collateral fissure (Figs. 58, 348). The roof and lateral walls are largely formed by the tapetum, but in the medial region of the roof a small part is furnished by the tail of the caudate nucleus and the accompanying stria terminalis. The most remarkable feature of the inferior horn is the *hippocampus* or *horn of Ammon* produced by the infolding of the pallium along the hippocampal fissure (Fig. 348). The hippocampus is a prominent sickle-shaped ridge on the medial wall of the horn, extending from the region of the splenium to the temporal tip of the ventricle where it is continuous with the ventricular surface of the uncus. Its broad anterior portion known as the *pes hippocampi,* shows a number of slight fingerlike elevations, the hippocampal digitations, separated by shallow radial furrows. Running along the dorsomedial surface of the hippocampus is a flattened white band, the *fimbria,* which extends from the uncus toward the splenium and is directly continued into the crus of the fornix. Hippocampus and fimbria are in part overlapped by the inferior portion of the choroid plexus which extends to the tip of the inferior horn (Fig. 47).

5

Blood Supply of the Central Nervous System

The central nervous system can be deprived of an adequate arterial blood supply for only a very short interval. If an adequate circulation is not maintained the tissues of the brain and spinal cord rapidly undergo softening (encephalomalacia) and degeneration (necrosis). The significance of an adequate blood supply is self evident, for vascular accidents are one of the most common types of injury to the central nervous system. One or more important arteries of the brain or spinal cord may be interrupted by injury, ligature, or blockage (occlusion). Either abnormal sacculations (aneurysms) or weak points along the vascular branchings may rupture to produce hemorrhage. Interruptions of an artery to the brain, followed by degeneration within the area of its vascular distribution, can often be correlated with the specific sensory and motor changes found in a neurological examination.

BLOOD SUPPLY OF THE SPINAL CORD

The arterial supply of the spinal cord is derived from two principal sources. Branches from the two vertebral arteries provide nutriment to the cervical cord segments. Communications from segmental vessels (i.e., deep cervical, intercostal, lumbar, and sacral arteries) course medially along the spinal nerves as *radicular arteries* and provide additional arterial blood to the thoracic, lumbar, and sacral segments of the spinal cord. The radicular arteries then sub-divide into smaller *anterior* and *posterior radicular arteries* which accompany the ventral and dorsal roots of the nerve to the spinal cord.

Each vertebral artery gives off two small, but highly important, arteries as it ascends along the ventrolateral surface of the medulla. The first, or most inferior branch, is the *posterior spinal artery* which turns dorsally and descends as a discrete vessel on the dorsal surface of the spinal cord (Fig. 61B). As the two posterior spinal arteries descend, they receive a variable number of contributions (5–8) from the posterior radicular arteries. The second, or more superior branch is the anterior spinal artery. These two vessels unite ventral to the pyramids to form a single descending *anterior spinal artery* (Fig. 61A). This vessel provides midline rami to the lower medulla, and more caudally it gives off sulcal arteries that enter the ventral median fissure to supply the spinal cord. The single anterior spinal artery varies in size as it descends. According to Suh and Alexander (1939) the continuity of this artery is dependent upon the anastomosing vessels it receives from the anterior radicular arteries (6–8). A plexus of smaller arteries within the pia mater, the *arterial vasocorona* interconnects the larger arterial vessels on the ventral and dorsal surfaces of the cord (Fig. 62A).

The blood supply of the cord may be jeopardized in certain transitional regions where its blood supply is derived from two different sources. For example, the cervical segments are supplied primarily by branches of the vertebral and to a lesser extent by small branches of the ascending cervical

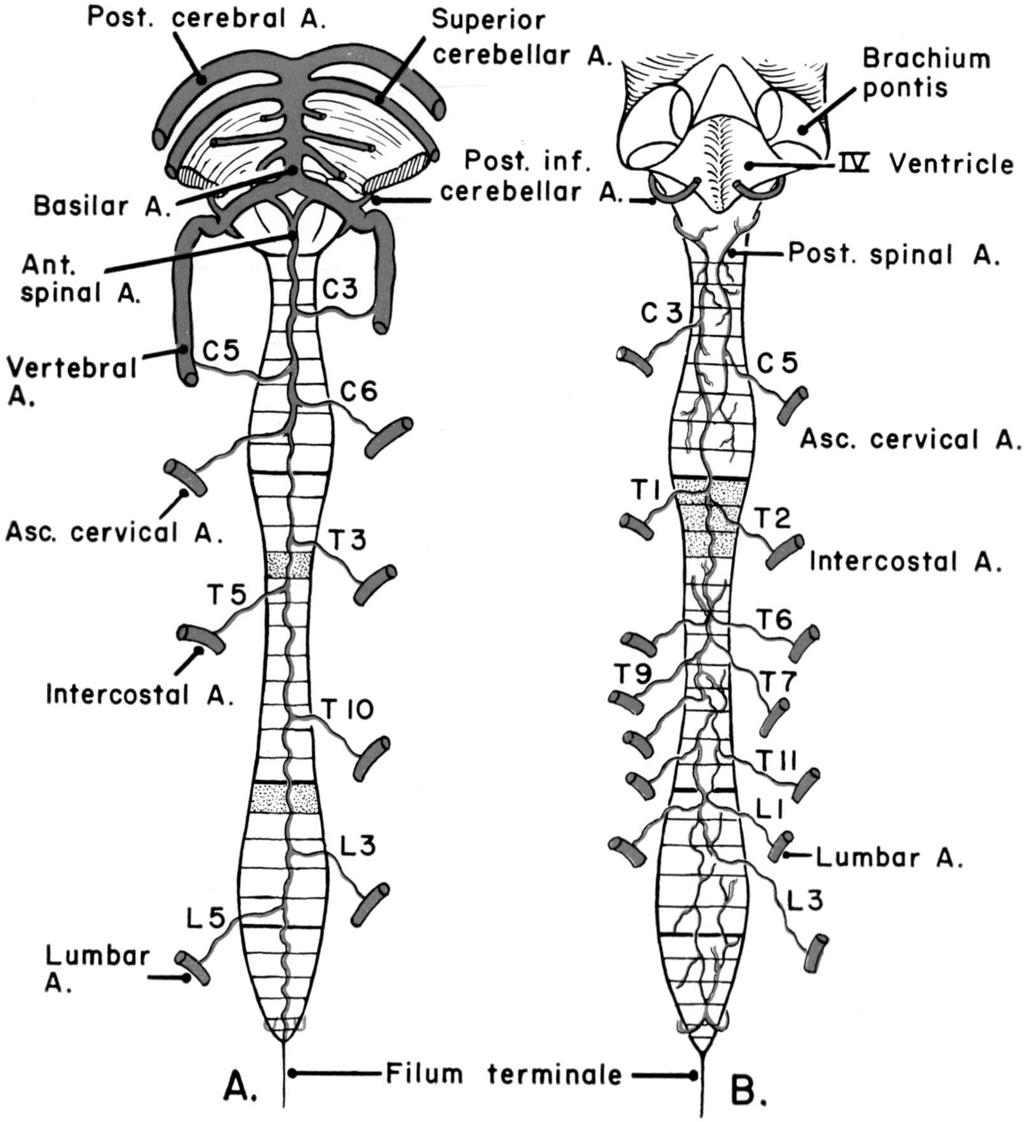

FIG. 61. Diagram of vessels that contribute arterial blood to the spinal cord. A. Ventral surface and arteries. B. Dorsal surface and arteries. Vulnerable segments of the spinal cord are stippled. Letters and numbers indicate most important radicular arteries (based on the work of Bolton, 1939; Suh and Alexander, 1939; and Zülch, 1954.)

artery. The upper segments of the thoracic spinal cord on the other hand, are dependent upon the radicular branches of the intercostal arteries. If one or more of the parent intercostal vessels are compromised by injury or ligature, segments of the spinal cord T1–4 could not be adequately maintained by the small sulcal branches of the anterior spinal artery (Fig. 61A). For this reason, thoracic segments T1–4, particularly T4, are considered vulnerable areas in the distribution of the anterior spinal artery (Zülch, 1954). Cord segment L1 is an equally vulnerable region. The posterior surface of the cord most susceptible to vascular insult is also in segments T1–4 (Fig. 61B). Such vascular injuries may result in necrosis of an entire segment and produce

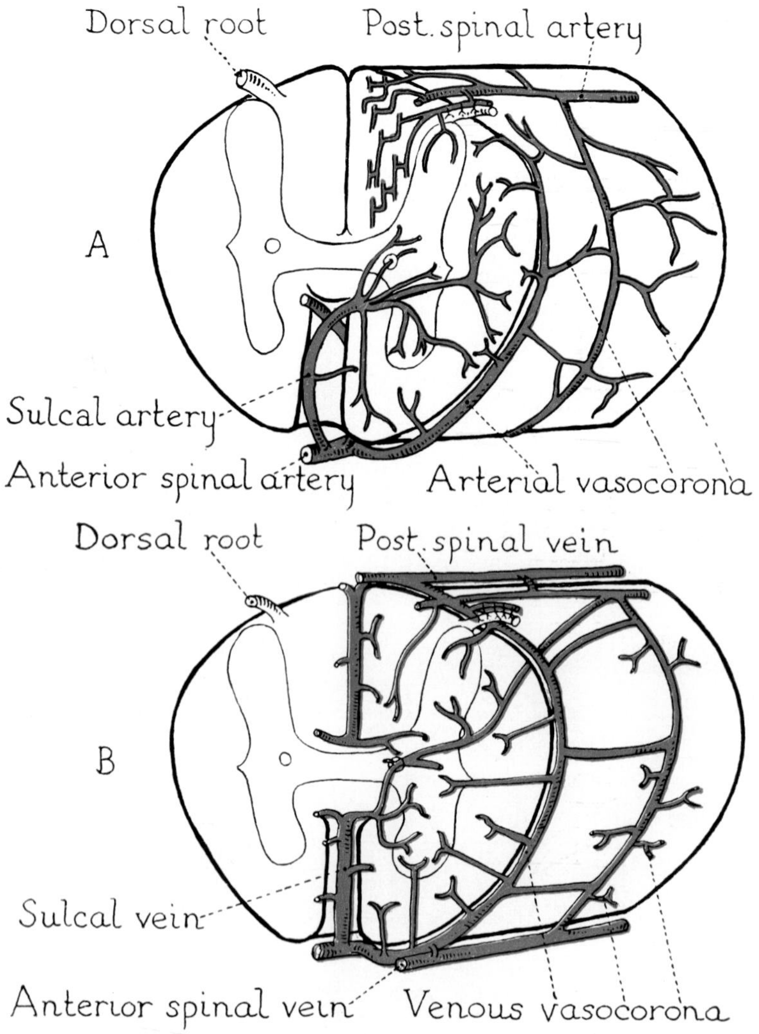

FIG. 62. Diagram of the blood supply of the spinal cord. *A*, arterial; *B*, venous. (After Herren and Alexander.)

neurologic symptoms comparable to complete cord transection (p. 230).

The anterior spinal artery gives off a number of *sulcal* (sulcocommissural) branches which pass dorsally in the ventral fissure and enter the cord alternately to the right and left. Only in the lumbar and sacral segments does an occasional single sulcal artery penetrate into the fissure and divide into a left and right branch. The anterior sulcal arteries are most numerous in the lumbar region and fewest in the thoracic where the segmental blood supply is poorest and there may be but one sulcal artery to an entire segment (Herren and Alexander, 1939).

The anterior spinal artery through its sulcal branches supplies the ventral and lateral horns, central gray and Clarke's column (Fig. 62A). It also supplies the ventral and lateral white funiculi including the lateral pyramidal tract. To a smaller degree the lateral white is also supplied by branches from the arterial vasocorona. The posterior spinal arteries feed the dorsal horn and dorsal white column.

The venous distribution is in the main similar to that of the arteries (Fig. 62B). There are 6–11 anterior and 5–10 posterior radicular veins, one of which, situated in the lumbar region, is of considerably greater caliber and is known as the *vena radicularis magna* (Suh and Alexander). The posterior radicular veins form a more or less distinct posterior median spinal vein or trunk along the whole extent of the cord as well as smaller paired posterolateral trunks. Similarly, an anterior median and paired anterolateral venous trunks are formed from the anterior radicular veins. As in the case of the arteries, a meningeal plexus of veins, the vasocorona, connects the longitudinal trunks. From the anterior spinal vein, sulcal branches pass dorsally in the ventral fissure and enter the cord, each sulcal vessel as a rule supplying both sides of the cord.

The posterior radicular veins (and posterior trunks) drain the dorsal white column, dorsal horn including Clarke's column, and a narrow strip of lateral white immediately adjacent to the dorsal horn (Fig. 62B). The anterior spinal vein, through the sulcal vessels, drains the sulcomarginal white and the medial portion of the ventral horn. The lateral portions of the ventral horn, the lateral horn, and the ventral and lateral white columns are drained by branches of the venous vasocorona (Fig. 62B).

THE BLOOD SUPPLY OF THE BRAIN

The entire brain is supplied by two pairs of arterial trunks, the two *internal carotid*

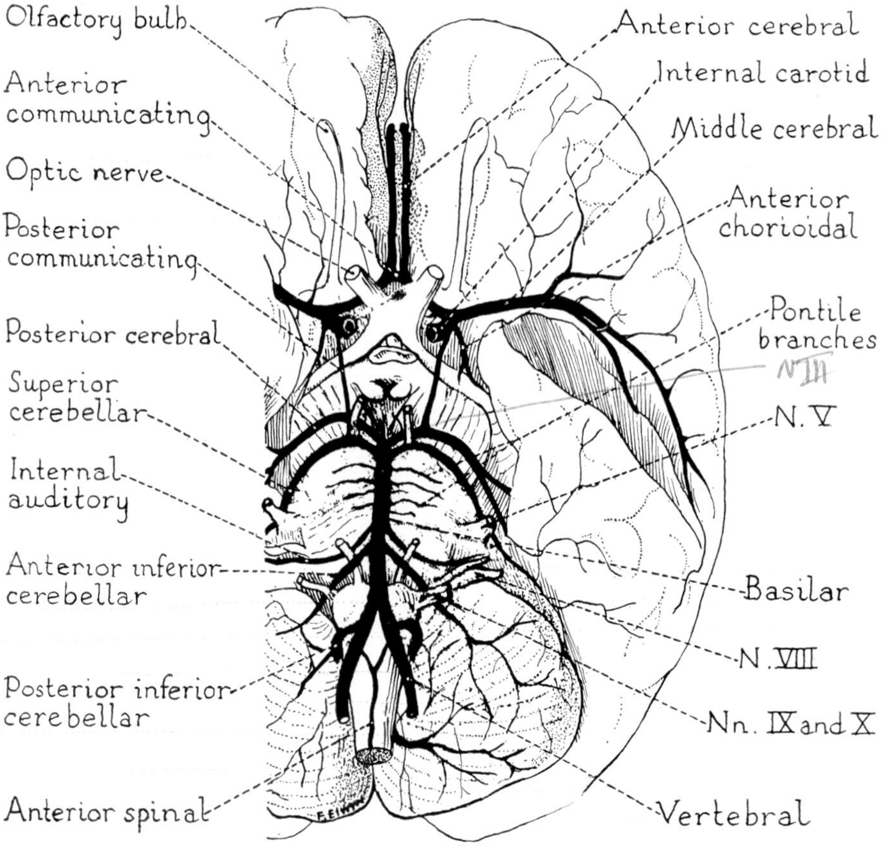

FIG. 63. The basal surface of the brain showing the main cerebral arteries and some of their branches.

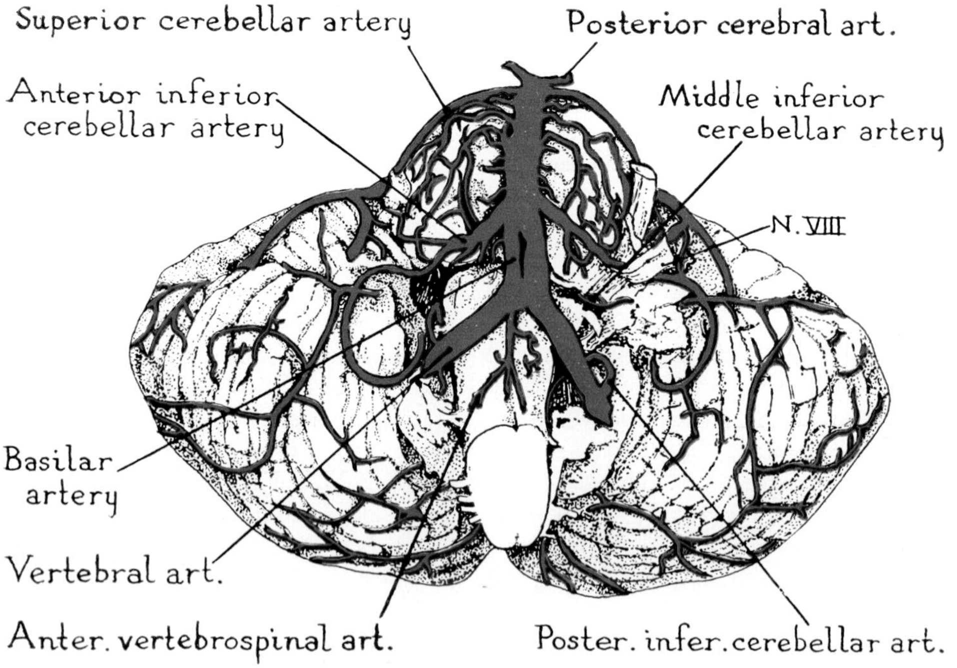

FIG. 64. The arterial supply of the human cerebellum. (After Jakob.)

and the two *vertebral arteries*. In a general way the branches derived from the vertebral arteries supply the caudal half of the brain including the hindbrain, midbrain, caudal half of the thalamus, occipital lobes, and basal portions of the temporal lobes. The anterior half of the thalamus, the corpus striatum, practically all of the internal capsule, the frontal, parietal, and lateral portions of the temporal lobes, are fed by branches of the internal carotids.

The circle of Willis. On the basal surface of the brain the four main arterial trunks form an anastomosing system known as the *arterial circle of Willis* (Figs. 63, 64). The two *vertebral* arteries entering through the foramen magnum run obliquely forward on the ventral surface of the medulla and near the caudal border of the pons fuse to form the unpaired *basilar artery*. At the rostral border of the pons this artery bifurcates into the two *posterior cerebral arteries* which run laterally in front of the oculomotor nerves and encircle the cerebral peduncles. The internal carotid artery enters the cranial cavity through the carotid foramen and reaches the base of the brain just lateral to the optic chiasma. Here it divides into its two terminal branches: the smaller *anterior cerebral artery* and the larger *middle cerebral artery* which may be regarded as the direct continuation of the *carotid.* At or immediately before its division the carotid gives off the *posterior communicating artery* which runs backward and anastomoses with the proximal portion of the posterior cerebral. The *anterior cerebral artery* runs medially and rostrally toward the interhemispheric fissure and in front of the optic chiasma is joined to its mate by a short connecting channel, the *anterior communicating artery.* In this manner there is formed a circular or rather heptagonal arterial wreath, the *circle of Willis,* surrounding the optic chiasma, tuber and interpeduncular fossa, composed of the posterior and anterior communicating arteries and the proximal portions of the anterior and posterior cerebrals. This anastomosis serves to equalize the blood flow to various parts of the brain and furnishes collateral circulation in cases of occlusion of one or more of the arteries contributing to the circle.

From the circle of Willis and the main cerebral arteries (anterior, middle, and posterior) arise two types of branches: the (1) *paramedian* or *central* also known as the *ganglionic*, and the *circumferential* or *cortical*. (2) The central and cortical arteries are not connected with each other but form two distinct systems. The *central* arteries arise from the circle of Willis and the proximal portions of the three cerebral arteries dip perpendicularly into the brain substance and irrigate the diencephalon, corpus striatum, and internal capsule. They are terminal arteries, i.e., the branches of one artery do not anastomose with those of others, hence occlusion of one of these vessels will produce a softening in the area deprived of its blood supply. The anterior and posterior chorioidal arteries, respectively branches of the middle and posterior cerebral arteries, may be included in this group.

The larger *cortical* branches of each cerebral artery enter the pia mater where they form a superficial plexus of more or less freely anastomosing vessels, in some places continuous with the plexuses derived from the other main arteries. From these plexuses arise the smaller terminal arteries which enter the brain substance at right angles and run a variable distance, the shorter ones arborizing in the cortex, the longer ones supplying the medullary substance of the hemispheres. Due to the anastomosis of the larger cortical branches, the occlusion of one of these vessels is compensated to a variable extent by the blood supply from neighboring branches, though such collateral circulation is rarely sufficient to prevent brain damage. The great majority of vascular occlusions occur in the cerebral vessels before they enter the substance of the brain. Areas of the cerebral cortex, internal capsule, or basal ganglia which lie between the territorial distributions of two primary arteries are the sites most severely involved after vascular injury (Mettler, Cooper, Liss, Carpenter, Noback, 1954). The degree of brain damage is variable and depends upon several factors (e.g., site of injury; amount of vascular overlap and confluence; rapidity with which an occlusion develops).

The cortical branches. The *anterior cerebral artery* passes medially and forward to the interhemispheric fissure, approaching the corresponding artery of the opposite side with which it is connected by the anterior communicating artery (Figs. 63, 65). It then runs on the medial surface of the hemisphere, curving over the genu of the corpus callosum and continuing along the dorsal surface of that commissure. The branches of the anterior cerebral artery supply the olfactory lobe, gyrus rectus and medial portion of the orbital gyri, the gyrus cinguli and the whole medial surface of the frontal and parietal lobes to the parieto-occipital sulcus where they anastomose with small branches of the posterior cerebral (Fig. 66). Some of the branches curve over to the lateral surface to supply the superior frontal gyrus, while numerous small branches are distributed to the corpus callosum. Thus the territory irrigated by the anterior cerebral includes the somesthetic and motor leg area of the paracentral lobule. One of the basal branches of the anterior cerebral is peculiar in having both a cortical and central distribution. This *medial striate artery* or *recurrent artery of Heubner* arises near the level of the anterior communicating artery, runs backward, and after giving off a few branches to the orbital cortex, dips into the anterior perforated space and supplies the anteroventral portion of the head of the caudate nucleus and adjacent portions of the putamen and internal capsule (Fig. 69). Occlusion of this vessel produces a softening of the rostral part of the internal capsule with a consequent supranuclear paralysis of the face, tongue and shoulder.

The *middle cerebral artery* passes laterally over the anterior perforated substance

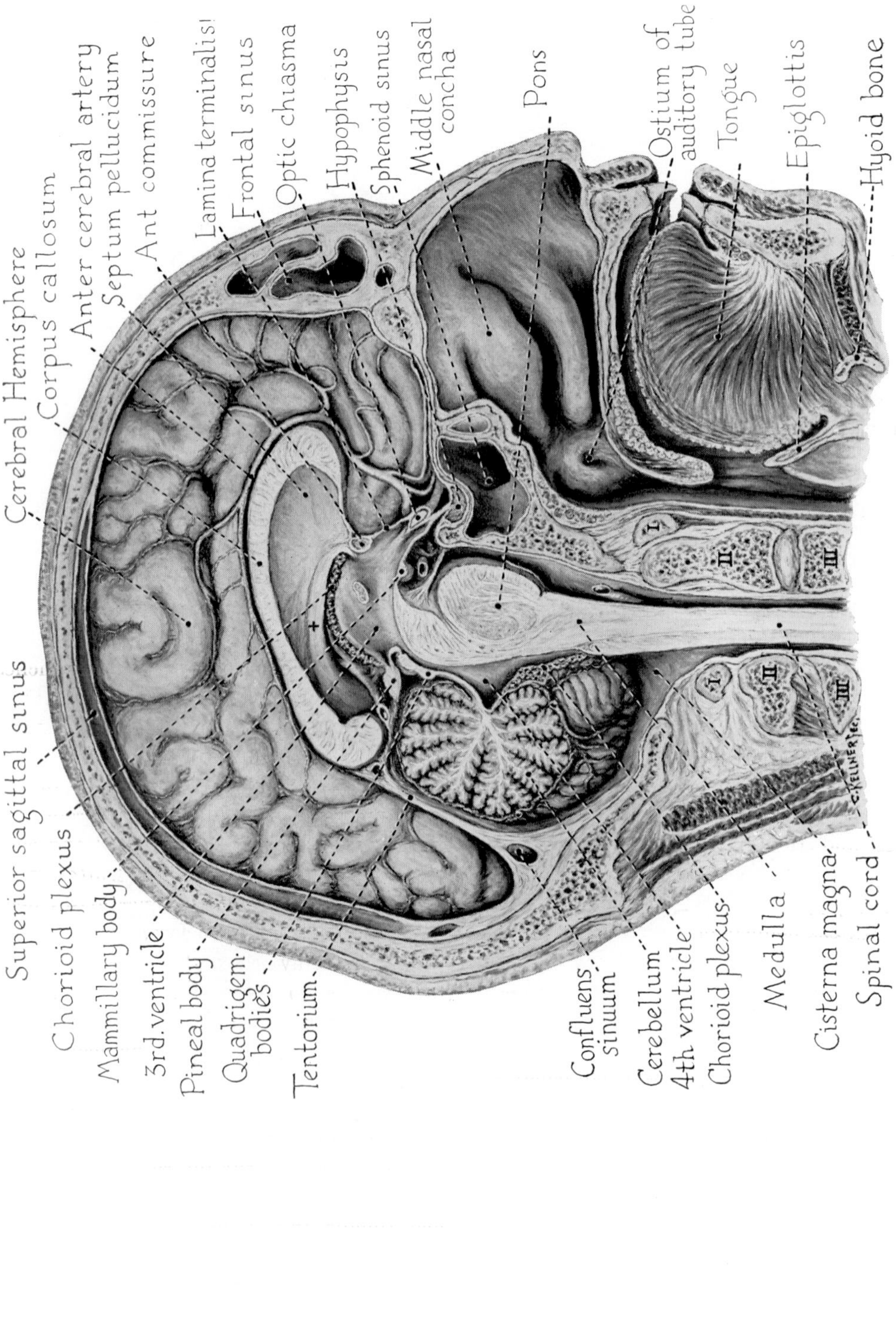

Fig. 65. Median sagittal section of head, showing brain and upper portion of spinal cord. I, atlas; II, axis; III, third cervical vertebra; +, fornix.

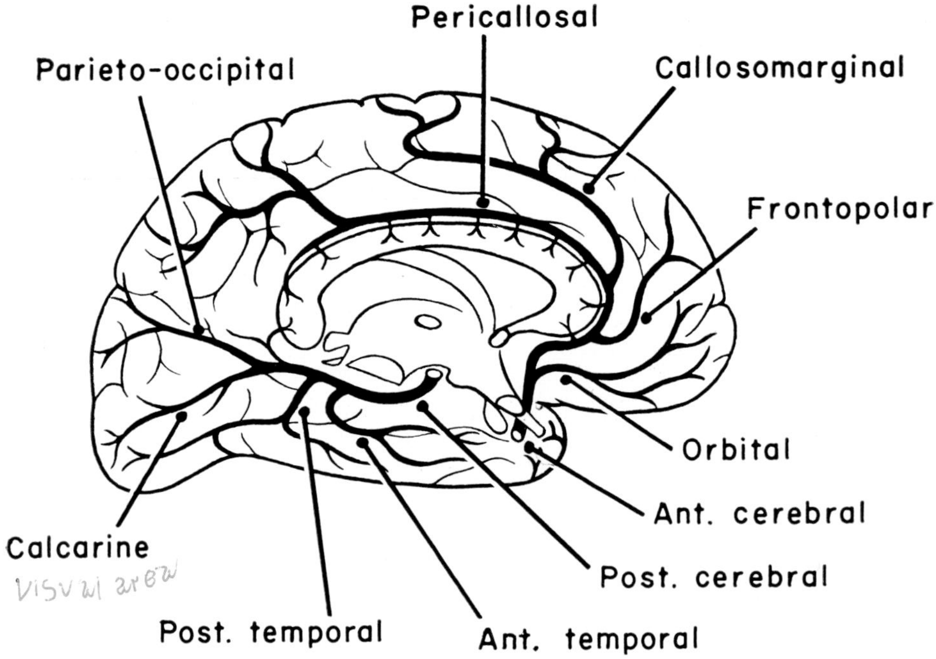

FIG. 66. Diagram of the main arteries on the medial surface of the left hemisphere.

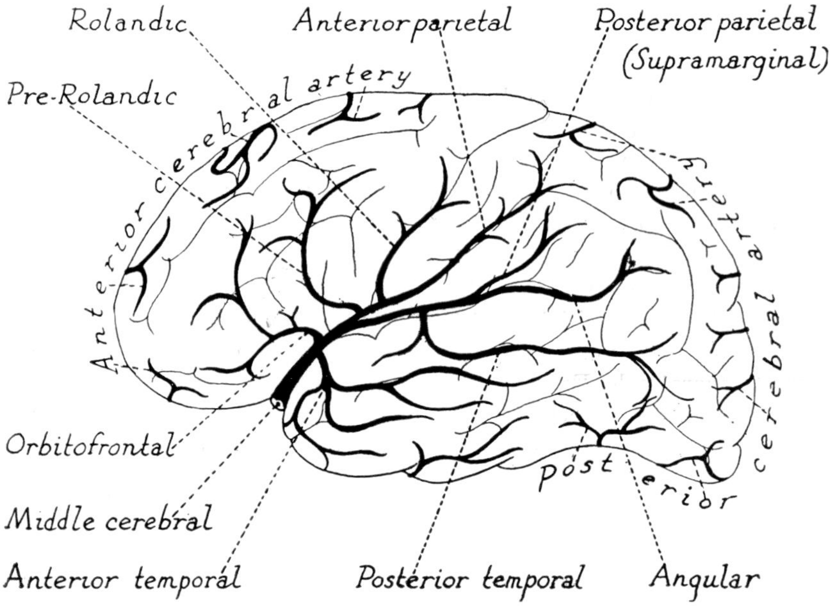

FIG. 67. The main arteries on the lateral surface of the hemisphere. Semischematic.

into the Sylvian fossa and there divides into a number of cortical branches which curve outward over the opercular margins of the lateral fissure and spread over the convex surface of the brain (Fig. 67). Besides the insula, these branches supply the lateral parts of the orbital gyri, the inferior and middle frontal gyri, the portions of the precentral and postcentral gyri seen on the lateral surface of the brain, the superior and inferior parietal lobules, and the superior and middle temporal gyri including the temporal pole. In many instances the territory of the middle cerebral artery is extended caudally to take in most of the lateral gyri of the occipital lobe. Thus the extensive and important territory irrigated by this artery includes the motor and premotor areas, the somesthetic and auditory projection areas and the higher receptive association areas. Occlusion of the middle cerebral artery near the origin of its cortical branches, when not fatal, produces a contralateral hemiplegia most marked in the upper extremity and face, and a contralateral sensory loss of the cortical type, such as astereognosis and the inability to distinguish between different intensities of stimuli. When the left or dominant hemisphere is involved there are also severe aphasic disturbances both as to the motor formulation of speech (verbal aphasia) and the comprehension of spoken or written words (p. 464).

Each of the *posterior cerebral arteries* formed by the bifurcation of the basilar, passes laterally and backward over the cerebral peduncles. After receiving the posterior communicating artery it continues to the inferior surface of the hemisphere, where it divides into four cortical branches (Fig. 66). These supply the medial and inferior surfaces of the occipital lobe and the inferior surface of the temporal lobe exclusive of the temporal pole. Especially important is the calcarine branch which is distributed to the visual area. The branches also extend to the lateral surface, supplying the inferior temporal gyrus and a variable portion of the lateral occipital region, and may invade a considerable part of the superior parietal lobule. In all these regions the branches come in contact and anastomose with the marginal branches of the anterior and middle cerebral arteries. This extensive anastomosis probably explains the fact that occlusion of the posterior cerebral rarely produces a complete softening of the deprived area. The most striking symptom is a contralateral homonymous hemianopia in which macular vision is often spared, due to the overlapping of the middle and posterior cerebral territories at the occipital pole.

The central or ganglionic branches. The ganglionic arteries which supply the diencephalon, corpus striatum, and internal capsule are arranged in four general groups: anteromedial, anterolateral, posteromedial, and posterolateral (Fig. 68). The *anteromedial* arise from the domain of the anterior cerebral and anterior communicating arteries, some twigs coming directly from the carotid at its place of bifurcation (Fig. 69). They enter the most medial portion of the anterior perforated space and are distributed to the anterior hypothalamus including the preoptic and suprachiasmatic regions.

The numerous *posteromedial arteries* which enter the tuber cinereum, mammillary bodies, and interpeduncular fossa are derived from the most proximal portion of the posterior cerebral and from the whole extent of the posterior communicating arteries. Some twigs come directly from the carotid just before its bifurcation (Fig. 69). A rostral and caudal group may be distinguished. The rostral group supplies the hypophysis, infundibulum and tuberal regions of the hypothalamus. A number of vessels, known as the *thalamoperforating arteries*, penetrate more deeply and are distributed to the anterior and medial portions of the thalamus. The caudal group supplies the mammillary region of the hypothalamus, the subthalamic structures, and likewise sends fibers to the medial wall and nuclei of the thalamus including the massa intermedia. Other vessels from the caudal group are distributed to the midbrain, supplying the raphéal region of the tegmentum, the nucleus ruber and medial portions of the pes pedunculi.

The *posterolateral* or *thalamogeniculate* arteries arise more laterally from the posterior cerebral arteries (Figs. 68, 70). They

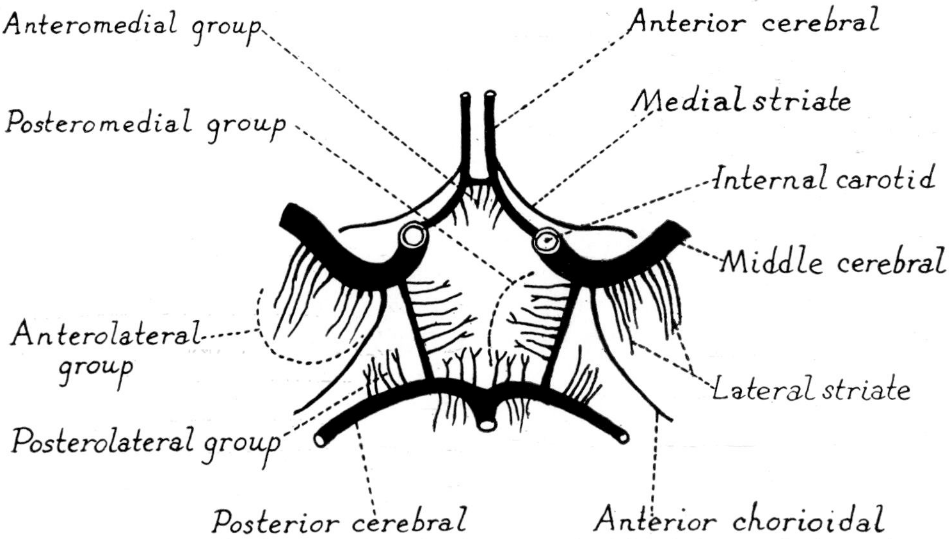

FIG. 68. Diagram showing arterial circle of Willis and origin of the ganglionic arteries.

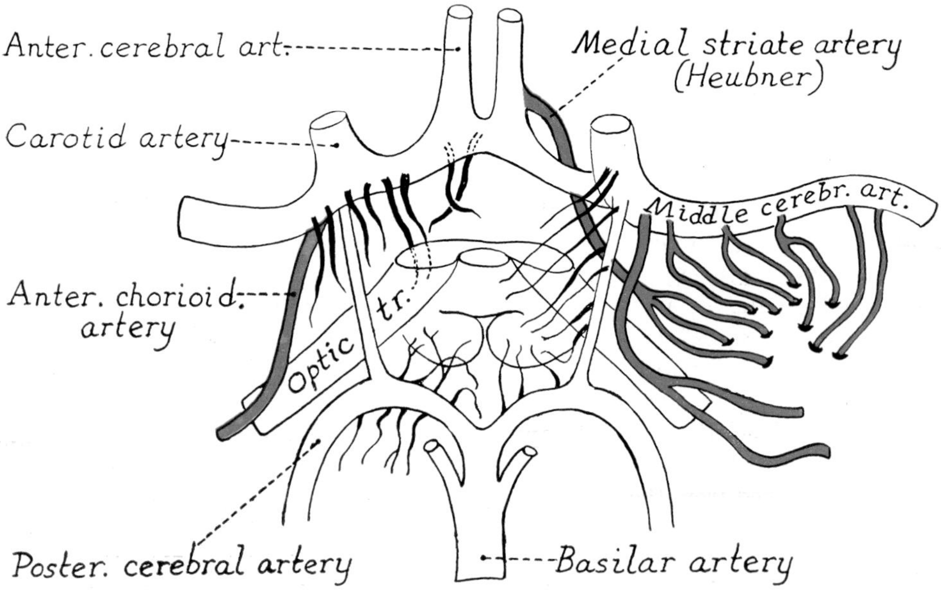

FIG. 69. The circle of Willis and the ganglionic arteries. On the left side the carotid artery has been turned to expose its dorsal surface. Anterior chorioidal and striate arteries in red; hypothalamic arteries in black. (Based on data from Alexander and from Foley, Kinney, and Alexander.)

penetrate the lateral geniculate body and supply the larger caudal half of the thalamus including the geniculate bodies, pulvinar and most of the lateral nuclear mass.

The *anterolateral* or *striate arteries* which pierce the anterior perforated substance arise mainly from the basal portion of the middle cerebral artery and to a lesser extent from the anterior cerebral (Figs. 69, 70). As a rule, those from the anterior cerebral supply the anteroventral portion of the head of the caudate nucleus and adjacent

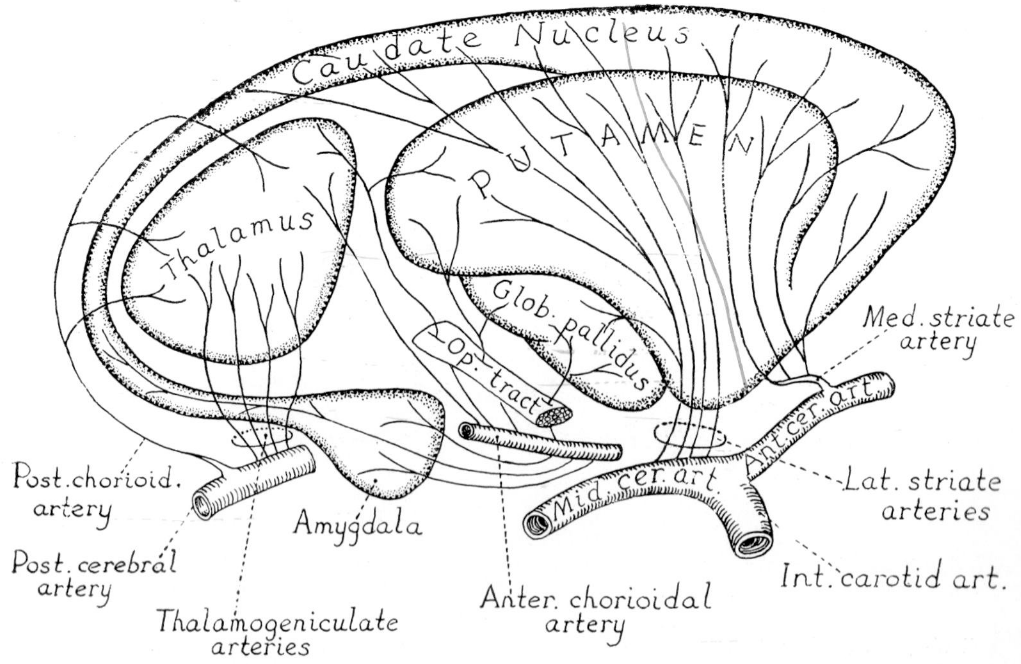

FIG. 70. Diagram of arterial supply to the corpus striatum. (Modified from Aitken.)

portions of the putamen and internal capsule. The rest of the putamen, caudate nucleus and anterior limb of the internal capsule are supplied by branches from the middle cerebral, excepting only the most caudal tip of the putamen and the recurving portion of the caudate tail (Fig. 70). These branches also feed the lateral part of the globus pallidus and the dorsal portion of the posterior limb of the internal capsule (Fig. 70). In some cases all the striate arteries may be derived from the middle cerebral (Alexander). One of the striate arteries has been described as the vessel most prone to rupture under pathological conditions and has hence been called the "artery of cerebral hemorrhage" (Charcot). Anatomically such an artery cannot be usually distinguished. It is very doubtful that the striate arteries aid in the vascular supply of the thalamus, though such vessels (lenticulo-optic) have been described by some investigators.

The anterior and posterior chorioidal arteries may also be regarded as central branches. The *anterior chorioidal* arises from the middle cerebral, close to the origin of the posterior communicating artery (Figs. 68, 69). It passes backward along the optic tract, some of its branches actually perforating the latter, and enters the chorioidal fissure in the lower part of the inferior horn. The artery supplies the chorioid plexus of the lateral ventricle, the hippocampus, the medial and intermediate portions of the globus pallidus and the larger ventral part of the posterior limb of the internal capsule, including the entire retrolenticular portion of the capsule (Fig. 71). It also sends branches to the amygdaloid nucleus, the recurving ventral portion of the caudate tail, and the posterior tip of the putamen (Fig. 70). Some of the twigs are believed to go to the pulvinar and superior surface of the thalamus. According to Alexander the anterior chorioidal artery is the vessel most susceptible to thrombosis on account of its long free subarachnoid course and its relatively small caliber. It is significant that the globus pallidus and hippocampus, the

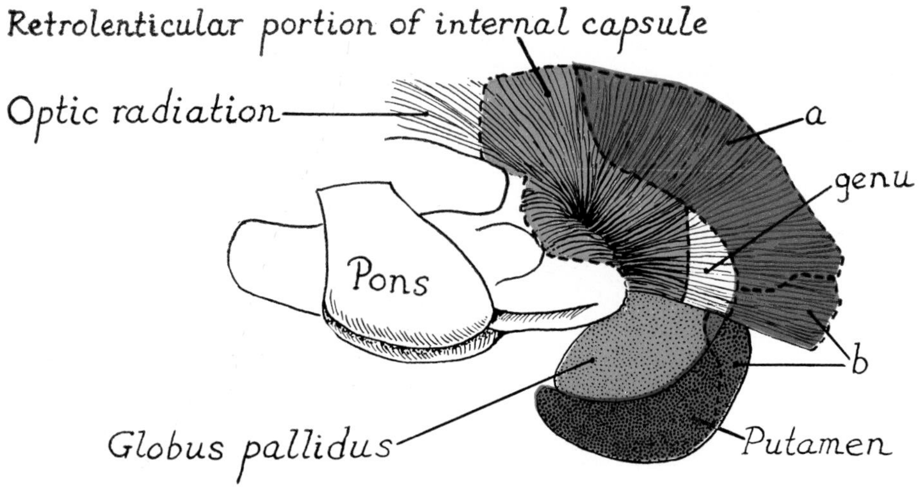

FIG. 71. Lateral view of internal capsule. The lenticular nucleus has been detached from capsule and depressed ventrolaterally. Supply of anterior chorioidal artery shown in yellow; that of striate arteries in red. a, branches of middle cerebral artery; b, branches of anterior cerebral artery. The genu is supplied by one or two direct branches from the carotid arteries. (Alexander.)

two most vulnerable parts of the brain, are supplied by this artery (Alexander).

The *posterior chorioidal arteries* of which there are usually two, are branches of the posterior cerebral. They encircle the cerebral peduncles and after giving off branches to the midbrain roof, are distributed to the tela chorioidea and chorioid plexus of the third ventricle, furnishing also a number of small twigs to the superomedial surface of the thalamus (Fig. 70).

The arterial supply of the diencephalon, basal ganglia and internal capsule may be briefly summarized. The *striatum* (caudate nucleus and putamen) is supplied by the striate arteries derived mainly from the middle cerebral and to a lesser extent from the anterior cerebral. Only the recurving portion of the caudate tail and the posterior tip of the putamen are supplied by the anterior chorioidal artery (Fig. 70). The medial and intermediate segments of the *pallidum* are fed by the anterior chorioidal artery. The lateral segment of the pallidum has a variable supply. It may be fed by the striate vessels or by the anterior chorioidal. More commonly it receives branches from both.

The *thalamus* is irrigated mainly by the posterolateral (thalamogeniculate) and posteromedial (thalamoperforating) arteries. The posterolateral supply the caudal and lateral regions, the posteromedial arteries supply the anterior and medial regions. Smaller contributions, especially for the superior surface are made by the posterior and perhaps the anterior chorioidal arteries. The anterior *hypothalamus* and preoptic region receive their blood supply from the anteromedian ganglionic arteries, the rest of the hypothalamus from the posteromedian group which also irrigates the *subthalamic structures*.

The anterior limb of the *internal capsule* and the dorsal part of the posterior limb are irrigated by the striate arteries (Fig. 71). The ventral part of the posterior limb and the retrolenticular portion are fed by the anterior chorioidal artery. The genu as a rule receives one or two direct twigs from the internal carotid (Alexander).

Arteries of the dura. The cranial dura mater is supplied by a number of meningeal arteries derived from several sources. The largest and most important is the *middle meningeal artery* which supplies most of the dura and practically its entire calvarial portion. It is a branch of the internal maxillary artery which enters the cranial cavity through the foramen spinosum and then divides into an anterior and a posterior branch (Fig. 25). Each of the branches run outward and upward and extend to the superior sagittal sinus, giving off numerous subsidiary branches which run forward and backward. A small *accessory meningeal artery,* which may arise from the internal maxillary or from the middle meningeal artery, enters the middle fossa through the oval foramen to supply the adjacent dura and the Gasserian ganglion. The middle fossa also receives a meningeal branch from the cavernous portion of the internal carotid artery.

In addition, the dura of the anterior and the posterior fossa receive a number of arteries, respectively known as the *anterior* and *posterior meningeal rami* or *arteries.* The anterior meningeal rami, usually two in number, are branches of the anterior and posterior ethmoidal arteries. The dura of the posterior fossa below the tentorium is mainly supplied by a variable number of posterior meningeal arteries. These include (1) one or several meningeal branches from the occipital artery entering through the jugular and hypoglossal foramina, (2) meningeal branches of the vertebral artery reaching the posterior fossa through the foramen magnum, and (3) several branches of the ascending pharyngeal artery entering through the foramen lacerum and hypoglossal canal.

Arteries of the midbrain and hindbrain. With the exception of the most anterior portion of the cerebral peduncles, which gets a variable contribution from the anterior chorioidal arteries, the blood supply to the midbrain and hindbrain is furnished by branches of the vertebral system. Each vertebral artery while passing over the ventral surface of the medulla gives off three branches which enter the brain substance: the larger *posterior inferior cerebellar artery,* and the smaller *anterior and posterior spinal arteries* (Fig. 64). The vertebrals then fuse into the unpaired *basilar artery* which extends to the superior border of the pons and there bifurcates into the posterior cerebral arteries. During its course the basilar gives off the following branches: the *anterior inferior cerebellar arteries,* the *internal auditory arteries* which do not supply the brain but pass laterally through the internal auditory meatus, a number of paramedian and circumferential *pontile branches,* and the *superior cerebellar arteries* (Fig. 64). From the proximal portion of each posterior cerebral artery arise a number of branches which furnish the main blood supply of the midbrain. The further course and distribution of these arterial trunks to the medulla, pons, and midbrain are discussed in their respective chapters.

BLOOD SUPPLY OF THE CEREBELLUM

Each half of the cerebellum is supplied by two inferior and one superior cerebellar arteries going respectively to the inferior and superior surfaces (Fig. 64). The *posterior inferior cerebellar artery* springs from the vertebral artery, runs for a short distance along the medulla oblongata whose dorsolateral portion it supplies and goes to the inferior vermis, especially the uvula and nodulus, also giving branches to the chorioid plexus. The *anterior inferior* cerebellar artery arises from the basilar artery and supplies the pyramis, tuber, flocculi and hemispheral portions of the inferior surface. It also sends branches to the deep portion of the corpus medullare, and according to Shellshear (1922) the dentate nucleus is mainly supplied by this artery. In some cases, the flocculus and portions of the tonsil and biventral lobule may be supplied by an inconstant middle inferior cerebellar artery (Jakob), (Fig. 64). The *superior cerebellar artery* emerges in back of the oculomotor nerve from the rostral end of the basilar artery. On reaching the cerebellum, it divides into two main branches, a median one for the superior vermis and adjacent lateral portions, and a lateral for the remaining hemispheral portions of the superior surface. From these arteries numerous branches extend deeply into the cerebellum to go to the superior medullary velum, middle and superior peduncles, deep portion of the corpus medullare and to the nuclei including part of the dentate nucleus. Twigs are also given to the chorioid plexus of the fourth ventricle.

The veins have a course generally similar to the arteries. A superior and an inferior median vein drain the respective portions of the vermis and adjacent regions and the deep cerebellar nuclei, the superior vein terminating in the *vein of Galen*, the inferior in the straight and lateral sinuses. Superior and inferior lateral veins bring blood from the hemispheres and flocculi to the lateral, and in part also to the superior petrosal sinuses.

THE CEREBRAL VEINS AND VENOUS SINUSES

The veins of the brain do not run together with the arteries. Emerging as fine branches from the substance of the brain, they form a pial plexus from which arise the larger venous channels or cerebral veins proper. These likewise run in the pia for a variable distance, then pass through the subarachnoid space and empty into a system of intercommunicating endothelium-lined channels, the *sinuses of the dura mater* placed between the meningeal and periosteal layers of the dura. The walls of these sinuses, unlike those of other veins, are composed of the tough fibrous tissue of the dura, hence they exhibit a greater tautness and do not collapse when sectioned. The various sinuses converge at the internal occipital protuberance into two transversely running sinuses, one for each side, which enter the jugular foramen to form the internal jugular vein. Besides draining the blood from the brain, the sinuses communicate with the superficial veins of the head by a number of small vessels which perforate the cranial bones as *emissary veins* (Fig. 72).

The *superior sagittal sinus* extends from the foramen cecum to the internal occipital protuberance, lying along the attached border of the falx cerebri, constantly increasing in caliber as it proceeds caudally. In its middle portion it gives off a number of lateral diverticula, the *venous lacunae*, into which protrude the arachnoid villi or Pacchionian granulations (p. 27). The narrow and shorter *inferior sagittal sinus* extends caudally along the free border of the falx. On reaching the anterior border of the tentorium it is joined by the *great cerebral vein of Galen* which drains the deeper structures of the brain, and the two together are continued as the *sinus rectus*. The latter runs backwards and downwards along the line of attachment of the falx and tentorium and joins the superior sagittal sinus near the internal occipital protuberance (Fig. 72). From this place arise the two *transverse sinuses*, each of which passes laterally and forward in the transverse groove of the occipital bone. On reaching the occipitopetrosal junction it curves sharply caudally and as the *sigmoid sinus* leaves the skull through the jugular foramen. The place of union of the superior sagittal, straight and transverse sinuses is known as the *sinus confluens* which also receives the small unpaired *occipital sinus* coming from the region of the foramen magnum and ascending in the falx cerebelli. The *confluens* is of asymmetrical form and shows many individual variations. In relatively few cases is there an actual union of the four sinuses. Most often the superior sagittal sinus turns to the right to become continuous with the right transverse sinus, while the

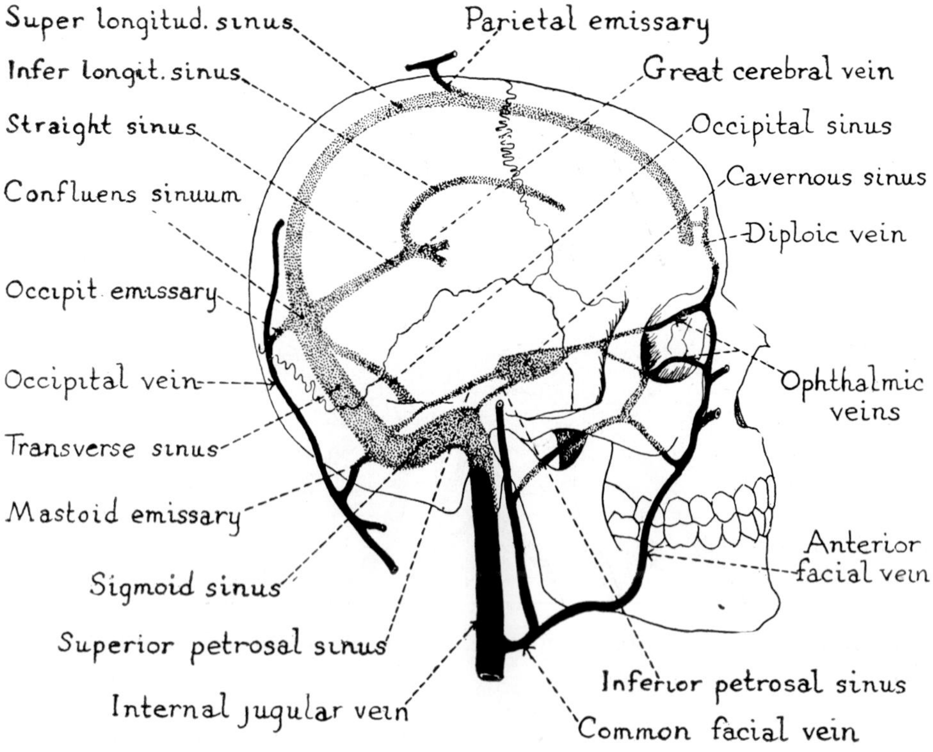

FIG. 72. The dural sinuses (stippled) and their principal connections with the extracranial veins. (After Blumberg from Tandler-Ranzi.)

straight sinus bends to the left as the left transverse sinus. In a general way, the venous blood of the superior cerebral veins, superior sagittal, right transverse, and sigmoid sinuses is drained by the right internal jugular vein. Most of the venous blood of the Galenic vein, straight sinus, left transverse, and sigmoid sinuses is usually drained by the left internal jugular vein.

The important *cavernous sinus* is a large irregular space located on the sides of the sphenoid bone, lateral to the sella turcica. It is really a mass of intercommunicating cavernous channels enclosing the internal carotid artery, the oculomotor, trochlear, and abducens nerves, and the ophthalmic branch of the trigeminal. It is connected with the opposite sinus by channels which pass anterior and posterior to the hypophysis, and by the *basilar venous plexus* which extends along the basilar portion of the occipital bone to the foramen magnum and there communicates with the venous plexuses of the vertebral canal (Fig. 73). The venous ring surrounding the hypophysis and composed of the two cavernous sinuses and their connecting channels, is often known as the *circular sinus*. Each cavernous sinus may likewise be regarded as a confluens sinuum. In front it receives the two ophthalmic veins through the orbital fissure and the small *sphenoparietal sinus* which runs along the under surface of the lesser wing of the sphenoid (Figs. 72, 73). Posteriorly it empties into the superior and inferior petrosal sinuses through which it is connected respectively with the transverse sinus and the bulb of the internal jugular vein.

As already stated the dural sinuses communicate with extracranial veins by a number of emissaries (Fig. 72). Thus the superior sagittal sinus is connected with the

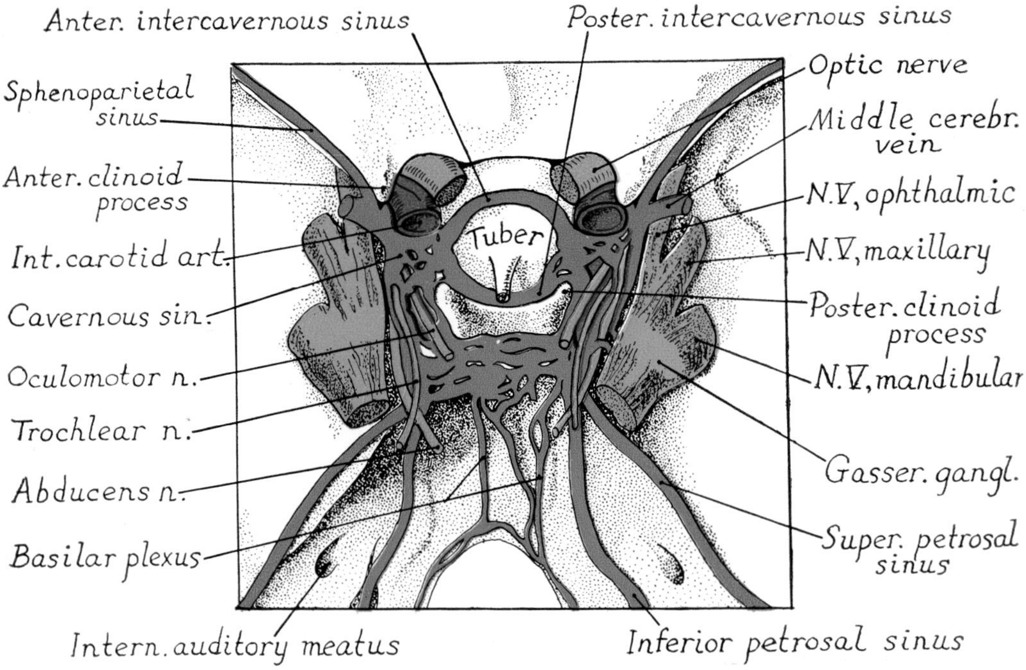

FIG. 73. Topography of the cavernous sinus and related structures. (After Corning.)

frontal and nasal veins through the frontal diploic veins and the emissaries of the foramen cecum, and also sends a *parietal emissary* to the superficial temporal vein. The confluens sinuum usually gives off an *occipital emissary* to the occipital vein which is also connected with the transverse sinus by the larger *mastoid emissary*. Smaller emissaries from the sigmoid sinus pass through the condyloid and hypoglossal foramina and communicate with the vertebral and deep cervical veins. The cavernous sinus, besides receiving the ophthalmic veins, is connected with the internal jugular vein and with the pterygoid and pharyngeal plexuses by fine venous nets or *rete* which pass through the oval, spinous, lacerated, carotid, and jugular foramina.

Baló (1950) has described a system of cavernous spaces in the dura mater, especially conspicuous around the superior sagittal sinus, the straight sinus and the confluens sinuum. This system is filled from small dural arteries, and it is drained into the sinuses. When the cavernous spaces become filled with blood, the lumina of the above named sinuses become narrowed, causing an obstruction of the venous outflow with resulting venous hyperemia in the brain. In severe engorgement of the spaces the lumen of the superior sagittal sinus or of the straight sinus may be reduced to a cleft.

The cerebral veins. The cerebral veins which, like the dural sinuses, are devoid of valves, are usually divided into an external or superficial and an internal or ventricular group. The cerebral veins drain the blood from the cortex and subcortical medullary substance and empty into the superior sagittal sinus or into the several basal sinuses, cavernous, petrosal, and transverse. The internal veins drain the chorioid plexuses of the forebrain, the deep medullary substance, the basal ganglia and dorsal portions of the diencephalon, and are collected into the *great vein of Galen* (*vena magna cerebri*) which enters the straight sinus at the junction of the latter with the inferior sagittal sinus (Fig. 72). The two groups are not anatomically distinct, but on the contrary are widely interconnected by numerous anastomotic channels, both intracerebral and extracerebral. Thus large surface areas can be drained through the vein of Galen, and conversely territories supplied by internal veins may be handled when necessity arises by surface vessels. This anastomotic venous arrangement facilitates the drainage of capillary beds by shifting the blood from one area to another and readily equalizes regional increases in pressure due to occlusion or other factors. As a result, the occlusion of even a large vein, if not too rapid, will produce but slight and transitory effects. Only when the occlusion or increase in pressure occur suddenly, will there be marked hyperemia and more or less extensive hemorrhages, as in birth injuries and occasionally in cases of adult thrombosis (Schlesinger; Schwartz and Fink).

The external cerebral veins arise from the cortex and subcortical medullary substance, anastomose freely in the pia and form a number of larger vessels which empty into the various sinuses. They include the superior and inferior cerebral veins and the superficial middle cerebral vein (superficial Sylvian vein). The *superior cerebral veins*, about 10 to 15 in number, collect the blood from the convex and medial surfaces of the brain and open into the superior sagittal sinus or its venous lacunae (Fig. 74). Many of them, especially the larger posterior ones, run obliquely forward through the subarachnoid space and enter the sinus in a direction opposed to that of the blood flow, often after a short intradural course parallel to the sinus. Some of the veins from the medial surface drain into the inferior sagittal sinus. The *inferior cerebral veins* drain the basal surface of the hemisphere and the lower portion of its lateral surface. Those on the lateral surface usually empty into the *superficial middle cerebral vein* (*superficial Sylvian vein*) which runs along the Sylvian

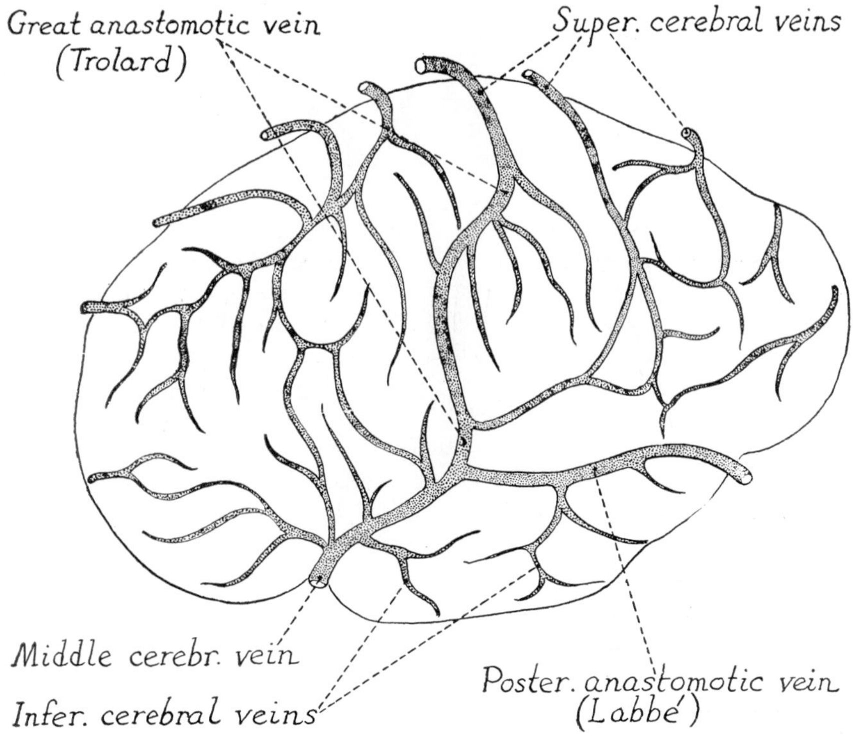

FIG. 74. External cerebral veins on the convex surface of the hemisphere.

fissure and terminates in the cavernous or sphenoparietal sinus (Figs. 73, 74). The middle vein receives many anastomotic branches from the superior cerebral veins and in many cases two of these channels become quite prominent. These are the *great anastomotic vein of Trolard* and the *posterior anastomotic vein* of *Labbé* which connect the middle cerebral vein respectively with tributaries of the superior sagittal and the transverse sinus. On the basal surface the small inferior veins arising from extensive pial plexuses drain in part into the basal sinuses. Those from the tentorial surface of the brain empty into the transverse and superior petrosal sinuses. Those from the anterior temporal lobe and from the interpeduncular regions drain partly into the cavernous and sphenoparietal sinuses, while some veins from the orbital region join the superior or the inferior sagittal sinus.

In addition, large cortical areas, especially on the basal and medial surfaces, are drained by a number of vessels which empty into the great vein of Galen before the latter bifurcates into the two internal cerebral veins (Figs. 75, 76). These vessels may be regarded as extracerebral anastomotic veins which connect the superficial and deep systems. The more important ones include the occipital vein, the basal vein (vein of Rosenthal), and the posterior callosal vein. Some of the veins draining the cerebellum likewise terminate in the great cerebral vein or in one of its larger tributaries.

The *occipital vein* drains the inferior and medial surfaces of the occipital lobe and possibly the adjacent parietal regions. The

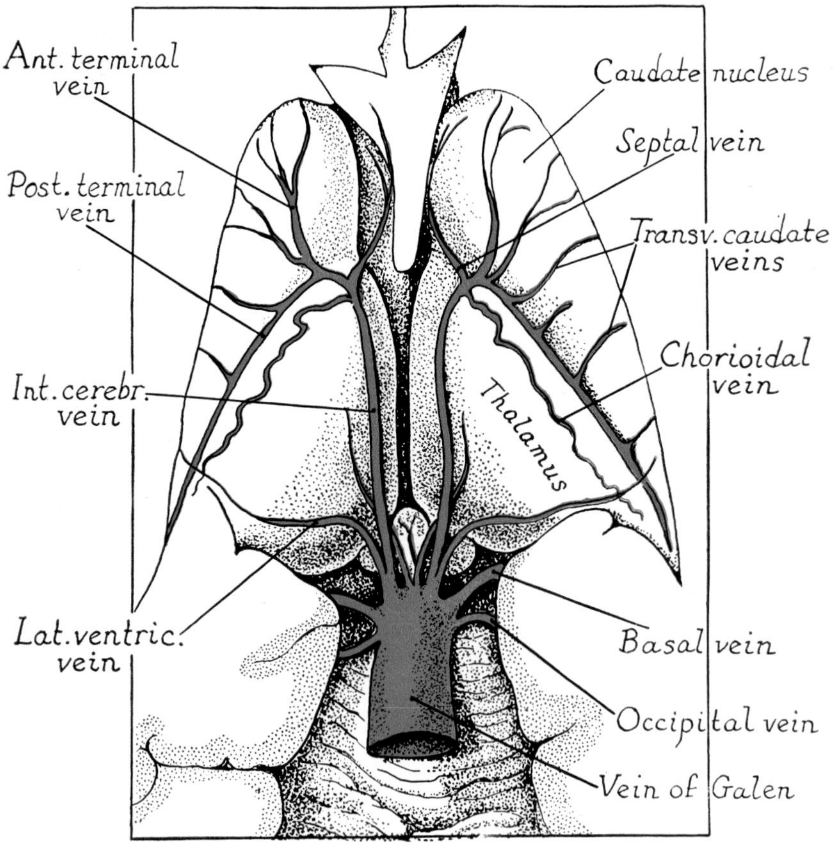

FIG. 75. The vein of Galen and its tributaries. (After Schwartz and Fink.)

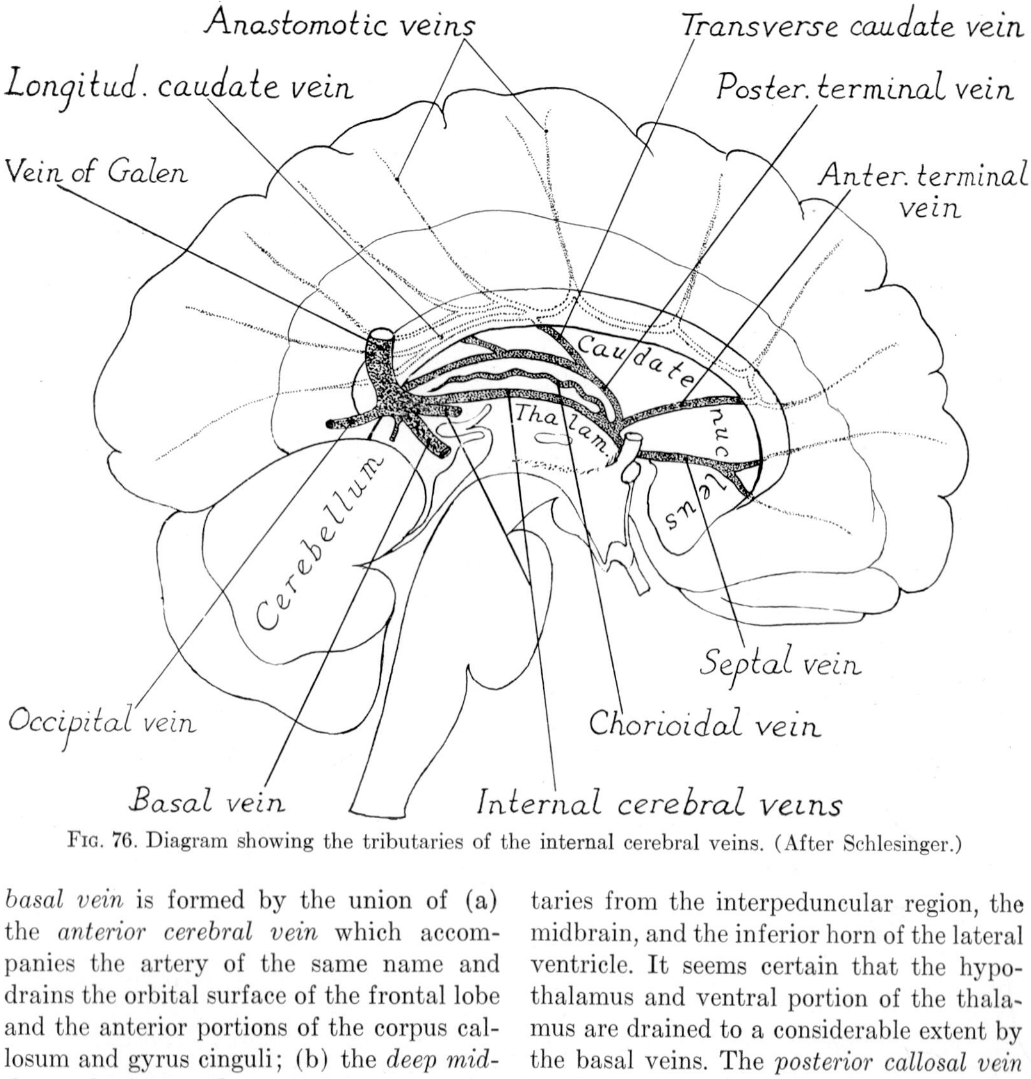

FIG. 76. Diagram showing the tributaries of the internal cerebral veins. (After Schlesinger.)

basal vein is formed by the union of (a) the *anterior cerebral vein* which accompanies the artery of the same name and drains the orbital surface of the frontal lobe and the anterior portions of the corpus callosum and gyrus cinguli; (b) the *deep middle cerebral* vein (*deep Sylvian vein*) which lies deeply in the lower portion of the lateral fissure and which aids in the drainage of the insular and adjacent opercular cortex; and (c) a number of vessels, the *inferior striate veins*, which come from the ventral portions of the corpus striatum, and emerge through the anterior perforated space, many of them emptying into the deep middle vein. At the anterior perforated space all these unite to form the basal vein which winds backward around the cerebral peduncles to reach the vein of Galen, receiving additional tributaries from the interpeduncular region, the midbrain, and the inferior horn of the lateral ventricle. It seems certain that the hypothalamus and ventral portion of the thalamus are drained to a considerable extent by the basal veins. The *posterior callosal vein* collects blood from the posterior portion of the corpus callosum and adjacent medial surface of the brain.

The following account of the internal veins is based mainly on the work of Schlesinger (1939) and Schwartz and Fink (1926). The *great vein of Galen* (*vena magna cerebri*) empties into the anterior end of the straight sinus (Fig. 72). It is a short trunk whose thin delicate walls are easily torn even in the adult. Peripherally, the vein curves ventrally beneath the splenium of the corpus callosum and after receiving the tributaries mentioned above, bifurcates into the two *internal cerebral veins* (*small veins of Galen*) which together with their branches comprise the ventricular or internal group of veins (Figs. 75, 76). At or near the bifurcation each internal cerebral vein gives off two branches, the *epithalamic* and the *lateral ventricular vein*. The former drains the dorsal portion of the diencephalon. Blood from the ventral portion of the thalamus and from the hypothalamus is collected by vessels which empty basally into the pial venous plexus of the interpeduncular fossa whence it is conveyed in part to the cavernous or sphenoparietal sinuses, in part to the basal vein of Rosenthal. The *lateral ventricular vein* runs laterally on the superior surface of the thalamus and tail of the caudate nucleus and is lost in the medullary substance at the angle of the lateral ventricle. One small branch of the vein usually goes to the chorioid plexus, another enters the white substance of the hippocampal gyrus. Occasionally, the lateral ventricular vein terminates directly in the vena magna (Schwartz and Fink).

The two internal cerebral veins then pass forward in the tela chorioidea of the third ventricle (velum interpositum), and in the region of the interventricular foramen each vein breaks up into its four terminal tributaries: the chorioidal, the septal and the anterior and posterior terminal veins (Figs. 75, 76). The tortuous *chorioidal vein* runs along the lateral border of the chorioid plexus into the inferior horn. It drains the plexus and adjacent hippocampal regions. Additional drainage of the plexus is through the chorioidal branch of the basal vein, and to a smaller extent through the small branch of the lateral ventricular vein.

The *posterior terminal vein* runs backward in the terminal sulcus between thalamus and caudate nucleus. The *anterior terminal vein* runs forward and branches in the head of the caudate nucleus. Both vessels receive a number of tributaries, the *transverse caudate veins*, which cross the caudate nucleus, reach the lateral angle of the ventricle and enter the adjacent white substance of the brain. Here they change their direction abruptly to form the *longitudinal caudate veins*. The latter divide at acute angles into a number of branches which fan

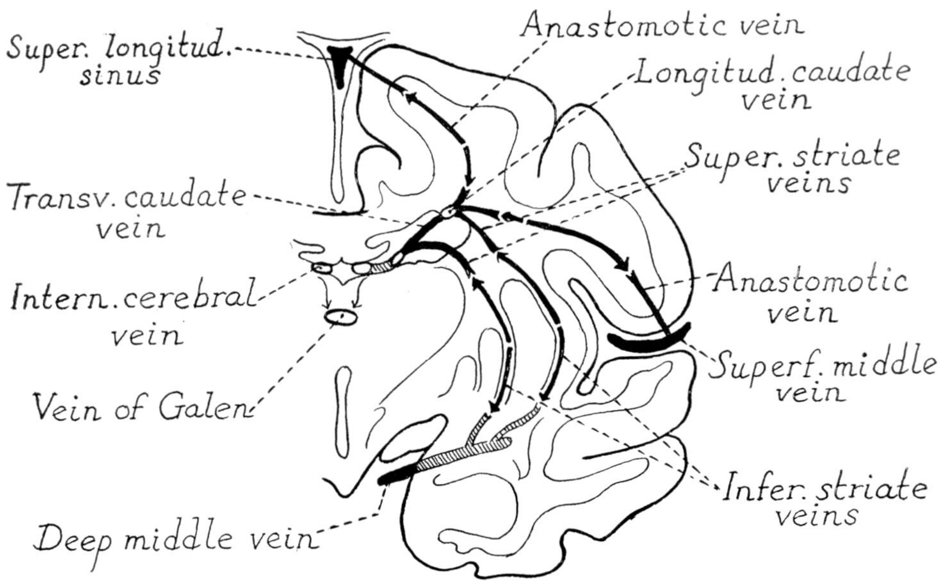

FIG. 77. Diagrammatic cross-section through the brain of a Rhesus monkey, showing the connections between the deep and the surface veins. (Schlesinger.)

out radially in the medullary substance, following as a rule the fibers of the corpus callosum (Fig. 76). Some of the branches are short and drain the deep capillary plexuses of the white matter. Others extend almost to the cortex and may be regarded as intracerebral anastomotic channels connecting the ventricular and surface veins. In addition, the transverse and longitudinal caudate veins give rise to another group of branches, the *superior striate veins.* These dip vertically into the brain substance, passing through and on both sides of the caudate nucleus, perforate the internal capsule, and break up into a number of smaller vessels which drain the dense capillary plexus of the lenticular nucleus (Fig. 77). Basally this capillary plexus is drained by the *inferior striate veins* which converge ventrally toward the anterior perforated space and enter the deep middle vein.

The *septal vein* (*vein of the septum pellucidum*) supplies the septum pellucidum and rostral portion of the corpus callosum. Then its distal branches dip beneath the head of the caudate nucleus and enter the medullary substance to be carried by the callosal fibers to the base of the frontal lobe (Figs. 75, 76).

It is evident from the above that the internal veins are primarily concerned with the drainage of the ventricular surface, the chorioid plexuses, the deep medullary substance, the caudate nucleus, and the dorsal portions of the lenticular nucleus and thalamus. All these structures can, however, be also drained by surface vessels through the numerous intracerebral and extracerebral anastomotic veins.

6

The Neuron

The structural units of the nervous system concerned specifically with the nervous functions of conduction and integration are the highly excitable *nerve cells* or *neurons,* each composed of a cell body and one or more elongated processes. These neurons are set in a framework of a peculiar type of interstitial tissue, the *neuroglia* or *glia,* which like the neurons themselves, is for the largest part derived from the ectoderm of the neural plate and ganglionic crest. Ordinary mesodermal connective tissue forms the envelopes (meninges) of the brain and spinal cord, the sheaths of the peripheral nerves and ganglia, and in scanty amounts accompanies the numerous blood vessels of the central nervous system.

The most striking morphological feature of the neuron is the presence of protoplasmic extensions or processes, some of which, the *nerve fibers,* may become exceedingly elongated, thus permitting a rapid and uninterrupted conduction of nerve impulses over considerable distances. The relation of these long processes to the cell body was not understood at first, and nerve tissue was long described as consisting of two elements, nerve cells and nerve fibers (Figs. 78, 79, 80). With the establishment of the continuity of nerve cell and nerve fiber, it became clear that the two together constituted a *single* structural unit, to which the name *neuron* is now given. A neuron may thus be defined as a nerve cell with all its processes. However, the term "nerve cell" is still used somewhat loosely to designate the neuron body and its processes exclusive of the nerve fiber.

The neurons, though showing wide variations in form and size, may be grouped in two main classes: those which possess dendrites and those which do not. The dendritic neurons which constitute the majority of nerve cells in the central nervous system and sympathetic ganglia, are *multipolar* in shape, being composed of a cell body or *perikaryon* from which extend a number of processes (Figs. 78, 79). One of these processes and one only, is structurally different from the others and is known as the *axon* (*neurite, axis cylinder process*) (Figs. 78, 80). It is a slender process, often of considerable length, characterized by a fairly uniform diameter and a smooth contour, and arises from a conical elevation on the cell body or one of the larger dendrites, known as the *implantation cone* or *axon hillock.* During its course it generally gives off several branches or *collaterals* which extend at right angles to the main fiber. Such collaterals may arise from any part of the axon but most commonly they are given off a short distance from the cell body. Both axon and collaterals finally terminate in complicated end branchings known as telodendria.

The other processes of a multipolar cell are structurally similar to the protoplasm of the cell body and are known as *protoplasmic processes* or *dendrites.* They may be considered as simple protoplasmic extensions which enormously increase the receptive surface of the cell and perhaps also aid in its nutritive processes. They are wide at the base, taper rapidly, have an irregular and roughened contour, and are often beset with fine spiny or knobby thickenings or *gemmules* (Fig. 79). Fox and Barnard (1957) reported the length of the spiny branchlets of a single Purkinje cell to be 40,700 microns. These dendritic branchlets with their 61,000 spines had a combined synaptic surface area of 222,000 square microns. They fork repeatedly at acute angles and generally terminate not far from the cell body.

Neurons without dendrites give off only one structural type of process which has the histological character of an axon. Some are *bipolar*, having two processes which arise one at each end of the cell body. Examples are the bipolar cells of the retina and the cells forming the spiral and the vestibular ganglion of the eighth cranial nerve. The olfactory cells of the nose likewise belong in this group. (Fig. 3, B, D).

The great majority of the neurons in the cerebrospinal ganglia are *unipolar cells* possessing a single process which divides not far from the cell body into two branches, one proceeding to some peripheral sense organ, the other entering the brain or spinal cord (Figs. 3E, 80). The single process as well as both of its arms have the structural features of an axon and may give off collateral branches. In early development these cells have a typical bipolar form but in later growth the two processes converge and fuse, forming the T or Y-shaped process characteristic of the adult cell (Figs. 129, 80A–D).

Physiologically the terms "axon" and "dendrite" are often used to denote the direction of conduction of nerve impulses. All processes conducting toward the cell body are considered dendrites, those conducting away from the cell body are axons. Regarded in this manner, the peripheral processes of the unipolar and bipolar neurons would be called dendrites though they have the histological features of an axon. This would obviously make difficult a structural definition of either dendrite or axon, since the direction of conduction can not be ascertained by microscopic study. Moreover, the peripheral branches of the unipolar sensory neurons actually can conduct distally, i.e., in a direction away from the cell body in the phenomenon of antidromic conduction. It is also known that axons by themselves, as in excised nerve, conduct nerve impulses in either direction. For these reasons, it seems advisable that the terms "axon" and "dendrite" should be used to denote processes possessing different structural characteristics.

The form of multipolar neurons show innumerable variations. However, neurons that populate some of the larger gray masses of the central nervous system often have characteristic features after metallic impregnation. Those neurons whose processes remain entirely within the brain and spinal cord are shown in Figs. 78 and 79. Neurons whose processes leave the central nervous system to form the peripheral nerves are illustrated in Fig. 80. Central nervous system neurons within a given group (nucleus) often "look alike" and aid in identifying the different nuclei. For example, the nerve cells of the inferior olive (Fig. 78A) have radiating dendrites with curly branches, whereas neurons of the thalamus (Fig. 78K) have radiating dendrites with longer and less kinked branches. The cells of the *substantia gelatinosa* of the spinal cord are best seen in stained longitudinal sections, and demonstrate only a few large dendrites that issue chiefly from one side of the cell body (Fig. 78G). Smaller branches of these dendrites then form a compact zone of fine parallel fibers.

It is instructive to compare the profuse dendritic branches of the central sensory and integrating neurons (Fig. 78A, B, D, E, G–K) with the more robust dendrites of motor neurons (Fig. 78C, F, L; Fig. 80M, N, O). This comparison is even more striking if one contrasts the two principal cell types of the cerebellar and cerebral cortex (Fig. 79). The Purkinje cell is ideally constructed for its essential role within the

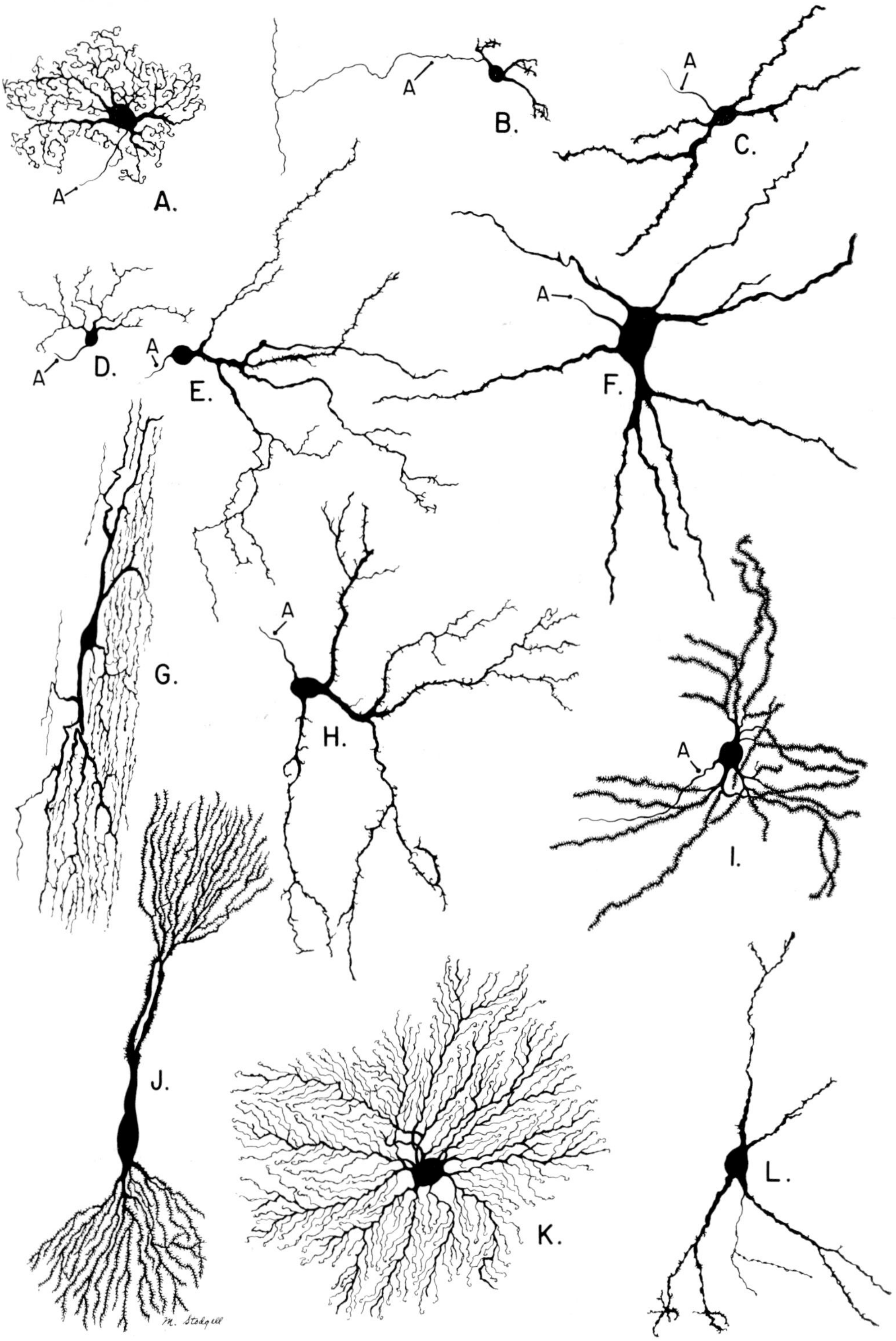

FIG. 78. Scaled drawings of some characteristic neurons whose axons (A) and dendrites remain within the central nervous system. A. Neuron of inferior olivary nucleus; B. granule cell of cerebellar cortex; C. small cell of reticular nucleus; D. small gelatinosa cell of spinal trigeminal nucleus; E. ovoid cell, nucleus of tractus solitarius; F. large cell of reticular nucleus; G. spindle-shaped cell, substantia gelatinosa of spinal cord; H. large cell of spinal trigeminal nucleus; I. neuron, putamen of lenticular nucleus; J. double pyramidal cell, Ammon's horn of hippocampal cortex; K. cell from thalamic nucleus; L. cell from globus pallidus of lenticular nucleus. Golgi preparations, monkey. (Courtesy Dr. Clement Fox, Marquette University.)

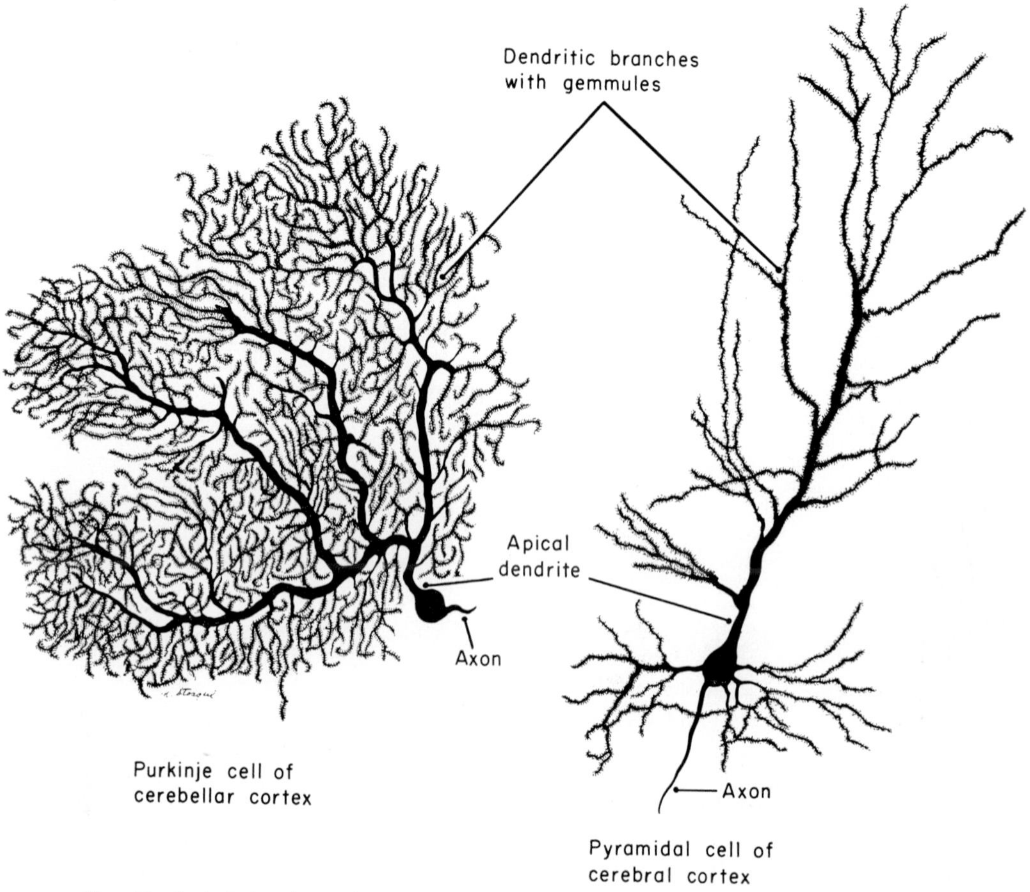

FIG. 79. Scaled drawings of two principal cell types in cerebellar and cerebral cortex. Dendritic branches provide extensive area for synaptic terminals of many other cortical and subcortical neurons. Golgi preparations, monkey. (Courtesy Dr. Clement Fox, Marquette University.)

cerebellar cortex where innumerable synaptic end-feet and climbing fibers terminate upon its dendrites (see p. 115). This dense, brush-like spread of dendrites is similar to that of other central integrating neurons (Fig. 78A, I, J, K) yet each has individual characteristics. The large pyramidal cell (Fig. 79) also has an extensive dendritic spread and tiny gemmules. However, its basic structure more closely resembles that of a motor neuron (Fig. 78F, L; Fig. 80 I, M–O). Thick sections prepared by the Golgi technic coat the neuron and its finest branches with a layer of silver chromate, so that it appears black against a light golden background. Successful preparations permit one to follow the processes of a neuron for considerable distances. The recent studies of Fox and Barnard, and Sheibel and Sheibel (1958) by the use of this method, have provided clearer concepts of neuron structure, dendritic ramification and axonal distribution within the cortex of the cerebellum, and brain stem reticular formation.

The somatic and visceral neurons of the central and peripheral nervous systems of man can be compared in Fig. 80. The peripheral processes and axons of such neurons form the peripheral cranial and spinal nerves. Nerve cells of the sensory and autonomic ganglia are surrounded by a thin

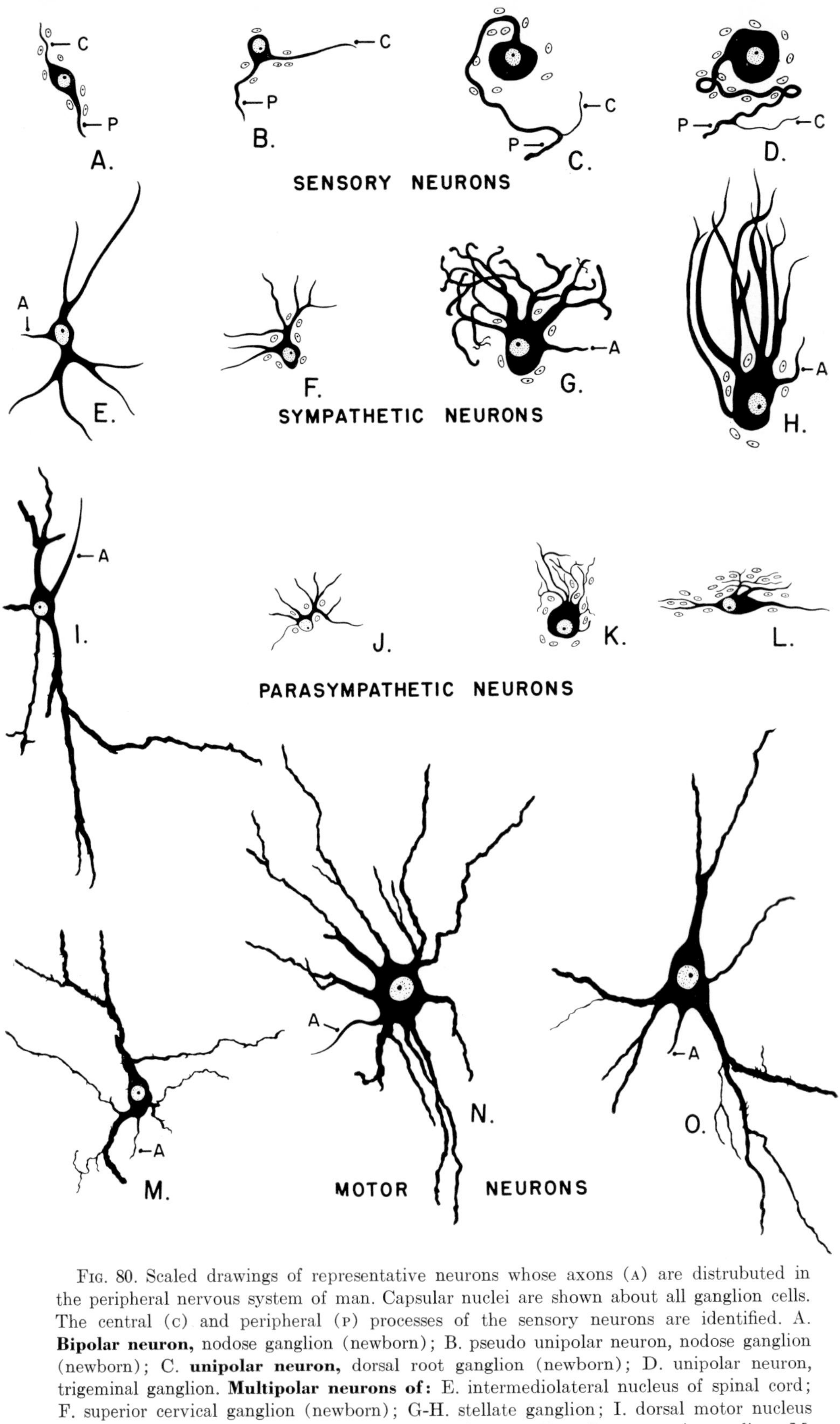

FIG. 80. Scaled drawings of representative neurons whose axons (A) are distrubuted in the peripheral nervous system of man. Capsular nuclei are shown about all ganglion cells. The central (C) and peripheral (P) processes of the sensory neurons are identified. A. **Bipolar neuron,** nodose ganglion (newborn); B. pseudo unipolar neuron, nodose ganglion (newborn); C. **unipolar neuron,** dorsal root ganglion (newborn); D. unipolar neuron, trigeminal ganglion. **Multipolar neurons of:** E. intermediolateral nucleus of spinal cord; F. superior cervical ganglion (newborn); G-H. stellate ganglion; I. dorsal motor nucleus N. X; J. ciliary ganglion (newborn); K. intracardiac ganglion; L. myenteric ganglion; M. nucleus ambiguus; N. motor nucleus N. XII; O. ventral horn cell.

nucleated capsule. Although nerve cells do not undergo mitotic division after birth, they probably do increase in cell size, as their axons and dendrites continue to grow in length. According to length of axon, Golgi has classified all nerve cells into long-axon (Type I) and short-axon (Type II) neurons. In the latter, the axon breaks up into an extensive terminal arborization in the immediate vicinity of the cell body.

The length of some nerve fibers is quite remarkable. Certain pyramidal cells of the cerebral cortex may send axons to the caudal tip of the spinal cord, i.e., from the top of the head to the lumbar region of the body (Fig. 193). Axons of motor neurons in the spinal cord may extend the whole length of the lower extremity to terminate in muscle fibers of the toes. A sensory unipolar neuron situated in the first sacral dorsal root ganglion may send a peripheral fiber to one of the toes, while its central fiber may ascend the whole length of the spinal cord and terminate in the medulla (Fig. 185). The total length of such a neuron would be approximately from toe to nape of neck. In a full grown giraffe such a fiber would reach the astounding length of over fifteen feet.

The size of the neuron body likewise fluctuates within wide limits, from a diameter of 4 micra in the smallest granule cells of the cerebellum (Fig. 78A) and cerebral cortex to well over 100 micra in the largest motor cells of the spinal cord. In general, the dimension of the cell body is proportional to the length, thickness, richness of branchings and terminal arborizations of its nerve fiber.

The cell body or perikaryon. The neuron body consists of a nucleus surrounded by a mass of cytoplasm whose surface layer forms a delicate plasma membrane. This membrane is of great physiological importance, especially in regulating the direction of transmission of nerve impulses from one cell to another.

The spherical nucleus, varying in size from 3–18 micra, is usually centrally placed, a striking exception being its eccentric position in the cells of Clark's column in the spinal cord (Figs. 172; 84J). In the larger and many of the smaller cells the nucleus has a characteristic vesicular appearance, composed of a definite nuclear membrane, a pale staining achromatic reticulum practically devoid of basichromatin, and usually one large deeply staining nucleolus in which most of the chromatin is apparently concentrated (Figs. 83, 85). In certain small cells such as the granule cells of the cerebellum and the substantia gelatinosa of the spinal cord, the small nucleus consists of a dense network of deeply staining chromatin without a nucleolus. These nuclei are often difficult to distinguish from the nuclei of neuroglia cells. Binucleate nerve cells are rare, but occur in some autonomic ganglia.

In the larger nerve cells of some animals a small deeply staining body about 1μ or less in diameter, has been found closely apposed to the nucleous (Fig. 81). Barr, Bertram and Lindsay (1950) have found that this "nucleolar satellite" is always present in the nerve cells of female cats but is often difficult to demonstrate in the cells of the male, due probably to the much smaller size of the satellite. According to other workers it appears to be present to the same extent in the cells of both sexes (Coidan, 1952). During intense metabolic activity as for instance following electrical stimulation, the satellite becomes somewhat enlarged and moves away from the nucleolus towards the nuclear membrane to return to its original position when normal conditions are reestablished (Barr and Bertram, 1951).

The chromatin of the nucleus is largely composed of nucleoproteins which are associations of basic proteins with nucleic acid. There are two main types of nucleic acid in the cell. In one, ribonucleic acid, the sugar of the nucleotide is ribose (pentose); in the other, desoxyribonucleic acid,

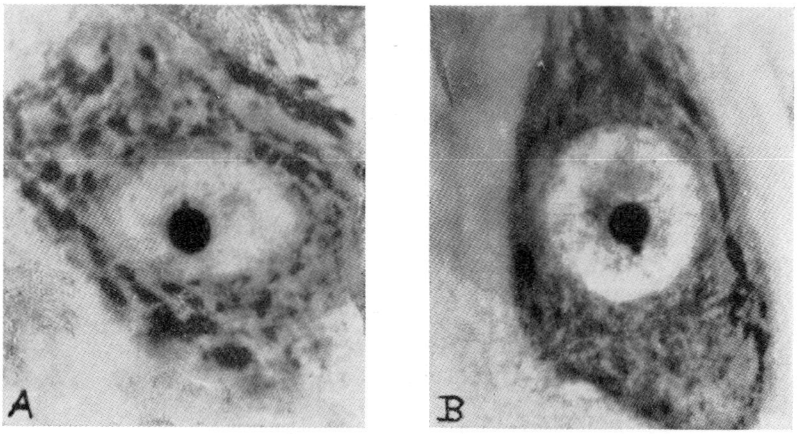

FIG. 81. Nucleolar satellite in motor cell of spinal cord (A) and Betz cell of motor cortex (B) Female cat. Cresyl violet. ×1200. (Barr, Bertram and Lindsay.)

the sugar is desoxyribose (desoxypentose). Recent cytochemical methods have furnished evidence that nucleoproteins of the desoxyribose type are found solely in the chromatin which forms the spireme and chromosomes in mitosis, and which during the intermitotic period is partly represented by chromatin bodies known as karyosomes. The nucleolar satellite apparently also contains desoxyribose nucleic acid. On the other hand, the true nucleolus is as a rule a dense, spherical, optically homogenous body rich in proteins, in which the nucleic acid when present is always of the ribose type. Similar ribonucleoproteins are found in the cytoplasm (see *chromophil substance*), and there is good evidence for the assumption that the nucleolus plays an important part in cytoplasmic protein formation (Caspersson, 1950).

In the cytoplasm are found the following structures: *neurofibrils, chromophil substance, Golgi reticular apparatus, mitochondria, central body,* and various *inclusions,* as pigment, fat, and lipoids. The neurofibrils are especially characteristic of nerve cells, but chromophil substance is also found in the cytoplasm of glandular and certain other cells where it is usually known as ergastoplasm or chromidial substance. Most of the other structures are normal constituents of any tissue cell.

It may be stated here that the above named constituents are demonstrated only by the employment of many special techniques, each of which may selectively stain one or a few of them. A composite picture of nerve cell structure can be obtained only from a study of many preparations treated with different technical methods.

The *neurofibrils* are found in *all* nerve cells. As demonstrated by the reduced silver methods of Cajal, Bielschowsky and others, they are delicate, homogeneous threads which are continuous throughout the cell body and its processes (Fig. 82). In the cell body they cross and interlace and in many preparations appear to anastomose into a true network (Cajal). In the processes they run straight and parallel to each other and are more closely grouped, especially in the axon which practically constitutes a cable of densely packed neurofibrils. They have been observed in the living nerve fibers of several invertebrates (de Renyi, Bozler) and more recently in the living ganglion cells of chick embryos (Weiss and Wang), and hence can not be regarded as artefacts. According to de Renyi, they are discrete threads of greater viscosity than the surrounding medium, which though interwoven do not branch or anastomose.

The neurofibrils lie imbedded in a sub-

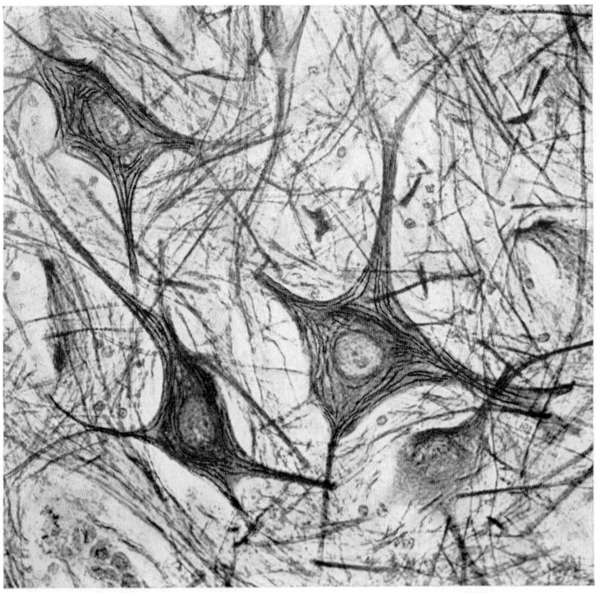

FIG. 82. Large motor cells from spinal cord of one month infant, showing neurofibrillar structure. Portions of dendrites and axons of other neurons fill the field. Cajal silver method. Photograph.

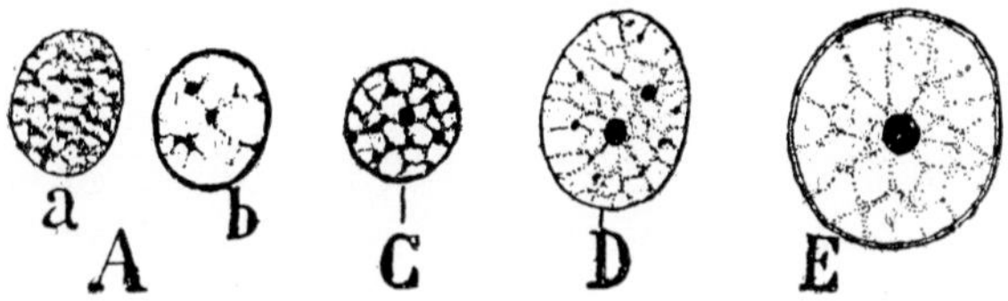

FIG. 83. Various types of nuclei in nerve cells and neuroglia cells of the rabbit. (Cajal.) *A, a* and *b,* neuroglia nuclei; *C,* nucleus of granule cell of cerebellum; *D,* nucleus of pyramidal cell of the cerebral cortex; *E,* nucleus of motor cell of the spinal cord.

stance collectively termed the *perifibrillar substance* or *neuroplasm* which obviously contains the other cytoplasmic constituents.

The function of the neurofibrils is not fully understood. Their universal occurence in all nerve cells and in all parts of nerve cells (dendrites, cell body, axon and terminal arborizations) and the fact that the chief conducting process consists practically of neurofibrils only, has led to the belief that they constitute the specific conductive substance of the neuron, a view which is still widely held. However, recent physiological evidence suggests that the propagation of the nerve impulses is primarily a surface phenomenon and has little to do with the internal structures of the cell. Some have suggested that the neurofibrils may be concerned with the nutritive transport of the cell and its processes, while others ascribe to them a purely mechanical supporting function.

In preparations stained with basic aniline dyes, the *chromophil substance* of *Nissl* appears in the form of deeply staining granules or clumps of granules known as *Nissl bodies* or *tigroid bodies.* They are found in the cell bodies and dendrites of all large and many of the smaller cells, but are invariably absent in the axon and axon hillock from which that process arises. They are most abundant and sharply defined in

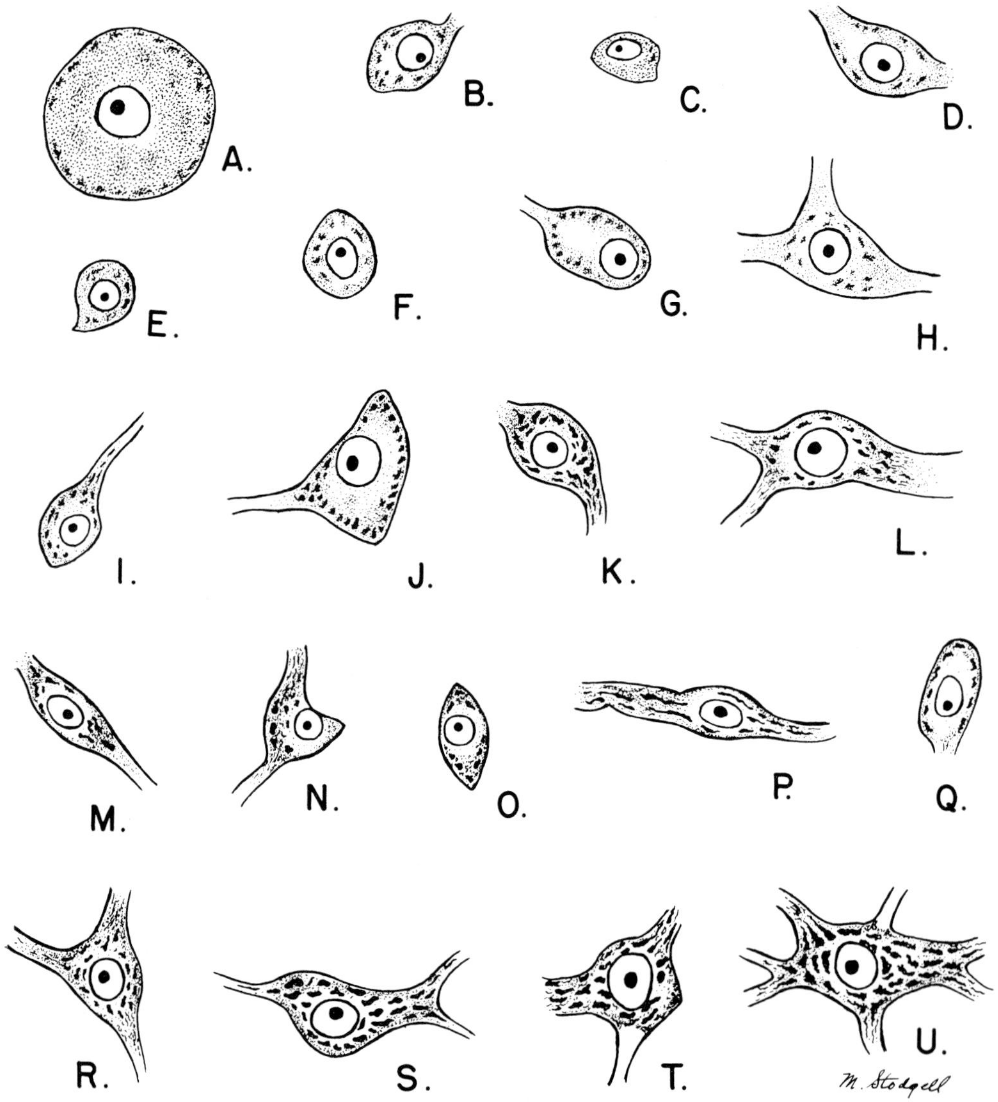

FIG. 84. Scaled drawings to demonstrate patterns of Nissl material in representative neurons of the human nervous system. **Sensory neurons** of: A. spinal ganglion; B. ventral cochlear nucleus; C. substantia gelatinosa; D. spinal nucleus of trigeminal nerve. **Neurons associated with cerebellum:** E. nucleus of inferior olive; F. Purkinje cell of cerebellar cortex; G. dentate nucleus; H. nucleus fastigii. **Neurons whose axons form tracts of C.N.S.:** I. nucleus gracilis; J. nucleus dorsalis (of Clarke); K. lateral vestibular nucleus; L. lateral reticular nucleus. **Autonomic or visceral motor neurons** from: M. nucleus of Edinger—Westphal; N. dorsal motor nucleus of N. X; O. intracardiac ganglion; P. intermediolateral nucleus of spinal cord; Q. lumbar sympathetic ganglion. **Motor neurons to skeletal muscle:** R. lateral nucleus N. III; S. nucleus ambiguus; T. motor nucleus N. XII; U. ventral horn cell.

the larger cells whose clear vesicular nucleus contains practically no basichromatin (Figs. 84, 85).

The Nissl bodies are larger in motor cells than in sensory, and attempts have been made to distinguish the many neuron types by the size, shape, distribution and staining capacity of the chromophil granules

(Fig. 84). There is often variation in the distribution of Nissl material within the neurons of one central nucleus. (See Olszewski, and Baxter, 1954). However, general patterns of intracellular Nissl material can be observed when different functional types of nerve cells are compared. For example, the Nissl pattern of the sensory and central integrating neurons are similar to each other (Fig. 84A–J). On the other hand, nerve cells whose axons form descending tracts (K–L) often possess a Nissl pattern similar to that seen in the larger motor neurons (R–U). The visceral motor nerve cells (M–Q) have a smaller size and the less prominent Nissl bodies often are arranged around the periphery of the cytoplasm.

The structure of the Nissl bodies is readily changed in pathological conditions or even in altered physiological states as in fatigue. They lose their appearance as discrete bodies and seemingly become dissolved in the cytoplasm, a phenomenon termed *chromatolysis.* The significance of the Nissl stain from a pathological standpoint lies in the fact that with a given technique, each type of nerve cell always presents the same appearance or "equivalent picture" in normal conditions. Such a picture thus furnishes a norm for comparison with cells which show pathological changes and which have been subjected to the same technique.

Nissl bodies cannot be seen in the living cell, and most investigators believe that the granules are precipitated in their characteristic form by the action of fixatives on a dissolved or suspended substance distributed uniformly through the cytoplasm. Some recent evidence, however, suggests that they may be present in the living protoplasm as definite bodies. In ganglion cells which have been centrifuged with tremendous force, the Nissl bodies become concentrated in the centrifugal pole of the cell without apparently losing their individual discreteness (Beams and King, Fig. 86). Bensley and Gersh, using the freezing-drying technique which eliminates many of the artifacts caused by commonly used fixation methods, have obtained Nissl pictures quite similar to those found in the usual histological preparations. Beams and King conclude that "Nissl bodies react like definite masses of greater density imbedded in lighter substance."

The chemical constitution of the Nissl substance has been investigated in recent years by means of microspectrographic studies in ultraviolet light (Caspersson, 1950) and also by means of new staining reactions (Gersh and Bodian, 1943). It has been definitely shown that the chromophil substance contains ribonucleic acid and proteins, and that similar nucleoproteins of the ribose type constitute the bulk of the large nucleolus present in those nerve cells which have abundant Nissl bodies in their cytoplasm. This is of considerable significance since ribonucleic acid also is found in the cytoplasm of other cells. It is especially prominent in cells concerned with intensive production of protein, such as growing cells where the total cell mass is increasing, and the exocrine cells of the pancreas and other glands where protein is constantly produced and excreted. In these cells there is also a well developed nucleolus likewise rich in ribonucleic acid. Caspersson and his associates have presented impressive evidence that those parts of the cell which are rich in nucleic acid form part of a cellular system for the formation of cytoplasmic protein.

The chemical organization of adult nerve cells suggests that they too are concerned with active protein metabolism, and this has been confirmed by cytochemical and experimental investigations (Hydén, 1943, 1947; Weiss and Hiscoe, 1948). Protein substances are constantly consumed in connection with motor activity and sensory stimulation and built up again with the aid of ribonucleic acid. Ordinarily the consumption and synthesis of the nucleopro-

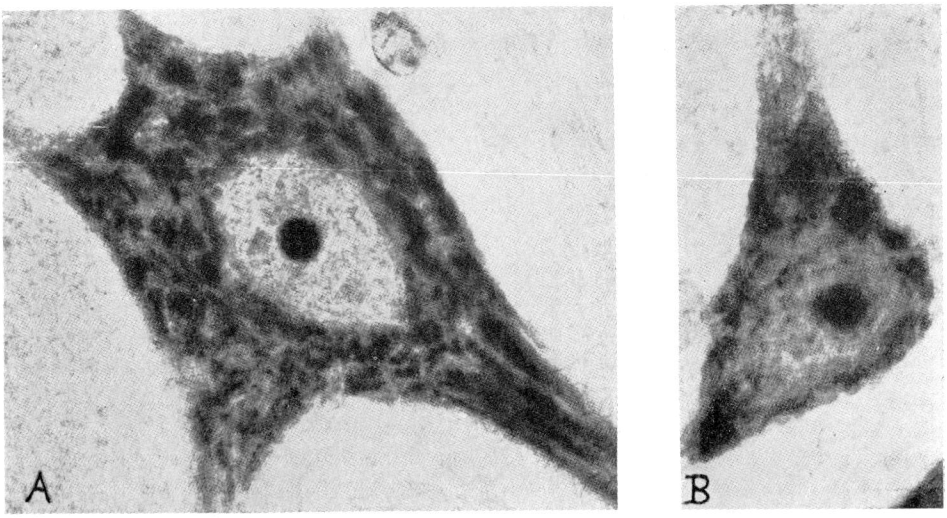

FIG. 85. A, ventral horn cell rabbit's spinal cord; B, pyramidal cell from human frontal cortex; showing Nissl bodies and nucleolus. Ultraviolet microphotograph of unstained preparations. A, ×1150; B, ×1450. (Hydén and Hartelius.)

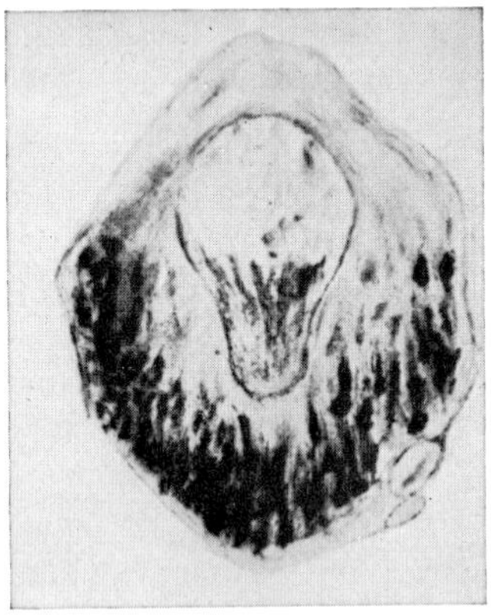

FIG. 86. Concentration of Nissl bodies at the centrifugal pole of a rat's spinal ganglion cell which had been centrifuged for half an hour at very great force. (Beams and King.)

teins is kept in balance, but under extreme conditions the formation of protein may be unable to meet the demand. During exhaustive muscular exercise, large amounts of protein and ribonucleic acid disappear in the cytoplasm of the motor cells affected, the loss of the nucleic acid giving the characteristic picture of chromatolysis. Similar effects are produced in the sensory ganglion cells after intensive stimulation. When normal conditions are reestablished, resynthesis of the nucleoproteins begins at once, and even in severely depleted cells the original concentration of the proteins is reconstituted within two or three days (Hydén and Hartelius, 1948.)

Thus the nerve cell has a mechanism, similar to that of growing and glandular cells, for the synthesis of protein which is constantly used up during its normal activity. Basically this is also the mechanism for maintaining the total mass of the cell which is relatively enormous in the larger nerve cells. Each cell has an elongated process, the axon or nerve fiber, whose volume may be several hundred times the volume of the cell body. Yet this axon depends for its maintenance on the cell body, and completely degenerates when severed from the latter. In the motor and sensory neurons of the peripheral nervous system regeneration usually occurs, and under favorable conditions the total mass of the severed portion may be reconstituted by peripheral growth from the central stump. This puts a terrific strain on the protein-forming system. Within 24 hours after section and continuing for about a week, the Nissl substance becomes tremendously reduced. Both protein and nucleic acid "appear to melt away in the central portion of the cell" (Bodian, 1947). By the end of the second week the Nissl bodies have practically disappeared. The severity of the chromatolytic changes is proportional to the mass of axon cut off. About the third week recovery begins, characterized by the appearance of ribonucleic acid and protein around the nuclear membrane. Full recovery may take from three to six months, and appears to be coincident with the reconstitution of most of the original cell mass (Bodian, 1947). In the central nervous system where regeneration does not occur, the affected cells atrophy and either completely disintegrate or persist permanently as small, shrunken cells.

The existence of a protein-forming mechanism in the cell body has also been demonstrated by the important experimental work of Weiss and Hiscoe (1948). These authors have definitely shown that a regenerating axon does not grow from local resources supplied by blood and tissue fluids, under some vaguely defined "trophic influences" of the nucleus. Synthesis of new axonal protoplasm (axoplasm) occurs only in the nucleated portion of the cell, and this axoplasm is kept in constant proximo-distal motion, streaming into the axon and causing its elongation and increase in diameter, until the total axonal mass is reconstituted. Moreover, the formation and centrifugal migration of the axoplasm, though at a slower rate, continues in fibers which have acquired their definitive size. These probably serve to replace the protoplasm and especially the proteins constantly consumed during the normal physiological activity. In the nerve fibers studied, Weiss and Hiscoe have estimated that the rate of normal axoplasmic convection is about 1 mm. a day, and this rate appears to be of the same order as that of protein consumption postulated from known values of ammonia production in nerve fibers.

The available evidence indicates that the Nissl bodies are parts of a mechanism for the synthesis of cytoplasmic proteins. This mechanism serves to replace the protein constantly consumed during normal physiological activity, and to restore the total cell mass when the neuron is suddenly deprived of a large amount of its protoplasm, as in axon amputation. It must be stated, however, that this view is not accepted by all investigators (Claude, 1950).

Granular or filamentous *mitochondria* are scattered throughout the entire cell body, dendrites, and axon (Fig. 87). A modified *central body* or *microcentrum* has been demonstrated in most nerve cells (Del Rio-Hortega). It usually consists of one or two granules surrounded by a clear cytoplasmic area from which in some cases fine wavy fibrils radiate. Occasionally a rod shaped body replaces one of the granules. The significance of the microcentrum is obscure, since adult neurons are incapable of cell division.

The *reticular apparatus* is most highly developed in the large nerve cells where it forms a complicated perinuclear reticulum which may extend a distance into the dendrites (Fig. 88). In other cells it may consist of disconnected granules or threads, and in some of the small cells it may be reduced to a single granule (Golgi body). The apparatus reflects altered physiological states and pathological conditions even more sensitively than the chromophil substance (Penfield). In the cell body of a neuron whose axon has been cut, the substance of the apparatus becomes dispersed toward the periphery, with subsequent fragmentation and dissolution (Fig. 89). These phenomena have been termed "retispersion" and "retisolution" respectively (Penfield).

Most of the larger adult nerve cells contain a yellowish pigment known as *lipochrome* or *lipofuscin*. It appears in the form of granules which are usually aggregated in a dense mass in some part of the cell body (Fig. 90). Occasionally they may be dispersed throughout the cell. They are in-

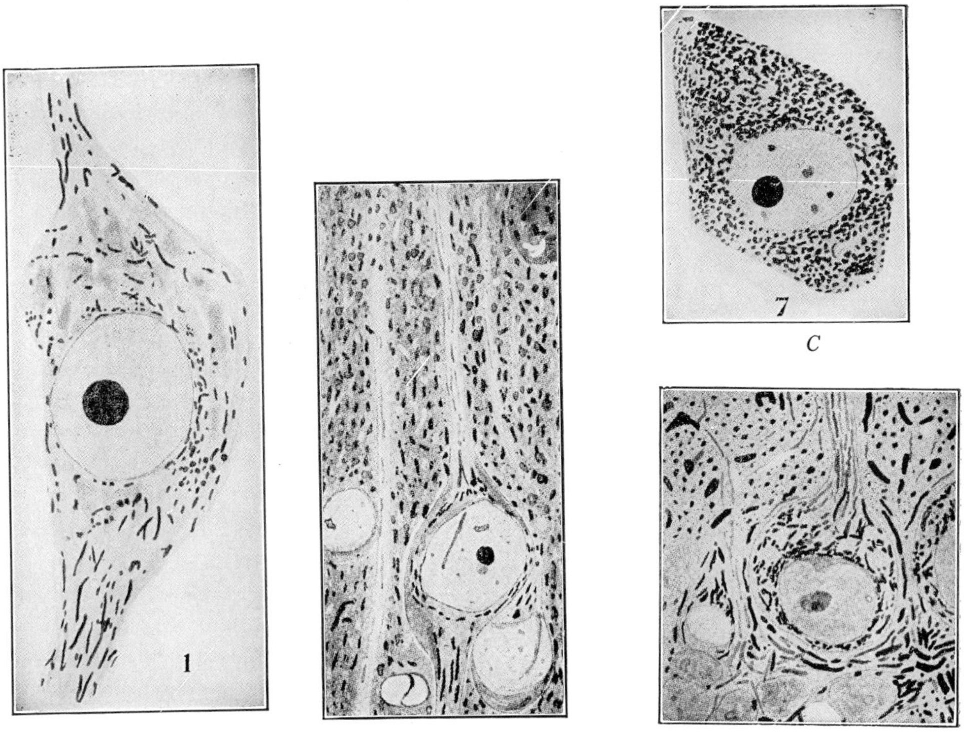

A B D

FIG. 87. Mitochondria in several types of nerve cells of the white mouse. *A*, large ventral horn cells; *B*, large pyramidal cell from the cortex; *C*, cell of Gasserian ganglion; *D*, Purkinje cell of cerebellar cortex. (Nicholson.)

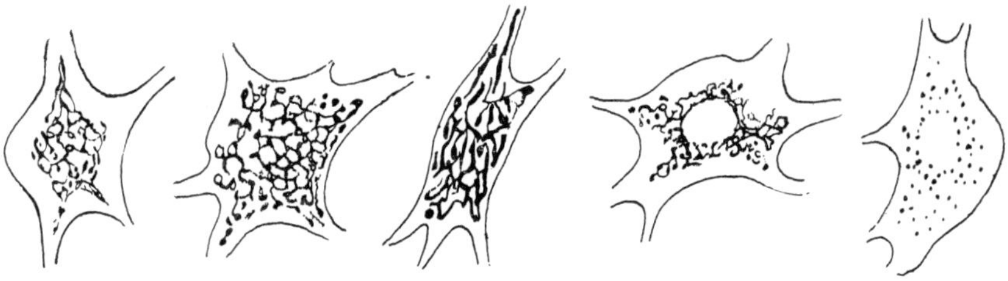

FIG. 88. Several forms of the Golgi apparatus in the motor neurons of the spinal cord of a 15 days old rabbit. (After Cajal.)

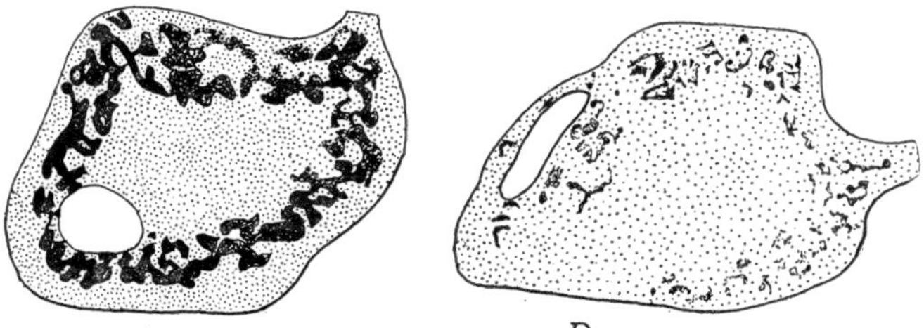

A B

FIG. 89. *A*, retispersion in cell of Clarke's column in spinal cord of cat four days after cutting its axon. *B*, same as *A* but showing retisolution as well. (Redrawn from Penfield.)

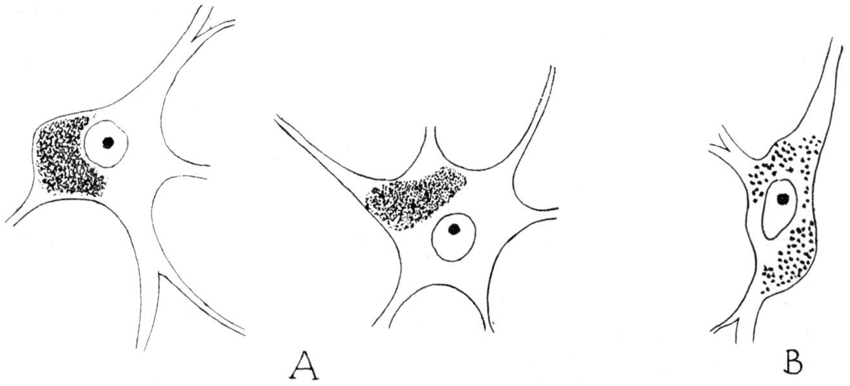

FIG. 90. *A,* lipochrome pigment in ventral horn cells of human spinal cord, blackened with osmic acid. *B,* cell from substantia nigra with melanin pigment granules.

soluble in the usual lipoid solvents, are blackened by osmic acid, and stain with Scharlach R. The cells of the newborn do not contain the pigment. It appears about the sixth year in the spinal ganglia, a few years later in the spinal cord, and after the twentieth year it is found in the cerebral cortex. It increases in amount with advancing years and during senescence it may take up the largest part of the cytoplasm (Truex, 1940).

Granules of a blackish pigment, known as melanin, are found in the substantia nigra, locus caeruleus and in certain pigmented cells scattered through the brain stem. It is also found in some cerebrospinal and sympathetic ganglion cells. Melanin appears at the end of the first year and increases in amount until puberty, after which it apparently remains constant until senescence. Little is known of the significance of either type of pigment.

The dendrites are simple protoplasmic extensions which have the same structure as the cytoplasm of the cell body.

The nerve fiber (the axon and its sheaths). The axon is a slender, usually long process which arises from a conical mass of specialized protoplasm known as the implantation cone or axon hill. It is composed of closely packed parallel running neurofibrils continuous with those of the cell body, and imbedded in a scanty amount of perifibrillar substance or axoplasm in which rodshaped mitochondria are scattered. It is distinguished from the cell body and dendrites by the complete absence of Nissl bodies which are also lacking in the axon hill. Distally each axon breaks up into more or less extensive terminal arborizations, the *effectors* (5 in Fig. 180).

In the central nervous system the axons may be *myelinated* or *unmyelinated.* The former possess a sheath of myelin for at least a portion of their course. In the unmyelinated fibers the sheath appears to be lacking. There is evidence, however, that even the finest unmyelinated fibers have a delicate layer resembling myelin enveloping the axon, too sparse to be seen histologically but detectable by special methods. Apparently the presence of such a layer is important for conduction of the nerve impulse. In the peripheral nervous system both myelinated and unmyelinated fibers have, in addition, an outer delicate nucleated membrane, the *neurilemma* or *sheath of Schwann.*

The *peripheral myelinated fiber* is structurally the most differentiated type, consisting of axon (axis cylinder), myelin sheath and neurilemma. The myelin sheath is not continuous, but is interrupted at fairly regular intervals, the parts of the fiber free from myelin appearing as constrictions known as the nodes of Ranvier (Fig. 96).

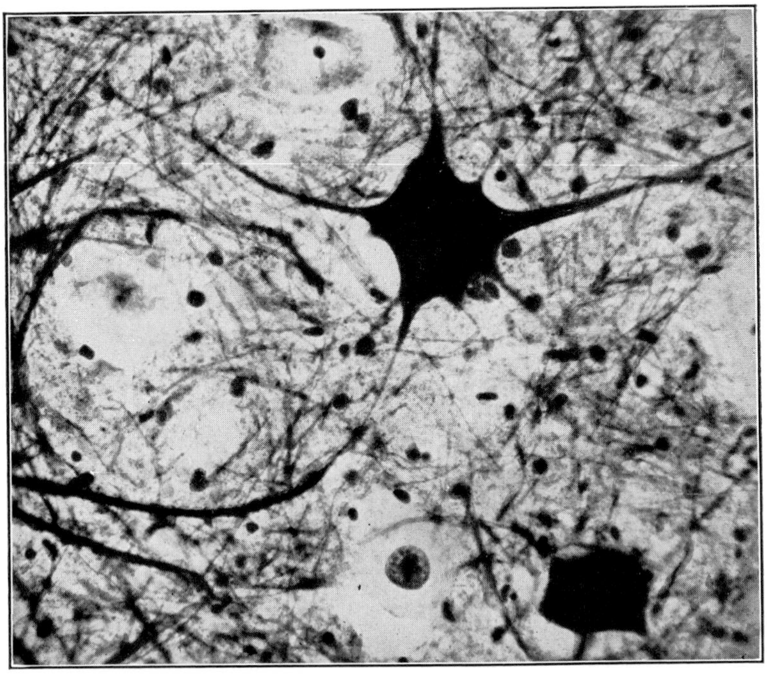

FIG. 91. Large motor cell from ventral gray horn of infant's spinal cord showing several dendrites and the origin of the axon. The latter arises from the lower side, tapers to a thin thread which runs for a short distance and then thickens at the point where the myelin sheath begins. Numerous small neuroglia nuclei, stained black, are shown. Modified Weigert's myelin stain. Photograph.

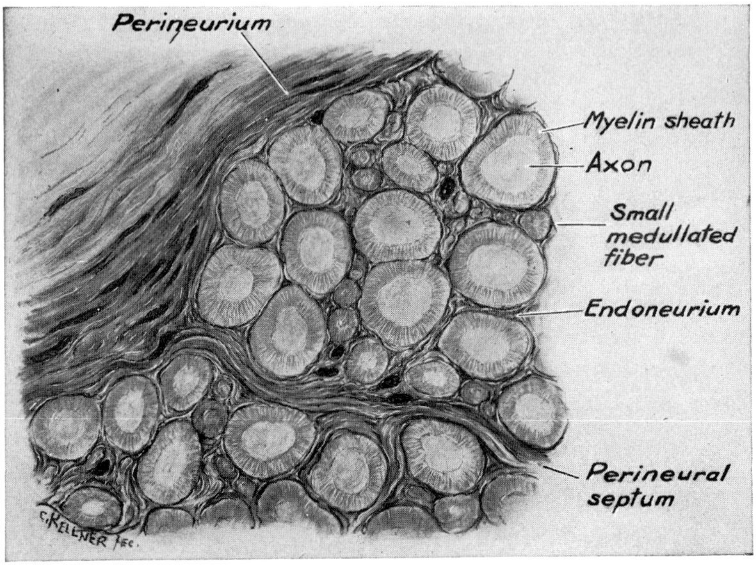

FIG. 92. Cross section of sciatic nerve of monkey. (From Bailey's Histology.)

In the fresh condition the semifluid axon is broad and homogeneous in appearance, occasionally showing faint longitudinal striations. In properly stained preparations it consists of closely packed parallel running neurofibrils imbedded in a scanty amount of homogeneous axoplasm. In most fixatives the axon usually shrinks down to a thin axial thread, but in careful preparations its normal size may be more nearly approximated (Fig. 92).

At each node of Ranvier the axon is slightly constricted and is traversed by a delicate membrane, the cross membrane or "Quermembran" which delimits adjacent internodal segments of the axon (Muralt, 1946). The membrane was first described by Bethe (1903) and later by Cajal (1928) who called it the "cementing disk" and regarded it as a supporting or connecting membrane (Fig. 93). Muralt has shown that the cross membrane is always demonstrable in the living nerve fiber when viewed in polarized light under proper optical conditions (Fig. 94), and ascribes to it an important part in the process of nerve excitation.

Between the axon and myelin sheath there is presumed to be a delicate layer or membrane, often known as the axilemma. Difficult to demonstrate histologically, the membrane may be seen clearly in ultraviolet photographs of the living nerve fiber, since both axilemma and neurilemma show a much greater ultraviolet absorption than the axon and myelin (Fig. 95). It is apparently a layer of peculiar physical properties, differentially permeable to various kinds of ions, and hence of utmost importance in the mechanism of impulse propagation.

The myelin sheath is acquired a short distance from the cell body, a short proximal portion of the axon being as a rule unmyelinated (Fig. 91). It is a sheath of varying thickness, composed of a semifluid doubly refracting substance known as *myelin* which in the fresh state has a glistening

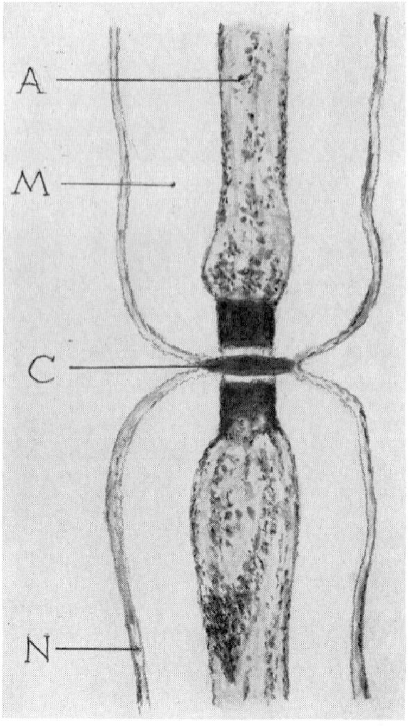

Fig. 93. Node of Ranvier. A, axon; C, cementing membrane; M, myelin sheath; N, neurilemma. (After Cajal.)

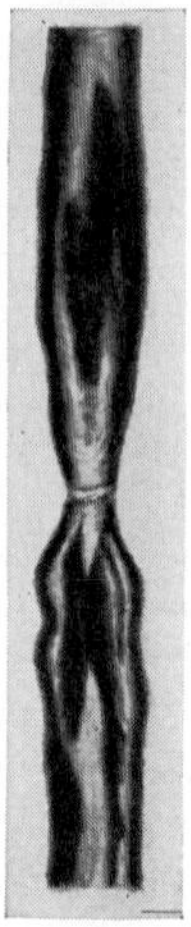

Fig. 94

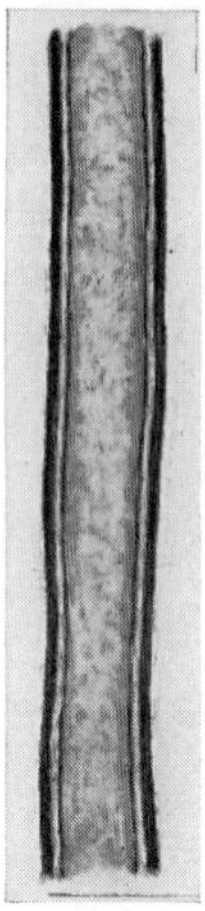

Fig. 95

Fig. 94. Portion of living nerve fiber, showing cross membrane in node of Ranvier. Photograph in polarized light. (Muralt.)

Fig. 95. Portion of living nerve fiber showing double contour of myelin sheath, produced by neurilemma and axilemma. Ultraviolet microphotograph. (Muralt.)

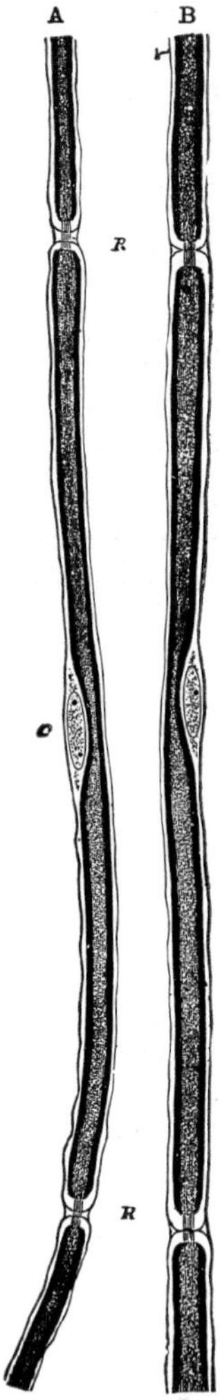

FIG. 96

FIG. 97

FIG. 96. Longitudinal section of portions of two myelinated fibers stained with osmic acid. Semidiagrammatic. *R, R,* nodes of Ranvier with axis cylinder passing through; *c,* nucleus surrounded by protoplasm, lying between neurilemma and myelin sheath. (J. E. Neale in Quain's Anatomy.)

FIG. 97. Longitudinal section of small portion of a myelinated nerve fiber. Osmic acid. *c,* cleft of Schmidt-Lantermann; *d,* node; *n,* nucleus; and *p,* cytoplasm of neurilemma cell. (Cajal.)

white appearance. Chemically it is composed of protein and several lipids such as cholesterol, lecithin, and cerebrosides. According to Schmitt, Bear, and Palmer (1941) the myelin sheath consists of thin concentric sheets of protein alternating with layers of lipids. As already stated the sheath is not continuous but is interrupted at intervals by constrictions known as the nodes of Ranvier (Figs. 96, 100). The length of the internodal segments varies considerably and is proportional to the diameter of the fiber, the thinner fibers having the shorter internodes. In the peroneal nerve of the rabbit the internodes on fibers 3–18μ in diameter range from 400–1500μ (Vizoso and Young, 1948) and these figures probably obtain for other mammals and man. Occasionally an internode may be twice the normal size without variation in the caliber of the fiber. Similarly there may be stretches where the internodes are shorter, and in these stretches the diameter may be sometimes reduced. Experimental studies on regenerating fibers which have much shorter internodes, indicate that there is no particular relation between conduction velocity and internodal length (Young, 1949). The myelin sheath of each internode is divided into conical segments by oblique funnel-shaped clefts, the *incisures of Schmidt-Latermann,* which extend from neurilemma to axon (Fig. 97). These are best seen in preparations treated with osmic acid but are also constantly visible in the living fiber, especially when viewed in polarized light (Muralt). Their significance is not understood, though a nutritive function has been ascribed to them by some investigators. In other preparations, the myelin sheath may exhibit a delicate trabecular reticulum, the *neurokeratin network* (Fig. 100). The network probably represents a precipitated protein residue of the myelin sheath rather than a true cytoplasmic reticulum. However, a delicate reticulum has been observed in the myelin sheath of the living nerve fiber photographed in ultraviolet light. The myelin sheath ends at or near the point where the terminal arborizations of the fiber are given off, the latter always being unmyelinated.

The neurilemma or sheath of Schwann is

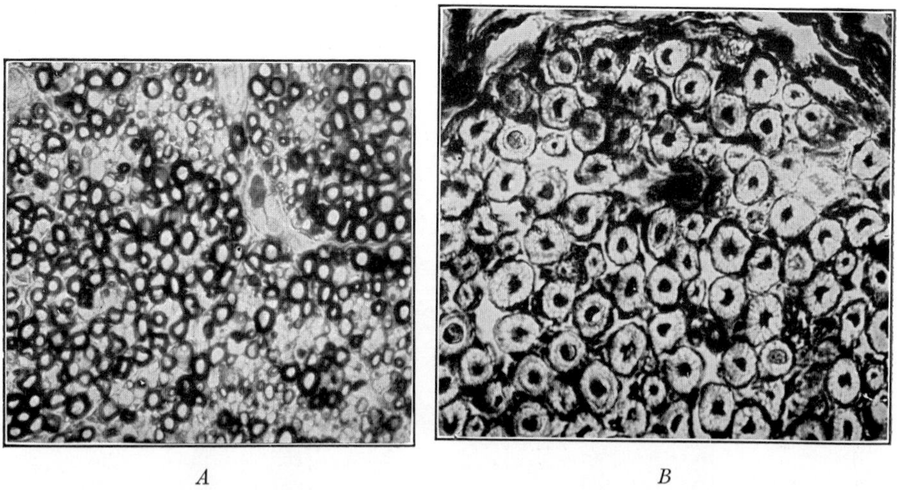

FIG. 98. Transverse sections through portions of a nerve trunk, each containing a number of myelinated fibers. In *A*, the myelin sheaths appear as black rings enclosing the unstained axis-cylinders. In *B*, the somewhat shrunken axis-cylinders appear black. The pale myelin sheath is covered externally by the dark staining neurilemma and displays a delicate neurokeratin reticulum. Photographs.

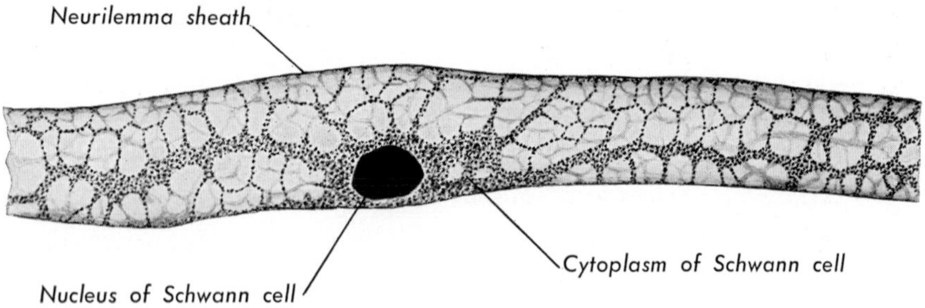

FIG. 99. Sheath of Schwann cell in nerve fiber from cauda equina of cat. (Bailey's Histology, after Nemiloff.)

a delicate membrane enclosing the myelin, which at the node of Ranvier dips inward and comes in contact with the axon. Underneath this membrane and outside the myelin, about halfway between two nodes, is found a flattened ovoid nucleus surrounded by an area of granular cytoplasm. From the region of the nucleus several strands extend along the length of the internode, branching and anastomosing to form a flat cytoplasmic network over the surface of the myelin (Fig. 99). Nucleus and cytoplasm constitute a *sheath cell* or *Schwann cell,* one for each internode. The neurilemma is probably the product of the Schwann cell, for recent studies indicate that the cytoplasm of the cell initially surrounded the naked axon. Subsequent rotation of a Schwann cell around the axon resulted in several concentric layers of cytoplasm, as though one had rolled a rug on a bamboo pole. Such concentric layers of Schwann cell cytoplasm later became blended to form a cytoplasmic layer which lined a thin investing neurilemma sheath. The first myelin to appear is deposited in what was originally the deeper layers of concentric Schwann cell cytoplasm surrounding the axon. Myelin formation is thus dependent upon the presence of such sheath or Schwann cells.

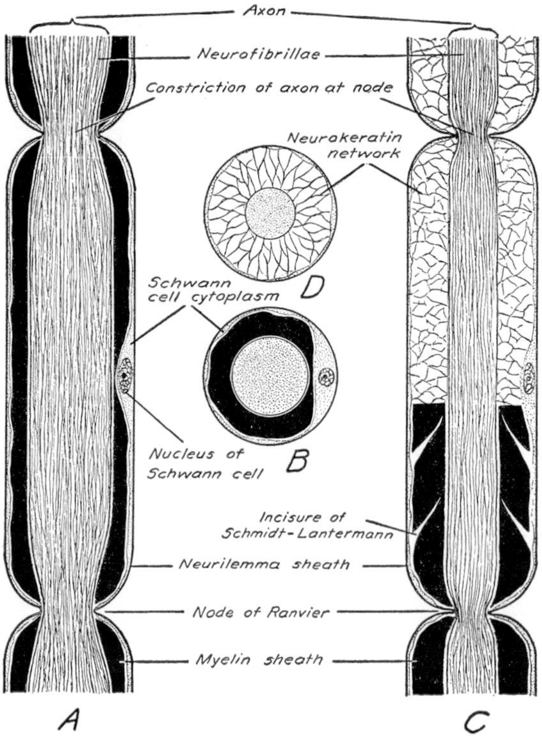

FIG. 100. Schematic drawings of peripheral myelinated nerve fibers. In *A* and *B* the relative diameters of axon and myelin sheaths are based on de Renyi's studies of living nerve fibers. *C* and *D* show them as seen in many fixed preparations. The cross membrane is not shown. (Bailey's Histology.)

Myelin formation occurs first in the vicinity of the nucleus and continues in either direction until an entire myelin segment is established between two nodes. The internodal segments are at first short, about 100–150μ, but progressively elongate as the nerve grows in length, accompanied by an increase in the diameter of the fiber. As a result the number of internodal segments in a given stretch of fiber remains constant throughout development. The adult relationship between internodal length and fiber diameter is due to the fact that the fibers which ultimately become the largest are the first to myelinate, hence their internodes are stretched to a greater degree in subsequent growth (Vizoso and Young, 1948). It is emphasized that sheath cells are also applied to peripheral fibers which do not become myelinated.

In addition to the above described structures, each myelinated peripheral nerve fiber is surrounded by a reenforcing sheath of delicate connective tissue, the *endoneurium* or *sheath of Henle* (*sheath of Key and Retzius*), which, however, does not form part of the nerve fiber proper. It is composed of delicate collagenous fibers disposed longitudinally for the most part, a homogeneous ground substance and scattered, flattened fibroblasts. The sheath is closely adherent to the neurilemma and is often difficult to distinguish from the latter. Both neurilemma and endoneurium remain as definite tubes during the processes of degeneration and regeneration of nerve fibers. The endoneurium is directly continuous with the more abundant connective tissue or *perineurium* which envelops bundles of fibers within a nerve trunk (Fig. 92). According to Denny-Brown (1946), the perineurial connective tissue is somewhat peculiar, consisting of

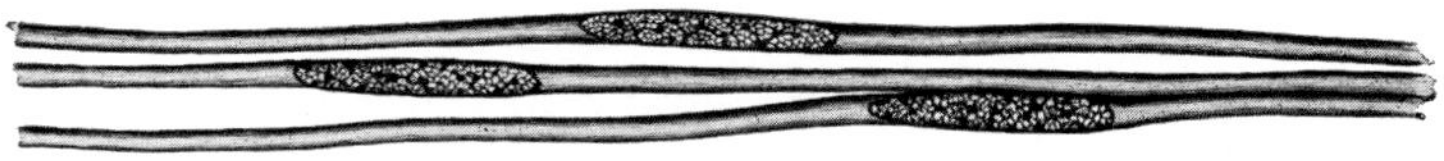

FIG. 101. Three unmyelinated fibers (fibers of Remak) with neurilemma nuclei. (After Cajal.)

flattened fibroblasts and smooth lamellae resembling mesothelium. Owing to the presence of neurilemma sheaths and reenforcing connective tissue layers, peripheral nerve trunks possess a considerable toughness as contrasted with the almost semifluid consistency of the white matter in the central nervous system.

The *unmyelinated peripheral nerve fibers*, or *fibers of Remak*, have a slender axon enveloped by a delicate nucleated sheath which is considered the equivalent of neurilemma and sheath cells (Fig. 101). The axons of most sympathetic ganglion cells and of many small cerebrospinal ganglion cells are unmyelinated.

The nerve fibers in the central nervous system do not possess a neurilemma sheath but are surrounded by neuroglia tissue (see neuroglia). In the myelinated fibers the nodes of Ranvier are less definite and more closely spaced (Cajal), and the incisures of Schmidt-Lantermann are not demonstrable in the myelin sheath. The unmyelinated fibers, of which there are many in the gray and white substance of the brain and spinal cord, appear as naked axons of small caliber imbedded in neuroglia.

Myelinated fibers vary greatly in size. The fine fibers have a diameter from 1–4μ, those of medium size from 5–10μ, the largest from 11–20μ.

Collaterals or branches are given off by most fibers of the central nervous system. They are usually of finer caliber than the parent stem, extend at right angles and often arise from the proximal unmyelinated part of the axon. In the myelinated portion they are given off at the nodes of Ranvier, and become myelinated themselves. In the peripheral nervous system the fibers of somatic motor neurons which supply striped muscle, branch repeatedly at acute angles before reaching the muscle. Within the latter the branching may be very extensive, so that a single nerve fiber may furnish motor terminals for many muscle fibers (Sherrington; Clark). Many sensory fibers probably branch in a similar manner since their terminal arborizations extend over a considerable area. According to Weddell a single myelinated fiber may supply sensory endings to more than 300 hair follicle groups. The term "sensory unit" has been suggested for a sensory fiber including all its terminals.

Myelinated fibers conduct more rapidly than unmyelinated ones. The speed is proportional to the diameter of the fiber, and more especially to the thickness of the myelin sheath. The latter may be regarded both as an insulator and as a source of energy for the rapid reversibility of the excitation processes, thus accounting for the speedy conduction and relative non-fatigability of the myelinated fiber.

Physical and physiological grouping of nerve fibers. When a wave of excitation, the nerve impulse, passes over a nerve fiber, it is invariably accompanied by an electrical change known as the *action potential* which can be recorded by an appropriate instrument such as the cathode ray oscillograph. The electrical record of an impulse consists of a strong negative deviation of short duration, the *spike potential*, usually followed by two longer but much weaker deviations known as the *negative* and *positive afterpotentials.* Since the traveling electric change and the impulse are inseparable from each other, a study of the electrical phenomena during excitation furnishes the most delicate and accurate information regarding the speed, frequency, and intensity of the nerve impulse. Thus the speed with which the spike potential travels over the nerve fiber constitutes the conduction velocity of the impulse, and the number of successive potentials traversing the fiber is regarded as representing the frequency of the impulses.

Erlanger and Gasser (1937) have shown that the different fibers in a nerve trunk conduct at greatly varying velocities, the speed being in the main proportional to the diameter of the fiber and of the myelin sheath. Also each nerve has a characteristic pattern of velocities corresponding to an analogous pattern of fiber diameters in the nerve trunk. As a result of extensive electrical investigations supported by histological studies, nerve fibers have been grouped into three main classes, the A, B, and C fibers, whose potentials are known as the A, B, and C waves. Each of the A and B groups includes several subdivisions. Criteria for the classification are fiber diameter, conduction velocity, and nature of the electrical record (Gasser and Grundfest; Bishop et al.; Grundfest; Heinbecker et al.; Lloyd; Quensel).

The A fibers are myelinated, range in diameter from 1–20μ and conduct at the rate of 5–120 meters per second, the rate proportional to the thickness of the fiber. The more finely myelinated B fibers have a diameter up to 3μ and a conduction rate of about 3–15 meters per second, though a higher velocity has been observed in some fibers of this group. The C fibers are unmyelinated and conduct very slowly, about 0.6–2 meters per second. It is obvious that there is a certain amount of overlapping so that a fiber of 2μ could belong to either A or B, but certain features of the electrical record permit a definite classification. Thus the duration of the spike potential is always much longer in B fibers than in any A fiber, and moreover the B fibers lack a negative afterpotential.

Studies on various types of nerves (muscular, cutaneous and autonomic) have indicated a general functional grouping of the three fiber types. This grouping must not be regarded too rigidly, since many fibers serving the same function may have widely different calibers. The A fibers include several subdivisions. The largest and most rapidly conducting fibers, 60–120 meters per second in man, transmit motor impulses to striped muscles, and carry afferent proprioceptive impulses from these muscles to the central nervous system. The rest of the A fibers, varying considerably in diameter and speed of conduction, carry afferent impulses from cutaneous receptors. The fibers of intermediate sizes are related to touch and pressure; the finest fibers are believed to transmit impulses of localized pain, and perhaps also some of temperature and touch.

The B fibers are mainly associated with visceral innervation, and are both efferent and afferent. All the preganglionic autonomic fibers belong to this group, and also the postganglionic fibers from the ciliary ganglion which are partly or wholly myelinated. The more rapidly conducting fibers transmit afferent impulses from the viscera (Muralt). The unmyelinated C fibers comprise the efferent postganglionic autonomic fibers, and afferent fibers which are believed to conduct impulses of poorly localized pain from the viscera and periphery.

Relationship of neurons. The synapse. The simplest segmental reflexes require a chain of at least two neurons (1 in Fig. 184). A wave of excitation, the nerve impulse, is set up in a peripheral sensory nerve ending and passes along the peripheral and central process of a ganglion cell into the spinal cord. There it activates a motor neuron whose impulse travels along the motor fiber and causes a muscular contraction (Fig. 201). Even such simple reactions have, as a rule, a third or *central* neuron interposed between the afferent and efferent cell (Fig. 184), while in the more complicated neural circuits the number of such intercalated central neurons may be tremendously multiplied. All neural pathways therefore consist of chains of neurons so related to each other as to make possible the physiological continuity of nerve impulse conduction over the complete circuit. The place of junction of neurons, i.e., where the axonal end arborizations of one neuron come in contact with the cell body or dendrites of another, is known as the *synapse*. It is generally accepted that the processes of one neuron do not fuse or become structurally continuous with those of other neurons. The relationship at the synapse is one of contact only, the axon terminals of one neuron being everywhere separated from the cell body and dendrites of other neurons by a delicate surface membrane. Such a membrane forms a site for the occurrence of various surface phenomena, thus offering increased resistance and otherwise modifying the transmission of impulses across the synapse; or may furnish a mechanism for the setting up of new nerve impulses. This view is supported by impressive histological as well as physiological evidence.

Synaptic junctions show many structural variations. Most commonly the axon terminals end in small bulb-like expansions or *neuropodia* (*end feet, boutons terminaux*) applied to the cell body or dendrites. Each neuropodium consists of a neurofibrillar loop imbedded in perifibrillar substance; sometimes there are simply small neurofibrillar rings (Fig. 102). A large motor cell in the spinal cord may receive several hundred of such endings. In another type of synapse the delicate axon terminals do not form end feet but come in lengthwise apposition with the dendrites or cell body, often for considerable distances (Figs. 103, 104). The most striking examples are the climbing fibers of the cerebellum. In some cases, unmyelinated axons run at right angles to the dendrites and apparently come in contact with the spiny excrescences or *gemmules* with which the dendrites are beset. It is obvious that one axon may carry impulses to a number of neurons and that conversely a single neuron may receive impulses from the axons of many neurons.

Many physiological peculiarities are associated with the synapse. While an activated nerve fiber conducts equally well in either direction, impulses are transmitted over the reflex arc, i.e., across the synapse in one direction only, from the axon of one neuron to the cell body and dendrites of

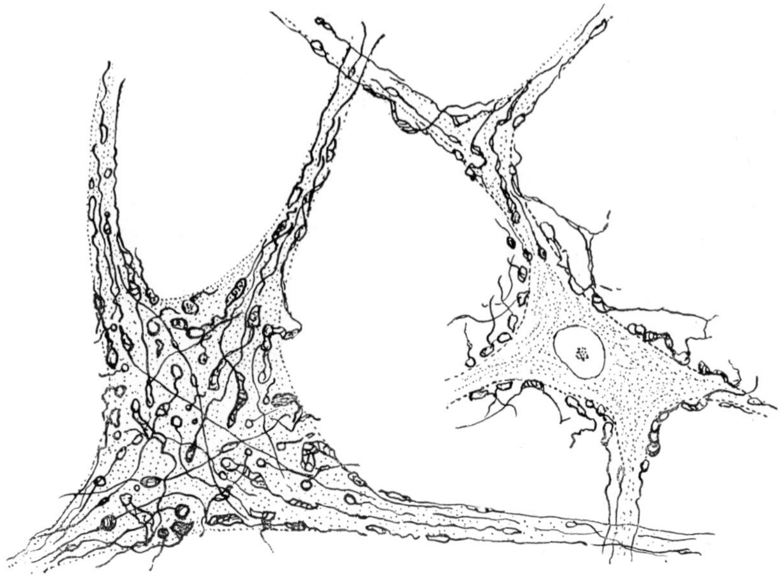

FIG. 102. Neuropodia (end feet) on body and dendrites of large cells in the reticular formation of the medulla. Adult rabbit. (Redrawn from Cajal.)

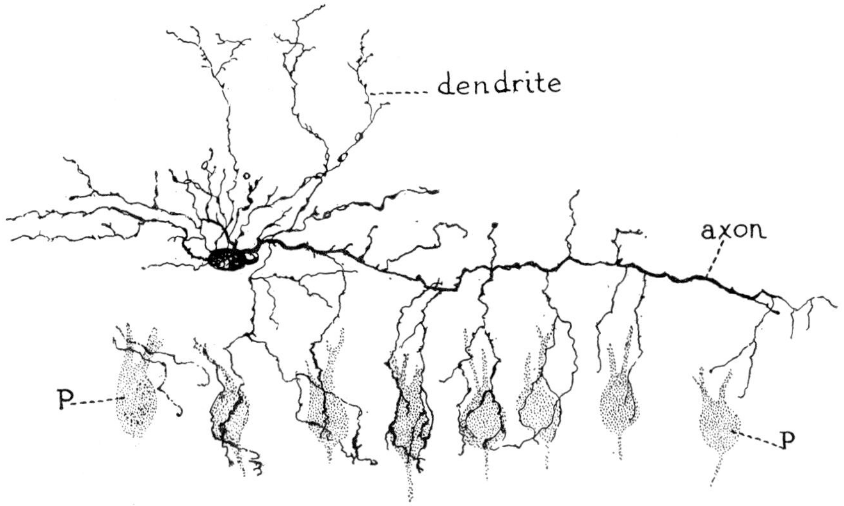

Fig. 103. Basket cell of human cerebellum with dendrites and axon. The collaterals of the axon end in terminal (synaptic) arborizations on the bodies of a number of Purkinje cells (*P*). (After Jakob.)

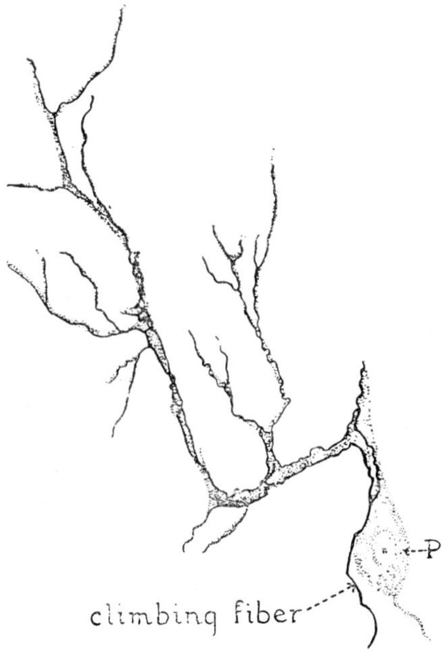

Fig. 104. Parallel axo-dendritic synapses formed by the terminal arborization of a climbing fiber with the dendrites of a Purkinje cell (*P*). Human cerebellum. (Redrawn from Jakob.)

another, a phenomenon known as *dynamic polarization.* Some of the other ways in which conduction across the synapse differs from that in a nerve fiber may be briefly mentioned (Sherrington). Over a reflex arc: (1) conduction is slower; (2) there may be persistence of response after cessation of the stimulus (after-discharge); (3) there is less close correspondence between the rhythm of stimulus and rhythm of response; (4) repetition of a given stimulus may produce a response where a single one will not (summation); (5) greater variability in the threshold value of a stimulus, i.e., the ease with which responses can be elicited; (6) much greater fatigability; (7) greater dependence on oxygen supply and greater susceptibility to anesthetics and other drugs; (8) greater refractory period; and (9) reenforcement and inhibition of one reflex by another.

Degeneration and regeneration of nerve fibers. The cell body is the trophic center of the neuron and any process detached from it disintegrates and completely disappears. When an axon is divided, degenerative changes of a traumatic character first affect the cut edges. In the proximal portion of the fiber which is attached to the cell body, the degenerative changes (retrograde degeneration) extend only a short though variable distance, depending on the nature of the injury. In a clean cut only one

FIG. 105. Diagrams showing several stages in the degeneration of end feet in the spinal cord of a cat, following section of a dorsal root. *A* normal end foot. *B, C, D, E,* after section of root. *B*, 2 days; *C*, 4 days; *D, E*, 5 days. (After W. C. Gibson.)

or two internodes may be involved. In more severe injuries, such as gunshot wounds or inflammatory processes the retrograde degeneration may extend as much as two or three centimeters. However, this is soon succeeded by reparative processes leading to the formation of new axonal sprouts from the central stump. In the distal portion, the axon and myelin sheath completely disintegrate, degeneration occurring throughout the whole length of the fiber and including its terminal arborization, a process known as *secondary* or *Wallerian degeneration.* The changes as a rule appear simultaneously along the whole length of the nerve fiber, distal to the point of injury.

Axonal changes begin almost at once. Twelve hours after injury the axon is swollen and irregular in shape, and in the second day begins to break up into fragments which undergo autolysis and finally disappear. However, the breaking-up process may continue for a considerable time in some fibers, and fragments of degenerating axons have been found as late as three or four weeks after the injury. The terminal arborizations are similarly affected. The neurofibrils lose their staining capacity, assume an irregular shape, and by the end of the fifth day have become broken up into granules (Fig. 105). The myelin sheath likewise degenerates. Two or three days after section, constrictions appear which break the myelin into elongated ellipsoid segments, which in turn fragment into smaller ovoid or spherical droplets or granules (Figs. 106, 107). The whole process resembles the break-up of a liquid column under surface tension, and is ascribed to the fact that the fiber is no longer kept in a turgid condition by the pressure emanating from the cell body (Young, **1949**). This view is supported by the work of Weiss and Hiscoe (**1948**) who have shown that under normal conditions there is a constant proximodistal flow of axoplasm from the nucleated portion of the cell. The myelin changes, at first purely physical, are soon followed by chemical changes as well, the myelin breaking down into simpler intermediate substances which react to the Marchi stain, and ultimately into neutral fat. The myelin break-down may in part occur in the Schwann cells whose protoplasm occasionally contains granular degeneration products. However, the main digestion and removal of the myelin is accomplished by macrophages which apparently enter the fiber from the endoneurium and perineurium (Young, **1942**). In the rabbit these macrophages appear about the seventh day, accumulate debris and become large vacuolated cells whose protoplasm is packed with granules and droplets of myelin in various stages of disintegration (Fig. 110). Often several macrophages lie close together, appearing as clumps or islands of fatty droplets along the course of the degenerating fiber (Fig. 107C). As the myelin is broken down and absorbed the macrophages gradually disappear, though occasional ones may be present three to four months after section. The way in which these debris-laden cells are removed from the nerve fiber is still undetermined.

While these changes take place, the nuclei

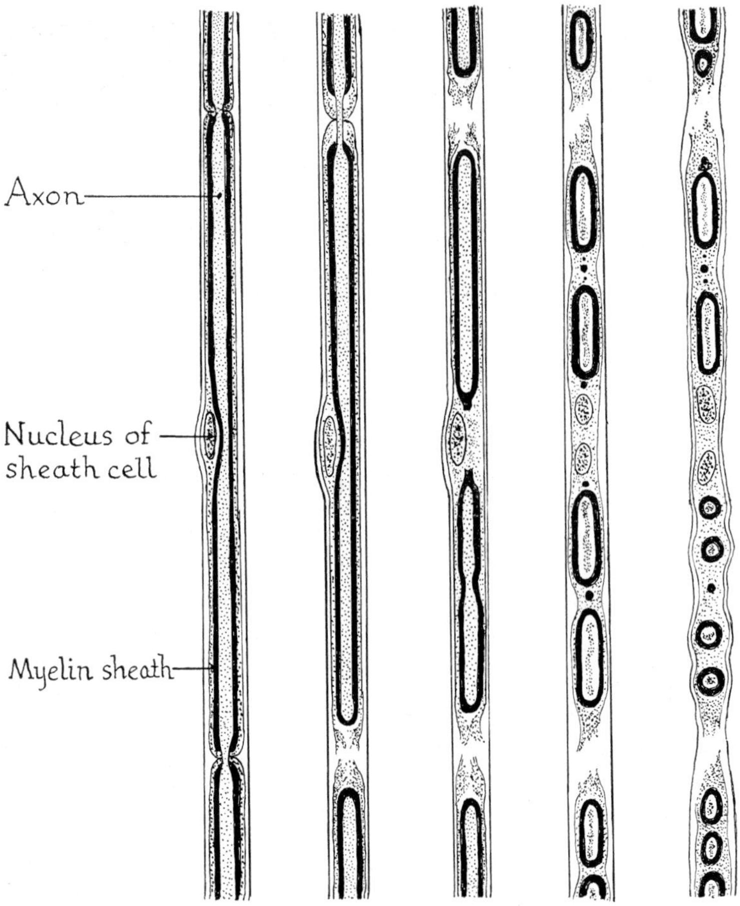

Fig. 106. Diagram showing breakup of myelin and axon during nerve degeneration. Note increase in sheath cell protoplasm and division of the nucleus. (Young.)

of the Schwann cells proliferate by mitotic division, and their cytoplasm increases in amount. Nuclear division begins around the fourth day and continues actively to about the 25th, mitosis occurring over the whole length of the fiber. The increase in the number of nuclei is very considerable, in some instances as much as 13 times the original population (Abercrombie and Johnson, 1947). In the view of many investigators, cytoplasmic division does not follow or is incomplete, and as a result, the sheath cells of each fiber now form a syncytial multinucleated cord or band, the *band fiber* or *band of Büngner* (Fig. 107C). According to Young, however, the syncytial character of the band is more apparent than real. After mitosis, each nucleus surrounded by a certain amount of cytoplasm becomes converted into an elongated tapering cell. Some may become syncytially connected at the ends, but often the ends overlap each other for some distance. Similarly the territories of two cells, which lie side by side and are apparently continuous, may be delimited by fine clefts present between them. Thus the band fiber is in part composed of elongated cellular elements which are independent of each other. The nuclei of the band fiber are able to move up and down within the tube and to migrate out of the tube at the cut surface. The sheath cells lie at first between the macrophages and the degenerating myelin; later they fill the entire tube.

The wall of the fiber, composed of the

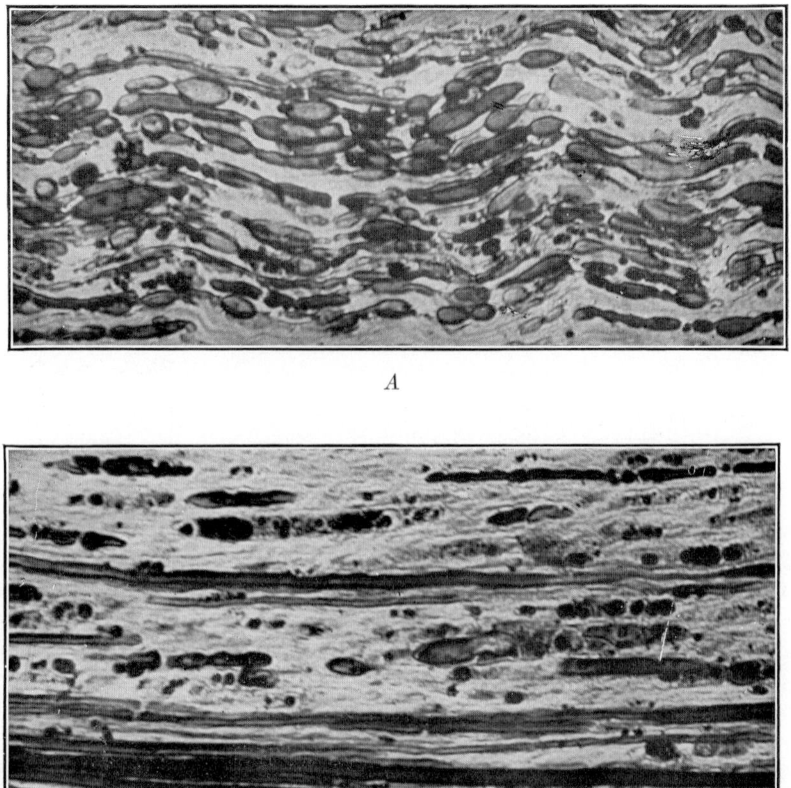

A

B

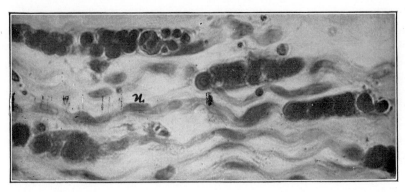

C

FIG. 107. *A*, distal stump of a nerve cut 3 to 5 days previously. Osmic acid. *B*, distal stump of a nerve partly cut 12 to 15 days previously. Osmic acid. Normal fibers and two nodes of Ranvier are shown at the bottom. *C*, distal stump of a nerve cut 12 to 15 days previously. Osmic and iron hematoxylin. In addition to the clumps or islands of degenerating myelin, several band fibers and their nuclei (*n*) are shown. Photographs.

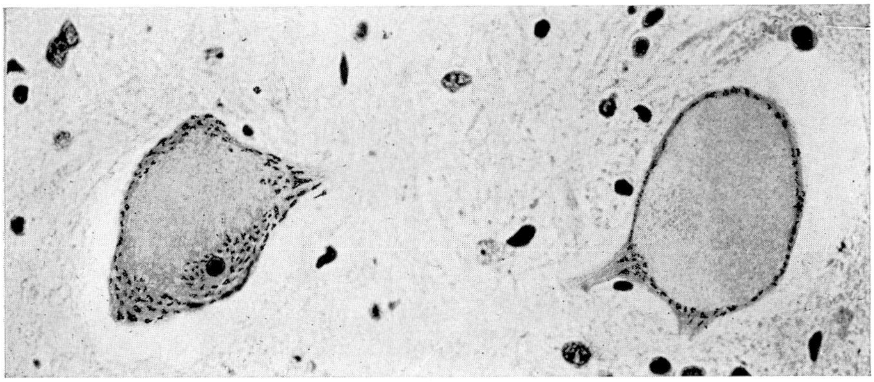

FIG. 108. Two motor cells from adult lumbar cord, showing "central chromatolysis", nuclear eccentricity and swelling of cell body. Photograph. The lumbosacral nerve roots had some time previously been crushed in an accident.

neurilemma tube and endoneurium, remains essentially unchanged. In the early stages the tube retains its diameter or may even become dilated by the accumulating debris. In later stages, especially if no axonal sprouts enter, the tube shrinks considerably, perhaps to one half of its original size, and the walls thicken, due primarily to the increase in the collagen content of the endoneurium. More severe shrinkage of tubes has been reported by Sunderland and Bradley (1950) in the degenerating stumps of the median and ulnar nerves of the opossum. Three months after severance all the fibers were less than 3 or 4μ in diameter, and after 16 months there were no tubes over 2μ in caliber.

The neuron body whose axon is injured likewise shows marked degenerative changes (Fig. 108). The cell body swells and becomes turgescent, the nucleus is displaced toward the periphery, and the Nissl bodies undergo dissolution, the chromatolysis beginning in the center of the cell and spreading outward (central chromatolysis). The extent and rapidity of these changes depend on the type of neuron involved, the nature of the injury and especially on the location of the injury, a lesion near the cell body producing a greater central effect than one more distantly placed. In other words, the effect depends upon the percentage of the neuron cut off. If the lesion is very near the cell body, the latter may ultimately die with consequent degeneration of the proximal portion of the nerve fiber which remains attached to it.

If the neuron survives the injury, *regeneration* takes place. Recovery in the cell body begins about the third week, characterized by the appearance of Nissl bodies around the nuclear membrane. The turgescence gradually subsides, the nucleus returns to its central position, and the Nissl bodies are restored to their normal amount and distribution. Full recovery may take from three to six months, the time depending on the mass of axon to be reconstituted. While this is going on, regenerative processes appear in the axons of the central stump. As early as the tenth hour the axonal ends begin to swell, due to pressure emanating from the cell body. Each axon splits into numerous fine strands or fibers (Fig. 109) which traverse the scar formed at the site of the injury and reach the neurilemma tubes of the degenerating stump. Many of these fibers enter a single tube where at first they are disposed peripherally, between the neurilemma and the surface of the sheath cells forming the Büngner bands (Fig. 110). Later some of them move to a more central position and become completely surrounded by the protoplasm of the sheath cells (Figs.

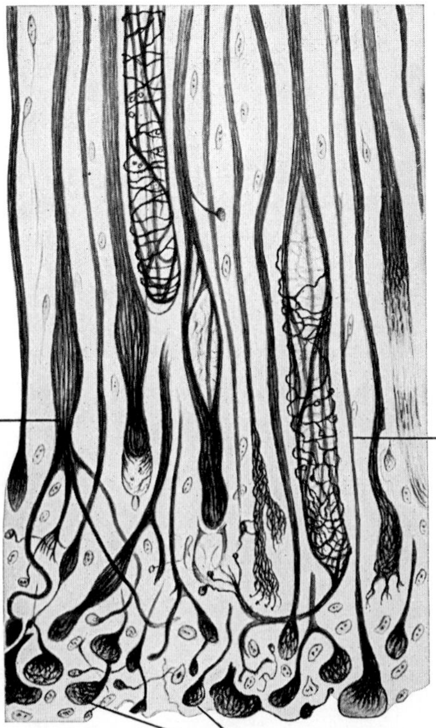

FIG. 109. Regenerating axons in the central stump of a cat's sciatic nerve 2½ days after section of the nerve. (After Cajal, from Bailey's Histology.)

111, 112). Along or within the Büngner bands, the regenerating axons grow down for long distances to their peripheral destinations. However, only one of the fibers in a tube usually goes to full functional maturity, gradually acquiring its original diameter and appropriate myelin sheath. The others apparently atrophy and ultimately disappear. The elimination of excess fibers may take considerable time, and some of them may still be seen in tubes three or four months after section. Of importance is the fact that the enlargement of one fiber and the elimination of the others occurs only if the regenerating axons make contact with the periphery. How this selective effect on the maturation of the fibers is exerted by the end organs in skin and muscle is still undetermined.

The thin regenerating axons, at first about 0.5–3μ in diameter, gradually enlarge, the increase in diameter advancing progressively down the tube, as if propelled by some centrifugal force from the central stump. On reaching the periphery, growth in length ceases, but the increase in diameter continues until the original thickness is approximated. Myelinization may occur as early as the second or third week in some fibers and likewise advances in a proximodistal direction, the process becoming somewhat slower in the more distant regions of the fiber. The myelin is at first laid down as a thin continuous sheath which subsequenetly becomes broken up into short internodal segments, about 150–700μ in length. In fully regenerated nerve fibers, therefore, the internodes are shorter and more numerous, and there is no longer any definite relation between internodal length and diameter, fibers of varying thickness possessing similar internodal lengths.

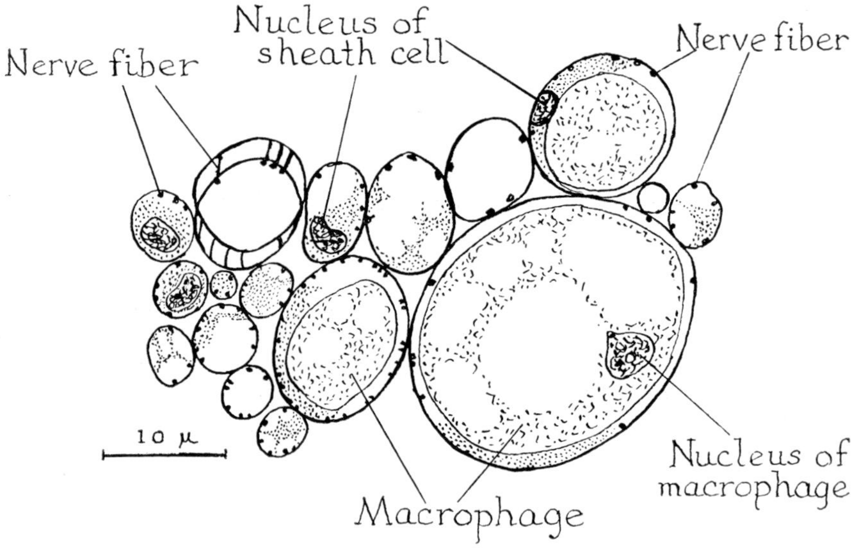

FIG. 110. Transverse sections of fibers in a peripheral stump 2 cm. distal to a suture made 25 days previously. Note the many fine nerve fibers running along the inner wall of each tube. (After Young.)

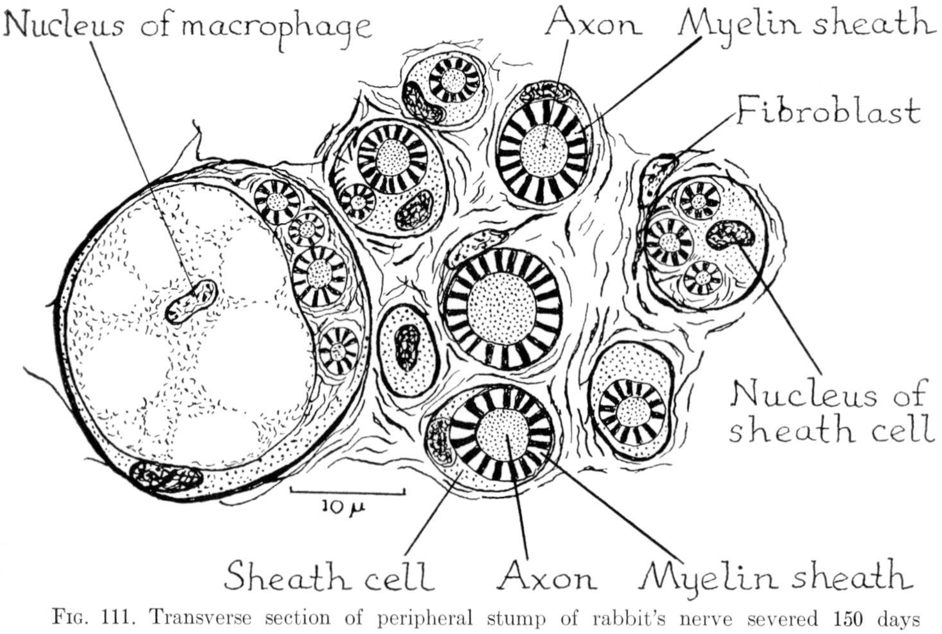

FIG. 111. Transverse section of peripheral stump of rabbit's nerve severed 150 days previously. The stumps were left unsutured but a union was established by outgrowth. Most of the tubes contain one or several myelinated fibers surrounded by protoplasm of sheath cell. (After Young.)

The growth processes observed during regeneration are truly remarkable. A slender axonal filament is ultimately transformed into a mature fiber whose volume in some instances may be several hundred times the volume of the original filament (Fig. 113 B–E). The manner in which this new axoplasm is formed has been investigated by

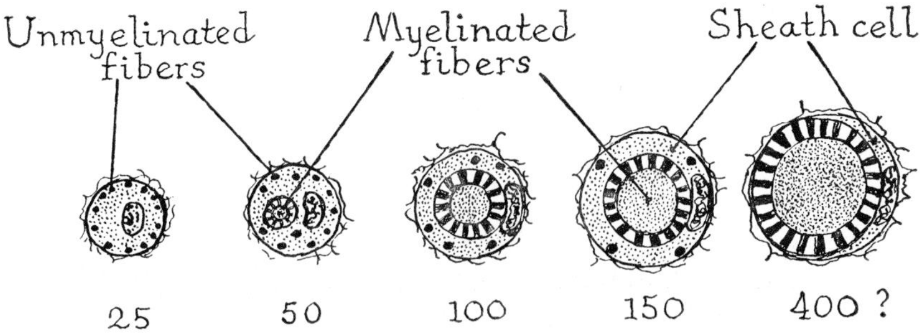

FIG. 112. Diagram showing progress of regeneration within a neurilemma tube of a rabbit's nerve distal to a good suture, with approximate number of days for the various stages. 25 days, many fibers at edge of tube; 50 days, one or two have enlarged and are surrounded by Schwann protoplasm; 100 days, one myelinated fiber in center of tube, others still at periphery. Time of final disappearance of excess fibers and attainment of normal diameter uncertain. (Young.)

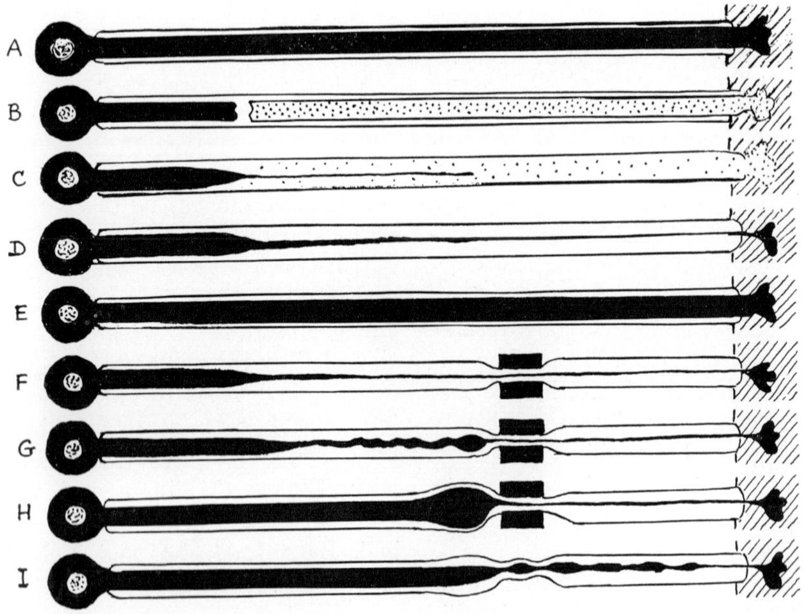

FIG. 113. Diagram of stages of nerve regeneration without and with constriction. A, normal fiber; B-E, ordinary regeneration after simple crushing; F-H, regeneration after constriction; I, after release of constriction. (Weiss and Hiscoe.)

Weiss and Hiscoe (1948) in a series of ingenious experiments. They fashioned small arterial rings which, when distended, could be slipped over the end of a cut nerve and placed in the desired position. The subsequent contraction of these rings produced localized constrictions with consequent reduction in the diameter of the individual fiber tubes (Fig. 113 F–H). The reduction in the lumen of the tube does not at first interfere with the advance of the slender regenerating axon which passes through the constricted zone and makes contact with the periphery. "But when the fiber, as it continues to enlarge, attains the dimensions of the constricted zone, a remarkable difference appears between those parts lying at the distal and at the proximal sides of the narrow neck. The distal segment ceases to grow and remains permanently under-

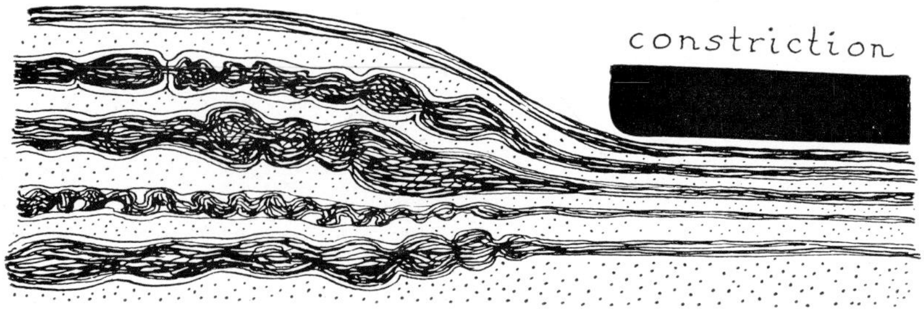

FIG. 114. Composite diagram of principal fiber deformations ("damming") proximal to a constriction. (Weiss and Hiscoe.)

sized, while the proximal segment not only continues to enlarge, but near the entrance of the constricted zone, enlarges excessively.... One gets the impression that a column of axoplasm is pressing distad and becomes dammed up where its channel narrows" (Figs. 113H, 114). The damming increases in intensity with time, and varies with the amount of constriction and the size of the fiber. Morphologically it is expressed in several ways, such as ballooning, beading, telescoping, and coiling of the fibers (Fig. 114). On release of the constriction, some of the dammed axoplasm flows into the distal portion which consequently increases in thickness (Fig. 113 I). The authors conclude that the formation of new axoplasm, i.e., growth in volume, occurs only in the cell body, and that this axoplasm is maintained in constant proximodistal motion, causing the elongation and enlargement of the regenerating fiber.

A knowledge of the mode of nerve regeneration is important as a basis for intelligent surgical treatment. Thus in human trauma it is desirable to approximate the severed ends of the nerve or, if some time has elapsed since the injury, to remove the scar tissue which forms an obstacle to the passage of the growing axons to the band fibers and thence to their destination. Further details concerning the regenerative processes following injury of peripheral nerves are given on page 180.

Regeneration within the central nervous system of mammals has been restudied in recent years using both anatomic and physiologic technics (Sugar and Gerard, 1940; Brown and McCouch, 1947; Windle and Chambers, 1950; Scott and Clemente, 1952; Freeman, 1952; Campbell, Bassett, Husby, and Noback, 1957, 1958). Such studies indicate that the central axons of injured nerve cells do make abortive attempts to regenerate across an experimental gap in the spinal cord. Factors that influence and often hamper central regeneration are similar to those influencing regeneration in the peripheral nervous system, (e.g., length of gap between severed stumps; hemorrhage; scar formation by ingrowth of connective tissue, etc.). Central regeneration is further thwarted by the absence of sheath cells and neurilemmal tubes to guide the regenerating axonal sprouts. Recent investigators used a nontoxic nylon tube impregnated with cellulose (Millipore) to bridge gaps of 1 cm. in the spinal cord of the cat (Campbell, Bassett, Husby, and Noback, 1958). This material provided a scaffold for the regenerating nerve fibers, and also minimized the ingrowth of connective tissue. They have observed bridging of the gap by nerve fibers as soon as 30 days after complete cord transection. As noted by these authors, "it is probable that both ascending and descending fibers are participating, because the configuration of the proximal and distal regenerating cord are similar". Sugar and Gerard (1940) found evidence of functional regeneration in adult rats whose thoracic cords had been transected with care to prevent injury to the blood supply. No return of function has been noted in the higher mammals following complete transection of the spinal cord. However, Scott and Clemente (1952) have presented electrophysiological evidence of partial regeneration in severed spinal cords with gaps of less than 1 mm. (cat). For a more complete discussion on regeneration in the central nervous system the reader is referred to Windle (1955).

The importance of secondary degeneration from the standpoint of anatomy lies in the fact that by using appropriate methods one is enabled to trace the connections between cells and nerve fibers throughout the nervous system. The Weigert method and osmic acid, which stain normal myelin, will bring out the fragmentation of the myelin sheath. On the other hand the Marchi method (osmic staining after treatment with bichromate) will bring out the intermediate products of myelin disintegration and leave the normal myelin practically unstained. By this method, if used at the proper stage of degeneration (about one to three weeks after injury), even scattered degenerating nerve fibers can be traced throughout their whole length as black granules easily distinguished from the normal fibers (Fig. 188). In later stages when the myelin has completely disappeared, the Weigert method for normal myelin is again helpful. This, of course, only gives a negative picture, the degenerated fibers being indicated by unstained areas (Fig. 186). Only bundles of fibers, not isolated ones, can be thus distinguished. By means of the Nauta technic (Nauta and Gygax, 1951, 1953) one can trace the course and terminations of isolated and small numbers of nerve fibers soon after their injury. In such preparations the injured nerve fibers are beaded and fragmented, and stain more intensely than adjacent normal nerve fibers. Finally, to ascertain the cell bodies to which the cut fibers belong, the Nissl method is usually employed and the abnormal cells distinguished by the characteristic changes described above. The Luxol Fast Blue-Cresyl Fast Violet staining technic (Kluver and Berrera, 1953) is a valuable method in such studies for it permits one to examine normal myelinated fibers and the Nissl material of nerve cells simultaneously.

The neuron doctrine. The various facts regarding the individuality of the neuron were formulated by Waldeyer in 1891 into the *neuron doctrine*. Briefly summarized, this states that the neuron is the *genetic* and *anatomical* unit of the nervous system. The neuron including all its processes constitutes an anatomical entity related to other neurons by contact only, each derived from a single embryonic cell.

The neuron is likewise the *trophic* unit. The nucleus is the regenerative center of the cell and processes cut off from the cell body completely degenerate. Regeneration may occur by new outgrowth from the nucleated portion.

Finally, the neuron is the *"functional"* unit of the nervous system and is the only element which conducts nerve impulses. All the neural circuits are composed of chains of such units.

7

Neuroglia, the Interstitial Tissue of the Nervous System

As already stated, the intersitial supportive framework of the brain and spinal cord is formed by a special tissue, the *neuroglia* or *glia,* composed of cells, fibers and a homogeneous intercellular substance. The structural features of this tissue are difficult to demonstrate except by selective and often complicated staining methods. In ordinary preparations with basophil dyes as a rule only the nuclei are seen (Fig. 120). Our knowledge concerning the structure and function of neuroglia has been greatly increased by the investigations of Cajal, Achucarro, Del Rio-Hortega, Penfield, and others.

Neuroglia in the broadest sense may be divided into the following types: (1) *astroglia* or *macroglia,* whose cells are known as *astrocytes;* (2) *oligodendroglia;* (3) *microglia* or *mesoglia;* (4) *ependyma.* To these should be added, for the peripheral nervous system, the *neurilemma cells* of the nerve fibers and at least the inner *capsule cells* surrounding the neuron bodies of the spinal and cranial ganglia. The neurilemma and capsule cells differentiate from cells which have migrated from the neural plate and hence represent a sort of peripheral neuroglia, although that term is usually not applied to them. According to Penfield, they most closely resemble the oligodendroglia of the central nervous system. With the exception of microglia, all of the above types are derived from the neural ectoderm.

(1) **Astroglia.** The **astrocytes** or neuroglia cells proper are branched stellate cells whose cytoplasm contains small rounded or ovoid granules, the *gliosomes* (Figs. 115, 116). The nucleus is irregularly ovoid and pale staining, with scant amounts of chromatin and no nucleolus. Centrosome, reticular apparatus, and usually a small amount of lipochrome pigment are found in the granular cytoplasm. Two types of astrocytes may be distinguished, *protoplasmic* and *fibrous.* The former, also known as mossy cells, have numerous freely branching processes and are destitute of fibers. They are found principally in the gray matter of the spinal cord and brain, where they often partly envelop the neuron bodies and thus constitute one of the varieties of perineuronal *satellite cells.*

The fibrous astrocytes or spider cells are characterized by thin unbranched fiber-like processes which radiate from the cell in all directions and extend for a considerable distance (Figs. 116, 118). With adequate staining it can be seen that these processes are composed of delicate fibers which extend through the cell body, coursing mainly in the peripheral cytoplasm. Whether these fibers actually leave the cell and become intercellular structures, as is the case in connective tissue, is still a somewhat open question. There appears to be considerable evidence that normally the neuroglia fibers no matter how long, are surrounded by a thin film of cytoplasm. Fibrous astrocytes are found mainly in the white matter.

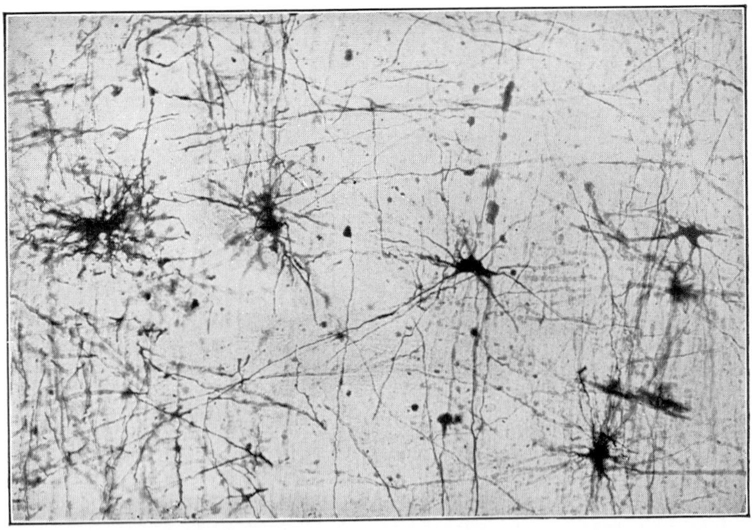

FIG. 115. Several fibrous astrocytes in the white matter of the spinal cord. The one to the left appears to be transitional to the protoplasmic form. A number of unbranched neuroglia fibers are seen coursing through the field. Golgi silver method. Photograph.

Cajal and others have described a mixed type of astrocyte which contains both protoplasmic and fibrous processes.

In both the protoplasmic and fibrous astrocytes, one or more of the processes have peculiar terminal expansions, the *foot plates* or *perivascular feet,* which are anchored to the outer walls of the blood vessels lying within the central nervous system (Figs. 116, 117). According to some, these foot plates form a continuous glial membrane around the blood vessels, the *perivascular limiting membrane.* Another glial membrane, the external glial limiting membrane, is found directly underneath the pia by a condensation of neuroglia, formed in part at least by foot plates of fibrous astrocytes anchored to the inner pial surface. These glial membranes are thus everywhere interposed between the true nervous tissue and the mesodermal coverings and blood vessels.

(2) **Oligodendroglia** consists of somewhat smaller cells with rather few and exceedingly slender processes which never form foot plates (Figs. 116, 121). The spherical nucleus is more darkly staining than that of an astrocyte, the cytoplasm contains gliosomes but no fibers. In the white matter, they are often seen lying in rows between the myelinated fibers (interfascicular glia), their delicate processes wrapping around the myelin sheath. In the gray matter, they may lie closely apposed to neuron bodies as *perineuronal satellite* cells, while in both gray and white matter some of them have their cell bodies closely applied to the walls of capillaries as *perivascular satellites.*

The function of oligodendroglia cells is probably metabolic rather than supportive. It has been suggested (Penfield) that they regulate the formation of myelin and hence correspond most closely to the neurilemma cells of peripheral nerves. Similar to the latter, they also seem to be concerned with the breaking down of the axon and myelin and the elimination of debris in secondary degeneration of nerve fibers in the central nervous system. In the same way, the perineuronal satellites may be compared to the inner capsule cells of the spinal ganglia. It is probable that in certain pathological conditions these satellites play a part in the

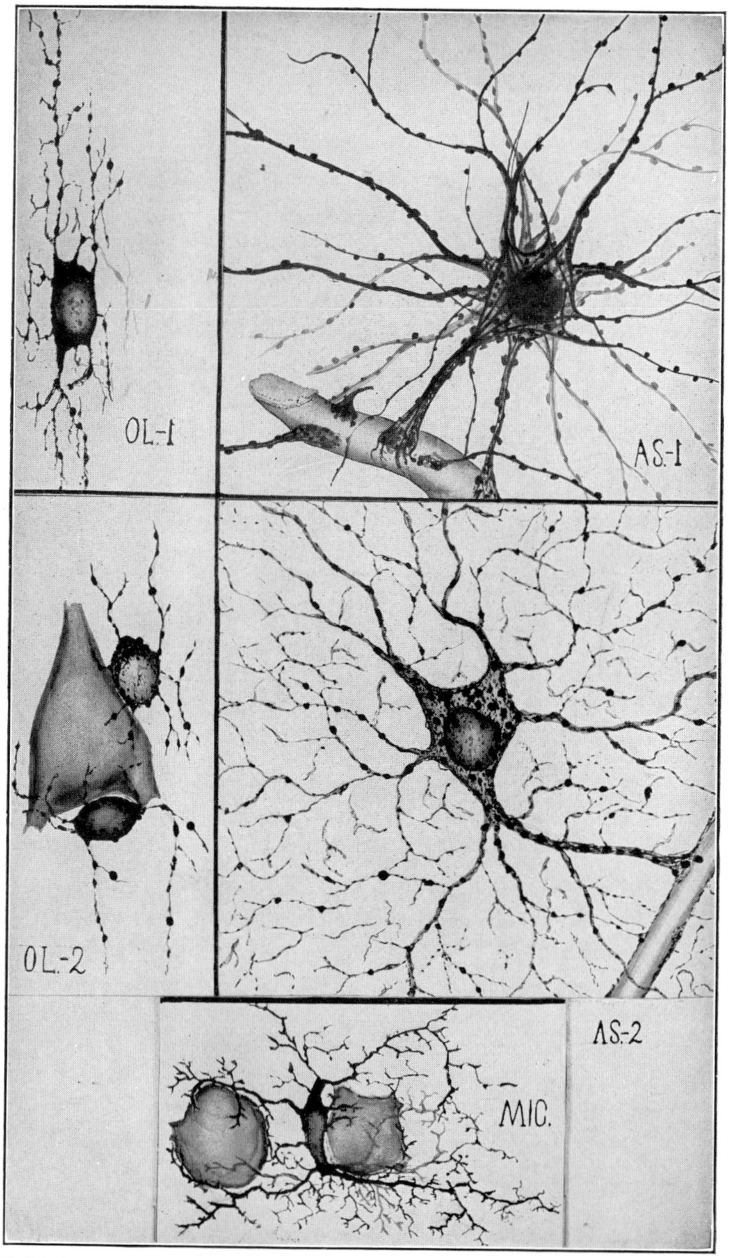

FIG. 116. Various types of neuroglia cells. *AS-1,* fibrous astrocyte with one or two processes forming foot plates against a neighboring blood vessel; *AS-2,* protoplasmic astrocyte with foot plate, and containing gliosomes (dark granules) in its body and processes; *MIC,* microglia cell whose delicate spiny processes embrace the bodies of two neurons; *OL-1,* oligodendroglia cell in the white matter (interfascicular form); *OL-2,* two oligodendroglia cells lying against a nerve cell (perineuronal satellites). (Penfield.)

eroding and even complete removal of weakened nerve cells, a process known as *neuronophagia.*

(3) **Microglia.** The microglia cells, unlike the other types of neuroglia, are of mesodermal origin and appear to enter the nervous system not long before birth. They are apparently fibroblasts or histoblasts

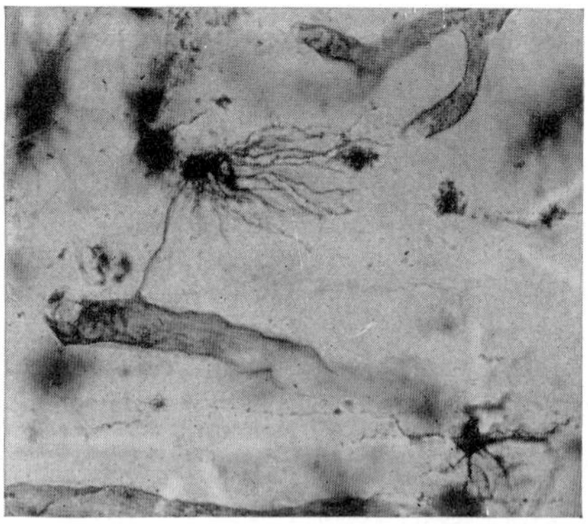

FIG. 117. Astrocyte with process adhering to wall of blood vessel. Golgi silver stain. Photograph.

are often closely apposed to neuron bodies as perineuronal satellites or to the walls of blood vessels as perivascular satellites.

In normal conditions the function of microglia is obscure, but in trauma or other destructive lesions of the nervous system they undergo striking changes. The protoplasm swells and becomes granular and the small cells are transformed into large actively phagocytic scavenger cells which exhibit ameboid movement. In certain pathological conditions (glioma), they may devour the processes of the giant astrocytes present in such cases (Penfield). On ac-

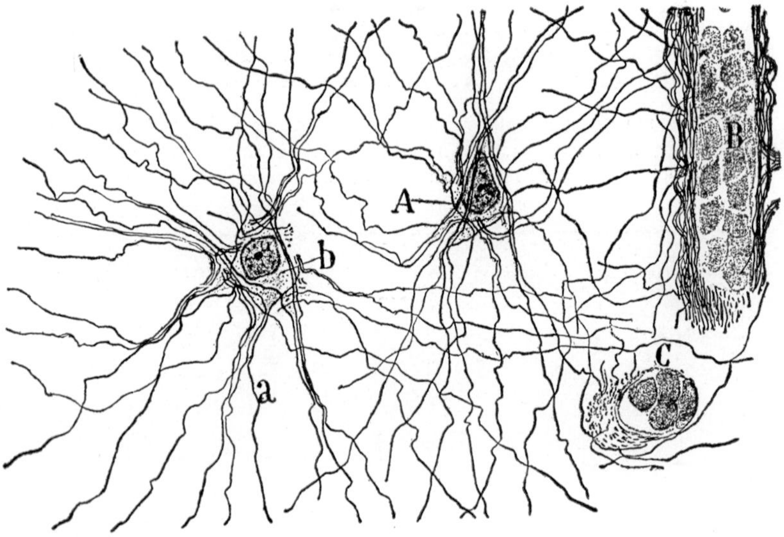

FIG. 118. Fibrous astrocytes from white matter of the human cerebellum. Weigert's neuroglia stain. *A*, cell body; *B, C*, blood vessels; *a*, neuroglia fibers; *b*, cytoplasm of neuroglia cell. (Cajal.)

which have migrated from the pia and it is possible that some arise by detachment of similar cells from the adventitial connective tissue of the neural blood vessels. The cells are very small with scanty cytoplasm and several delicate tortuous processes which bear small spines (Figs. 116, 121). Occasionally only two processes may be present. The deeply staining nucleus is irregularly elongated triangular or kidney-shaped, the cytoplasm devoid of gliosomes and fibers. Microglia cells are found in both gray and white matter. They have no foot plates but

count of its origin and behavior in pathological conditions, microglia is considered by many as part of the reticulo-endothelial system. (See texts of histology).

(4) **Ependyma.** The ependyma lines the central canal of the spinal cord and the ventricles of the brain, and in ordinary preparations has the appearance of a simple columnar epithelium (Fig. 167). With adequate staining methods the cytoplasm is seen to contain neuroglia fibers which are continued into the slender process projecting from the base of each cell (Fig. 122). In

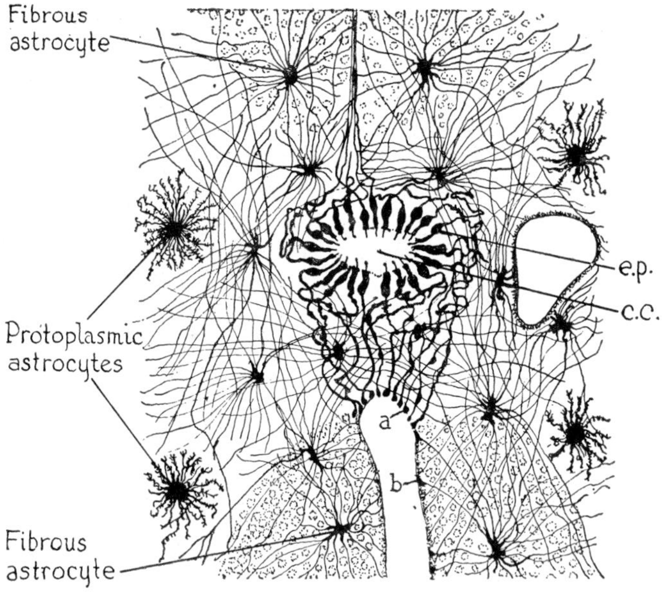

FIG. 119. Ependyma and neuroglia in the central portion of the spinal cord of an infant eight days old. Golgi impregnation. *a,* terminal foot plate of ependyma cell; *b,* terminal foot plate of fibrous astrocyte; *c.c.,* central canal; *e.p.,* ependyma cell. (After Cajal.)

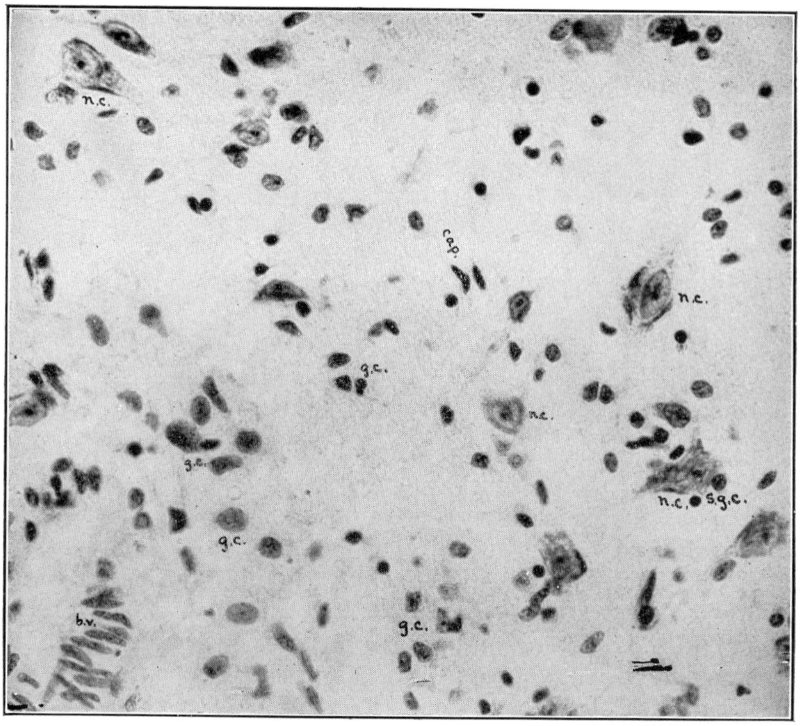

FIG. 120 Portion of intermediate gray of infant's spinal cord. Nissl stain. Photograph. *bv,* blood vessel with nuclei of circular smooth muscle coat; *cap,* capillary with two endothelial nuclei; *gc,* nuclei of neuroglia cells. The larger pale nuclei belong to astrocytes, the darker smaller round nuclei to oligodendroglia, and the darkest, smallest, round or elongated nuclei to microglia. *nc,* small and medium sized nerve cells showing Nissl bodies.

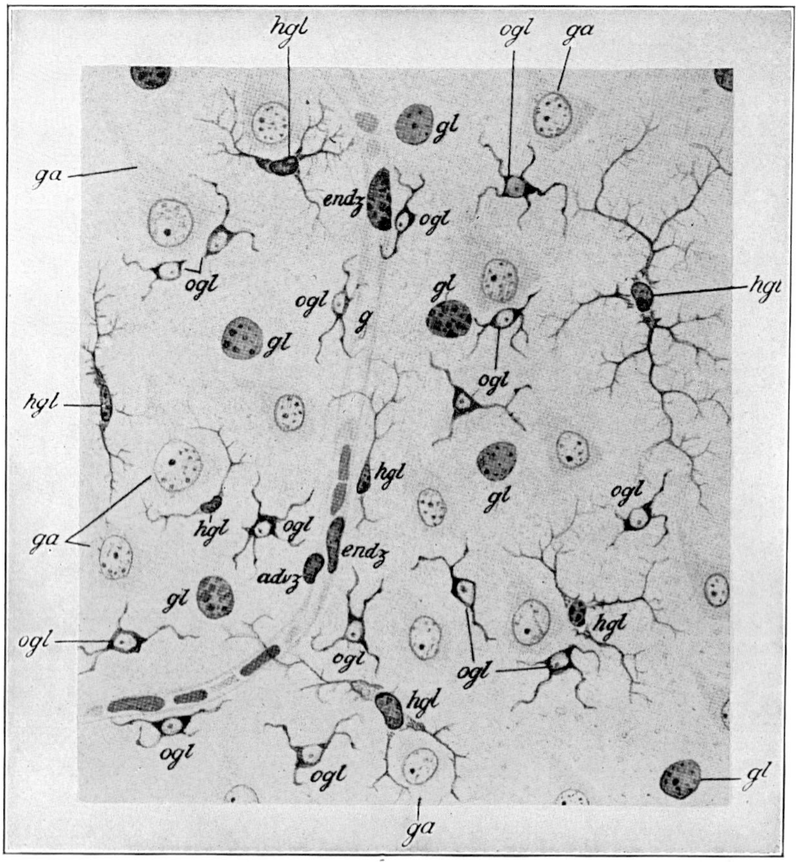

FIG. 121. Various types of neuroglia cells in human cerebral cortex. Hortega silver stain. *advz*, adventitial cell; *endz*, endothelial cell; *g*, capillary; *ga*, nerve cell; *gl*, nuclei of protoplasmic astrocytes; *hgl*, microglia; *ogl*, oligodendroglia. (Jakob.)

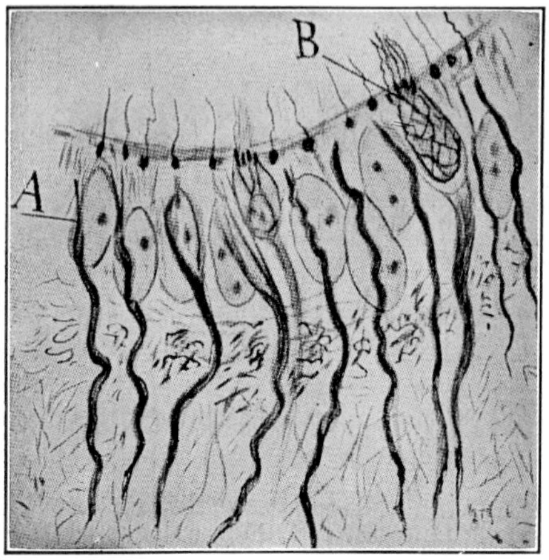

FIG. 122. Ependymal cells in spinal cord of a one and one-half months old cat. *A*, uniflagellate ependyma cell; *B*, pluriflagellate ependyma cell. (Cajal.)

embryonic life these processes traverse the whole thickness of the neural wall to become attached to the pia by terminal expansions or end feet, and this condition is still seen in the adult in places where the neural wall is relatively thin, as in the ventral floor plate of the spinal cord (Fig. 119). In the thick-walled portions the ependymal fibers usually end within a short distance from the cell body. In certain forms and in certain places at least, cilia or flagellae protrude from the free surface of the ependymal cells into the neural cavity (Fig. 122), and may perhaps assist in the circulation of the cerebrospinal fluid. In man such cilia are only observed in embryological stages and appear to be absent in the adult. Ependyma may be regarded as composed of neuroglia

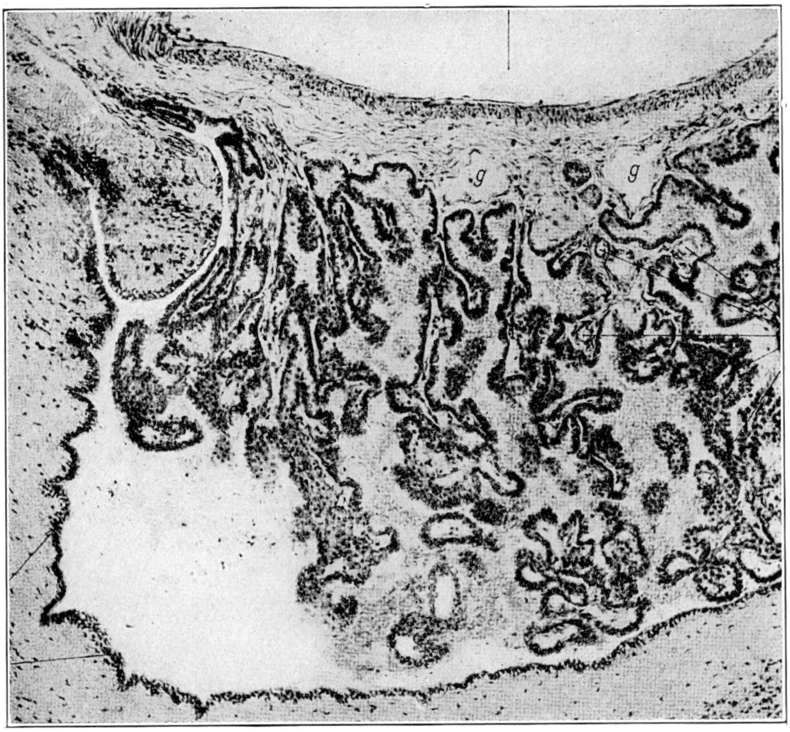

FIG. 123. Normal human chorioid plexus. Nissl stain. Photograph. *g*, blood vessel. (Jakob.)

cells which have retained their embryonic shape and position.

In certain places the wall of the brain is exceedingly thin and is composed solely of a simple epithelial membrane of modified ependyma cells, the *epithelial chorioid lamina.* The cells are cubical in shape, contain cytoplasmic granules, and are believed to be concerned with the production of the cerebrospinal fluid, though the mode of such production is not entirely clear. This epithelial lamina is thrown into complicated folds and invested externally by highly vascularized pial connective tissue, the two together constituting the telae chorioideae and chorioid plexuses of the fourth, third, and lateral ventricles (Fig. 123).

An analogous structure is the pars ciliaris retinae of the eye, where part of the neural wall is likewise composed of a single layer of cubical epithelial cells. Here too a similar function probably exists in the formation of the fluids filling the eye cavity.

8

Histogenesis of the Neural Elements and their Segmental Distribution

The neural plate originally consists of a simple layer of columnar epithelium. As the plate is closing, the epithelium thickens and assumes a stratified appearance. The cell outlines become indistinct and disappear and the nuclei assume positions in varying depths of the wall, except for a narrow outer zone, the marginal layer, which contains no nuclei (Fig. 124). Near the central canal, mitotic figures are present, the ovoid or rounded dividing cells being known as *germinal cells*. The protoplasm between the nuclei becomes alveolar, giving the appearance of a reticulum of anastomosing protoplasmic trabeculae. The trabeculae unite along the inner and outer surface of the wall to form the internal and external limiting membranes. By rapid proliferation of the germinal cells, more and more nuclei become displaced toward the periphery, increasing the depth of the *nuclear* or *ependymal layer* which, however, is always separated from the external limiting membrane by the *marginal* non-nucleated zone (Fig. 124).

By means of the Golgi and other silver methods, two kinds of cells may be demonstrated in these early developmental stages: *spongioblasts* and *germinal cells*. The former are spindle-shaped bipolar cells which extend through the whole thickness of the wall, their nuclei placed close to the lumen, their processes attached to the internal and external limiting membranes (Fig. 125). Many of these soon lose their connection with the central canal and withdraw to deeper portions of the wall as unipolar spongioblasts which later develop numerous processes and are ultimately transformed into neuroglia cells, probably protoplasmic and fibrous astrocytes (Figs. 125, 131). Others retain their original position and become ependyma cells, their peripheral processes as a rule losing their connection with the external limiting membrane and extending only a short distance from the cell body. In the thin-walled portion of the fourth, third, and lateral ventricles, the ependyma cells are modified into cubical granular cells, the chorioidal epithelial cells, which form the inner lining of the chorioid plexuses (Figs. 123, 131). The microglia alone is not formed from the medullary ectoderm but from connective tissue which later invades the neural tube.

Differentiation of neurons. Many of the germinal cells or medulloblasts begin to increase in size and a neurofibrillar zone appears in the cytoplasm on the side away from the central canal. This is the apolar stage of the neuroblast. The cell migrates away from the lumen to which it often remains attached by a process and at the same time sends out a neurofibrillar process, the axon, toward the periphery (Fig. 126). This bipolar stage lasts only a short time, the central process disappearing and the cell becoming a unipolar neuroblast. Somewhat later, dendritic processes grow out from the cytoplasm and the neuroblast assumes the multipolar shape characteristic of the adult neuron. While these changes

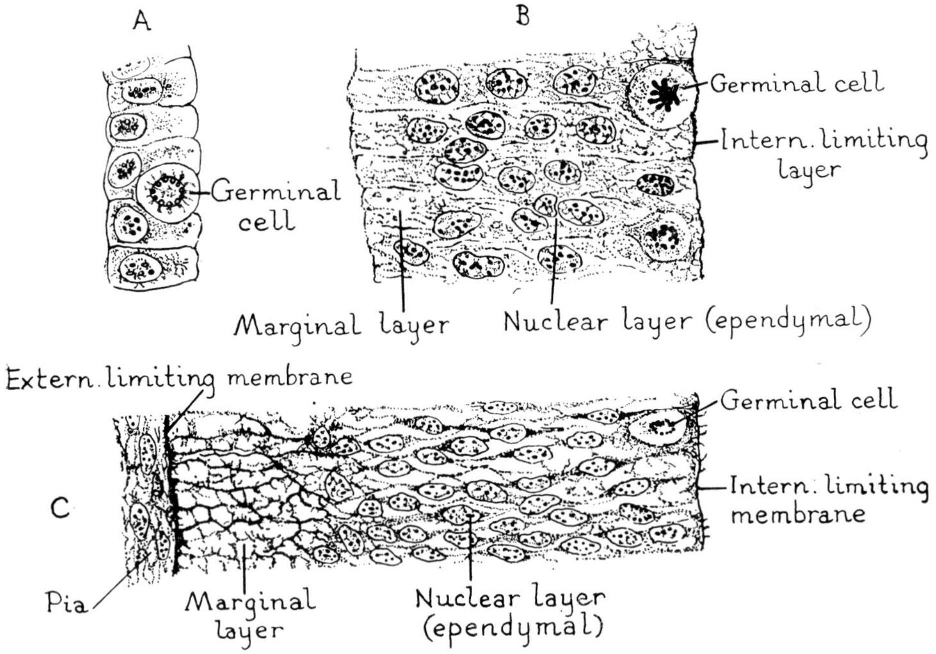

FIG. 124. Three stages in the histogenesis of the neural tube. *A*, from rabbit embryo before closure of tube. (After His.) *B*, from 5 mm., and *C*, from 10 mm. pig embryos. (After Hardesty.)

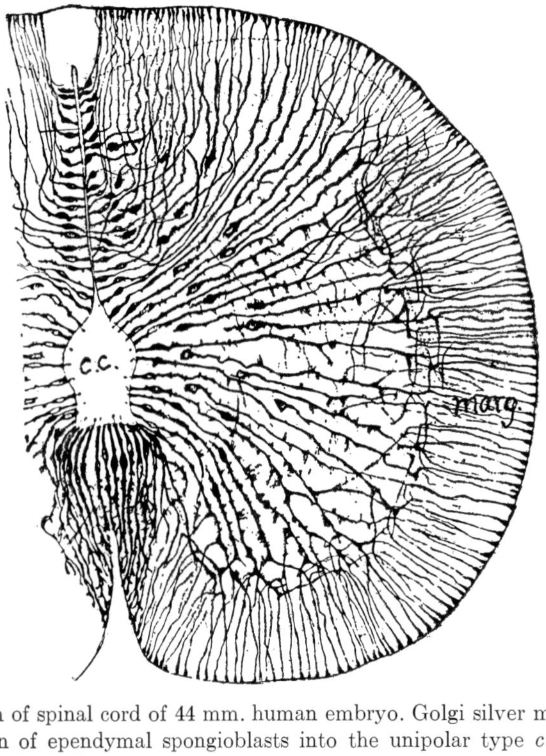

FIG. 125. Section of spinal cord of 44 mm. human embryo. Golgi silver method. Migration and transformation of ependymal spongioblasts into the unipolar type *c.c.*, central canal; *marg.* marginal layer. (Cajal.)

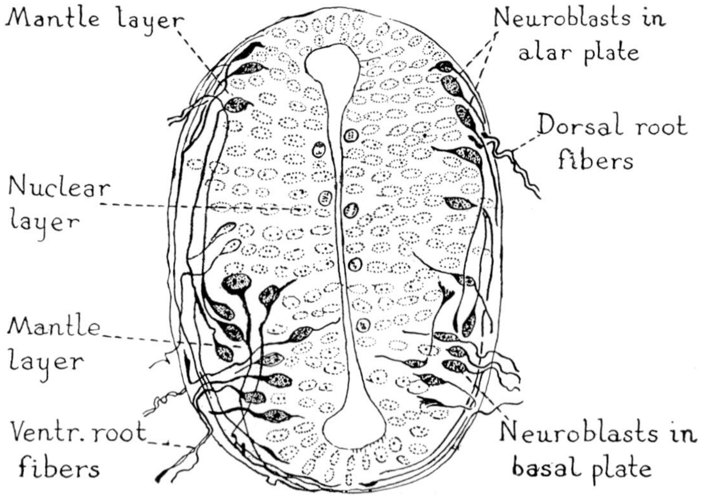

FIG. 126. Section through spinal cord of 56 hour chick embryo. (After Cajal.)

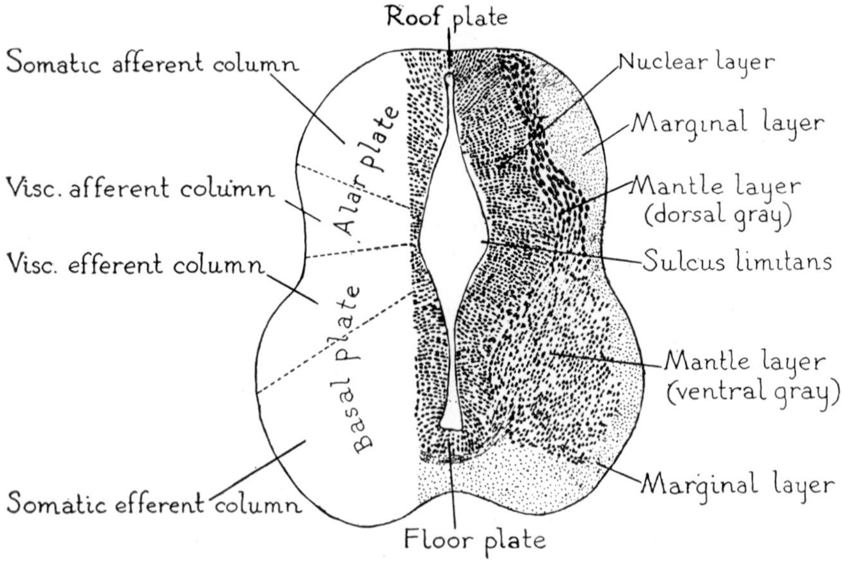

FIG. 127. Section through spinal cord of a 7 mm. human embryo. (Modified from Fischel.)

occur, the differentiating neuroblasts become displaced peripherally and now form a more or less distinct layer, the *mantle layer*, between the nuclear and marginal layers (Fig. 126).

The mantle layer is not formed uniformly throughout the neural wall. The floor and roof plates remain relatively thin and furnish only spongioblastic elements. But even in the lateral wall the neuroblasts are primarily concentrated in the most dorsal and the most ventral portion, corresponding to the alar and basal plate respectively (Figs. 126, 127). Between these regions the cells are few and scattered. The mantle layer constitutes the future gray of the spinal cord, the alar portion developing into the dorsal horn, the basal into the ventral horn.

The neuroblasts of the basal plates become the *efferent peripheral neurons.* Their axons penetrate the marginal layer and external limiting membrane and leave the cord as ventral root fibers which go directly to striped muscle or to autonomic ganglia for the innervation of visceral structures (Figs. 126, 128, 180). The axons of cells from the alar plate all remain within the central nervous system. Some arch ventrally, cross through the basal plate to the opposite side and reach the marginal layer where they ascend or descend for variable distances. Other axons remain on the same side and likewise ascend or descend in the marginal layer. These cells whose processes are entirely confined to the central nervous system constitute the *central*, or *intermediate* cells. Those whose axons remain on the same side are known as *association* cells, those whose axons cross are *commissural*.

As development proceeds, the proliferation of the germinal cells gradually decreases and ultimately stops altogether. As more and more indifferent cells are transformed into neuroblasts, the nuclear layer progressively diminishes in size and is ultimately reduced to a single layer of columnar ependymal cells. In certain places, as in the ventral commissure of the spinal cord, some of the ependymal cells may retain their embryonal spongioblastic character and extend the whole thickness of the neural wall (Fig. 119).

The mantle layer, on the other hand, progressively increases in size and furnishes the gray matter of the spinal cord, surrounded by a constantly expanding marginal layer which contains the descending and ascending axons of the central cells. At a much later period, most of the axons become myelinated and the marginal layer assumes the whitish, glistening appearance characteristic of the white matter of the cord.

In the spinal ganglia, derived from the neural crest, a similar differentiation takes place. Many of the cells originally polygonal or rounded become spindle-shaped and bipolar by the development of two neurofibrillar processes, a central and a peripheral one (Figs. 80, 128, 129). The central processes enter the spinal cord as dorsal root fibers and there bifurcate into ascending and descending arms which contribute to the formation of the marginal layer (Figs. 128, 130). The peripheral processes continue as

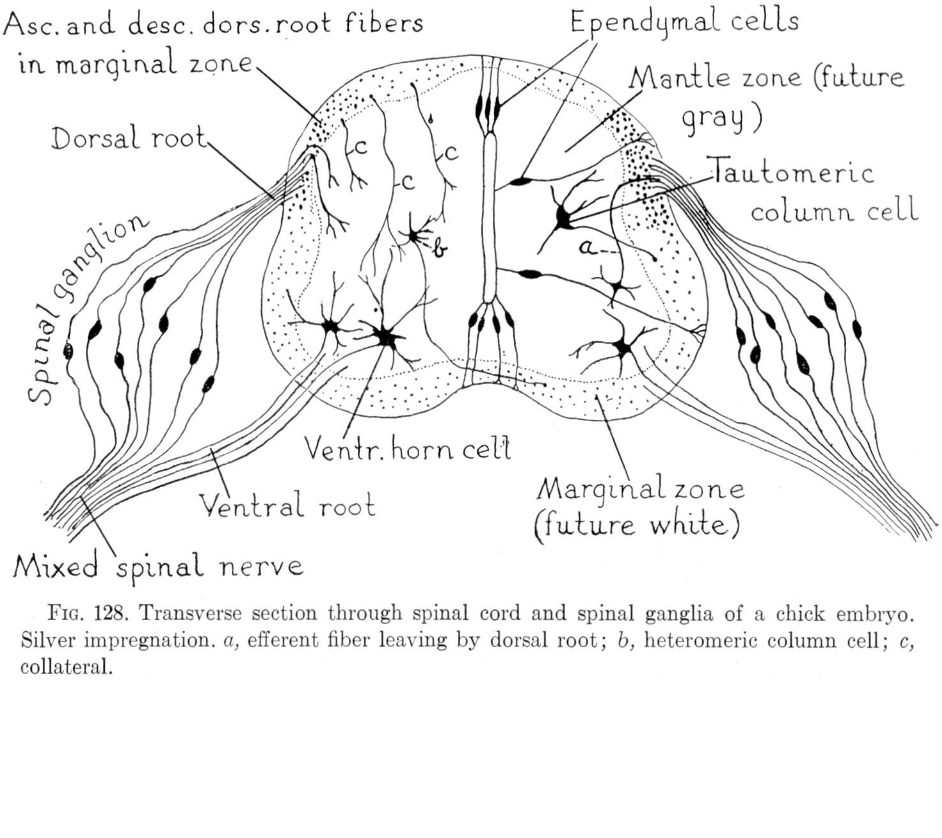

FIG. 128. Transverse section through spinal cord and spinal ganglia of a chick embryo. Silver impregnation. *a,* efferent fiber leaving by dorsal root; *b,* heteromeric column cell; *c,* collateral.

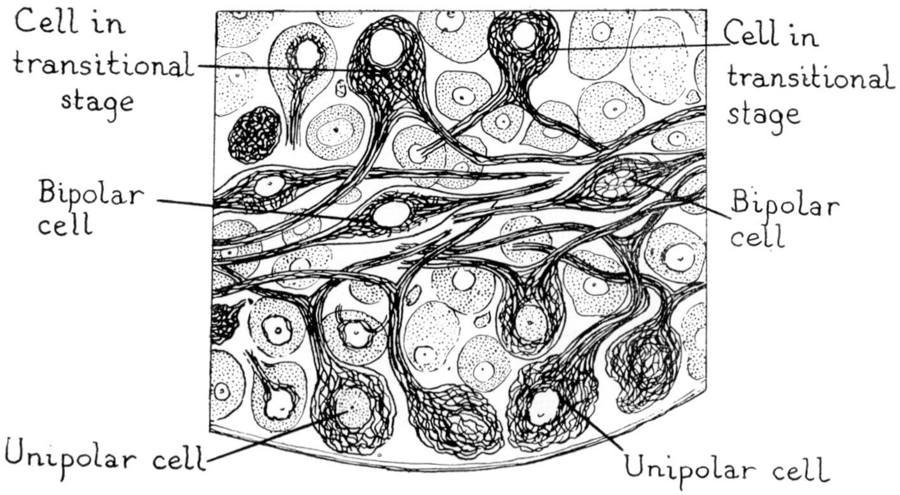

FIG. 129. Section through spinal ganglion of twelve day chick embryo. Reduced silver stain. (After Cajal.)

afferent or sensory fibers to terminate in various receptors of the body. These spinal (or cranial) ganglion cells constitute the *afferent peripheral neurons* (sensory neurons). At first bipolar, the majority of these cells become subsequently unipolar by the fusion of the two original processes, the single process thus formed now dividing into a central and a peripheral arm (Fig. 129).

Not all of the cells in the spinal ganglia differentiate into neuroblasts. Some develop into *capsule cells* or *amphicytes* which form a capsule around the bodies of the spinal ganglion cells. Others wander out along the course of the growing peripheral nerve fibers, envelop the latter and ultimately become neurilemma cells (*lemnocytes*). As already stated, these play some part in the formation of myelin and may be considered as a peripheral type of neuroglia, perhaps most closely related to oligodendroglia (Penfield).

Besides the spinal ganglia there are other peripheral aggregations of nerve cells known as *autonomic* or *sympathetic* ganglia. Arising in part probably from the neural crest, in part migrating from the ventral part of the cord along the ventral roots, these cells form two ganglionic chains on the ventro-

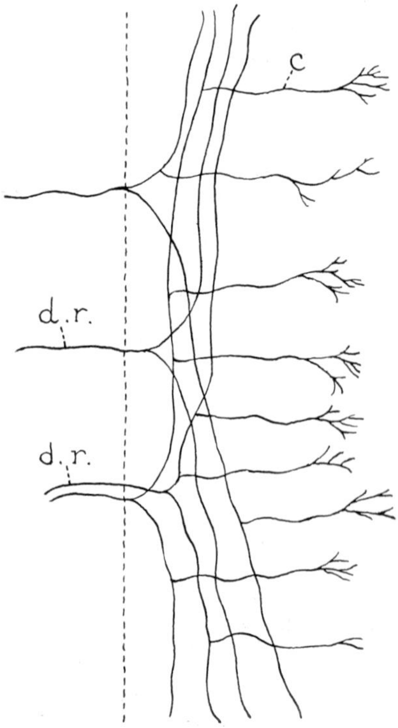

FIG. 130. Dorsal root fibers (*d.r.*) entering cord and bifurcating into ascending and descending arms. *c*, collateral terminating in gray of spinal cord. Eight day chick embryo. Silver impregnation.

lateral aspect of the vertebral column (vertebral sympathetic ganglia). Others wander still further to form the ganglia of the mesenteric plexuses (collateral or prevertebral ganglia), while still others actually invade the walls of the viscera or settle close to them as the terminal or peripheral autonomic ganglia. Here too differentiation occurs along several directions. Some enlarge to form the multipolar sympathetic ganglion cells whose axons terminate in visceral effectors, smooth muscle, heart muscle, and glandular epithelium. Others, as in the case of the spinal ganglia, give rise to amphicytes which envelop the bodies of one or several ganglion cells. Finally, there are some which differentiate into the chromaffin cells found in the adrenal medulla, carotid bodies and other portions of the body.

The origin of the autonomic ganglia is still in dispute. While some believe they are formed from the neural crest (Müller and Ingvar, Detwiler, Hammond), others maintain that the largest part is derived from the ventral part of the spinal cord, the cells migrating by way of the ventral roots (Kuntz). It is probable that in mammals at least, both neural crest and cord contribute to such formation. It has been reasoned that inasmuch as the sympathetic cells are efferent in character their origin would most likely be from the efferent part of the spinal

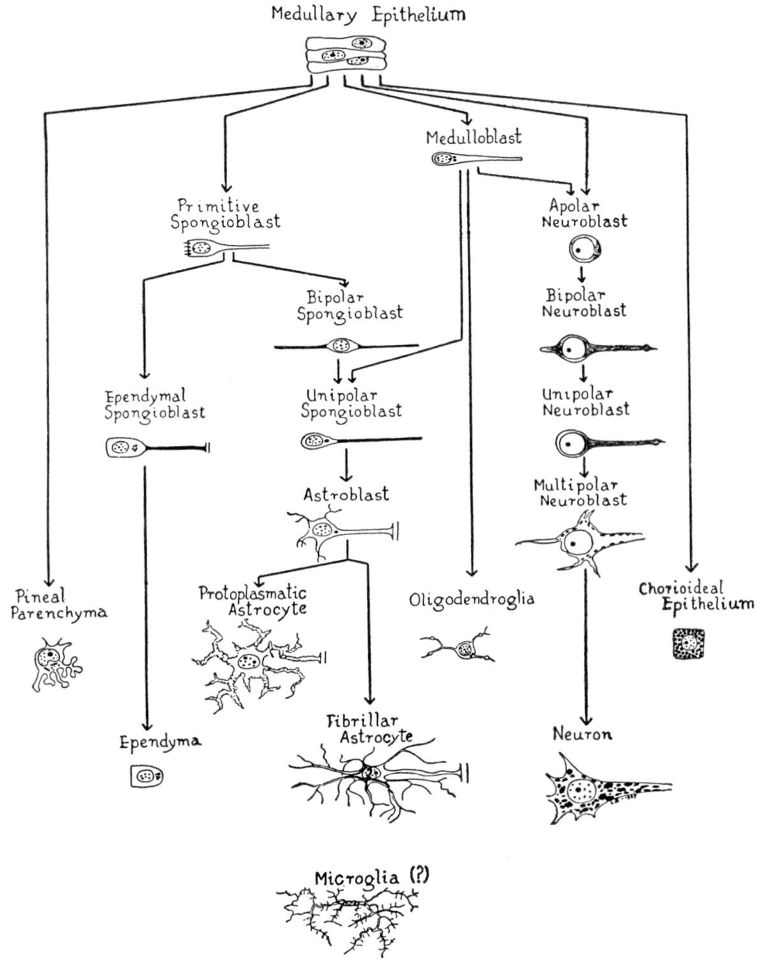

FIG. 131. Schema showing histogenesis of neuroglia cells and neurons. (Bailey and Cushing.)

cord, i.e., the ventral horn. It must be remembered, however, that efferent fibers have been demonstrated in the dorsal roots of many animals, and that some afferent fibers may enter the cord through the ventral roots (Foerster and Gagel).

Segmental arrangement of the peripheral nerve elements. With the differentiation of the various types of nerve cells, there is established in early stages of development a neuronal mechanism adequate for complete, if simple, reflex arcs and consisting of afferent, intermediate, and efferent neurons and their peripheral extensions. However, the synaptic junctions of these cells which would make such an arc functional are as yet unformed.

In embryos of about 10 mm. the various components of the peripheral nervous system are already laid down and may be recognized in a transverse section of any typical body segment (Fig. 132). The central processes of the spinal ganglion cells form the *dorsal* roots, the ventral root is composed of axons from cells in the ventral gray of the spinal cord (mantle layer). Distal to the ganglion, the ventral root unites with the peripheral processes of the ganglion cells to form the mixed *spinal nerve* which now contains afferent and efferent fibers. Each

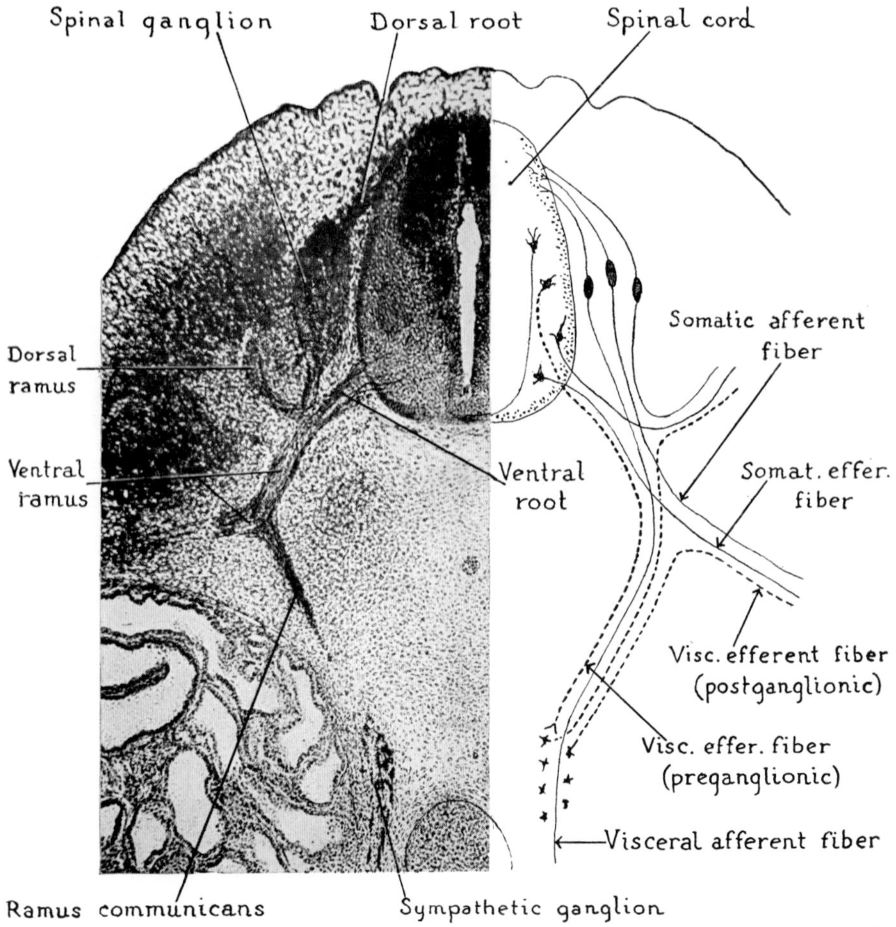

Fig. 132. Transverse section through 14 mm. pig embryo. Bielschowsky's silver stain. Photograph.

spinal nerve divides into a *dorsal* and a *ventral ramus*, and also sends a fiber bundle known as the *ramus communicans* to the vertebral sympathetic chain. The dorsal ramus supplies the muscles and skin of the back, the larger ventral one goes to the ventrolateral parts of the body wall. Four functional types of peripheral nerve fibers may be distinguished: somatic efferent, somatic afferent, visceral efferent, and visceral afferent, all of these types being found in both dorsal and ventral rami. The somatic efferent or "motor" fibers arise from large cells in the ventral gray matter, pass out through the ventral roots and go directly to the striped voluntary muscles of the body wall. The somatic afferent or "sensory" fibers are the peripheral processes of spinal ganglion cells, which terminate as receptors in the skin and deeper portions of the body wall. The central processes enter the cord as dorsal root fibers (Fig. 180).

The efferent innervation of visceral structures is somewhat different from that of the somatic muscles, for two neurons are always involved in the conduction of impulses from the central nervous system to the effector organs (Figs. 132, 180). The *preganglionic visceral efferent* fibers are axons from cells of the spinal cord which pass through the ventral root and ramus communicans to terminate in a vertebral or prevertebral sympathetic ganglion. The axons of sympathetic cells then form the *postganglionic visceral efferent* fibers which course through the ramus communicans in the reverse direction, join the main branches of the spinal nerve and are distributed to the smooth muscle and glandular epithelium of the body wall. In the adult the ramus communicans is seen to consist of a white and a gray portion. The former contains the *myelinated* preganglionic fibers, the latter the *unmyelinated* postganglionic fibers.

Finally, there are the *visceral afferent* fibers which bring in impulses from the thoracic and abdominal viscera. Like the somatic afferent ones, they have their cell bodies in the spinal ganglia and enter the cord through the dorsal root.

9

The Peripheral Nerves and their Ganglia

The spinal cord is connected with the various parts of the body by 31 pairs of segmentally arranged spinal nerves: eight cervical, twelve thoracic, five lumbar, five sacral and usually one coccygeal. The first cervical nerve emerges between the occipital bone and the atlas, the eighth cervical between the seventh cervical and first thoracic vertebrae. Below this each spinal nerve emerges from the intervertebral foramen between its own and the next lower vertebra (Fig. 31).

Each spinal nerve arises from the cord by two roots, a dorsal afferent and a ventral efferent one. The two roots traverse the dural sac, penetrate the dura and reach the intervertebral foramen where the dorsal root swells into the spinal ganglion which contains the cells of origin of the afferent fibers (Figs. 133, 180). Distal to the ganglion, the dorsal and ventral roots unite and emerge from the intervertebral foramen as the *mixed spinal nerve* or *common nerve trunk*, which now contains both afferent and efferent fibers. The dorsal roots are, as a rule, stouter than the ventral ones and vary with the size of their respective ganglia. The only exception is the first cervical nerve whose dorsal root is greatly reduced and often missing altogether.

Each dorsal root is composed of myelinated and unmyelinated fibers which vary in caliber from 2–20 micra. The larger myelinated fibers, 10–20 micra in thickness, are sensory fibers from muscles and tendons and from tactile receptors, while the finer myelinated and the unmyelinated ones are believed to be mainly concerned with the conduction of temperature and pain. Though mainly afferent in character, there is evidence that some efferent fibers from cells of the spinal cord also pass through the dorsal roots (Fig. 128), and join the spinal nerves as vasodilators of the cutaneous blood vessels (Cajal, Kahr and Sheehan, Young and Zuckerman).

The ventral root is composed of large and small myelinated fibers originating from cells in the ventral and lateral horns of the spinal cord. The large ones are somatic motor fibers going to striped muscle. The smaller ones are preganglionic fibers from spinal cord to sympathetic ganglia (Fig. 134). These fibers are found only in the thoracic, and upper lumbar roots. In the cervical and lower lumbar nerves the ventral roots contain only the large somatic fibers. According to Foerster and Gagel (1933), some finely myelinated and unmyelinated *afferent* fibers enter the cord through the ventral roots. They are in part processes of spinal ganglion cells and may be concerned with the conduction of painful impulses.

THE SPINAL NERVE

After fusion of the dorsal and ventral roots, the common nerve trunk divides into four branches or rami: dorsal ramus, ventral ramus, meningeal ramus, and ramus communicans (Figs. 133, 132). The dorsal rami supply the muscles and skin of the back, the larger ventral ones innervate the ventrolateral portion of the body wall and

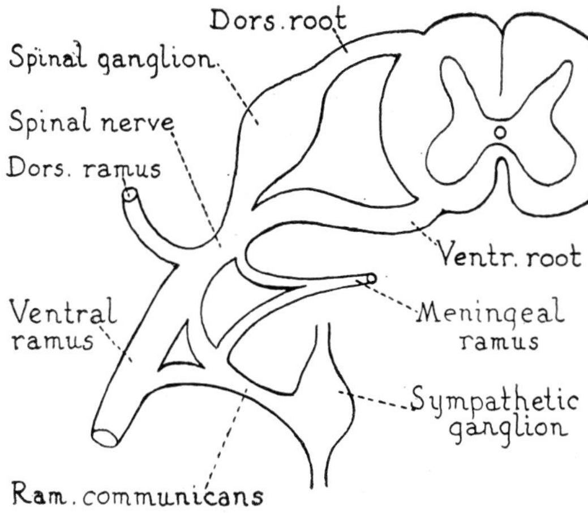

FIG. 133. Diagram of a spinal nerve.

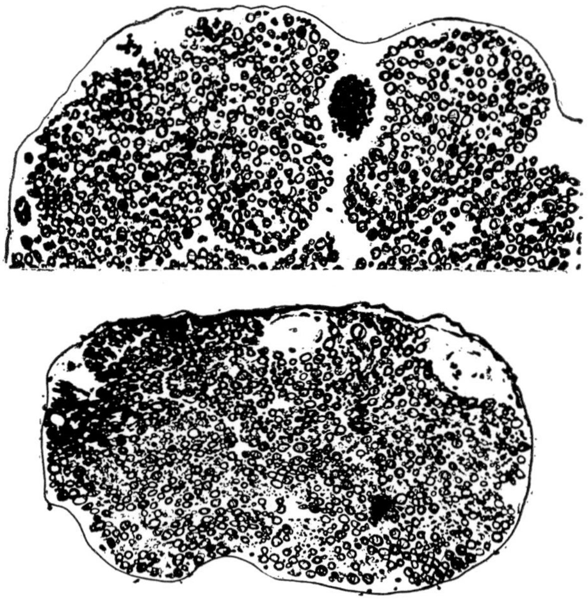

FIG. 134. Sections of lumbar (upper figure) and thoracic ventral rootlets. Weigert's myelin stain. Photograph. Same magnification for both sections. The lumbar root is composed almost entirely of coarse nerve fibers. In the thoracic root, the coarse fibers are somewhat smaller than in the lumbar root and there are in addition numerous fine myelinated preganglionic autonomic fibers. The greater caliber of the coarse fibers of the lumbar root is related to the greater length and larger cell bodies of the somatic motor neurons innervating the muscles of the lower extremity as compared with those innervating the muscles of the trunk.

all the extremities. The ramus communicans connects the common spinal trunk with the sympathetic ganglia and consists of a white and a gray portion. The former contains the myelinated preganglionic fibers from cord to sympathetic ganglion, the latter the unmyelinated postganglionic fibers which join the dorsal and ventral rami to be distributed to the body wall. In the white rami are also afferent fibers from the viscera whose cell bodies are situated in the spinal ganglia (Fig. 180).

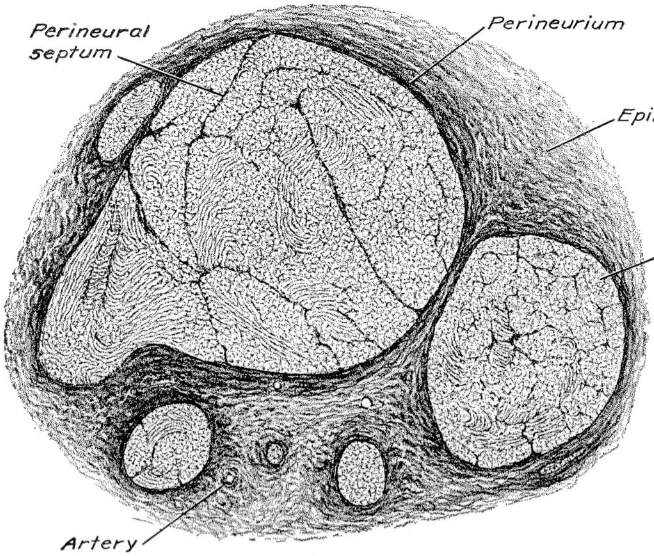

FIG. 135. Cross section of sciatic nerve of monkey. (Bailey's Histology.)

The meningeal branch is a small nerve trunk which usually arises by several twigs from both the common trunk and the ramus communicans (Fig. 133). It reenters the intervertebral foramen to supply the meninges and vertebral column.

The dorsal and ventral rami divide into superficial (cutaneous) and deep (muscular) peripheral nerves. These nerve trunks branch repeatedly and become progressively smaller as they extend toward the periphery, ultimately breaking up into individual nerve fibers which terminate in their respective receptors or effectors. The cutaneous nerves are composed mainly of sensory fibers of various size, but also contain efferent vasomotor, pilomotor, and secretory fibers for the blood vessels, hair, and glands of the skin. In the nerves to muscle there is a greater mixture of sensory and motor fibers. There are somatic motor for the striped muscle fibers, vasomotor for the blood vessels, and numerous afferent fibers from the receptors in muscle, tendon, and bone. Thus in each peripheral nerve there are fibers of various categories, myelinated and unmyelinated, large and small, sensory and motor, which can not be morphologically distinguished from each other (Figs. 136, 137).

While each spinal nerve in a general way supplies its own body segment, there is considerable intermixture and "anastomosis" of adjacent nerve trunks. The dorsal rami remain relatively distinct, though even here interconnections between rami of adjacent segments are common in the cervical and sacral regions. The ventral rami, however, form more extensive connections. With the exception of the thoracic nerves which retain their segmental distribution, the cervical and lumbosacral ventral rami branch and anastomose to form the cervical, brachial, and lumbosacral plexuses. In these plexuses a regrouping of fibers occurs, and each of the peripheral nerves which arise from them now contains contributions from two or three or even four ventral rami. The peripheral nerves are therefore "mixed" in a double sense, consisting not only of afferent and efferent fibers, but also of fibers which come from several segments of the spinal cord.

Morphologically each peripheral nerve consists of parallel running nerve fibers invested by a thick sheath of rather loose

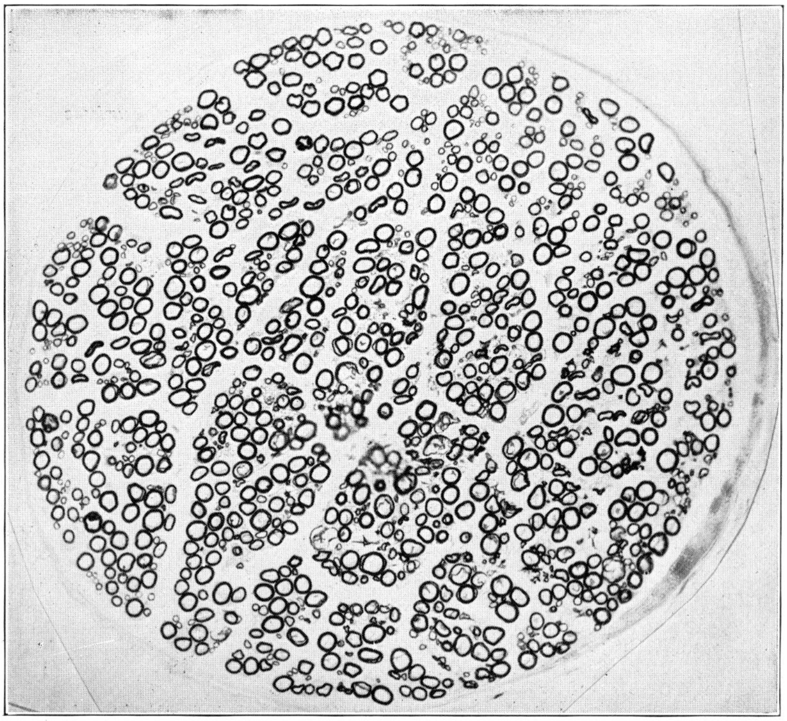

FIG. 136. Transverse section of a fasciculus from the sciatic nerve of a cat. Osmic acid. From a preparation of S. W. Ranson. Large and small myelinated fibers are shown.

connective tissue, the *epineurium* (Fig. 135). From this sheath septa extend into the interior and divide the fibers into bundles or *fascicles* of varying size, each of which is surrounded by a fairly distinct perifascicular sheath or *perineurium*. These fascicles do not run like isolated cables but may split at acute angles and connect with adjacent fascicles for an interchange of fibers. As a result, the fascicular arrangement varies in different portions of the nerve.

From the perineurium delicate strands invade the bundle as intrafascicular connective tissue or *endoneurium*. This separates the fibers into smaller and smaller bundles and ultimately invests each fiber as a delicate tubular membrane, the *sheath of Henle*. In the epineurial and perineurial connective tissue are blood vessels and spaces lined with endothelium which communicate with lymph channels within the fascicle.

On emerging from the spinal cord, the dorsal and ventral roots receive an investment of connective tissue as they pass through the pia. This is reinforced by additional connective tissue as they pass through the arachnoid and dura, the latter becoming continuous with the epineurium of the spinal nerve.

Functional considerations. Injury to the spinal nerves or their peripheral branches will naturally cause disturbances of sensation and movement. Section of a dorsal root produces a loss of all sensation (anesthesia) and loss of all reflexes (areflexia) initiated by stimulation of the areas supplied by that root. Owing to the overlapping distribution of fibers of adjacent roots, the anesthesia may not be marked unless two or more contiguous roots are cut. The areflexia is not only a loss of the superficial and deep kinetic reflexes but also of the tonic proprioceptive ones, resulting in a diminution of tone (hypotonia) in the muscles

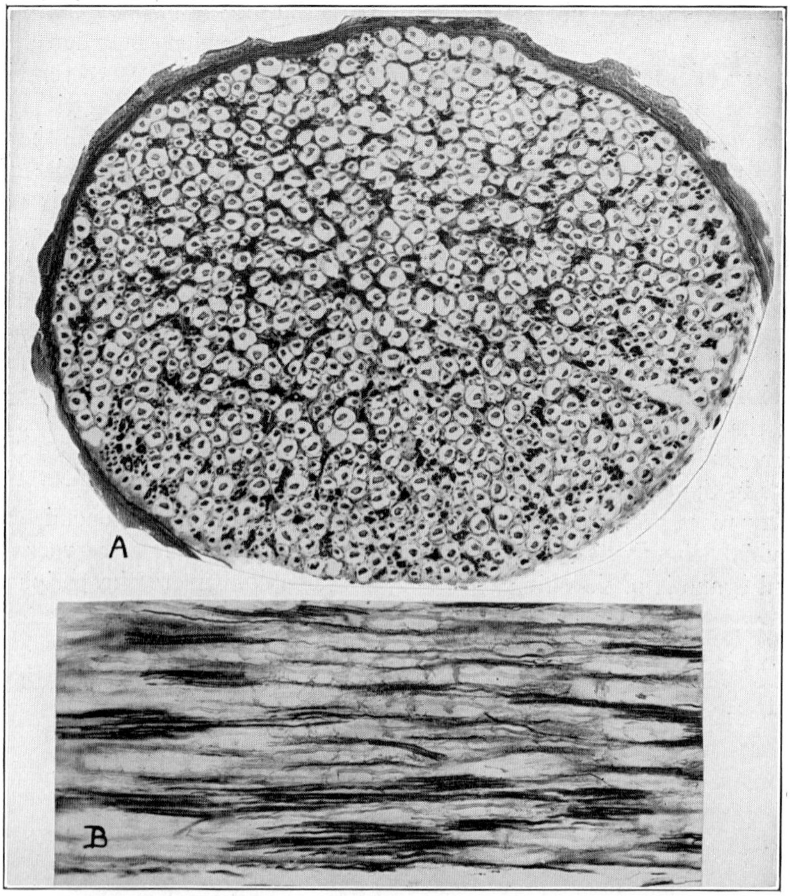

Fig. 137. Transverse (*A*) and longitudinal (*B*) sections of parts of the sciatic nerve of a sympathectomized cat. Ranson's silver pyridin stain. From a preparation by S. W. Ranson. The myelinated fibers appear as brown dots in *A* and bands in *B* surrounded by clear spaces (myelin sheaths). Besides, there are a great number of deeply stained fine unmyelinated fibers not seen in Fig. 136. As the sympathetic ganglia had previously been removed, these are not postganglionic fibers but are peripheral processes of small spinal ganglion cells.

affected. Also, failure of impulses from the muscles to reach the higher cerebellar and cortical centers may result in irregularity or incoordination of movement usually termed *ataxia*.

The various activities of the central nervous system can only take effect by impulses passing through the efferent peripheral neurons, somatic and visceral, whose axons form the ventral roots. These neurons, also known as the *lower motor neurons*, constitute the *final common pathway* (Sherrington).

Destruction of the ventral root produces a complete paralysis of reflex and voluntary movement with loss of tone (flaccidity) and degenerative atrophy of the striped muscle fibers affected. The muscle also shows certain changes in its reaction to electrical stimulation, these changes constituting the *reaction of degeneration* (R D). Healthy muscle responds to stimulation by both the faradic (interrupted) and galvanic (continuous) current. In faradic stimulation the response lasts as long as the stimulus is applied. In galvanic stimulation the response occurs only on closing or opening the circuit, and normally it is the application of the negative pole or cathode which produces the strongest contraction on closing the current. In the complete reaction of degeneration which appears 10–14 days after the injury, the muscle no longer reacts to faradic or galvanic stimulation when applied to its motor nerve. However, it still responds to direct stimulation with the galvanic current by sluggish wave-like contractions, but now it is the positive pole or anode which induces the strongest response on closing the current.

If preganglionic visceral fibers are also involved, as in the case of the thoracic and upper lumbar roots, there will be vasomotor (and atrophic) disturbances expressed by dryness and cyanosis of the skin.

Section of the mixed spinal nerve immediately after union of the dorsal and ventral roots will naturally cause combined symptoms of muscular paralysis and sensory loss in the affected area. In the case of the peripheral nerves a knowledge of the exact distribution of each nerve is essential for an understanding of the sensory and motor defects resulting from injury to such nerve. Since familiarity with the structure of the spinal cord will aid in understanding the formation and composition of the more complex spinal nerves, a full account of peripheral innervation is given in chapter XI.

THE SPINAL GANGLIA

The spinal and autonomic ganglia are part of the peripheral nervous system and contribute fibers to the peripheral nerves.

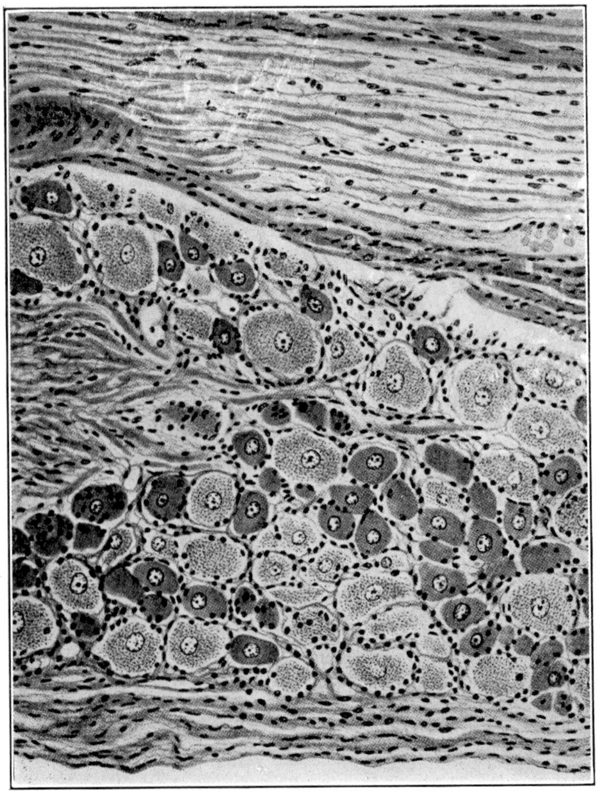

Fig. 138. Section of human spinal ganglion. Hematoxylin-eosin stain. The cells are of two types, a large clear type with well marked Nissl bodies and a smaller, more darkly staining type ("obscure cells"). The nuclei of the capsule cells are also seen. (Ph. Stoehr, Jr., from v. Moellendorff's Handbuch der mikroskopischen Anatomie des Menschen.)

The majority if not all of the afferent fibers, both somatic and visceral, have their cell bodies in the spinal ganglia. All the efferent visceral fibers which go directly to visceral muscle and glandular epithelium wherever found, are axons of cells in the autonomic ganglia. The structure of the latter is described in chapter XIV.

The *spinal ganglia* are aggregations of nerve cells appearing as spindle-shaped swellings on the dorsal roots (Figs. 30, 133). Each ganglion is surrounded by a connective tissue capsule continuous with the epineurium and perineurium of the spinal nerves. From this capsule trabeculae extend into the interior and form a connective tissue framework which contains the blood vessels and surrounds the nerve cells and their processes. The nerve cells themselves are separated into irregular groups by bundles of nerve fibers which run through the long axis and constitute the central and peripheral processes of the ganglion cells.

The majority of the ganglion cells are unipolar cells of irregularly ovoid or spherical shape, which vary tremendously in size,

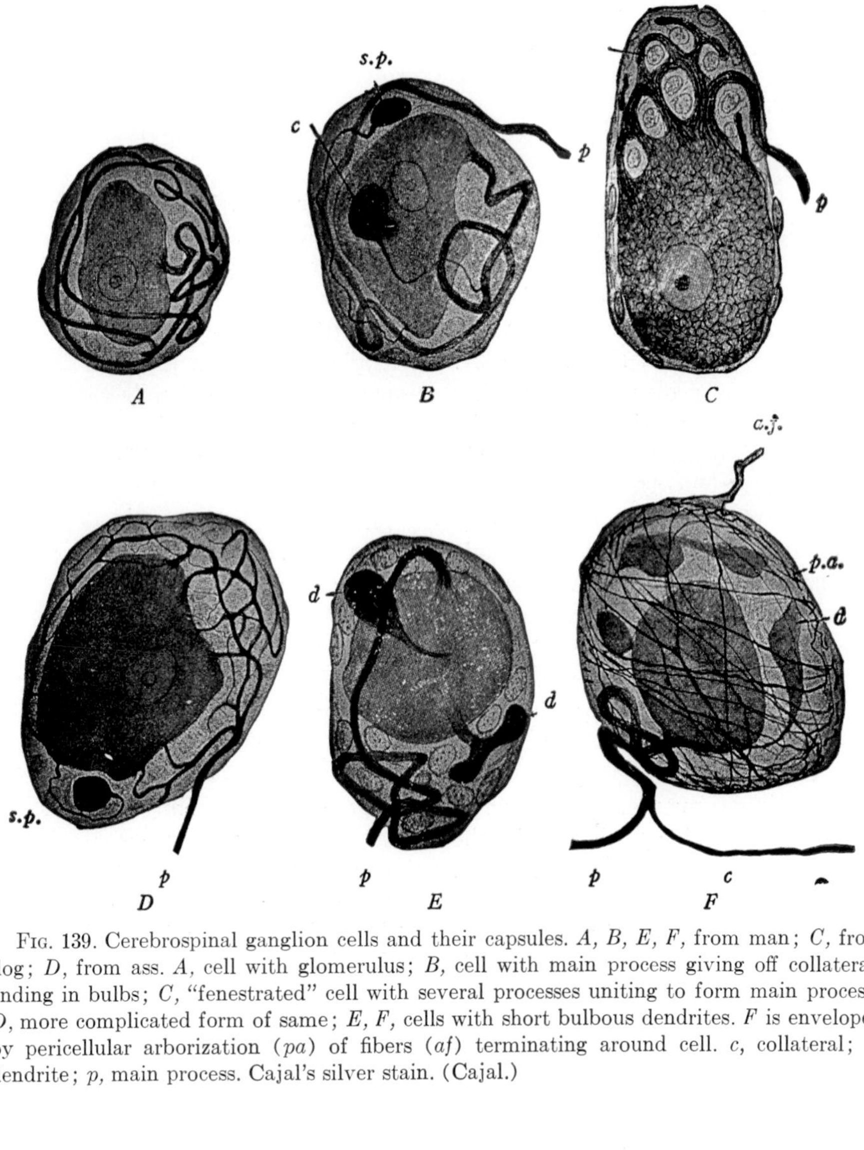

FIG. 139. Cerebrospinal ganglion cells and their capsules. *A, B, E, F,* from man; *C,* from dog; *D,* from ass. *A,* cell with glomerulus; *B,* cell with main process giving off collaterals ending in bulbs; *C,* "fenestrated" cell with several processes uniting to form main process; *D,* more complicated form of same; *E, F,* cells with short bulbous dendrites. *F* is enveloped by pericellular arborization (*pa*) of fibers (*af*) terminating around cell. *c,* collateral; *d,* dendrite; *p,* main process. Cajal's silver stain. (Cajal.)

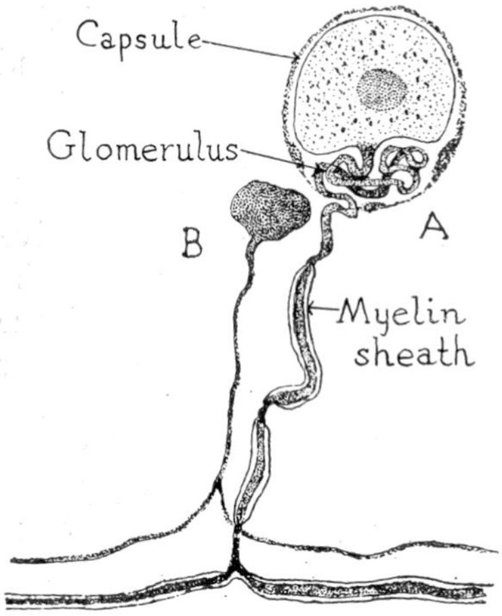

FIG. 140. Two cells from vagus ganglion of cat. Ehrlich's methylene blue. *A,* large clear cell; *B,* small "obscure" cell with deeply staining cytoplasm. (After Cajal.)

from less than 20 micra for the smallest to over 100 micra for the largest. Each ganglion cell is surrounded by a capsule of flat, concentrically arranged cells, the inner ones of which are probably derived from the ectodermal cells of the neural crest and are known as capsule cells (Figs. 80, 140). This capsule extends over the emerging process and becomes continuous with the neurilemma sheath of that fiber. The single process always has the structure of an axon and if myelinated acquires a medullary sheath soon after leaving the cell. It winds and coils about itself in an intricate manner near the cell body, resembling the structure of a glomerulus. Then the process straightens out, extends deeper into the ganglion and bifurcates into a central process which enters the cord through the dorsal root, and a peripheral one which becomes an afferent fiber of the peripheral nerve. The glomeruli are most complex and conspicuous in the axons of the large cells (Figs. 139, 140). In the unmyelinated axons of the small cells they are reduced or altogether lacking. It is evident from the above that the longitudinal fiber bundles of the ganglion consist of myelinated and unmyelinated processes of spinal ganglion cells, which run centrally into the cord, and peripherally into the spinal nerve.

As a result of careful studies with methylene blue and reduced silver stains, many types of ganglion cells have been distinguished on the basis of size, shape, distribution of chromophilic bodies, and types of processes (Dogiel, Hirt, Warrington, Ranson). Of these the large *clear cells* and the small *obscure cells* form the main types (Warrington). The former are light staining cells with vesicular nuclei and fine chromophilic bodies (Fig. 138). Usually considered as the typical spinal ganglion cells, they constitute less than 30 per cent of the total number. The axons of these cells form the glomeruli described above, but many variations occur (Fig. 139). The axon may split into a number of processes which then unite again into a single process. Or a number of processes may arise from the cell, anastomose with one another and then give rise to a single process. In some of the cells the process may give off collaterals which terminate in the ganglion by end bulbs or other terminal arborizations. The axons of these larger cells are probably all myelinated.

The *obscure* cells are smaller, stain more deeply and diffusely and comprise about 50–75 per cent of the ganglion cells (Figs. 138, 140). The fibers of some of these also may give off collaterals which end in bulb-shaped terminations within the ganglion. The obscure cells supply in considerable part the fine unmyelinated fibers which are concerned with the transmission of impulses of a painful and possibly otherwise affective character. These fibers remain intact after the postganglionic efferent fibers, also unmyelinated, have been removed by destruction of the sympathetic ganglia from which they arise (Fig. 137).

10

Peripheral Terminations of Afferent and Efferent Nerve Fibers

TERMINATION IN RECEPTORS

Those parts of the body which are excitable to stimuli and contain the terminations of the afferent peripheral nerve fibers are known as *receptors.* They have the general function of transforming various kinds of physical and chemical changes affecting them into nerve impulses, and there is considerable evidence that each receptor is activated by only one particular kind of physical or chemical change. In other words, it lowers the threshold to one kind of stimulus and raises it to all others. The nature of the reaction also depends on the central connections of the afferent fibers to which the receptors are related and on the effectors with which they are ultimately connected. However, the capacity of reacting differently to different kinds of stimuli depends primarily on the analytic capacity of the receptors.

The receptors and their associated modalities of sensation have been classified in several more or less overlapping ways. (1) Topographically, many kinds of receptors are found more or less profusely distributed over all parts of the body, and collectively represent *general somesthetic sensibility* (body sense). They include the receptors for touch, pressure, pain, temperature, sense of position and movement, and visceral sense. Others comprising smell, taste, sight, hearing, and head position and movements are found only in certain parts of the head and constitute the *organs of special sense.*

(2) Sherrington (1906) has classified all receptors into three main groups: *exteroceptors, proprioceptors,* and *interoceptors.* The exteroceptors, situated on the external surface of the body, receive impressions from the outside which result in somatic movements. They include touch, light pressure, cutaneous pain and temperature, smell, sight, and hearing. Some of these are *contact receptors*; others, such as smell, sight, hearing and part of temperature, are stimulated by distant objects and are known as *teloreceptors.* It is possible that deeply acting agencies such as radium emanations, X-rays and diathermy which directly affect the tissues may be partly picked up by some of these receptors.

The proprioceptors receive stimuli from the deeper portions of the body wall, especially from the muscles, tendons and joints, and give rise to sensations of position and movement. Since they are primarily concerned with the regulation of movement in response to exteroceptive stimuli, the proprioceptors and exteroceptors may be grouped together as somatic receptors. The deeper portion of the body wall also contains receptors for deep pain and pressure.

The interoceptors are the visceral sense organs receiving internal impressions and concerned with the visceral activities of digestion, excretion, circulation, etc., which are primarily under control of the autonomic system. They give rise to sensations of taste, visceral pain and temperature, and to the more obscure forms of visceral sensibility such as hunger, thirst, sexual feeling and to the general feelings of well-being or of *malaise*. Smell, though not interoceptive, has close visceral affiliations and may be in part at least considered as visceral.

(3) Sensibility may also be divided into *superficial* and *deep*. The former obviously coincides with exteroceptive sense, the latter comprises both interoceptive and proprioceptive, including also deep pressure. A special form of sensation is the ability of recognizing the vibrations of a tuning fork applied to bone or of a faradic current to the skin. This is usually known as *vibratory* sense. The nature of its receptors is not known.

(4) An analysis of sensation, important from a clinical and comparative viewpoint, was introduced by Head (1905). He distinguishes two systems in sensibility, one *protopathic* or affective, the other *epicritic* or discriminative, and believes that the two have their separate receptors, at least for the cutaneous innervation. Protopathic sensation is of a marked affective character, agreeable or disagreeable, but gives little information of the nature or exact location of the stimulus. In epicritic sensibility, the discriminative element predominates. The stimulus is accurately localized, two points simultaneously applied are properly discriminated and variations in intensity of stimuli are appreciated. Affective sensations are primarily related to reactions which most directly involve bodily welfare and in which there is reason to suppose that the thalamus plays an important part. They are consequently often termed *vital* or *thalamic*. Discriminative sensibility forms the basis for the complex associative and cognitive reactions of the cerebral cortex, hence it is called *gnostic* or *cortical*. In a general way, pain, temperature, visceral sensibility, and part of touch are predominantly affective, while part of touch and the proprioceptive and teleceptive sensibilities are predominantly discriminative. From neither category is one or the other element entirely absent.

FIG. 141. Sensory nerve terminations in corneal epithelium. (Cajal.)

Structurally the terminations of afferent fibers in receptors are extremely varied and often of a very complicated character. They may be classified into two main groups: (a) the *free* or *diffuse* endings, and (b) the *encapsulated* endings which are enclosed in a connective tissue capsule.

Free nerve endings. The free nerve endings are the most widely distributed in the body. They are most numerous in the skin, but are also found in the mucous and serous membranes, in muscle and in the connective tissue of many visceral organs. The skin is supplied by many cutaneous nerve trunks composed of myelinated and unmyelinated fibers. Some of the myelinated fibers are large and are destined for the encapsulated organs described below, but the majority have a relatively small caliber. The fibers of these small nerve trunks separate as they approach the epidermis, lose their myelin sheath, undergo branching and form extensive unmyelinated plexuses in the deeper portion of the dermis, and immediately beneath the epidermis (Fig. 142). From this subepithelial plexus, delicate fibers penetrate the epithelium, divide repeatedly and form an end arborization of delicate terminal fibrils which wind vertically through the epidermis and end in small knob-like thickenings, often within the cytoplasm of the epithelial cells (Figs.

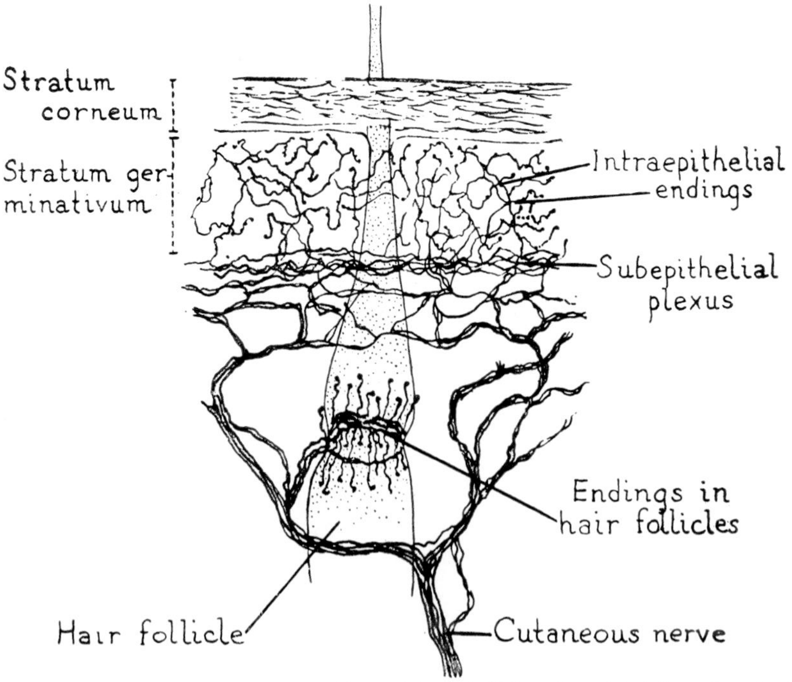

FIG. 142. Nerves and nerve endings in skin and hair follicles. (Modified from Retzius.)

141, 142). In the cornea, which has no horny layer, these intraepithelial endings may reach the surface, but in other portions of the skin they do not extend beyond the germinative layer. Intraepithelial endings are also found in mucous membranes which are lined by stratified epithelium, as the esophagus and bladder, and probably in many simple columnar epithelia as well.

Other nerve fibers form unmyelinated arborizations or terminal nets in the connective tissue of the dermis. There is some evidence that the intraepithelial endings are derived from fine myelinated fibers, while the subepidermal arborizations and plexiform nets are in the main terminals of unmyelinated ones (Woollard). Diffuse nerve endings in the form of nerve nets or arborizations of varying complexity are widely distributed through the visceral organs. They have been described in the serous membranes, heart, bronchial tree, alimentary canal, and blood vessels (Fig. 143). They are also found in the chorioid plexuses of the brain and in striped muscle. They are for the larger part terminals of unmyelinated fibers. Complicated arborizations have been found in the smooth muscle of the bronchi by Larsell who terms them "smooth muscle spindles" (Fig. 143). They are endings of medium sized or large myelinated fibers and may perhaps initiate proprioceptive bronchial reflexes.

An important type of diffuse cutaneous receptors is represented by the *peritrichial* endings of the hair follicles, which are activated by the movements of the hairs. They vary considerably in complexity and are best developed in the vibrissae of certain mammals. In the simpler forms several myelinated fibers approach the hair follicle just below its sebaceous gland, lose their myelin sheath and divide in several branches which encircle the outer root-sheath (Fig. 142). From these spring numerous fine flattened fibers which run for a short distance upward and often also downward in the outer root-sheath and terminate in flattened or bulbous endings.

Besides the intraepithelial endings de-

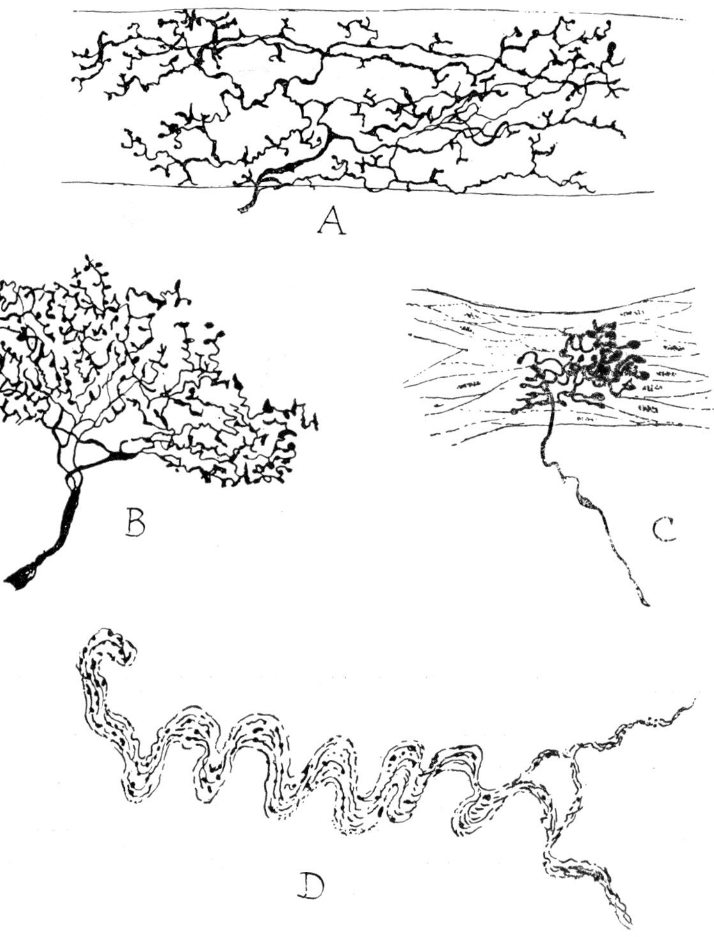

FIG. 143. Afferent nerve endings in various visceral structures. *A*, on a large pancreatic blood vessel. (After Castro.) *B*, in endocardium of dog. (After Smirnow.) *C*, in bronchial musculature of child. (After Larsell and Dow.) *D*, in longitudinal muscle coat of stomach of cat. (After Carpenter.)

scribed above, which end among or within ordinary epithelial cells, there are found in the deeper portion of the germinative layer somewhat more specialized endings known as the *tactile discs* of Merkel (Fig. 144). Each consists of a concave neurofibrillar disc or meniscus closely applied to a single epithelial cell of modified structure. A single epidermal nerve fiber may by repeated branching give rise to a number of such discs. This type of termination is transitional to more specialized forms, such as the corpuscles of Grandry, found in the skin of birds. In these the flat tactile discs lie between two or more specialized epithelial cells.

The tendency to modification of epithelial cells receiving sensory nerve endings is exemplified in various *neuroepithelial* cells which have special forms and show staining affinities similar to nerve cells. The specific cells of the taste buds (Fig. 145) and the hair cells in the sensory epithelia of the cochlear and vestibular apparatus are examples of such neuroepithelial cells.

Encapsulated endings. These include the *tactile corpuscles of Meissner,* the *end bulbs,* the *Pacinian corpuscles,* the *corpus-*

FIG. 144. Tactile discs in epithelium of pig's snout. (After Ranvier.)

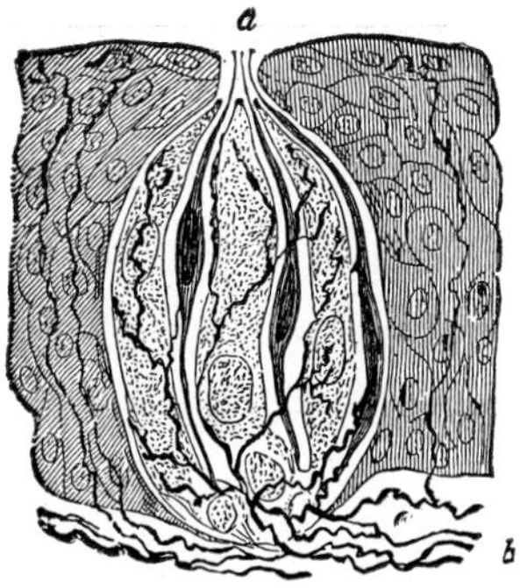

FIG. 145. Taste bud from circumvallate papilla of tongue. *a,* taste pore; *b,* nerve fiber entering taste bud and ending upon neuroepithelial cells. On either side are some free intraepithelial endings. (Merkel-Henle.)

cles of *Ruffini* and of *Golgi-Mazzoni,* the *neuromuscular spindles* and the *neurotendinous organs* of *Golgi.*

The *tactile corpuscles of Meissner* are elongated ovoid bodies, about 90–120 micra in length, which are found in the dermal papillae, close to the epidermis (Fig. 146). Each corpuscle is surrounded by a thin nucleated connective tissue sheath and the interior consists of many flattened epithelioid cells whose nuclei are placed transversely to the long axis of the corpuscle. From one to four myelinated nerve fibers supply each corpuscle. As each fiber enters, its connective tissue sheath becomes continuous with the fibrous capsule, the myelin sheath soon disappears and the naked axon winds spirally among the epithelioid cells, giving off numerous branches which likewise course spirally, show numerous varicosities and end in flattened neurofibrillar expansions. Besides the myelinated fibers, the corpuscles may also receive one or more fine unmyelinated fibers whose source is not definitely known (Fig. 147). Meissner corpuscles occur mainly in the hairless portion of the skin and are most numerous on the volar surface of the fingers, toes, hands, and feet. In lesser numbers they are also found in the lips, eyelids, tip of tongue, and volar surface of the forearm.

The *end bulbs* resemble the tactile corpuscles in structure and are spherical or ovoid bodies which vary greatly in dimension. The simplest and smallest ones are found in the conjunctiva, the largest in the connective tissue of the external genitalia where they are also known as *genital corpuscles.* In its simplest form (Fig. 148A) the end bulb consists of a nucleated capsule enclosing a soft gelatinous core in which nuclei may often be seen. One or more myelinated fibers lose their myelin on entering the capsule and give off numerous lateral branches which form a complicated terminal arborization. Some end bulbs may be compound. End bulbs of various form have a wide distribution, being found in the conjunctiva, mouth, tongue, epiglottis, nasal cavity, peritoneum, and other serous membranes, lower end of rectum and external genitalia, especially the glans penis and clitoris. They are also found in tendons, ligaments and synovial membranes and in the connective tissue of nerve trunks.

The *Pacinian bodies* or *corpuscles of Vater-Pacini* are the largest and most widely distributed of the encapsulated receptors (Fig. 149). They are laminated, elliptical structures of whitish color, each supplied by a large myelinated fiber, and differ from the other encapsulated organs mainly in the greater development of their perineural capsule. This capsule is formed by a large number of concentric lamellae, each lamella of the outer bulb consists of a single continuous layer of flattened cells and is supported by collagen fibers of

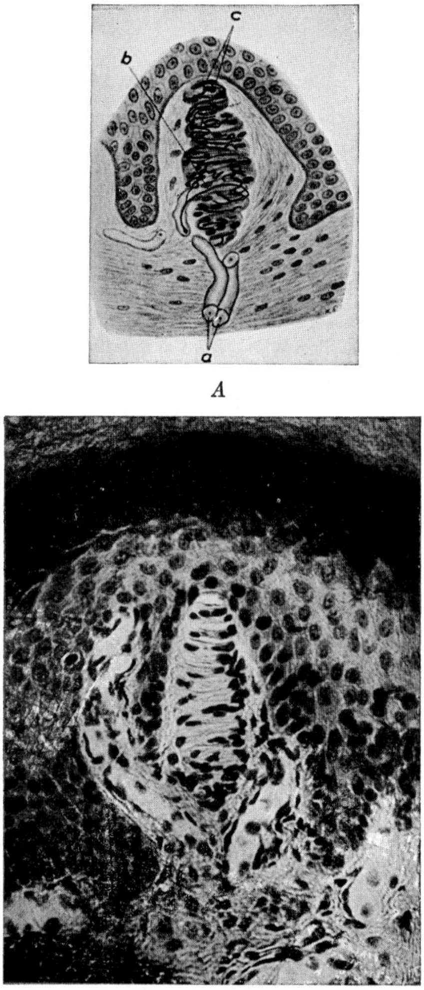

A

B

FIG. 146. *A*, Meissner's corpuscle from sole of human foot. (After Braus.) *a*, myelinated fibers; *b*, terminal arborization; *c*, end swellings. *B*, Meissner's corpuscle in dermal papilla of human finger tip. Photograph.

the interlamellar spaces. The interlamellar spaces contain a network of fine fibers, blood vessels and some free cells in a semifluid substance. Blood vessels accompany the nerve fiber to the capsule but ramify only in the outer bulb. At birth the neurilemmal and myelin sheaths are lost as the large nerve fiber enters the inner bulb. However, the capsule continues to grow and enlarge, so that in the human adult both neurilemmal and myelin elements can at times be identified within the inner bulb (Cauna and Mannan, 1958). No fine nerves enter the inner bulb with the large fiber. These authors also found that the average length of the corpuscle at birth was from 500 to 700 microns. The size increased gradually throughout life to become 3–4 mm. in length. In persons over 70 years of age the corpuscles show regressive changes, becoming smaller and more irregular. They conclude that the Pacinian corpuscle is a receptor mechanism for signalling changes in local blood supply rather than for changes in pressure. The corpuscles are found in the subcutaneous tissue, especially of the hand and foot, in the peritoneum, pleura, mesenteries, penis, clitoris, urethra, nipple, mammary glands, pancreas, and in the walls of many viscera. They are especially numerous in the periosteum, ligaments and joint capsules, and also occur in the muscular septa and occasionally in the muscle itself.

Related to the Pacinian bodies are the

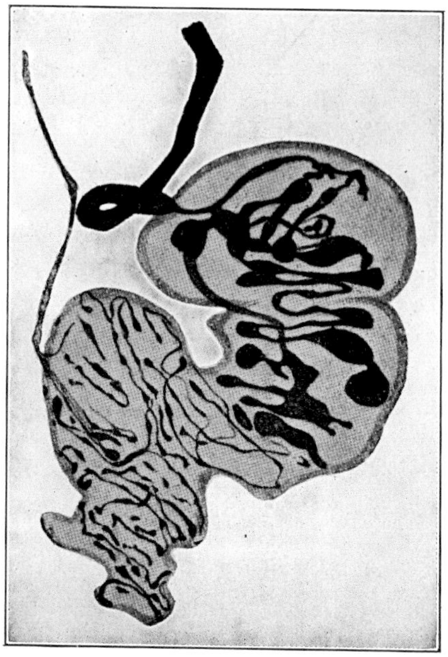

FIG. 147. Meissner's corpuscle showing termination of a large myelinated and a fine unmyelinated fiber. (Ruffini.)

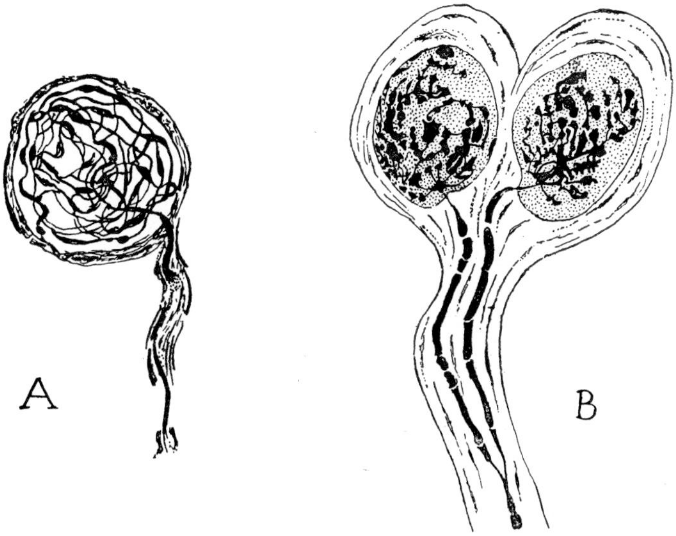

FIG. 148. *A*, end bulb of Krause from conjunctiva. (Dogiel.) *B*, compound corpuscle of Golgi-Mazzoni from the subcutaneous tissue of the finger tip. (Ruffini.)

lamellated *corpuscles of Golgi-Mazzoni,* found in the subcutaneous tissue of the fingers and on the surface of tendons (Fig. 148 B). They are ovoid bodies with lamellated capsules of varying thickness and a central core of granular protoplasm in which the single myelinated fiber which supplies the corpuscle forms a rich arborization with varicosities and terminal expansions. In the subcutaneous tissue of the finger tips are also found the *corpuscles of Ruffini,* elongated bodies of considerable size whose capsule encloses several bundles of connective tissue fibers. Several nerve fibers enter the corpuscle and ramify extensively, the branches lying between and partly encircling the small connective tissue bundles.

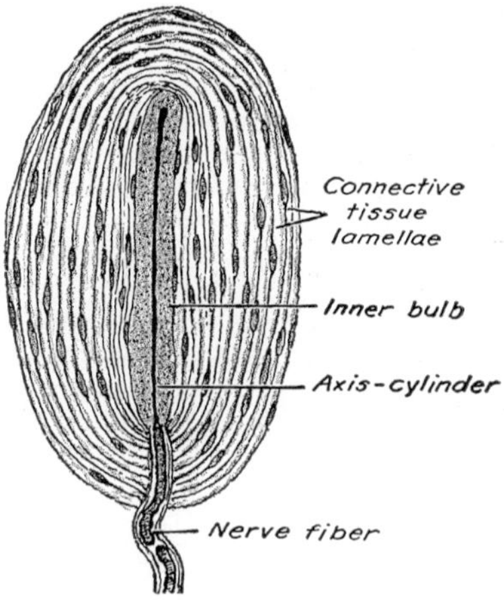

FIG. 149. Human Pacinian corpuscle. (After Cajal, from Bailey's Histology.)

It is obvious that the different types of encapsulated receptors described above have a fundamentally similar structure, with numerous and often transitional variations as regards the size of the corpuscles and the complexity of the capsule and terminal ramification.

In the striped muscles there are found complicated nerve endings known as *neuromuscular spindles* (Figs. 150, 151, 180). Each spindle consists of a bundle of slender muscle fibers enclosed within a lamellated capsule and supplied with several nerve fibers which arborize in an exceedingly complicated manner (Fig. 151). The spindles may be simple or compound. The former are usually fusiform, thicker in the center and tapering toward the ends. The compound spindles show a number of dilatations but also become pointed at the ends. Each spindle has its own blood and lymph supply.

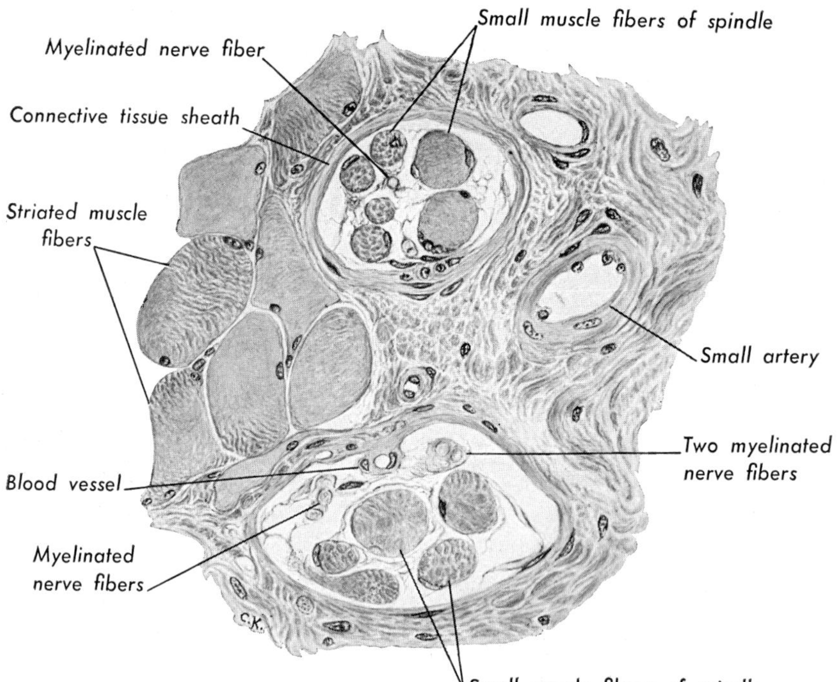

FIG. 150. Cross section of two muscle spindles in skeletal muscle of monkey. (Bailey's Histology.)

The muscle fibers of the spindle, considerably thinner than ordinary muscle fibers, branch and anastomose like those of heart muscle. Each fiber shows a definite cross-striation except at one place, usually in the belly of the spindle, where the striations disappear and the fiber contains a closely packed mass of bubble-like structures. Each spindle is supplied with both sensory and motor endings which are spatially separated. Two or more myelinated fibers enter the spindle, their endoneurial sheaths becoming continuous with the fibrous capsule. The thicker sensory fibers divide into secondary and tertiary branches. These then become closely applied to the muscle fibers, lose their myelin sheath and give rise to two types of endings. In one, the naked axons break up into a most extensive flower or ivy-like arborization consisting of varicosities connected by fine filaments. These "flower-sprays" (Ruffini) terminate on that portion of the muscle fiber which contains the bubble-like structures. In the other type of ending, the naked axons become flattened like ribbons and either wind spirally around the muscle fiber, terminating in free expansions, or the ribbon runs along one side of the muscle fiber and gives off band-like branches which, like tendrils, clasp the circumference of the muscle fibers. This "annulo-spiral" ending may terminate in portions of the spindle where normal cross-striations are found. The perfect annulo-spiral endings described in the spindles of many mammals (Ruffini) are not characteristic for human muscle spindles, while the ivy-like endings are always present and show a truly remarkable complexity and extent.

The usually thinner motor fibers terminate in typical end plates situated at the poles of the spindles. Each spindle contains also a number of fine unmyelinated fibers. Some are vasomotor fibers for the blood vessels of the spindle.

The recorded dimensions of human mus-

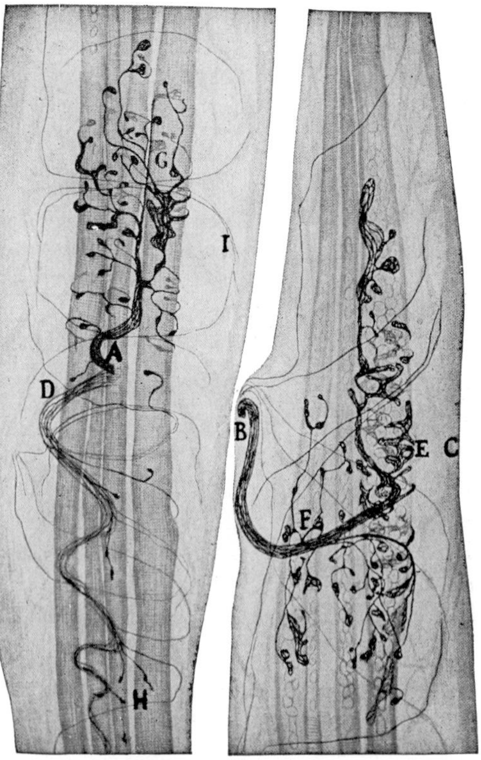

FIG. 151. Neuromuscular spindle in a human fetus of six months. *A,* coarse nerve fiber with arborescent (flower-spray) terminations at *G*; *B,* coarse fiber with spiral and annular terminations at *E* and *F*; *H,* motor fibers; *I,* fine unmyelinated fibers; *C,* connective tissue capsule. (Tello.)

cle spindles fluctuate enormously, the extremes for length being 0.05 to 13 mm. The more usual length is 2 to 4 mm. The spindles have been found in practically all muscles and are more numerous in the extremities than in the trunk. They are especially abundant in the small muscles of the hand and foot (lumbricals) and in the eye muscles (Cooper and Daniel, 1949; Merrillees, Sunderland, and Hayhow, 1950). In the eye muscles the spindles have more delicate capsules, are smaller than in other skeletal muscles, and are mainly confined to the distal and proximal portions of the muscles.

The *neurotendinous organs of Golgi* are spindle-shaped structures most commonly found at the junction of muscle and tendon, but occasionally also in the muscular septa

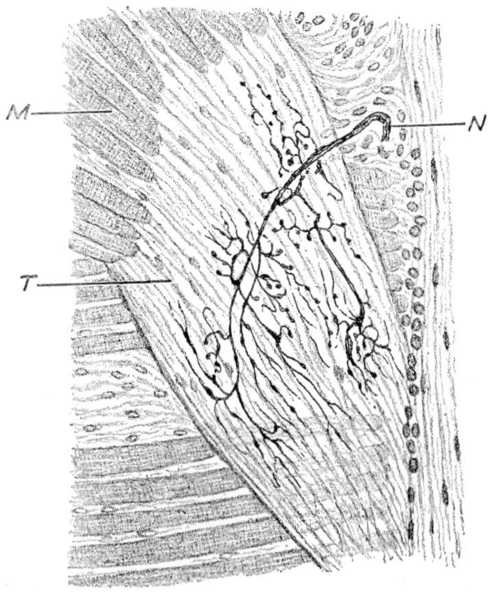

FIG. 152. Neurotendinous organ from six months human fetus. *M,* muscle fibers; *N,* nerve fiber; *T,* tendon fibers. (After Tello.)

and sheaths (Fig. 152). They have been demonstrated in practically all muscles. The spindle consists of several tendon fascicles surrounded by a lamellated connective tissue capsule and, as a rule, supplied by one, occasionally two or three myelinated nerve fibers. On penetrating the spindle, the fiber loses its sheath of Henle which becomes continuous with the capsule, and divides into primary, secondary, and tertiary branches which still retain their myelin sheath. The latter then split into numerous unmyelinated branches which wind between and around the primary tendon bundles, meanwhile giving off side branchlets which again repeatedly divide. All these terminal branches show numerous flat leaflike expansions, the whole ramification appearing as a delicate net enveloping the tendon bundles. In man these spindles have a length of about 1.35 mm. and a thickness of about 200 micra.

Besides the neuromuscular and neurotendinous organs, muscle and tendon have a variety of other sensory structures: free nerve endings, end bulbs, and Pacinian corpuscles. The latter are especially numerous in tendons.

RELATION OF RECEPTORS TO SENSORY MODALITIES

It is generally maintained, though not proven conclusively, that each type of receptor is activated by only one kind of physical or chemical change and is hence associated with only one kind of sensory modality. The problem of relating the various receptors to their specific sensory modalities has been an exceedingly difficult one and many important details are still to be elucidated.

It seems probable that painful impulses are received by the diffuse cutaneous end arborizations. Not only would their universal presence and unspecialized type indicate this but also their sole presence in places where stimuli give rise to pain only, such as the tympanic membrane of the ear, the cornea of the eye and the pulp of the teeth. Recent evidence suggests that the intraepithelial endings derived from fine myelinated fibers are related to sharply localized pain, while poorly localized pain is represented by the subepidermal terminations of unmyelinated fibers (Woollard). It is probable, however, that the intraepithelial fibers also mediate a low form of tactile sensibility (Waterston).

Touch is represented by the endings in hair follicles, Meissner's corpuscles and similar encapsulated organs, and probably also by the tactile discs and some other intraepithelial endings. The peritrichial endings stimulated by movements of the hair give rise to a sensibility quite delicate and discriminative yet having a marked affective tone. Shaving greatly reduces the sensibility to touch. On the hairless parts of the body tactile stimuli are received primarily by the corpuscles of Meissner which are probably the chief sense organs of discriminative touch.

The receptors for temperature are not known as well, but are probably end bulbs of various kinds and possibly also some diffuse endings. It is known that the margin of the cornea is sensitive only to cold and pain and is provided only with diffuse endings and end bulbs of Krause. Hence the latter and similar subcutaneous end bulbs are believed to be receptors for cold. In the same way, the corpuscles of Ruffini are considered as related to warmth. There is still much to be learned about the temperature receptors.

The different parts of the body surface vary considerably as to their capacity for affective and discriminative sensibility. The hands and fingers represent the highest development of the latter, being practically stalked sense organs for cortical sensibility. In other parts such as the back, abdomen, and especially the genitalia, affective sensibility predominates, to the partial exclusion of the other type.

The corpuscles of Pacini are both deep subcutaneous and visceral structures. Their form and position indicate that they are stimulated by deep or heavy pressure. It is probable that other lamellated corpuscles as those of Golgi-Mazzoni have a similar function.

The proprioceptive stimuli of position and movement, initiated by the constant or varying tension states of the voluntary muscles and their tendons and by the movements of the joints, are undoubtedly received by the muscle spindles and tendon organs and by the Pacinian corpuscles found in the joint capsules, ligaments, and periosteum. The important proprioceptive, kinetic, and tonic reflexes and mnemonic reactions initiated by these stimuli have already been mentioned.

There is much that is still obscure about visceral sensibility. It is known that the viscera are insensitive to many mechanical and chemical stimuli, yet they may be the source of intense pain as well as of the organic sensations of hunger, thirst, etc. Visceral pain is mainly due to either distension or to abnormal contraction or spasm of the muscle coats. Hence the intramuscular diffuse nerve endings would appear to be the probable receptors for these stimuli. The blood vessels may also give rise to painful sensation, likewise due to muscular spasms in their walls and to the resulting stimulation of similar diffuse endings. The totality of stimuli which are constantly initiated by these diffuse visceral receptors during normal or abnormal organic functioning probably gives rise to the general affective sensibility of internal well-being or of *malaise*.

One peculiarity of visceral pain is that painful visceral stimuli are often "felt" in the corresponding somatic segment or segments of the external body wall, a phenomenon known as "referred pain". Centrally the receptive nuclei for somatic and visceral pain impulses are closely associated within the dorsal gray column of the spinal cord. For this reason referred pain is most likely due to altered central mechanisms within the spinal cord although the precise neurons involved have not been ascertained. A common explanation is that the constant bombardment of pain impulses from a diseased viscus lowers the threshold of stimulation of adjacent central (somatic) relay neurons. Normally these relay neurons are concerned with somatic sensations and are not concerned with transmission of visceral pain. As a result, normal incoming somatic sensory impulses that terminate in this "sensitized" neuron pool are now relayed to higher centers where they are misinterpreted as painful stimuli coming from body surfaces.

Sinclair, Weddell, and Fiendel (1948) have suggested that the production of referred pain may be due to the branching of the sensory fibers which conduct painful impulses. One limb of a branched axon goes to the visceral site where the disturbance originates, while others go to the peripheral places to which the pain is referred. This mechanism works in two ways. The first leads to a misinterpretation by the central nervous system of the true origin of the pain impulses. Secondly, the liberation of metabolites at the nerve terminals in the region where the pain is felt gives rise to secondary pain impulses which actually have their origin in the periphery. The first factor is more important initially; the second gains in importance with time and becomes predominant in the later stages.

Referred pains correspond to the dermatome distribution of a spinal nerve, not to the distribution of a peripheral nerve. The following are some classical examples where a diseased viscus causes pain to be referred to the overlying soma and dermatome: diaphragm referred to dermatome C4; heart referred to dermatomes C8-T8; bladder referred to dermatomes T1-10; stomach referred to dermatomes T6-9; intestine referred to dermatomes T7-10; testes, prostate, and uterus referred to dermatomes T10-12; kidneys referred to dermatomes T11-L1; rectum referred to dermatomes S2-4 (Figs. 157, 159, 160).

TERMINATIONS IN EFFECTORS

The endings of the efferent peripheral fibers in the effector organs of the body fall into two groups: somatic efferent and visceral efferent. The somatic efferent are terminations of myelinated fibers whose cell bodies are situated in the ventral horn of the spinal cord and which go directly to the striped skeletal muscles. The visceral endings are terminals of unmyelinated fibers which arise from cells of the various autonomic ganglia. These fibers supply the heart (cardiomotor), visceral muscle (visceromotor), blood vessels (vasomotor), hair (pilomotor), and glands (secretory). Pigment cells and possibly the endothelium of capillaries may be innervated by such autonomic fibers.

Somatic effectors. The somatic efferent fibers terminate in the striped muscle fibers in small flattened expansions of oval shape, known as the *motor end plates* (Figs. 153,

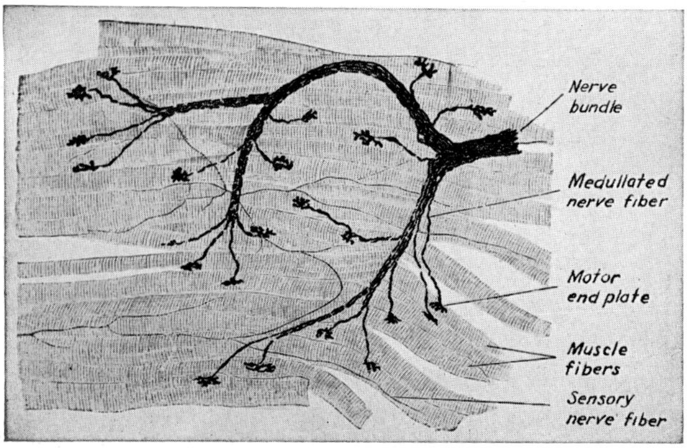

FIG. 153. Motor endings in intercostal muscle of rabbit. (After v. Moellendorf, from Bailey's Histology.)

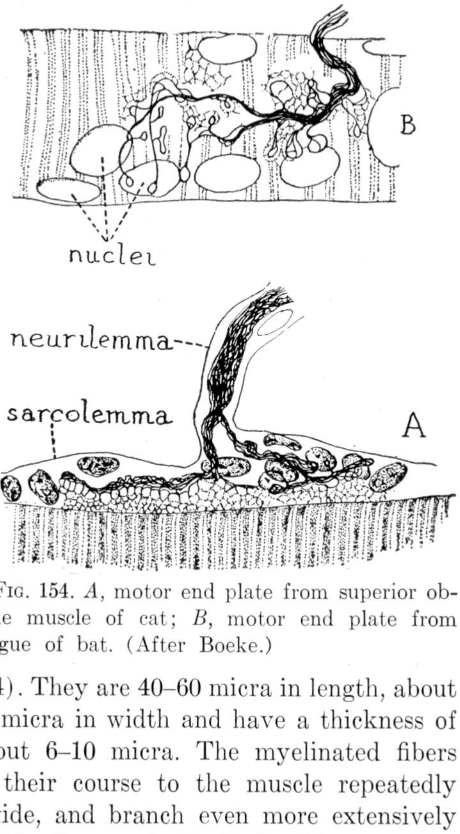

FIG. 154. *A*, motor end plate from superior oblique muscle of cat; *B*, motor end plate from tongue of bat. (After Boeke.)

154). They are 40–60 micra in length, about 40 micra in width and have a thickness of about 6–10 micra. The myelinated fibers in their course to the muscle repeatedly divide, and branch even more extensively within the muscle itself. In this manner a single nerve fiber may furnish end plates to a variable number of muscle fibers. Each of the terminal fibers on reaching the sarcolemma suddenly loses its myelin sheath and the neurilemma becomes continuous with the sarcolemma. The naked axon enters the muscle fiber and immediately beneath the sarcolemma forms a delicate localized arborization of flattened or club-shaped neurofibrillar terminals. This arborization is embedded in a mass of finely granular protoplasm, the *sole* of the plate, containing a number of light staining nuclei derived in part from the muscle, in part from the neurilemma.

Boeke and others have described small "accessory" motor end plates innervated by fine unmyelinated fibers. These may be placed within the sole of the larger end plates or may be found as isolated structures underneath the sarcolemma. Their significance is not understood, but they are believed by some to be of autonomic origin.

The axon of one motor neuron supplies a variable number of skeletal muscle fibers. In the larger back muscles (e.g., sacrospinalis, gluteus maximus), a single ventral horn cell may provide motor end plates to over 100 muscle fibers. Each motor neuron to a muscle of the thumb or an extrinsic eye muscle may only supply a few skeletal muscle fibers. All the skeletal muscle fibers supplied by one motor neuron and its axon constitute a *motor unit*. A muscle with many motor units for a given number of muscle fibers is capable of more precise movements than a muscle with a few motor units for the same number of muscle fibers. It also follows that only a few ventral horn cells and motor units are required to maintain reflex muscle tone during periods

FIG. 155. Motor nerve terminations in the smooth muscle bands of a bronchus. Rabbit. *tfi*, terminal fibrils. (Larsell.)

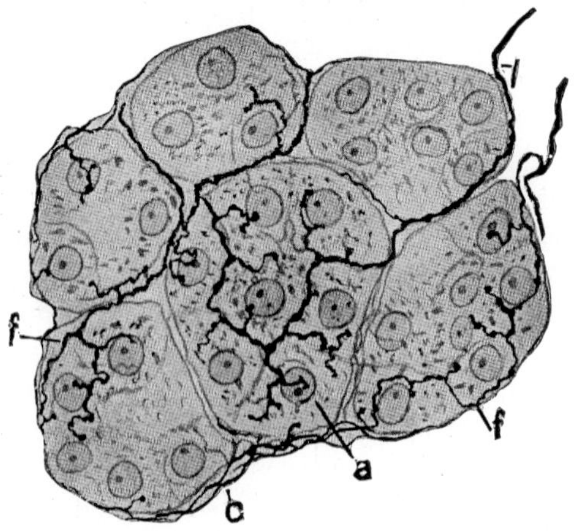

FIG. 156. Nerve terminations around and within acini of the pancreas of an adult mouse. *c*, periacinous fibers; *f*, interepithelial and intraepithelial fibers. (Castro.)

of rest or sleep. However, many or all motor units may be called into operation when demands are made upon the muscles for maximal contraction.

Visceral effectors. The unmyelinated autonomic fibers which supply visceral muscle either end in simple arborizations, or first form extensive intramuscular plexuses from which the terminals arise. The terminal fibrils wind between the smooth muscle cells and end in small neurofibrillar thickenings or delicate loops on the surface or more probably within the protoplasm of the muscle fibers (Fig. 155). Similar terminals arise from delicate plexuses which surround the tubules or acini of glands, pass between the cells and terminate in part at least within the cytoplasm of the glandular cells (Fig. 156).

11

Segmental and Peripheral Innervation

SEGMENTAL (RADICULAR) INNERVATION

The "segmental" character of the cord, as evidenced by its spinal nerves, corresponds to the general metamerism of the body, each pair of nerves supplying a body segment (metamere). The ventral roots contain the efferent fibers which go to the somatic musculature (myotomes) and by way of the autonomic ganglia to the blood vessels (vasoconstrictor), visceral muscle and glandular epithelium. The dorsal roots contain all the afferent fibers, superficial, deep and visceral, and probably also some efferent fibers which act as vasodilators of cutaneous blood vessels. That cutaneous area supplied by a single dorsal root and its ganglion is called a *dermatome.*

In the adult, the correspondence between neural and body metameres is easily recognized in the trunk and neck regions where each spinal nerve supplies the musculature and cutaneous area of its own segment. Here the dermatomes follow one another consecutively, each forming a band encircling the body from the middorsal to the midventral line. In the extremities, however, the conditions are far more complicated. During development the metameres migrate distally into the limb buds and arrange themselves parallel to the long axis of the future limb (Fig. 157). In each extremity, there is thus formed an axial line along which are placed a number of consecutive segments which have wandered out from the axial portions. The result is that in the trunk and neck portion of the adult the fourth cervical dermatome is in contact with the second thoracic, and the second lumbar with the third sacral, the intervening segments having migrated to form the dermatomes of the extremities (Figs. 159, 160). This mode of migration explains the seemingly confusing arrangement and sequence of the limb dermatomes, and may still be recognized in the adult when the fetal position is approximated (Fig. 157B).

Sherrington (1894) experimentally demonstrated in the monkey the exact cutaneous areas supplied by the various dorsal roots. Section of a single root did not produce a marked anesthesia anywhere, so he selected a special root for study and cut two or three adjacent roots above and below. The area of "remaining sensibility" bounded above and below by an area of anesthesia obviously represented the dermatome supplied by the normal root. He found that each dermatome overlapped the sensory cutaneous areas of adjacent roots, being coinnervated by the one above and the one below (Fig. 158), hence at least two contiguous roots had to be sectioned to produce a region of complete anesthesia. Pictures similar to those of Sherrington were obtained by irritating single roots or ganglia with strychnine and noting the resulting hypersensitive areas (Dusser de Barenne).

Clinically, Head was the first to outline the human dermatomes by studying the areas of eruption and hyperalgesia occurring in herpes zoster, a disease which often attacks isolated spinal ganglia. More recently Foerster (1933, 1936) has furnished a remarkably complete map of human der-

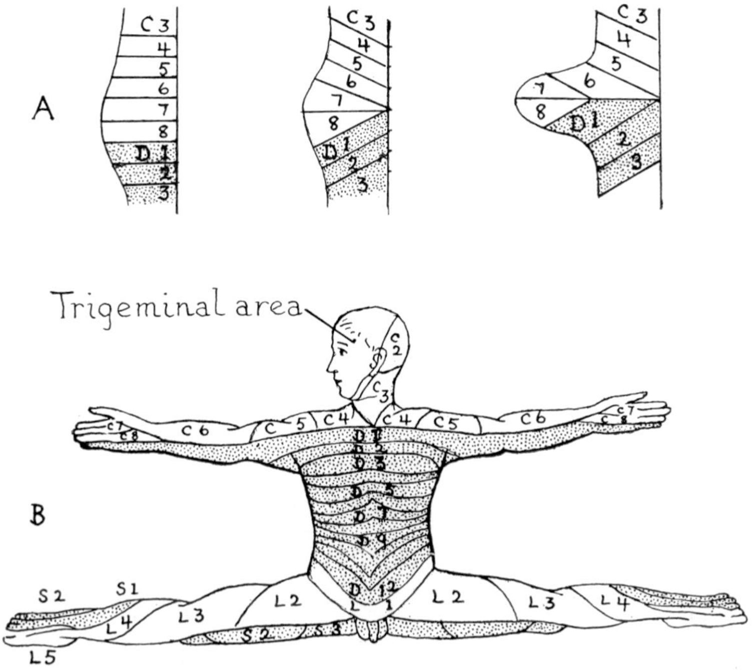

Fig. 157. *A*, schema of migration of metameres during development. (After Bing.) *B*, segmental arrangement of dermatomes. (After Luciani.) *c*, cervical; *d*, thoracic; *l*, lumbar; *s*, sacral.

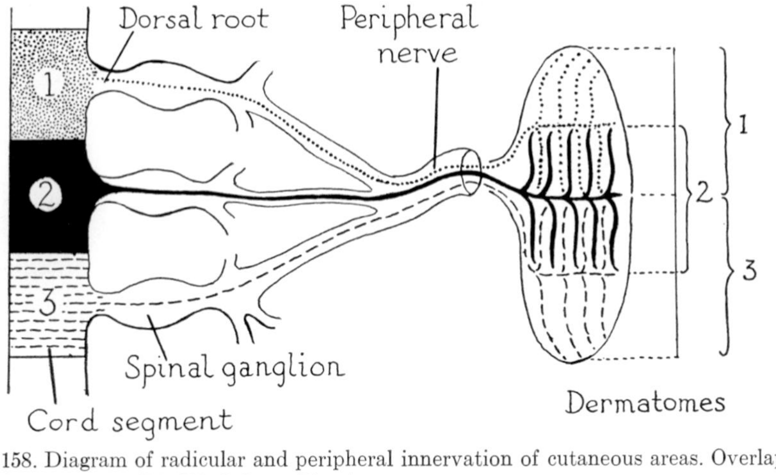

Fig. 158. Diagram of radicular and peripheral innervation of cutaneous areas. Overlapping of the dermatomes. (Modified from Bing.)

matomes, based on numerous resections of dorsal roots for the alleviation of spastic conditions and in cases of root injury due to tumors or other causes. They correspond in the main with the fields of Head and show the same overlapping given by Sherrington for monkeys. Most dermatomes are supplied by three, occasionally even four, dorsal roots. The only root whose section produces an area of complete anesthesia is C2, neither C3 nor the trigeminal nerve invading to any considerable extent the back of the head. It is interesting that the overlapping of adjacent dermatomes is greater for

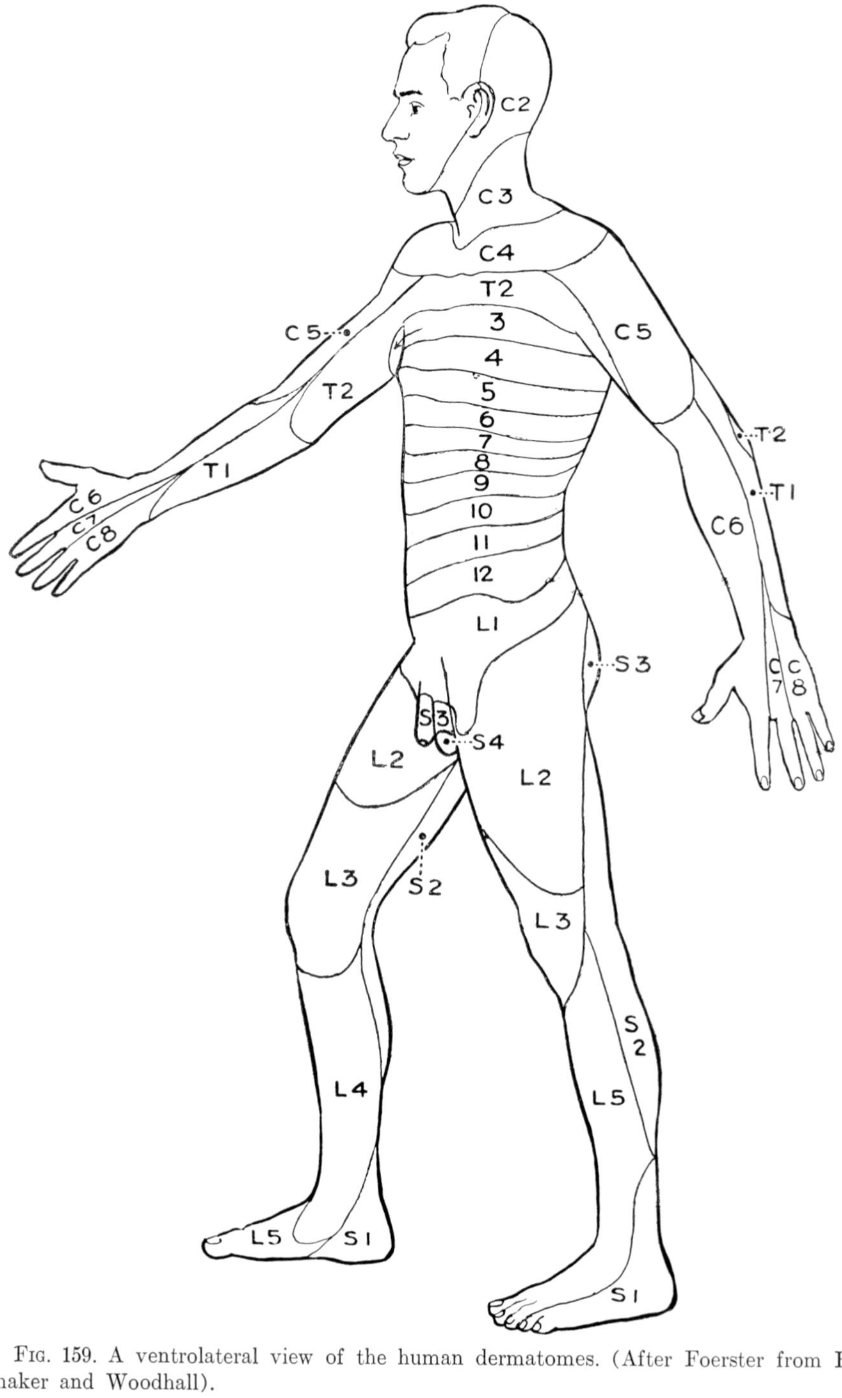

Fig. 159. A ventrolateral view of the human dermatomes. (After Foerster from Haymaker and Woodhall).

touch than for pain and temperature. The distribution of the human dermatomes is shown in Figs. 159, 160.

A somewhat different chart of the human dermatomes was recently published by Keegan and Garrett (1948) who outlined areas of diminished cutaneous sensibility caused by compression of individual roots. These

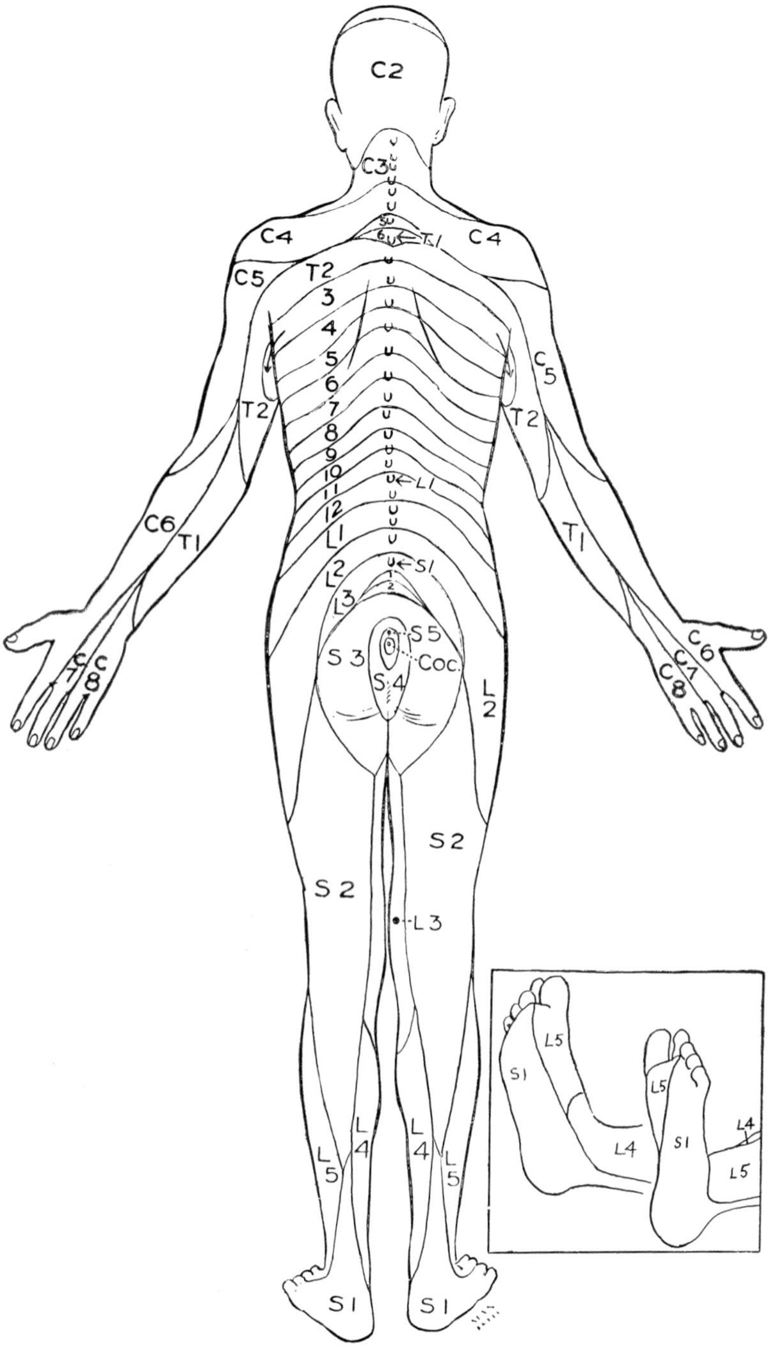

FIG. 160. Back view of the human dermatomes. Arrows in the region of the spinal column point to the spinous processes of the first thoracic, first lumbar, and first sacral vertebrae. (After Foerster from Haymaker and Woodhall.)

areas, which they called *primary dermatomes*, did not show any significant overlapping. Moreover, there was no evidence that the dermatomes of the extremities had wandered out and lost their connection with the axial portion of the body. The dermatomes presented a regular pattern of serial elongated bands, continuous from the dorsal midline down the arms and legs.

The segmental innervation of the striped musculature (myotomes) has likewise been worked out, by direct stimulation of ventral roots, by study of the pathological changes which occur in the ventral horn cells when a motor nerve is cut, and by secondary degeneration of peripheral nerve fibers. As in the case of the dermatomes, the majority of the muscles, especially those of the extremities, are innervated by two or three and occasionally even four ventral roots. Hence injury to a single root may only weaken the muscle or have no apparent effect whatever. Only the very short muscles of the trunk and spinal column and a few others such as the abductor pollicis, are formed from single myotomes and retain a monosegmental innervation. The peripheral projection of the myotomes coincides in the main with that of the dermatomes.

Following are the locations in the cord of the ventral horn cells which carry out some of the important reflex and other activities.

Movements of the head (by muscles of neck), C1–C4.

Movements of diaphragm (phrenic center), C3–C5.

Movements of upper extremity, C5–T1.

Biceps tendon reflex (flexion of forearm on percussion of biceps tendon), C5, C6.

Triceps tendon reflex (extension of forearm on percussion of triceps tendon), C6–C8.

Radial periosteal reflex (flexion of forearm on percussion of distal end of radius), C7, C8.

Wrist tendon reflexes (flexion of fingers on percussion of wrist tendons), C8-T1.

Movements of trunk, T1–T12.

Abdominal superficial reflexes (ipsilateral contraction of subjacent abdominal muscles on stroking skin of upper, middle, and lower abdomen), upper (epigastric), T6, T7; middle, T8, T9; lower, T10–T12.

Movements of lower extremity, L1–S2.

Cremasteric superficial reflex (elevation of scrotum on stroking skin of inner thigh), T12–L2.

Genital center for ejaculation, L1–L2 (smooth muscle); S3, S4 (striped muscles).

Vesical center for retention of urine, T12–L2.

Patellar tendon reflex or knee jerk (extension of leg on percussion of patellar ligament), L2–L4.

Gluteal superficial reflex (contraction of glutei on stroking skin over glutei), L4–S1.

Plantar superficial reflex (flexion of toes on stroking sole of foot), L5–S2.

Achilles tendon reflex or ankle jerk (plantar flexion of foot on percussion of Achilles tendon), L5–S2.

Genital center of erection, S2–S4.

Vesical center for evacuation of bladder, S3–S5.

Bulbocavernosus reflex (contraction of bulbocavernosus muscle on pinching penis), S3–S4.

Anal reflex (contraction of external rectal sphincter on stroking perianal region), S4, S5, and coccygeal.

PERIPHERAL INNERVATION

While each spinal nerve in a general way supplies its own body segment, there is considerable intermixture and anastomosis of adjacent nerve trunks before they reach their peripheral destination. The primary dorsal rami (Fig. 133) remain relatively distinct, though even here interconnections are common in the cervical and sacral regions. The ventral rami, however, form far more elaborate connections. Except for the thoracic nerves which largely retain their segmental distribution, the cervical and lumbosacral rami innervating the extremities anastomose and branch to form extensive plexuses in which a radical regrouping of fibers occurs. Each of the peripheral nerves arising from these plexuses now contains fibers contributed from two, three, four or even five ventral rami. As a result the cutaneous areas supplied by the peripheral nerves do not correspond with the cutaneous areas supplied by the individual dorsal roots (dermatomes). Similarly, several ventral roots may contribute fibers to a single muscle, and conversely several muscles may receive fibers from a single ventral root. A knowledge of the cutaneous and muscular distribution of the peripheral nerves is of great importance to the neurologist for determining the segmental level of peripheral nerve injuries, hence the more important morphological features are presented briefly. A more complete account will be found in the larger handbooks of anatomy and clinical neurology.

The **dorsal** or **posterior rami** of the spinal nerves innervate the intrinsic dorsal muscles of the back and neck, which constitute the extensor system of the vertebral column, and the overlying skin from vertex to coccyx. In the middle of the back the cutaneous area roughly corresponds to that of the underlying muscles, but in the upper and lower portions it widens laterally to reach the acromial region above and the region of the great trochanter below. With certain exceptions the dorsal rami have a typical segmental distribution, the field of each overlapping with that of the adjacent segment above and below. Each ramus usually divides into a medial and a lateral branch, both of which may contain sensory and motor fibers, though the lateral branches of the cervical rami are purely motor in character. Deviations are found in the upper two cervical and in the lumbosacral rami. The first or *suboccipital* nerve is purely motor and terminates in the short posterior muscles of the head (rectus capitis and obliquus capitis). The main branch of the second cervical ramus, known as the *greater occipital* nerve, ascends to the region of the superior nuchal line where it becomes subcutaneous, and supplies the scalp on the back of the head to the vertex, occasionally extending as far as the coronary suture (Fig. 164). The nerve is joined by a filament from the third cervical ramus. The lateral branches of the upper three lumbar and upper three sacral rami send cutaneous twigs which supply the upper part of the gluteal area, extending laterally to the region of the great trochanter. These branches are usually known as the *superior* (lumbar) and *medial* (sacral) *clunial* nerves (Fig. 164).

The **ventral** or **anterior rami** of the spinal nerves supply the ventrolateral muscles and skin as well as the extremities which are outgrowths of the ventral body wall. With the exception of most thoracic nerves, the ventral rami of adjacent nerves unite and anastomose to form the cervical, brachial, and lumbosacral plexuses.

Cervical plexus. The cervical plexus is formed from the ventral rami of the four upper cervical nerves. It furnishes cutaneous nerves for the ventrolateral portions of the neck, the shoulder, the upper part of the breast, and the lateral portions of the back of the head. The muscular branches supply the deep cervical muscles of the spinal column, the infrahyoid muscles, and the diaphragm. They also aid in the innervation of the trapezius and sternocleidomastoid which are chiefly supplied by the accessory nerve (N.XI).

The *lesser occipital* nerve (C2, C3) is distributed to the upper pole of the pinna and to the lateral area on the back of the head, overlapping only slightly the field of the greater occipital nerve (Fig. 164). The *great auricular nerve* (C2, C3) supplies the larger, lower portion of the pinna and the skin over the angle of the mandible. The *anterior cervical cutaneous* (C2, C3) innervates the ventral and lateral parts of the neck from chin to sternum (supra- and infrahyoid region). The *supraclavicular nerves* (C3, C4) variable in number of branches, are distributed to the shoulder, the most lateral regions of the neck, and to the upper part of the breast where their end branches overlap with those of the second intercostal nerve (Figs. 163, 164).

The chief muscular nerve is the *phrenic* which supplies the diaphragm and is derived mainly from C4, with smaller contributions from C3 or C5 or from both (Fig. 161). It frequently receives an anastomotic branch from the subclavian nerve of the brachial plexus, which enters the phrenic at a variable height. Hence in high lesions of the phrenic, paralysis of the diaphragm may not occur. The deep cervical muscles are innervated by direct segmental branches from the ventral rami. The lateral and the anterior rectus capitis receive twigs from C1 and C2; the longus capitis from C1–C3; the longus colli from C3–C6; the intertransversarii from all the cervical rami. Branches from C4 also aid in the innervation of the median scalene muscle.

The hyoid muscles, excepting those supplied by the cranial nerves, are innervated by twigs from C1–C3. These twigs unite into a common trunk known as the *ansa hypoglossi*. The geniohyoid and thyreohyoid are supplied entirely from C1; the sternohyoid, sternothyreoid and omohyoid from C2 and C3 as motor twigs from the ansa hypoglossi. The cervical plexus also aids in the innervation of the sternocleidomastoid and trapezius muscles which are mainly supplied by the accessory nerve. The sternocleidomastoid receives twigs from C2 and C3. The trapezius receives its main contributions from C3 and C4. The nerve filaments form one or more bundles which are often incorporated in the supraclavicular cutaneous nerves, and are distributed to the upper portion of the muscle. The middle and lower portions appear to be solely innervated by the accessory nerve (Foerster). The levator scapulae is supplied by nerves C3–C5.

Paralysis of the neck muscles as a result of peripheral injuries is relatively rare and is usually associated with involvement of the spinal cord.

The brachial plexus. The nerves supplying the upper extremity and forming the brachial plexus are derived as a rule from the ventral rami of the four lower cervical and the first thoracic nerves with a small contribution from the fourth cervical (Fig. 161). There are, however, considerable variations. If the contribution from the fourth cervical is strong and that of the first thoracic negligible the plexus belongs to the *prefixed* type. It is called *postfixed* when the fourth cervical does not participate at all, but the contribution of the first thoracic is strong and in addition the second thoracic sends a branch to the plexus. Between these extremes there are many intermediate conditions, depending on the stronger or weaker participation of the fourth cervical on the one hand and the first thoracic on the other. These variations are probably dependent on embryological factors. The limb buds of both arms and legs may vary in longitudinal extent and especially in their relative position to the neuraxis. The more cephalic the position of the limbs, the more cephalic will be the nerves contributing to the plexus, and vice versa (Stookey).

The ventral rami supplying the plexus give rise to three *primary trunks*. C5 and C6 unite to form the *upper trunk*; C8 and T1 form the *lower*, while C7 is continued as the *middle trunk*. Then passing underneath the region of the clavicle, each trunk splits into a dorsal and a ventral division. The dorsal divisions of all three trunks fuse to form the *posterior cord* placed behind the axillary artery. The ventral divisions of the upper and middle trunk form the *lateral cord*, while the ventral division of the lower trunk is continued as the *medial cord* (Fig. 161).

Many of the nerves supplying the shoulder muscles are given off directly from the ventral rami or from the primary trunks and their branches before these unite to form the secondary cords. Here also dor-

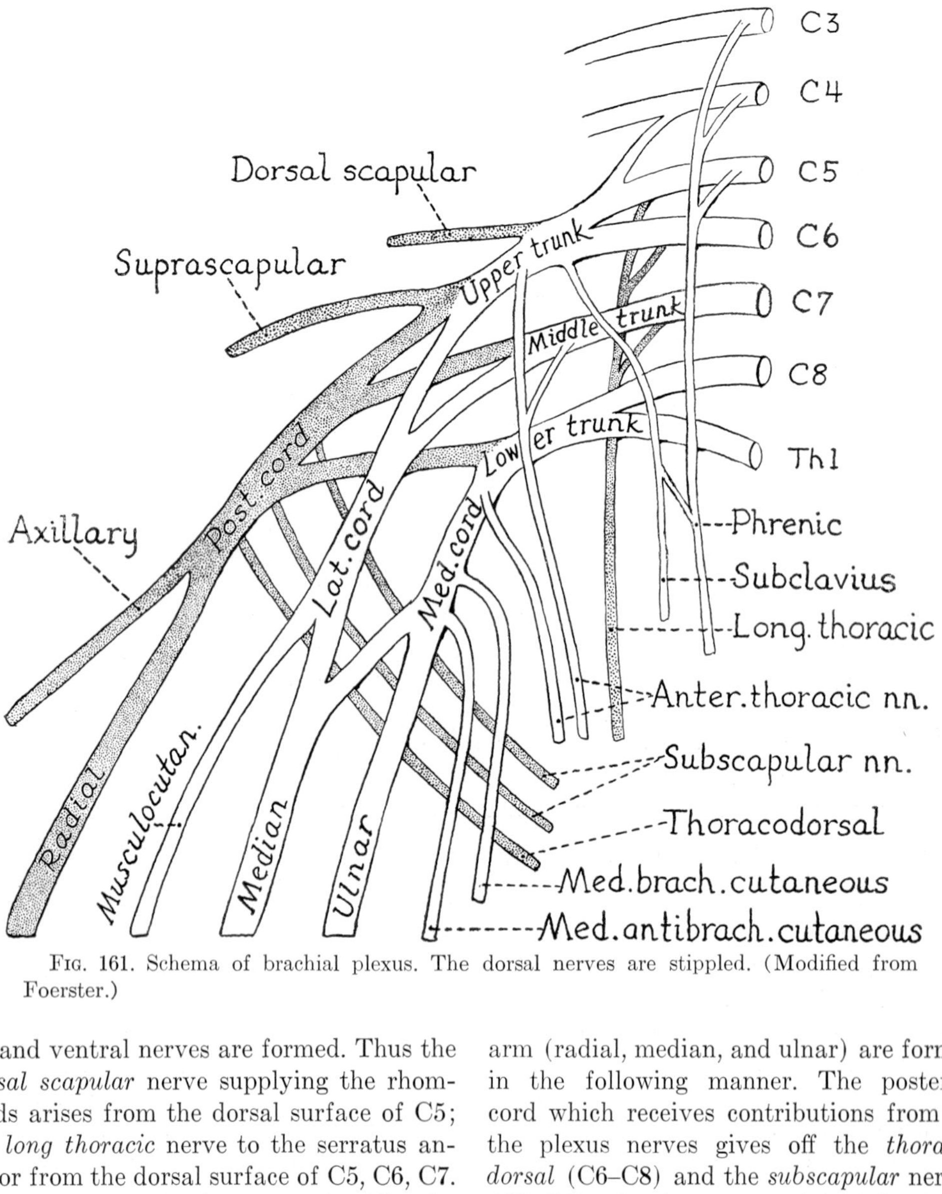

FIG. 161. Schema of brachial plexus. The dorsal nerves are stippled. (Modified from Foerster.)

sal and ventral nerves are formed. Thus the *dorsal scapular* nerve supplying the rhomboids arises from the dorsal surface of C5; the *long thoracic* nerve to the serratus anterior from the dorsal surface of C5, C6, C7. From the upper trunk emerge dorsally the *suprascapular* nerve (C4, C5, C6) for the supraspinatus and infraspinatus; ventrally the small nerve to the subclavius (C5, C6). The roots of the *anterior thoracic* nerves (C5–T1) which innervate the pectoralis major and minor arise in part from the ventral surface of the upper and middle trunks, in part from the medial cord (Fig. 161).

The three large peripheral nerves of the arm (radial, median, and ulnar) are formed in the following manner. The posterior cord which receives contributions from all the plexus nerves gives off the *thoracodorsal* (C6–C8) and the *subscapular* nerves (C5–C8), the former supplying the latissimus dorsi, the latter the teres major and subcapularis. Then the posterior cord splits into its two terminal branches, the larger *radial* and the smaller *axillary* nerve. The lateral and medial cords each split into two branches, thus forming four nerve trunks. The two middle branches, one from the lateral and one from the medial cord, unite to form the *median* nerve. The outer branch derived from the lateral cord be-

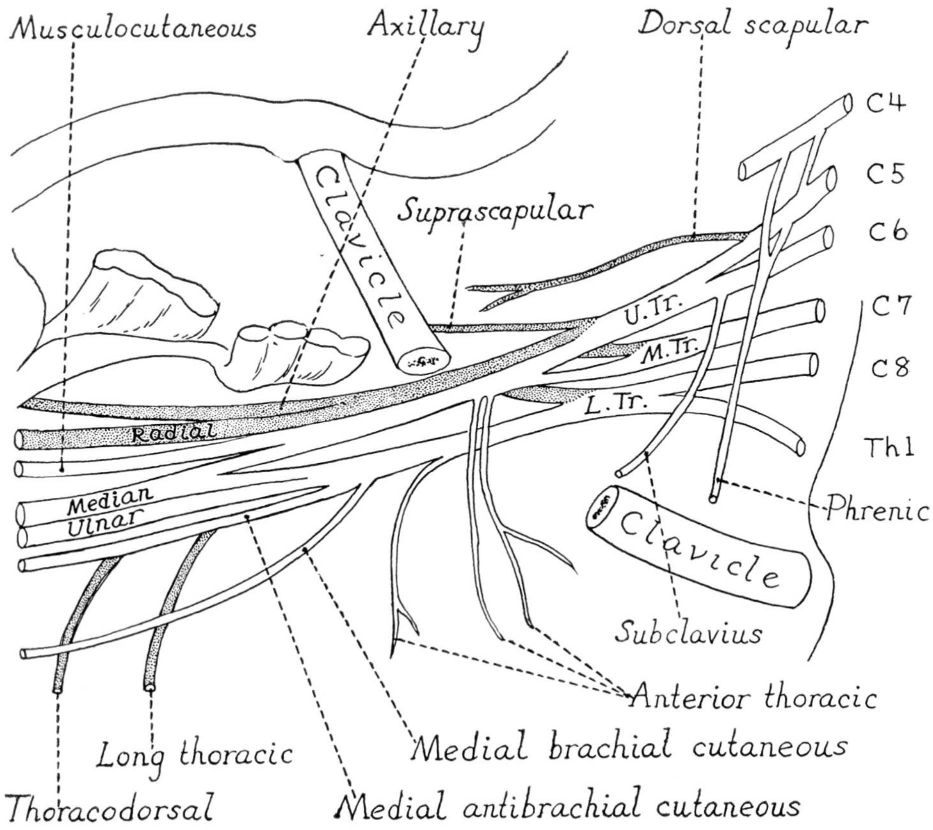

FIG. 162. The brachial plexus. The dorsal nerves are stippled. U.Tr., M.Tr., L.Tr., upper, middle, and lower trunk. (After a dissection by Borchardt.)

comes the *muscluocutaneous nerve.* The large innermost branch derived from the medial cord gives off the purely sensory *medial brachial cutaneous* and *medial antibrachial cutaneous* nerves, and is then continued as the *ulnar nerve* (Figs. 161, 162).

A brief reference to embryological conditions will aid in explaining the formation of the plexus. During early development the primitive muscle mass of the limb is split into a dorsal and a ventral layer, separated by the anlage of the humerus. The primary ventral nerve rami invading the limb likewise split into dorsal and ventral branches to supply the corresponding muscles and the overlying skin. Within the primitive musculature, many simple muscles fuse to form larger and more complex ones and become supplied by two or more spinal nerves, with resulting interlacing of nerve fibers and plexus formation. Such fusion usually occurs within the dorsal or the ventral musculature and the muscles are innervated respectively by dorsal or ventral nerves. However, at the cephalic (preaxial) and the caudal (postaxial) border of the limb some muscles may be derived from both the dorsal and ventral musculature. These are then supplied by both dorsal and ventral nerves. A well known example is the brachialis muscle which receives branches from the radial and musculocutaneous nerves. Thus the plexus primitively shows a division into a dorsal and a ventral plate, the former innervating the dorsal or extensor half of the arm and the dorsal shoulder muscles; the ventral supplying the volar or flexor half and the ventral muscles of the shoulder. The nerves arising from the dorsal plate are the dorsal scapular, long thoracic, suprascapular, subscapular, thoracodorsal, axillary, and radial. Those from the ventral plate include the subclavian, anterior thoracic, musculocutaneous, median, ulnar, and the purely sensory medial brachial and medial antibrachial cutaneous nerves.

Following is a summary of the peripheral distribution of the principal arm nerves, including the segmental supply of the individual muscles. The cutaneous areas are shown in Figs. 163, 164.

The *axillary* nerve supplies motor branches to the deltoid (C4–C6) and teres minor (C5, C6) and sends the *lateral brachial cutaneous* nerve to the skin of the upper outer surface of the arm, mainly the deltoid region (Figs. 163, 164). In complete section of the nerve, abduction of the arm without external rotation is practically im-

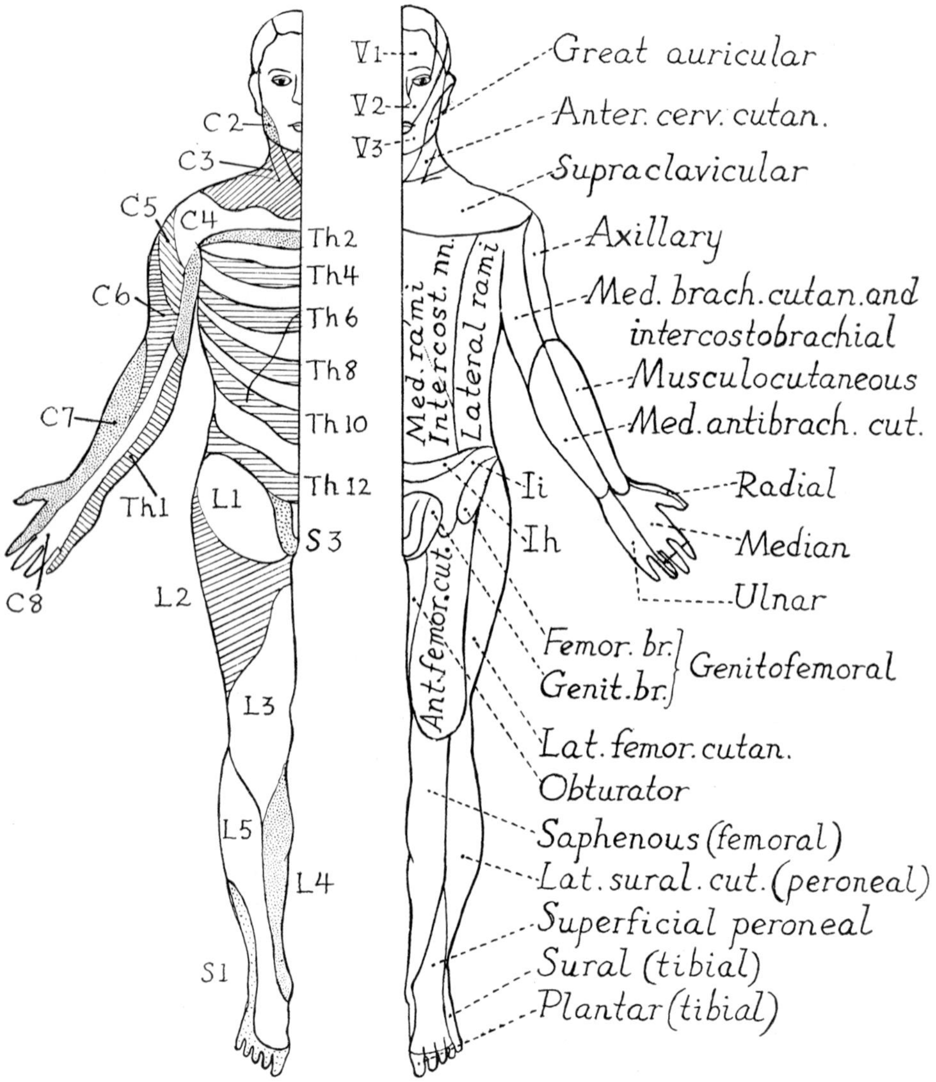

FIG. 163. Dermatomes (left) and cutaneous fields of peripheral nerves. Front view. Ih, iliohypogastric; Ii, ilioinguinal.

possible. The sensory loss is less extensive than the area supplied, due to the overlap of neighboring cutaneous nerves.

The *radial* nerve (C5–T1) supplies motor branches to all the extensors of the elbow, hands and fingers, to the brachioradialis, supinator and abductor pollicis longus. In addition it usually sends a twig to the brachialis. Its cutaneous branches, all distributed to the dorsal surface of the extremity, are the *posterior brachial cutaneous nerve* to the arm, the *dorsal antibrachial cutaneous* to the forearm, and the *superficial radial nerve* to the radial half of the dorsum of the hand and fingers as far as the distal interphalangeal joints (Fig. 164). The muscular branches are given off to the muscles in the following order:

Triceps and Anconeus, C7, C8, T1.
Brachioradialis, C5, C6.
Extensor carpi radialis longus, C6, C7.
Supinator, C5, C6.
Extensor digitorum communis, (C6), C7, C8.
Extensor carpi radialis brevis, C7.
Abductor pollicis longus, C7, C8.
Extensor carpi ulnaris, C7, C8.
Extensor digiti quinti proprius, C7, C8.
Extensor pollicis longus, C7, C8.
Extensor pollicis brevis, C8, T1.
Extensor indicis proprius, C8, T1.

Injuries of the radial nerve will give variable symptoms depending on the height of the lesion. Complete section of the nerve above all its branches will produce inability to extend the elbow, wrist, fingers, and thumb, with wrist drop as the most striking feature. The sensory loss is most marked on the dorsum of the hand in the territory supplied by the superficial ramus. The anesthesia is negligible on the arm, but is usually present in a narrow strip on the dorsal surface of the forearm from elbow to wrist. The limited sensory loss is due to overlap of adjacent cutaneous nerves.

The *musculocutaneous* nerve (C5–C7) sends muscular branches to the coracobrachialis (C6, C7), biceps (C5, C6) and brachialis (C5, C6), and continues as the *lateral antibrachial cutaneous* nerve to supply the radial half of the forearm, both dorsal and volar (Figs. 163, 164). In complete section of the nerve flexion and supination of the forearm are weakened. The lateral portion of the brachialis may be spared since it receives as a rule a branch from the radial nerve, and in addition flexion can still be produced by the brachioradialis. The sensory loss is variable in extent. It is poorly defined dorsally, due to overlap with the dorsal antibrachial cutaneous nerve of the radial. On the volar side it is more extensive and more nearly approximates the territory supplied by the nerve.

The *median* nerve (C6–T1, sometimes also C5) supplies all the muscles on the volar surface of the forearm except the flexor carpi ulnaris and the ulnar heads of the flexor digitorum profundis. In the hand its branches go to the outer lumbricals (I, II) and to the muscles of the thenar eminence, excepting the adductor pollicis and deep head of the flexor pollicis brevis. The sensory innervation is practically limited to the hand, comprising the volar surface of the thumb, index, and middle fingers and the radial half of the fourth finger, with corresponding portions of the palm (Fig. 163). Dorsally the nerve supplies the distal phalanx of the index, middle and radial half of the fourth finger. An inconstant *palmar* branch is distributed to the radial half of the volar surface of the wrist, but this area is usually completely overlapped by the antibrachial branch of the musculotaneous nerve. The order of the muscular branches is as follows:

Pronator teres, C6, C7.
Flexor carpi radialis, C6–C8.
Palmaris longus, (C7), C8, T1.
Flexor digitorum sublimis, C7–T1.
Flexor digitorum profundis, radial head, (C7), C8, T1.
Flexor pollicis longus, (C7), C8, T1.
Pronator quadratus, C8., T1.

Flexor pollicis brevis, superficial head, C8, T1.
Abductor pollicis brevis, C8. T1; opponens pollicis, C8, T1.
Lumbricals I and II, (C7), C8, T1.

Injury to the nerve along its course in the arm will affect all its branches. Complete interruption causes severe impairment of pronation of the forearm and weakened flexion of the wrist. The wasting of the thenar eminence and the abnormal position of the thumb may give the hand a characteristic appearance. Normally the thumb is partially rotated and its metacarpal bone is in a more volar plane than the other metacarpals. In injury of the median nerve the rotation is lost, the thumb is extended and now lies in the same plane as the rest of the palm (simian hand).

Flexion of the index finger is practically abolished, and is only slightly compensated by the flexor action of the interossei at the metacarpophalangeal joint. The middle finger is more variably affected. In the thumb, flexion of the terminal phalanx is completely lost, as are abduction and opposition of the thumb. Makeshift movements of opposition, without abduction and rotation, can still be effected by the abductor pollicis and the deep head of the flexor brevis (pseudo-opposition). The motor defects are especially brought out in making a fist. The fourth and fifth fingers flex, the thumb and index finger, and to a variable degree the middle finger, remain partially extended.

Disturbances of cutaneous sensibility occur in the area supplied by the nerve. Complete anesthesia is, however, much smaller in extent and is most constant on the volar surface of the index and middle finger.

The *ulnar* nerve (C8, T1, some fibers also from C7) supplies in the forearm the flexor carpi ulnaris and the ulnar head of the flexor digitorum profundis. In the hand it is distributed to the adductor pollicis, the deep head of the flexor pollicis brevis, the interossei, the two inner lumbricals, and the muscles of the hypothenar eminence. It gives off three cutaneous branches. The *palmar cutaneous* branch supplies the ulnar half of the volar surface of the wrist, an area extensively overlapped by the medial antibrachial cutaneous nerve. The *dorsal* branch goes to the ulnar half of the dorsum of the hand and all of the little finger, and to the proximal phalanx of the ulnar half of the fourth or ring finger. The *superficial volar* branch supplies the volar surface of the fifth and ulnar half of the fourth finger and the corresponding ulnar portion of the palm (hypothenar region), (Figs. 163, 164). The muscle branches are given off in the following order:

Flexor carpi ulnaris, (C7), C8, T1.
Flexor digitorum profundis, ulnar head, (C7), C8, T1.
Palmaris brevis, C8, T1.
Hypothenar muscles, C8, T1:
  Abductor digiti quinti.
  Flexor digiti quinti brevis.
  Opponens digiti quinti.
Interossei, C8, T1.
Adductor pollicis, C8, T1.
Flexor pollicis brevis, deep head, C8, T1.
Lumbricals III and IV, C8, T1.

As in the case of median nerve, injury to the ulnar nerve in the arm region will affect its whole distribution. Flexion of the wrist is weakened, as are also flexion of the fourth and fifth fingers and adduction of the thumb. There is marked wasting of the hypothenar muscles and of the interossei. The paralysis of these small muscles is particularly disturbing, making it exceedingly difficult to execute the finger movements required for writing, sewing and other skilled activities. The interossei flex the basal phalanges and extend the middle and distal ones. Hence paralysis of the interossei may cause an overextension of the basal phalanges by the extensor digitorum communis, and a flexion of the middle and distal ones by the flexor digitorum sublimis (claw hand).

Sensory disturbances are variable, cor-

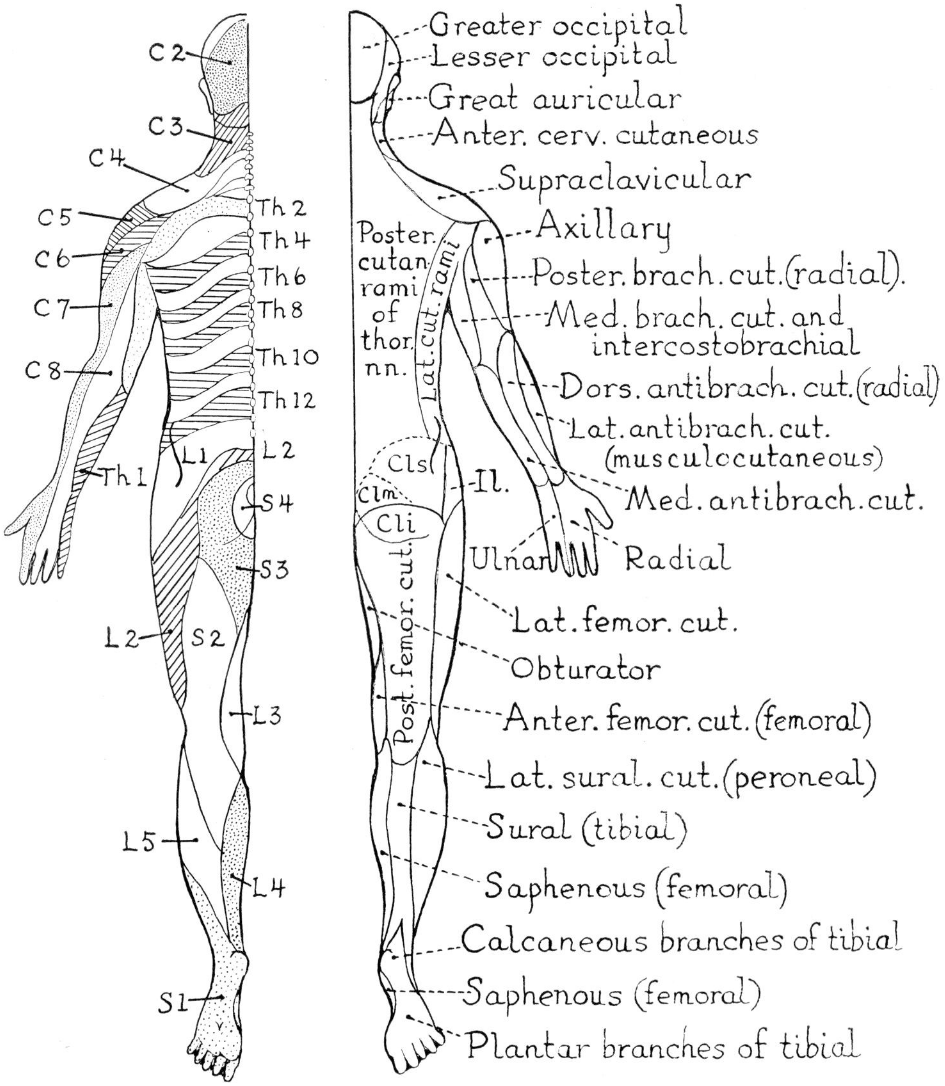

FIG. 164. Dermatomes (left) and cutaneous fields of peripheral nerves. Back view. Cls, Clm, and Cli, superior, medial, and inferior clunial nerves; Il, iliohypogastric nerve.

responding in the main to the anatomical distribution. Total anesthesia is as a rule limited to the little finger and hypothenar region.

The *medial antibrachial cutaneous* nerve (C8, T1) supplies the medial half of the forearm, both dorsal and volar (Figs. 163, 164). The extent of the sensory deficits caused by injury varies in individual cases. On the volar side it often reaches to the middle of the arm. On the dorsal side it is smaller than the area of supply.

The *medial brachial cutaneous* nerve (T1) is usually associated with the *intercostobrachial* nerve derived from the second and often from the third thoracic (intercostal) nerves. The two nerves supply the axillary region and the inner surface of the arm, the area being considerably larger on the volar than on the dorsal surface (Figs. 163, 164). The area is extensively overlapped by adjacent cutaneous nerves. Injury to one or the other produces negligible symptoms or none at all. In injury of both the anesthesia is limited to the axillary region and medial surface of the upper arm.

Injuries of the brachial plexus. The motor and sensory deficits of plexus lesions vary considerably, depending on the extent of the injury and whether the primary trunks or secondary cords are involved. In injury of the trunks the symptoms are segmental in character, and two main types of symptom complexes may be recognized, affecting respectively the upper or the lower primary trunk. The upper type (syndrome of Duchenne-Erb) involves the muscles supplied by C5 and C6, namely the deltoid, biceps, brachialis, brachioradialis, supinator, teres major, teres minor, supraspinatus, and infraspinatus. There is difficulty in the elevation and external rotation of the arm, accompanied by a severe loss of flexion and supination of the forearm. Owing to the overlap of adjacent roots, the sensory deficit is as a rule limited to the deltoid region and outer aspect of the arm.

The lower type (syndrome of Klumpke or of Duchenne-Aran) is relatively rare and affects primarily the small muscles of the hand innervated by C8 and T1. The palmaris longus and the long digital flexors are usually involved, hence the chief disabilities are in the finger and wrist movements. The sensory defects are along the inner aspects of the arm, forearm, and hand. If the preganglionic sympathetic fibers of the first thoracic root are included in the injury, there will be drooping of the eyelid, diminution of the pupil, and narrowing of the palpebral fissure (Horner's syndrome, Fig. 204).

Injuries of the secondary cords produce symptoms similar to those of peripheral nerves, except that several peripheral nerves are affected at the same time. Thus a lesion of the posterior cord will involve the radial and axillary nerves, and often the thoracodorsal and subscapular. Interruption of the lateral cord will affect the musculocutaneous and the lateral portion of the median nerve. Injury to the medial cord will involve the ulnar and the medial portion of the median nerve, as well as the medial brachial and antibrachial cutaneous nerves. The motor and sensory disabilities resulting from injury of these nerves have already been discussed.

The lumbosacral plexus. The plexus innervating the lower extremity is as a rule formed by the primary ventral (anterior) rami of L1–S2 and the larger portion of S3, frequently with a small contributing branch from T12. As in the case of the brachial plexus there may be anatomic variations. The plexus is *prefixed* when supplied by T12–S2, *postfixed* when formed from L2–S4, with many intermediate conditions, the maximum shift in either direction rarely exceeding the extent of a single spinal nerve. These conditions are probably determined by the individual variations in the position of the limb buds during development. According to Foerster (1929) prefixed plexuses are rare, since in none of his cases did faradic stimulation of the twelfth thoracic nerve produce a contraction of a single muscle in the lower extremity.

The lumbosacral plexus, excluding the pudendal and coccygeal portions which are not distributed to the leg, is conveniently subdivided into an upper *lumbar* and a lower *sacral* plexus. The lumbar plexus is formed by L1, L2, L3 and the larger part of L4, and there is usually a communicating branch from T12 (Fig. 165). The more extensive sacral plexus is supplied by the smaller portion of L4 (furcal nerve) which joins L5 to form the stout lumbosacral trunk, and by S1, S2 and the greater portion of S3 (Fig. 166). Except for the uppermost portion supplied mainly by L1, where the conditions are somewhat obscure, both plexuses show an organization into dorsal and ventral divisions. The arrangement is simpler than in the brachial plexus. The undivided lumbosacral primary rami do not form interlacing trunks but split directly into dorsal and ventral divisions related

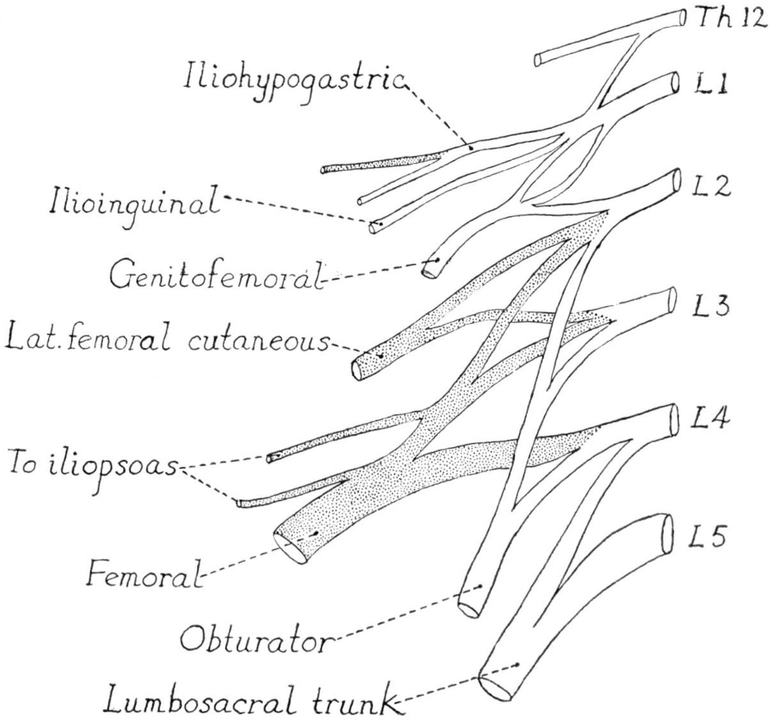

FIG. 165. Schema of lumbar plexus. The dorsal nerves are stippled.

respectively to the primitive dorsal and ventral musculature of the leg. The peripheral nerves to the extremity are then formed by the union of a variable number of either dorsal or ventral divisions (Figs. 165, 166). In the lumbar plexus the ventral divisions give rise to the iliohypogastric (ventral branch), ilioinguinal, genitofemoral, and obturator nerves; the dorsal to the iliohypogastric (dorsal branch), femoral, and lateral femoral cutaneous nerves. In the sacral plexus the ventral divisions furnish the tibial nerve and the nerve to the hamstring muscles; the dorsal divisions form the common peroneal and the superior and inferior gluteal nerves. The posterior femoral cutaneous nerve which supplies the back of the thigh receives fibers from both dorsal and ventral divisions. As in the case of the arm, muscles derived from both the dorsal and the ventral primitive musculature, are innervated by both dorsal and ventral divisions. Thus the biceps femoris receives branches from the tibial as well as peroneal portions of the sciatic nerve.

Following is a summary of the peripheral distribution of the principal leg nerves including the segmental supply of the individual muscles. The cutaneous areas are shown in Figs. 163, 164.

The *obturator* nerve (L2–L4) supplies the adductor muscles of the thigh and the gracilis, and sends an inconstant branch to the pectineus which is more often innervated by the femoral nerve. Its cutaneous branch is distributed to the inner surface of the thigh (Figs. 163, 164), the area being extensively overlapped by adjacent cutaneous nerves. The muscle branches are as follows:

Obturator externus, L3–L4.
Adductor magnus, L2–L4.
Adductor brevis, L2–L4.
Adductor longus, L2–L4.
Gracilis, L2–L4.
(Pectineus, L2–L4).

In injury of the nerve, adduction of the

thigh is severely weakened but not completely lost since the adductor magnus also receives some fibers from the sciatic nerve. The sensory defects usually involve only a small triangular area of the anatomical field.

The *femoral* nerve (L2–L4, also L1) sends motor branches to the extensors of the leg, the iliopsoas, the sartorius and also to the pectineus. Occasionally a branch may go to the adductor longus. The cutaneous branches are the *anterior femoral cutaneous* nerves for the thigh and the *saphenous* nerve for the leg and foot (Figs. 163, 164). The former supply the ventral and ventromedial surface of the thigh, comprising a relatively large autonomous sensory field. The saphenous nerve sends an infrapatellar branch to the skin in front of the knee-cap and is then distributed to the medial side of the leg, the lowermost terminal branches going to the medial margin of the foot to about the proximal phalanx of the great toe. The order of muscular branches is as follows:

Iliopsoas, L1–L4, mainly L1, L2.
Pectineus, L2–L4.
Sartorius, L1–L3.
Quadriceps femoris:
  Rectus femoris, L2–L4.
  Vastus lateralis and vastus intermedius, L2–L4.
  Vastus medialis, L2–L4.

Injury of the femoral nerve causes inability to extend the leg. If the lesion is high enough to involve the iliopsoas, flexion of the thigh is severely impaired. Sensory disturbances are manifested throughout the field of supply with relatively large areas of total anesthesia. If the thigh nerves alone are involved the anesthesia is most extensive on the ventral surface of the thigh above the knee. In isolated lesions of the saphenous nerve, the anesthetic field extends on the inner surface of the leg from just below the knee to the medial margin of the foot.

The *lateral femoral cutaneous* nerve (L2, L3) supplies the lateral half of the thigh, both dorsal and ventral, extending from the lateral buttock region to the knee (Figs. 163, 164). In spite of considerable overlapping with adjacent cutaneous nerves, injury produces a considerable strip of anesthesia on the lateral aspect of the thigh.

The cutaneous areas supplied by the *iliohypogastric* (L1), *ilioinguinal* (L1), and *genitofemoral* (L1, L2) nerves are shown in Figs. 163, 164. The iliohypogastric and ilioinguinal also send motor fibers to the internal oblique and transverse abdominal muscles. Sensory loss due to injury to one of these nerves is relatively small or lacking altogether, but such lesions frequently cause neuralgia.

The *sciatic* nerve (L4–S3), the largest nerve in the body, is the chief continuation of all the roots of the sacral plexus. It is in reality composed of the two main leg nerves, the tibial and the common peroneal, enclosed for a variable distance within a common sheath (Fig. 166). Emerging from the greater sciatic foramen, or while still within it, the nerve sends branches to the main external rotators of the thigh, comprising the obturator internus, the gemelli and the quadratus femoris (L5, S1, S2). Lesions of these nerves are comparatively rare and there is only a weakening of external rotation, since other external rotators are available. In the region of the thigh branches are given off to the flexors of the knee (hamstring muscles) and to the adductor magnus, the latter being also innervated by the obturator nerve. These branches, all derived from the tibial portion of the sciatic, often spring from a common trunk which either runs independently or is loosely incorporated in the medial side of the sciatic nerve. An additional branch from the common peroneal nerve supplies the short head of the biceps femoris. In injuries of the hamstring nerves flexion of the knee is severely impaired, but weak flexion may still be produced by the action of the gracilis and sartorius muscles.

The sciatic splits into its two terminal

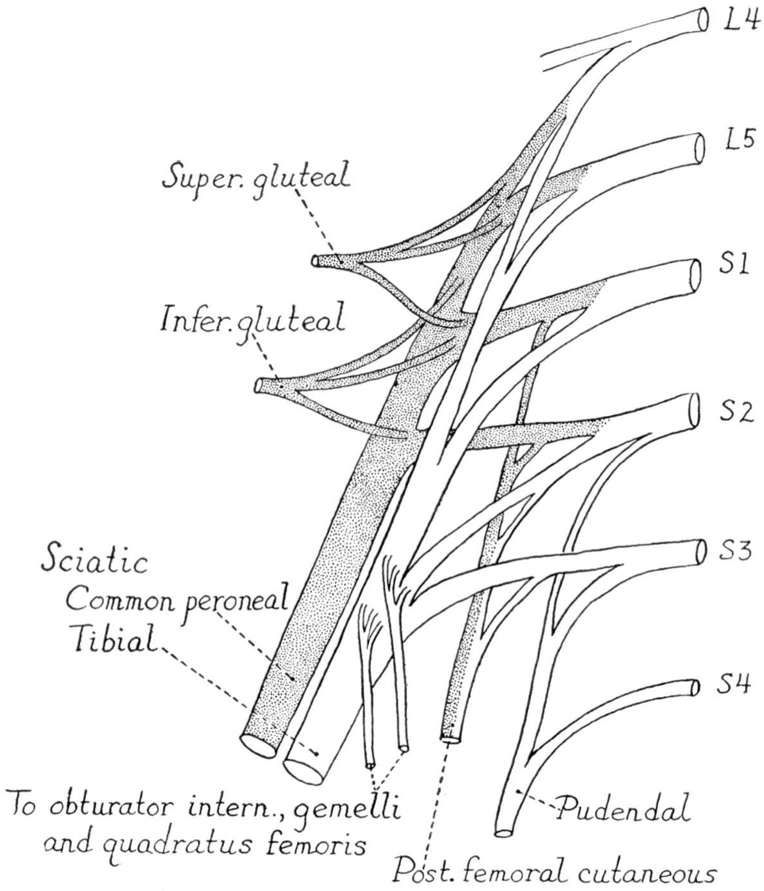

FIG. 166. Schema of sacral plexus. The dorsal nerves are stippled.

nerves at greatly varying levels of the thigh region. The muscular branches of the common trunk are as follows:

Quadratus femoris, obturator internus, gemelli, L5, S1, S2.
Semitendinosus, L5–S2.
Semimembranosus, L5–S2.
Biceps femoris, long head, L5–S2.
Biceps femoris, short head, S1, S2 (common peroneal nerve).

The *tibial* nerve (L4–S3) supplies the dorsal calf muscles concerned with plantar flexion and inversion of the foot and with plantar flexion of the toes, and the intrinsic muscles of the sole which aid in maintaining the arch of the foot. One cutaneous branch given off in the thigh, the *sural* nerve, is distributed to the dorsal and medial surface of the calf where it is extensively overlapped by the end branchings of the saphenous and lateral sural (peroneal) nerves. The terminal branches of the sural (*lateral calcaneal*) supply the outer margin of the heel and a triangular area on the outer surface of the foot to the lower portion of the Achilles tendon. Other cutaneous branches of the tibial nerve (*medial calcaneal* and *plantar*) supply the back and medial margin of the heel, the plantar surface of the foot and toes and the dorsal surface of the distal phalanges (Figs. 163, 164). The terminal branches of the tibial nerve are the *medial* and *lateral plantar* nerves. The muscle branches are as follows:

Gastrocnemius, S1, S2.
Plantaris, S1, S2.
Popliteus, L5, S1, S2.
Soleus, S1, S2.

Tibialis posterior, L4, L5.
Flexor digitorum longus, S1, S2.
Flexor hallucis longus, S1, S2.
Muscles of the sole:
Flexor digitorum brevis, S2, S3.
Interossei and lumbricals, S1–S3.
Flexor brevis and abductor digiti quinti, S1–S3.
Abductor hallucis, S1–S3.
Flexor hallucis brevis, S1–S3.
Adductor hallucis, S1–S3.

Complete interruption of the tibial nerve above all its branches will abolish plantar flexion of the foot and toes, and severely impair inversion of the foot. Atrophy of the sole muscles will increase the concavity of the plantar arch (pes cavus). Sensory disturbances are negligible in the calf region in which only a narrow strip may show reduced sensitivity. Total anesthesia is found on the sole of the foot, the plantar surface of the toes and on the heel, and often on a triangular area on the outer surface of the foot.

The *common peroneal* nerve (L4–S2) supplies the lateral and ventral muscles of the leg and the dorsal muscles of the foot, effecting dorsal flexion and eversion of the foot and dorsal flexion of the toes. The chief cutaneous nerves are the *lateral sural cutaneous* and the *superficial peroneal* nerve (Figs. 163, 164). The former, given off in the thigh, is distributed to the outer side of the leg from the knee region to nearly the outer margin of the sole where it invades the territories of the superficial peroneal and sural nerves. The superficial peroneal supplies the dorsum of the foot and toes to the distal phalanges and a portion of the ventral surface of the leg. A small branch of the deep peroneal nerve is distributed to the cleft between the adjacent surfaces of the great and second toe. The muscle branches are as follows:

Peroneus longus, L5–S1.
Peroneus brevis, L5–S2.
Tibialis anterior, L4, L5.
Extensor digitorum longus, L5, S1.
Peroneus tertius, L5, S1.
Extensor hallucis longus, L5, S1.
Extensor digitorum brevis, S1, S2.
Extensor hallucis brevis, S1, S2.

Complete section of the peroneal nerve causes paralysis of dorsal flexion and eversion of the foot and of dorsal flexion (extension) of the toes. The most striking feature is the inability to elevate the foot and toes (foot-drop). If the condition is prolonged, shortening of the Achilles tendon will produce a permanent plantar overflexion and the foot will assume the appearance of equinovarus. Sensory defects will be found on the dorsum of the foot, the outer part of the leg, and the skin between the great and second toe. The extent is much smaller than the anatomical field, since both foot and leg areas are extensively overlapped by the adjacent cutaneous nerves.

The *superior gluteal* nerve (L4–S1) supplies the gluteus medius, gluteus minimus, and tensor fasciae latae, which abduct the hip and rotate it internally. These movements will be impaired by injury to the nerve.

The *inferior gluteal* nerve (L5–S2) is distributed to the gluteus maximus which is the strongest extensor of the hip. Injury causes wasting of the buttock. There is difficulty in rising from a sitting position, walking uphill, or climbing stairs, where powerful contraction of the muscle is required for raising the body.

The *posterior femoral cutaneous* nerve (S1–S3) gives off several branches (*inferior clunial*) which supply the lower portions of the buttocks where they overlap with the branches of the lumbar and sacral dorsal rami (superior and medial clunial nerves), (Fig. 164). Another small branch (*perineal*) goes to the lower innermost part of the buttock and the dorsal surface of the scrotum (or labia majora) and reaches the inner surface of the thigh. The main nerve supplies the dorsal aspect of the thigh, often extending considerably below the knee and widely overlapping with adjacent nerves. Injuries produce a relatively broad strip of anesthesia on the dorsal surface of the thigh from buttocks to the level of the knee-cap.

Regeneration of injured peripheral nerves. Our knowledge of the processes of degeneration and regeneration has been greatly increased in recent years by intensive investigations on mammalian nerves under various experimental conditions. Valuable information was obtained by clinical and surgical studies of the many peripheral nerve injuries resulting from the war. Seddon (1944) distinguishes three types of nerve injury: (1) Complete anatomical division (*neurotmesis*), practically always demanding surgical intervention, such as suture, for a more or less successful recovery. The recovery is never complete since many of the regenerating fibers fail to reach their respective end organs. (2) Injuries in which the continuity of the nerve fibers is broken but the sheath and supporting tissue remain intact (*axonotmesis*), due to crush or severe compression. There is complete degeneration of the severed nerve fibers as in neurotmesis, and the clinical symptoms such as loss of sensation and movement, wasting of muscles and reaction of degeneration, are likewise the same. But since the damaged nerve fibers are in close anatomical contiguity, spontaneous regeneration always leads to good recovery. (3) Temporary impairment or block, with varying degree of paralysis but with persistence of normal electrical excitability (*neurapraxia*). The nerve fibers are not severed, hence there is no peripheral degeneration. Recovery is rapid, beginning in a few weeks and usually completed in two or three months. The three types may appear as separate entities or in various combinations. Since the clinical symptoms of neurotmesis and axonotmesis are the same until recovery begins, surgical exploration is usually indicated to determine the nature of the injury (Stookey and Scarff).

In a simple crush (axonotmesis), though the continuity of the axons is interrupted, the endoneurium and other supporting tissue remain essentially intact. As a result, new fibers from the central stump can grow straight down, traverse the relatively insignificant scar formed between the severed axonal ends and enter appropriate tubes of the distal stump. After complete anatomical severance (neurotmesis), the conditions are quite different at the site of injury. The cut ends are separated by a gap of variable extent, which soon becomes filled with connective tissue and sheath cells, forming a scar of union between the stumps. The behavior of the sheath cells is especially significant. About the fourth day, they become elongated and migrate out of the stumps into the scar, coming mainly from the peripheral stump and to a lesser extent from the central one. These cells arrange themselves end to end, and form strands which traverse the fibrous tissue of the scar and establish continuity between the intact axons and the degenerating tubes of the peripheral stump. In some animals under suitable conditions, gaps of 2 cm. have been naturally bridged in this manner, and it is probable that in man gaps of several millimeters may be similarly bridged. Ordinarily, however, the mass of scar tissue is too extensive to be handled by the sheath cells themselves, and surgical intervention is required. Most of the scar tissue is removed and the ends approximated and held in the desired position by a proper suture. Meanwhile the central axonal tips swell and produce a number of fine branches which enter the scar on the third day. At first they appear free in the connective tissue, but soon they apply themselves to the surface of the sheath cell strands and are led by these to the peripheral stump where many of the branches enter the old tubes. However, the number of fibers entering the tubes is always smaller after section of the nerve than after crush, and moreover many fibers enter tubes which are structurally unsuitable for full functional maturation. Once the fibers have entered the old tubes, the further processes of growth and maturation are the same as after crush. These are described in Chap. VI.

The rate of nerve regeneration has been studied by a number of investigators. After primary suture of the peroneal nerve in the rabbit it takes about seven days for the growing axon tips of the central stump to traverse the scar of the gap and reach the peripheral stump (Gutmann, Guttmann, Medawar and Young). After crush the "scar" delay is about five days. Then the fastest tips grow at the rate of 3.5 mm. a day after suture, 4.4 mm. after a crush. The growing axons must reach their respective end organs before the return of function. The latter is dependent on the maturation of a sufficient number of fibers, including increase in diameter and myelinization, for the carrying of effective impulses, a state which has been termed "functional completion" (Young). Hence the rate of functional recovery is slower than that of the advancing axonal tip. In rabbits it is about 3 mm. a day after crush and 2 mm. after suture. The total latent period in the rabbit is about 36 days after suture and 20 days after a crush. In the longer nerves of man the process is probably somewhat slower, though a rate of 4.4 mm. a day for growing axons was found after a crush of one of the digital nerves (Bowden and Gutmann). However, the rate of functional regeneration falls off with the distance traversed, since increase in diameter and myelination occur more slowly in the distal portions of the fiber. A justifiable assumption for axonal growth in man is about 3 mm. per day, with an average latent period to functional maturity of 20 days after crush and 50 days after suture.

While regeneration can occur when two stumps are sutured after being left apart for a considerable time, it is generally agreed that the functional recoveries after long delayed sutures are usually unsatisfactory. This is due to a number of factors whose operation interferes with the regenerative processes and whose effects become progressively more serious. Some of the factors may be briefly mentioned. After a long delay, the distal stump atrophies and the outgrowth of sheath cells is reduced or ceases altogether. Hence good apposition of the cut nerve ends is difficult, and many axons fail to reach the degenerating tubes of the distal stump. The tubes themselves are greatly shrunken and receive fewer fibers, thus lessening the chances for appropriate peripheral connections. Myelinization is severely delayed, and increase in diameter is made difficult by the fixation of the thickened endoneurium which now forms a large portion of the tube. Of especial importance is the progressive atrophy of the muscles and end organs. In early stages the motor plates remain intact and connected with the tubes, hence new fibers can enter directly and restore the original pattern. As degeneration proceeds, the channels become occluded and the plates may completely disintegrate. The regenerating fibers often fail to enter the old plates or their previous locations. They then wander along the muscle fibers, ultimately forming new plates of a more primitive character, whose distribution is irregular and different from the original pattern of innervation. The indications are therefore for early suture, perhaps three or four weeks after injury, when sheath cell activity is at its height and the somewhat thickened perineurium permits easier surgical connections (Young, 1949). After a month the factors mentioned above begin to operate to some extent and become progressively more important. Delays of six months or more before suture may seriously interfere with the reparative processes and possibly prevent them altogether. This does not necessarily apply to all cases. Good recovery is possible after long delayed suture if enough axons manage to reach appropriate tubes and if the muscles are maintained in good condition by appropriate therapy. Sunderland (1950) has reported very good restoration of function in human hand and finger muscles which had been denervated for at least 12 months.

12

Internal Structure of the Spinal Cord

The microscopic appearance of the adult spinal cord has become vastly altered when compared to the three layered tube observed in embryonic development. The incoming and outgoing processes of ganglion cells and intrinsic neurons produce marked changes in the embryonic marginal and mantle layers (Figs. 126, 127). The embryonic layers become longitudinal columns of gray and white matter in the adult spinal cord, each having microscopic landmarks and subdivisions (Figs. 32, 33). Individual segments of the spinal cord show variations at different levels, for there is great variation in the size and number of fibers in the individual spinal nerves (Figs. 132, 133, 180). A microscopic knowledge of the gray and white matter in different regions of the cord is of fundamental importance, if one is to fully understand the material presented in subsequent chapters.

FINER STRUCTURE OF GRAY AND WHITE SUBSTANCE

The gray and white matter is composed of nervous elements supported by an interstitial framework of neuroglia. The mesodermal structures comprise the blood vessels and their contents. The larger vessels are accompanied by prolongations of pial connective tissue. The gray matter contains all the nerve cells and dendrites and portions of myelinated and unmyelinated fibers which generally run in a transverse plane, hence are cut longitudinally in a transverse section of the cord. These fibers are axons of nerve cells located in the gray matter passing to the white matter, and terminal portions of fibers in the white entering the gray to terminate there. All synapses are thus in the gray since there alone the cell bodies and dendrites are found. The white matter contains no neuron bodies or dendrites, the nervous elements being confined to myelinated and unmyelinated fibers and their branches. The fibers are longitudinally arranged but are connected with the gray by the many transverse fibers mentioned above.

The neuroglia. The central canal is lined by a layer of ependymal cells resembling a simple columnar epithelium after routine staining (Fig. 167). They have elongated nuclei and their cytoplasm contains neuroglia fibers which extend basally from the cell for some distance to merge with the diffuse glial network which permeates the gray and white matter. The ependymal cells are practically embryonal neuroglia cells (spongioblasts) which have retained their primitive form and position. In the region of the ventral median fissure and dorsal median septum, the basal processes of the ependymal cells actually reach the pia to which they are attached by terminal expansions or end feet, a condition characteristic of all spongioblasts during early development (Fig. 119).

In most adults the central canal is often obliterated, the ependyma being represented by clumps of apparently rounded cells. Surrounding the ependyma is the clear central gelatinous substance, composed of neuroglia fibers and clumps of fibrous astrocytes

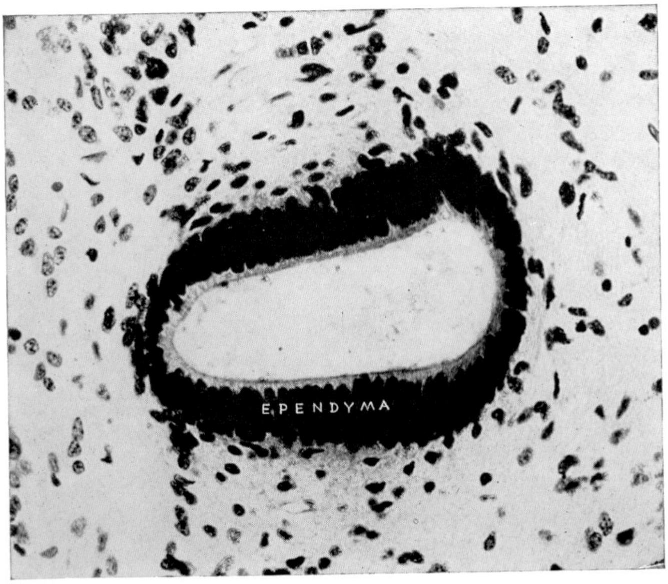

FIG. 167. Ependyma lining central canal of infant's spinal cord. Photograph. The area surrounding the ependyma is the central gelatinous substance (substantia gliosa) in which numerous neuroglia nuclei are seen.

which are otherwise rather scarce in the gray matter. In the gray and white matter the neuroglia forms a diffuse network, enveloping the neuron bodies, dendrites and nerve fibers. In the gray it consists mainly of protoplasmic astrocytes with rather few scattered fibrous ones. Special condensations of neuroglia cells and fibers are found in the substantia gelatinosa of Rolando and the zona spongiosa. The neuroglia of the white matter is composed chiefly of fibrous astrocytes whose fibers form a meshwork around the longitudinally coursing myelinated and unmyelinated fibers. Oligodendrocytes and microcytes are found in both gray and white. In the latter, the oligodendrocytes are often seen lying in rows, their delicate processes wrapping around the nerve fibers. Externally, the neuroglia condenses to form a narrow peripheral zone, *the marginal glia,* devoid of nerve fibers and composed solely of branching glia cells and their fibers (Fig. 168). This marginal glia forms a continuous investment of the spinal cord, its outer boundary appearing as a thin line, the *superficial glial limiting membrane,* closely applied to the inner surface of the pia. From the marginal glia processes extend into the white matter, the largest of them being the dorsal median septum.

The blood vessels which penetrate into the cord from the pia are always invested by tubular prolongations of the marginal glia forming the perivascular glial membranes which thus everywhere separate the nervous elements from the mesodermal tissues. The clefts between vessel wall and glia constitute the perivascular spaces which communicate with the subarachnoid spaces.

The structural features of neuroglia are difficult to demonstrate, and special stains are required to bring out the cytoplasm of neuroglia cells and the glia fibers. The nuclei are always seen in preparations stained with basic dyes, scattered through the gray and white matter (Fig. 169). They are easily distinguished from the vesicular nuclei of the medium sized and larger nerve cells, but with greater difficulty from those of the small ones and from the nuclei of connective tissue and endothelium. In general, the smallest, most deeply staining nu-

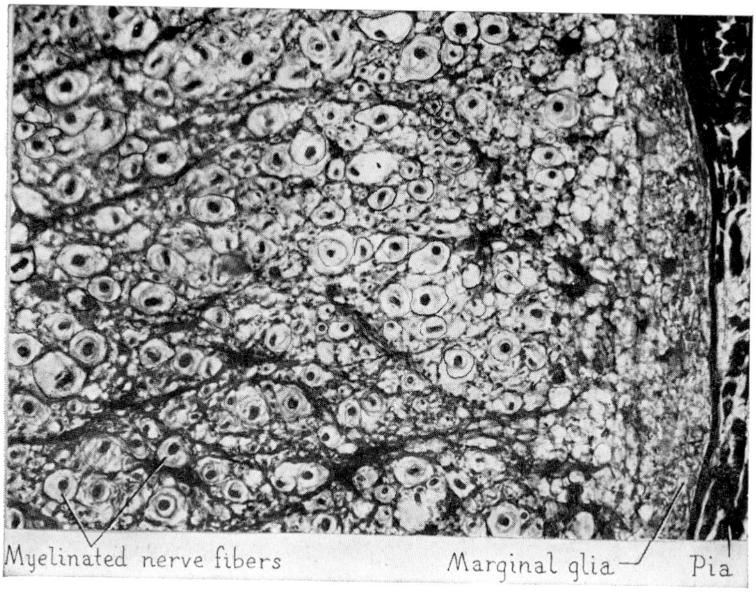

FIG. 168. Portion of white matter and adjacent pia of adult spinal cord. Mallory's phosphotungstic hematoxylin stain. Photograph. Among the myelinated fibers are seen darker staining strands composed of neuroglia cells and fibers. In upper portion of pia is a blood vessel filled with red blood corpuscles.

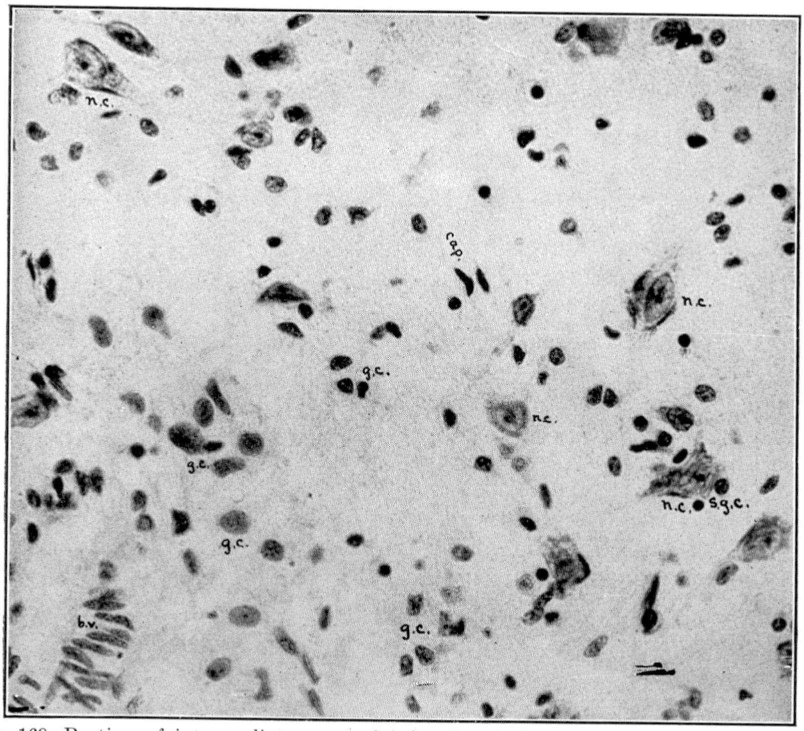

FIG. 169. Portion of intermediate gray of infant's spinal cord. Nissl stain. Photograph. *bv,* blood vessel with nuclei of circular smooth muscle coat; *cap,* capillary with two endothelial nuclei; *gc,* nuclei of neuroglia cells. The larger pale nuclei belong to astrocytes, the darker, smaller, round nuclei to oligodendroglia; and the darkest, smallest, round or elongated nuclei to microglia. *nc,* small and medium sized nerve cells showing Nissl bodies.

clei belong to microcytes, the somewhat larger, round nuclei to oligodendroglia, while the larger, paler ones are those of astrocytes.

The nuclei or cell groups. The gray matter contains numerous multipolar cells of varying size and structure, which may be grouped into two main classes, the *root cells* and the *column cells.* The root cells, situated in the ventral and lateral gray, are the efferent peripheral neurons whose axons pass out of the cord as ventral root fibers to innervate the somatic and visceral effectors. The column cells, on the other hand, are entirely confined to the central nervous system. They constitute the *central, internuncial* or *association* neurons. The majority send their axons to the white where, by bifurcating or bending, they form the longitudinal fibers of the white columns. Some are Golgi's type II cells whose short unmyelinated axons do not reach the white but terminate in the gray close to their origin. Those cells whose fibers remain on the same side are known as association or *ipsilateral* column cells, those whose axons cross are *contralateral* or *commissural* cells, while some cells may have axons which split into a crossed and uncrossed fiber. The Golgi's type II cells may likewise be association or commissural, their axons ending in the gray of the same side or crossing over to the gray of the opposite side. Some of the longitudinal fibers arising from the column cells, both crossed and uncrossed, may reach the brain as long tracts which are part of suprasegmental pathways (Figs. 185, 190). Others ascend or descend a variable distance as intersegmental fibers connecting various levels of the cord. Still others may be very short and terminate within a segment. This is especially true of the Golgi cells which obviously are intrasegmental in character (Fig. 184).

The nerve cells are not scattered uniformly through the gray, but are organized in more or less definite columns or *nuclei* which may be recognized in transverse sec-

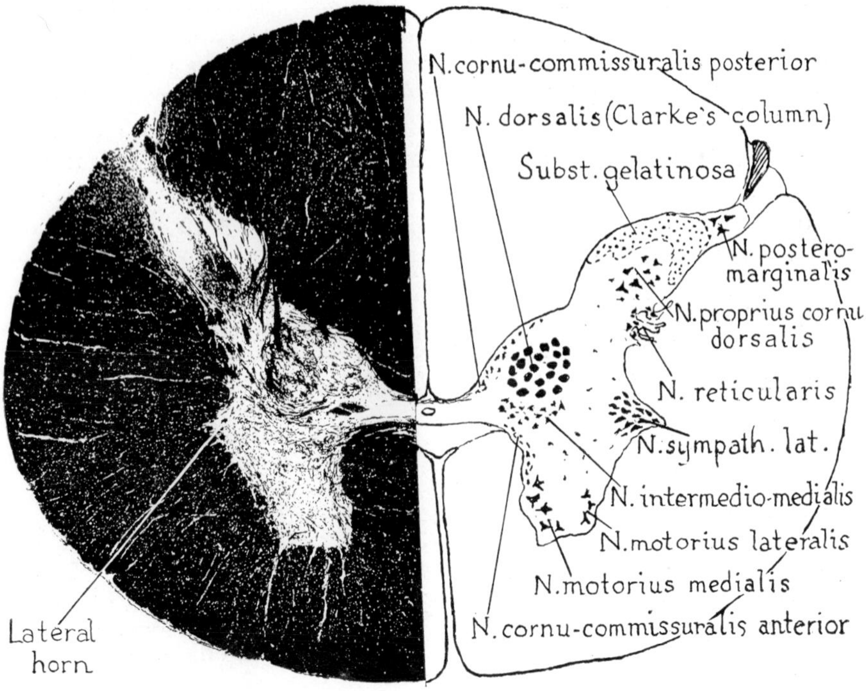

FIG. 170. Section through twelfth thoracic segment of adult human spinal cord. Weigert's myelin stain. Photograph. On the right side the more constant cell columns have been schematically indicated.

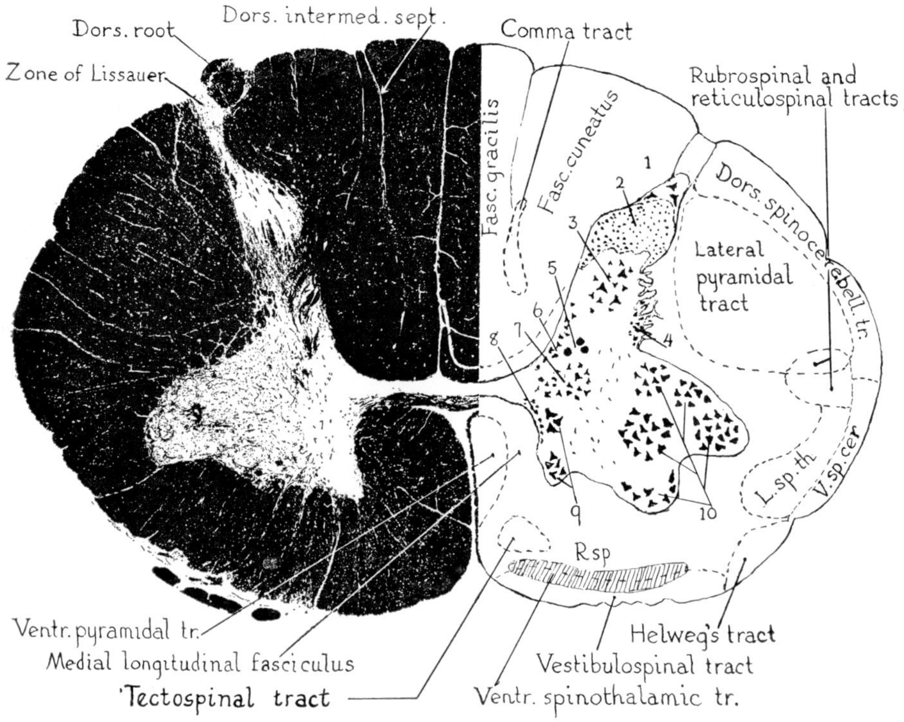

FIG. 171. Section through adult human spinal cord at level of C7–C8. Weigert's myelin stain. Photograph. On the right side the cell groups (*1–10*) and fiber tracts are diagrammatically indicated. *1*, cellulae posteromarginales; *2*, substantia gelatinosa; *3*, nucleus proprius cornu dorsalis; *4*, nucleus reticularis; *5*, Clarke's column; *6*, nucleus cornucommissuralis posterior; *7*, nucleus intermediomedialis; *8*, nucleus cornucommissuralis anterior; *9*, nuclei motorii mediales; *10*, nuclei motorii laterales; *L.sp.th.*, lateral spinothalamic tract; *R.sp.*, reticulospinal fibers; *V.sp.cer.*, ventral spinocerebellar tract.

tions as separate groups distinguished from others by their location, size, form and internal structure (Figs. 170, 171, 173, 175, 177). Some of these cell groups extend the whole length of the cord, though varying in extent in different levels. Others may be limited to certain regions only. There is still considerable disagreement as to the distribution and terminology of many cell columns. The following is based mainly on the work of Jacobsohn, Massazza and Bok.

A. The **root cells** are organized into the following groups:

1. *Nuclei motorii cornu ventralis.* These are the groups of somatic motor cells located in the ventral horn, whose axons pass without interruption to the striped voluntary muscles. They are the largest cells of the spinal cord reaching a long diameter of well over 100 micra and having a transverse diameter of 30–60μ. They are elongated multipolar cells with 3–10 or even 20 dendrites, a large vesicular nucleus and coarse Nissl bodies. (Figs. 80, 82, 84). They are largest in the lumbosacral and cervical enlargements, smaller in the thoracic levels. Two main groups are distinguished, each of which shows several subdivisions:

(a) The *medial* cell group or column is divisible into a dorsomedial and ventromedial group. The latter extends throughout the whole cord, being most prominent in C1, C2, C4, T1, T2, L3, L4, S2, S3. The nucleus of the hypoglossal nerve in the medulla appears to be a continuation of this column. The dorsomedial group is smaller, most distinct in the cervical and lumbar enlargements, and may be altogether missing in the thoracic and sacral portions. The medial motor column innervates the short and long muscles of the spine.

(b) The *lateral* motor cell group innervates the rest of the musculature. In the thoracic segments it is small and undivided and innervates the intercostal and other ventrolateral trunk muscles (Fig. 170). In the cervical and lumbar enlargements it becomes considerably enlarged and a number of sub-groups may be distinguished, accounting for the massive ventral horns found in these regions. It is especially prominent in those segments which participate in the innervation of the most distal portions of the extremities. Here there may be distinguished ventrolateral, dorsolateral, ventral (anterior), central, and retrodorsolateral groups (Figs. 171, 175). The exact innervation of the various extremity muscles by each of these groups has not been completely worked out, but in general the more distal muscles are supplied by the more lateral cell groups. Passing thus from the most mesial part of the ventral horn to its lateral periphery, the successive innervation is spine, trunk, shoulder and hip girdle, upper leg and arm, lower leg and arm, the retrodorsolateral group finally supplying the muscles of hand and foot. It is interesting that in all the lateral cell groups the ventrally placed cells supply the dorsal musculature and vice versa (Bok).

2. *Nuclei sympathici.* (Preganglionic autonomic neuron groups.) These are the cells whose axons pass out by way of the ventral roots and white rami communicantes to the various sympathetic ganglia. They are ovoid or spindle-shaped cells with thinner shorter dendrites, vesicular nuclei, and finer chromofilic bodies (Figs. 80, 84). They are considerably smaller than the somatic motor cells, ranging in size from 12–45μ. In Weigert preparations they appear to be surrounded by a clear homogeneous substance resembling the gelatinous substance of Rolando. They may be divided into the following two groups:

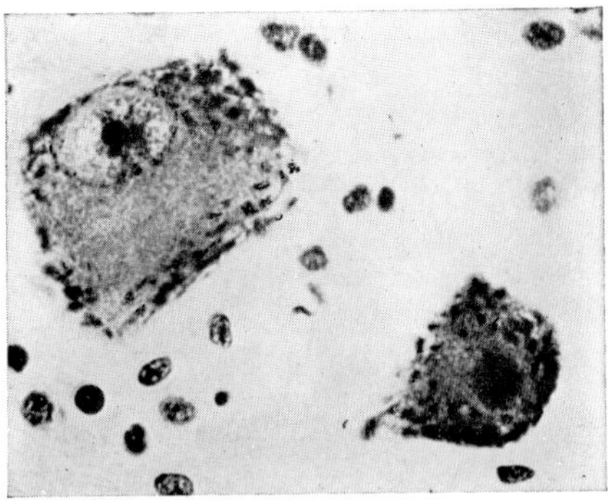

FIG. 172. Two cells from Clarke's column of human spinal cord. Nissl stain. Photograph.

(a) *Nucleus sympathicus lateralis* (*intermediolateral column*) (Figs. 170, 173). This nucleus really consists of several adjacent cell columns. The most lateral apical cell group constitutes the lateral horn (intermediolateral column). The nucleus begins in the lower portion of C8, and extends caudally to L2 or L3. The nucleus is usually divided into a *superior* portion corresponding to the extent of the apical group, and an *inferior* portion continuing into the sacral cord. In the lower sacral segments the inferior nucleus breaks up into irregularly scattered cells which apparently mingle with those of the medial sympathetic nucleus to be described below, the two together occupying a considerable part of the ventral horn.

(b) *Nucleus sympathicus medialis* (*nucleus myoleioticus*). This nucleus begins about L3, is largest in L5 and continues to the caudal end of the cord. It lies along the medial border of the ventral horn, but in the lower sacral segments becomes mingled with the inferior lateral sympathetic nucleus (Figs. 175, 177).

The axons of the sympathetic nuclei appear to run into the ventral roots (Bok, 1922; Poliak, 1924). It is at present believed that the axons of the superior lateral nucleus (intermediolateral column) go to

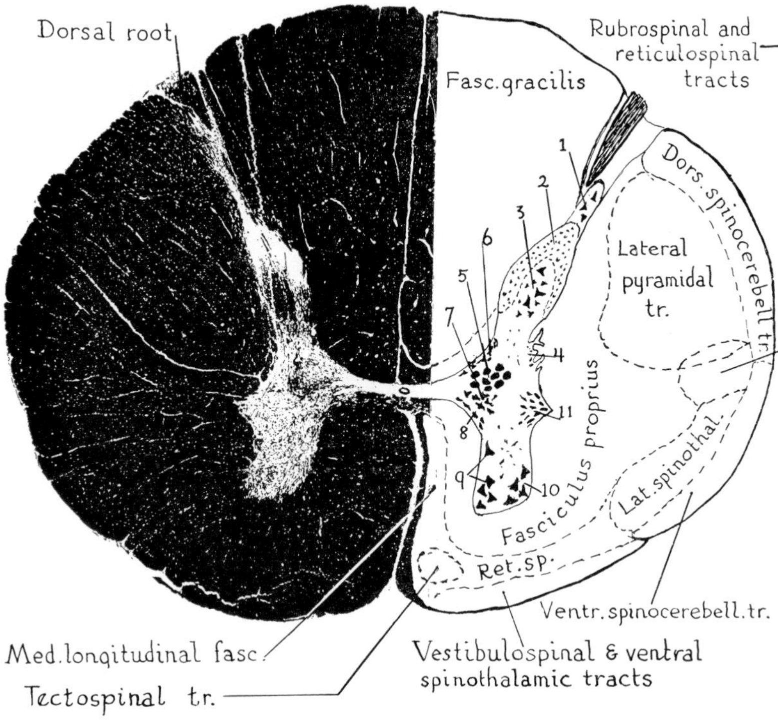

FIG. 173. Section through seventh thoracic segment of adult human spinal cord. Weigert's myelin stain. Photograph. *1,* nucleus posteromarginalis; *2,* substantia gelatinosa; *3,* nucleus proprius cornu dorsalis; *4,* nucleus reticularis; *5,* Clarke's column; *6,* nucleus cornucommissuralis posterior; *7,* nucleus intermediomedialis; *8,* nucleus cornucommissuralis anterior; *9,* nucleus motorium medialis; *10,* nucleus motorius lateralis; *11,* nucleus sympathicus lateralis; *Ret.sp.*, reticulospinal fibers.

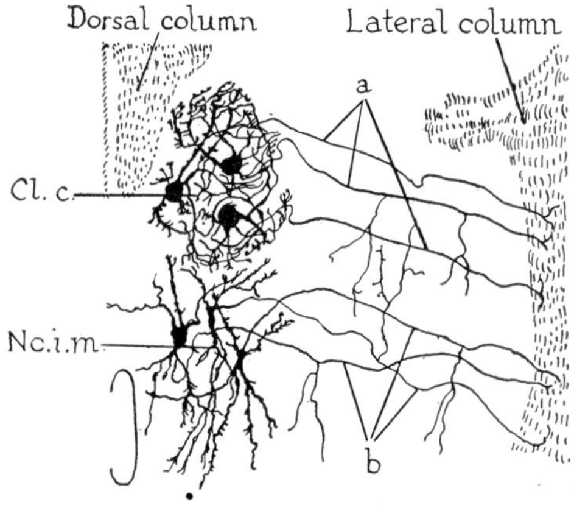

FIG. 174. Clarke's column (*Cl.c.*) and nucleus intermediomedialis (intermediate gray, *Nc.i.m.*) in transverse section of thoracic cord of newborn mouse. Golgi impregnation. *a,* fibers from Clarke's column entering lateral column (dorsal spinocerebellar fibers); *b,* fibers from intermediate gray entering lateral column. Some of these may be ventral spinocerebellar fibers. (After Cajal.)

the verterbral and prevertebral ganglia of the thoracolumbar autonomic system. The inferior lateral and the medial sympathetic nuclei send their preganglionic axons to the pelvic ganglia located within or near the wall of the pelvic viscera. Short postganglionic fibers then supply the smooth muscle and glands of each viscus as sacral autonomic elements of the parasympathetic (craniosacral) nervous system.

B. **Central cells** (Column cells and Golgi's type II cells). These cells and their processes are entirely confined to the central nervous system. In the dorsal and intermediate gray especially, they receive the collaterals or direct terminations of dorsal root fibers. They in turn send their axons either directly to ventral horn cells of the same segments, or to the white matter where by bifurcating or bending upward or down-

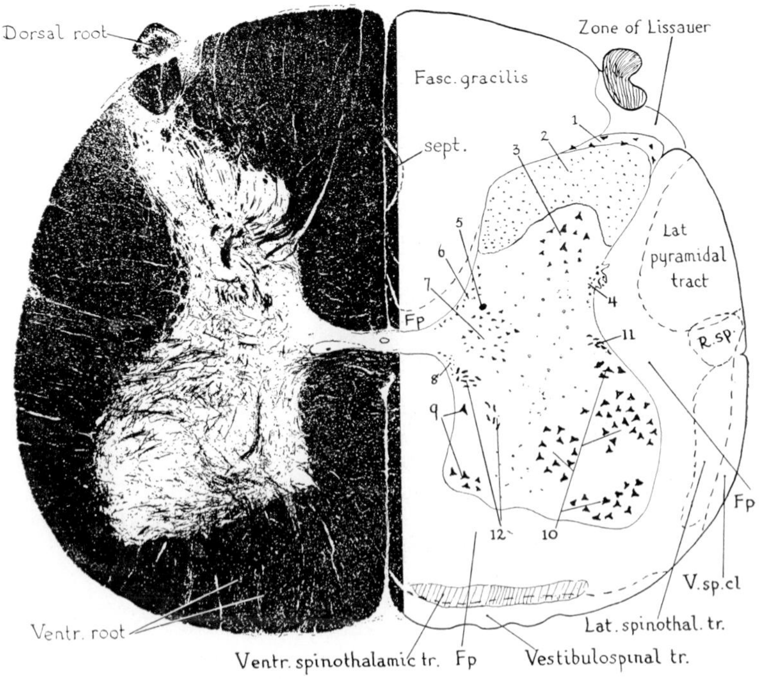

FIG. 175. Section through lower portion of fourth lumbar segment of adult human spinal cord. Weigert's myelin stain. Photograph. *1,* nucleus posteromarginalis; *2,* substantia gelatinosa; *3,* nucleus proprius cornu dorsalis; *4,* nucleus reticularis; *5,* cell from Clarke's column; *6,* nucleus cornucommissuralis posterior; *7,* nucleus intermediomedialis; *8,* nucleus cornucommissuralis anterior; *9,* nucleus motorius medialis; *10,* nucleus motorius lateralis; *11,* nucleus sympathicus lateralis; *12,* nucleus sympathicus medialis; *Fp,* fasciculus proprius; *R.sp.,* rubrospinal and reticulospinal tracts; *sept.,* septomarginal fasciculus; *V.sp.cl.,* ventral spinocerebellar tract.

ward they become longitudinal fibers, forming intersegmental tracts of varying length. The longest fibers reach the brain as parts of suprasegmental pathways (Fig. 184). The cells vary in size, form, and internal structure. Some are organized into definite cell groups easily distinguishable in transverse sections, others are scattered irregularly in the gray matter.

The *nucleus posteromarginalis* (*nucleus magnocellularis pericornualis, marginal cells*) forms a thin layer of cells covering the tip of the dorsal horn and situated in the zona spongiosa. They are large tangentially arranged stellate or spindle-shaped cells reaching a diameter of over 50 micra (Ziehen). Their axons pass into the lateral white and bifurcate into ascending and decending fibers, probably forming intersegmental pathways. The cells are found throughout the cord, most numerous in the lumbosacral segments, less in the cervical and least in the thoracic. In sections 10–20μ thick, their number varies from 1 or 2 in the thoracic to 6 or 10 in the lumbar cord (Fig. 175).

Beneath the marginal cells is the *substantia gelatinosa of Rolando* (*nucleus sensibilis proprius*) which forms the outer caplike portion of the head of the dorsal horn. It extends the whole length of the cord, being largest in the lumbosacral and first cervical segments. Its variations in size are to some extent related to the size of the dorsal roots, the increase in the first cervical segment being due to the considerable number of decending fibers from the trigeminal nerve (Fig. 268). The nucleus is composed of rows of small ovoid or polygonal cells with deeply staining nuclei (cells of Gierke), about 6–20μ in diameter (Fig. 78). The unmyelinated or finely myelinated axons end in considerable numbers in the substantia gelatinosa or dorsal horn. Others pass into the zone of Lissauer, adjacent lateral white, and the dorsal white column. The large number and small size of the cells suggest that they give rise to short, principally intrasegmental fibers. The nucleus constitutes the chief associative center of the dorsal horn for incoming impulses and probably also forms an important part of the pathway for painful, thermal, and some tactile impulses, either conscious, reflex or both.

The head and cervix of the dorsal horn is occupied by the *nucleus proprius cornu dorsalis* (*nucleus centrodorsalis, nucleus magnocellularis centralis, nucleus spinothalamicus*). Some are spindle-shaped cells of rather more than medium size, others are large polygonal cells with numerous dendrites, which may approach the size of a motor ventral horn cell. This rather poorly defined cell column is found in all segments, the cells being most numerous in the lumbosacral cord. It seems certain that the long crossed spinothalamic and spinotectal fibers arise from these cells, but axons also pass to the adjacent white of the same side. Lateral to this nucleus, the small and medium sized cells found in the reticular process have been termed the *nucleus reticularis* (Bok). They send their axons to the same as well as to the opposite ventrolateral white.

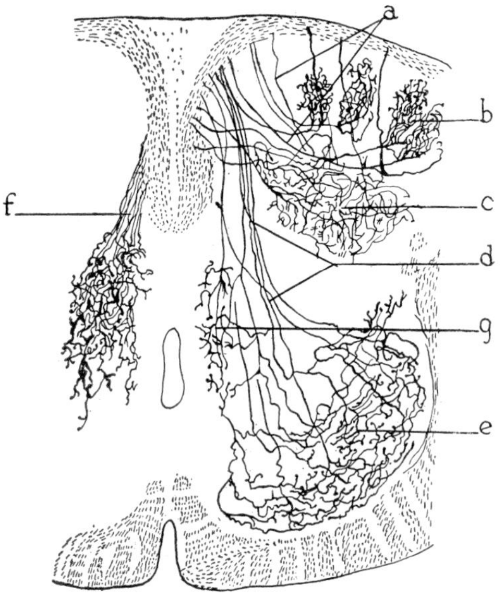

Fig. 176. The more important collaterals from the fibers of the dorsal funiculus. Newborn rat. Golgi impregnation. *a,* collaterals to substantia gelatinosa and to the nucleus proprius (central nucleus) of dorsal horn. Terminal arborizations of these fibers are seen in substantia gelatinosa (*b*) and nucleus proprius (*c*); *d,* sensorimotor collaterals with terminal arborizations around cells of ventral horn (*e*); *f,* collaterals to intermediate gray (nucleus intermediomedialis); *g,* terminal branching of a collateral from a sensori-motor fiber in intermediate gray. (After Cajal.)

The *Column of Clarke* (*nucleus dorsalis, nucleus magnocellularis basalis, nucleus spinocerebellaris*) is a striking cell column placed in the medial portion of the base of the dorsal horn. The nucleus begins to be well defined in C8 and extends through the thoracic and upper lumbar segments, being most prominent in T11, T12 and L1. Below L3 it becomes indistinguishable, though occasional cells are found in the lower cord segments as well as in the cervical region. In sections 10–20μ thick, the number of cells range from 3 or 4 in the upper thoracic to 10 or 15 in the lower thoracic, with about 20 in T12 and L1. The cells are large, many of them as large as the somatic motor cells. They are multipolar neurons with large vesicular, often eccentrically placed nuclei, and coarse chromofilic bodies usually confined to the periphery of the cell body (Figs. 172, 174, 84J). Their large thickly myelinated axons pass uncrossed to the lateral white where they ascend to the vermis of the cerebellum as the dorsal spinocerebellar tract (Figs. 174, 182, 192).

In the intermediate gray a rather diffusely organized cell group constitutes the *nucleus intermediomedialis*, as contrasted

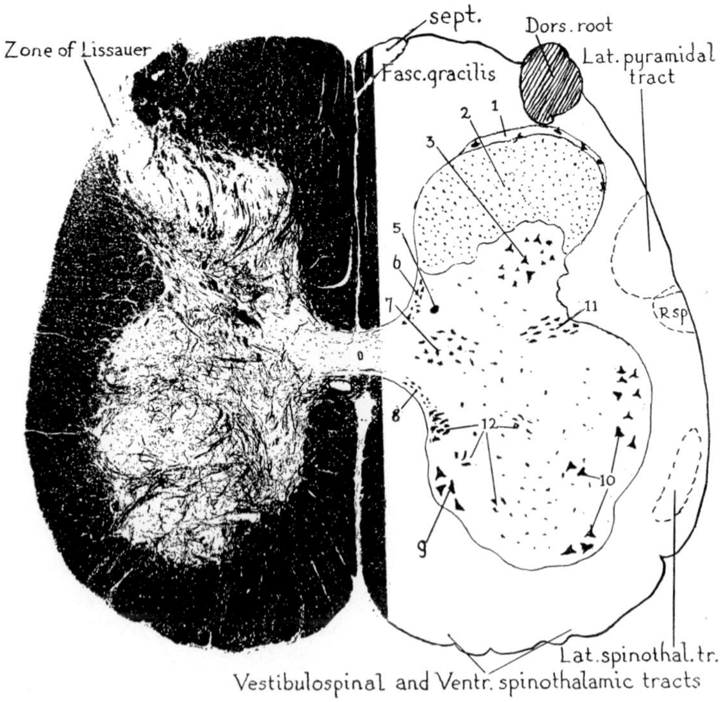

FIG. 177. Section through third sacral segment of adult human spinal cord. Weigert's myelin stain. Photograph. Numbers of cell groups as in Fig. 175. *R.sp.*, rubrospinal and reticulospinal tracts; *sept.*, septomarginal fasciculus.

with the intermediolateral or sympathetic column described under the root cells. The small and medium sized cells, 10–24μ in size, are found in varying numbers throughout the cord but are most numerous in the upper cervical segments. Their axons pass mostly to the lateral white of the same side and are believed to contribute to the ventral spinocerebellar tract (Fig. 192).

Two less definite cell columns extending the length of the cord are the *nuclei cornucommissurales posterior* and *anterior* (dorsomedial and ventromedial diffuse cell groups of Jacobsohn). The former, in section, is a thin cell strip occupying the medial margin of the dorsal horn and extending along the border of the dorsal gray commissure, lying over the column of Clarke where the latter is present. The anterior is a similar cell group along the medial surface of the ventral horn and ventral gray commissure. These nuclei consist of small and medium sized spindle-shaped cells whose axons probably form intersegmental tracts in the dorsal and ventral white respectively.

Besides the more organized groups, there are diffusely scattered cells (*cellulae disseminatae*) throughout the gray matter. In the interior of the ventral horn, scattered between the somatic motor cells, these small triangular or spindle-shaped cells are often collectively termed the *nucleus proprius cornu ventralis*. They are most numerous in C5–C8 and L2–L4 and may serve for intranuclear connections. As a rule, the cells are largest in the lumbosacral cord.

Arrangement of fibers. It has been noted that the white matter is composed principally of longitudinal fibers while in the gray the fibers have a transverse direction, running from gray to white or vice versa (Figs. 178, 179). The reason for the transverse course of these fibers is obvious. The gray matter contains all the cell bodies and dendrites, hence all synapses are in the gray. Any fiber or collateral terminating in any level of the cord enters the gray as a transverse fiber. Similarly, axons arising from column cells leave the gray as transverse fibers to pass into the white where they assume a longitudinal course. The transverse fibers are therefore either fibers of origin or fibers of termination and include: (a) root fibers entering or leaving the cord, (b) axons of column cells passing to the white where they become ascending or descending fibers, and (c) collaterals and terminals of fibers of the white matter, which come from other parts of the spinal cord or from the brain and enter the gray to terminate there.

The dorsal roots, as already stated, are composed of coarse, thickly myelinated fibers and of finer fibers, many of which are unmyelinated. The coarse fibers are processes of the larger spinal ganglion cells, bringing in impulses from muscle and tendon spindles, Meissner's corpuscles, Pacinian corpuscles, and probably from diffuse tactile receptors (position and movement, touch, vibration). The finer myelinated and unmyelinated fibers which are processes of the smaller ganglion cells conduct impulses from diffuse endings, end bulbs, and other encapsulated endings (primarily pain and temperature, also some touch). The dorsal roots break up into a number of filaments or rootlets which enter the cord in a linear manner. Each of these filaments on entering the cord separates into a smaller lateral bundle composed of fine fibers which enters the zone of Lissauer, and a larger medial bundle composed of the coarser fibers, which pass into the main portion of the dorsal funiculus lying medial to the dorsal horn (Figs. 180, 181). Each root fiber bifurcates into a longer ascending and a shorter descending arm as soon as it enters the cord. The fine fibers which pass to the zone of Lissauer divide into very short arms, the longer ascending ones extending only for one or two segments (Ranson). The descending and ascending arms sooner or later enter and terminate

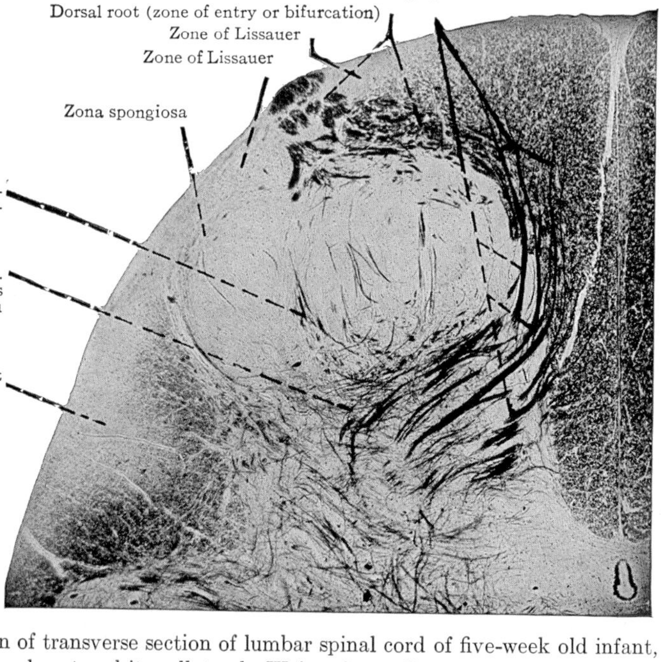

Fig. 178. Portion of transverse section of lumbar spinal cord of five-week old infant, showing entrance of dorsal root and its collaterals. Weigert's myelin stain. Photograph.

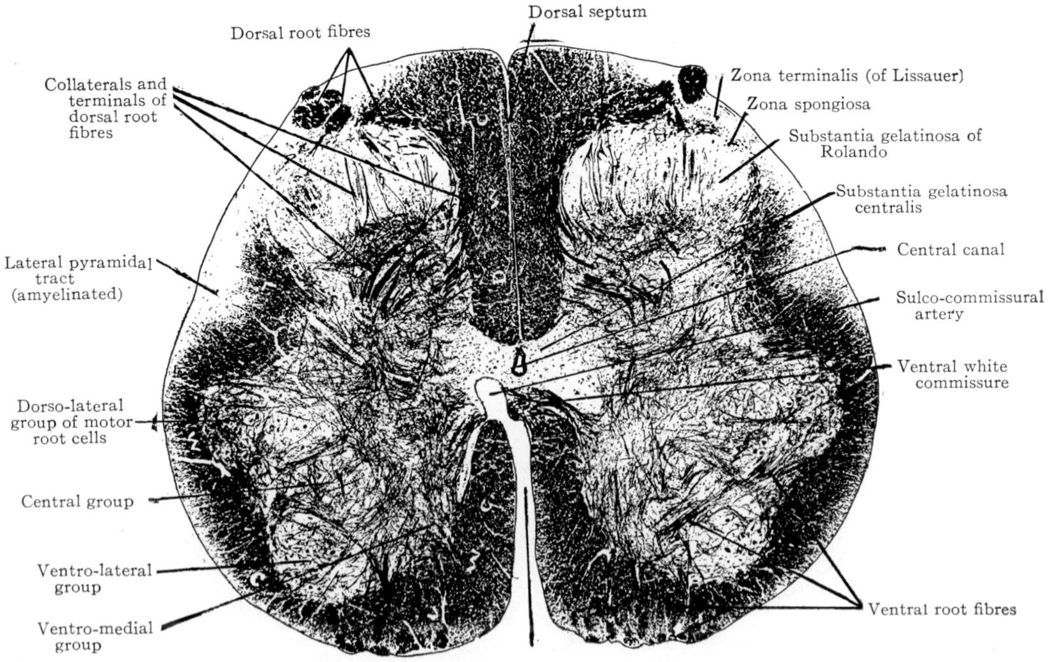

FIG. 179. Section through fourth lumbar segment of spinal cord of five-week infant. Weigert's myelin stain. Photograph ×20. *DWC* (white letters), dorsal white column; *LWC,* lateral white column; *VWC,* ventral white column. The vertical line lies in the ventral median fissure.

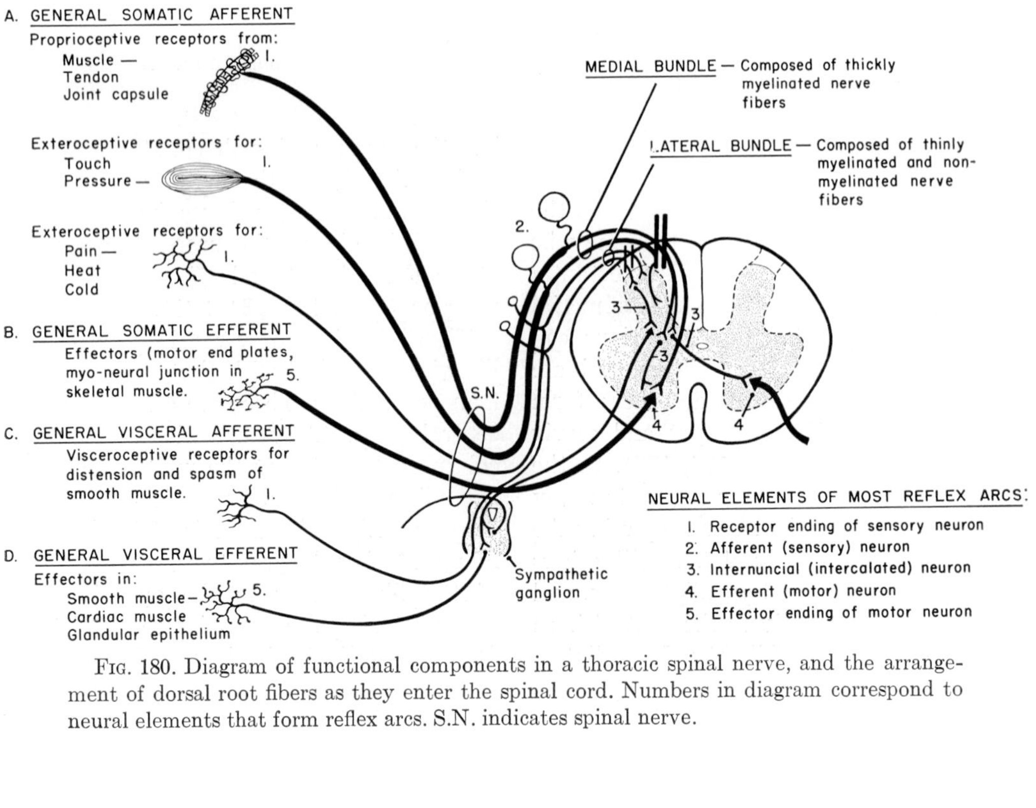

FIG. 180. Diagram of functional components in a thoracic spinal nerve, and the arrangement of dorsal root fibers as they enter the spinal cord. Numbers in diagram correspond to neural elements that form reflex arcs. S.N. indicates spinal nerve.

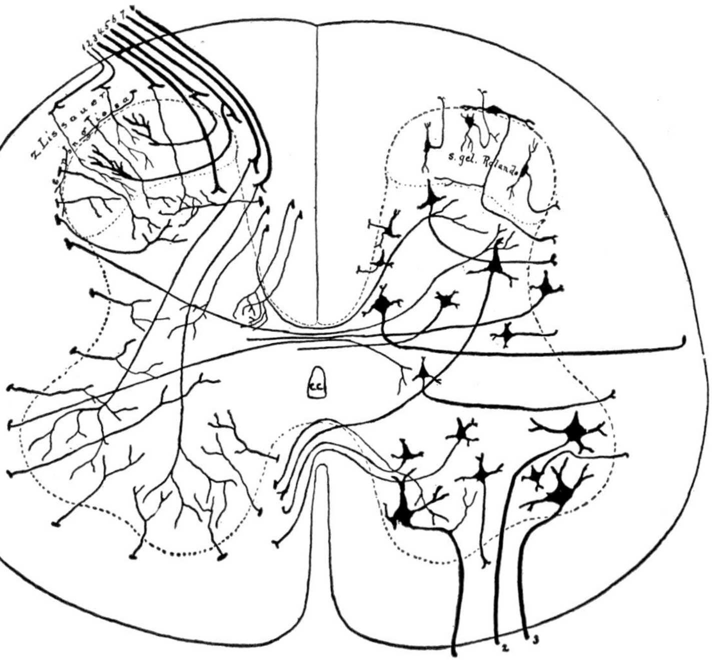

FIG. 181. Section through spinal cord, showing arrangement of collaterals (left) and cell bodies and their axons (right) as seen in Golgi preparations. *1* and *2* represent fine dorsal root fibers passing laterally to the zone of Lissauer. *3* to *8* represent coarse dorsal root fibers passing to the dorsal white column. Collaterals from *1* and *2* enter the substantia gelatinosa, those from *3* to *8* enter the gelatinosa, head and neck of the dorsal horn, intermediate gray, and ventral horn. Some collaterals from dorsal root fibers of other, probably lower, levels are seen leaving the dorsal white column and ending in the dorsal horn, intermediate gray, and in the colmun of Clarke. Preganglionic autonomic root cells are not shown. *cc*, central canal. (After Cajal and Lenhossék.)

in the gray matter. In any transverse section of the cord, bundles of fine fibers composed of collaterals and terminals from the entering roots or dorsal funiculus may be seen passing radially through the substantia gelatinosa or sweeping around its mesial side to be distributed to the various cell groups of the gray matter. Some terminate in the substantia gelatinosa, others form terminal plexuses in the caput and cervix of the dorsal horn (Figs. 176, 178). In the thoracic and upper lumbar segments many myelinated collaterals are seen entering the column of Clarke (Fig. 182). Still others can be traced to the intermediate gray, and finally some go directly to the ventral horn as "sensorimotor" or "direct reflex collaterals". By means of the last named collaterals, two-neuron reflex arcs are made possible, but the number of such collaterals terminating directly on the motor cells is relatively small. Most reflexes have at least one additional central neuron interposed between the afferent and efferent peripheral neurons (Figs. 180, 184, 201).

The lateral and ventral funiculi are likewise connected with the gray by many transverse fibers. These are all processes of central cells. They are either axons of column cells entering the white to become ascending or descending longitudinal fibers, or collaterals and terminals of longitudinal fibers entering the gray to terminate. Many of the fibers cross to the opposite side. The ventral white commissure consists of decussating fibers of column cells which lie near the level of crossing. The much smaller dorsal white commissure contains a few crossing axons of column cells, and collaterals from the dorsal white column.

Finally, in the ventral part of the cord may be seen the coarser transverse fibers which are axons of the various somatic motor cell groups. The bundles of somatic motor fibers leave the ventral gray horn, pass through the white matter, and emerge as ventral root fibers (Figs. 179, 180). In the thoracic and upper lumbar segments and in some of the sacral ones, the ventral roots contain also a large number of fine myelinated fibers from cells of the lateral horn. These fine fibers constitute the preganglionic fibers of the autonomic system.

VARIATIONS IN STRUCTURE AT DIFFERENT LEVELS

While the general structure described above obtains throughout the cord, the different levels vary considerably as regards the shape and size of the cord, the shape and size of the gray matter, and the relative amount of gray and white. These differences are primarily due to two factors: (1) Variations in size of the nerve roots, causing corresponding variations in the white and especially in the gray matter which receives the afferent fibers and contains the cells of origin of the efferent ones. Thus the larger nerves of the extremities produce the cervical and lumbar enlargements marked primarily by the great increase in the gray columns. Similarly the outflow of the preganglionic sympathetic fibers in the thoracic cord is represented by the lateral horn (intermediolateral column). (2) Since all levels of the cord are connected with the brain by long ascending and descending

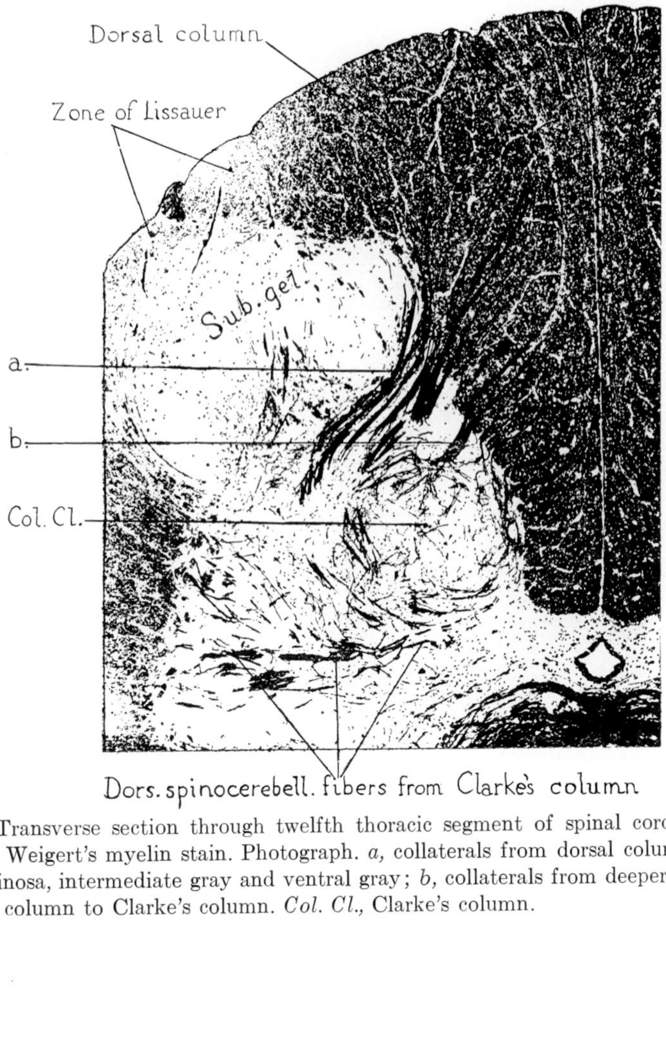

FIG. 182. Transverse section through twelfth thoracic segment of spinal cord of a five week infant. Weigert's myelin stain. Photograph. *a,* collaterals from dorsal column to substantia gelatinosa, intermediate gray and ventral gray; *b,* collaterals from deeper portion of dorsal white column to Clarke's column. *Col. Cl.,* Clarke's column.

fibers, there will naturally be an increase in the white matter as we proceed from lower to higher levels, the first cervical containing the largest number of fibers. Some of the variations seen at different levels may be briefly summarized.

In the *third sacral* segment (Fig. 177), the gray columns are massive with a large substantia gelatinosa and a short gray commissure. The white matter is relatively small in amount and the total area of the section is likewise small. The area is much larger in the *fourth* or *fifth lumbar* segment, with a transverse diameter of about 12 mm. and a sagittal of 9 mm. (Fig. 175). There is a considerable increase in the white matter. The gray columns are massive and the ventral horns are bayed out laterally, due to the increase of the lateral motor cell groups. In sections of the *thoracic* cord (Figs. 170, 173) the area is smaller than in the lumbar enlargement, due primarily to the great reduction of the gray. Both dorsal and ventral horns are slender and there is a well marked lateral horn (intermediolateral column). On the mesial surface of the base of the dorsal horn is seen the column of Clarke. It is especially prominent in the twelfth thoracic which also has a stouter ventral horn than the more typical thoracic segments (Fig. 182). Myelinated collaterals from the dorsal funiculus may be seen entering Clarke's column to terminate among its cells. From the nucleus coarse myelinated fibers gather at its ventral side and pass outward to the

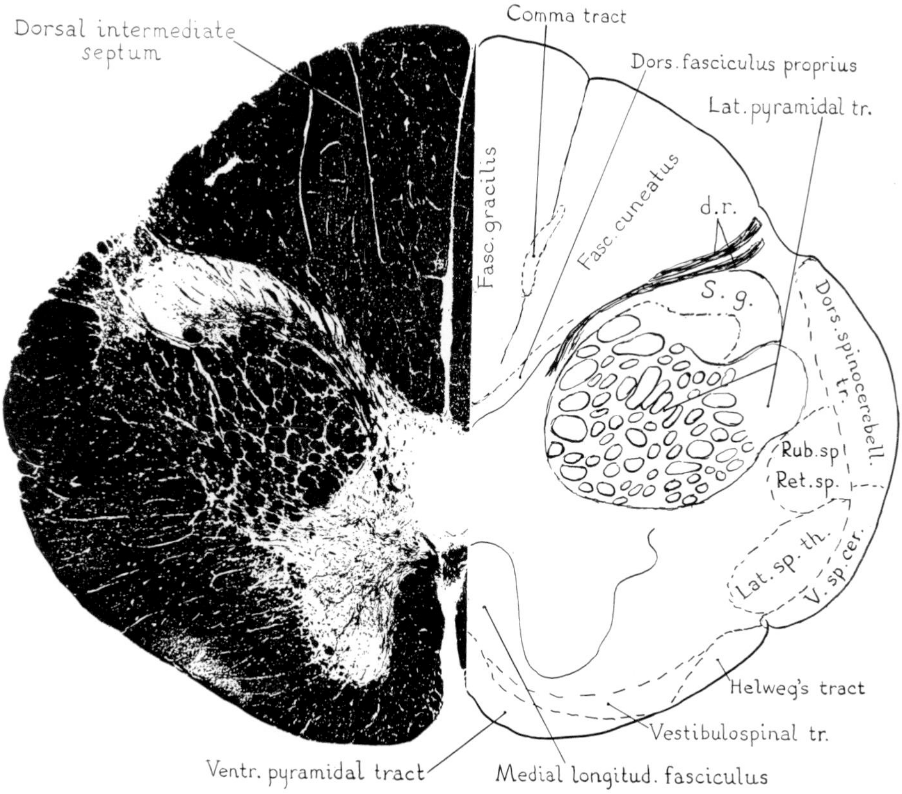

FIG. 183. Section through upper portion of first cervical segment of adult cord. Myelin stain. Photograph. *d.r.*, dorsal root; *Lat.sp.th.*, lateral spinothalamic tract; *Ret.sp.*, *Rub.sp.*, reticulospinal and rubrospinal tracts; *S.g.*, substantia gelatinosa; *V.sp.cer.*, ventral spinocerebellar tract.

lateral periphery of the cord where they bend upwards as fibers of the dorsal spino-cerebellar tract (Fig. 192). The white matter is considerable and increases in amount at successively higher levels. In the mid-thoracic region the transverse diameter is about 10 mm., the sagittal about 8 mm. (Ziehen).

The largest area is found in sections of the *cervical enlargement* and especially in C7 and C8 where the transverse and sagittal diameters are about 13–14 mm. and 9 mm. respectively (Fig. 171). The shape of the section is oval, flattened dorsoventrally. The dorsal horn is enlarged, though relatively slender, and the ventral horns are again massive, with lateral extensions accommodating the lateral motor cell groups innervating the upper extremities. The reticular process is prominent, and there is a great increase in the white matter. A more or less complete septum divides the dorsal funiculus into a medial fasciculus gracilis and a lateral fasciculus cuneatus. In the *upper cervical* segments as C2 or C1, the gray matter becomes again reduced but the area of the section is large, due to the great amount of white matter (Fig. 183). The diameter is about 12 mm.

13

The Fiber Tracts of the Spinal Cord

The ascending and descending fibers of the spinal cord do not run in a haphazard manner but are organized into more or less distinct functional bundles which occupy definite areas in the white matter. When such bundles consist of fibers having the same origin, termination, and function they are known as *tracts*. When composed of a mixture of functionally distinct fibers they are usually termed *fasciculi*. A *funiculus* is a larger bundle of nerve fibers composed of two or more fascicles. The various tracts and fascicles are not sharply demarcated, but on the contrary show considerable overlapping and intermingling. In general, the long fibers are peripherally placed, the shorter lying nearest the gray matter.

ARRANGEMENT OF INCOMING SENSORY FIBERS

The thick, heavily myelinated central processes of dorsal root ganglion cells form a compact *medial bundle* (division) as they enter the dorsolateral surface of the spinal cord (Fig. 180). A smaller less conspicuous *lateral bundle* (division) is composed of thinly myelinated and non-myelinated nerve fibers that enter the zone of Lissauer. The large fibers are central processes of large dorsal root ganglion cells that convey impulses from large encapsulated somatic afferent receptors. In a similar manner the thin fibers represent central processes of small and medium size ganglion cells related to small, unspecialized somatic and visceral afferent receptors (Fig. 180). The receptors, sensory neurons, internuncial neurons, outgoing motor neurons, and terminal effectors are the five essential neural elements needed to complete most spinal reflexes.

Upon entering the dorsal funiculus of the spinal cord, the central process of each dorsal root ganglion cell divides promptly into ascending and descending branches (Fig. 184). Numerous smaller branches, or collaterals, are given off as these ascending and descending fibers extend through many segments of the spinal cord. Most of the collateral branches are given off in the segment of entry where they participate in intrasegmental reflexes, or relay their impulses to a second neuron which ascends as a discrete sensory pathway. The primary ascending and descending branches also provide many collaterals to adjacent cord segments for intersegmental reflexes and secondary sensory pathways. The ascending primary branches are usually longer, and in the case of the thickly myelinated fibers, many of them extend upward into the medulla. The central course and branches of one dorsal root ganglion cell may be far more extensive than shown schematically in red in Fig. 184.

The myotatic, or stretch reflex is composed of two neurons with only one synapse interposed (1 in Fig. 184). Thus tapping of the quadriceps femoris tendon and the subsequent muscular extension at the knee represents a stretch (monosynaptic) reflex. In this example, both the sensory and motor nerve fibers leave and enter the quadriceps muscle as constituents of the femoral nerve. It will be recalled that parts of two, three, or more myotomes are incorporated in each

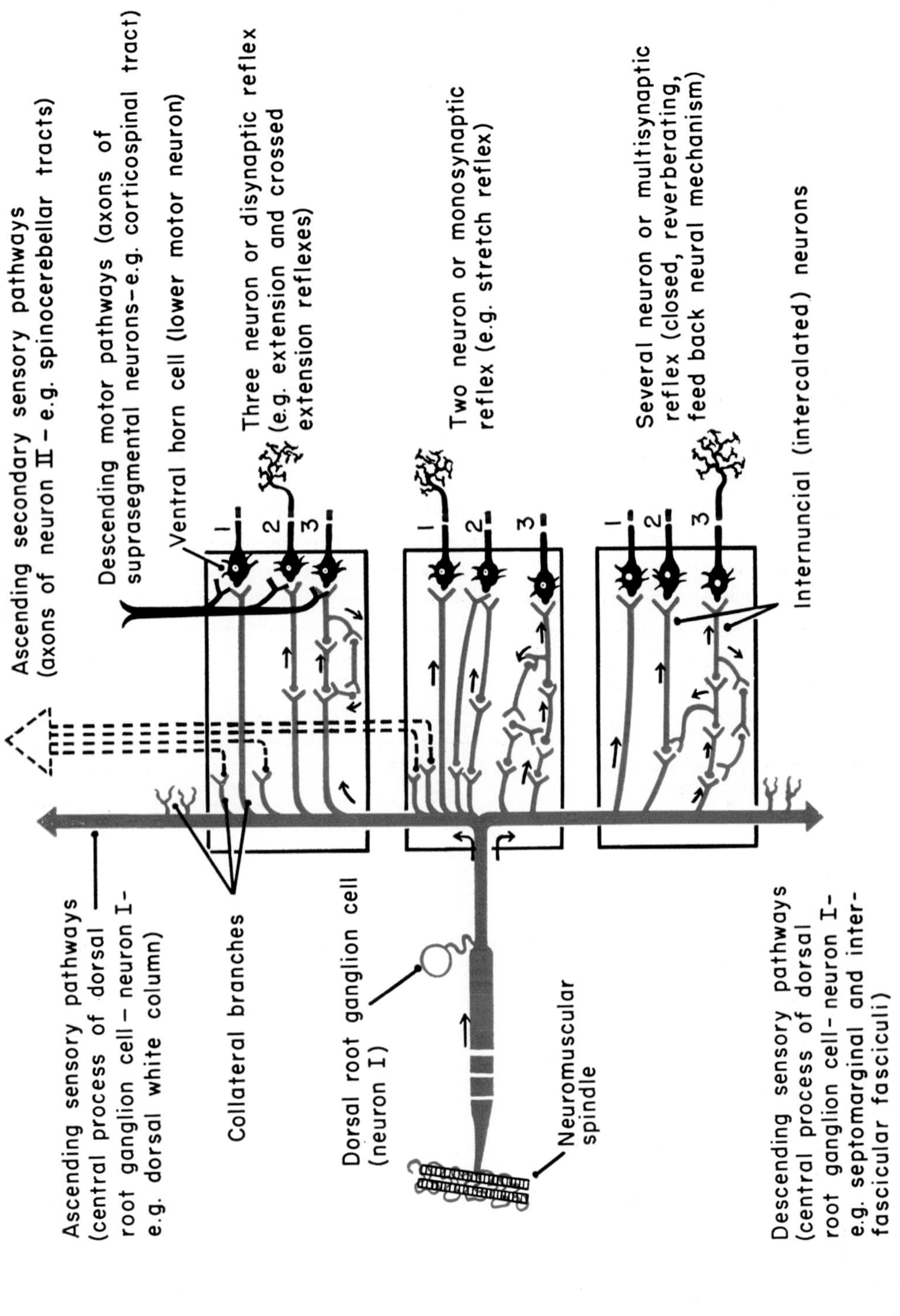

FIG. 184. Diagram of the major branches and collaterals of a dorsal root ganglion cell within three segments of the spinal cord. Black arrows indicate direction of nerve impulse conduction. The stretch or myotatic reflex (1) is a two neuron circuit with one central synapse (monosynaptic). Other reflex circuits consist of (2. disynaptic) three or more neurons (3. multisynaptic).

muscle, and two, three, or more spinal nerves and cord segments provide sensory and motor fibers. The femoral nerve is composed of sensory and motor fibers from spinal nerves L2, L3, and L4. Thus, the synapses between these sensory and motor fibers must be within spinal cord segments L2, L3, and L4.

As shown in this schema, the other spinal reflexes have one or more internuncial neurons interposed between sensory and motor neurons (2 and 3 in Fig. 184), and some of these may be quite complex reverberating circuits. A ventral horn cell (lower motor neuron) may thus be facilitated, or inhibited, by the sum total of all the impulses that play upon it through literally thousands of tiny synaptic end feet. Such synaptic boutons may be terminal endings of incoming sensory fibers, internuncial neurons, or the several descending motor pathways from the brain stem and cortex. This is the basic organization of a spinal cord segment and its attached spinal nerves. One should remember that each central segment of the spinal cord is also related with gross peripheral structures and the maintenance of their normal function. The following diagrams of the major pathways have included as many cross references to gross anatomy as space permits.

THE LONG ASCENDING TRACTS

I. **The dorsal white column.** (*Fasciculus gracilis and fasciculus cuneatus.*) Since the dorsal funiculus and zone of Lissauer are predominantly composed of dorsal root fibers, both the ascending and descending course of these fibers are described under this heading.

The coarser fibers of the medial bundle enter the dorsal white column just medial to the dorsal gray horn where they bifurcate into ascending and descending arms. The ascending fibers from lower levels are gradually shifted medially and dorsally as they continue upward in the dorsal white funiculus of the spinal cord. The longest fibers are thus displaced medially by shorter ascending dorsal root fibers which enter the spinal cord at successively higher levels. Within this segmental arrangement of ascending dorsal root fibers, the long sacral fibers are most medial, whereas the shorter cervical fibers are located laterally (Fig. 185).

In the cervical region the massive dorsal funiculus is divided by the dorsal intermediate septum into a medial *fasciculus gracilis* (column of Goll) and a lateral *fasciculus cuneatus* (column of Burdach) (Figs. 171, 185). The former contains the long ascending root fibers from the sacral, lumbar, and lower thoracic ganglia, i.e., from the lower extremity and lower portion of the trunk. The fasciculus cuneatus consists of similar fibers from the upper thoracic and cervical ganglia representing upper trunk, upper extremity, and neck.

Since many ascending arms are relatively short, it is evident that only a portion of the root fibers terminate in the medulla, the others ending in the dorsal gray column at various intermediate levels. Those which reach the medulla constitute the first relay of an important afferent pathway to the cerebral cortex. According to Winkler, they come primarily from the lumbosacral and cervical segments, the thoracic contributing relatively few long arms to the medulla.

The central processes of dorsal root ganglion cells thus constitute the first neuron (Neuron I, uncrossed) of this ascending pathway. Ascending fibers that reach the medulla within the fasciculus gracilis terminate upon the cells of the *nucleus gracilis,* while the fibers of the fasciculus cuneatus end about cells of the *nucleus cuneatus* (Fig. 185). The neurons of the nucleus gracilis and cuneatus constitute the second neuron (Neuron II) in this afferent tract. The axons of Neuron II sweep ventrally and medially as *internal arcuate fibers,* cross the midline, and again turn upward as a discrete bundle known as the *medial lemniscus.* This crossed tract ascends through

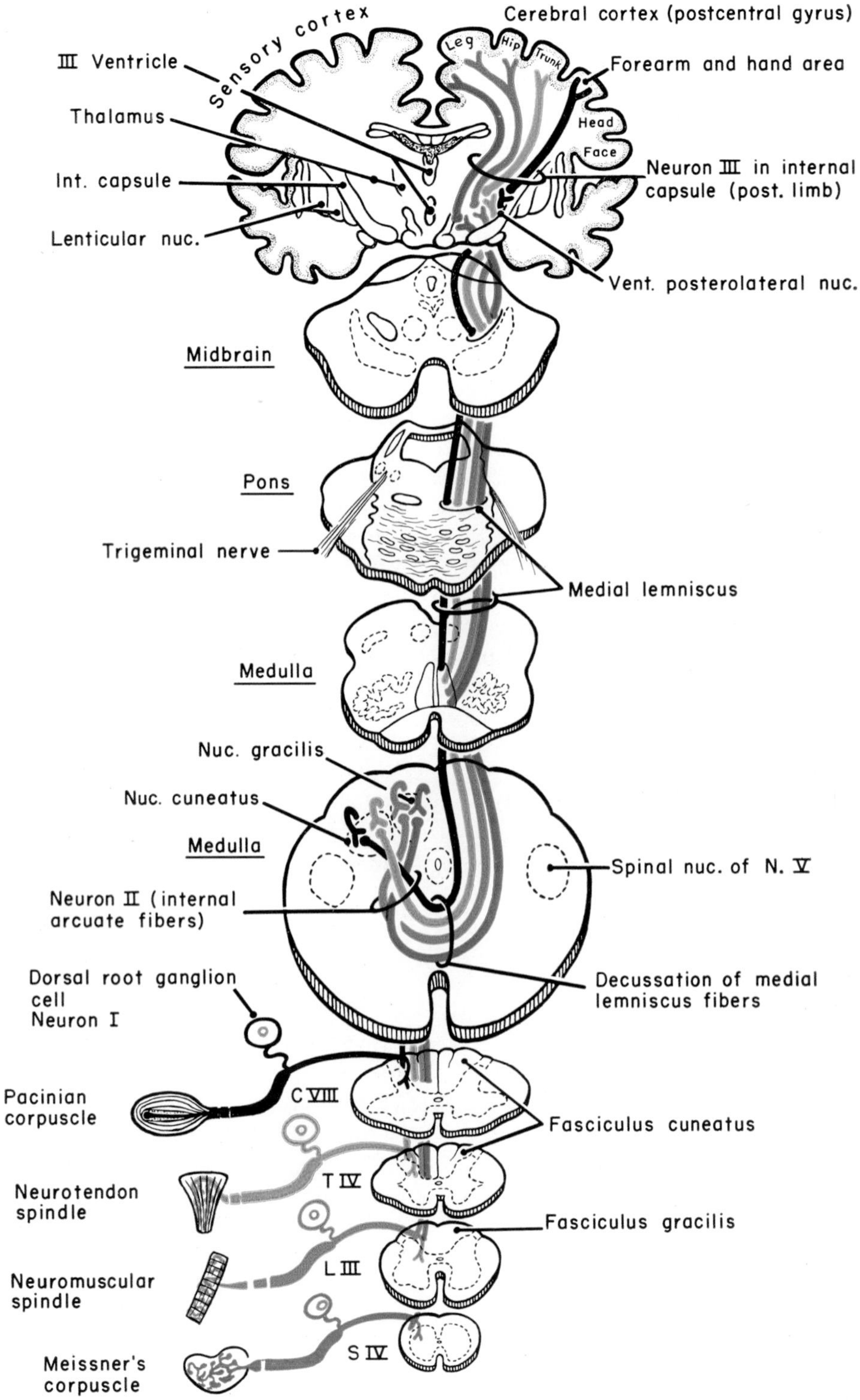

FIG. 185. Diagram of the dorsal white column and medial lemniscus. The pathway for discriminative sensations and conscious proprioception. Letters and numbers indicate corresponding segments of the spinal cord.

the pons and midbrain levels to terminate in the ventral posterolateral nucleus of the thalamus. Relay neurons of this thalamic nucleus (Neuron III) send their axons through the posterior limb of the internal capsule to terminate in the appropriate sensory areas of the cerebral cortex (Fig. 185). In this figure one can follow the respective sacral, lumbar, thoracic, and cervical fibers as they ascend from their level of entrance in the spinal cord to the sensory (somesthetic) cortex. We reiterate, that the ascending fibers of Neuron I in the dorsal white column of the spinal cord constitute an uncrossed tract. The medial lemniscus is a continuation of this pathway, and above the decussation of the medial lemniscus its constituent nerve fibers are crossed. This neural pathway will again be encountered as we study higher levels of the brain stem.

The dorsal white columns are among the newer acquisitions of the nervous system (Brouwer), receiving principally impulses from the arms and legs. In animals without extremities they are poorly developed and consist mainly of shorter fibers. When we consider the great importance of the upper extremity, especially the hand, as an organ for discriminative sensibility and acquisition of skill, and the lower extremity for the maintenance of erect posture, it is not surprising that this phylogenetically younger fiber system constitutes the principal path for the conduction of discriminative (epicritic) sensibility related to cortical function.

The long fibers of the dorsal column convey impulses from the proprioceptors which give rise to sensations of position and movement. They also conduct impulses from tactile receptors necessary for the proper discrimination of two points simultaneously applied (spatial discrimination) and for exact tactile localization. Rapidly successive stimuli produced by the application of a tuning fork to bone or faradic current to skin, which give rise to the sense of vibration (temporal discrimination), are likewise conducted along these fibers.

Lesions of the dorsal column will naturally abolish or diminish these forms of sensibility, the symptoms appearing on the same side as the lesion. Mere contact and pressure are apparently normal, but tactile localization is poor, and two-point discrimination and vibratory sense are lost or greatly diminished. There is loss of appreciation of differences in weight and inability to identify objects placed in the hand by feeling them. These symptoms are most acute on the fingers and more acute on the extremities than on the trunk. Position and movement sense is severely affected, especially in the distal parts of the extremities, and as a rule accompanied by a diminution of muscular tone (hypotonia). Small passive movements are not recognized as movements at all but as touch or pressure. But even in long excursions the direction and extent of the movement are not perceived or only very poorly. With the loss of muscle sense there is inability to perform voluntary active movements properly, the latter being clumsy, uncertain and incoordinated (sensory or dorsal column ataxia).

Since a fiber severed from its cell of origin degenerates, it is obvious that injury to these central ascending fibers of the dorsal white column will produce microscopic evidences of fiber degeneration. These large myelinated fibers are frequently involved totally, or in part, by toxins, demyelinating or metabolic diseases. Sections prepared by the Weigert method yield a "negative picture of myelin degeneration" after injury, for only the normal intact fibers are stained (Figs. 186, 189). A knowledge of tract formation (Fig. 185) enables one to distinguish which region of the spinal cord may have been injured sometime prior to death. The series shown in Fig. 186 were made following injury in the lumbosacral region, and the antemortem neurologic signs and symptoms involved the lower extremities and pelvis. Note the decrease of ascending degeneration in the fasciculus gracilis as it ascends to the second cervical segment. Also observe the progressive increase of normal

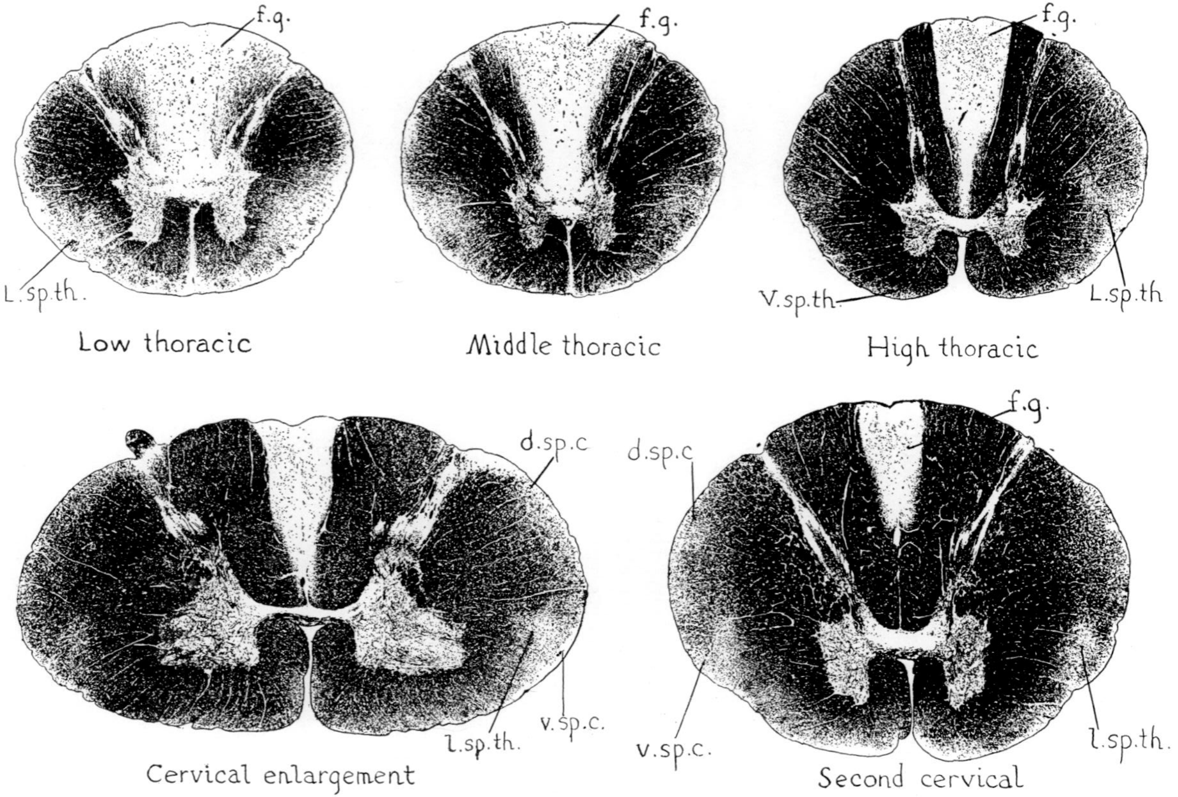

FIG. 186. Transverse sections of a human spinal cord which had been crushed some time previously in the lumbo-sacral region. Weigert's myelin stain. Photographs. *d.sp.c.*, dorsal spinocerebellar tract; *f.g.*, fasciculus gracilis; *l.sp.th.*, lateral spinothalamic tract; *v.sp.c.*, ventral spinocerebellar tract. In the dorsal column the progressive diminution of the degenerated area is due to the passing into the gray of the short and medium ascending arms of the lumbo-sacral dorsal root fibers. Also the progressive increase of normal fibers, next to the dorsal horn, is due to the addition of ascending arms of dorsal root fibers entering the cord above the injury.

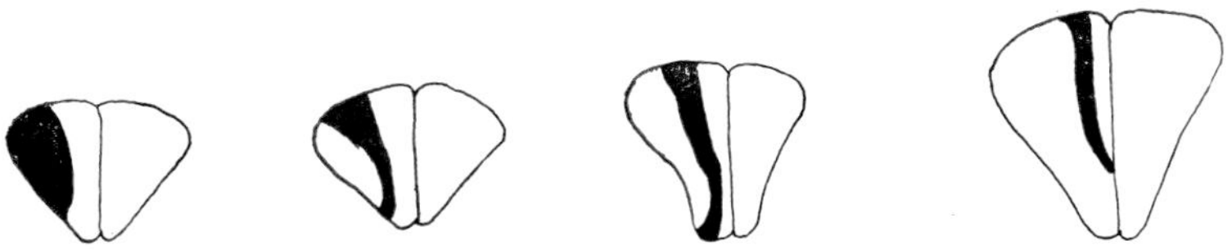

FIG. 187. Ascending degeneration after section of dorsal roots L1, T12 and T11. Marchi method. (After Foerster.)

fibers that have entered the cord above the level of the injury. Contrast the appearance of the second cervical segments shown in Figs. 186 and 189. The antemortem dorsal column symptoms were far more extensive in the patient with a cervical cord crush (Fig. 189). Here all ascending dorsal column fibers were interrupted bilaterally including part of the fibers of the brachial plexus. Note that only a few normal cervical fibers have entered the fasciculus cuneatus above the level of injury.

Sections of the cord prepared by the Marchi method demonstrate a "positive picture of fiber degeneration" (Figs. 187, 188). In such preparations the broken down myelin sheaths stain as fine brown or black granules. The ascending degeneration after destroying only the dorsal roots of L1, T12, and T11 is shown in Fig. 187. In such an injury outside the spinal cord normal sacral and lumbar fibers remain and are visible in the most medial part of the fasciculus gracilis. The fasciculus cuneatus is completely normal. A section of the cervical cord after lumbar injury (Fig. 188) shows that degeneration is limited to the lowest fibers within the fasciculus gracilis. The Marchi method yields excellent results even though some time may have intervened between injury and death. Great care must be exercised by the inexperienced in interpreting Marchi preparations for this method, like many others, often produces deceiving artefacts (Smith, 1951, 1956).

The descending arms of the dorsal roots, also varying in length, likewise become displaced medially and somewhat dorsally as they pass to lower segments of the cord. They are relatively short fibers but some may descend a distance of ten or more segments. In the cervical and most of the thoracic cord they form a small plug-shaped bundle, the *fasciculus interfascicularis* or *comma tract of Schultze,* lying about the middle of the dorsal funiculus (Figs. 185, 200). In the lumbar region they descend near the middle of the dorsal septum in the *septomarginal fasciculus* (*oval area of Flechsig*) which in the sacral cord occupies a small triangle near the dorsomedian periphery (*triangle of Phillippe-Gombault,* Figs. 175, 177). Besides the descending root fibers, the above named fascicles also contain descending fibers from cells of the dorsal horn.

The zone of Lissauer (*fasciculus dorsolateralis*) is composed of fine myelinated and unmyelinated arms of the dorsal root fibers which mainly convey impulses of pain and temperature. Some of these fibers pass through the substantia gelatinosa and terminate in the nucleus proprius of the dorsal horn which gives origin to the spinothalamic tracts. Others end in the substantia gelatinosa and are thence relayed to the posteromarginal cells and the nucleus proprius (Pearson, 1952). Mingled with the root fibers are fibers from cells of the substantia gelatinosa, which likewise ascend or descend for only a few segments. These are probably associative in character, connecting different levels of the dorsal horn.

II. **The ventral spinothalamic and spinotectal tracts** arise from the large cells of the dorsal horn (nucleus centrodorsalis) and probably also from similar cells of the intermediate gray. The majority of the axons

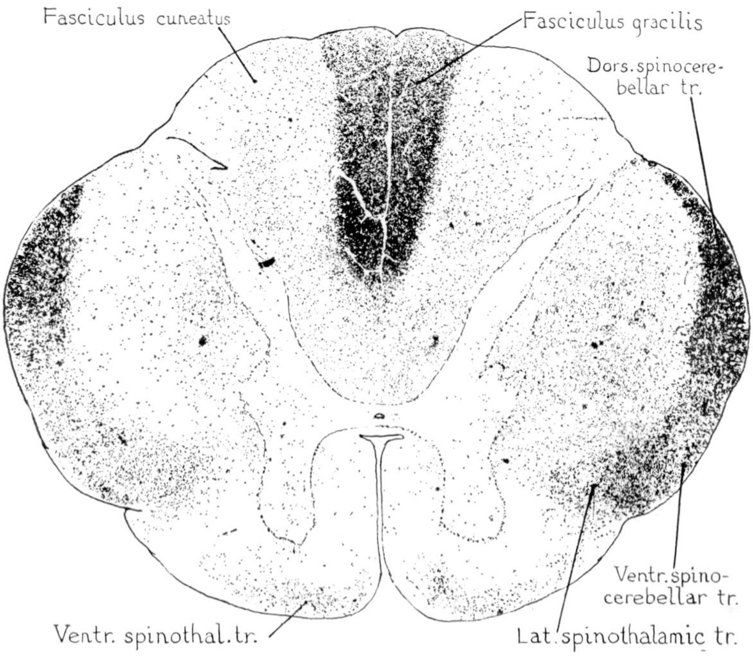

FIG. 188. Section through second cervical segment of a human spinal cord which had been crushed several weeks previously in the upper lumbar region. Marchi stain for degenerating fibers. Photograph. The ascending degenerating fibers are seen as black granules.

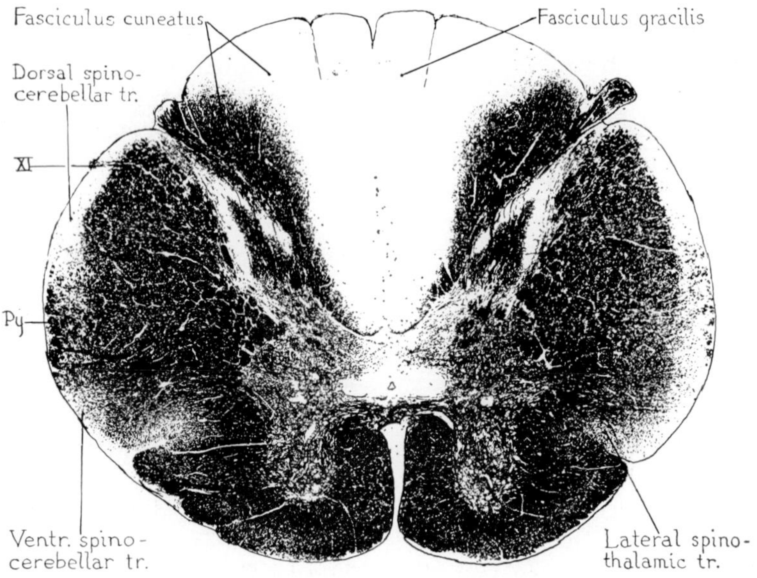

FIG. 189. Section through second cervical segment of a human spinal cord which had been crushed some time previously in the lower cervical region. Weigert's myelin stain. Photograph. Owing to the high level of the injury, practically all the fibers of the spinocerebellar and spinothalamic tracts have undergone degeneration; also all ascending root fibers in the dorsal white column except those of dorsal root fibers which have entered above the upper level of the lesion (about C6). *Py*, aberrant pyramidal fibers; *XI*, root fibers of spinal accessory nerve.

cross obliquely in the ventral white commissure, the decussation extending through several segments, and ascend in the ventral and ventrolateral funiculi of the opposite side as the *ventral spinothalamic* and *spinotectal tracts* (Fig. 190).

Although not included in Fig. 190, a smaller number of uncrossed fibers ascend in the homolateral ventral spinothalamic tract. The large dorsal root ganglion cells and secondary neurons of this tract are believed to convey impulses of touch and pressure supplementing the tactile path of the dorsal white column. The ventral spinothalamic tract becomes incorporated with the fibers of the medial lemniscus in the medulla and higher levels of the brain stem. As in most crossed ascending sensory tracts the axon of Neuron II decussates and ascends to the thalamus. The ventral spinothalamic tract terminates in the ventral posterolateral nucleus of the thalamus. Neuron III then relays touch and pressure impulses to the cerebral cortex (Fig. 190). Inasmuch as touch and pressure impulses are conveyed in both ventral spinothalamic tracts and the dorsal white column, these sensory modalities are of little use clinically in localizing injury in the spinal cord. However, such is not the case in the medulla and higher levels, for presumably both crude and discriminative touch from the opposite side are incorporated in or near the medial lemniscus. Injury to the ventral spinothalamic tract in the spinal cord produces little if any disturbance in tactile sensibility, though such may be ascertained by more precise methods (heightened threshold, reduction of touch and pressure points per unit of skin area). Discriminative sensibility is undisturbed for such impulses are conveyed in the dorsal white column. The pleasant or unpleasant character of sensation, however, is definitely related to conduction in the ventrolateral funiculi. In bilateral destruction of these columns, there is apparently complete loss of such affective qualities as itching, tickling, and libidinous feeling (Foerster).

The small spinotectal tract has an origin similar to that of the spinothalamic tract, and conveys somatic sensory impulses (tactile, pain, and perhaps some pressure). Considered by many as a component of the spinothalamic tracts, the spinotectal paths parallel their course in the ventrolateral funiculus as it ascends to terminate in the superior colliculus of the midbrain (Fig. 190).

III. **The lateral spinothalamic tract** is closely related to the ventral spinothalamic and spinotectal tracts. It is treated separately in view of its tremendous clinical importance. Its component fibers are more concentrated than those in the ventral tract. It also contains more numerous long fibers that go directly to the thalamus without relay. The receptors of pain and temperature represent peripheral endings of the small and medium sized dorsal root ganglion cells, and their thin central processes enter the zone of Lissauer (Fig. 191). Axons from the cells of nucleus centrodorsalis, and perhaps some from the substantia gelatinosa, cross in the ventral white commissure and ascend in the opposite lateral funiculus mesial to the ventral spinocerebellar tract. Most of the axons of Neuron II cross obliquely to the opposite side within the segment of entry, although some ascend one segment before crossing in the ventral white commissure.

The fibers show a ventromedial segmental arrangement in the lateral spinothalamic tract. The most lateral and dorsal fibers represent the lowest portion of the body, whereas the more medial and ventral fibers are related to the upper extremity and neck (Fig. 191). As shown on the left of level C 8, there is also a lamination of the sensory modalities within this tract; the temperature fibers are placed dorsally, and pain fibers are located more ventrally. Injuries of this compact pathway ordinarily affect both pain and temperature. At higher

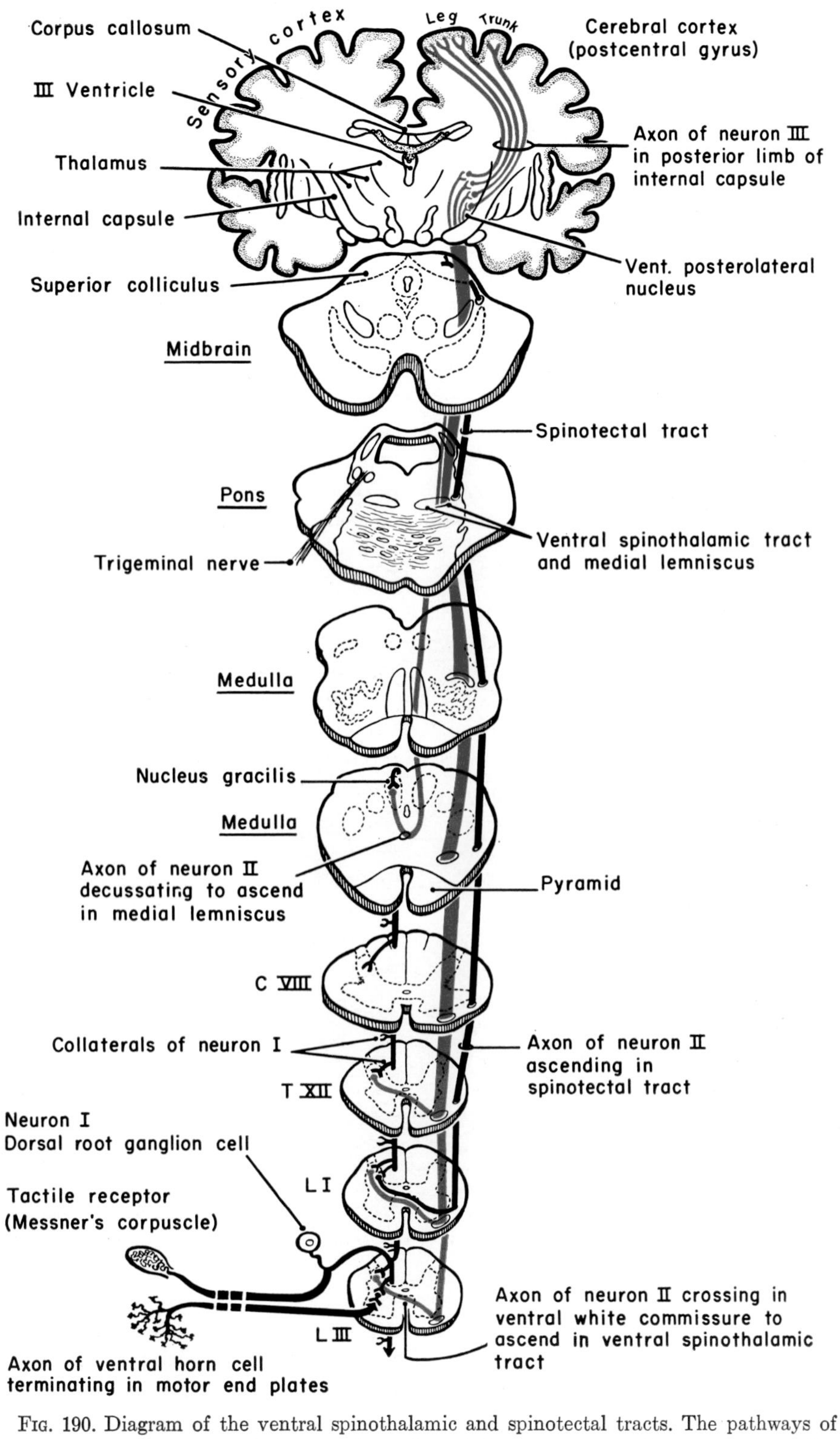

FIG. 190. Diagram of the ventral spinothalamic and spinotectal tracts. The pathways of crude touch and pressure. Letters and numbers indicate corresponding segments of the spinal cord.

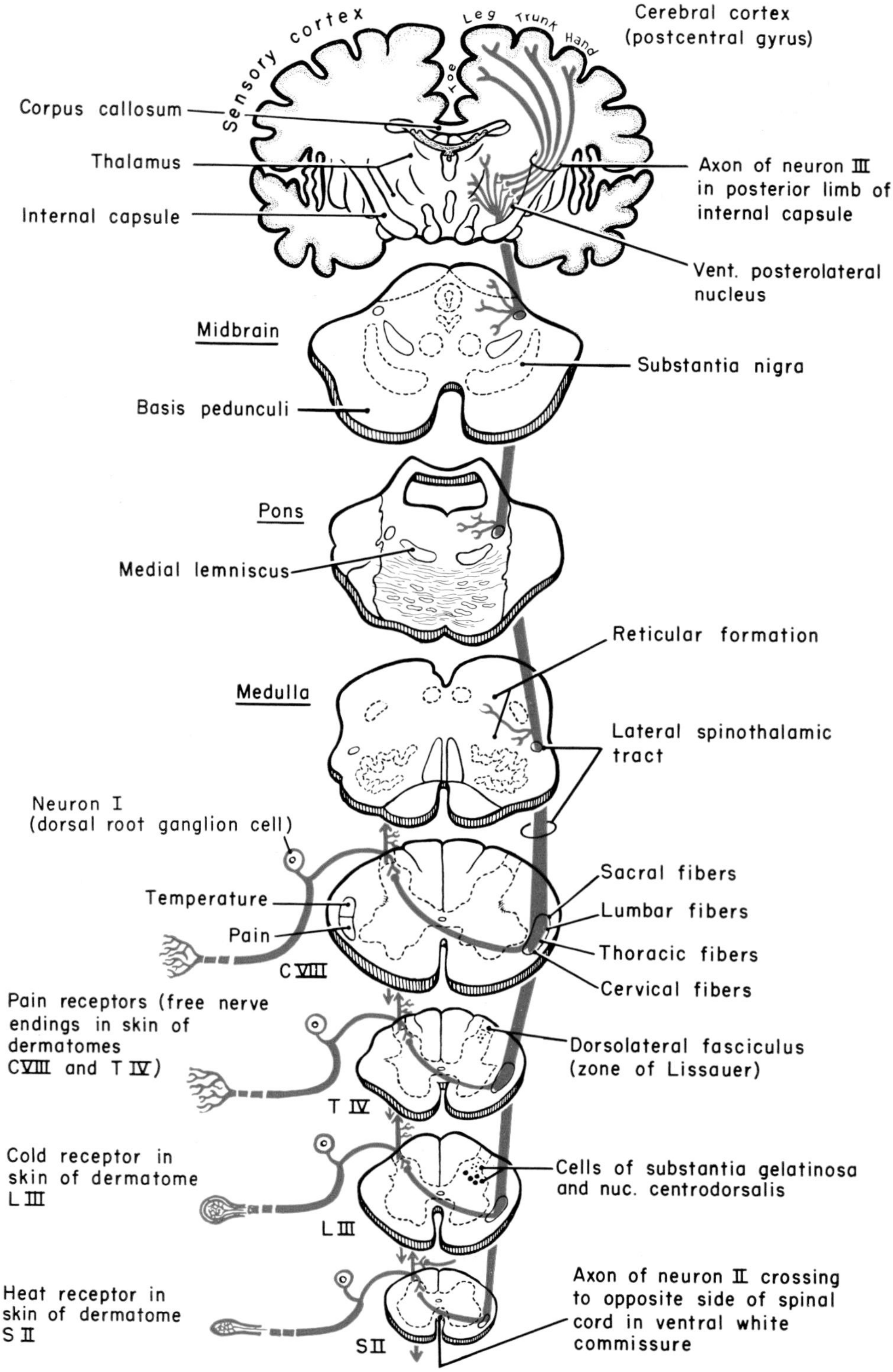

FIG. 191. Diagram of the lateral spinothalamic tract. The pathway of pain and temperature. Letters and numbers indicate corresponding segments of the spinal cord.

brain stem levels this tract sends numerous collaterals into the reticular formation and tegmentum before terminating in the ventral posterolateral nucleus of the thalamus.

Unilateral section of this tract produces a complete loss of pain and temperature (analgesia and thermoanesthesia) on the opposite side of the body. This contralateral sensory loss extends to a level one segment below that of the lesion, due to the oblique crossing of Neuron II fibers (Fig. 204). The anesthesia involves the superficial and deep portions of the body wall, but not the viscera which appear to be represented bilaterally. The anogenital region is not markedly affected in unilateral lesions. After a variable period there is often some return of painful sensibility, due perhaps to the presence of uncrossed spinothalamic fibers. Such pain impulses may also ascend by shorter relays along the spinospinal and spinoreticular pathways. A return of temperature sensations may also be encountered. In certain instances a bilateral surgical section of the lateral spinothalamic tracts (chordotomy) is performed on selected patients to relieve pain and produce a complete and more enduring sensory loss. The spinothalamic and trigeminothalamic pathways may both be destroyed by one laterally placed lesion in the medulla or midbrain where these two tracts occupy a superficial position (Figs. 191, 268). Interruption of both tracts at the level of the midbrain results in a loss of pain and temperature of the face, neck, trunk, and extremities on the opposite side of the body.

Nathan and Smith (1951) have presented evidence that in man the fibers subserving the sensation of bladder fullness, desire to micturate, and pain fibers from the bladder, urethra, and lower ureter are all located in the lateral spinothalamic tract. They believe that fibers mediating touch, pressure, or tension in the urethra ascend in the dorsal white column.

It is evident from the above that the sensory impulses brought in by the dorsal roots are organized in the spinal cord into two main systems, discriminative (epicritic) and affective (vital, protopathic), the former related to the long fibers of the dorsal white column, the latter to the shorter root fibers and the ventrolateral white column. Discriminative sensibility carried by the longest fibers remains uncrossed in the spinal cord. Pain and temperature brought in by the shortest fibers in the zone of Lissauer cross almost at once via the lateral spinothalamic tract. The rest of tactile sense (mere contact and pressure) is carried upward in the dorsal column by ascending root fibers of varying length which terminate in the gray of the cord and connect with the ventral spinothalamic neurons at various intermediate levels (Stopford). This distribution of afferent impulses accounts for the curious sensory dissociation occurring in hemisection of the spinal cord (Brown-Sequard) where there is loss of pain and temperature on the opposite half of the body below the level of the lesion, while the sense of position and movement, two-point discrimination and vibration are lost on the same side as the lesion (see p. 231).

It seems certain that cells of the substantia gelatinosa are intercalated between some of the root fibers which conduct pain and the neurons of the lateral spinothalamic tract. It is probable that the larger more quickly conducting pain fibers terminate directly in the nucleus proprius, while the finer more slowly conducting ones are relayed through cells of the substantia gelatinosa, accounting perhaps for the high threshold and diffuse character of some pain reactions.

IV. **The dorsal spinocerebellar tract** (*tract of Flechsig, direct cerebellar tract*) is a prominent uncrossed fiber bundle lying along the dorsolateral periphery of the cord, bounded medially by the lateral pyramidal tract (Figs. 192, 200). Its large fibers arise from the cells of Clarke's column, pass laterally to the white matter of the same side and there ascend the whole length of the cord. In the medulla they form part of the inferior cerebellar peduncle and pass to the cerebellum, terminating in both the cephalic and caudal portion of the vermis. The tract appears first in the upper lumbar cord (L3) and increases in size until the upper limit of Clarke's column has been reached (C8).

Since the column of Clarke is not present to any extent in the sacral and lower lumbar regions of the cord, impulses destined for the cerebellum are carried upward by the large myelinated ascending arms of the dorsal roots which give off bundles of collaterals to Clarke's column when the latter nucleus is reached (Figs. 182, 192). But even in the thoracic cord the dorsal root fibers usually ascend a few segments before sending collaterals to Clarke's column. The large fibers of cervical spinal nerves entering the cord above C8 ascend in the dorsal white column to end in the lateral cuneate nucleus. Axons from this nucleus course along the dorsolateral surface of the medulla as *dorsal external arcuate fibers.* They join the dorsal spinocerebellar fibers within the restiform body and terminate in the anterior lobe of the cerebellum.

This uncrossed pathway from periphery to cerebellum is composed of two neurons, the spinal ganglion cells and the cells of Clarke's column (Fig. 192). Extensive degeneration studies in man have emphasized that the ventral and dorsal spinocerebellar tracts are difficult to delimit as they form the margins of the lateral funiculus in the spinal cord. Many fibers of the ventral spinocerebellar tract move dorsally as they ascend and become incorporated within the dorsal spinocerebellar tract(Smith, 1957). The latter includes most of the spinocerebellar fibers from the spinal cord, particularly those proprioceptive fibers that come mainly from the trunk and lower extremity.

V. **The ventral spinocerebellar tract** is likewise situated along the lateral periphery of the cord, extending from the ventral limits of the direct cerebellar tract to about the exit of the ventral roots (Figs. 192, 200). Mesially it is in intimate contact with the lateral spinothalamic tract, the two together constituting the *anterolateral fasciculus of Gower.* The tract is more diffusely organized than the direct cerebellar, and is composed of finer fibers which probably arise from cells scattered through the intermediate gray (intermediomedial nucleus) and perhaps also from cells in the base of the dorsal horn. The majority of the fibers are uncrossed, but a smaller number come from cells of the opposite side. The tract appears in the upper sacral or lower lumbar cord. At higher cord levels many of these small fibers become incorporated into the dorsal tract. In the brain stem of man the ventral tract is small and composed of few fibers (Smith, 1957). Some of the ventral tract fibers probably terminate in the reticular formation, and are then relayed to the cerebellum by reticulocerebellar fibers.

The ventral spinocerebellar tract reaches the cerebellum by a somewhat different route, ascending considerably higher than the dorsal spinocerebellar tract, and then turning back along the outer side of the superior cerebellar peduncle to terminate in the cephalic portion of the vermis. This path to the cerebellum is likewise composed of two neurons (Fig. 192). Though this tract is composed of crossed and uncrossed fibers in the spinal cord, the fibers terminate in the opposite part of the anterior lobe after decussating with fibers of the cerebellar vermis (Carrea and Grundfest, 1954; Combs, 1956). The proprioceptive impulses conducted by the tract come from all parts of the body including the neck and upper extremities.

The spinocerebellar tracts convey to the cerebellum impulses from the muscle, tendon, and joint receptors, which enable the cerebellum to exercise its regulative tonic and synergizing influence upon the voluntary muscles. The effects of injury to these tracts in the spinal cord are often difficult to judge since other tracts are simultane-

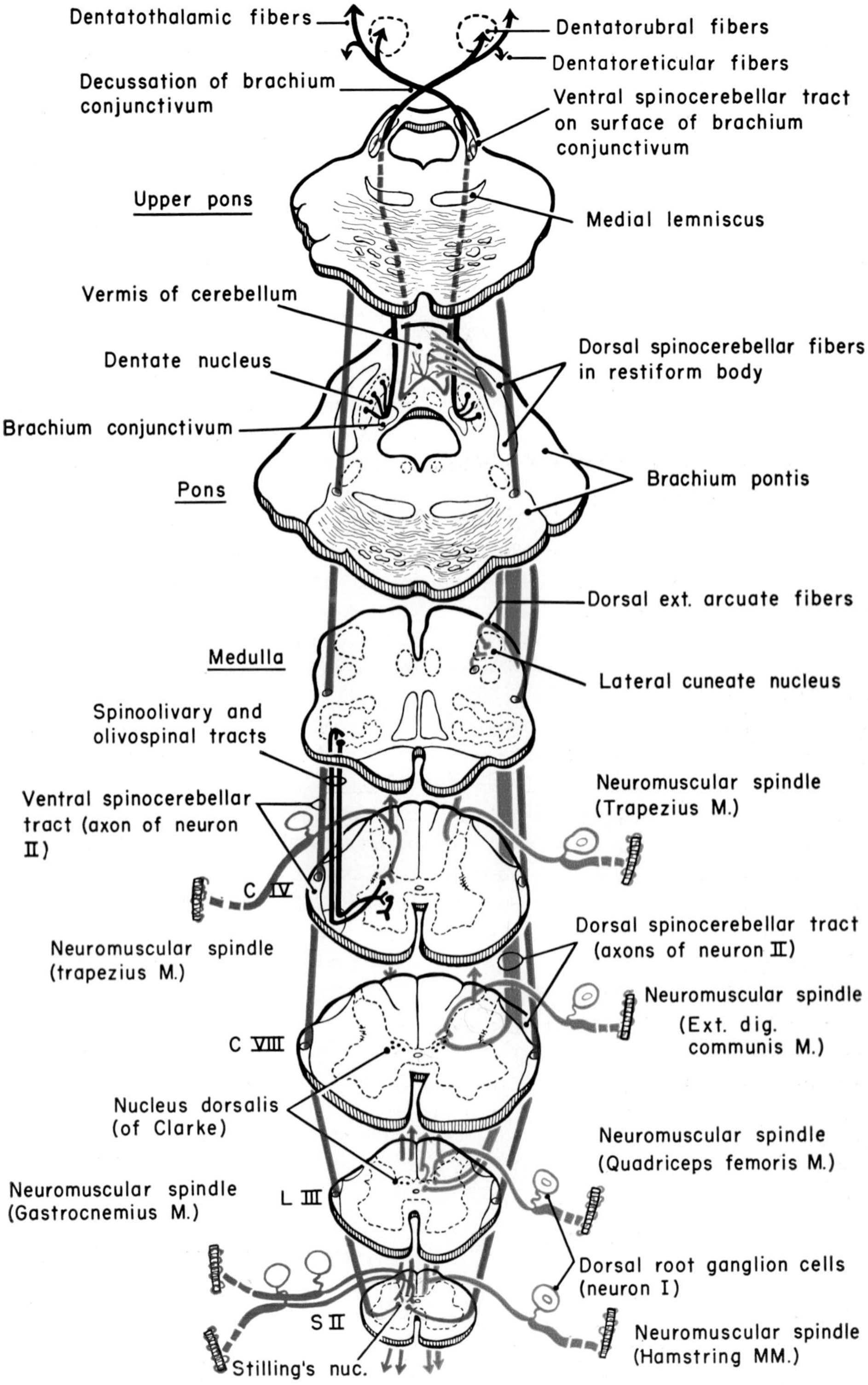

FIG. 192. Diagram of the ventral (red) and dorsal (blue) spinocerebellar tracts; spinoolivary and olivospinal tracts (black). The proprioceptive pathways for subcortical integration and reflexes.

ously involved. Injury to the cerebellum itself results in reduced muscular tone and in an incoordination of muscular action producing disturbances of posture and movement (cerebellar ataxia or asynergia). There is no sensory loss of position and movement, the impulses to the cerebellum remaining on an unconscious level.

The cervical segments of the spinal cord send proprioceptive fibers to the inferior olivary nucleus, and receive descending fibers in return. These ascending and descending tracts (*spinoolivary* and *olivospinal*) lie close together at the junction of the ventral and lateral white funiculi. They are shown on the left side of Fig. 192. These reciprocal paths are proprioceptive in nature, for the nucleus of the inferior olive is intimately related to the opposite hemisphere of the cerebellum.

VI. **Spinoreticular and spinocortical tracts.** A spinoreticular tract has been described in the cat by Brodal (1949, 1958). The fibers originate from cells in the dorsal horn, ascend in the lateral funiculus and terminate in the lateral reticular nucleus of the medulla. The majority of the fibers appear to be uncrossed (Fig. 197). Since the lateral reticular nucleus sends projections to the cerebellum, this pathway may be concerned with the transmission of exteroceptive impulses to the cerebellum.

A spinocortical tract has been described in man by Nathan and Smith (1955). In their degeneration studies ascending spinal fibers from the upper cervical cord became intermingled with the descending fibers of the corticospinal tract. The ascending fibers accompanied the corticospinal tract through the medulla and pons. In the midbrain the ascending fibers were intermingled with another descending path, the temporopontine tract. If the work of Nathan and Smith is substantiated by others, this direct spinocortical tract will be of considerable neuroanatomic significance.

THE LONG DESCENDING TRACTS

I. **The corticospinal or pyramidal tracts** constitute the most important and conspicuous descending fiber bundles of the cord. Each tract is composed of over a million fibers of which some 700,000 are myelinated (Lassek and Rasmussen, 1939; Lassek, 1942, 1954). The great majority of the myelinated fibers, nearly 90%, have a diameter of 1–4μ; most of the remaining fibers range in caliber from 5–10μ but include among them some 30,000–40,000 very large fibers having a thickness of 11–22μ. The fibers arise in part from the giant pyramidal cells of Betz in the precentral gyrus of the cerebral cortex (motor area, area 4 of Brodmann), in larger part from other cells of this and adjacent frontal areas (premotor area, area 6) and probably also from other cortical areas. They converge in the corona radiata and pass downward through the internal capsule, basis pedunculi, pons and medulla (Fig. 193). This robust tract is closely related to the emerging motor fibers of cranial nerves III, VI and XII as it descends through the brain stem. The corticobulbar tract bringing impulses to brain stem motor nuclei is close to the corticospinal tract in the internal capsule and midbrain. However, the corticobulbar fibers pass dorsally and these tracts become separated from each other in the pons and medulla. The corticospinal tract comes to the surface in the medulla as the pyramid. At the junction of medulla and cord, the fibers undergo an incomplete decussation giving rise to two tracts in each half of the spinal cord, a *lateral* or *crossed pyramidal* and a *ventral uncrossed* or *direct pyramidal* tract (Figs. 193, 229).

The majority of the fibers, 75–90 per cent, cross in the pyramidal decussation and descend in the dorsal part of the lateral funiculus as the lateral or crossed pyramidal tract, lying between the dorsal spinocerebellar tract and the lateral fasciculus proprius (Figs. 194, 195, 196). It comes to

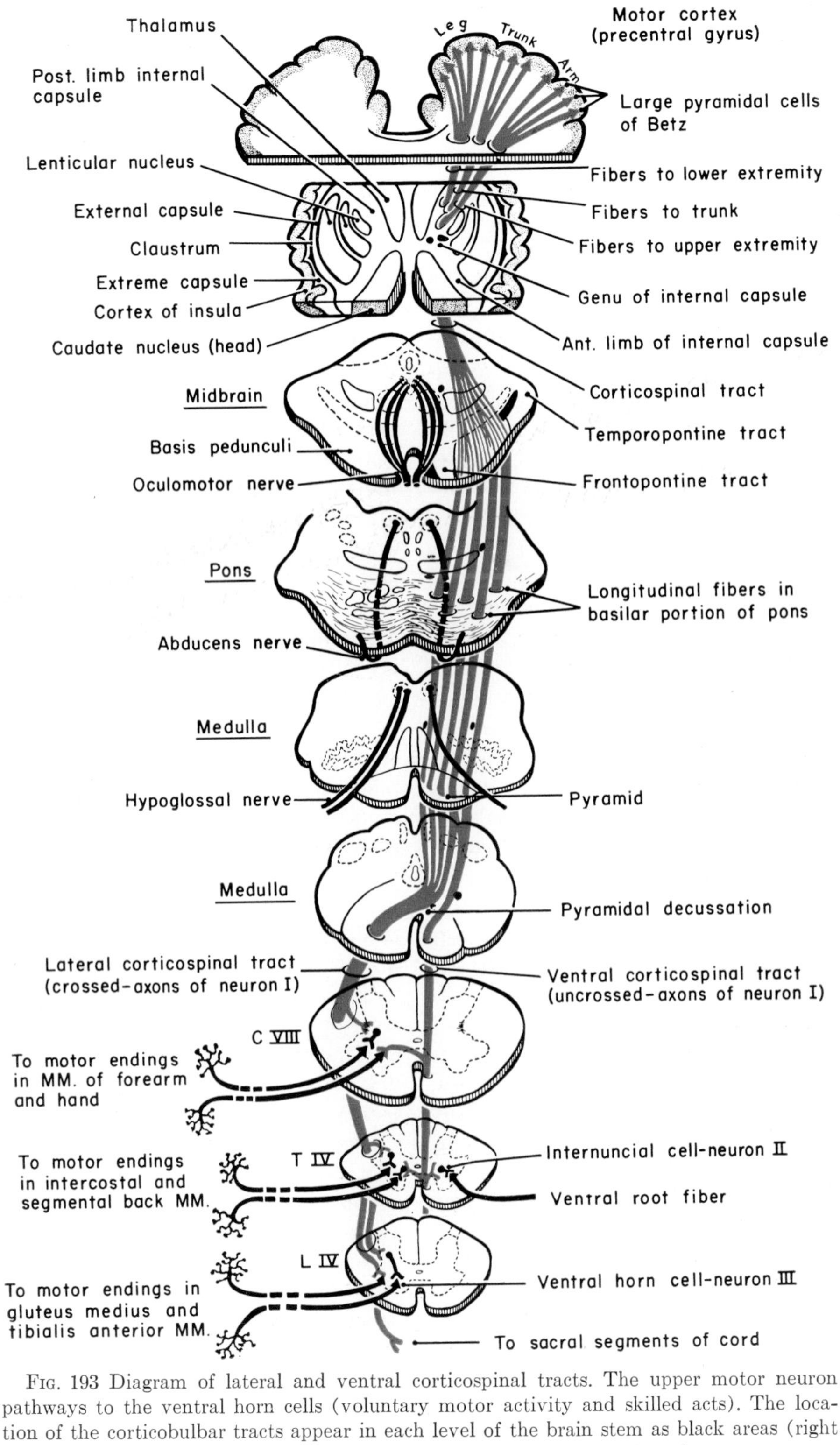

FIG. 193 Diagram of lateral and ventral corticospinal tracts. The upper motor neuron pathways to the ventral horn cells (voluntary motor activity and skilled acts). The location of the corticobulbar tracts appear in each level of the brain stem as black areas (right side). Letters and numbers indicate corresponding segments of spinal cord.

the surface in the lumbar and sacral regions before the dorsal cerebellar tract has appeared. In the uppermost cervical segments some fibers occupy for a short distance an aberrant position outside the dorsal spinocerebellar fibers (Figs. 193, 189). The tract extends to the lowermost part of the cord, constantly diminishing in size as more and more fibers leave to terminate in the gray matter.

A smaller portion of the pyramidal fibers descend uncrossed as the ventral or direct pyramidal tract (bundle of Türck), occupying an oval area adjacent to the ventral median sulcus (Figs. 193, 194). It normally extends only to the upper thoracic cord, though fibers have been traced to the lower thoracic and even lumbar region, thus innervating primarily the muscles of the upper extremities and neck. This tract is found only in man and the higher apes and its size shows considerable variations, due to the fact that the proportion of decussating fibers is not constant. In extreme cases they may be altogether absent, practically all of the fibers crossing in the pyramidal decussation. In other isolated cases, the pyramidal fibers of one or both sides may not cross at all and give rise to huge ventral pyramidal tracts.

Besides the two tracts discussed, there are other uncrossed corticospinal fibers which form the *ventrolateral pyramidal tract* of Barnes ("Fibres pyramidales homolaterales superficielles" of Déjérine). The bundle is composed of rather fine fibers which descend more ventrally in the lateral funiculus, in or near the area occupied by the tract of Helweg (olivospinal tract, Fig. 192).

The fibers of the lateral pyramidal tract terminate in the gray of the same side. The termination of the direct tract is not fully ascertained. It is probable that most fibers cross individually through the ventral commissure to terminate on the opposite side, a smaller number ending on the same side. The majority of all pyramidal fibers are not projected directly on the ventral horn cells but terminate in arborizations around intercalated cells in the intermediate or ventral gray. Only a relatively small number (10–20 per cent) come in direct synapse with the motor cells(Hoff and Hoff, 1934).

It is evident from the above that the corticospinal system is primarily a crossed one, but nevertheless has considerable homolateral representation through the ventrolateral tract of Barnes and the fibers of the direct pyramidal tract which end on the same side. Hoff and Hoff (1934) conclude that in the chimpanzee, 20–25 per cent of the fibers establish ipsilateral connections.

It has been estimated that about 55 per cent of all pyramidal fibers end in the cervical cord, 20 per cent in the thoracic, and 25 per cent in the lumbosacral (Weil and Lassek, 1930). This would suggest that pyramidal control over the upper extremity is much greater than over the lower. Myelinization of the fibers begins around birth and is not fully completed until the end of the second year.

The pyramidal tract conveys to the spinal cord impulses which result in volitional movements, especially those isolated individual movements of finger, hand, etc., which form the basis for the acquisition of skill. Destruction of the tract therefore produces a loss of voluntary movement, most marked in the distal parts of the extremities. The proximal joints, and grosser movement are less severely and less permanently affected. At the onset of a vascular accident, there is at first a loss of tone in the affected muscles. But after a period of days or even weeks the muscles gradually become more resistant to passive movement (spasticity), and the deep kinetic reflexes, especially in the leg, are increased in force (hyperreflexia). On the other hand, the superficial reflexes, such as the abdominals, cremasteric and normal plantar, are lost or diminished.

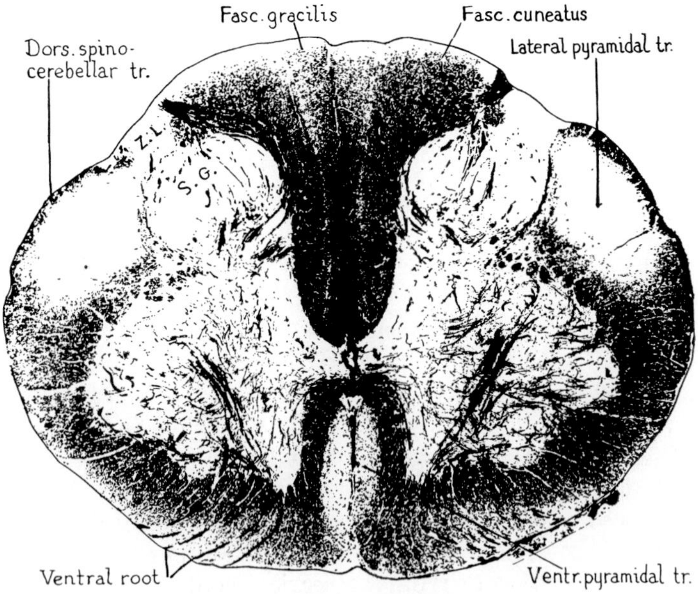

FIG. 194. Section through cervical enlargement of spinal cord of seven to eight months human fetus. Weigert's myelin stain. Photograph. The pyramidal tracts are unmyelinated at this stage, hence are unstained. *S.G.*, substantia gelatinosa; *Z.L.*, zone of Lissauer.

In individuals of advanced age there is a tendency for the abdominal reflexes to be absent. These reflexes are absent more often in females than in males (Madonick, 1957). He found the cutaneous abdominal reflexes absent in 16 per cent of 2500 non-neurologic cases, and concludes that the absence of this reflex is not in itself an indication of nervous system disease. In the case of the plantar reflex, stimulation of the sole is followed by dorsiflexion of the big toe instead of the normal plantar flexion (sign of Babinski), a symptom usually present in injury of the pyramidal tract. However, it is not an infallible sign, for it was absent in some human cases with established corticospinal lesions (Nathan and Smith, 1955). The Babinski response is commonly observed in the human newborn due to incomplete maturation of the central nervous system, and should not be regarded as indicative of birth injury.

After a prolonged interval, some individuals show a considerable restitution of the more gross muscle movements about the shoulder and hip. The residual defects are most marked in the distal parts of the extremities, and at this time the pathologic reflexes are often diminished or may no longer be elicited.

The cause of the spasticity usually occurring in human hemiplegia is still a subject of considerable controversy. Lesions of the pyramidal tract in cats and monkeys produce a hypotonic paralysis or paresis of discrete movements, though in the chimpanzee the hypotonia is obscure and more difficult to demonstrate (Tower). Similarly, Fulton and Kennard (1934) have reported that ablation of the motor area (area 4) in monkeys and chimpanzees produces paralysis of a flaccid character. Only when the premotor area (area 6) is also involved, is there increased resistance to passive movements. These investigators conclude, therefore, that the spasticity is due to injury of "extrapyramidal" pathways descending in close conjunction with the pyramidal tract.

More recently, however, in a series of experiments on the monkey, Denny-Brown

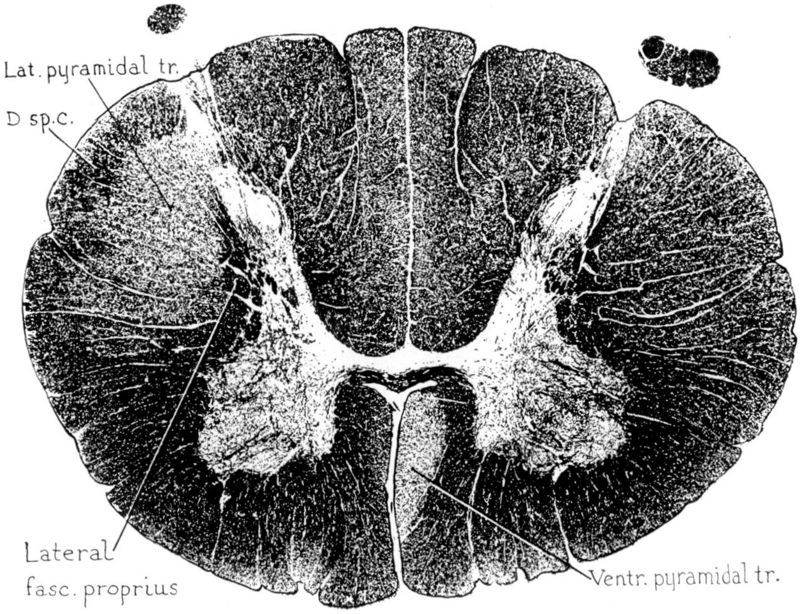

FIG. 195. Transverse section through cervical enlargement of spinal cord of hemiplegic man. Weigert's myelin stain. Photograph. The lateral pyramidal tract of one side and the ventral pyramidal tract of the other side are degenerated. *d.sp.c.*, dorsal spinocerebellar tract.

and Botterell (1948) have found that spasticity accompanies the paralytic manifestations of all area 4 lesions, and is most enduring in total ablations. In total lesions where the motor deficit is greatest, the onset of spasticity is considerably delayed; it is more rapid with the milder symptoms produced by partial lesions of area 4. The authors regard hemiplegic spasticity as a sign of pyramidal or motor area involvement.

It must be remembered that the pyramidal tract is a complex fiber system arising from more extensive cortical areas than was formerly supposed, and originating only in part from the giant pyramidal cells of Betz in the precentral gyrus. These cells are relatively few in number, about 25,000 according to Campbell, some 34,000 in the more careful recent count of Lassek (1940). They probably furnish the larger fibers, 10–22 micra in diameter, whose number has been estimated around 40,000 (Lassek and Rasmussen, 1939). The more numerous finer fibers come in considerable part from the premotor area (area 6) and perhaps from other cortical regions (Häggquist, Kennard, Foerster, Verhaart). Thus there are at least two components in the pyramidal tract, a large-fibered component from the motor area, and a fine-fibered one from the motor, premotor, and perhaps other areas. Lesions of the entire pyramidal tract involve both components, ablation of the motor area alone destroys only the large-fibered one (Häggquist, 1937). It is probable that the fibers of the Betz cells are concerned with the finer isolated movements of the distal parts of the extremities, which are primarily affected in pyramidal lesions. The more numerous finer fibers may be related to grosser movement and tonic control, and injury to them may be the cause of the increase in muscle tone and the more active deep reflexes. These fibers are not, however, "extrapyramidal". They form an integral part of the pyramidal tract, its largest portion indeed, descending uninterruptedly from cerebral cortex through the medullary

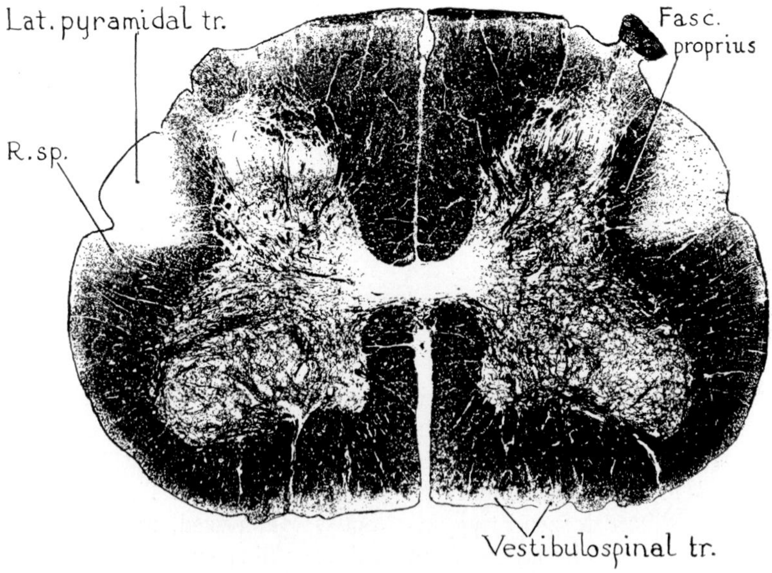

FIG. 196. Section through fourth lumbar segment of a human spinal cord which had been crushed some time previously in the lower cervical region. Weigert's myelin stain. Photograph. The degenerated long descending tracts are unstained. Note that the lateral pyramidal tract reaches the lateral periphery of the cord. *R.sp.*, rubrospinal and reticulospinal tracts.

pyramids to the spinal cord. They come from cortical areas which also send true extrapyramidal tracts, i.e., tracts which are relayed in subcortical nuclei before reaching the cord.

The pyramidal cells and their axons constitute the "upper motor neurons" in contrast to the "lower motor neurons" (ventral horn cells) which directly innervate the striped muscle. The symptoms of pyramidal lesion, characterized by loss of volitional movement, spasticity, increased deep reflexes, loss of superficial reflexes, and the sign of Babinski, are therefore often designated as "upper motor neuron" paralysis (spastic or supranuclear paralysis). In "lower motor neuron" paralysis, there is loss of all movement, reflex and voluntary, with loss of tone and rapid atrophy of the affected muscles.

Paralysis of both arm and leg on one side is termed a *hemiplegia,* that of a single limb a *monoplegia. Diplegia* denotes the paralysis of two corresponding parts on opposite sides, such as both arms, though when both legs are involved the term *paraplegia* is often used. Paralysis of all four extremities is usually known as *tetraplegia,* or *quadraplegia.*

II. **The reticulospinal tracts** are fairly extensive, but diffuse, fiber bundles which originate from large cells scattered through the reticular formation of the medulla, pons, and midbrain (Fig. 78C, F). Both crossed and uncrossed fibers are present, all terminating in the ventral horn (Fig. 197). Some descending axons may terminate upon the ventral horn cells directly, while most of them probably synapse with internuncial neurons located in the ventral gray horn. The reticular nuclei, particularly at medulla levels, give origin to the *lateral reticulospinal tract.* These fibers are chiefly uncrossed and are located medially in the brain stem (Fig. 197). In the lateral funiculus of the cord this tract lies close but medial to the rubrospinal and corticospinal tracts. Autonomic fibers from higher centers probably descend in intimate relation with both the lateral reticulospinal and corticospinal fibers to end about visceral motor cells of the intermediate gray matter.

Reticular nuclei within the pons, and possibly some in the midbrain, contribute chiefly uncrossed fibers that form the *medial reticulospinal tract.* In the lower brain stem this pathway is located close to the medial longitudinal fasciculus, which it follows into the ventral funiculus of the spinal cord. Like the lateral tract, its component fibers end in synapses upon internuncial and ventral horn cells.

Through this descending multisynaptic pathway fibers are relayed from numerous higher structures (e.g., globus pallidus, substantia nigra, red nucleus, cerebellum) to spinal cord levels. Fibers transmitting facilitative and inhibitory impulses from brain stem centers descend in these tracts to influence the neural activity of ventral horn cells and thus help regulate muscle tone (Fig. 197). The lateral reticulospinal tract conveys most of the facilitatory fibers, while inhibitory fibers are more heavily concentrated in the medial reticulospinal tract and ventral funiculus. The reticulospinal tract as well as descending autonomic fibers may be included in some injuries of the lateral corticospinal tracts. Their destruction help explain some of the change in muscle tonus, as well as visceral symptoms of the bladder and rectum that often accompany lesions of the corticospinal tracts. Other descending autonomic fibers enroute to the ciliospinal center of the cord lie in the lateral reticular formation of the medulla and very likely within the lateral reticulospinal tract of the cervical spinal cord.

III. **The vestibulospinal tract** originates from the lateral vestibular nucleus of the medulla which receives fibers from the vestibular division of the eighth nerve and from the cerebellum. The largest number of fibers descend uncrossed as the *lateral vestibulospinal tract* along the ventral periphery of the cord, intermingled with ascending fibers of the ventral spinothalamic tract (Figs. 196, 198, 200). It is reduced in man, but its fibers have been traced to the lowermost part of the cord, all terminating in the ventral gray. A smaller number of fibers from the medial and lateral vestibular nuclei form chiefly a crossed, descending tract designated the *medial vestibulospinal tract.* These fibers are intimately related with the medial longitudinal fasciculus, and have not been traced below the upper thoracic levels of the spinal cord (Fig. 198).

The vestibulospinal tracts bring to the ventral horn cells impulses from the vestibular mechanism of the ear and from the cerebellum. The lateral vestibulospinal tract conveys impulses that facilitate the spinal motor mechanism. The medial tract, though not yet analyzed, may be part of the inhibitory fiber system of the ventral funiculus. Both of these tracts exert their influence upon the musculature of the upper trunk and extremities, which aid in maintaining position and equilibrium, especially in correlation with positions of the head.

Examples of their activity are seen in the tendency to fall after being rapidly rotated, and in the "past-pointing" reaction. In the latter, after being rotated in a certain direction, vertical voluntary movements tend to deviate in that direction and the person misses objects he endeavors to touch with his eyes closed.

IV. **The rubrospinal tract** is a small fiber bundle arising from certain large cells of the red nucleus (nucleus ruber) situated in the tegmentum of the midbrain. The fibers cross immediately as the *ventral tegmental decussation* and descend to the cord where they lie ventral to and intermingled with the lateral pyramidal tract (Figs. 196, 199, 200). The descending rubrospinal fibers send numerous collaterals into the bulbar reticular formation, and in the spinal cord they have terminal synapses upon internuncial and ventral horn neurons. The rubrospinal tract does not extend below thoracic levels of the spinal cord (Stern, 1938). Though conspicuous in most mammals this tract is greatly reduced in man. It is possible that

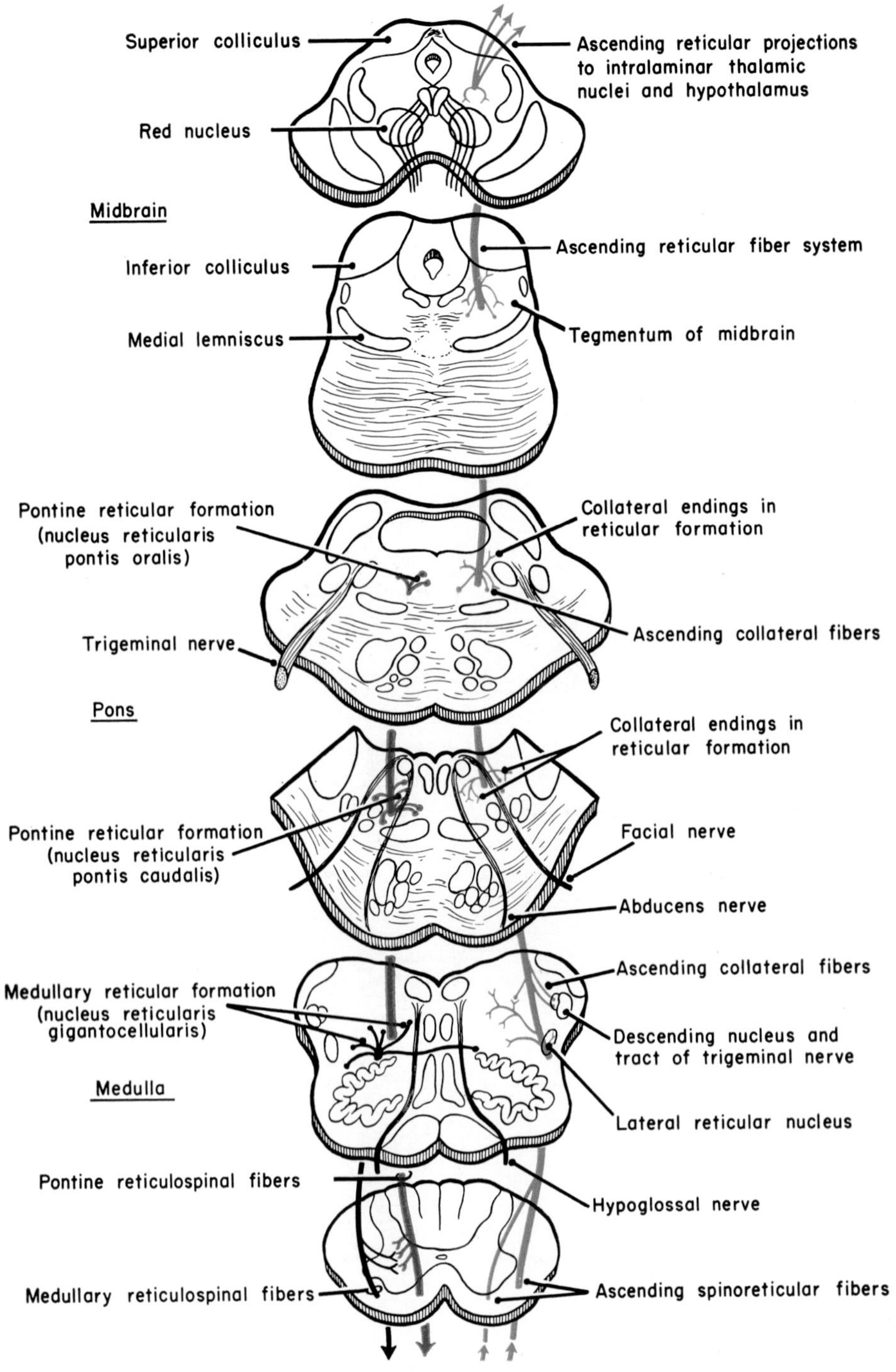

Fig. 197. Schematic diagram of ascending and descending reticular fiber systems. Ascending spinoreticular and collateral reticular projections are shown on the right (blue). This system gives off collateral fibers at various brain stem levels and is augmented by rostrally projecting reticular fibers. Pontine reticulospinal fibers (medial reticulospinal tract, red) are uncrossed and originate largely from the nucleus reticularis pontis caudalis. Medullary reticulospinal fibers (lateral reticulospinal tract, black) are predominantly uncrossed and arise from the nucleus reticularis gigantocellularis. Fibers from these sources are not sharply segregated in the spinal cord. [Based upon Olszewski and Baxter (1954), Brodal (1958) and Nauta and Kuypers (1958).]

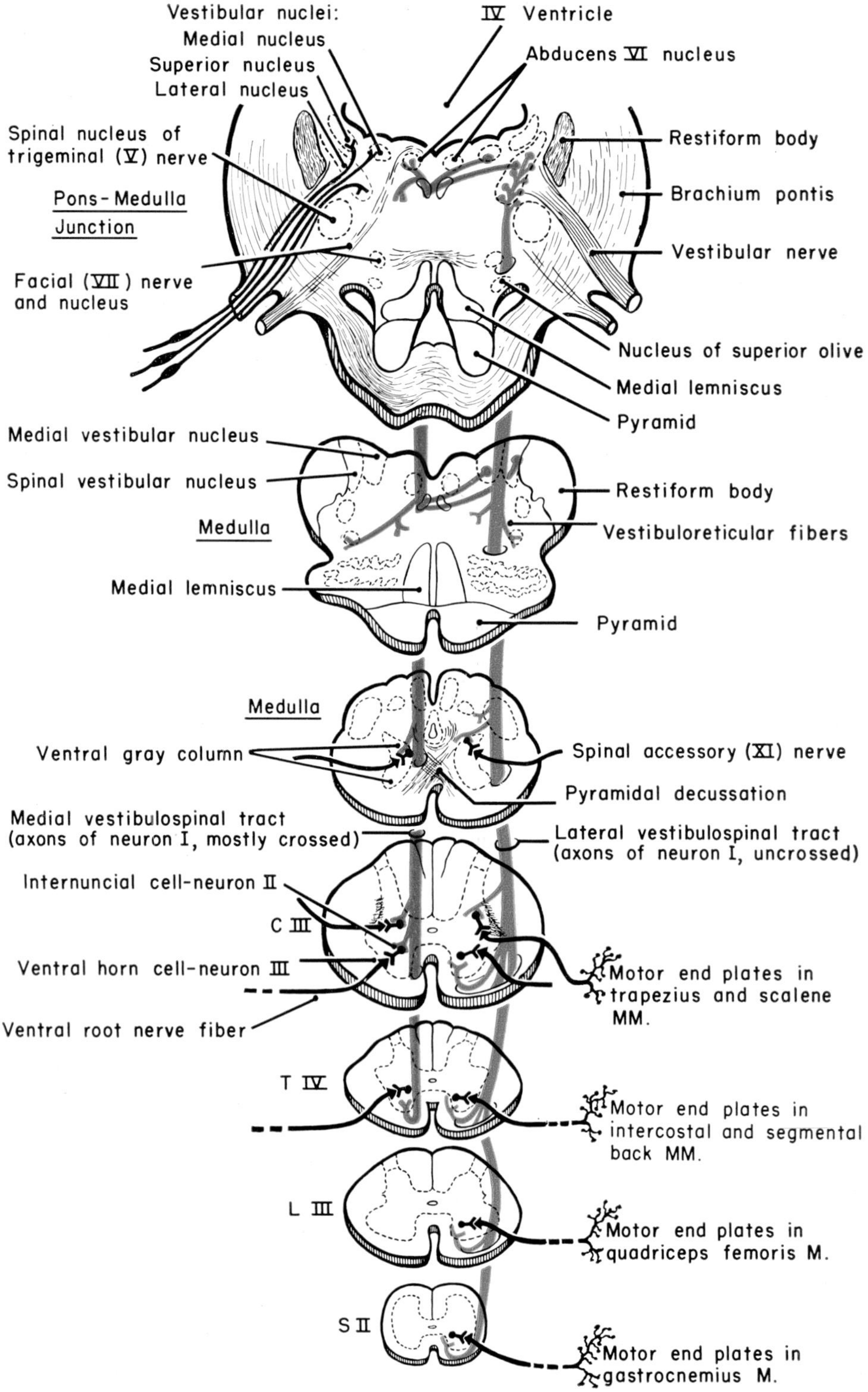

FIG. 198. Diagram of the lateral (blue) and medial (red) vestibulospinal tracts. These are extrapyramidal pathways. Letters and numbers correspond to segments of the spinal cord.

much of its influence on spinal motor neurons may be relayed downward through the reticular nuclei and their tracts (Fig. 199). It has not been determined whether the rubrospinal fibers have a facilitative or inhibitory influence on ventral horn cells.

V. **The tectospinal and tectobulbar tracts.** These two tracts arise from neurons lying in the deeper layers of the superior colliculus, which is primarily an optic relay center. Other fibers come from the region of the inferior colliculus. The contributing fibers cross the midline as the *dorsal tegmental decussation,* and descend as a small compact bundle. In the upper brain stem levels these tracts are placed between the medial longitudinal fasciculus and the medial lemniscus. Those tectal fibers destined for synapses on motor neurons of the cranial nerves and reticular nuclei form the *tectobulbar tract* (Fig. 199). The remainder of the tectal fibers form a small tract that descends into the ventral funiculus of the upper spinal cord as the *tectospinal tract.* These fibers terminate upon internuncial and ventral horn cells and convey impulses which mediate reflex postural movements in response to visual and auditory stimuli.

VI. **The medial longitudinal fasciculus.** In the dorsal part of the ventral funiculus are found diffusely organized descending fiber bundles of mixed origin (Figs. 198, 200, 264). Some come from the interstitial nucleus of Cajal (interstitiospinal) and from the nucleus of the posterior commissure (commissurospinal), two nuclei located in the tegmentum of the midbrain just cephalad to the oculomotor nucleus. These fibers are mainly uncrossed. Other fibers, both crossed and uncrossed, are axons from cells of the medial and other vestibular nuclei (medial vestibulospinal). All the fibers terminate in the ventral horn. In the brain stem these various fibers form a well defined bundle, the medial longitudinal fasciculus, from which a considerable number of fibers are continued into the ventral white of the upper cervical cord. Below that region the fibers are few in number and difficult to follow, but some of them have been traced to the lumbar levels of the cord.

VII. **The olivospinal tract (of Helweg)** is a complex tract composed of fine fibers which stain lightly with the Weigert method. Some of the fibers undoubtedly originate in the inferior olivary nucleus of the medulla and terminate in the ventral horn of the upper cervical cord (Fig. 192). Others which come from higher brain regions have in part been identified with the ventrolateral pyramidal tract described by Barnes and Déjérine. According to some, there are also present ascending spinoolivary fibers. The tract as a whole is only found in the upper cervical cord where it forms a light staining triangular area on the periphery just lateral to the ventral roots (Fig. 183). It disappears below the fourth or fifth cervical segments, but individual fibers have been traced to lower cord levels.

The **ascending** and **descending** tracts of the spinal cord have been represented in the schematic diagrams as discrete tracts. It is emphasized that there is always considerable overlapping and intermingling of fibers in adjacent fiber pathways. All the major ascending and descending pathways of the spinal cord have been included in Fig. 200.

It is evident that the ventral horn cells, which constitute the "final common path" to the muscles, are not only stimulated by pyramidal impulses, but are also under the influence of various other descending tracts which impinge upon them, directly or through intercalated neurons. The rubrospinal, reticulospinal, tectospinal, vestibulospinal, etc., may be collectively termed *extrapyramidal* tracts and constitute the older descending motor systems from higher neural centers before the evolution of the pyramidal system. They not only exert a regulatory control over reflex and other automatic activities, but are able to produce the grosser synergic movements of a volitional nature. These gross movements have been partly superseded by and blended with

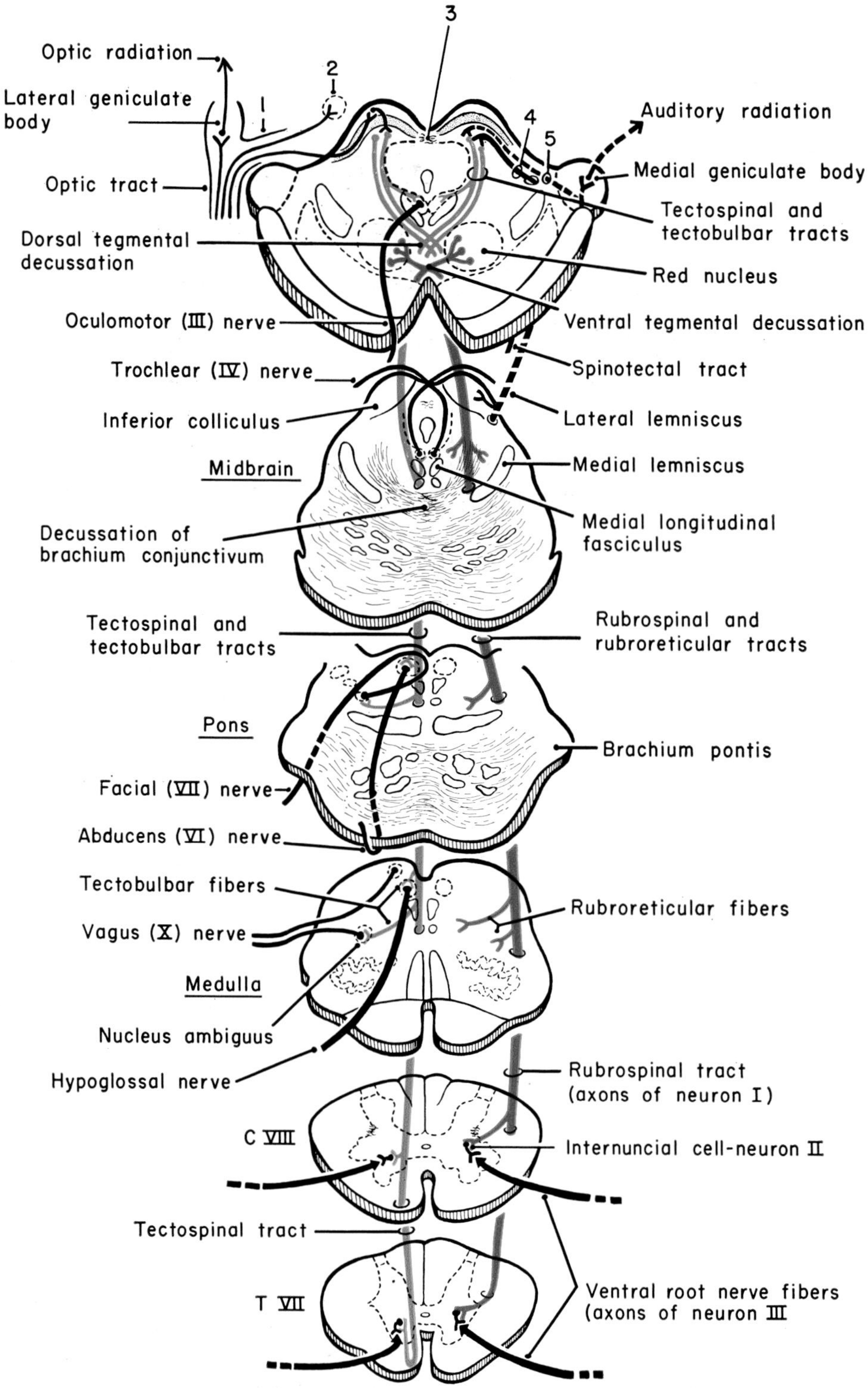

Fig. 199. Diagrams of the rubrospinal and rubroreticular tracts (red); tectospinal and tectobulbar tracts (blue). These are extrapyramidal and reflex pathways. Other midbrain structures include 1, the brachium of the superior colliculus; 2, pretectal area; 3, commissure of superior colliculus; 4, spinotectal tract; 5, collicular fibers from lateral lemniscus.

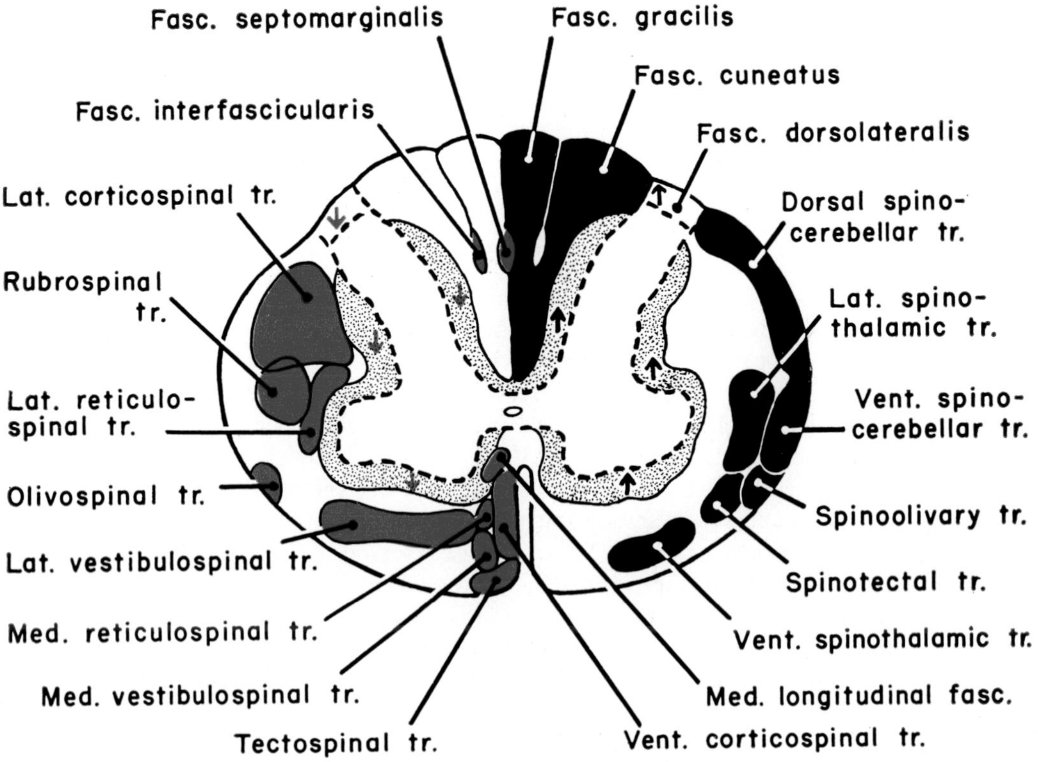

FIG. 200. Diagram of ascending (black) and descending (red) pathways of the spinal cord. The fasciculus proprius system (stippled) and dorsolateral fasciculus contain both ascending and descending nerve fibers.

the finer pyramidal movements. However, they can be independently performed and persist in a modified form when the pyramidal tract is destroyed. It is probable that the recovery of the larger, grosser movements after pyramidal injury is in part due to the fuller utilization of the old motor tracts.

DESCENDING AUTONOMIC TRACTS

The descending tracts described in the preceding pages are parts of pathways ultimately reaching the voluntary striped muscles through the somatic ventral horn cells. The spinal cord also contains descending fibers which come in relation with the intermediolateral column and other preganglionic cell groups for the innervation of visceral structures (smooth muscle, heart muscle, and glandular epithelium). The highest coordinating center of this pathway is the hypothalamus which in turn is under the influence of visceral neurons within the cerebral cortex and thalamus. Other important autonomic centers lie in the tegmentum of the midbrain and pons, and in the medulla. The descending paths are diffuse and are probably interrupted by relay neurons. In the cord these fibers descend mainly in the ventral and ventrolateral portions of the white matter, in close relation to the lateral fasciculus proprius system, and lateral reticulospinal tract.

THE FASCICULI PROPRII

Equally important as the long ascending and descending tracts are the shorter fiber systems which form part of the intrinsic reflex mechanism of the cord. In its simplest form a spinal reflex arc may consist of only two neurons, an afferent peripheral neuron (spinal ganglion cell) and an efferent peripheral neuron (ventral horn cell) with a single synapse in the gray (Figs. 201, 184). These monosynaptic reflexes are as a rule uncrossed and usually involve only one segment or closely adjacent ones, i.e., they are primarily segmental reflexes. It is quite probable that some of the periosteal and tendon reflexes and the tonus maintaining stimuli from a muscle back to itself, are represented by such arcs.

There are, however, only a few collaterals of dorsal root fibers which terminate directly on ventral horn cells (Hoff, 1932; Foerster, 1933). Hence in most reflex arcs there is at least one central or internuncial neuron interposed between the afferent and efferent peripheral neurons (Fig. 201). These central cells then send their axons to the motor cells of the same segment or to higher and lower segments for the completion of various intersegmental arcs (Fig. 202). Many of the fibers are axons of internuncial cells which ascend or descend in the white of the same side. Others come from commissural cells and pass to the white of the opposite side. All these ascending and descending fibers, crossed and uncrossed, which begin and end in the spinal cord and connect its various levels, constitute the *spinospinal* or *fundamental* columns (*fasciculi proprii*) of the spinal cord (Figs. 200, 173). To this spinal reflex mechanism also belong the descending root fibers of the interfascicular and septomarginal bundles previously described, and the collaterals and many terminals of ascending dorsal root fibers. Impulses entering the cord at any segment may travel along these fibers to higher or lower levels before connecting directly or through internuncial neurons with the ventral horn cells (Figs. 184, 202).

The spinospinal fibers are found in all the white funiculi; dorsal, ventral, and lateral. They occupy the area adjacent to the gray matter, between the latter and the more peripherally placed long fiber tracts with which they naturally intermingle. They are most numerous in the ventrolateral white columns. In the dorsal funiculus they form a narrow zone along the dorsal commissure and adjacent portions of the dorsal horn. In general, the shortest fibers lie nearest the gray and connect adjacent segments. The longer fibers lie more peripherally and continue up or down through several or many segments.

It must be kept in mind that under normal circumstances there are no *isolated* reflexes, and that every neural reaction involving any given arc always influences and is influenced by other parts of the nervous system. The primitive nervous system is organized for the production of generalized muscle movements and total response. Studies of fetal behavior suggest that local reflexes appear later (Coghill, Herrick and Coghill, Hooker).

LESIONS AND DEGENERATION IN THE SPINAL CORD

The origin, course, and terminations of most of the ascending sensory paths, as well as the descending corticospinal tract, are the most documented paths in man and higher mammals (Nathan and Smith, 1955; Van Beusekom, 1955). However, much anatomic and physiologic information remains to be ascertained, particularly for some of the small and diffuse pathways that descend from higher levels into the spinal cord. Additional facts are constantly being amassed by studying material chiefly from three sources: experimental lesions in animals followed by neuroanatomic staining technics; neurophysiologic stimulation and recording of neuron potentials, with or without subsequent histologic examination; and lastly, from antemortem and postmortem neuropathologic studies of human nerve tissue after injury, or surgical procedures.

In determining the fiber tracts, the method of secondary or Wallerian degeneration has been especially valuable (Fig. 203). When a nerve fiber is cut, not only does the part severed from the cell body undergo

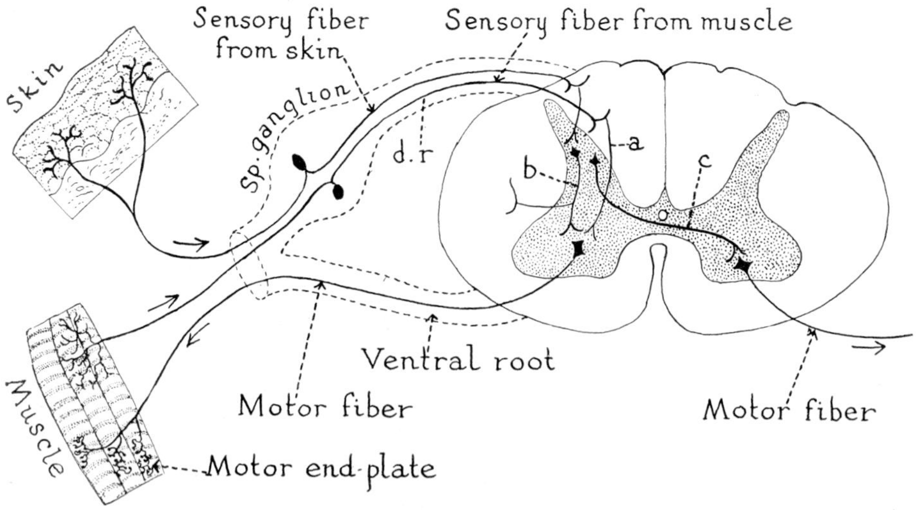

FIG. 201. Diagram illustrating two-neuron and three-neuron intrasegmental spinal reflexes, crossed and uncrossed. *a*, collateral of dorsal root fiber; *b*, association or internuncial neuron; *c*, commissural cell.

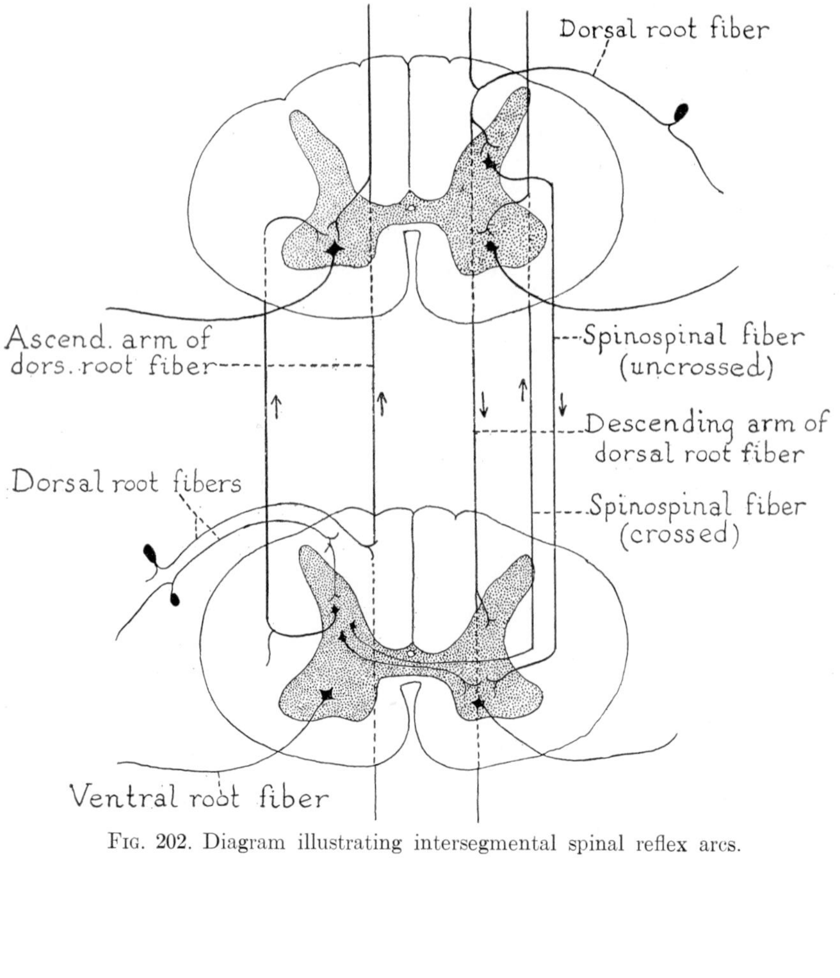

FIG. 202. Diagram illustrating intersegmental spinal reflex arcs.

complete degeneration, but the cell body itself exhibits certain pathological changes, such as central chromatolysis, swelling and nuclear eccentricity. Thus if the spinal cord is cut or injured, all the ascending fibers will degenerate above the level of injury ("ascending" degeneration). Their cell bodies, located below the injury, will show the above pathological changes (Fig. 108). Below the level of injury the descending fibers will degenerate ("descending" degeneration) since their cell bodies are placed above the cut. In the same way the central continuations of the dorsal root fibers may be determined by following their secondary degeneration in the cord after cutting the dorsal roots proximal to the spinal ganglia (Fig. 203). In this case the chromatolysis will occur in the spinal ganglion cells. The location of the cell bodies whose axons form the ventral roots may be similarly determined by cutting the ventral root and ascertaining which cell bodies in the cord show regressive changes (axon reaction). The Marchi and Nauta (Nauta and Gygax, 1951, 1953; Glees and Nauta, 1955) methods are used extensively to give precise information, particularly when smaller numbers of degenerating nerve fibers are being traced within the brain and spinal cord.

It should now be obvious that cutting a dorsal root of a spinal nerve will abolish all of its incoming sensory impulses as well as to interrupt the afferent arms of some segmental reflexes (Figs. 202, 203). Due to the overlap of dermatomes in the periphery, destruction of one dorsal root results in diminished cutaneous innervation (hypesthesia), whereas three consecutive dorsal roots must be destroyed before there is complete *anesthesia* in a dermatome (Fig. 158). Muscle tone is also dependent upon the integrity of segmental reflexes, although two or more segments usually supply a single muscle. For example, total resection of dorsal root C5 will result in severe loss of muscle tone in the supraspinatus and rhomboid muscles (derived from cervical myotomes 4 and 5—mostly 5). Such a lesion also diminishes, but does not abolish, reflex tone in the deltoid, subscapularis, biceps brachii, brachialis, and brachioradialis muscles (derived from cervical myotomes 5 and 6). However, if dorsal roots C5 and 6 are both destroyed, all proprioceptive sensory nerve fibers from these muscles are lost and there are no reflexes (*areflexia*). As a result the normal tone of these muscles is now abolished completely (*atonia*). These muscles can still contract, however, for their ventral root fibers remain intact.

Injury to the emerging ventral root of a spinal nerve produces deficits in segmental motor responses due to interruption of somatic efferent axons (Figs. 180, 203, 204). If the injury is in a thoracic or upper lumbar spinal nerve, visceral efferent neurons (and reflexes) would also be involved (Figs. 208, 209). Thus the destruction of spinal ventral root C8 would partly paralyze the small muscles of the hand (via median and ulnar nerves), whereas a lesion of both ventral roots C8 and T1 would produce a complete flaccid paralysis, and a positive reaction of degeneration in these muscles (pp. 145, 229). The inclusion of ventral root T1 in the injury also interrupts most of the preganglionic visceral efferent fibers enroute to the superior cervical sympathetic ganglion (Figs. 209, 204). Loss of these visceral motor fibers to the smooth muscle of the eye and levator palpebrae muscle results in a triad of clinical symptoms known as Horner's syndrome (p. 248). This syndrome is usually accompanied by altered sweating on the face. It should be noted that destruction of either the ventral horn cells (e.g., poliomyelitis), or their peripheral axons will result in a lower motor neuron lesion (Fig. 204), and the appropriate muscles are deprived of the tonic influence of motor nerves.

If the mixed nerve is injured distal to the junction of the dorsal and ventral root (Fig. 203), the combined sensory and motor losses enumerated above will be present. It should be noted that if such combined nerve

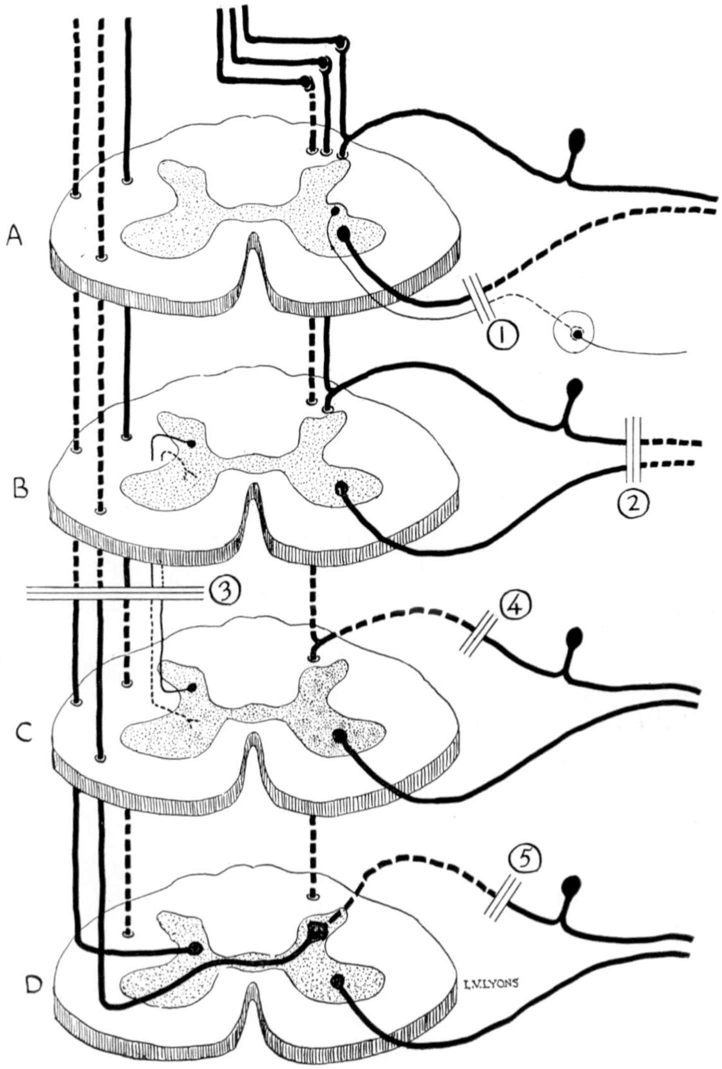

FIG. 203. Diagram illustrating the secondary degeneration of nerve fibers separated from their neuron bodies by lesions of the spinal roots or spinal cord. *A,B,C,D,* various levels of spinal cord. *1,2,3,4,5,* various lesions severing nerve fibers. The portions undergoing secondary degeneration are indicated by broken lines. (After a figure from Ranson.)

lesions are extensive, they may be followed by trophic changes in the skin (smoothness, dryness) and capillary circulation (cyanosis). The trophic alterations are presumably due to the loss of peripheral vasomotor and afferent nerve fibers.

The ventral root fibers may be injured centrally along with secondary ascending sensory pathways. The ependymal cells and glial elements about the central canal (Fig. 167) at times undergo degenerative changes and liquefaction which results in a small medially placed cavity (syringomyelia). Oft times destruction of the crossing fibers of the lateral spinothalamic tract are the only neural structures involved initially. Later the cavity may enlarge in a lateral, dorsal, cranial, or caudal direction, and destroy adjacent fiber tracts or gray matter. A typical example of such a case is illus-

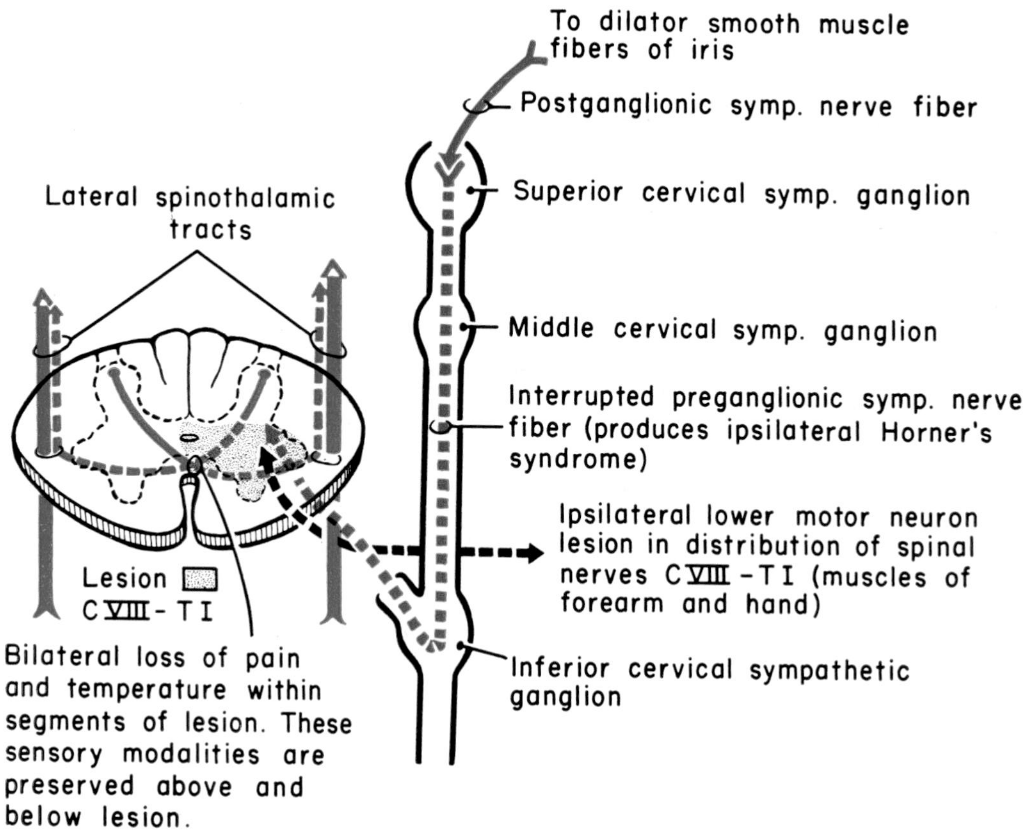

FIG. 204. Diagram of syringomyelia with lateral extension into ventral gray horn of spinal cord. Arrows show direction of impulse conduction; broken lines indicate interrupted nerve fibers.

trated schematically in Fig. 204. Here the lesion interrupts the crossing fibers of the lateral spinothalamic tract in cord segments C8 and T1. Injured axons distal to the point of the lesion are separated from their cells of origin, and undergo degeneration (broken lines in Fig. 204). Destruction of these crossing fibers from both sides of the cord result in a detectable bilateral loss of pain and temperature sensations in the distribution of spinal nerves and dermatomes of C8-T1. All pain and temperature fibers of T1 are destroyed, but some of the C8 fibers are spared inasmuch as a few fibers ascend and cross in cord segment C7. The remainder of the lateral spinothalamic tracts contain normal fibers that have crossed the spinal cord in segments either above or below the area of the lesion. In this case, the lateral extension of the cavity has also destroyed the ventral gray horn and nerve fibers passing through it (Fig. 204). In view of the involved segments, such a case would possess antemortem signs and symptoms of a lower motor neuron lesion involving the muscles of the hand, and a Horner's syndrome. These neurologic findings aid in localizing the lesion in cord segments C8 and T1.

Occasionally a different type of spinal cord lesion is seen which results in a lower motor neuron lesion involving parts of both upper extremities, and an upper motor neuron (pyramidal) lesion affecting the trunk and both lower extremities (amyotrophic lateral sclerosis, Fig. 205). These findings may be accompanied by functional disturbances of the bladder and rectum due to injury of descending autonomic fibers

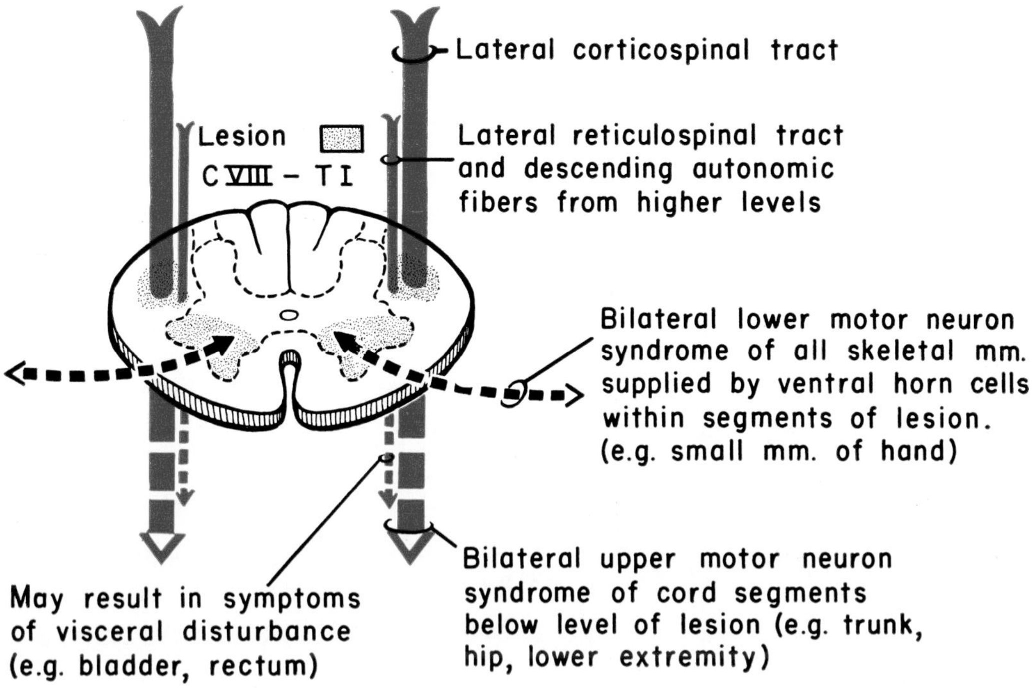

FIG. 205. Diagram of a spinal cord lesion in amyotrophic lateral sclerosis. Arrows show direction of impulse conduction; broken lines indicate interrupted nerve fibers.

enroute to lumbar and sacral segments of the cord. Such fibers lie close to both the lateral reticulospinal and corticospinal tracts, and can be looked upon as "supra-segmental" to the visceral nuclei of the spinal cord.

The large myelinated fibers of the dorsal and lateral funiculi of the spinal cord are frequently involved simultaneously in certain neurologic diseases (e.g., subacute combined degeneration, multiple sclerosis, and Friedreich's disease). The dorsal white column and the lateral corticospinal tracts are most often affected, although the adjacent spinocerebellar tracts and other pathways may also be involved (Fig. 206). Lesions in other regions of the nervous system can precede or accompany the demyelinating process shown here in the cervical cord. Essential findings will depend upon the level of the cord lesion, and the amount of the destruction within the different tracts. This cervical lesion (Fig. 206) will result in more extensive signs than will a similar lesion in the lumbar region of the spinal cord, for in the cervical region more ascending sensory and descending motor fibers are destroyed. Destruction of the dorsal white columns will produce marked sensory deficits in the hands, trunk, and lower extremities (p. 202). Injury of the corticospinal tracts at this level result in release phenomena characteristic of an upper motor neuron lesion (p. 217) in the same body areas. Interruption of autonomic and spinocerebellar fibers may add cerebellar symptoms and serious visceral disturbances. The tottering, stiff gait is characteristic of the patient in whom there is paresis, as well as sensory and cerebellar deficits.

Hemisection of the spinal cord is a most useful lesion for teaching purposes (Fig. 207). It will rarely, if ever, be encountered clinically for injuries usually extend across midline to include one or more neural elements. The combined signs and symptoms of a hemisected spinal cord comprise the *Brown-Sequard syndrome.* Neurologic find-

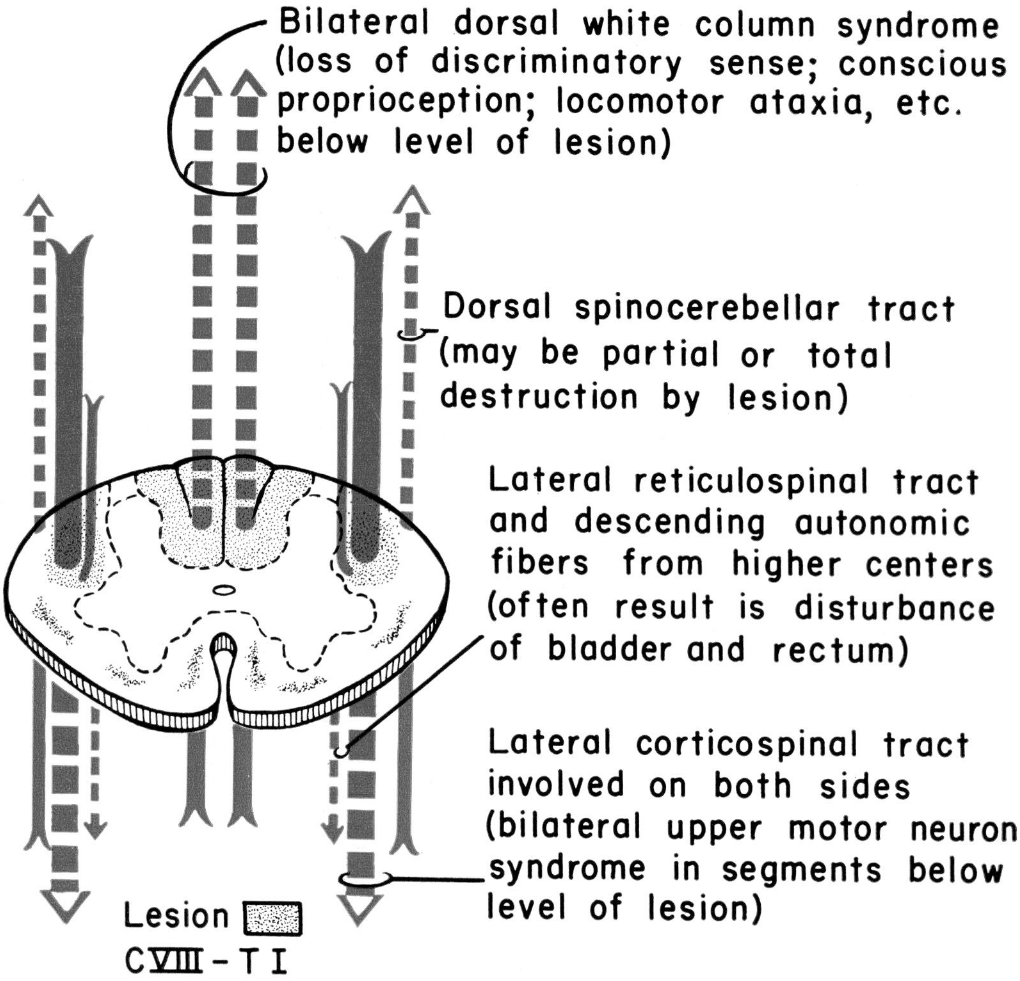

FIG. 206. Diagram of spinal cord lesions in subacute combined degeneration. Arrows show direction of impulse conduction; broken lines indicate interrupted nerve fibers.

ings in the illustrated hemisection would include: (1) Loss of sensory impulses in the dorsal white column below the lesion on the same side; (2) Upper motor neuron lesion below the level of injury on the same side; (3) Lower motor neuron symptoms and vasomotor paralysis in areas supplied by the injured segments on the same side; (4) Bilateral loss of pain and temperature sensations within the area of the lesion; (5) Loss of pain and temperature sensations below T12 on the opposite side of the body (i.e., lower extremity, genitals, and perineum). With a lesion at cord segment T12, sensory and pyramidal symptoms would be manifested through spinal nerves of the lumbar and sacral plexuses. The lower motor neuron damage at cord segment T12 would produce no significant loss in motor function, or reflex activity.

Complete and incomplete transections of the human spinal cord may result from missile wounds or fracture-dislocation of a vertebra. Similar damage may follow ischemic necrosis due to occlusion or interruption of radicular arteries that supply the vulnerable upper thoracic segments of the spinal cord (Bolton, 1939; Mettler, 1948; Zülch, 1954). Neoplasms may also compress the cord as they enlarge and secondarily

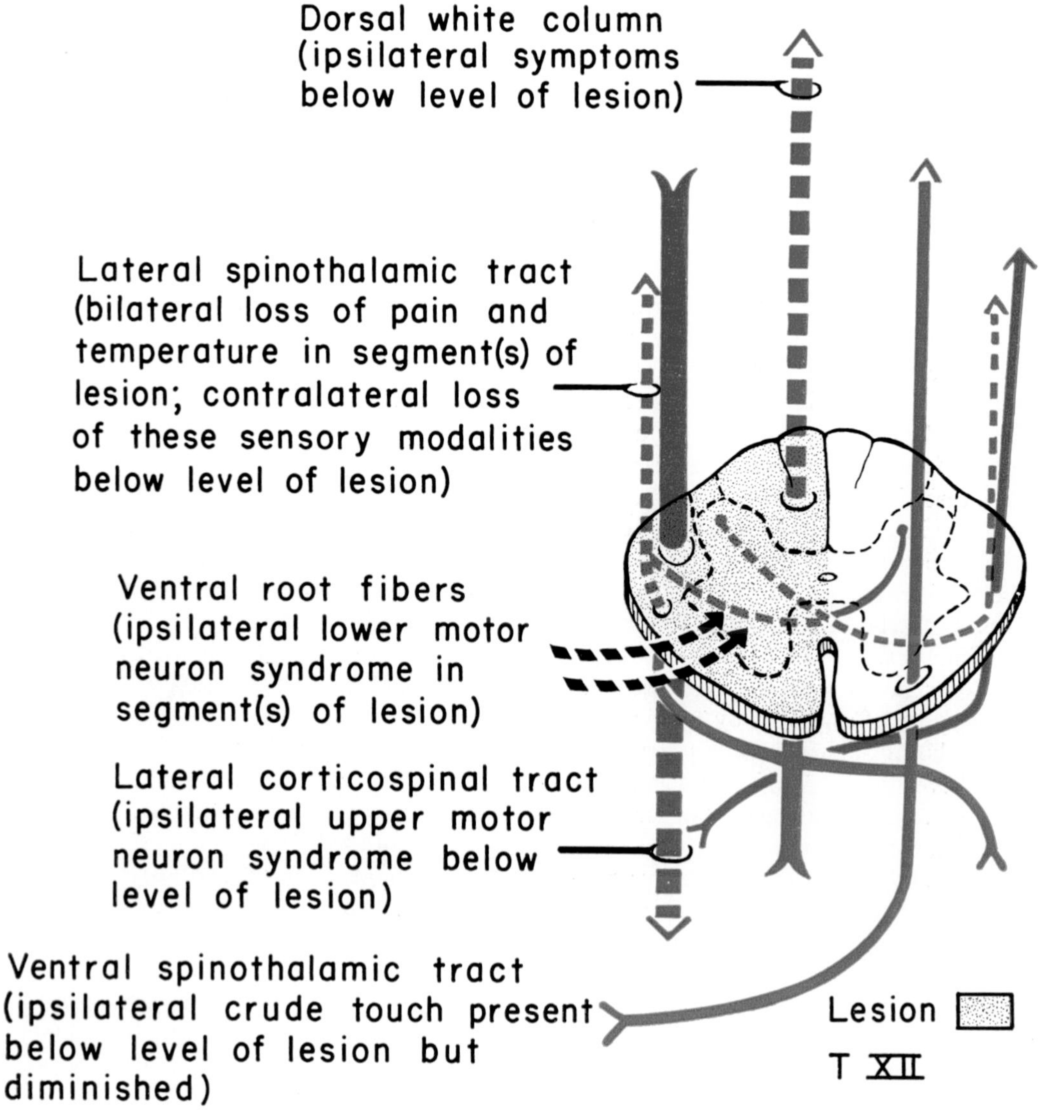

FIG. 207. Diagram of spinal cord hemisection. This lesion results in a Brown-Sequard syndrome. Arrows show direction of impulse conduction; broken lines indicate interrupted nerve fibers.

compromise the blood supply. In such cord damage, the symptoms are severe and the complications many, regardless of the level of injury.

Complete transection is followed by loss of all sensibility below the injury since all ascending pathways are destroyed. Total anesthesia extends up to and includes the level of transection. There is a loss of all voluntary movement (absolute paralysis) due to interruption of all descending pathways. In view of the acute cord injury, there may even be suppression of sensory and motor functions and loss of reflexes in several cord segments above the level of spinal transection. Such suppression usually lasts no longer than two weeks (Haymaker, 1956).

Below the transection all somatic and visceral reflex activity, including muscle tone, is abolished for a variable period of time. This severe depression or collapse of intrinsic cord function is known as neural or "spinal shock". Reflex activity within the isolated caudal segments may begin to reappear within a few days, or may not become evident until six weeks after injury. Once reasserted, caudal to the transection, the deep reflexes increase in intensity until they are obviously exaggerated (Babinski response). Superficial reflexes are rarely observed. The caudal spinal segments, released from the control of suprasegmental structures, initiate and maintain a marked increase in reflex muscle tone (hypertonus). Such uncontrolled muscle tone leads to alternating spasms of the flexor and extensor muscles. Eventually there is a predominant contraction of either the extensor or flexor muscles of the paralyzed limbs. The position assumed by the paralyzed limbs during the early stages of paraplegia is believed to be a most important factor in determining whether flexor or extensor spasms will eventually predominate. In paraplegics who have survived two years or longer, Guttmann (1946, 1952) noted that extensor spasms predominate over flexor spasms in the majority of cases (65 per cent), and that persistent flaccid paralysis is more uncommon (18 per cent). Kuhn (1950) also believes that predominant extensor activity is the final outcome of complete cord transection.

Bladder and rectal functions are disturbed in all transections of the cord for they are no longer under voluntary control. Interruption of descending autonomic fibers, particularly those enroute to parasympathetic nuclei in the sacral cord (S3, 4, 5), leads to loss of rectal motility. There is reflex spasm of the external anal sphincter and fecal retention. Defecation occurs involuntarily after long intervals. If cord segments S3, 4, and 5 are destroyed there is a permanent paralysis of the external sphincter and fecal incontinence. When these sacral segments are involved there is in addition: paralytic incontinence, and usually bladder distention; impotence; perianal or saddle anesthesia; but normal sensory and motor function is retained in the lower extremity (conus medullaris syndrome).

Bladder disturbances usually occur in three phases after cord transection. At the outset there is always *retention,* due to paralysis of the muscular bladder wall (detrusor muscle), and spasm of the vesicle sphincter. Two or three weeks later (range 2 days to 18 months) the second phase or *overflow incontinence* is observed. This phase consists of an intermittent dribbling of urine, and is due to the gradual hypertrophy of the detrusor smooth muscle. The muscle can now overcome the resistance of the internal sphincter for short periods of time. In most cases continued hypertrophy of the bladder wall eventually permits the bladder to expel small amounts of urine automatically, providing bladder infections have not intervened. This is the third phase, known as *automatic micturition.* Such automaticity of the bladder is poor if the lumbar segments are involved, and absent (paralytic incontinence) when the sacral segments are destroyed.

In partial or incomplete transection of the spinal cord, some of the ascending or descending fibers escape injury. The sensory deficits may not correspond to the level of motor loss, and some voluntary function may return within a week or two. Vasomotor and visceral disturbances are usually less pronounced, and irritative sensory phenomena are more common (e.g., pains, paresthesias, hyperesthesias). Marked priapism is more likely to accompany an incomplete transection of the cord. Haymaker (1956) has stated the only reliable criterion of total transection, in the early stages after spinal injury, is "a complete flaccid paraplegia with areflexia and complete sensory loss which lasts longer than 2 to 5 days".

14

The Peripheral Portions of the Autonomic System

Those portions of the central and peripheral nervous system primarily concerned with the regulation of visceral activities are often collectively termed the *visceral, autonomic* or *vegetative* nervous system in contrast to the *somatic* or *cerebrospinal.* The visceral reactions initiated in the main by internal changes acting on the visceroceptors and taking effect in the smooth musculature and glands are to a large extent involuntary and unconscious. Such visceral reactions as do reach the conscious level are vague and poorly localized and of a predominantly affective character. Tactile sensibility is practically absent, and temperature is apparently appreciated only in certain places such as esophagus, stomach, colon, and rectum. On the other hand, distention or muscular spasms of the walls of the hollow viscera or blood vessels may produce severe distress or acute pain.

The division of the nervous system into a somatic and visceral portion, convenient from a physiological standpoint, does not imply the presence of two anatomically distinct systems. They are merely two aspects of a single integrated neural mechanism, closely interrelated both centrally and peripherally. The higher brain centers regulate both somatic and visceral functions and throughout most neural levels there is intermingling and association of visceral and somatic neurons. Peripherally, visceral efferent fibers are found in all the spinal and many of the cranial nerves, and the visceral afferent fibers have their cell bodies in the cerebrospinal ganglia. Moreover, visceral reflexes may be initiated by impulses passing through somatic afferent fibers and coming from any receptor, and conversely visceral changes may give rise to active somatic movement.

THE AUTONOMIC SYSTEM

Interposed in the efferent peripheral pathway from the central nervous system to the visceral structures are aggregations of nerve cells known as the *autonomic ganglia.* The cells of these ganglia are in synaptic relation with fibers from the spinal cord or brain, and send out axons which terminate in the visceral effectors: smooth muscle, heart muscle, and glandular epithelium. Thus unlike striped muscle, which is directly innervated by axons of centrally placed neurons, the transmission of impulses from the central nervous system to the viscera always involves two different neurons. The first neuron situated in the brain or spinal cord sends its fine myelinated axon as a *preganglionic* fiber to some autonomic ganglion to synapse with one or more ganglionic cells. The usually unmyelinated axons of the autonomic ganglion cells then pass as *postganglionic* fibers to the visceral effectors. It is therefore evident that even the simplest visceral reflex arc will involve

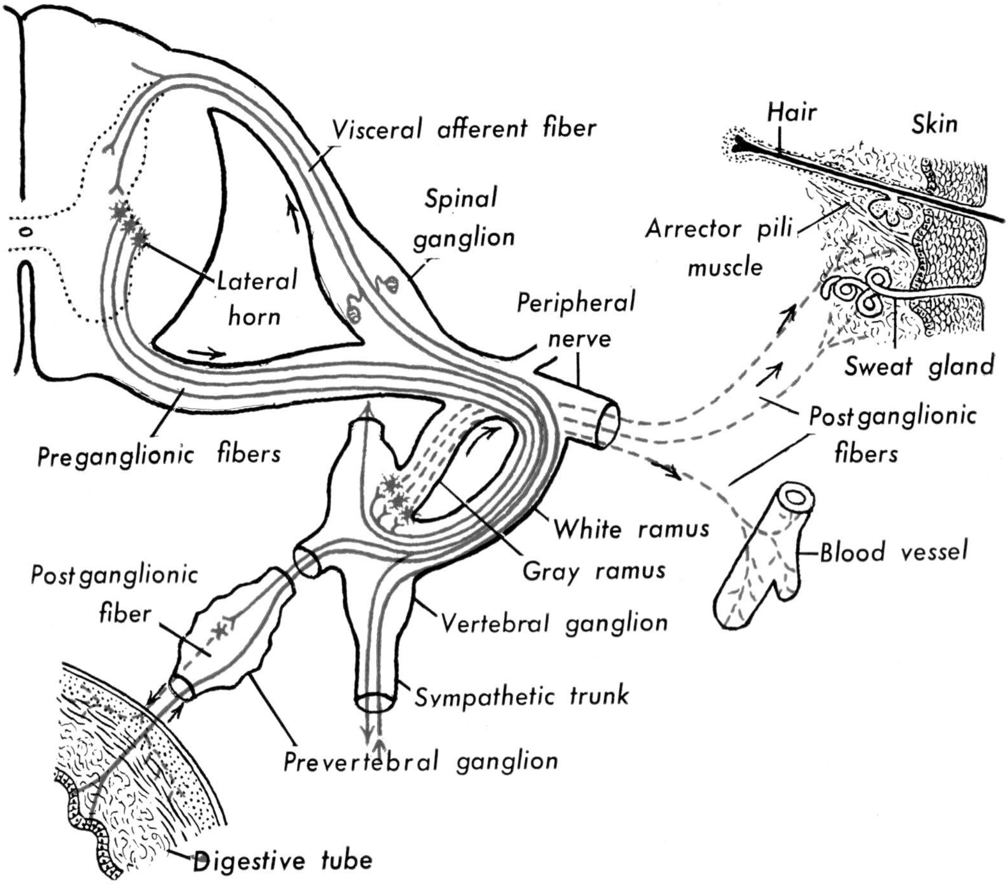

FIG. 208. Diagram of neural reflex arcs involving sympathetic system. (Bailey's Histology.)

at least three neurons: afferent, efferent preganglionic visceral, and efferent postganglionic visceral neurons (Figs. 180, 208).

All these "nerve cells and nerve fibers, by means of which visceral efferent impulses pass to tissues other than multinuclear striated muscle" form the *autonomic system* as defined by Langley (1921). By this definition, the autonomic represents only the peripheral efferent portion of visceral innervation. The visceral afferent fibers which run by way of the autonomic but have their cell bodies in the cerebrospinal ganglia are not included in this system, nor are the higher brain centers which influence and regulate vegetative activities. In recent years, there has been a definite tendency to make the term "autonomic" more synonymous with "visceral" and to include the whole neural apparatus, both peripheral and central, concerned with visceral functions (Hess, 1948).

The autonomic ganglia which have a wide distribution in the visceral periphery, may be placed in three groups: the *vertebral*; the *prevertebral* (*collateral*); and the *terminal* or *peripheral* ganglia. The vertebral ganglia are arranged in a segmental fashion along the ventrolateral surface of the vertebral column and connected with each other by longitudinal fibers to form the two *sympathetic trunks* or ganglionated cords. The collateral ganglia are irregular aggregations of cells found in the mesenteric neural plexuses surrounding the abdominal aorta and larger visceral arteries, while the terminal ganglia are located within or close to the structures they innervate. The ganglia show extreme variations as to size and compactness of organization. They may be organized into anatomically distinct encapsulated structures, as in the case of the sympathetic trunks and the autonomic ganglia of the head; they may form extensive plexuses of nerve fibers, as in the intramural intestinal plexuses; or they may be found as small ganglionic masses or scattered cell groups within or near the walls of visceral structures, as in the heart, bronchi, pancreas, and urinary bladder.

Three outflows of preganglionic fibers connect the central nervous system with the autonomic ganglia (Fig. 209). The *cranial outflow* contains preganglionic visceral motor fibers within the oculomotor, facial, glossopharyngeal, and vagus nerves. Such visceral fibers terminate in either cranial autonomic ganglia (i.e., ciliary, otic, sphenopalatine, submandibular) or terminal ganglia within the wall of a viscus (e.g., heart, lung, stomach). The *thoracicolumbar outflow* is composed of fibers from the lateral sympathetic nucleus (intermediolateral column) of the spinal cord, which pass out by way of the ventral roots of the thoracic and upper two lumbar nerves, a few passing through the eighth cervical. These fibers leave the ventral roots as the white rami communicantes, enter the sympathetic trunk and end in the vertebral ganglia of the trunk or in the collateral mesenteric ganglia. The *sacral outflow* contains efferent visceral fibers from the inferior lateral and medial sympathetic nuclei of the spinal cord. They pass through the ventral roots of the second, third, and fourth sacral nerves and go to the terminal ganglia associated with the pelvic viscera.

Most of the viscera receive a double autonomic innervation, the effects of the two being as a rule antagonistic. One is through the thoracicolumbar division which supplies all the visceral structures of the body. The other innervation is by the craniosacral division. The cranial portion supplies the visceral structures of the head and the thoracic and abdominal viscera with the exception of the pelvic organs which are supplied by the sacral division. The cranial and sacral divisions have other features in common. They react in a similar manner to certain drugs. They have no white rami communicantes which enter the sympathetic trunk, but their preganglionic fibers run directly to the terminal ganglia. The autonomic thus comprises two main divisions: the *thoracicolumbar* or *sympathetic* system and the *craniosacral* or *parasympathetic* system.

The sympathetic system. The sympathetic trunks are two ganglionated cords symmetrically placed along the ventrolateral aspects of the vertebral column and extending from the base of the skull to the coccyx (Figs. 209, 211). The cervical portion contains three ganglia probably formed by the fusion of the original eight segmental ganglia. The superior cervical ganglion is the largest autonomic ganglion and is situated near the second and third cervical vertebrae. The small middle cervical ganglion, often absent, may lie near the sixth cervical vertebra or close to the inferior cervical ganglion (Fig. 212). The latter, placed at the lower border of the seventh cervical vertebra, frequently fuses with the first thoracic ganglion to form the stellate ganglion. In the thoracic, lumbar, and sacral portions the ganglia are segmentally arranged. There are 11–12 thoracic, 3–4 lumbar, and 4–5 sacral ganglia. In the sacral portion, the two trunks gradually approach each other and fuse at the coccyx into the unpaired coccygeal ganglion.

The prevertebral ganglia are irregular ganglionic masses situated in the mesenteric neural plexuses surrounding the visceral branches of the aorta. The largest are the coeliac ganglia, the others comprise the superior mesenteric, aorticorenal, phrenic,

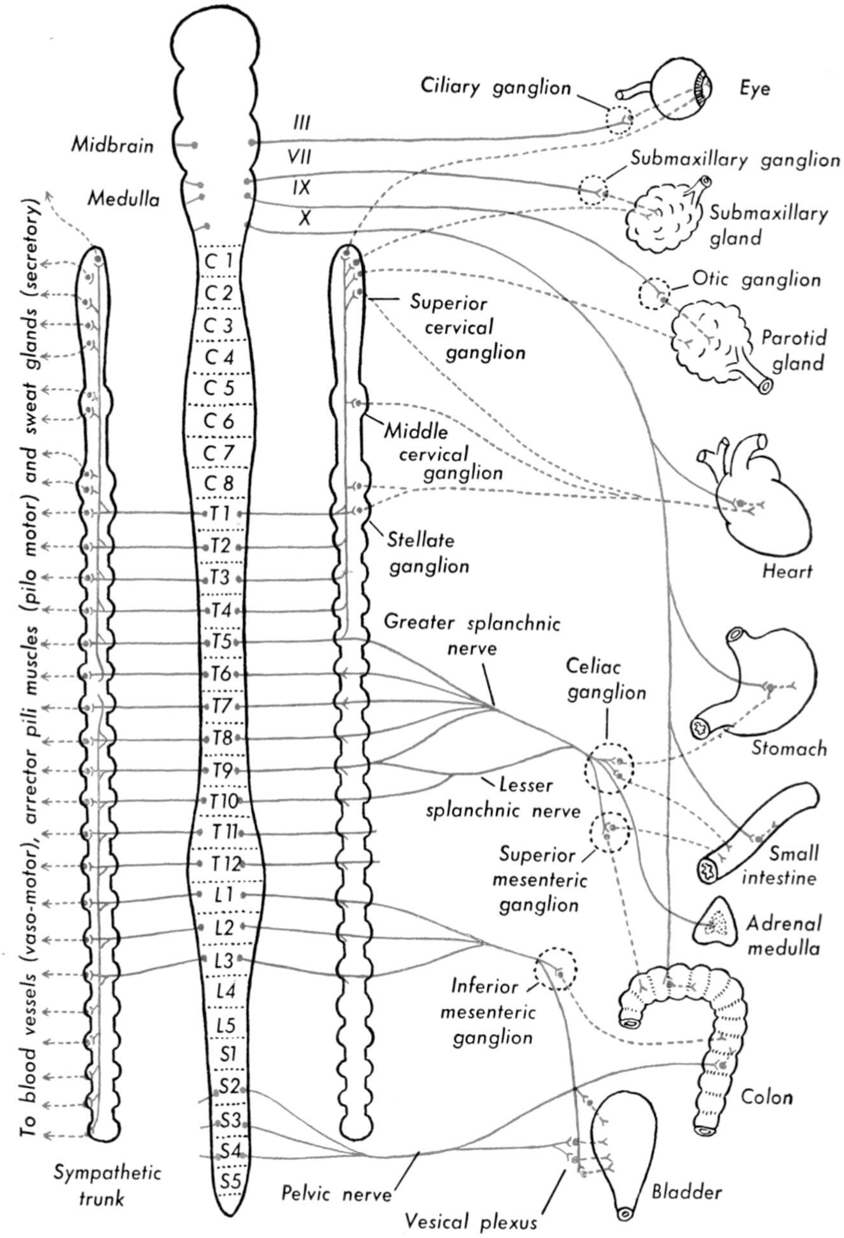

FIG. 209. Diagram showing general arrangement of the autonomic system. Sympathetic shown in red, parasympathetic in blue. Solid lines represent preganglionic fibers, broken lines postganglionic fibers. For clearness the sympathetic fibers to the blood vessels, hair, and sweat glands are shown separately on the left side. (Bailey's Histology.)

and inferior mesenteric ganglia (Fig. 213). These will be described in relation to the coeliac and subsidiary plexuses.

The sympathetic ganglia receive preganglionic fibers from the spinal cord through the ventral roots of all the thoracic and the upper two lumbar nerves (Sheehan, 1941; Pick and Sheehan, 1946). These fibers leave the ventral roots, pass through the white rami communicantes and enter the sympathetic trunk where they have two general destinations: (a) They terminate in the vertebral ganglia, either the one which they enter first, or they pass up or down in the sympathetic cord giving off collaterals, and terminate in vertebral ganglia above or below the level of their entrance (Fig. 210). The preganglionic fibers from the upper five thoracic nerves pass mainly upward and in the cat, T1 contributes the smallest number of ascending fibers in the cervical sympathetic trunk (Foley and Schnitzlein, 1957). Those from the middle thoracic (T7–10) pass up or down, while those of the lumbar and lowest thoracic pass only downward. (b) Other preganglionic fibers do not synapse in the vertebral ganglia but merely pass through them and emerge as the splanchnic nerves (efferent rami) to terminate in the prevertebral ganglia (Figs. 210, 213). Thus while the sympathetic pathway from the spinal cord to the viscera always involves two neurons, there are apparently never more than two, the synapse occurring either in the vertebral or prevertebral ganglia (Langley).

While the white rami communicantes are limited to the thoracic and upper lumbar nerves, each spinal nerve receives a gray ramus communicans from the sympathetic trunk. These consist of unmyelinated fibers which innervate the blood vessels, hair, and glands of the body wall. There is some

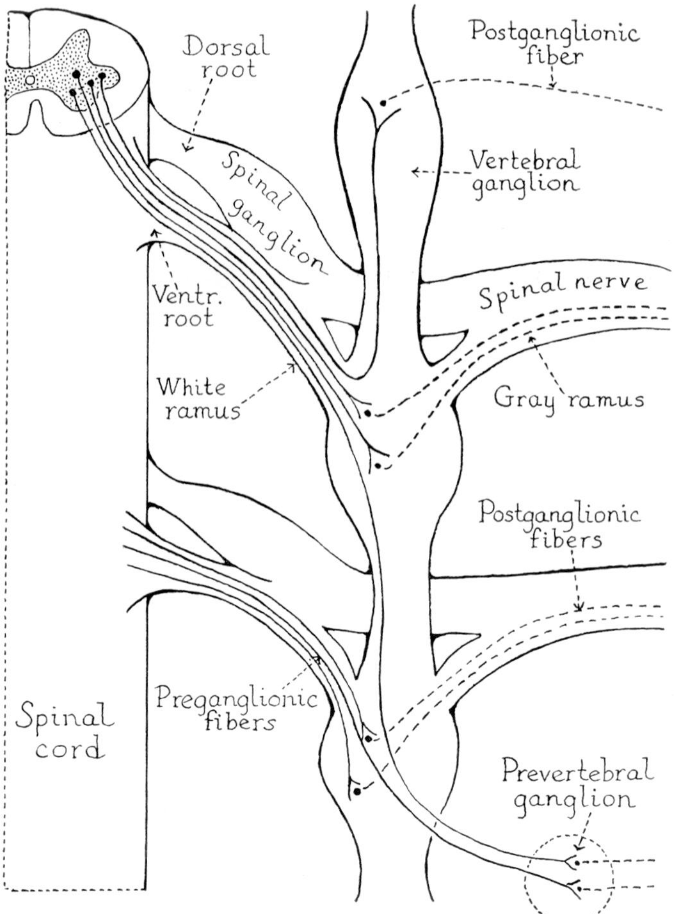

FIG. 210. Diagram of portion of sympathetic trunk showing course of preganglionic and postganglionic fibers. (After Edinger.)

histological evidence that fine unmyelinated fibers also terminate in striped muscle fibers where they form accessory motor end plates (Boecke). The suggestion that these are of sympathetic origin has been opposed by many investigators.

The cervical sympathetic ganglia receive ascending preganglionic fibers from the white rami of the upper thoracic nerves, most of them going to the superior cervical ganglion. From the latter arise numerous gray strands composed of postganglionic fibers (Fig. 211). These are distributed as gray rami to the adjacent cranial nerves (IX, X, XI, XII) and to the upper three or four cervical nerves, to the pharynx, and to the external and internal carotid arteries around which the fibers form corresponding plexuses (Fig. 212). From these plexuses the fibers accompany the branches of the cranial nerves and supply the dilator muscle of the iris, the smooth muscle portion of the levator palpebrae, the orbital muscle of Müller; the blood vessels, sweat glands, and hairs of the head and face, and the lacrimal and salivatory glands. Another important branch passes as the superior cervical cardiac nerve to the cardiac plexuses innervating the heart. The middle cervical ganglion, when lying at the level of the sixth cervical vertebra, supplies gray rami to cervical nerves C5 and C6, and at times also to C4 and C7. When absent or when placed close to the inferior cervical ganglion, these nerves receive their gray rami from the sympathetic trunk (Fig. 212). The inferior cervical ganglion furnishes gray rami to C7 and C8 and T1. Thus a single ganglion may supply two or more of the lower cervical nerves, and a single nerve may be supplied by two ganglia. Potts (1925) has found that the lower four cervical nerves may each receive three gray rami derived from the sympathetic trunk and the middle and inferior cervical ganglia. In addition, the middle and inferior ganglia give off respectively the middle and inferior cardiac nerves which go to the heart by way of the cardiac plexuses (Fig. 211).

The thoracic, lumbar, and sacral ganglia furnish gray rami to the remaining spinal nerves. Delicate branches from the upper five or six thoracic ganglia go to the cardiac plexuses as the thoracic cardiac nerves, while fibers from the stellate ganglion (and inferior cervical) reach the pulmonary plexuses to innervate the bronchial musculature and blood vessels of the lungs. Shorter mediastinal branches from both the thoracic and lumbar ganglia form plexuses around the thoracic and abdominal aorta. In addition to these, there are two, sometimes three, important branches known as the *splanchnic nerves* which arise from the thoracic portion of the sympathetic trunk, pierce the diaphragm and terminate in the preveterbral ganglia of the mesenteric plexuses. The *greater splanchnic nerve* arises by roots from the fifth to the ninth thoracic ganglia and goes to the coeliac plexus. The *lesser splanchnic* usually arises by two roots from the tenth and eleventh ganglia and either unites with the greater splanchnic or continues as an independent nerve to that portion of the coeliac plexus which surrounds the roots of the renal arteries and there terminates in the aorticorenal ganglion (Fig. 213). The *smallest splanchnic nerve* sometimes arises from the last thoracic ganglion and goes to the renal plexus. Often this nerve is represented by a branch from the lesser splanchnic. The splanchnic nerves, though appearing as branches of the thoracic ganglia, are composed of preganglionic fibers from the white rami which merely pass through the sympathetic trunk on their way to the coeliac ganglia (Figs. 209, 210).

The *coeliac* plexus is an extensive plexus surrounding the roots of the coeliac and superior mesenteric arteries. It extends cranially to the diaphragm, caudally to the renal arteries, and laterally to the suprarenal bodies. It becomes continuous above with the thoracic, below with the abdominal

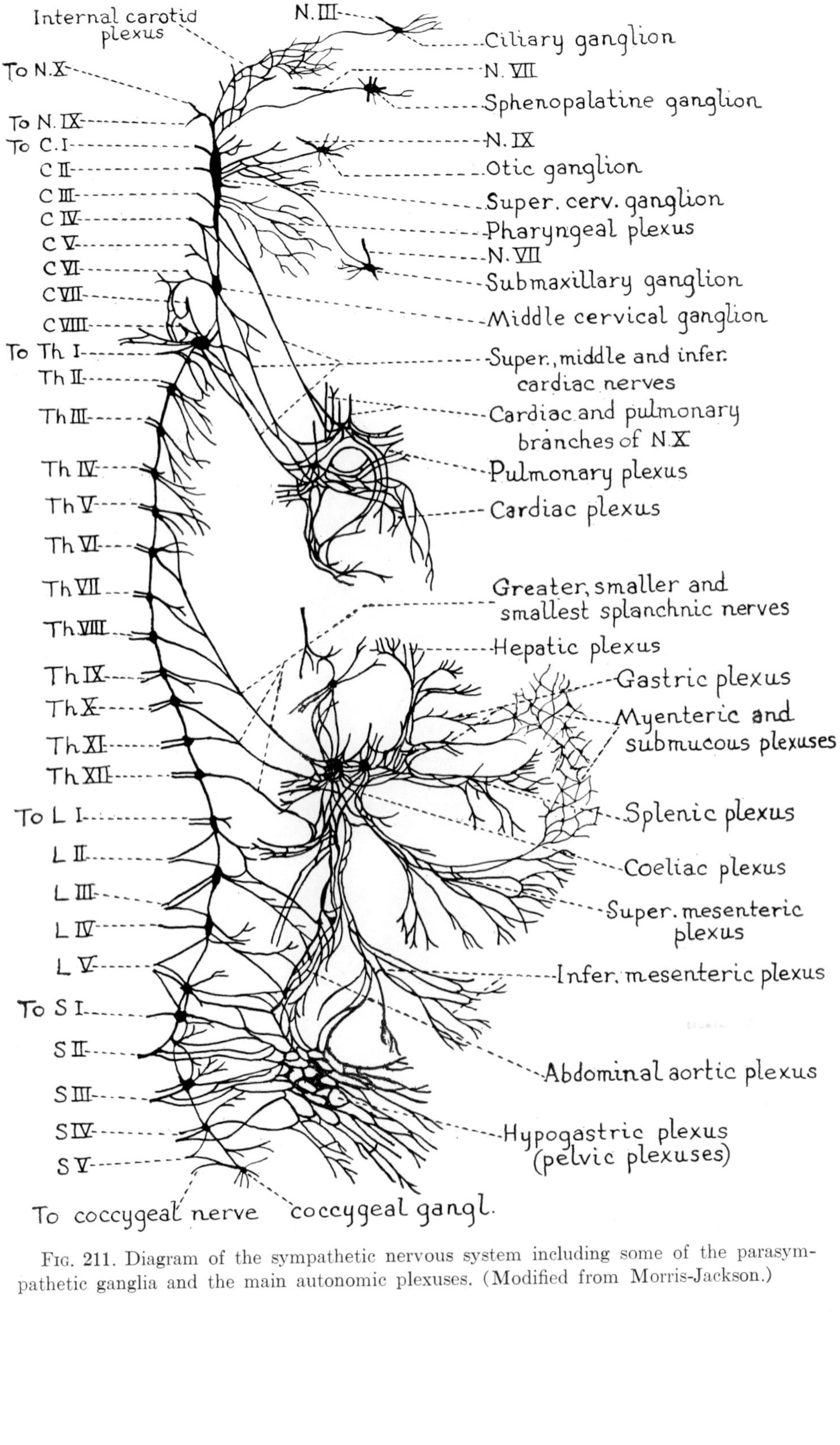

FIG. 211. Diagram of the sympathetic nervous system including some of the parasympathetic ganglia and the main autonomic plexuses. (Modified from Morris-Jackson.)

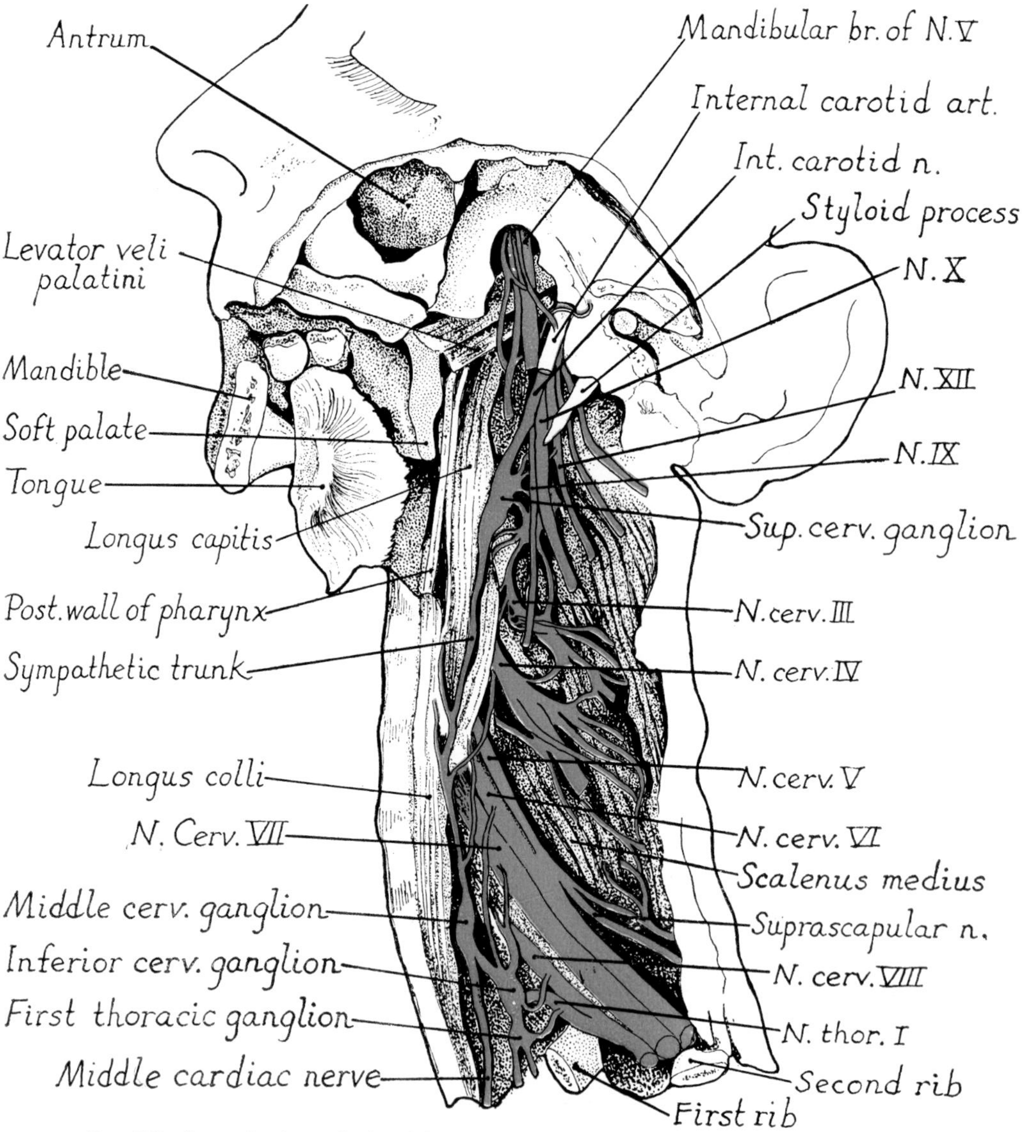

FIG. 212. Lateral view of the left cervical sympathetic trunk and its connections. (Somewhat modified from Potts.)

aortic plexuses. From the main plexus are given off paired and unpaired subsidiary plexuses which accompany the branches of the coeliac and superior mesenteric arteries and other branches of the abdominal aorta. The paired ones include the phrenic, suprarenal, and spermatic (or ovarian), while the gastric, hepatic, splenic, and superior mesenteric plexuses are unpaired. Within the coeliac plexus are found two relatively large ganglionic masses of flattened semilunar shape, the *coeliac ganglia*, lying on either side of the coeliac artery and connected with each other by delicate fiber strands (Fig. 213). Occasionally the two may be so close as to form a single unpaired ganglion encircling the artery. Other ganglionic masses found in the plexus include the paired aorticorenal ganglia and the superior mesenteric ganglion lying near

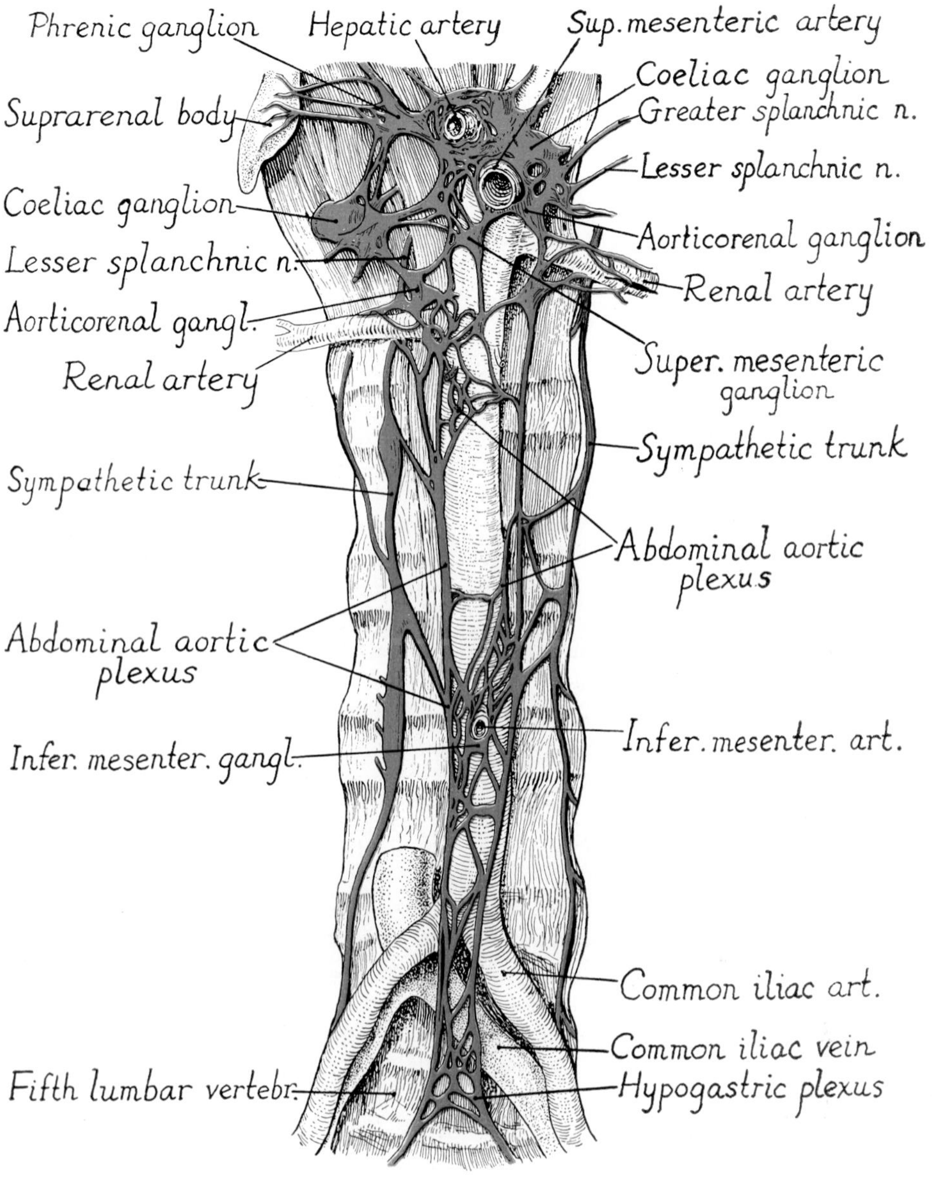

FIG. 213. Portion of the abdominal sympathetic trunk and related plexuses. (Henle.)

the roots of their respective arteries, and the small phrenic ganglion present only on the right side at the junction of the phrenic nerve with the phrenic plexus (Fig. 213). All these ganglia receive preganglionic fibers from the splanchnic nerves.

Caudally the coeliac plexus becomes continuous with the abdominal aortic plexuses lying on either side of the aorta (Fig. 211). From these plexuses nerve strands pass to the root of the inferior mesenteric artery and form the inferior mesenteric plexus which surrounds that artery and its branches. Within this plexus and lying close to the root of the artery is another prevertebral ganglionic mass known as the *inferior mesenteric ganglion* (Figs. 209, 213). Still further caudally the abdominal aortic plexuses are continued into the unpaired *hypogastric* or *pelvic plexus* which also receives strands from the inferior mesenteric plexus. On entering the pelvis the plexus breaks up into a number of subsidiary plexuses surrounding the rectum, bladder, and accessory genital organs. The preganglionic fibers supplying the pelvic organs come from the white rami of the two upper lumbar nerves and from the lowest thoracic one, pass through the corresponding ganglia of the sympathetic trunk and terminate in the inferior mesenteric ganglion. The cells of this ganglion then send postganglionic fibers which pass by way of pelvic and inferior mesenteric plexuses to the pelvic viscera.

The parasympathetic system. The preganglionic fibers of the craniosacral division form synaptic relations only with the terminal ganglia. In the cephalic region there are four such ganglia topographically related to the branches of the trigeminal nerve (Figs. 209, 211). The *ciliary ganglion* lying against the lateral surface of the optic nerve receives preganglionic fibers from the oculomotor nerve (III) and sends postganglionic to the sphincter of the iris and the smooth muscle of the ciliary body. The *sphenopalatine ganglion* in the sphenopalatine fossa and the *submandibular ganglion* lying over the submaxillary gland receive fibers from the intermediate portion of the facial nerve (VII). The preganglionic fibers pass by way of the greater superficial petrosal nerve to the sphenopalatine ganglion, and by way of the chorda tympani to the submandibular ganglion. The latter is usually broken up into a submaxillary and a sublingual portion. The sphenopalatine ganglion sends postganglionic fibers to the lacrimal glands and to the blood vessels and glands of the mucous membranes of the nose and palate. Postganglionic fibers from the submandibular ganglion go to the submaxillary and sublingual glands and also to the mucous membrane of the floor of the mouth. The *otic ganglion* situated mesially to the mandibular nerve receives preganglionic fibers from the glossopharyngeal nerve (IX) by way of the lesser superficial petrosal nerve and sends postganglionic fibers to the parotid gland. All of these cranial autonomic ganglia receive nerve filaments from the superior cervical ganglion, passing by way of the internal and external carotid plexuses. These, however, do not synapse with the ganglionic cells but merely pass through to furnish the sympathetic innervation of the same structures.

The largest preganglionic source of the cranial autonomic is furnished by the vagus nerve (X) which supplies the pharynx, larynx, and practically all the thoracic and abdominal viscera except those in the pelvic portion (Fig. 209). In the thorax these preganglionic fibers enter the pulmonary, cardiac, and esophageal plexuses to be distributed to the terminal (intrinsic) ganglia of the heart and bronchial musculature, from which short postganglionic fibers go to the heart and bronchial muscle. In the abdomen the vagus fibers go to the stomach and pass through the coeliac and its subsidiary plexuses to end in the terminal ganglia of the intestine, liver, pancreas, and probably the kidneys. In the alimentary canal these terminal ganglia form the extensive ganglionated plexuses of Auerbach (myenteric) and of Meissner (submucosal). They extend the whole length of the digestive tube from the upper portion of the esophagus to the internal sphincter of the anus. These plexuses are composed of numerous small aggregations of ganglion cells intimately connected to each other by delicate transverse and longitudinal fiber bundles. From these cells postganglionic fibers terminate in the smooth muscle and glandular epithelium. The alimentary innervation of the vagus extends to the descending colon.

The sacral autonomic consists of preganglionic fibers from the second, third, and fourth sacral nerves which form the pelvic nerve (N. erigens) and go to the terminal ganglia of the pelvic plexuses as well as the myenteric and submucosal plexuses of the descending colon and rectum (Fig. 209). Postganglionic fibers from these ganglia then supply the effectors of the pelvic organs including the urinary bladder, descending colon, rectum, and accessory generative organs. The sacral autonomic thus innervates those viscera not supplied by the vagus.

The enteric plexuses differ from the other autonomic plexuses in one important respect. They apparently contain some mechanism for local reflex action, since coordinated peristalsis occurs on stimulation of the gut after section of all the nerves which connect them with the central nervous system. The nature of this reflex mechanism is not fully understood.

It is evident from the above that all the autonomic plexuses consist of complicated intermixtures of sympathetic and parasympathetic fibers which are difficult to distinguish morphologically. It must, however, be emphasized again that the sympathetic preganglionic fibers are interrupted in the vertebral and prevertebral ganglia, while the parasympathetic ones pass by way of the plexuses to the terminal ganglia.

In addition to the craniosacral outflow, it is believed by a few investigators that efferent parasympathetic fibers from the spinal cord pass through the dorsal roots as vasodilators of the cutaneous blood vessels. Stimulation of the distal end of a cut dorsal root causes vasodilation and a rise in temperature in the skin of the corresponding dermatome. Recently it has been shown that centrifugal discharges occur normally at the proximal ends of cut sensory nerves (Tönnies). The anatomical data are still inadequate and conflicting. Some have definitely demonstrated efferent fibers in the dorsal roots of many forms (Fig. 128), others have been unable to locate them.

VISCERAL AFFERENT FIBERS

There are numerous receptors in the viscera whose afferent fibers, myelinated or unmyelinated, travel centrally by way of the autonomic nerves, both sympathetic and parasympathetic. The largest myelinated fibers come principally from Pacinian corpuscles, the smaller myelinated and the unmyelinated ones from the more numerous diffuse visceral receptors. All these fibers have their cell bodies in the cerebrospinal ganglia. Those traveling within the sympathetic nerves are peripheral processes of ganglion cells from the thoracic and upper two lumbar spinal ganglia (Fig. 180). These pass through the white rami communicantes, enter the sympathetic trunk and run uninterruptedly to the abdominal and thoracic viscera by way of the splanchnic nerves or by way of the cardiac, pulmonary, and other sympathetic nerves. The parasympathetic nerves likewise contain many visceral afferent fibers. The afferent fibers of the vagus whose cell bodies are in the nodosal ganglion are distributed to the heart, lungs, and other viscera. Similar fibers from the bladder, rectum, and accessory genital organs pass by way of the pelvic nerves and enter the cord through the second, third, and fourth sacral nerves, their cell bodies presumably located in the corresponding sacral spinal ganglia.

The afferent visceral fibers are important for the initiation of various visceral and viscero-somatic reflexes mediated through the spinal cord and brain stem for the regulation and adjustment of vegetative functions. Many of these reactions remain on a subconscious level, but afferent impulses also give rise to visceral sensation, such as visceral pain, distress, nausea, hunger, and other more vague visceral sensations. It is probable that the constant stream of afferent visceral impulses is responsible for the general feeling of internal well being or of *malaise*. There is considerable uncertainty as to the sensory nature of the various visceral afferent fibers. Visceral pain is carried chiefly by fibers running in the sympathetic nerves, while most of the vagal fibers are concerned with specific visceromotor, vasomotor, and secretory reflexes which do not reach consciousness or only vaguely so. However, the sense of taste is mediated by the vagus, glossopharyngeal and facial nerves, and impulses giving rise to hunger are probably also carried by the vagus. Similarly, the sensation of bladder distention appears to be mediated by fibers running in the sacral autonomic, since such sensation is abolished by section or block of the pelvic nerves (p. 209).

STRUCTURE OF AUTONOMIC GANGLIA

The autonomic ganglia are cellular aggregations of varying size and shape, each surrounded by a connective tissue capsule. Trabeculae extending from the capsule form an internal framework which contains numerous, often pigmented, cells between which are irregular plexuses of myelinated and unmyelinated fibers. Besides these ganglia, isolated autonomic cells or nonencapsulated aggregations of such cells are found widely distributed throughout the viscera.

The autonomic cells are typically multipolar in shape (Fig. 80G–H). The size of the cells fluctuates between 20–60 micra and the number of their branching dendrites is exceedingly variable, as few as three or four in some and as many as twenty in others. The cells have a clear spherical or ovoid nucleus, delicate neurofibrils and fine chromofilic bodies. Binucleated or even multinucleated cells are not uncommon. Most of the cells are surrounded by cellular capsules similar to those surrounding the spinal ganglion cells (Fig. 80).

Some of the cells have short dendrites which ramify within the capsules. These are numerous in the autonomic ganglia of man (Fig. 214). Others have long slender dendrites which pierce the capsule and run for varying distances in the intercellular plexuses. Some cells possess both short and long processes. The intracapsular dendrites may arborize symmetrically on all sides of the cell or they may form "glomerular" structures on one side. These "glomeruli" are often formed by the interlocking dendritic processes of two or more cells, and all the cells so interlocked are enclosed within a single capsule (Fig. 215A). Such cells probably receive common terminal arborizations of preganglionic fibers. The extracapsular dendrites end in similar end arborizations at varying distances from the cell body which may likewise interlock with those of other cells. These long dendrites together with preganglionic fibers and axons of autonomic cells form the intricate fiber

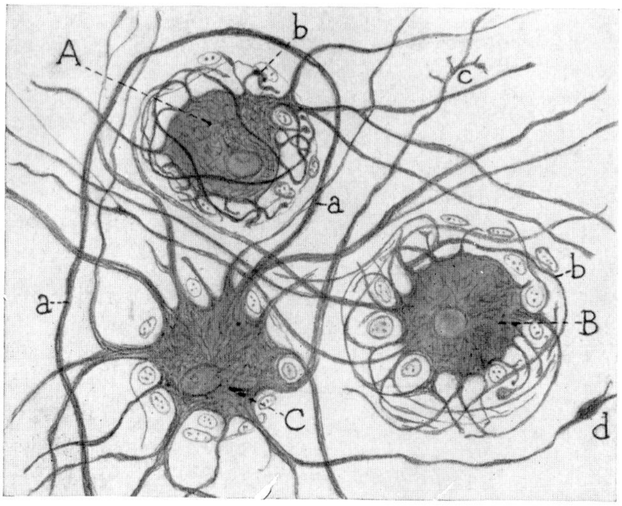

FIG. 214. Human sympathetic cells. *A,B*, cells whose dendrites (*b*) form a pericellular plexus. *C*, cell with long dendrites. *a*, axon; *c,d*, terminal portions of dendrites. Cajal's silver stain. (Cajal.)

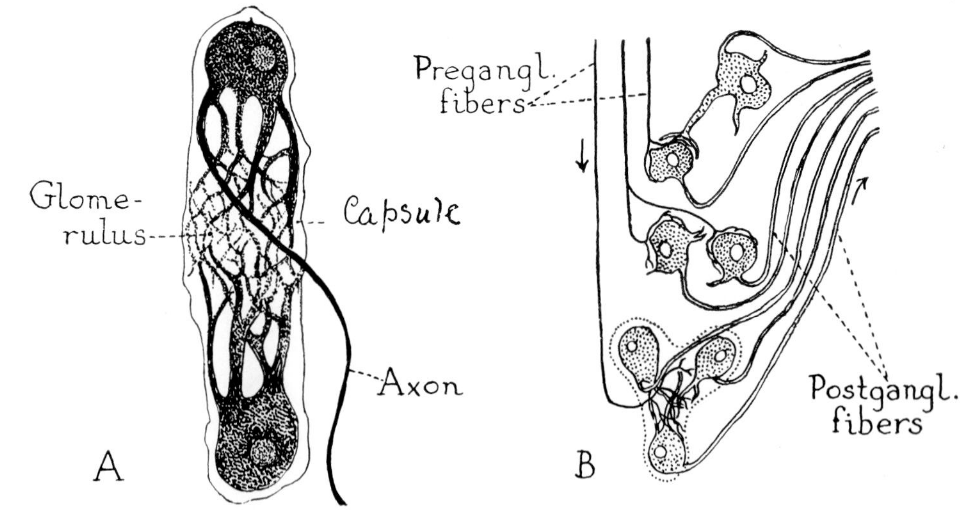

FIG. 215. *A*, Glomerulus formed by dendrites of two sympathetic cells. (After Cajal.) *B*, Diagram showing ways by which one preganglionic fiber may come into relation with two or more sympathetic ganglion cells. (After Ranson and Billingsley.)

plexuses between the cells. Many autonomic cells, especially in the terminal ganglia, have long slender dendrites almost indistinguishable from axons.

Most of the axons of the autonomic ganglion cells are unmyelinated, but myelinated ones are found in many places, as in the ciliary ganglion. Some axons are partly myelinated and partly unmyelinated. All are postganglionic fibers terminating in the visceral effectors.

Numerous preganglionic fibers end in synaptic relation with the bodies and dendrites of the autonomic cells. They are fine myelinated fibers which may branch repeatedly within the ganglion and form pericellular arborizations, the terminal fibrils ending by neurofibrillar rings or loops on the cell body (Fig. 216). More common than such axosomatic synapses are the axodendritic ones where the preganglionic fibers end in diffuse arborizations about the intracapsular and extracapsular dendrites. The preganglionic character of the several endings described above has been demonstrated experimentally, since they degenerate and disappear when the appropriate preganglionic fibers, such as the vagus or white rami, are cut (Fig. 217). There is convincing anatomical evidence that a single preganglionic

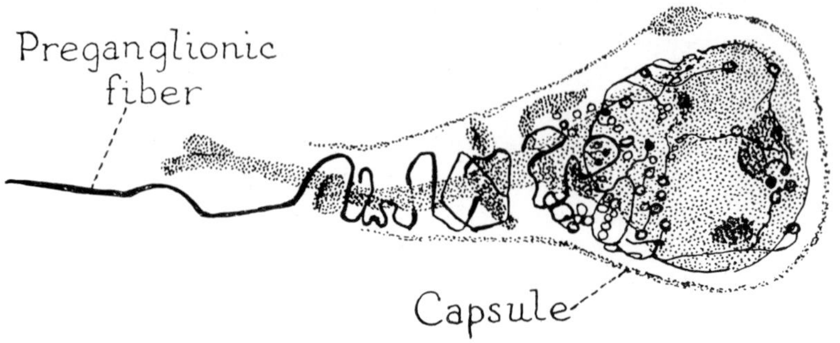

FIG. 216. Terminations of a preganglionic fiber on the body of a sympathetic cell. (After Huber.)

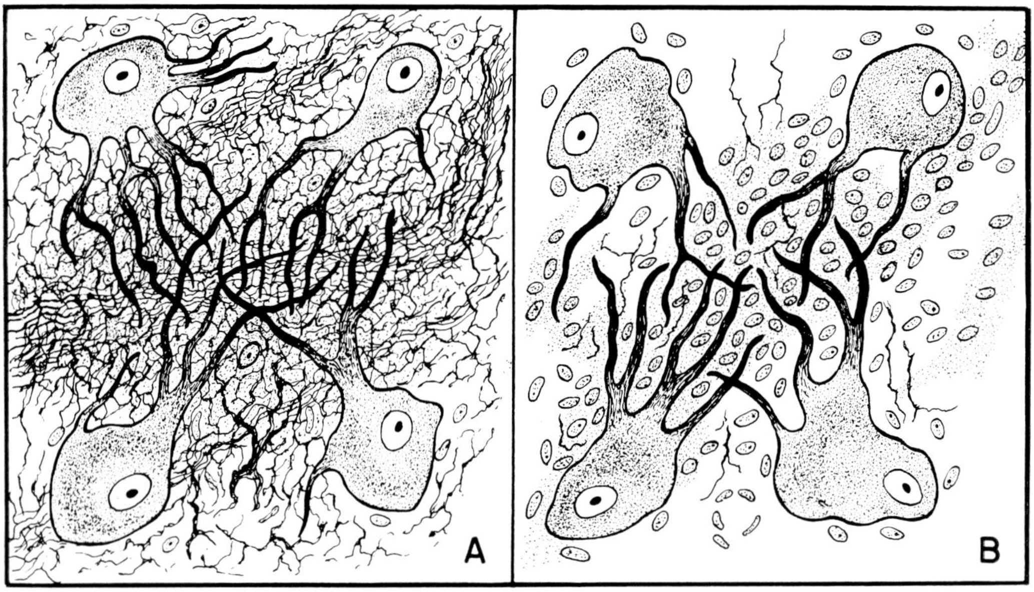

FIG. 217. Terminations of preganglionic vagus nerve fibers (parasympathetic) upon postganglionic neurons within an intracardiac ganglion. A. both vagii intact; B. 32 days after bilateral vagectomy. Dog, Bodian stain.

fiber may form synaptic relations with several or even a large number of autonomic neurons (Fig. 215B).

FUNCTIONAL CONSIDERATIONS

The investigations of Loewi, Dale, Cannon, and others have demonstrated that autonomic effects are mediated by chemical substances liberated at the postganglionic nerve terminals. Stimulation of the vagus releases acetylcholine, while stimulation of the sympathetic is followed by the liberation of an adrenaline-like substance, known as sympathin (Cannon and Rosenblueth). As a result, Dale introduced the terms "adrenergic" and "cholinergic" to distinguish between the two types of postganglionic fibers. Subsequent investigations showed, however, that the terms "adrenergic" and "cholinergic" did not correspond completely with "sympathetic" and "parasympathetic" respectively. Thus the postganglionic fibers to the sweat glands, though anatomically part of the sympathetic, are cholinergic, and moreover react to certain drugs such as pilocarpine and atropine in the same way as parasympathetic fibers. Hess (1948) therefore maintains that the sudomotor innervation belongs functionally to the parasympathetic system. There are other instances of mixed autonomic nerves. In the splanchnic and lumbar sympathetic nerves, which are composed preponderantly of adrenergic vasoconstrictor fibers, there are also some cholinergic vasodilator ones. Thus when the vasoconstrictor and other sympathetic activities are abolished by ergotoxin, stimulation of the splanchnics and of the lower abdominal sympathetic chain produces vasodilation in the intestine and lower extremity respectively (Dale). The vagus may likewise contain some vasodilator fibers and some which inhibit gastrointestinal peristalsis (Hess). These can not be detected by electrical stimulation since the resultant effect is dominated by the preponderant group. In physiological conditions, however, they may be selectively activated by appropriate stimuli from the central nervous system. Hess believes that the differentiation of the sympathetic and parasympathetic components can not be based on morphological principles alone, but must take into account the criterion of functional activity.

Gaskell has pointed out that whenever a visceral structure is innervated by both the sympathetic and parasympathetic, the effects of the two are as a rule antagonistic. The sympathetic dilates the pupil, accelerates the heart, inhibits intestinal movements, and contracts the vesical and rectal sphincters. The parasympathetic constricts the pupil, slows the heart, furthers peristaltic movement, and relaxes the above named sphincters. The apparently haphazard effects on involuntary muscle produced by each autonomic division in different organs, contraction in one, inhibition in another, are more readily explained when the *overall* activities of the two systems are taken into consideration. The parasympathetic deals primarily with anabolic activities concerned with the restoration and conservation of bodily energy and the resting of vital organs. In the words of Cannon, "a glance at these various functions of the cranial division reveals at once that they serve for bodily conservation; by narrowing the pupil they shield the retina from excessive light; by slowing the heart rate they give the cardiac muscle longer periods for rest and invigoration; and by providing for the flow of saliva and gastric juice, and by supplying the necessary muscular tone for the contraction of the alimentary canal, they prove fundamentally essential to the processes of proper digestion and absorption, by which energy-yielding material is taken into the body and stored. To the cranial division belongs the great service of building up reserves and fortifying the body against times of need and stress." The sacral division supplements the cranial by ridding the body of its intestinal and urinary wastes.

On the other hand, stimulation of the sympathetic component equips the body for the intense muscular action required in offense and defense. It is a mechanism of "war" quickly mobilizing the existing reserves of the body. This is especially brought out in emergencies or emotional crises. The eyes dilate, respiration is deepened and the rate and force of the heart is increased. The blood vessels of the viscera and the skin are constricted, the blood pressure raised, and the blood driven to the striped muscles, lungs, heart, and brain. The peaceful activities are slowed down or even paralyzed, the blood drained from the huge intestinal reservoir, peristalsis and alimentary secretion inhibited, the urinary and rectal outlets blocked by contraction of their sphincters.

The two systems are reciprocally innervated and their dual activities integrated into coordinated responses ensuring the maintenance of adequate internal conditions to meet the demands of any given situation. The parasympathetic activities are primarily initiated by internal changes in the viscera themselves. The sympathetic is in considerable part activated by exteroceptive impulses passing over the somatic afferent fibers and initiated by favorable or unfavorable changes in the external environment.

The preganglionic fibers of the sympathetic arise from a continuous cell column of the spinal cord, and a single fiber may form synaptic relations with many cells in different vertebral ganglia or in the prevertebral ones (Fig. 215B). Both types of ganglia are placed at considerable distances from the organs innervated, and from them relatively small numbers of postganglionic fibers are distributed to extensive visceral areas. Such a mechanism permits a wide radiation of impulses, hence sympathetic discharges are profuse and expressed in widely spread visceral effects. Thus the stimulation of a thoracic ventral root or white ramus will cause erection of hair and vasoconstriction in five or six or even more segmental skin areas.

In the parasympathetic the preganglionic neurons are represented by more isolated cell groups whose fibers pass out in separate nerves and go directly to the terminal ganglia within or near the organs. Moreover each preganglionic fiber enters into synaptic relations with fewer postganglionic neurons than is the case in the sympathetic division. Thus in the superior cervical ganglion of the cat the ratio of preganglionic fibers to postganglionic neurons is about 1:15 or more, while in the ciliary ganglion the ratio is only 1:2 (Wolf, 1941). Parasympathetic action is therefore more discrete, and limited in effect to the portion stimulated. Thus stimulation of the glossopharyngeal nerve will increase parotid secretion and stimulation of the oculomotor will constrict the pupil, in each case without the appearance of other parasympathetic effects. Similarly, stimulation of the distal end of a cut dorsal root will cause vasodilation limited to the corresponding dermatome.

SOME IMPORTANT PERIPHERAL AUTONOMIC PATHWAYS

Eye

(a) ***Parasympathetic.*** Preganglionic fibers from nucleus of Edinger-Westphal in midbrain by way of third nerve to ciliary ganglion. Postganglionic fibers from cells of ciliary ganglion to ciliary muscle and sphincter of iris.

Action: Contraction of pupil (constriction, miosis) and accommodation to near and far vision.

(b) ***Sympathetic.*** Preganglionic fibers from cells of lateral sympathetic nucleus in spinal cord passing by way of upper two or three thoracic white rami and sympathetic trunk to superior cervical ganglion. Postganglionic fibers from the latter ganglion via the internal carotid plexus and long and short ciliary nerves to the radial muscle fibers of the iris, the superior tarsal muscle of Müller, and the blood vessels of the eyeball.

Action: Dilation of pupil (mydriasis).

Interruption of the pathways passing through the cervical sympathetic trunk causes a number of symptoms clinically known as Horner's syndrome. There is a constriction of the pupil (miosis), drooping of the eyelid (ptosis) and a sinking in of the eyeball (enophthalmos). This is accompanied by vasodilation and dryness of the skin of the face, due to damage of the vasoconstrictor and sudomotor fibers which likewise pass through the cervical trunk. The reason for the enophthalmos is not clear. It was commonly believed to be due to paralysis of the orbital muscle of Müller, a band of smooth muscle lying obliquely on the floor of the orbit, whose contraction supposedly causes a slight protrusion of the eyeball (exophthalmos). However, the muscle is vestigial in man, and according to many ophthalmologists is incapable of causing even the slightest displacement of the eyeball. Moreover, careful measurements have failed to disclose any significant changes in position between the affected and the normal eyeball. It is possible, therefore, that the enophthalmos may only be apparent, due perhaps to the drooping of the eyelid.

Horner's syndrome may be caused by lesions of the intermediolateral column in the upper two or three thoracic segments of the cord (ciliospinal center), which gives origin to the preganglionic fibers; by section of the upper thoracic white rami, or of the cervical sympathetic trunk through which the preganglionic fibers run; or by damage to the superior cervical ganglion and the postganglionic fibers which arise from the latter (Fig. 204). The symptoms may also appear in lesions of the cervical cord, medulla and other portions of the brain stem, if descending tracts from higher sympathetic centers to the ciliospinal center are involved.

Submaxillary, Sublingual and Lacrimal Glands

(a) ***Parasympathetic.*** Preganglionic fibers from superior salivatory nucleus of medulla by way of facial nerve, chorda tympani and lingual nerve to submandibular ganglion; by way of facial nerve and great superficial petrosal nerve to sphenopalatine ganglion. Postganglionic fibers from submandibular ganglion to submaxillary and sublingual glands; from sphenopalatine ganglion via zygomatic and maxillary nerves to lacrimal gland.

Action: Increases secretion.

(b) ***Sympathetic.*** Preganglionic fibers from lateral sympathetic nucleus in spinal cord passing by way of upper thoracic white rami and sympathetic trunk to superior cervical ganglion. Postganglionic fibers from that ganglion by way of external and internal carotid plexuses to submaxillary, sublingual, and lacrimal glands.

Action: Some increase in lacrimal secretion; apparently some increase of thick viscid salivary secretion.

Heart

(a) ***Parasympathetic.*** Preganglionic fibers from dorsal motor nucleus of vagus by way of vagus nerve and its cardiac branches and cardiac plexus to intrinsic ganglia of heart. Postganglionic fibers from these ganglia, located in the walls of the atria and in the interatrial septum, to nodal tissue and heart muscle.

Action: Cardiac inhibition and coronary vasoconstriction.

(b) ***Sympathetic.*** Preganglionic fibers from lateral sympathetic nucleus of cord by way of the white rami of the upper four or five thoracic nerves to the cervical and upper thoracic ganglia. Postganglionic fibers from these ganglia via cervical and thoracic cardiac nerves to heart muscle.

Action: Cardiac acceleration and coronary vasodilation.

The exact distribution of the sympathetic and parasympathetic fibers to the heart is not fully determined. The postganglionic parasympathetic fibers appear to go to the atrial musculature, to the nodes and bundles of the conduction system, and to the coronary blood vessels. The sinoatrial node is chiefly innervated by the right vagus, the atrioventricular node by the left vagus (Nonidez, 1939). Others believe that the atria and the nodes are supplied by both vagal and sympathetic fibers, while the ventricles receive sympathetic fibers only (Chapman et al., 1948). According to Stotler and McMahon (1947) the motor innervation of the human heart is restricted to the conduction system, no nerve fibers terminating on ordinary cardiac muscle fibers. The numerous nerve fibers running in the connective tissue between the muscle bundles are regarded as supplying the coronary vessels.

Afferent fibers are found in both the parasympathetic and sympathetic cardiac nerves. The afferent vagal (and glossopharyngeal) fibers serve mainly as afferent links in cardiac and vascular reflexes, such as the aortic and the carotid sinus reflex. Afferent pain fibers from the heart run by way of the sympathetic, passing chiefly through the five thoracic cardiac branches and probably also through the inferior and middle cervical cardiac nerves (Fulton, 1949). The cardiac pain of angina pectoris is relieved by upper thoracic sympathectomy.

Lungs and Bronchi

(a) ***Parasympathetic.*** Preganglionic fibers from dorsal motor nucleus of vagus by way of vagus nerve and its pulmonary branches to intrinsic ganglia of trachea, bronchi, and lung. Postganglionic fibers from these ganglia to musculature and glands of bronchial tree.

Action: Constriction of bronchial musculature and the secretion of mucus.

(b) ***Sympathetic.*** Preganglionic fibers from lateral sympathetic nucleus through upper thoracic white rami to stellate ganglion. Postganglionic fibers from stellate ganglion via pulmonary plexuses to bronchial musculature and blood vessels.

Action: Dilatation of bronchi.

Gastrointestinal Tract to Descending Colon Pancreas, Liver

(a) ***Parasympathetic.*** Preganglionic fibers from dorsal motor nucleus of vagus by way of vagus nerve and its corresponding branches to the terminal ganglia of the digestive tube, pancreas, and liver. Postganglionic fibers from the latter to smooth muscle and glands of these organs.

Action: Excites peristalsis of digestive tube and gall bladder. Increases secretion of gastrointestinal and pancreatic juices.

(b) ***Sympathetic.*** Preganglionic fibers from lateral sympathetic nucleus via white rami from the fifth to twelfth thoracic nerves and splanchnic nerves to coeliac and related ganglia. Postganglionic fibers from the latter to smooth muscle and glands of the digestive tube, and to pancreas.

Action: Inhibits peristalsis of digestive tube and gall bladder. Vasoconstriction of intestinal blood vessels. Little effect on pancreatic secretion.

Descending Colon and Rectum, Urinary Bladder

(a) ***Parasympathetic.*** Preganglionic fibers from inferior lateral and from medial parasympathetic nuclei of cord by way of second, third, and fourth sacral nerves, and pelvic nerve to terminal ganglia of colon, rectum, and urinary bladder. Postganglionic fibers from the latter to the smooth muscle of those organs.

Action: Excites peristalsis of colon and rectum and inhibits internal anal sphincter. Excites detrusor muscle and inhibits vesical sphincter with resulting urination.

(b) ***Sympathetic.*** Preganglionic fibers from lateral sympathetic nucleus by way of lumbar white rami and continuing uninterruptedly through the lumbar ganglia and abdominal aortic plexuses to inferior mesenteric ganglion, and perhaps to smaller scattered ganglia in hypogastric plexus. Postganglionic fibers from these ganglia to smooth muscle of descending colon, rectum, and bladder.

Action: Inhibits peristalsis of colon and rectum and excites contraction of anal sphincter. Inhibits detrusor muscle of bladder and excites contraction of internal sphincter with consequent retention of urine.

Cutaneous Blood Vessels, Sweat Glands, and Arrector Pili Muscles

(a) ***Parasympathetic.*** The anatomical pathway of such parasympathetic fibers, if at all present, has not been demonstrated. There is some evidence that vasomotor fibers leave the cord in the dorsal roots and act as vasodilator fibers of cutaneous blood vessels. The origin and course of these fibers are still obscure.

(b) ***Sympathetic.*** Preganglionic fibers from lateral sympathetic nucleus by way of thoracic and lumbar white rami to all the ganglia of the sympathetic trunk. Postganglionic fibers from superior cervical ganglion by way of the external and internal carotid plexuses and by way of gray rami of upper cervical nerves to blood vessels, sweat glands, and hair muscles of the head and neck. Postganglionic fibers from all other trunk ganglia via gray rami and corresponding spinal nerves to blood vessels, sweat glands, and hair muscles of trunk and extremities.

Action: Vasoconstriction, excitation of arrector pili muscles, and of sweat gland secretion.

15

The Internal Structure of the Medulla

The cranial nerves and their nuclei, ascending and descending neural pathways, the fourth ventricle and new nuclear groups are all responsible for the altered, compact appearance of the medulla (Figs. 218, 219) as contrasted to the spinal cord. It will be recalled that these structural alterations in the medulla account for the rearrangement of the functional neurons related to the cranial nerves (contrast Figs. 222, 127 and 180). Within the medulla the special somatic afferent nuclei related to incoming auditory and vestibular fibers occupy a dorsolateral position. Taste fibers of cranial nerves VII, IX, and X (special visceral afferent) form the *fasciculus solitarius.* Such taste fibers terminate in the *nucleus solitarius.* They are located in the floor of the rhomboid fossa lateral to the sensory and visceral motor nuclei of the vagus nerve (Figs. 220–222). A conspicuous column of motor neurons is present in the ventrolateral area of the reticular formation, dorsal to the nucleus of the inferior olive. This is the *nucleus ambiguus.* These nerve cells constitute the lower motor neuron to muscles derived from the mesoderm of the third and fourth branchial arches (branchiomeric muscles). The axons from this nucleus supply the muscles of the larynx, pharynx, and lateral neck via cranial nerves IX, X, and XI. Other motor nuclei have a similar location in the pons and provide motor fibers to muscle derivatives of the first and second branchial arches via cranial nerves V and VII. Visceral motor or parasympathetic neurons whose axons become incorporated in cranial nerves III, VII, IX, and X are indicated in yellow in Figs. 220 and 221. The student will find Figs. 218 to 223 extremely useful for purposes of orientation as ascending levels of the brain stem are presented.

Thus the relatively uniform picture seen in any section of the spinal cord is rapidly altered in the medulla oblongata and here the changes continue from level to level. The centrally placed H-shaped gray matter of the cord becomes broken up into more or less definite cell groups distributed throughout the whole area of the section. The white matter no longer surrounds the gray as a continuous peripheral mantle of longitudinal fibers but is now composed of fiber bundles intermingled with the gray masses. It is characterized by numerous transversely or obliquely running fibers, the whole constituting the *reticular formation* of the medulla, pons, and upper portion of the brain stem. An understanding of these bewildering changes may best be gained by the study of a closely graded series of transverse sections in which the appearance and changing relationships of the various structures can be followed continuously. The series selected is that of a one month baby in which myelinization of several fiber systems is still incomplete, hence many tracts may be distinguished from others by the relative intensity of their staining capacity. Thus the fully myelinated fibers stain black in myelin stains, while others, as the pyramidal tract, are only partly myelinated and appear gray. Still others, such as the pontile fibers, are entirely unmyelinated and remain unstained. Whenever necessary, adult sections

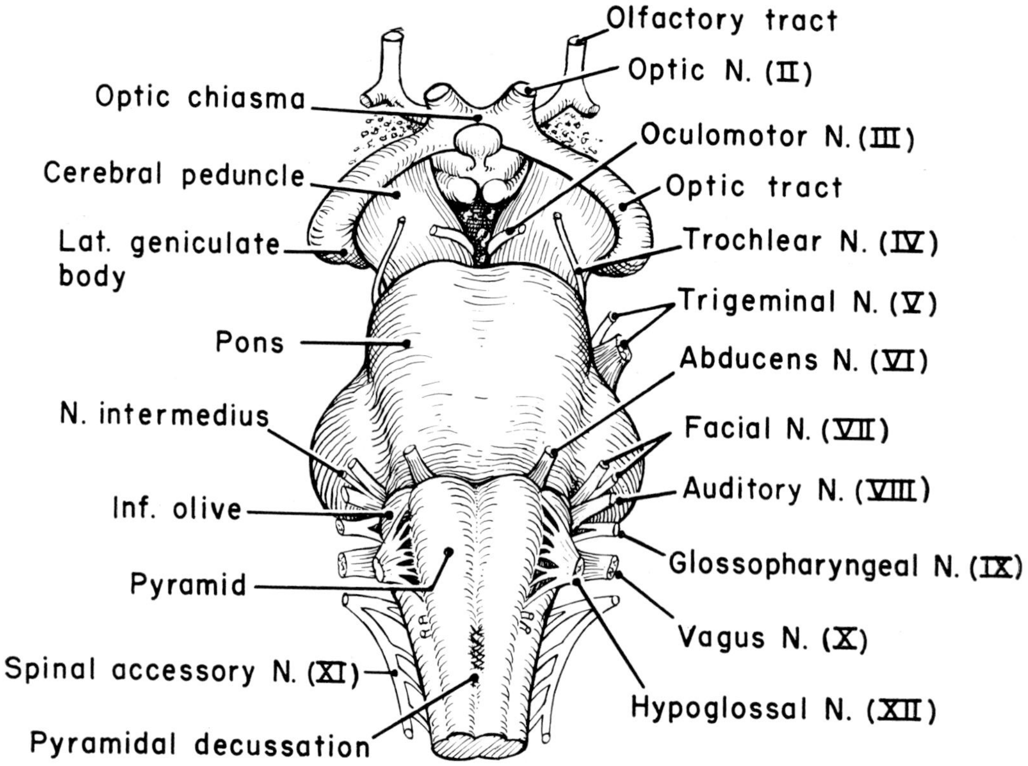

FIG. 218. Diagram of medulla, pons, and midbrain. Ventral view.

have been introduced to bring out structures not easily seen in the infant.

At the junction of the spinal cord and medulla (Fig. 224) the picture is still typical of the upper cervical cord, though with certain significant modifications. The substantia gelatinosa has increased in size and in the zone of Lissauer coarser myelinated fibers have made their appearance. The zone at this level is a mixed bundle, consisting in part of fine ascending root fibers of the uppermost cervical nerves, in part of coarser descending fibers of the trigeminal nerve (N.V), which enter at a much higher level (pons) and descend in the dorsolateral fasciculus to terminate in the substantia gelatinosa.

The lateral pyramidal tract is detaching itself from the lateral white column and has invaded the gray. It is broken up into a number of obliquely or transversely cut bundles between which are strands of gray matter, and partially separates the dorsal from the ventral gray. The central gray has increased in amount and is expanding dorsally.

SPINAL ACCESSORY NERVE

In the ventral gray are the somatic motor cells of the first cervical nerve, whose axons emerge as ventral root fibers. These cells extend for a short distance into the medulla where they are known as the supraspinal nucleus (Jacobsohn, Fig. 228). Dorsal and lateral to them is the nucleus of the spinal accessory nerve (N.XI), some roots of which are present at this level (Fig. 226). The accessory nerve is often divided into a bulbar and spinal portion, forming respectively the internal and external branches of the nerve (Fig. 239). The bulbar portion arises from neurons in the caudal end of the nucleus ambiguus. Axons of these cells emerge on the lateral surface of the medulla slightly

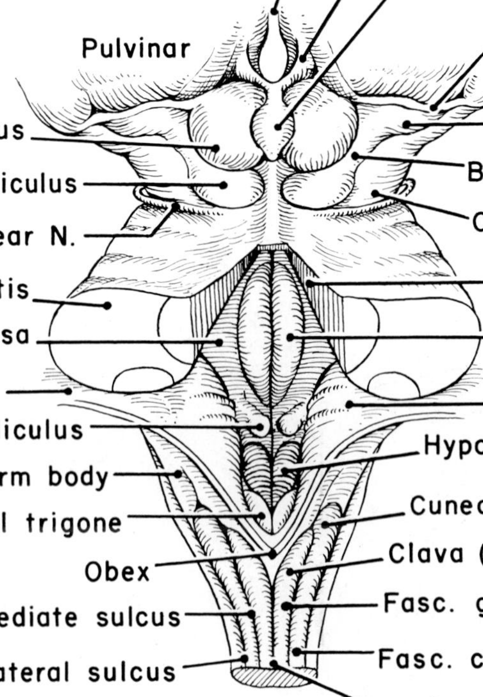

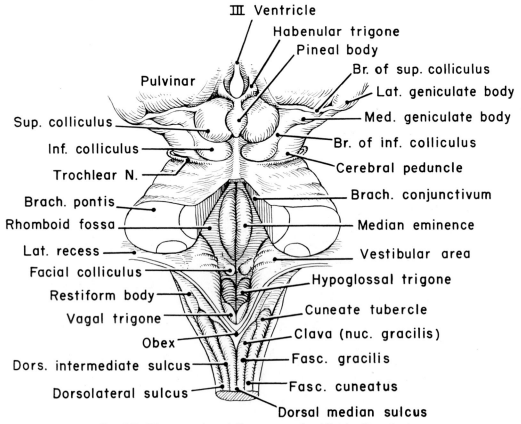

FIG. 219. Diagram of medulla, pons, and midbrain. Dorsal view.

inferior to the lowest fibers of the vagus. The bulbar portion of XI promptly joins the vagus nerve, and as motor fibers of the inferior (recurrent) laryngeal nerve supply the intrinsic muscles of the larynx. The spinal portion constitutes the accessory nerve and supplies the sternocleidomastoid and portions of the trapezius muscles. It originates from a cell column in the ventral horn extending from the fifth or sixth cervical segments to about the middle of the pyramidal decussation. Caudally the cells of the column are in the lateral part of the ventral horn, but in the oral portion the cells assume a more central position. The root fibers arch dorsally and laterally, some of them first ascending within the cord for a distance, and emerge on the lateral aspect of the cord in a series of rootlets extending as low as the fifth or sixth cervical segments (Figs. 223, 239). The rootlets of the accessory nerve unite to form a common trunk (external branch) which ascends in the spinal canal, enters the skull through the foramen magnum, and makes its cranial exit through the jugular foramen together with the vagus and glossopharyngeal nerves. The nucleus of N.XI, like all motor nuclei, receives terminations of fibers bringing to it reflex, cerebellar, extrapyramidal, and pyramidal influences related to cephalogyric movements. Since contraction of the sternomastoid muscle turns the head to the opposite side, in lesions of the XIth nerve the head will have a tendency to deviate to the side of the injury.

In the white matter the fiber tracts have the same arrangement as in other sections of the cervical cord. The dorsal column shows a massive fasciculus cuneatus and a

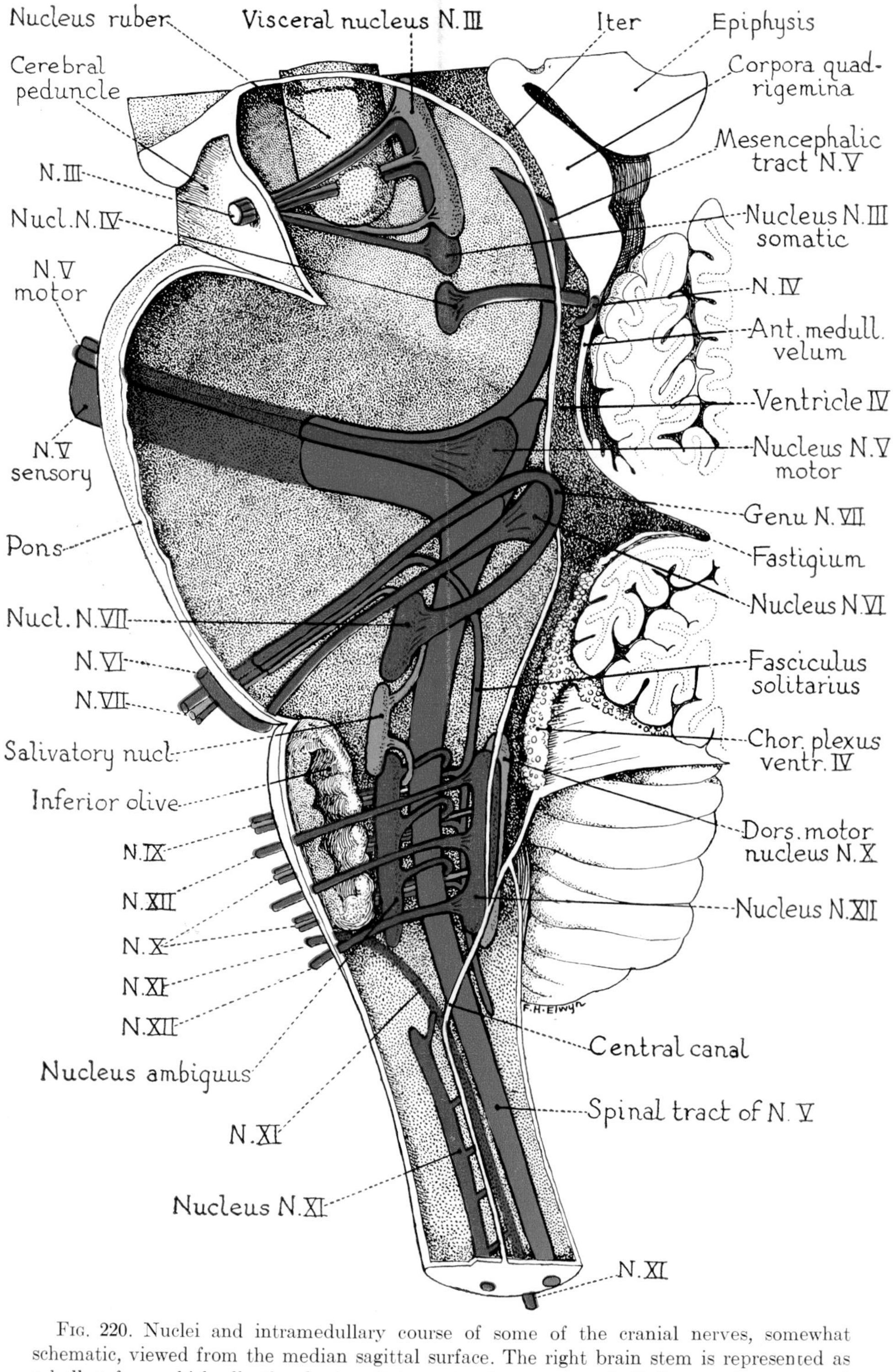

FIG. 220. Nuclei and intramedullary course of some of the cranial nerves, somewhat schematic, viewed from the median sagittal surface. The right brain stem is represented as a hollow from which all other brain substance has been removed. *Red*, somatic motor and special visceral motor components (to striped muscle); *yellow*, general visceral motor; *blue*, sensory components. (After Braus-Elze.)

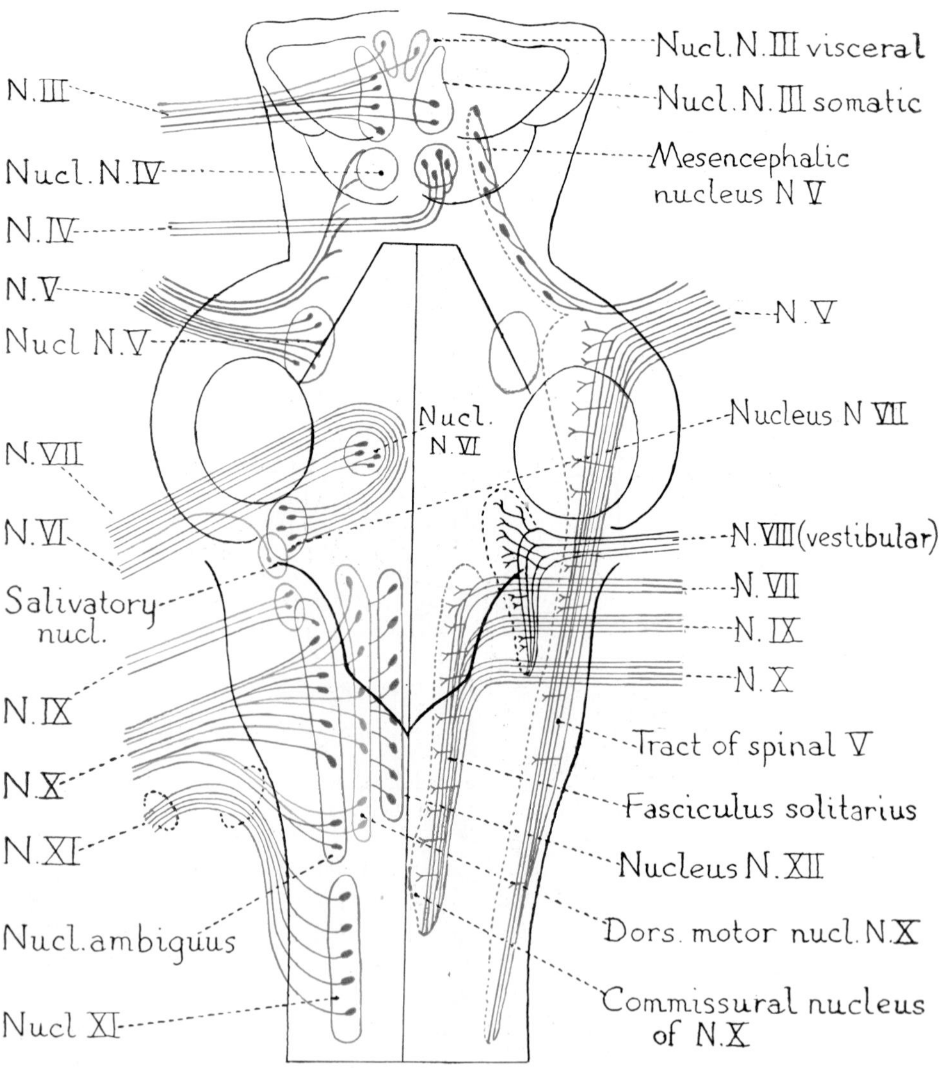

FIG. 221. Diagram showing nuclei of origin, nuclei of termination and intramedullary course of the cranial nerves, projected on the dorsal surface of the brain stem. *Red*, somatic motor and special visceral motor (to striped muscle); *yellow*, general visceral motor; *blue*, general sensory (somatic and visceral); *black*, special somatic sensory (proprioceptive). (Modified from Van Gehuchten.)

somewhat smaller fasciculus gracilis. In the latter, lighter areas represent the caudal tip of the nucleus gracilis in which the whole tract ultimately terminates. In the peripheral part of the lateral and ventral white columns are the dorsal and ventral spinocerebellar, the olivospinal (Helweg), and ventral pyramidal tracts. Somewhat deeper are the rubrospinal, spinothalamic, and vestibulospinal tracts. The ventral white contains the medial longitudinal fasciculus and, more ventrally, the tectospinal fibers. The shorter intersegmental (spinospinal) tracts lie close to the gray matter.

SECTIONS OF MEDULLA THROUGH PYRAMIDAL DECUSSATION (MOTOR DECUSSATION) (FIGS. 226, 227)

The most conspicuous features are the decussation of the pyramidal tracts, the

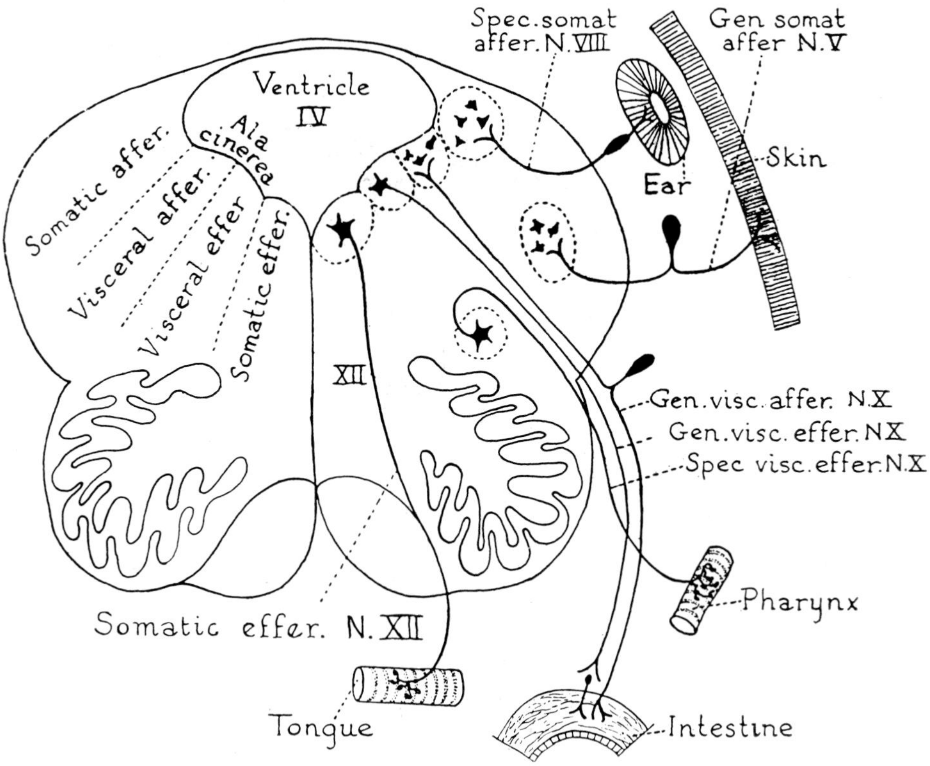

FIG. 222. Diagrammatic section through the medulla showing the functional components of the cranial nerves and the cell columns to which they are related.

appearance of the dorsal column nuclei, and the beginning of the gray reticular formation. The central gray dorsal to the central canal has greatly increased in amount.

Bundles of fibers from the lateral pyramidal tract are crossing the midline to join the ventral pyramidal tract of the opposite side, and in their passage through the gray are cutting off the ventral horn from the rest of the gray matter. In a series of ascending sections the decussation is naturally seen in the reverse. The pyramidal tract is a massive descending fiber bundle arising from cells in the motor and premotor cortex. In the pyramidal decussation most of the fibers cross to the dorsolateral portion of the cord where they descend as the lateral or crossed pyramidal tract (Figs. 193, 229). The rest of the fibers remain in their original ventral position as the uncrossed or ventral tract. Some uncrossed fibers pass to the lateral tract of the same side. The fibers cross in interdigitating bundles having a downward as well as transverse direction, hence the bundles are cut obliquely and in any section there may be more pyramidal fibers on one side than on the other. The pyramidal decussation forms the anatomical basis for the voluntary motor control of one half of the body by the opposite cerebral hemisphere. Injury of the pyramidal tract anywhere above the decussation will cause the pyramidal symptoms already described in the contralateral extremities.

The greatly enlarged substantia gelatinosa is capped externally by the zone of Lissauer whose fibers are constantly increasing in number. The zone no longer contains ascending spinal root fibers but is composed of descending afferent fibers of the trigeminal nerve (N.V.), which terminate directly or by collaterals in the gelatinous

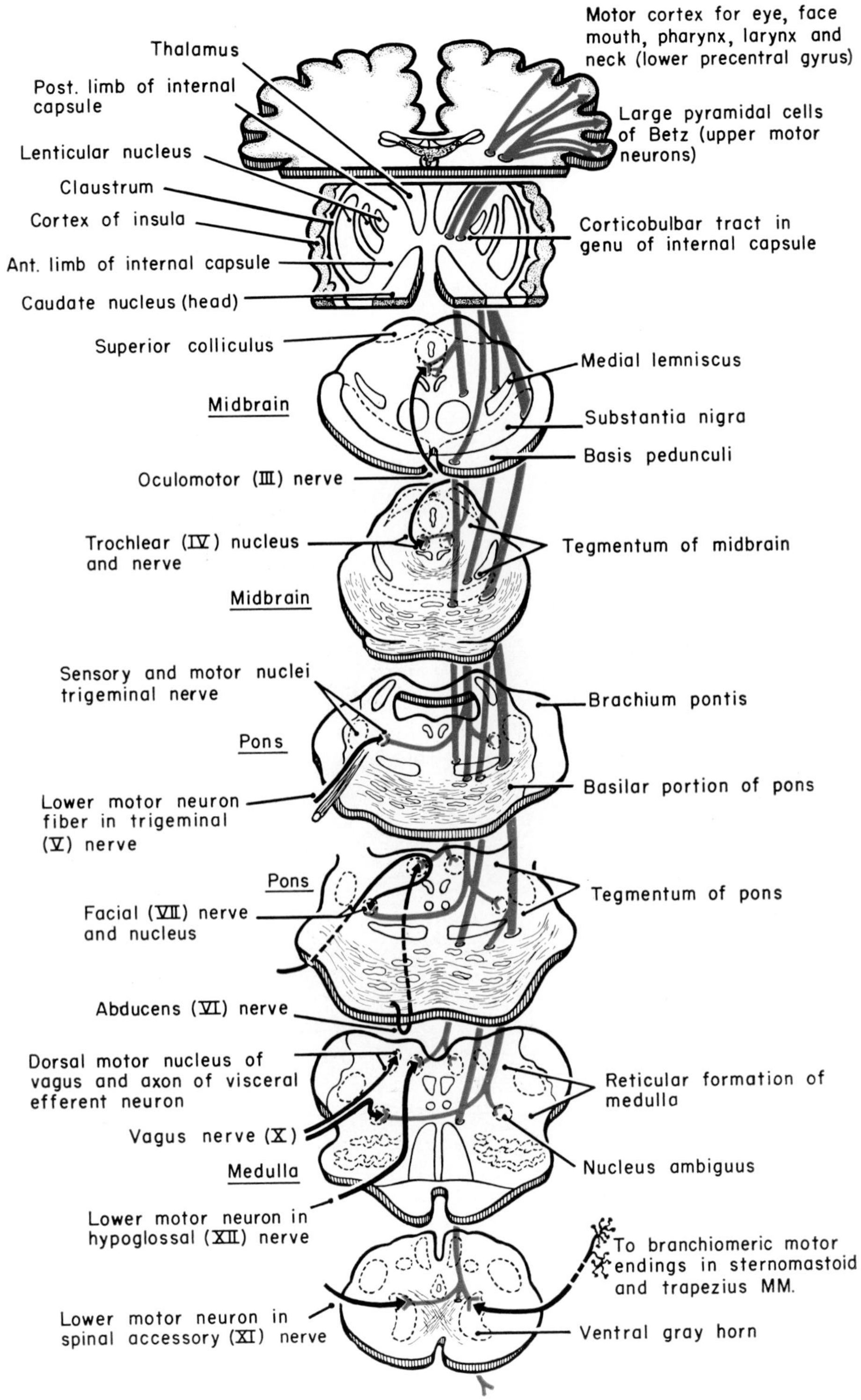
Motor cortex for eye, face mouth, pharynx, larynx and neck (lower precentral gyrus)
Thalamus
Post. limb of internal capsule
Large pyramidal cells of Betz (upper motor neurons)
Lenticular nucleus
Claustrum
Cortex of insula
Corticobulbar tract in genu of internal capsule
Ant. limb of internal capsule
Caudate nucleus (head)
Superior colliculus
Medial lemniscus
Midbrain
Substantia nigra
Basis pedunculi
Oculomotor (III) nerve
Trochlear (IV) nucleus and nerve
Tegmentum of midbrain
Midbrain
Sensory and motor nuclei trigeminal nerve
Brachium pontis
Pons
Basilar portion of pons
Lower motor neuron fiber in trigeminal (V) nerve
Pons
Tegmentum of pons
Facial (VII) nerve and nucleus
Abducens (VI) nerve
Dorsal motor nucleus of vagus and axon of visceral efferent neuron
Reticular formation of medulla
Vagus nerve (X)
Medulla
Nucleus ambiguus
Lower motor neuron in hypoglossal (XII) nerve
To branchiomeric motor endings in sternomastoid and trapezius MM.
Lower motor neuron in spinal accessory (XI) nerve
Ventral gray horn

Fig. 223. Diagram of the corticobulbar tract. The upper motor neuron pathway to the motor nuclei of cranial nerves.

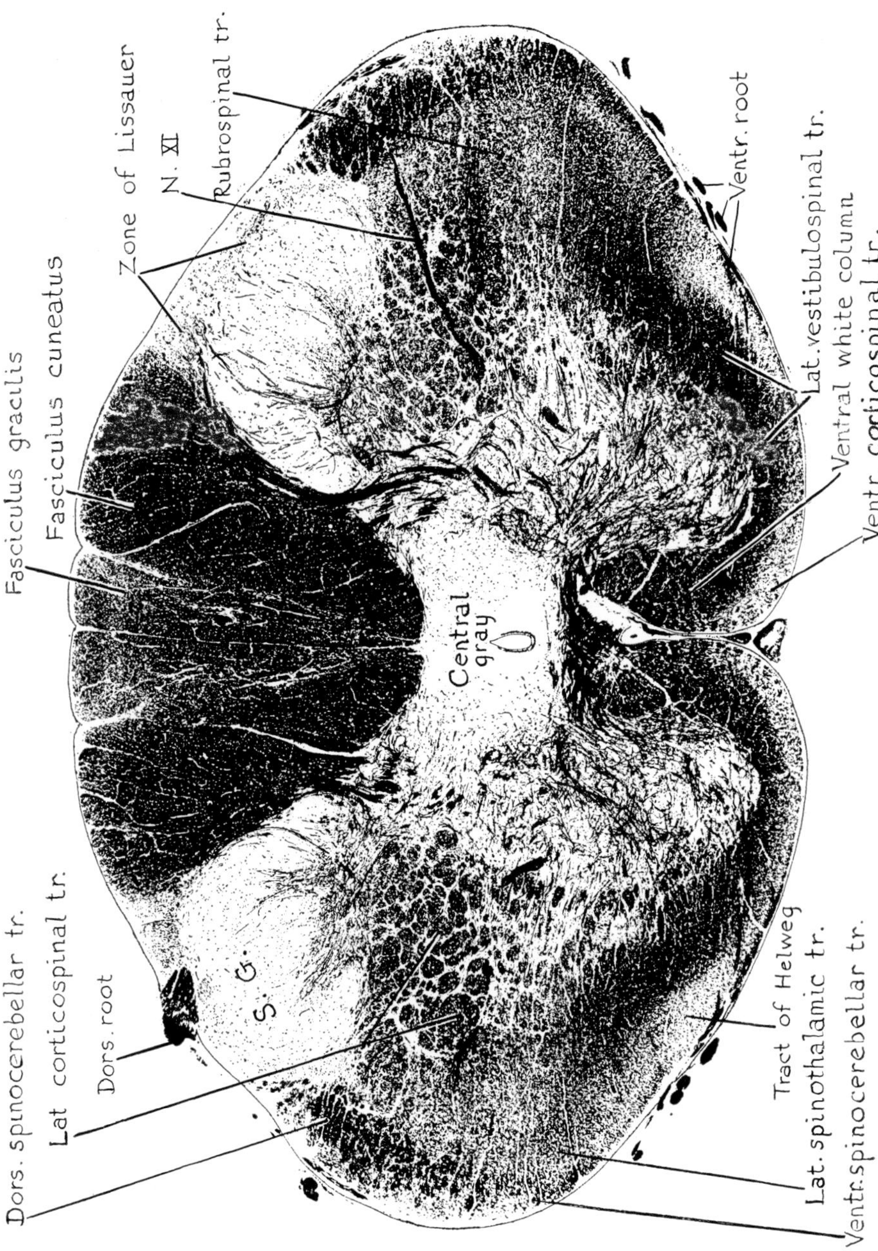

FIG. 224. Transverse section through uppermost portion of spinal cord of one month infant. Weigert's myelin stain. Photograph. S. G., substantia gelatinosa.

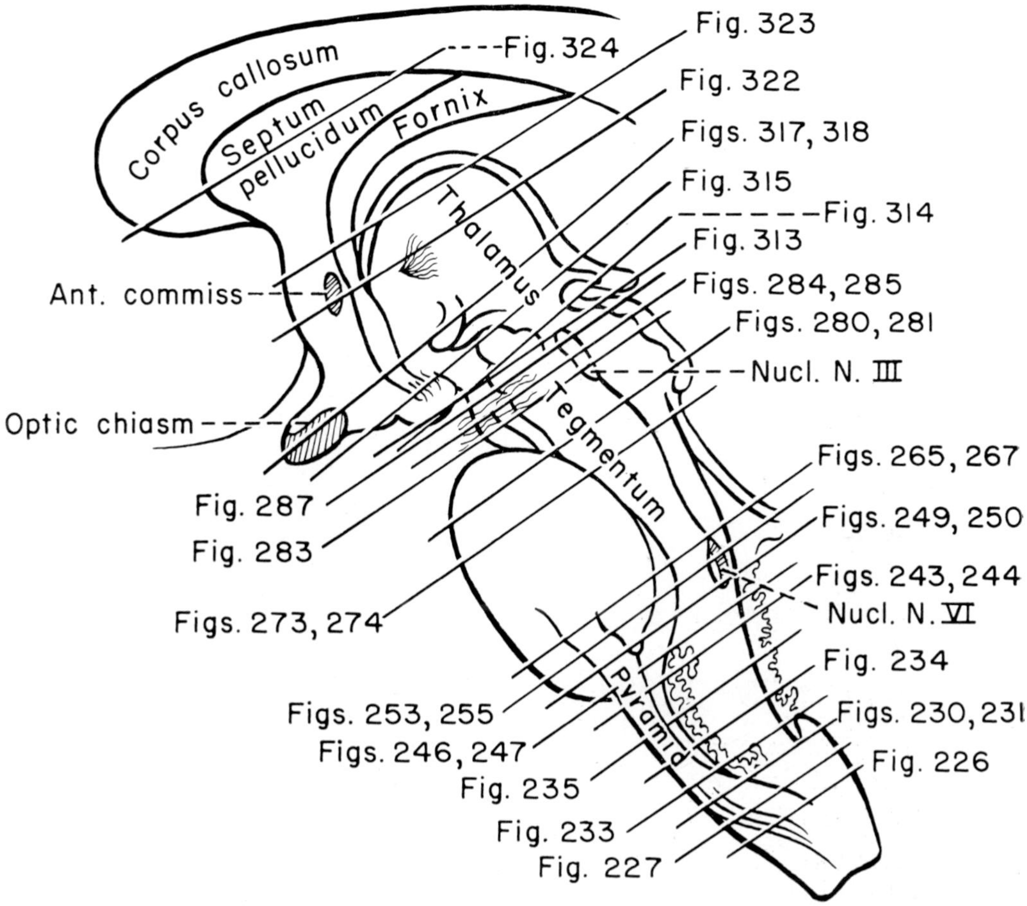

FIG. 225. Outline of paramedian sagittal section of brain stem, showing level and plane of the transverse sections of the figures indicated. For identification of structures see Fig. 311.

substance. This fiber bundle now constitutes the *tract of the spinal V* or *descending trigeminal tract* and the substantia gelatinosa similarly becomes the *terminal nucleus of the spinal V* (Fig. 268).

The ventral horn is still recognizable and as before contains the motor nuclei of the first cervical and accessory nerves. The rest of the gray, between gelatinous substance and ventral horn, has lost its definite form and continuity and is now composed of a mixture of scattered nuclear masses and fiber bundles, the latter mainly composed of the short intersegmental fibers which in the cord were placed next to the gray. This area of closely intermingled gray and white substance is known as the *reticular formation* which is caudally continuous with the reticular process of the spinal cord.

In the dorsal white columns nuclear masses have appeared in the fasciculi gracilis and cuneatus. These are the nuclei of the dorsal column, known respectively as the *nucleus gracilis* and *nucleus cuneatus*, in which the fibers of the dorsal column end. Their termination marks the ending of that system of fibers which has been traced upward from their origin in the spinal ganglia, the completion of the course of the peripheral afferent neurons with long ascending arms (Figs. 184, 185). The fasciculus cuneatus is still massive and its nucleus small in

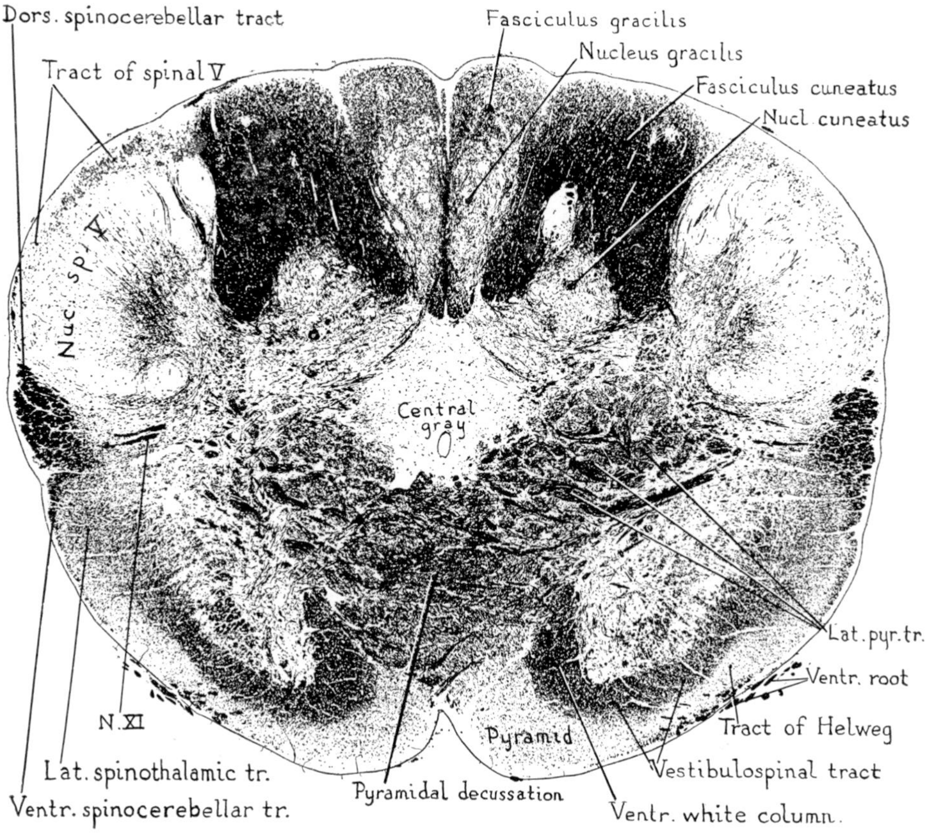

FIG. 226. Transverse section of medulla of one month infant, through the decussation of the pyramidal tracts. Weigert's myelin stain. Photograph. *Lat. pyr. tr.*, lateral pyramidal tract.

these levels. The nucleus gracilis is larger with consequent diminution of the gracile fasciculus. As progressively higher levels are reached, more and more fibers will terminate in these nuclei with constant increase in the size of the latter and a corresponding decrease in the size of the two fasciculi. At the caudal tip of the inferior olive, the whole fasciculus gracilis and most of the fasciculus cuneatus have been replaced by their respective nuclei. The secondary tracts which arise from these nuclei are better seen in higher levels.

The tracts of the lateral and ventral white columns occupy the same relative positions, though the shorter intersegmental fibers have become part of the reticular formation. The ventral white column has been pushed laterally by the pyramidal decussation.

SECTION OF MEDULLA THROUGH THE DECUSSATION OF THE MEDIAL LEMNISCUS (SENSORY DECUSSATION) (FIGS. 230, 231)

The most conspicuous features are the large extent of the nuclei gracilis and cuneatus, the decussation and formation of the medial lemniscus, and the increase of the gray reticular formation. Elements belonging to the hypoglossal (N.XII) and vagus (N.X) nerves have appeared in the central gray. Ventral to the central canal is the nucleus of the hypoglossal nerve and dorsolateral to it the dorsal nucleus of the vagus. Dorsal to the central canal is the commis-

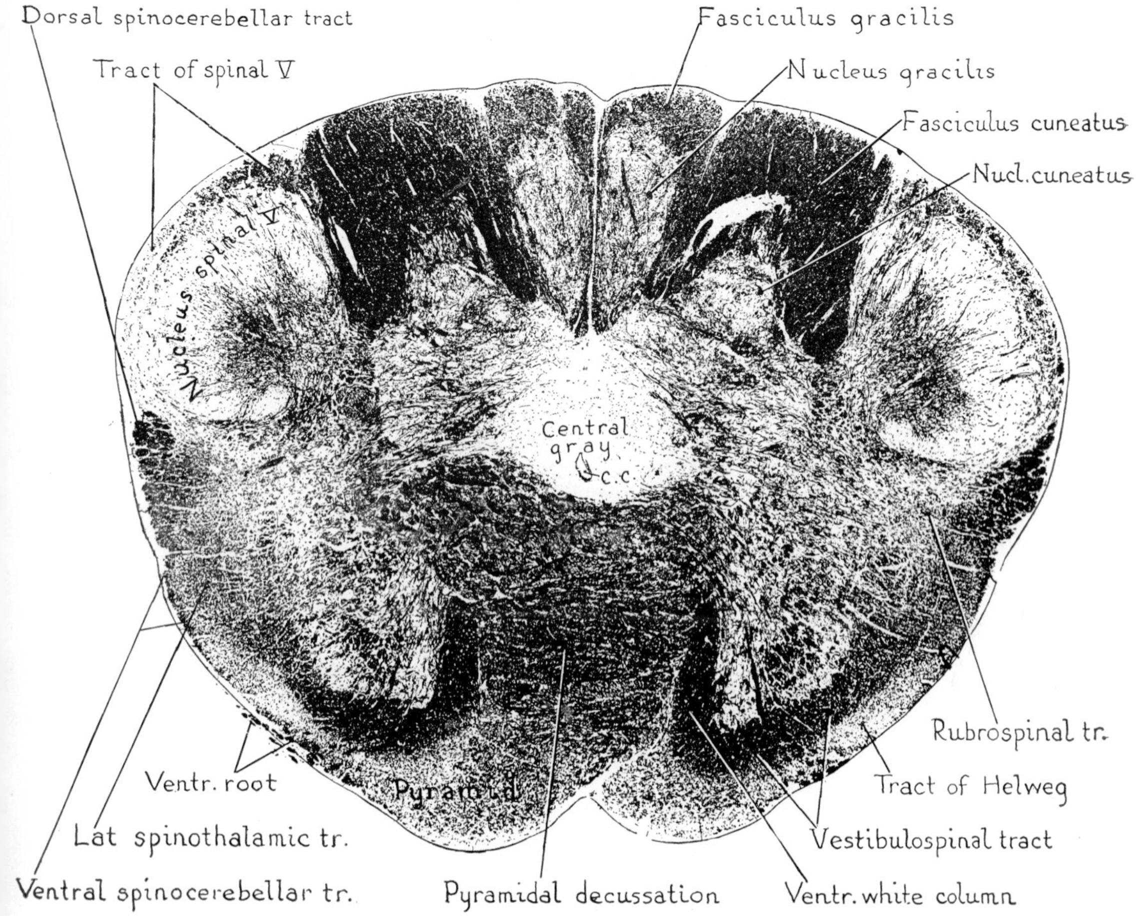

Fig. 227. Transverse section of medulla of one month infant, through upper portion of pyramidal decussation. Weigert's myelin stain. Photograph. *c.c.*, central canal.

sural nucleus of the vagus. These nerves are best studied at somewhat higher levels.

The descending corticospinal fibers are here observed above their decussation where they form a massive pyramid on either side of the deep median ventral sulcus (Figs. 229, 230).

In the dorsal column the nucleus gracilis has reached its greatest extent, practically all of the fibers of the fasciculus gracilis having terminated between this and the preceding level. The nucleus cuneatus is likewise much larger, though still covered by a considerable portion of the cuneate fasciculus. From these nuclei new myelinated fibers arise which, as *internal arcuate fibers,* sweep ventrally around the central gray, cross in the midline or *raphé,* and at once turn upward to form the ascending fiber bundle known as the *medial lemniscus* or *fillet,* which terminates in the ventral nuclei of the thalamus (Fig. 185). This tract constitutes the second neuron of the dorsal column pathway conveying muscle sense and discriminative touch, and the decussation of the medial lemniscus is the basis for the sensory representation of one half of the body by the opposite cerebral hemisphere. Injury to the medial lemniscus above the decussation will hence cause the character-

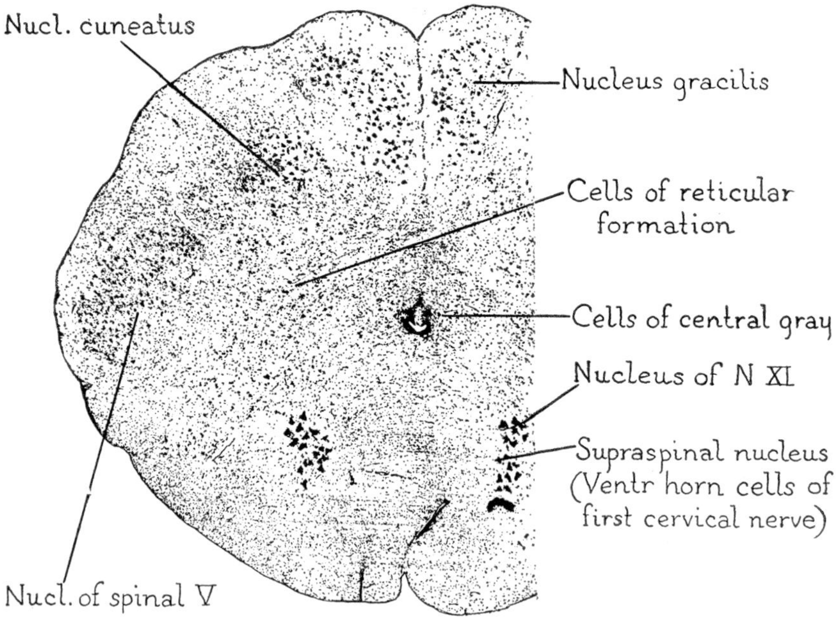

FIG. 228. Section through medulla of one month infant, about same level as Fig. 226. Cresyl Violet. Photograph, with cell groups blocked in schematically.

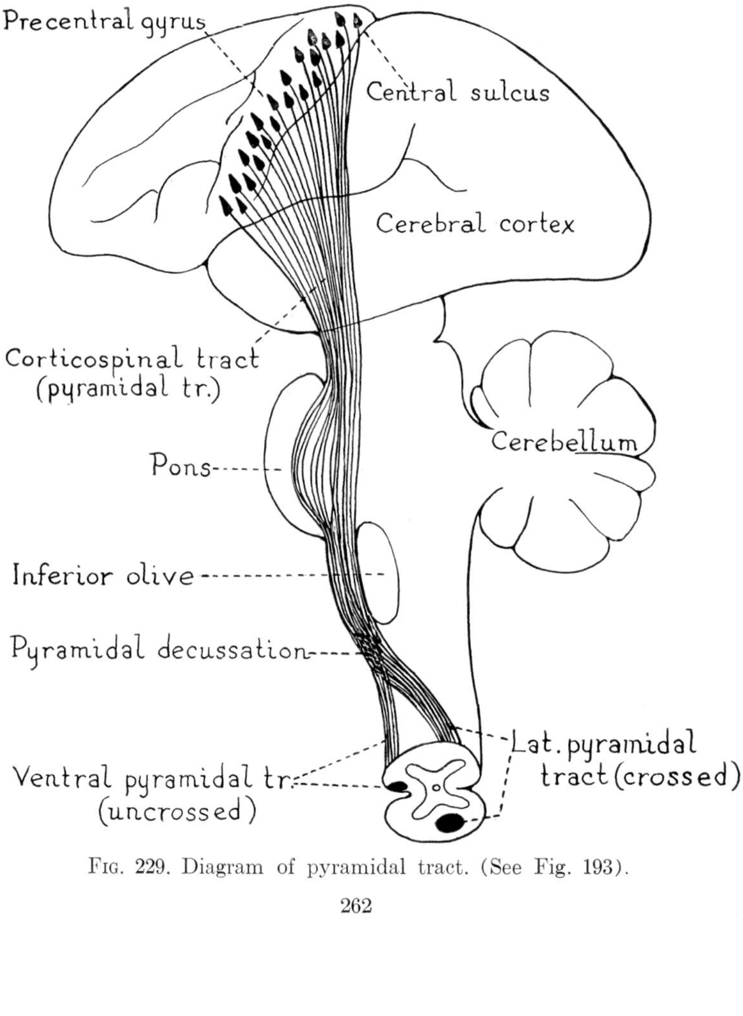

FIG. 229. Diagram of pyramidal tract. (See Fig. 193).

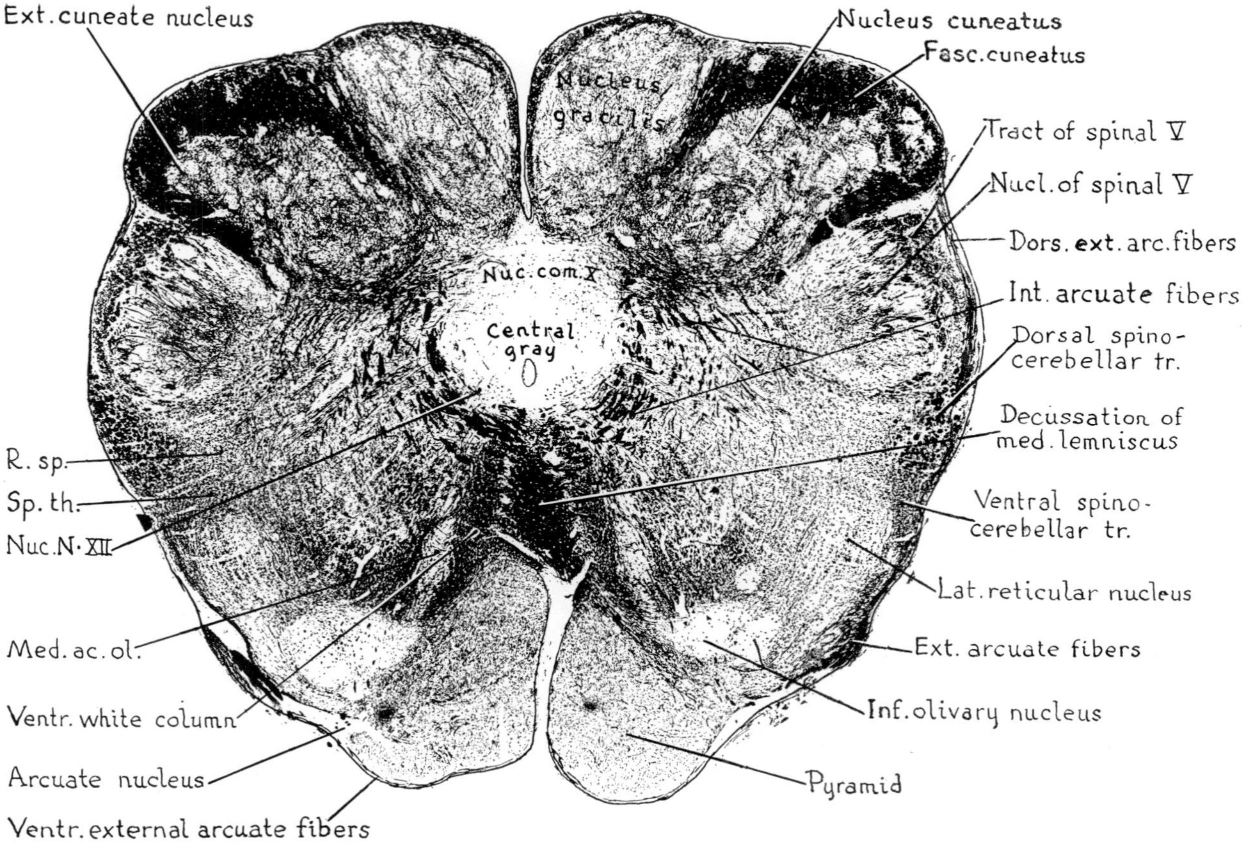

Fig. 230. Transverse section of medulla of one month infant, through the decussation of the medial lemniscus. Weigert's myelin stain. Photograph. *Med.ac.o.*, medial accessory olivary nucleus; *Nuc.com.X*, nucleus commissuralis; *R.sp.*, rubrospinal tract; *Sp.th.*, spinothalamic tract.

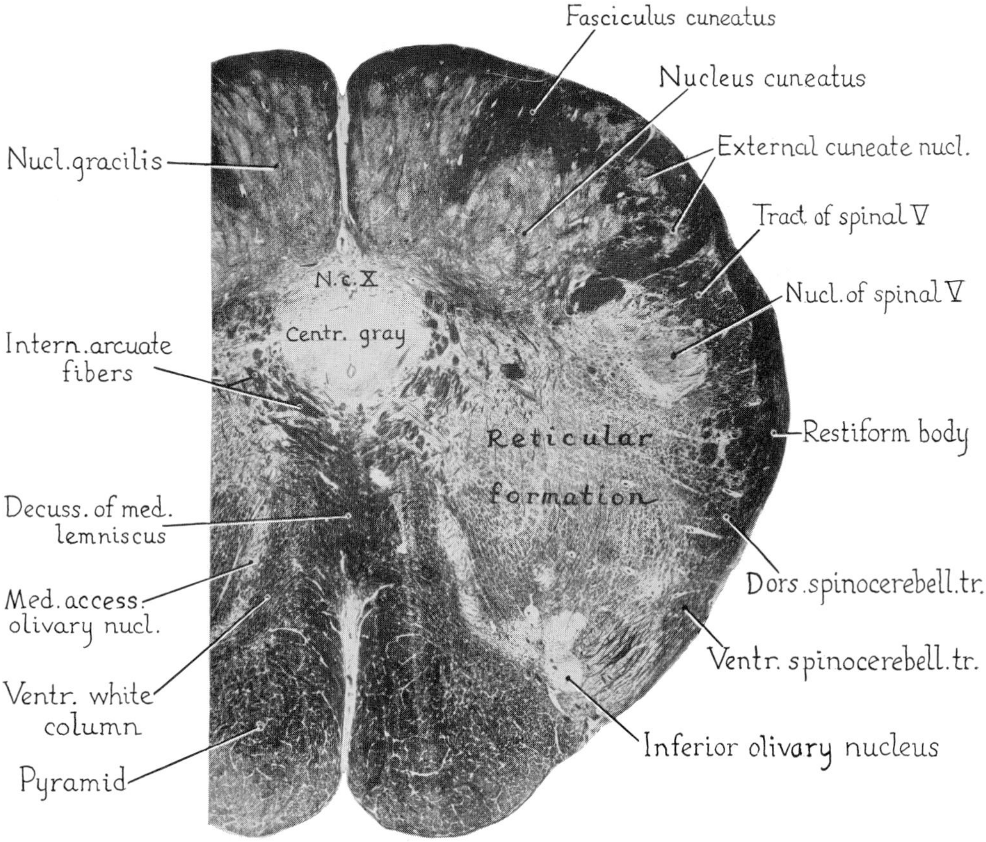

FIG. 231. Transverse section of adult medulla, through decussation of medial lemniscus. Weigert's myelin stain. Photograph, ×13. N.c.X., nucleus commissuralis of N.X.

istic dorsal column disturbances on the contralateral side.

Lateral to the nucleus cuneatus is a group of larger cells resembling in structure those of the column of Clarke. This group is known as the *lateral* or *external cuneate nucleus* (magnocellular nucleus of the dorsal column, nucleus of Monakow, Figs. 192, 230, 232). Its fibers do not participate in the formation of the medial lemniscus but course over the dorsolateral periphery as *dorsal external arcuate* fibers to enter the cerebellum at a higher level. This nucleus may be regarded as a medullary extension of Clarke's column, whose fibers supplement the dorsal spinocerebellar tract, conveying uncrossed impulses to the cerebellum from the muscles of the upper extremity and neck.

The *tract of the spinal V* has increased in size. As already stated, the afferent root of the trigeminal nerve enters the brain stem at a much higher level (pons) but many of its fibers descend as the tract of the spinal V which occupies the region of the zone of Lissauer. In its descent the tract becomes progressively smaller as more and more of its fibers end in the terminal nucleus of the spinal V which is an upward continuation of the substantia gelatinosa extending rostrally to the mid-pontile region. Hence in a series of ascending sections the tract will continue to increase to the level of entry of the trigeminal nerve (Fig. 268). These descending fibers convey sensory impulses, primarily pain and temperature, from the face, forehead, and mucous membranes of the mouth and nose, hence injury to the tract will cause a diminution of these sensations on the same side of the face. From the terminal nucleus arise fibers which form the secondary trigeminal tracts. The fibers arise, a few at each level, and many cross to the opposite side where they ascend in the reticular formation to terminate in the thalamus. These trigeminothalamic fibers constitute the second neuron system in the sensory pathway from face to cortex. Other uncrossed fibers ascend and descend on the same side, forming reflex connections with the motor nuclei of the hypoglossal, vagus, facial and other cranial nerves (Figs. 268, 271). Since the nucleus and tract of spinal V are located not far from the spinothalamic tract, injury to the dorsolateral region of the medulla produces the curious clinical picture of an alternating hemianalgesia and hemithermoanesthesia of the face and body. There is loss or diminution of pain and temperature on the same side of the face and on the opposite side of the body and neck.

Exclusive of the dorsal column nuclei, the nucleus and tract of the spinal V, and the pyramid, the bulb of the medulla now consists of the much increased *reticular formation* composed of gray matter and longitudinal fiber bundles. Through it course many transverse fibers representing the beginnings or endings of the longitudinal bundles, such as the internal arcuate fibers of the medial lemniscus and secondary trigeminal fibers. In the peripheral portion of the reticular formation, the long tracts of the lateral and ventral columns retain their relative positions but the ventral white is now situated dorsal to the pyramids and lateral to the medial lemniscus.

The **reticular formation** contains numerous cells which are organized in more or less definite groups. In the central and medial portion the cells are diffusely arranged. Many of them are medium sized or small, but scattered among them are found unusually large cells or aggregations of such cells with coarse chromofilic bodies and generally resembling the structure of motor cells (Figs. 78, 84). In the upper portions of the medulla and in the pons there are greater concentrations of such cells and here also the cells are largest. These large cells, whose number throughout the brain stem is considerable, are collectively known as the *motor reticular nucleus.* Their axons, in large part uncrossed, usually split into ascending and descending branches. Many descend to the spinal cord as reticulospinal fibers, others go to the motor nuclei of the cranial nerves (Fig. 197). They receive collaterals or terminals from secondary afferent neurons (medial lemniscus, secondary trigeminal, etc.), from the nucleus ruber and tectum of the midbrain, the corpus striatum, and probably from the cerebral cortex. Hence they represent intermediate links between the above-named structures and the peripheral motor neurons. They form an extensive if diffuse old motor system, an important part of the extrapyramidal pathway. Some of the reticulospinal and reticulobulbar fibers which descend from the midbrain are believed to play a part in the regulation of extensor tonus of the antigravity muscles. Intermingled with the large cells are smaller ones whose connections are poorly understood. They are intersegmental in character and may represent relays in central autonomic or visceral pathways. The reticular formation, like the spinospinal system of the cord, may be regarded as the intrinsic associative system of the medulla, mediating important bulbar reflexes, and also forming relay stations in longer conduction paths to and from higher centers. In a general way, the large cells are related to somatic pathways discharging on striped skeletal muscle, while many of the smaller cells are probably parts of central visceral (autonomic) pathways.

More laterally in the reticular formation close to the ventral spinocerebellar tract is the *lateral reticular nucleus* (Figs. 232, 237), usually subdivided into a ventral and a dorsal nucleus. The ventral is the larger

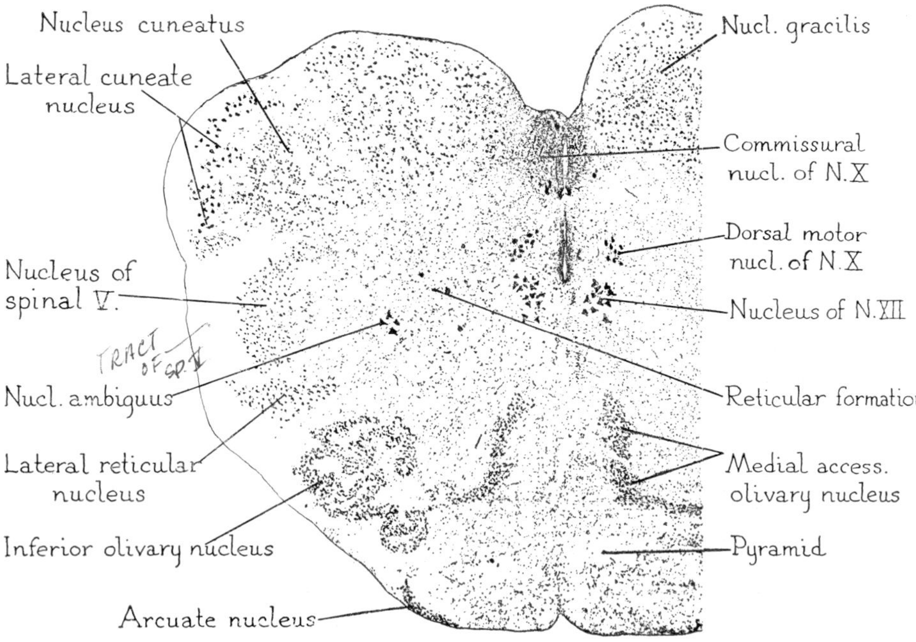

FIG. 232. Section through medulla of one month infant, about same level as Fig. 230 Cresyl Violet. Photograph, with cell groups blocked in schematically.

and is best developed in the caudal portion of the olivary region (Figs. 233, 235). These neurons appear to be relay stations in a spinocerebellar pathway, receiving spinoreticular fibers from the dorsal gray columns of the spinal cord (Brodal, 1949) and possibly collaterals from the ventral spinocerebellar tract. Most of the axons arising in the nuclei form ventral external arcuate fibers which reach the restiform body and enter the homolateral cerebellum (Fig. 236). Fewer fibers cross the median raphé and pass to the restiform body and cerebellum of the opposite side.

On the basal aspect of the pyramid is the *arcuate nucleus* whose position varies somewhat in different levels (Figs. 232, 237). In the superior portion of the medulla the nucleus enlarges considerably (nucleus precursorius pontis) and appears to become continuous with the nuclei of the pons. Its afferent connections are obscure. It may possibly receive fibers from the lateral reticular nucleus, and send axons as ventral external arcuate fibers to the cerebellum (arcuatocerebellar, Fig. 236). Thus in this portion of the medulla there is formed a diffuse though relatively small, system of afferent cerebellar fibers that arises in the lateral cuneate, lateral reticular and arcuate nuclei.

Dorsolateral to the pyramids new nuclear masses have appeared which become more extensive in the succeeding levels. They represent the caudal tip of the inferior olivary complex.

SECTIONS OF MEDULLA THROUGH LOWER AND MIDDLE PORTIONS OF INFERIOR OLIVARY NUCLEUS (FIGS. 233, 234, 235)

These represent the most characteristic pictures of the medulla, passing dorsally through the fourth ventricle and showing three large surface eminences: the pyramids, inferior olives, and restiform bodies. The central canal has opened into the fourth ventricle, narrow at first but widening progressively in higher levels as the dorsal walls of the medulla diverge more and more laterally. The thin roof is formed by the tela

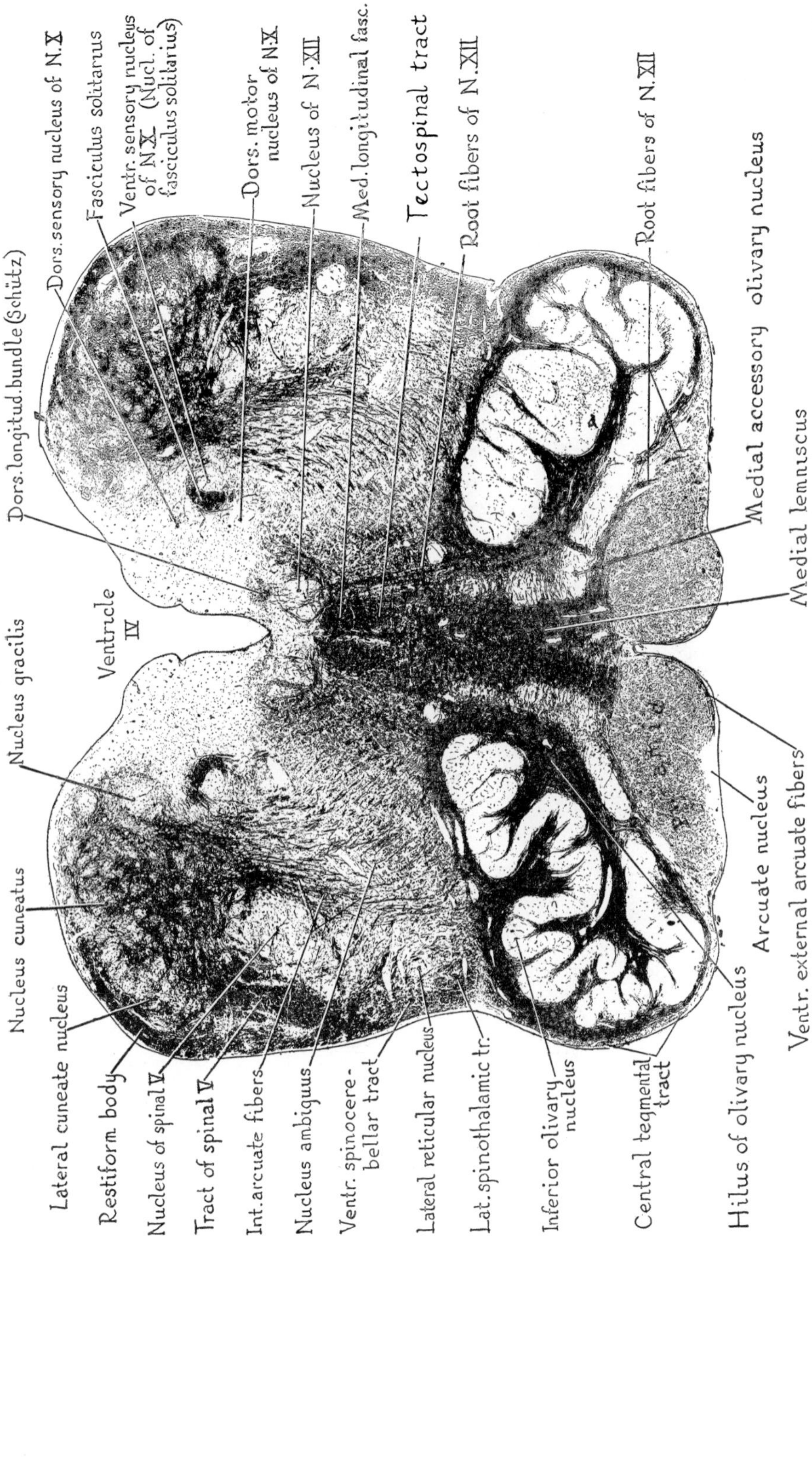

FIG. 233. Transverse section of medulla of one month infant, through lower part of inferior olivary nucleus. Weigert's myelin stain. Photograph.

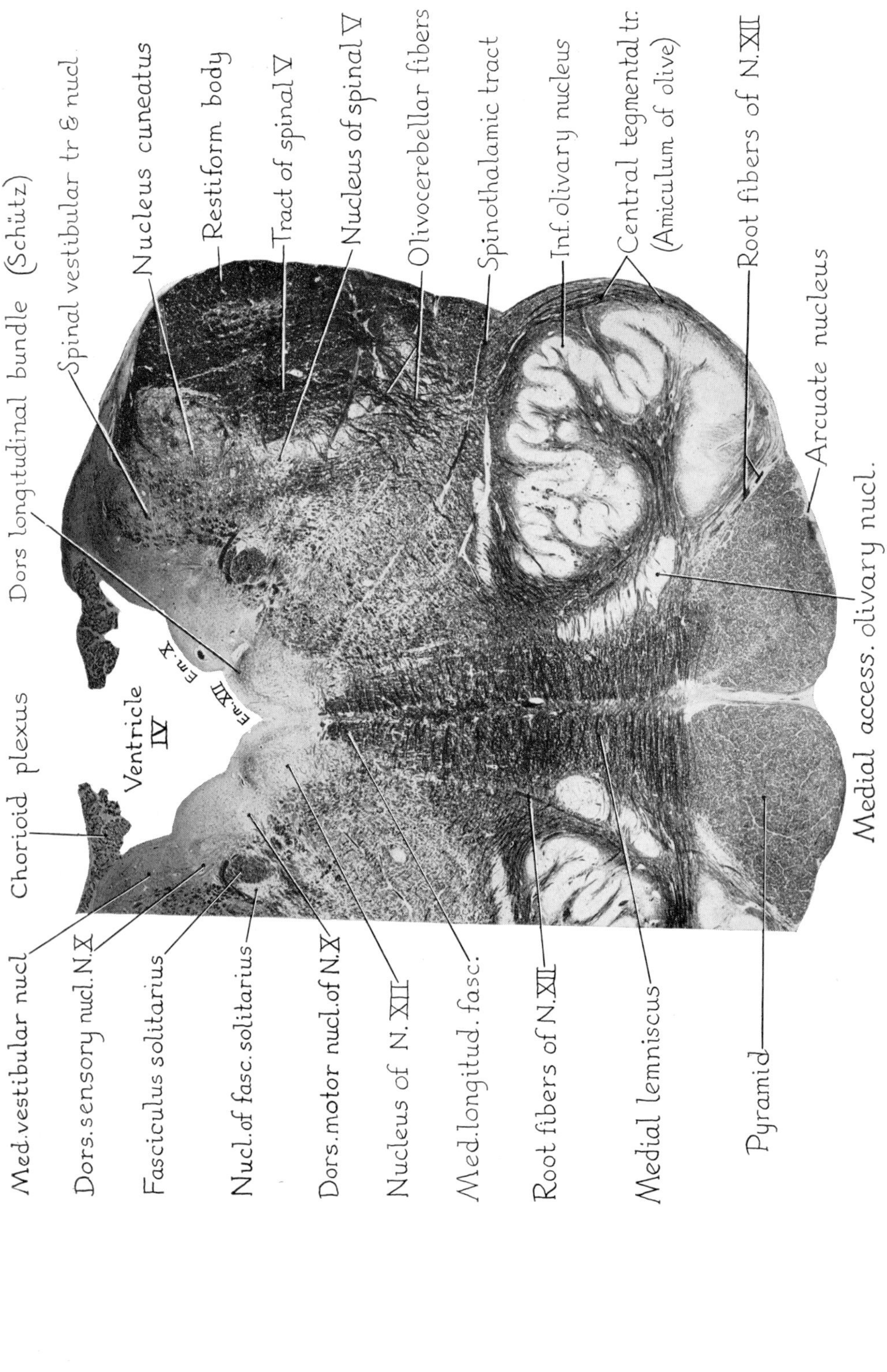

FIG. 234. Transverse section of adult medulla, through inferior olive, somewhat higher than Fig. 233. Weigert's myelin stain. Photograph, ×12. Em. X, eminentia vagi; Em. XII, eminentia hypoglossi.

chorioidea and chorioid plexus. The central gray is now spread out on the ventricular floor. On the latter are seen the eminentia media, or the *trigonum hypoglossi* occupied by the nucleus of the XIIth nerve; the *trigonum vagi* or *ala cinerea* containing certain vagal nuclei, and lateral to this the *area vestibularis* occupied by the medial vestibular nucleus (Figs. 234, 235).

The nucleus gracilis has disappeared in sections cut through the middle of the inferior olivary nucleus. The larger nucleus cuneatus is also diminished in size. However, both nuclei, while present, continue to furnish internal arcuate fibers which sweep medially and ventrally through the reticular formation to cross midline and turn upward in the opposite medial lemniscus. The medial lemnisci at this level constitute two conspicuous, triangular-shaped fiber bundles lying dorsal to the pyramids and medial to the olivary nuclei (Fig. 234). The spinal nucleus and tract of the trigeminal nerve are less conspicuous structures in Weigert sections for they are not always sharply demarcated from the lateral cuneate nucleus dorsally, or the fibers of the restiform body more laterally.

The larger fibers of the dorsal spinocerebellar tract have moved dorsally to join with olivocerebellar fibers and thus contribute to the formation of the **restiform body** or **inferior cerebellar peduncle.** This large mass of myelinated nerve fibers forms the dorsolateral margin of the upper half of the medulla and is a conspicuous ridge lying dorsal to the emerging fibers of the glossopharyngeal and vagus nerves. Although the restiform body is composed primarily of afferent fibers enroute to the cerebellum from the spinal cord and medulla, it also contains efferent cerebellovestibular and cerebelloreticular fibers (Figs. 192, 236, 260). At the medulla-pons junction the restiform body becomes covered laterally by the fibers of the middle peduncle or brachium pontis.

The most striking new structure is the convoluted gray band of the *inferior olivary nucleus,* appearing in section as a much folded bag with the opening or hilus directed mesially. Placed near the hilus is the *medial accessory olivary nucleus* and near the dorsal aspect of the main nucleus is the *dorsal accessory olivary nucleus.* The main nucleus is composed of relatively small round or pear-shaped cells with numerous short and richly branching dendrites. Their axons form the olivocerebellar fibers distributed to all parts of the opposite side of the cerebellum. The fibers fill the interior of the bag-shaped nucleus, emerge from the hilus, cross through the medial lemniscus, and pass through or around the opposite olivary nucleus. Then they turn dorsolaterally and, gathered into more compact bundles, traverse or surround the spinal V, and enter the restiform body. The accessory nuclei and the most medial portion of the main nucleus are phylogenetically the oldest (paleo-olive) and send their fibers to the cerebellar vermis (paleocerebellum). The larger convoluted lateral portion of the main nucleus (neo-olive) is related principally to the cerebellar hemisphere (neocerebellum). As more and more olivocerebellar fibers are given off, the restiform body assumes massive proportions and forms a prominent bulge on the dorsolateral surface of the medulla (Figs. 235, 243). Thus the restiform body is composed of the olivocerebellar, dorsal spinocerebellar and to a smaller extent of the external arcuate fibers from the cuneate, arcuate, and lateral reticular nuclei (Fig. 236).

The main olivary nucleus is always surrounded by a dense band of myelinated fibers, the *amiculum olivae,* composed in large part of axons terminating in the nucleus. These are principally fibers of a rather extensive tract arising in the upper portion of the midbrain (nucleus ruber, reticular formation) and perhaps from other regions, and known as the *central tegmental tract* (Figs. 234, 235). This tract is well developed in man, and together with the olivocerebellar fibers constitutes a newer path-

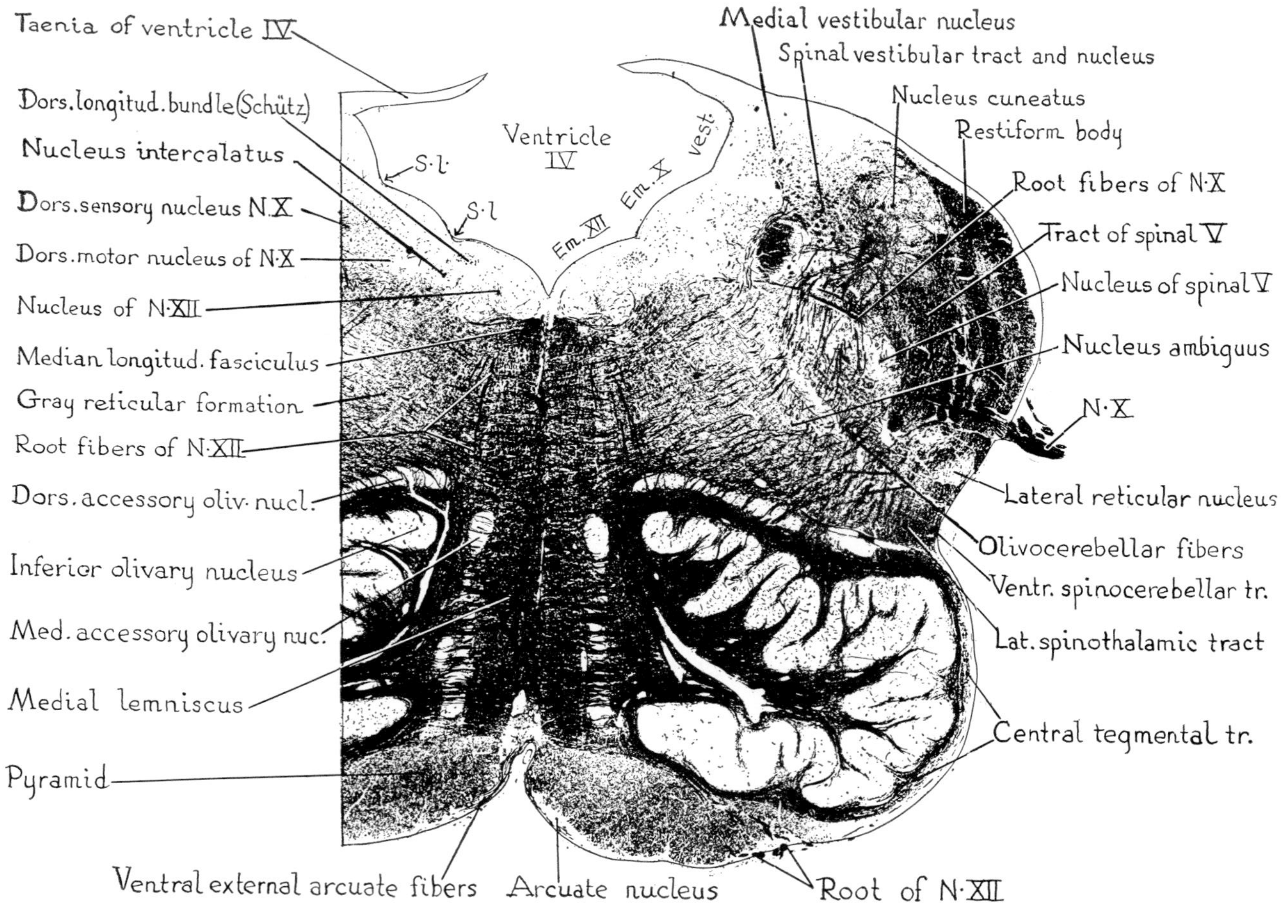

FIG. 235. Transverse section of medulla of one month infant, through middle of olive. Weigert's myelin stain. Photograph. *Em.X*, eminentia vagi (ala cinerea); *Em.XII*, eminentia hypoglossi; *S.L.*, sulcus limitans; *Vest.*, area vestibularis.

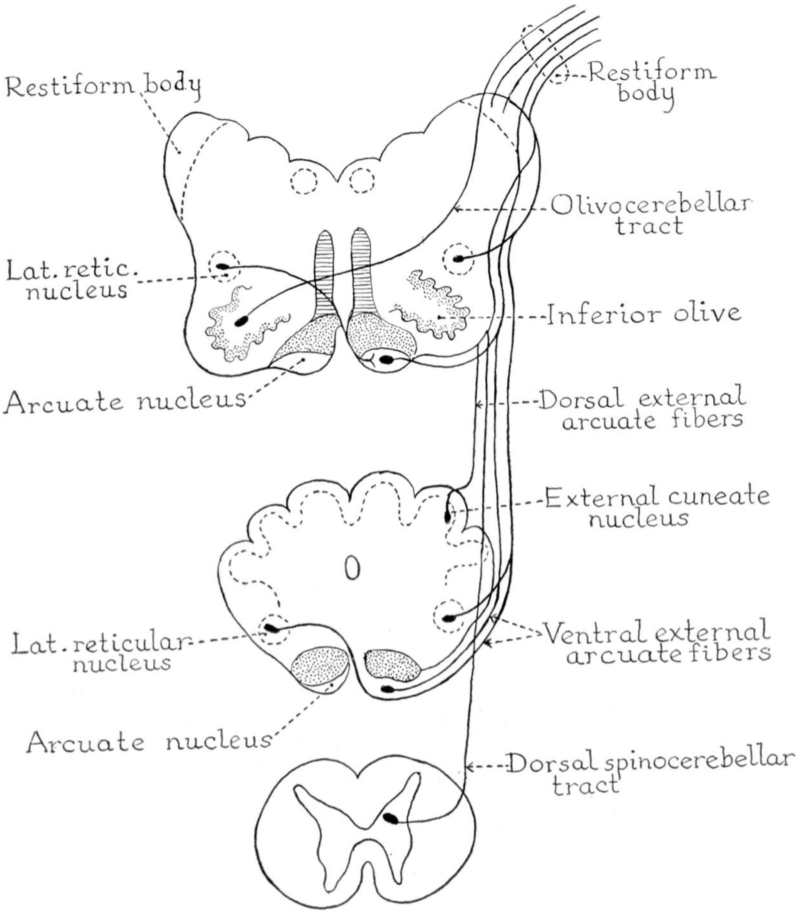

FIG. 236. Diagram showing composition of restiform body.

way linking the corpus striatum, thalamus, red nucleus, and reticular formation to the newer portion of the cerebellum. The amiculum also contains efferent olivary fibers which descend to the upper cervical cord as the olivospinal tract of Helweg. Some of these may be spinoolivary fibers.

The ventrolateral tracts of the reticular formation have been pushed dorsally by the olivary nuclei. The ventral spinocerebellar, rubrospinal, and spinothalamic tracts occupy the lateral periphery between the restiform body and olive. The vestibulospinal fibers are scattered along the dorsal surface of the olive, and the remnants of the ventral white column now lie on either side of the raphé directly above the medial lemniscus. Its dorsal compact portion constitutes the *medial longitudinal fasciculus*, a descending fiber bundle of mixed origin. In these levels the fasciculus contains fibers from two nuclei in the tegmentum of the midbrain (interstitial nucleus and nucleus of the posterior commissure) and fibers from the vestibular nuclei (medial vestibulospinal tract). Ventral to the medial longitudinal fasciculus is the more loosely organized *predorsal bundle* composed of tectospinal fibers (Fig. 199).

The **reticular formation** has reached its fullest extent and contains the above named long tracts. It may now be divided into two portions: (a) the white reticular formation near the raphé and containing the

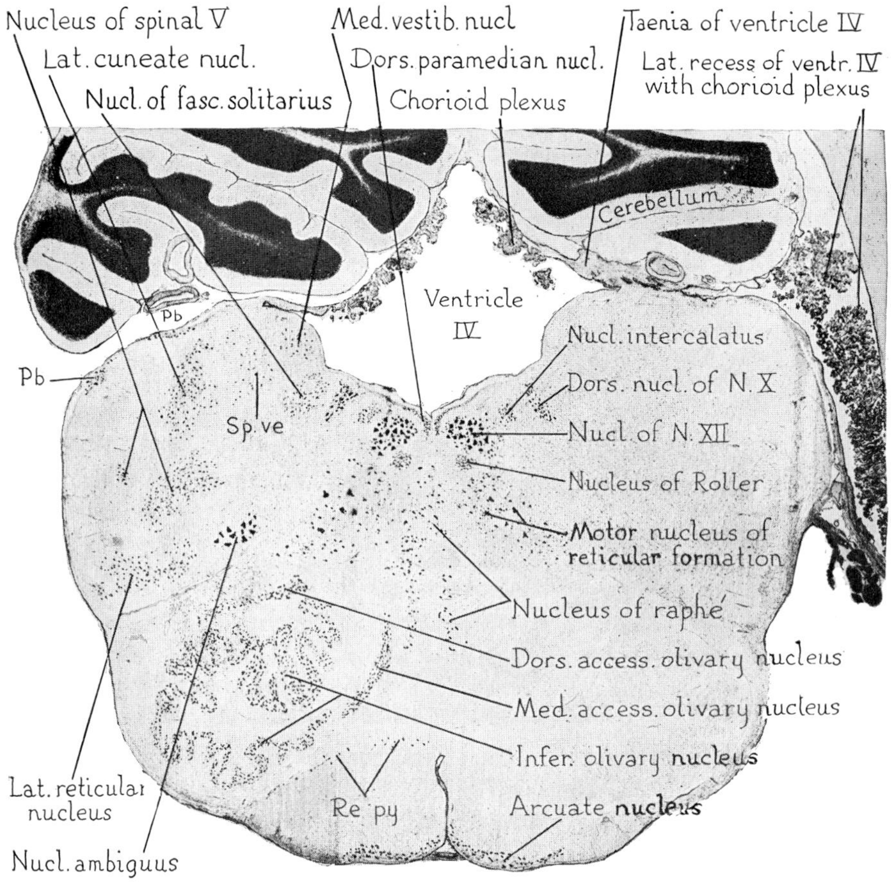

FIG. 237. Section through midolivary region of adult medulla. Cresyl Violet. Photograph, with schematic representation of main cell groups. *Pb*, pontobulbar nucleus; *Re.py.*, retropyramidal nucleus; *Sp.ve.*, spinal vestibular nucleus (nucleus of descending vestibular nerve).

compact fiber bundles of the medial lemniscus, medial longitudinal fasciculus and tectospinal tract; and (b) the gray reticular formation in which the gray masses predominate and the fiber bundles are more loosely arranged. The root fibers of the hypoglossal nerve mark the boundary between the two. In the most dorsal position on either side of the raphé is a band of small cells, the *dorsal paramedian nucleus*, lying immediately beneath the ependyma and extending the whole length of the fourth ventricle (Figs. 237, 244). Its lateral extension in the central gray of the ventricular floor, at this level lying dorsal to the hypoglossal nucleus, has been distinguished by some as a separate nuclear column, the *nucleus eminentiae teretis* (*eminentiae mediae*). Further ventrally and extending into the interolivary region is a larger cell complex, the nucleus (or nuclei) of the raphé (Fig. 237). This nucleus becomes especially large in the uppermost portion of the medulla where it is also known as the inferior central nucleus.

In the gray reticular formation the motor reticular nucleus is represented by considerable concentrations of large cells surrounded by scattered smaller ones (Fig. 237). The lateral reticular nucleus is best developed in this portion and contributes external arcuate fibers to the restiform body.

The arcuate nucleus is large and becomes more medially placed in the higher levels. A group of closely packed, medium sized cells placed on the dorsolateral aspect of the restiform body constitutes the caudal portion of the *pontobulbar* nucleus (Fig. 237). Proceeding rostrally, this cell column assumes a more and more ventral position, until at the junction of pons and medulla it forms a fairly large cell mass now placed ventral to the inferior cerebellar peduncle (Figs. 244, 246). The cells of this nucleus which thus partly encircles the restiform body, resemble those in the basilar portion of the pons and are regarded by some as a caudal extension of the pontile nuclei.

The cranial nerves of this portion are the *hypoglossus* (N.XII), the *vagus* (N.X), the *glossopharyngeal* (N.IX), and the *descending vestibular tract* (N.VIII).

THE HYPOGLOSSAL NERVE

The hypoglossal nerve is a motor nerve supplying the somatic striped musculature of the tongue. It also appears to contain some afferent proprioceptive fibers since the muscle spindles of the tongue degenerate on section of the nerve. These afferent fibers may in part be derived from inconstant ganglion cells found on the hypoglossal roots (Tarkhan and Abd-El-Malek, 1950) but their principal source is still obscure. During fetal life the nerve apparently contains dorsal root fibers related to a small ganglion (Froriep) but these disappear in a later period.

The nucleus of N.XII forms a column of typical multipolar motor cells, some 18 mm. in length and occupying the central gray of the median eminence. The column begins below the caudal tip of the olive and extends rostrally to the region of the striae medullares. Within the nucleus can be seen coarse myelinated fibers which are the root fibers of the motor cells, and a network of finer fibers representing terminals of axons ending in the nucleus. The root fibers gather on the ventral surface of the nucleus, forming a series of rootlets which pass ventrally lateral to the medial lemniscus and emerge

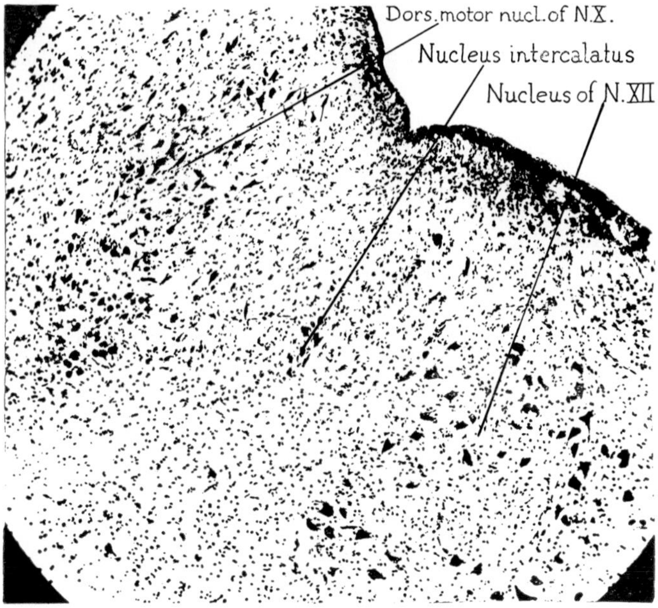

FIG. 238. Some of the nuclei in the floor of the fourth ventricle, about same level as Fig. 237. Medulla of three months infant. Cresvl Violet. Photograph.

on the surface in the ventrolateral (preolivary) sulcus between pyramid and olive (Fig. 223).

The terminal fibers form a delicate plexus within and around the nucleus. Some are corticobulbar fibers effecting voluntary movements of the tongue, which go in part to the nucleus of the same side, in larger part cross to the opposite nucleus. Others are secondary glossopharyngeal, vagal, and trigeminal fibers mediating reflex tongue movements in response to stimuli from the lingual mucous membrane (taste, touch, temperature, pain). Fibers from olfactory centers and from the medial vestibular nucleus likewise terminate in the hypoglossal nucleus. These fibers come in part from a descending bundle of fine myelinated fibers found in the central gray dorsolateral to the hypoglossal nucleus and known as the *dorsal longitudinal bundle of Schütz* (dorsal tegmental tract, Figs. 233, 234, 235). The constitution of this tract is not fully worked out. Some fibers appear to come directly from the hypothalamus, others from the dorsal tegmental nucleus of the midbrain. In the medulla, fibers from the medial vestibular nucleus are added. Some of its fibers terminate in the hypoglossal nucleus, either directly or through intercalated neurons (nucleus intercalatus, nucleus prepositus). Others probably come in relation with the motor and secretory nuclei of the vagus and glossopharyngeal nerves.

Injury to the hypoglossal nerve will naturally produce a lower motor neuron paralysis of the ipsilateral half of the tongue, with loss of all movement, loss of tone, and degenerative atrophy of the muscles affected. Since the genioglossus muscle effects protrusion of the tongue to the opposite side, the tongue when protruded will deviate to the side of the injury.

The juxtaposition of the emerging root fibers of N.XII and the pyramidal tract is the anatomical basis of the *inferior* or *hypoglossal alternating hemiplegia* resulting from ventral lesions of this area (Fig. 193). This consists of a lower motor neuron paralysis of the ipsilateral half of the tongue combined with an upper motor neuron (pyramidal, spastic) hemiplegia of the contralateral half of the body, especially pronounced in the extremities.

THE VAGUS NERVE

The vagus nerve (N.X) is both efferent and afferent. It contains (a) general somatic afferent fibers distributed through the auricular branch of the vagus to the skin in back of the ear and the posterior wall of the external auditory meatus. These fibers have their cell bodies in the *jugular ganglion* of the vagus nerve (ganglion of the root). (b) General visceral afferent fibers from the pharynx, larynx, trachea, esophagus, and from the thoracic and abdominal viscera; also some special visceral afferent fibers from scattered taste buds in the region of the epiglottis. The cell bodies of the visceral fibers are in the larger *nodosal ganglion* (ganglion of the trunk). (c) General visceral (preganglionic) efferent fibers to terminal parasympathetic ganglia innervating the thoracic and abdominal viscera. (d) Special visceral efferent (branchiomotor) fibers to the striped voluntary muscles of the larynx and pharynx.

The *dorsal motor nucleus* (preganglionic neurons) occupies the medial portion of the trigonum vagi or ala cinerea (Figs. 233–235, 238). It is a column of cells somewhat longer than the hypoglossal nucleus, extending both cranially and caudally a little beyond the hypoglossal nucleus. The nucleus is composed of relatively small spindle-shaped cells among which are larger ones with coarser chromofilic bodies and scattered pigmented cells. The functional significance of the several cell types is not clear. The cells which give rise to secretory fibers have not been definitely determined for the vagus, but probably lie more ventrally in the dorsal part of the reticular formation. In the more rostral portion of the medulla, a group of such cells is known as the *inferior saliva-*

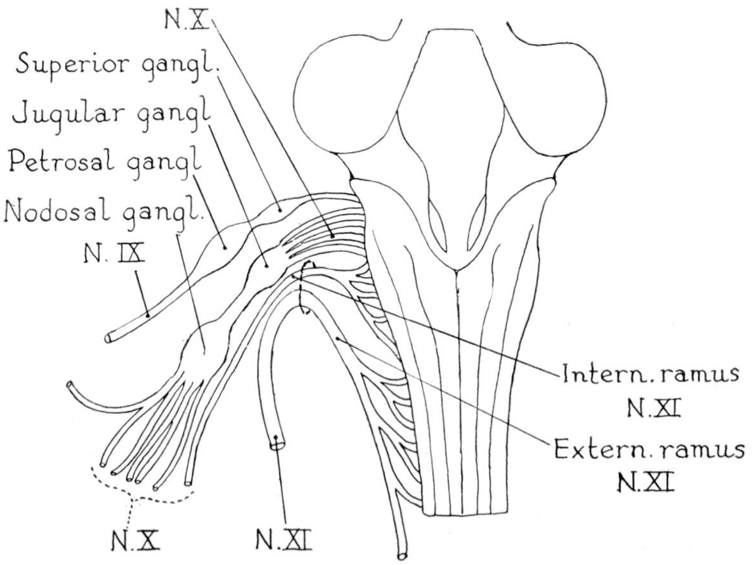

FIG. 239. Diagrammatic sketch of the roots of nerves IX, X, and XI. (After Bendz.)

tory nucleus, contributing secretory fibers to the glossopharyngeal nerve (see below). The axons of the cells from the dorsal nucleus pass ventrolaterally, traverse the nucleus and tract of the spinal V and emerge on the lateral surface of the medulla between the olive and the restiform body.

The dorsal motor nucleus contains relatively few myelinated fibers, indicating that many of the terminals entering it are unmyelinated. These are principally secondary fibers from the sensory nuclei of the glossopharyngeal and vagus nerves, from olfactory centers, and from the medial vestibular nucleus. Through excessive vestibular stimulation vomiting is often initiated. Terminals from central autonomic tracts linking the thalamus and cortex with the nucleus must likewise be present since emotional states may give rise to nausea, vomiting, and changes in heart rate.

The *ventral motor* nucleus or *nucleus ambiguus* is a column of cells placed in the reticular formation about halfway between the nucleus of the spinal V and the inferior olive (Figs. 220, 235, 237). It extends from about the caudal border of the lemniscal decussation to the level of the striae medullares, the uppermost portion contributing fibers to the glossopharyngeal nerve. The nucleus is composed of typical multipolar lower motor neurons whose axons go directly to the striped muscles of the larynx and pharynx. These axons have an arched intramedullary course (Figs. 220, 223, 241). They pass obliquely dorsally and medially, join the other fibers of the vagus, and then bending abruptly outward, pass with them to the lateral surface of the medulla. Some cross the midline to leave by the root of the opposite side (Obersteiner). The nucleus receives various terminals, among which are both crossed and uncrossed pyramidal fibers for the voluntary control of swallowing and phonation (Fig. 223). Others appear to come from the lateral columns (Marburg) and secondary trigeminal tracts. The nucleus receives stimuli from the pharyngeal and laryngeal muscles themselves for proprioceptive tonic control; and secondary vagal, glossopharyngeal, and trigeminal fibers. Fibers in these three nerves convey stimuli from the oral, pharyngeal, and respiratory mucosa mediating various reflexes such as coughing, vomiting, pharyngeal, and laryngeal reflexes; and also fibers conveying cerebellar and extrapyramidal impulses.

The afferent fibers of the vagus enter

along with the efferent ones. The few cutaneous fibers coming from the external ear apparently terminate in the nucleus of the spinal V, the latter thus forming the terminal nucleus for all the general somatic afferent impulses brought in by the cranial nerves. The more numerous afferent visceral fibers pass dorsomedially and either end immediately in terminal nuclei or bend sharply and form a long descending bundle known as the *fasciculus solitarius* (tract of the descending IX and X) (Figs. 220, 221). This bundle gives off collaterals and terminals en route, constantly diminishing in size until caudal to the fourth ventricle many of the remaining fibers decussate dorsal to the central canal (Fig. 241). The fasciculus solitarius is not formed by the vagus alone but receives contributions of afferent visceral fibers from the glossopharyngeal and facial nerves. The glossopharyngeal fibers convey taste impulses from the posterior third of the tongue, those of the facial bring in similar impulses from the anterior two-thirds of the tongue. Though entering at higher levels, the fibers of the facial nerve descend to form the upper portion of the fasciculus solitarius (Fig. 221). Just as the spinal V constitutes a descending bundle of somatic afferent fibers, so does the fasciculus solitarius represent a descending bundle of visceral afferent fibers. The upper portion, especially above the entry of N.X, is almost entirely related to taste, the lower portion represents general visceral sensation from the organs innervated by the vagus.

The fibers of the fasciculus solitarius end in two main terminal nuclei, the *dorsal sensory nucleus of the vagus* and the *nucleus of the fasciculus solitarius* (*ventral sensory nucleus*, Figs. 233, 234, 240). The dorsal nucleus is a column of small cells placed medial to the fasciculus in the central gray of the trigonum vagi, lateral to the dorsal motor nucleus. It extends from the middle

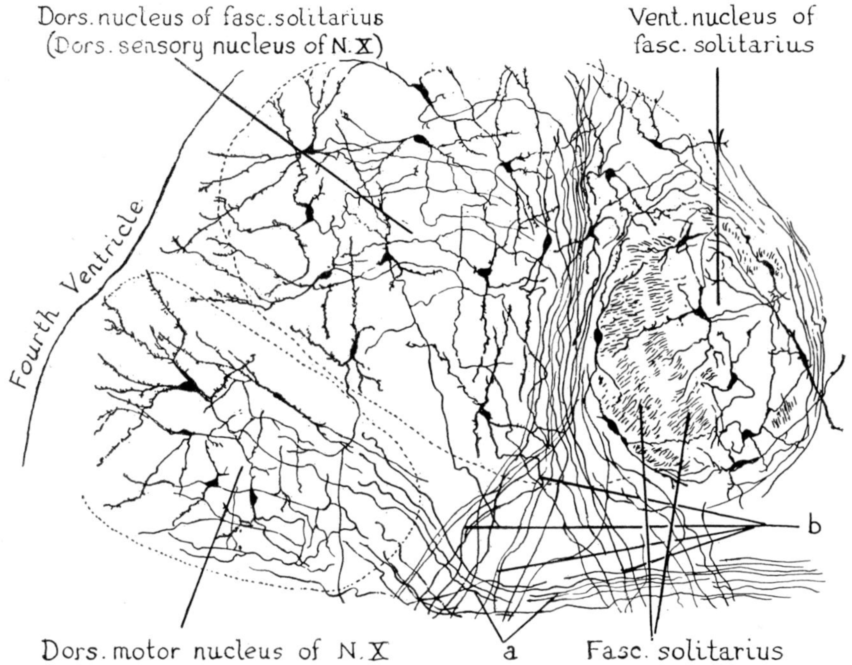

FIG. 240. The various vagus nuclei in the floor of the fourth ventricle. Medulla of newborn cat. Golgi impregnation. *a*, efferent (preganglionic) root fibers from dorsal motor nucleus; *b*, fibers from the sensory nuclei forming secondary vagoglossopharyngeal tracts. (After Cajal.)

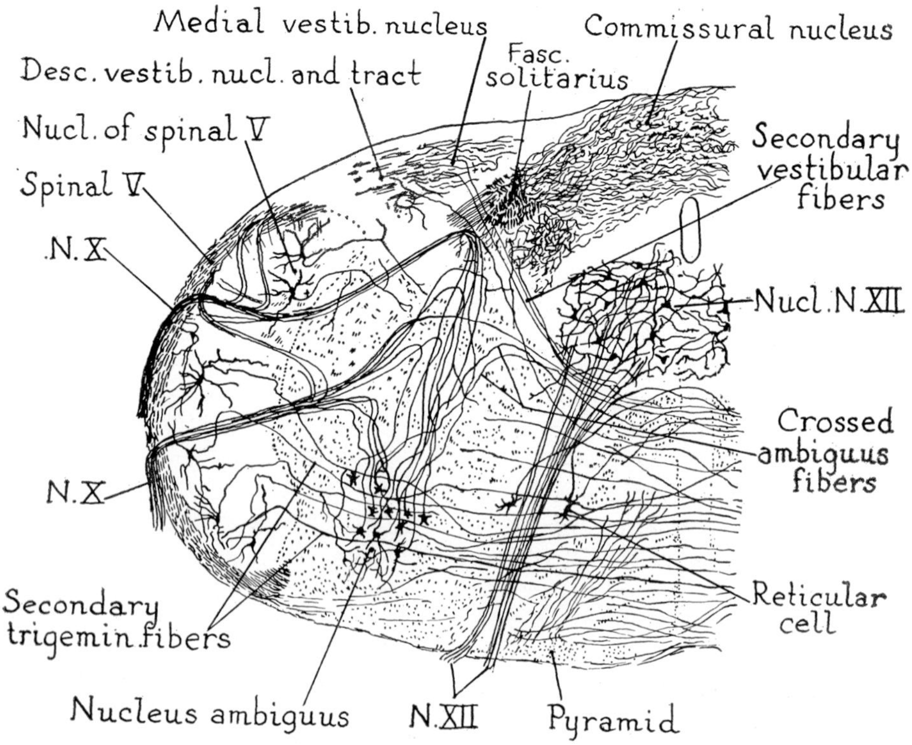

FIG. 241. Transverse section through medulla of mouse four days old, at level of hypoglossal nucleus and nucleus ambiguus. Golgi silver impregnation. (After Cajal.)

of the pyramidal decussation to the upper third of the olive. The ventral sensory nucleus lies ventrolateral to, and also within, the fascicle and in the uppermost portions completely surrounds the fasciculus. It is composed of both small and large cells, the latter mainly aggregated in the lateral portion. The nucleus forms a long column over an inch in length, extending upward almost to the inferior border of the pons and downward some distance below the fourth ventricle. Here the nucleus of each side becomes continuous with a median nuclear mass, the *commissural nucleus of N.X*, placed dorsal to the central canal (Figs. 241, 230, 231) and in which terminate many crossed fibers of the fasciculus solitarius. The uppermost enlarged portion of the nucleus solitarius which receives the taste fibers from N.VII and N.IX is also known as the *gustatory nucleus.*

The secondary fibers forming part of the afferent taste pathways to the thalamus and cortex are not well established. They appear to be both crossed and uncrossed fibers which ascend in the dorsal part of the reticular formation and possibly join the medial lemniscus (Allen). Other secondary fibers from the sensory nuclei of N.X and N.IX go to various motor nuclei of the cranial and spinal nerves. As already stated, such fibers go to the hypoglossal and salivatory nuclei for lingual and secretory reflexes, either directly or through intercalated neurons. Others relaying impulses from the pharyngeal, respiratory, and alimentary mucous membranes go to the nucleus ambiguus for pharyngeal and laryngeal reflexes. Additional impulses go to the dorsal motor nucleus, phrenic nucleus in the cervical cord, and the nuclei of the intercostal muscles in the thoracic cord involved in coughing, vomiting, and respiration. The connection with the spinal cord centers of the respiratory muscles is in large part by intercalated reticular neurons in the vicinity of the nucleus solitarius (reticulopsinal fibers).

It has been established for the cat and the monkey, that the maintenance of rhythmic respiratory movements is mediated by diffusely arranged cell groups in the reticular formation of the olivary region, roughly coextensive longitudinally with the sensory and motor nuclei of the vagus nerve (Pitts, 1946). The cells of this *"respiratory center"* are not only activated by vagal and other neural impulses, but are also affected directly by changes in their physical and chemical environment (CO_2 accumulation, etc.). The ventral cell groups lying immediately above the olive are concerned with inspiratory movements, the dorsal ones with expiration. The activities of the respiratory center are subject to regulation from higher neural levels, especially the cortex and diencephalon.

Bilateral destruction of the vagus nerves is rapidly fatal in man unless immediate precautions are instituted to prevent asphyxia for there is complete laryngeal paralysis. Paralysis and atonia of the esophagus and stomach induces pain and an incoercible vomiting with the hazards of aspiration. There is also a loss of vagal respiratory reflexes, dyspnea and cardiac acceleration.

A unilateral lesion of the vagus nerve is followed by ipsilateral paralysis of the soft palate, pharynx, and larynx, which results in hoarseness, dyspnea, and dysphagia. Anesthesia of the pharynx and larynx results in an ipsilateral loss of the cough reflex. Destruction of visceral motor fibers of the vagus accounts for the ipsilateral loss of the carotid sinus reflex.

THE GLOSSOPHARYNGEAL NERVE

The glossopharyngeal nerve (N.IX), though emerging at a somewhat higher level (Figs. 239, 243, 244), is intimately related to the vagus, the two having common intramedullary nuclei of origin and termination and similar functional components. Some of its connections have already been mentioned. Like the vagus, it is both afferent and efferent. The afferent fibers have their unipolar cell bodies in the small *superior ganglion* placed within the jugular canal and the larger extracranial *petrosal ganglion.* The nerve contains: (a) a few general somatic afferent fibers from the skin in back of the ear, distributed through the auricular branch of the vagus nerve. Their cell bodies are in the superior ganglion and they apparently terminate in the nucleus of the spinal V. (b) Visceral afferent fibers whose cell bodies are in the petrosal ganglion. Some are general visceral afferent fibers of touch, pain, and temperature supplying the mucous membrane of the posterior portion of the tongue, tonsil, and Eustachean tube. More numerous are the special visceral afferent fibers from the taste buds on the posterior third of the tongue. After entering the medulla, these fibers contribute to the upper portion of the fasciculus solitarius and terminate in the nucleus of the latter which is fairly large rostrally and known as the gustatory nucleus. Of interest is a special sensory branch, the *carotid* or *sinus nerve,* which innervates the carotid sinus, a dilatation of each common carotid at its bifurcation into the internal and external carotid arteries. Elevation of carotid arterial pressure initiates afferent impulses in the carotid sinus receptors, and these are conveyed along the sinus nerve to the medulla. Centrally these afferent fibers of the glossopharyngeal nerve send collaterals to the dorsal motor nucleus of the vagus nerve. Preganglionic axons from this vagal nucleus then proceed distally in the vagus nerve to terminate about ganglion cells in the atria of the heart. Short postganglionic fibers continue to the adjacent sinoatrial and atrioventricular nodes, as well as atrial heart muscle. This glossopharyngeal-vagus reflex pathway is constantly regulating arterial pressure, for stimulation of the sinus nerve produces slowing of the heart and a fall in

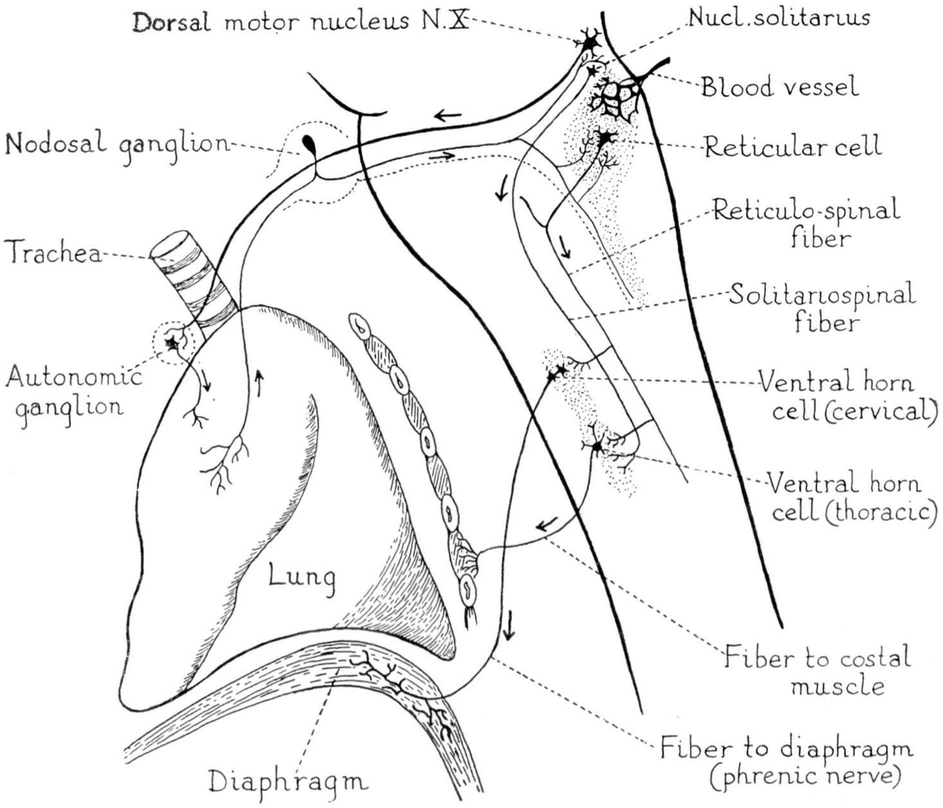

FIG. 242. Diagram of the intrinsic neural mechanism of respiration. (After Cajal and Herrick.)

blood pressure. In older people, particularly in patients with arteriosclerosis, the carotid sinus reflex may be hypersensitive. In such cases slight pressure on the carotid bifurcation may induce bradycardia, convulsions, and even loss of consciousness (carotid sinus syndrome). (c) General visceral efferent fibers, principally preganglionic secretory fibers to the parotid gland. These originate in the inferior salivatory nucleus already mentioned (Figs. 220, 221), the glandular homologue of the dorsal motor nucleus, and by way of the lesser superficial petrosal nerve reach the otic ganglion whence they are relayed to the parotid gland. (d) Special efferent visceral fibers arising from the rostral portion of the nucleus ambiguus aid in the innervation of the superior pharyngeal constrictor and the stylopharyngeus muscles. The secondary fiber systems originating from the sensory glossopharyngeal nuclei have been described with the vagus nerve.

Pure lesions of the glossopharyngeal nerve alone are infrequent. The major symptoms of ninth nerve involvement include loss of the pharyngeal (gag) and carotid sinus reflexes; loss of taste in the posterior third of the tongue; and deviation of the uvula to the normal side. Glossopharyngeal neuralgia, like that of the trigeminal nerve, is characterized by excruciating, paroxysmal pain within the distribution of its sensory fibers. In glossopharyngeal neuralgia the trigger zone is usually in the pharynx and the pain radiates to the Eustachian tube, middle ear, or behind the ear. It is most often initiated by coughing or swallowing.

Cranial nerves V, VII, and IX through XII may be involved, together or in varying combinations, as a result of bilateral interruption of the corticobulbar tracts centrally within the brain stem (see Fig. 223). Such bilateral destruction, between the pons below and the internal capsule above, is usually the result of an extensive demyelinating disease, vascular thrombosis, or neoplasms. In such cases the muscles do not exhibit atrophy, for the lower motor neurons remain intact. Instead there is a marked paresis of the muscles of mastication, the face, tongue, pharynx, and larynx. As a result there is difficulty in chewing, swallowing, breathing, and speech. Contractures of the lips, tongue, and palate may occur after a prolonged interval (Haymaker, 1956). Unrestrained outbursts of laughing and crying sometimes accompany these extensive brain stem lesions, as well as cerebellar symptoms. This combined symptom complex is often designated *pseudobulbar palsy.*

Another bundle of descending afferent fibers is the *descending* or *spinal vestibular root* lying dorsolateral to the fasciculus solitarius (Figs. 221, 234, 235). The fibers are arranged in small bundles (area fasciculata) accompanied by cells which constitute their terminal nucleus, the *nucleus of the descending or spinal vestibular tract.* Occupying the floor of the ventricle medial to the vestibular root and lateral to the trigonum vagi is another terminal nucleus of the vestibular nerve, the *medial* or *triangular vestibular nucleus.* The vestibular nerve and its central connections will be fully described in higher levels (p. 300).

In the central gray of the ventricular floor are several nuclear masses whose functions and connections are not fully understood. The *nucleus intercalatus* placed between the hypoglossal and the dorsal motor vagus nucleus (Figs. 237, 238) is composed of small cells among which are clumps of larger ones. It is probably a relay station in intersegmental visceral reflex pathways, gustatory, olfactory, and others. It receives secondary vago-glossopharyngeal fibers, fibers from the medial vestibular nucleus and the bundle of Schütz. This nucleus probably sends fibers to the hypoglossal and salivatory nuclei, and to the dorsal motor nucleus of the vagus. According to some, it is a detached portion of the medial vestibular nucleus.

The *nucleus of Roller*, also known as the "sublingual nucleus", lies ventral to the hypoglossal nucleus (Fig. 237) and is composed of small densely packed cells. It is considered by some to be a condensation of reticular cells, by others to be related to the medial vestibular nucleus. Like the nucleus intercalatus, it is probably a station for intersegmental visceral pathways.

SECTION OF MEDULLA THROUGH LATERAL RECESS AND ENTRANCE OF COCHLEAR NERVE (FIGS. 243, 244)

The fourth ventricle has reached its maximum width and is here continued into its lateral extensions, the *lateral recesses,* passing external to the restiform body and the dorsal and ventral cochlear nuclei which form its medial walls. The lateral wall of each recess is formed by a dense fiber bundle, the *peduncle of the flocculus,* related to the floccular lobe of the cerebellum which here becomes continuous with the lateral surface of the medulla. The nerves of this level are the *glossopharyngeal* (N.IX) and the *cochlear root* of the *acoustic nerve* (N.VIII).

The hypoglossal and the dorsal motor nucleus of the vagus have disappeared but the most rostral portion of the nucleus ambiguus is usually still present and contributes efferent fibers to the glossopharyngeal nerve. The afferent fibers of N.IX are shown entering on the lateral aspect of the medulla, ventral to the restiform body (Fig. 243). Such sensory fibers traverse the spinal V and pass to the fasciculus solitarius, some terminating in the nucleus of that tract here known as the gustatory nucleus, others descending to lower levels. The fasciculus solitarius is now very small and just above the entrance of N.IX can no longer be distinguished as a

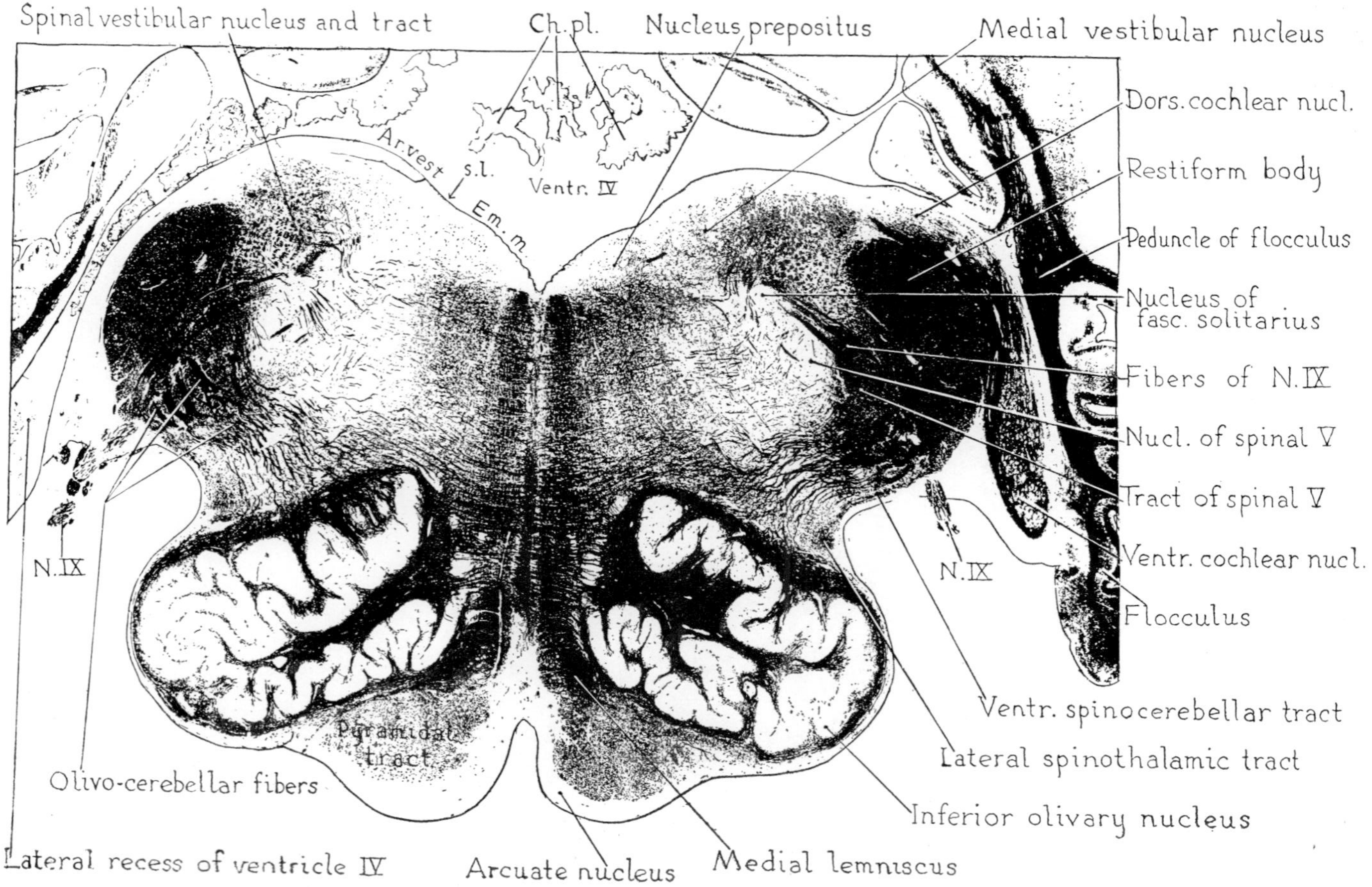

FIG. 243. Transverse section of medulla of one month infant, through cochlear nuclei and ninth nerve. Weigert's myelin stain. Photograph. *Ar. vest.*, area vestibularis; *Ch.pl.*, chorioid plexus; *Em.m.*, eminentia media (teretis); *S.l.*, sulcus limitans.

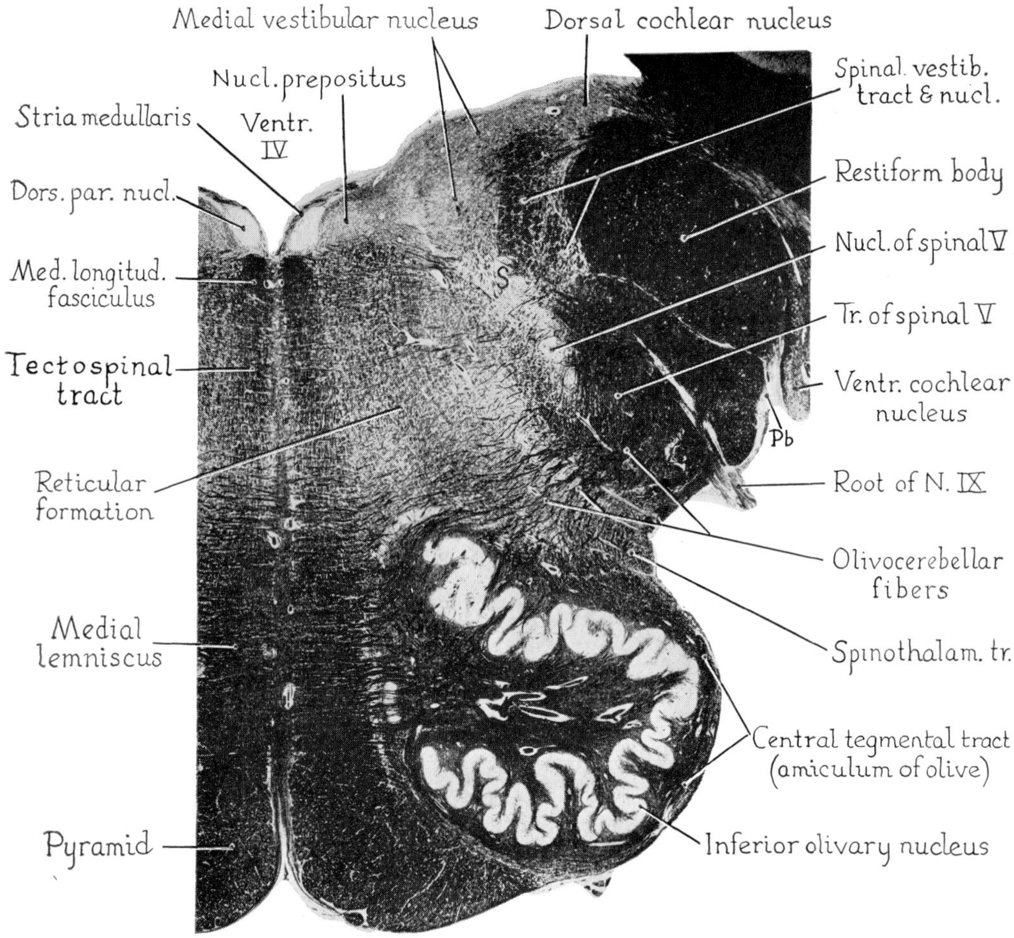

FIG. 244. Transverse section of adult medulla, through cochlear nuclei and ninth nerve. Weigert's myelin stain. Photograph, ×10. Dors. par. nucl., dorsal paramedian nucleus; Pb., pontobulbar nucleus; S, nucleus of fasciculus solitarius.

definite bundle, consisting of only a few descending afferent root fibers of N.VII.

The root fibers of the *cochlear nerve,* conveying impulses from the organ of Corti in the cochlea, enter at the extreme lateral angle of the medulla. Such auditory fibers terminate at once in two nuclear masses, the *ventral* and *dorsal cochlear nuclei,* the latter forming a prominence, the *tuberculum acusticum* on the floor of the rhomboid fossa (Fig. 244). The ventral nucleus is composed of rather large ovoid or rounded cells with dark-staining protoplasm. In the dorsal nucleus, the cells are smaller and fusiform (Figs. 84, 245). The secondary cochlear (auditory) fibers arising from these cells are not well seen until the cephalic end of the cochlear nuclei is reached.

The descending vestibular root and its terminal nucleus is large and forms a triangular area wedging ventrally between the restiform body and the nucleus of the spinal V. The medial vestibular nucleus has likewise enlarged and occupies practically all the ventricular gray lateral to the sulcus limitans. Secondary vestibular fibers from these nuclei form internal arcuate fibers which either enter the reticular formation of the same side or pass toward the raphé to become incorporated in the medial longi-

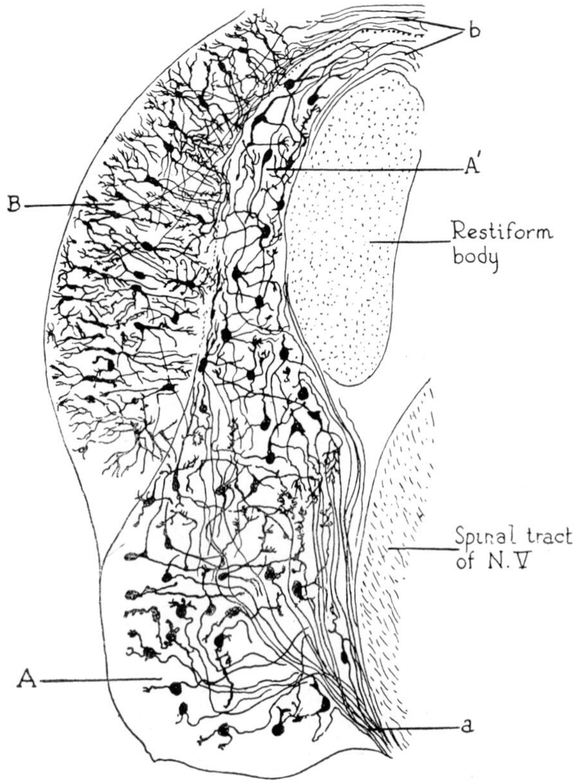

FIG. 245. Cochlear nuclei in medulla of rabbit eight days old. Golgi impregnation. *A*, ventral cochlear nucleus and its dorsal extension or tail (*A′*); *B*, dorsal cochlear nucleus (tuberculum acusticum); *a*, axons from ventral nucleus passing ventrally and medially to become fibers of the trapezoid body; *b*, axons from dorsal nucleus and tail of ventral nucleus passing dorsally and medially to form the superficial and intermediate trapezoid fibers. (After Cajal.)

tudinal fasciculus of the same and opposite side (Figs. 198, 261). It is probable that those from the descending nucleus convey vestibular (and cerebellar) impulses to the voluntary muscles for the regulation of postural tone, while those from the medial vestibular nucleus initiate such visceral reflexes as nausea and vomiting after excessive vestibular stimulation.

The main olivary nuclei are still large and send many bundles of olivocerebellar fibers to the opposite restiform bodies which have grown to massive proportions. The arcuate nuclei practically envelop the pyramids and may now represent the most caudal portion of the pontile nuclei (*nucleus precursorius pontis*, Ziehen). In favorable preparations the *striae medullares* (*striae cerebellares*) are seen passing transversely over the ventricular floor and dipping into the raphé (Fig. 244). These fibers probably arise from the arcuate nucleus, cross and ascend dorsally in the raphé and then pass laterally over the ventricular floor to terminate in the flocculus of the cerebellum (arcuatocerebellar tract).

With the disappearance of the cuneate nucleus, the medial lemniscus has reached its fullest extent, forming a vertical band of fibers on either side of the raphé, in intimate contact with the ventrally lying pyramid. The longest fibers of the ventral spinothalamic tract whose course is difficult to trace in the medulla are probably now incorporated in the medial lemniscus (Fig. 190). In the ventral portion of the lemniscus, here as well as in lower and higher levels, are seen bundles of lighter staining fibers. These are aberrant descending fibers detached from the pyramids, which either go to the more caudally lying motor nuclei of the cranial nerves (hypoglossal, accessory, ambiguus) or rejoin the pyramids lower down. The whole system of pyramidal fibers innervating the cranial motor nuclei is known as the *corticobulbar* or *corticonuclear tract* (Fig. 223). Owing to the close proximity of the pyramid and medial lemniscus in the inter-olivary region of the medulla, injury of this area may affect both tracts and produce a more or less severe contralateral anesthesia (touch, muscle sense, vibration) and hemiplegia (upper motor neuron paralysis) of the body and extremities.

The reticular formation is large and similar in structure to that of the previous level. The medial longitudinal fasciculus and predorsal bundle are now partially separated from the medial lemniscus by lighter areas occupied by the nucleus of the raphé which here, and in somewhat higher levels, increases in size and spreads laterally into the reticular formation (inferior central nucleus, nucleus pterygoideus). The rubrospinal, spinothalamic, and ventral spinocerebellar tracts are in the same position, but the vestibulospinal tract is moving from the dorsal surface of the olive to a more internal position. Its fibers cannot usually be distinguished but are bending dorsally toward the vestibular nuclei from which they originate (Fig. 198). Conspicuous transverse fibers in the reticular formation are the olivocerebellar and the secondary vestibular and trigeminal fibers.

Extensive lesions of the gray reticular formation throughout the medulla often produce the sympathetic disturbances already described as the syndrome of Horner. The disturbances are apparently due to interruption of central autonomic tracts (reticulospinal, Fig. 197) which connect higher autonomic centers with the lateral gray horn of the upper thoracic cord.

As already stated, there is found in the superficial gray of the median eminence a strip of closely packed small cells known as the nucleus eminentiae teretis (eminentiae medialis). Incorporated in this small-celled column at several places are groups of larger cells, the most conspicuous of which is the *nucleus prepositus* now found in the place previously occupied by the hypoglossal nucleus (Figs. 244, 247). The nucleus extends from the oral limits of the hypoglossal nucleus to about the caudal limit of the abducens nucleus. It is composed of numerous relatively large cells and few smaller cells, resembling those of the nucleus intercalatus with which it apparently becomes continuous in more caudal levels. Like the nucleus intercalatus, it is believed by some to have intimate relations with the medial vestibular nucleus. It is probably a relay station in olfactory and other visceral reflex pathways, receiving fibers from the bundle of Schütz, medial vestibular nucleus, and sending fibers to the reticular formation, hypoglossal, dorsal motor vagus, and secretory nuclei.

SECTION OF HINDBRAIN AT LEVEL OF JUNCTION OF MEDULLA AND PONS (FIGS. 246, 247)

The section which is cut somewhat obliquely, the right side being higher than the left, is immediately ventral to the lateral recess, and the roof of the fourth ventricle is now formed by the cerebellum, a portion of which is shown in Fig. 246. In the cerebellum are seen a portion of the *vermis* and two of the internal cerebellar nuclei, the *nucleus dentatus* and *nucleus emboliformis*. On the left side the cochlear nuclei are overhung laterally by a portion of the cerebellum known as the *flocculus*, from the interior of which a dense deeply staining fiber bundle, the *peduncle of the flocculus*, extends dorsally and medially. This peduncle, as already mentioned, forms

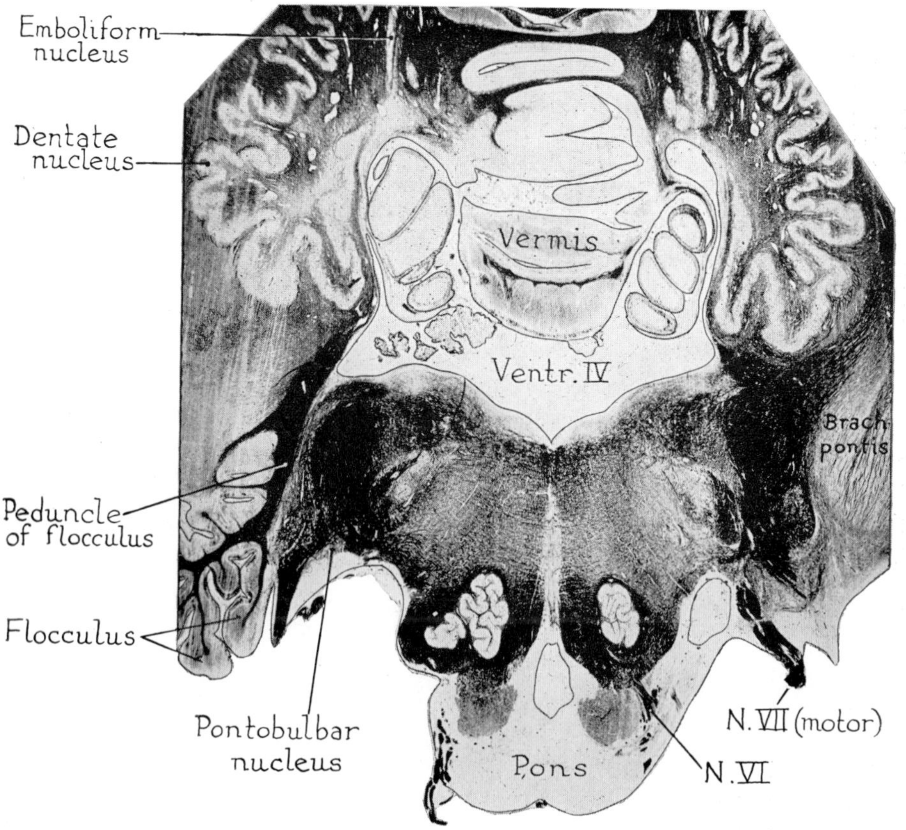

FIG. 246. Section through medulla and portion of cerebellum of one month infant, at level of caudal border of pons. Weigert's myelin stain. Photograph.

the outer wall of the lateral recess (Fig. 243).

On the right (higher) side the restiform body is bending dorsolaterally and entering the white substance of the cerebellum. It is covered externally by a broad band of fibers, the *brachium pontis* or *middle cerebellar peduncle,* which medially becomes continuous with the pons whose caudal tip now covers the ventral surface of the medulla and practically envelops the pyramidal tract. The blind end of the ventral median sulcus overhung by the pons is known as the *foramen caecum posterior.*

The greatly reduced olivary nucleus is flanked laterally by the considerably augmented central tegmental tract whose fibers terminate in the olive (Fig. 247). The medial lemniscus now in contact with the dorsal surface of the pons is flattening dorsoventrally and curving laterally along the ventral surface of the inferior olive (Fig. 185). The lighter staining area separating it from the medial longitudinal fasciculus and predorsal bundle is occupied by the inferior central nucleus (nucleus of the raphé).

The cochlear nerve has disappeared on the right side, but the cranial tip of the ventral cochlear nucleus is still visible and gives rise to secondary cochlear (trapezius) fibers which course medially along the dorsal border of the pons and can be traced better in the next level. A few fibers of the *vestibular nerve* are entering the medulla and are passing between the restiform body and the spinal V to the vestibular area. This area, besides the large medial vestibular

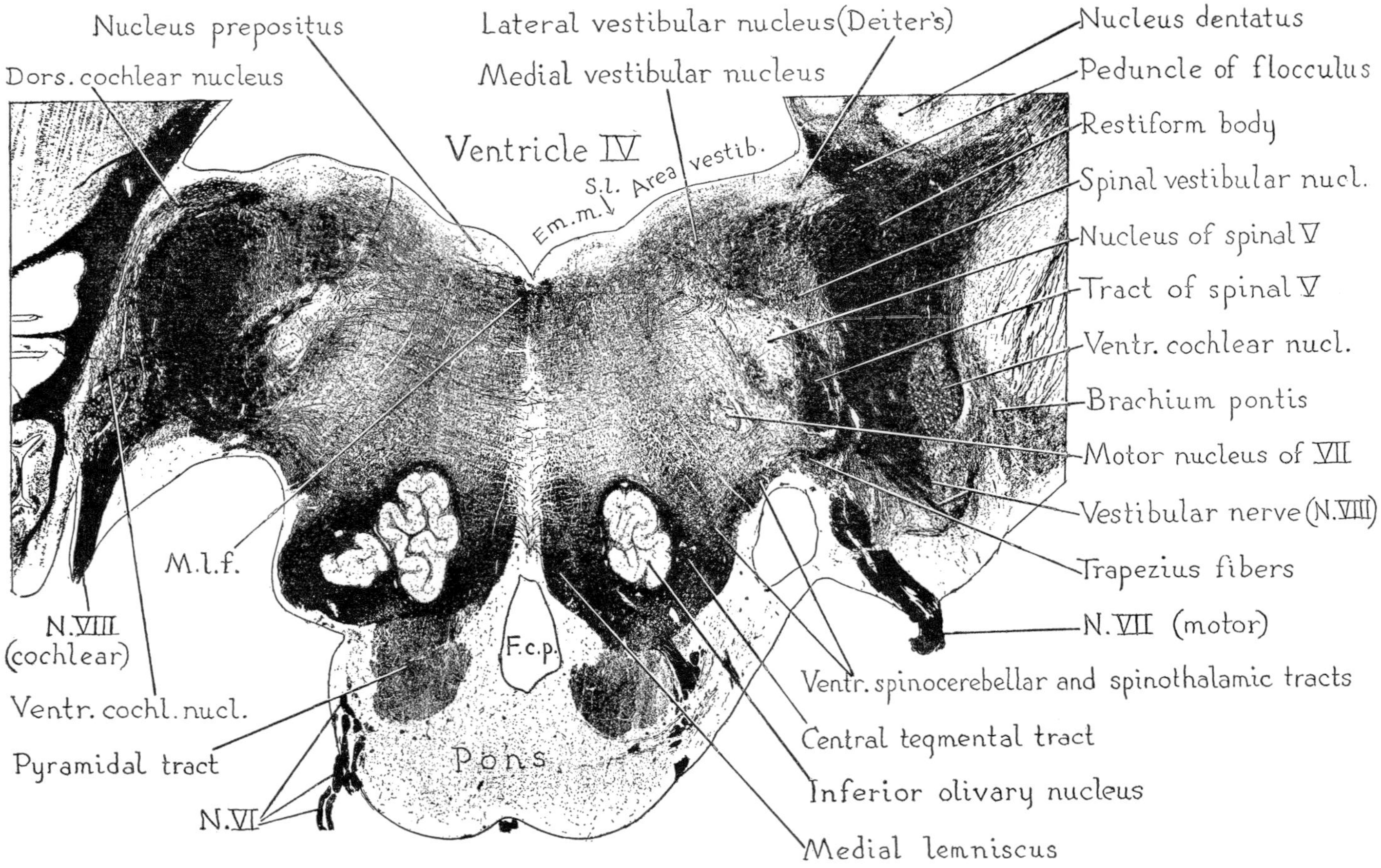

FIG. 247. Transverse section of medulla of one month infant, through caudal border of pons. Weigert's myelin stain. Photograph. *Em.m.* eminentia media; *F.c.p.*, foramen cecum posterior; *M.l.f.*, medial longitudinal fasciculus.

nucleus now includes the large-celled *lateral vestibular nucleus* of Deiters lying dorsal to the restiform body (Fig. 247).

In the lateral portion of the reticular formation is the caudal tip of the motor nucleus of the facial nerve, occupying a position similar to that of the nucleus ambiguus. Emerging at the junction of the medulla and pons are the roots of the facial (N.VII) and abducens (N.VI) nerves. The former emerges medial to the vestibular nerve and in line with the glossopharyngeal, the abducens emerges between the pyramid and the olive. The nuclei of the facial and abducens nerves are located dorsally in the pons and will be discussed in the next chapter.

The small, compact medulla thus differs structurally from the more caudal spinal cord. It contains the nuclei of origin and termination of cranial nerves IX to XII, as well as some of the nuclei related to hearing and equilibrium. Essential visceral reflexes governing respiration, circulation, swallowing, and digestion are dependent upon the integrity of cells and fibers lying dorsally within the reticular formation. The more recently acquired fiber tracts and related nuclei occupy a ventral and lateral position in the medulla (e.g., corticospinal tract, inferior olive, restiform body). Several of these medullary structures may be involved simultaneously by vascular lesions, neoplasms, or disease processes. The symptoms will naturally depend upon the neural structures involved and whether they be irritated, or partially or completely destroyed. With the gross and microscopic information of the medulla at hand, it is now desirable to reexamine its blood supply (Fig. 277, p. 326). Note the important neuronal structures that lie within the area of distribution of the vertebral artery, and each of its immediate branches to the caudal and midolivary levels of the medulla. Sudden rupture or occlusion of one artery will deprive certain medullary structures of their blood supply, and often results in recognizable symptom complexes.

16

The Internal Structure of the Pons

The rostral portion of the hindbrain which is the direct continuation of the medulla oblongata, and the caudal portion of the midbrain are covered ventrally by a massive band of cells and fibers constituting the *pons Varolii.* Hence in sections of this region two parts may be distinguished, a dorsal and a ventral (Fig. 248). The dorsal portion known as the *tegmentum* of the pons (tegmentum of the hindbrain) is the direct continuation of the medulla and besides its own new structures contains the upward prolongations of those already studied in lower levels, with the exception of the pyramidal tracts. The ventral part which now includes the pyramidal tracts forms the *basilar portion* of the pons or *pons proper.* In strict usage the term *pons* refers to the basilar portion only.

SECTIONS THROUGH CAUDAL PORTION OF PONS AND PONTILE TEGMENTUM (FIGS. 249, 250, 253, 255)

The roof of the now narrower fourth ventricle is formed by the cerebellum. Within the latter may be seen a portion of the vermis and the four pairs of internal cerebellar nuclei (Figs. 253, 265). The most lateral of these is the *nucleus dentatus,* a convoluted band of gray resembling the inferior olive, and medial to this the *nucleus emboliformis, nucleus globosus* and *nucleus fastigii* or *tecti.* The fastigial nucleus receives fibers from the cortex of the cerebellar vermis and is intimately related with the vestibular nerve and nuclei. The dentate and emboliform nuclei receive fibers principally from the cerebellar hemispheres, and their axons form an efferent cerebellar fiber cable, the *superior cerebellar peduncle* or *brachium conjunctivum,* conveying cerebellar impulses to the contralateral midbrain and thalamus (Fig. 192). The superior peduncle is not fully formed or observed in the lower pontile levels.

The basilar portion of the pons. The basilar portion or pons proper consists of transverse and longitudinal fibers between which there are numerous groups of small and medium sized polygonal cells, the *pontile nuclei.* The longitudinal fibers comprise (1) the pyramidal tracts (corticospinal and corticobulbar) which descend through the pons and give off a number of fibers to the motor nuclei of the cranial nerves (Fig. 223). The main body of fibers passes through the pons to enter the medullary pyramids (Fig. 193). Compactly arranged near the caudal border of the pons, the pyramidal fibers become broken up into a number of bundles separated by the transverse pontile fibers. At the rostral margin of the pons the pyramidal fibers are again organized into a compact mass which forms part of the cerebral peduncle of the midbrain. The pyramidal tract is believed to give off some collaterals or even terminals to the pontile nuclei (Cajal). (2) Other longitudinal fibers which likewise descend from the pallium terminate within the pontile nuclei themselves and are known as the *corticopontile* or *palliopontile fibers.* They arise from the cortex of the frontal lobe (frontopontile), from the temporal and

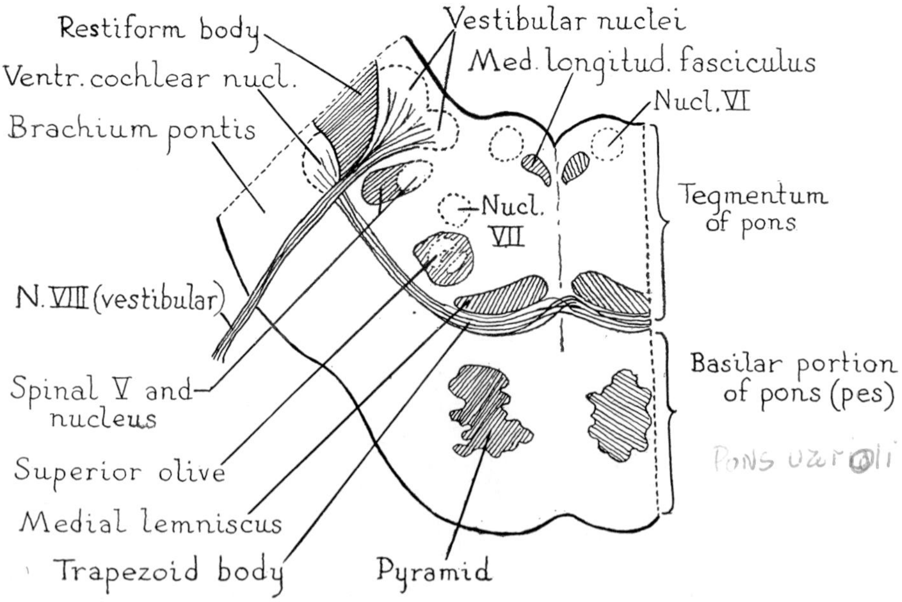

FIG. 248. Diagrammatic section of pons at level of entrance of vestibular nerve.

parietal cortex (temporo-, and parietopontile), and also from some portions of the occipital lobe. These fibers descend uncrossed to end in the homolateral nuclei of the pons. The corticopontine fibers are numerous in the upper portion of the pons where they form considerable bundles difficult to distinguish from the pyramidal tracts (Figs. 267, 274). Their number gradually diminishes as more and more of the fibers terminate in the pontile nuclei until in the most caudal portions only a few of them are left. The corticopontile fibers and the transverse fibers to be described below do not become myelinated till some time after birth and hence are not distinguishable in brain sections of a four weeks infant. They are shown in the adult pons in Figs. 267, 274.

The transverse fibers are axons of cells of the pontile nuclei which cross almost entirely to the opposite side and unite to form a massive bundle, the *brachium pontis* or *middle cerebellar peduncle.* They pass dorsal and ventral to the pyramidal tract, the dorsal ones forming the *deep layer,* and the ventral ones the *superficial layer* of the pons. The brachia ponti sweep dorsally and somewhat caudally into the cerebellum, lying external to the restiform bodies, and are distributed principally to the cortex of the cerebellar hemispheres. The pons is thus a relay station in an extensive and phylogenetically new two neuron pathway from the cerebral cortex to the cerebellar hemispheres. The first one is a cortical neuron sending an uncrossed corticopontile fiber to the pons. The second is a pontile neuron sending a crossed pontocerebellar fiber via the brachium pontis to the cerebellum.

Some of the transverse fibers connect the cerebellum with the reticular formation of the tegmentum (tegmentocerebellar). Fibers passing vertically in the raphé from tegmentum to pons are undoubtedly continuations of such transverse fibers. Other more laterally placed vertical fibers are cortical fibers which enter the tegmentum to innervate the motor nuclei of the cranial nerves (corticobulbar or aberrant pyramidal fibers, Figs. 223, 266).

The pontile nuclei are numerous, closely packed cellular aggregations of varying extent placed between the transverse and longitudinal fibers (Fig. 251). In the caudal

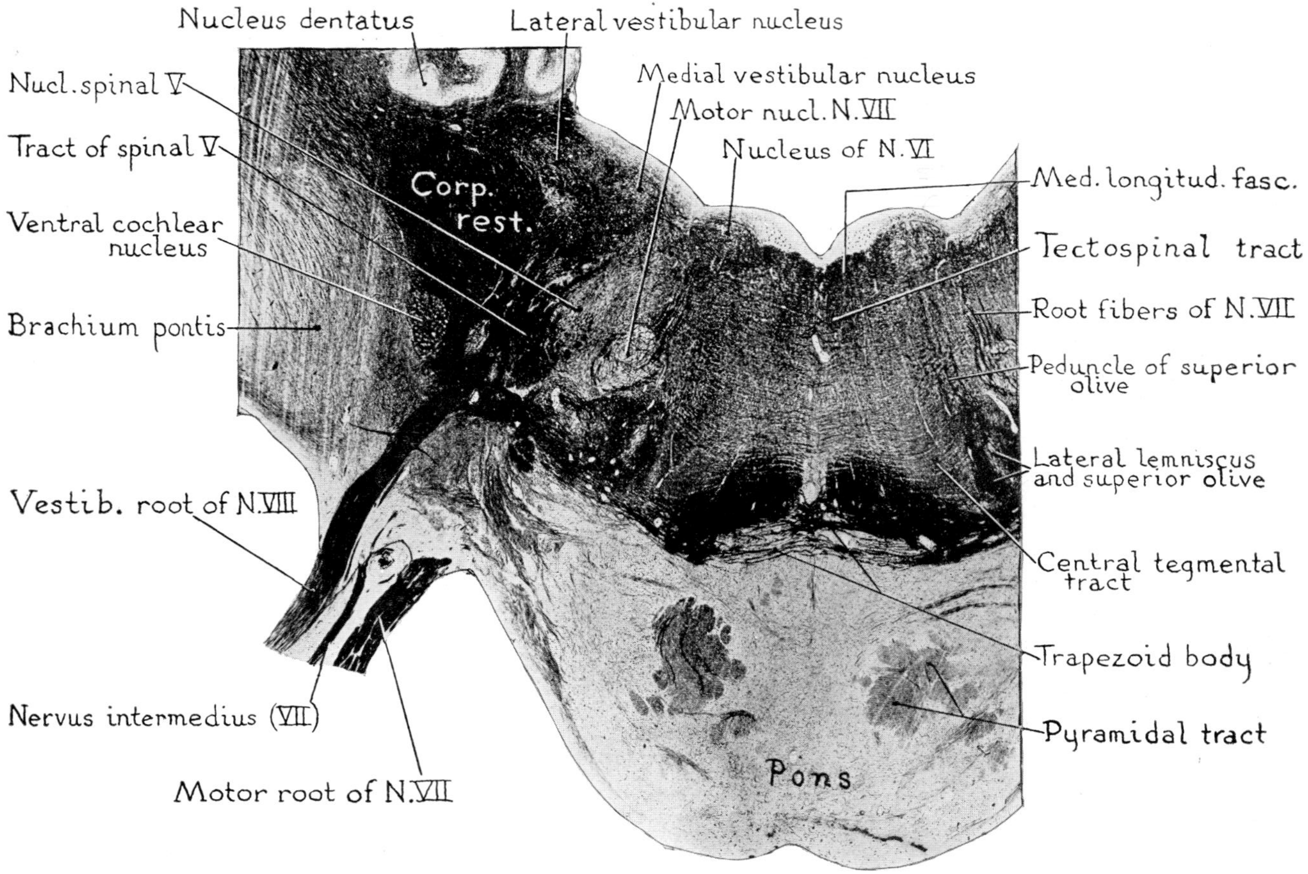

Fig. 249. Section of pons and pontile tegmentum of one month infant through vestibular and facial nerve roots. Weigert's myelin stain. Photograph. *Corp.rest.*, restiform body.

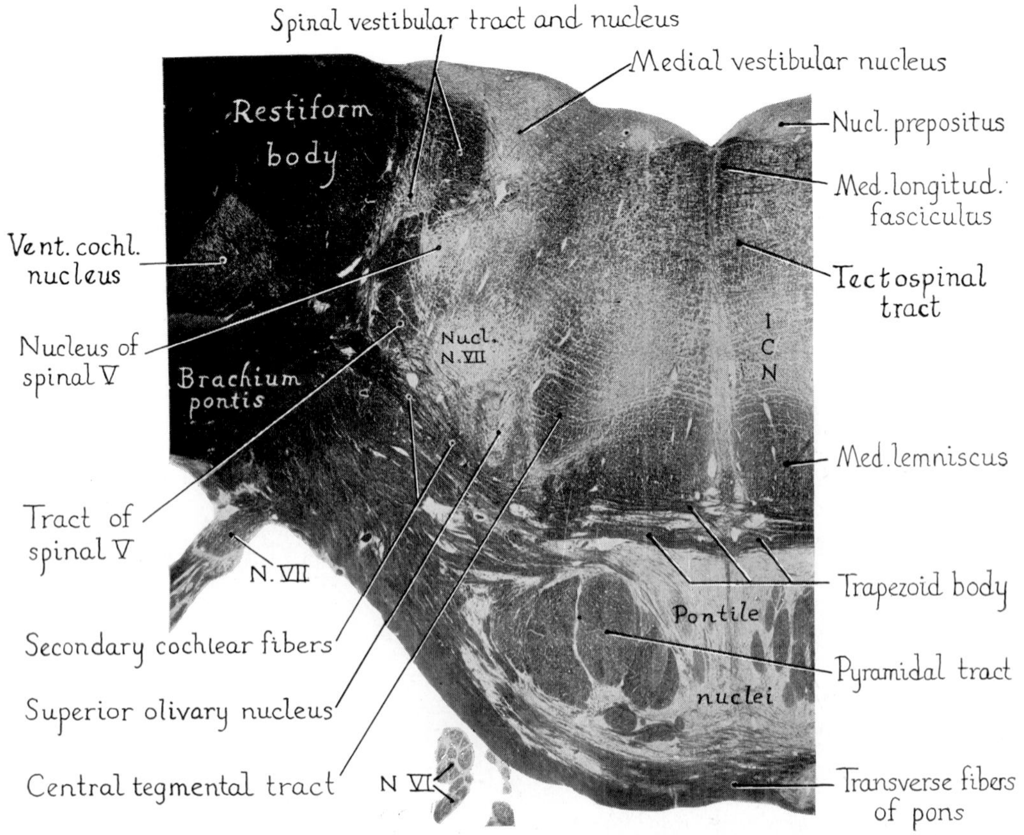

FIG. 250. Transverse section of adult pons and pontile tegmentum, through emergence of facial nerve. Weigert's myelin stain. Photograph, ×9. I.C.N., inferior central nucleus.

region the cells form a ring around the compact pyramidal tract, more rostrally the latter is broken up into smaller bundles by islands of pontile cells. In a general way the cells may be grouped into lateral, medial, dorsal, and ventral nuclear masses (Fig. 255). In the lateral groups the polygonal cells are relatively large or medium sized, in the paramedian region they are smaller. Their dendrites ramify around adjacent cell bodies, their axons, almost entirely crossed, form the brachium pontis. Among these cells are found curiously shaped Golgi Type II cells whose dendrites are beset with numerous hair-like processes and whose short, branching axons terminate in the vicinity of the cell body.

The pontile tegmentum. The inferior olivary nucleus is no longer present and the olivocerebellar fibers are here entering the cerebellum as part of the restiform body covered externally by the brachium pontis. The *central tegmental tract* at first occupies the ventral part of the reticular formation but in higher levels gradually shifts to a more central position (Figs. 254, 255). This tract constitutes a system of descending fibers terminating principally in the inferior olive. Most of them probably come from the upper tegmentum of the midbrain, in part from the nucleus ruber, in part from the reticular formation of that region (rubroolivary and tegmentoolivary). Many descend directly to the olive, others are relayed in the reticular formation. The tract, extensive in man, appears to be a link in a newer pathway connecting the corpus striatum and thalamus with the cerebellum, but

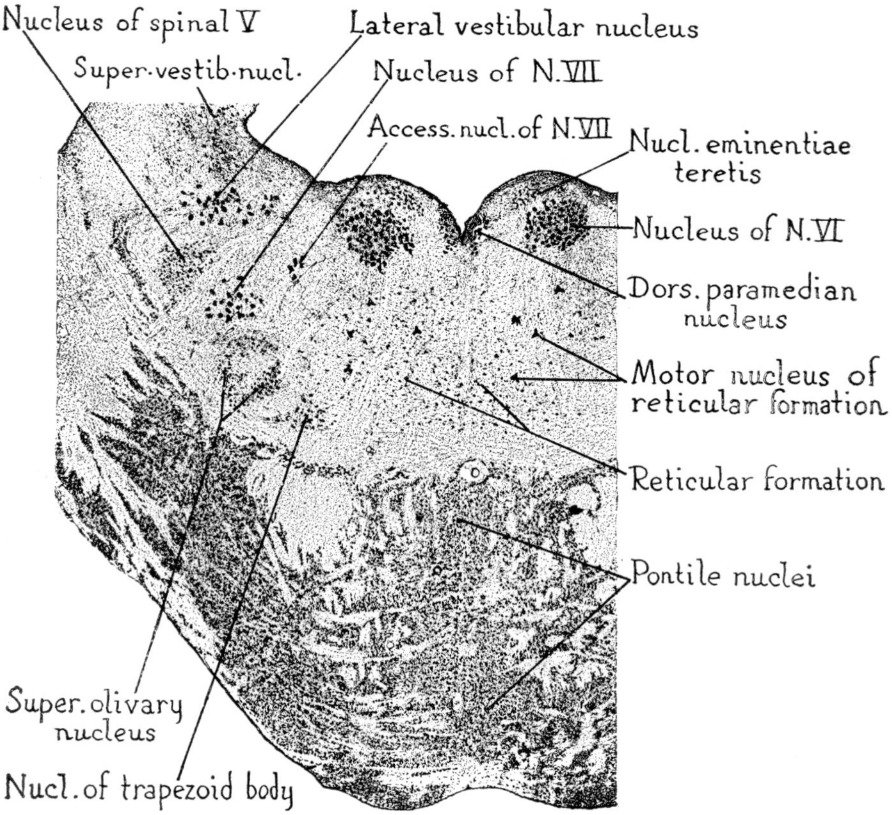

FIG. 251. Section through pons and pontile tegmentum of three months infant. About same level as Fig. 249. Cresyl Violet. Photograph, with schematic representation of cell groups.

its functional significance is poorly understood. Intermingled with the olivary fibers are probably descending and ascending fibers of other functionally distinct systems.

The medial lemniscus, no longer compressed between the two inferior olives, has lost the form of a longitudinal column and now appears as a flattened elliptical mass extending transversely, in close contact with the dorsal border of the pons. It is widely separated from the medial longitudinal fasciculus and tectospinal tract, the interval being occupied by the enlarged nucleus of the raphé, here known as the inferior central nucleus (Fig. 250). The tract and nucleus of the spinal V, the spinothalamic, and ventral spinocerebellar tracts are in the same position but are now separated from the surface by the pons and pontile brachium. The uncrossed vestibulospinal fibers are emerging from their nucleus of origin (lateral vestibular nucleus) and cannot be distinguished easily.

The reticular formation is extensive and contains the various nuclear masses already described. In its dorsal portion are the dorsal paramedian nucleus and the nucleus of the median eminence (nucleus eminentiae teretis). More ventrally is the enlarged nucleus of the raphé (inferior central nucleus), and scattered through the reticular formation are the large cells constituting the motor reticular nucleus. The lateral reticular nucleus furnishing arcuate fibers to the cerebellum has disappeared.

Secondary cochlear fibers and related nuclei. A striking feature in sections of these and somewhat higher levels is the *trapeziod body*, a conspicuous bundle of transversely running fibers in the ventral portion of the tegmentum. These fibers arise principally from the ventral cochlear nucleus and in a convex arc sweep medially toward the raphé. Most of them cross to the opposite side passing through or ventral to the medial lemniscus and reach the ventrolateral portion of the tegmentum. Here they turn sharply in a longitudinal direction to form a new ascending fiber bundle, the *lateral lemniscus* (Fig. 258). The turn is made just dorsolateral to a nuclear mass known as the *superior olive.* The dorsal cochlear nucleus likewise gives rise to secondary fibers which cross in a more dorsal position close to the floor of the fourth ventricle to join the lateral lemniscus. These do not form a conspicuous bundle and are difficult to distinguish from the secondary vestibular fibers which arise from the adjacent vestibular nuclei (Figs. 245, 252, 263).

Closely related to the trapezoid body are several cellular aggregations of which the most prominent is the nuclear complex of the *superior olive.* This is a cellular column, about 4 mm. long, extending from the level of the facial nucleus to the motor nucleus of the trigeminal nerve, in close contact ventrally with the lateral portion of the trapeziod body. It contains several distinct cell groups: an S-shaped lateral chief nucleus composed of medium sized polygonal cells, and a wedge-shaped medial or accessory nucleus of closely packed somewhat larger fusiform cells (Figs. 250, 251). The superior olive receives collaterals or terminals of secondary cochlear fibers and contributes fibers to the trapeziod body and lateral lemniscus. From its dorsal surface a bundle of fibers, the *peduncle of the superior olive,* passes dorsomedially toward the abducens nucleus, some ending in that nucleus, others going to the reticular formation and probably to the medial longitudinal fasciculus (Fig. 249).

Other smaller cellular aggregations related to the trapezoid body are difficult to see in Weigert preparations (Fig. 252). They include the *trapezoid nucleus,* scattered among the trapezoid fibers medial to the superior olive, and the *internal* and *external preolivary nuclei* lying ventral to the superior olive. All these nuclei appear to be intercalated in the secondary cochlear (auditory) pathways.

The new cranial nerves appearing in these sections are the vestibular root of N.VIII, the facial nerve (N.VII), and the abducens nerve (N.VI).

The afferent *vestibular root fibers* enter at the caudal border of the pons, pass between the restiform body and the spinal V, and reach the field previously occupied by the descending vestibular tract whose fibers form a downward continuation of the root. Scattered large cells in this area form the *lateral vestibular nucleus* of *Deiters.* The medial vestibular nucleus is still present, and dorsal to the lateral nucleus, at the extreme angle of the fourth ventricle, is the *superior vestibular nucleus* (Figs. 251, 253, 255). As in previous levels the vestibular nuclei are sending out secondary fibers which either enter the reticular formation of the same side or pass to the raphé to become incorporated in the medial longitudinal fasciculus of the same and opposite side. Other fibers are seen passing from the vestibular area to the cerebellum, coursing close to the fourth ventricle (Figs. 253, 265). These are in part vestibular root fibers and secondary fibers from the vestibular nuclei which go to the cerebellum, in part descending fibers from the cerebellum to the vestibular nuclei and to other cells in the reticular formation. These ascending and descending fibers which connect the vestibular area with the cerebellum constitute the *internal* or *juxtarestiform* portion of the inferior cerebellar peduncle (Fig. 260).

The facial nerve is composed of two portions: a medial large *motor root* innervating the facial musculature, and lateral to this a slender strand known as the *nervus intermedius* or *nerve of Wrisberg* (Fig. 249). The

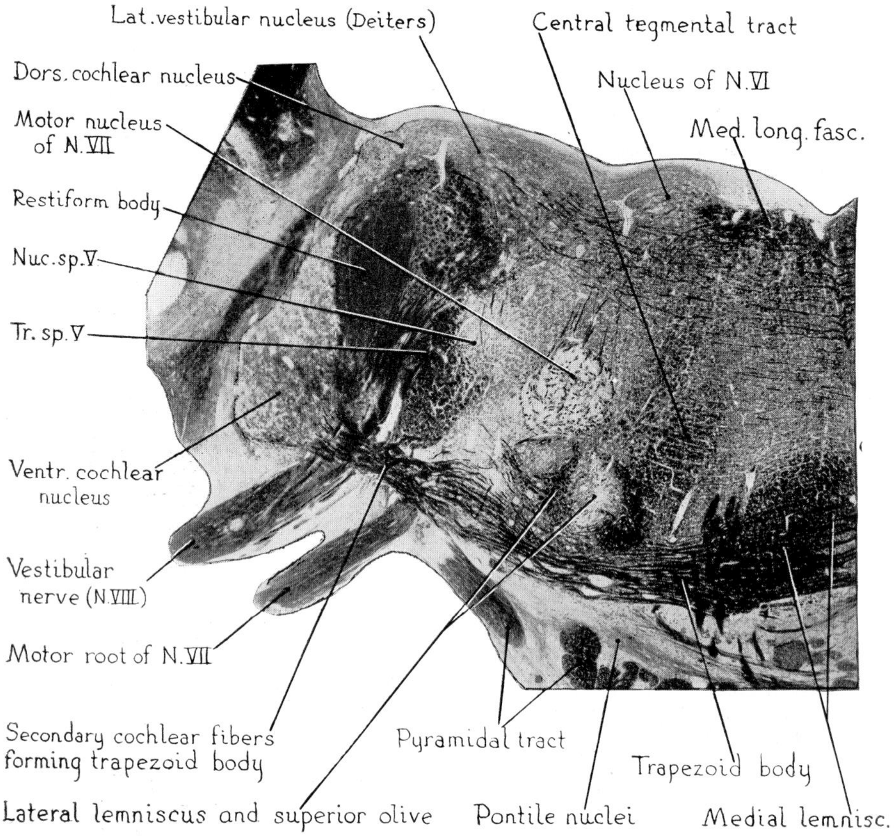

FIG. 252. Section of left half of pons and pontile tegmentum of three year old child whose brain showed a complete absence of the left cerebellar hemisphere and middle cerebellar peduncle. Weigert's myelin stain. Photograph. The origin of the trapezoid fibers from the ventral cochlear nucleus is clearly shown. Note also the dorsal trapezoid fibers passing into tegmentum from dorsal cochlear nucleus. (Strong.)

intermediate nerve contains both afferent and efferent visceral fibers.

The *motor nucleus of N.VII* appears as a pear-shaped gray mass in the lateral part of the reticular formation immediately dorsal to the superior olive (Figs. 249, 250, 251). Within it may be seen the usual plexus of fine terminals and the coarser fibers which give origin to the facial root. The root fibers form a rather complicated intramedullary loop whose continuity can not be seen in any one section (Figs. 220, 221, 223). Emerging as fine bundles of fibers from the dorsal surface of the nucleus they proceed dorsomedially to the floor of the ventricle. There they form a compact longitudinal bundle which ascends for a distance of about 2 mm. medial to the abducens nucleus and dorsal to the medial longitudinal fasciculus. At the cranial extremity of the abducens nucleus the bundle makes a sharp lateral turn over the dorsal surface of the abducens nucleus, forming the *internal facial genu* or bend. It then proceeds ventrolaterally and caudally to emerge on the lateral aspect of the caudal border of the pons (Fig. 249). While near the midline some of the fibers may possibly cross over to join the nerve of the opposite side (Obersteiner).

The *nucleus of N.VI* is a rounded gray mass placed in the lateral part of the median eminence of the fourth ventricle and to-

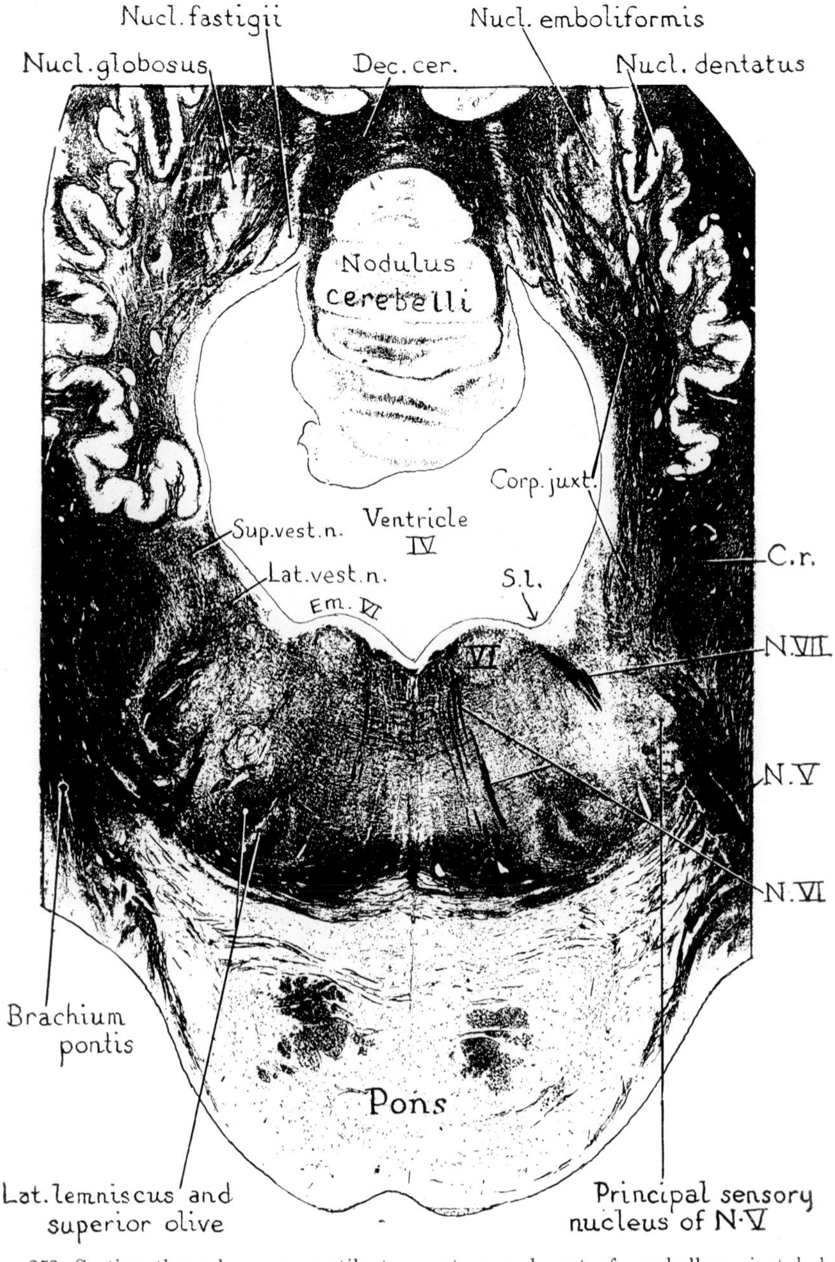

FIG. 253. Section through pons, pontile tegmentum and part of cerebellum, just below entrance of trigeminal nerve. One month infant. Weigert's myelin stain. *C.r.*, restiform body; *Corp.juxt.*, juxtarestiform body; *Dec.cer.*, cerebellar decussation; *Em.VI*, eminentia abducentis; *S.l.*, sulcus limitans; *VI*, nucleus of sixth nerve.

gether with the genu of the facial nerve forms the rounded prominence in the ventricular floor known as the *colliculus facialis* or *eminentia abducentis* (Figs. 219, 253). Its root fibers emerge from the medial surface of the colliculus and descend for a short distance to emerge at the caudal border of the pons.

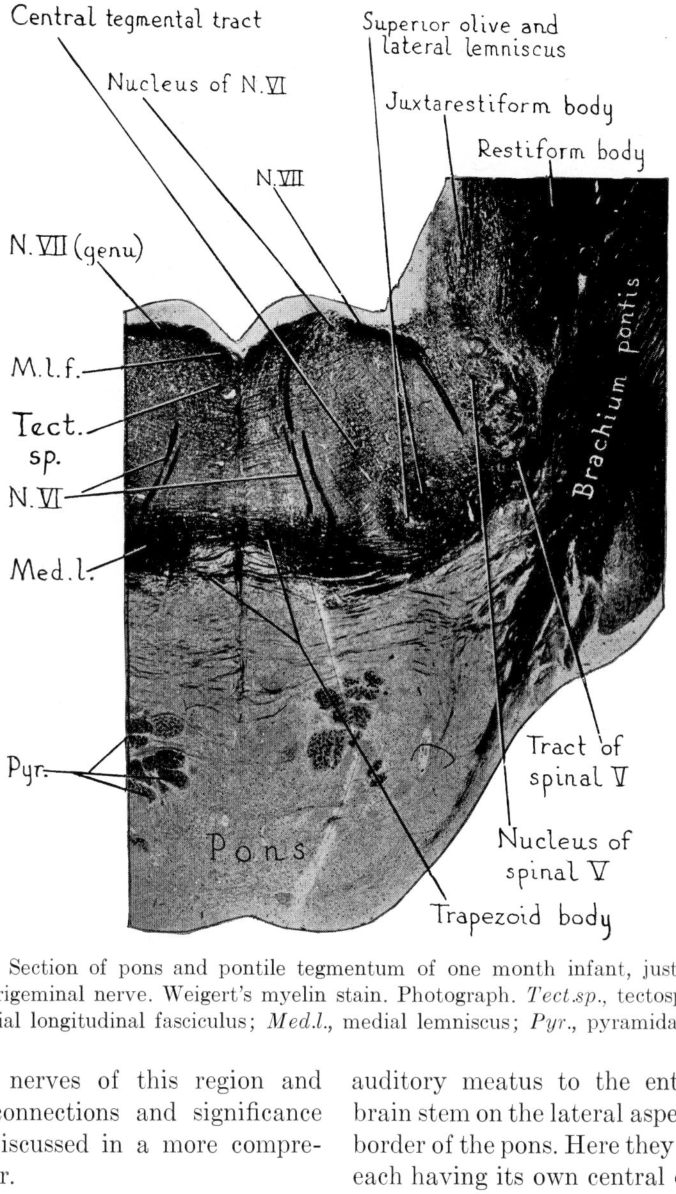

FIG. 254. Section of pons and pontile tegmentum of one month infant, just below entrance of trigeminal nerve. Weigert's myelin stain. Photograph. *Tect.sp.*, tectospinal tract; *M.l.f.*, medial longitudinal fasciculus; *Med.l.*, medial lemniscus; *Pyr.*, pyramidal tract.

The cranial nerves of this region and their central connections and significance may now be discussed in a more comprehensive manner.

THE ACOUSTIC NERVE

The acoustic nerve (N.VIII, N. acusticus) is composed of two parts:—(a) the *cochlear nerve* which supplies the cochlea and is concerned with hearing, and (b) the *vestibular nerve* which innervates the utricle, saccule, and semicircular canals and is concerned with postural and equilibratory functions (Fig. 256). The two run together as the acoustic nerve from the internal auditory meatus to the entrance into the brain stem on the lateral aspect of the caudal border of the pons. Here they separate again, each having its own central connections.

The cochlear nerve and the auditory pathways. The cochlear nerve is the larger portion of N.VIII and enters the brain at a somewhat lower level than the vestibular nerve. Its fibers originate in the *spiral ganglion*, an aggregation of bipolar cells situated in the modiolus of the cochlea. The longer central processes of these cells form the cochlear nerve, the short peripheral ones end in relation to the hair cells of the organ of Corti (Fig. 257). The

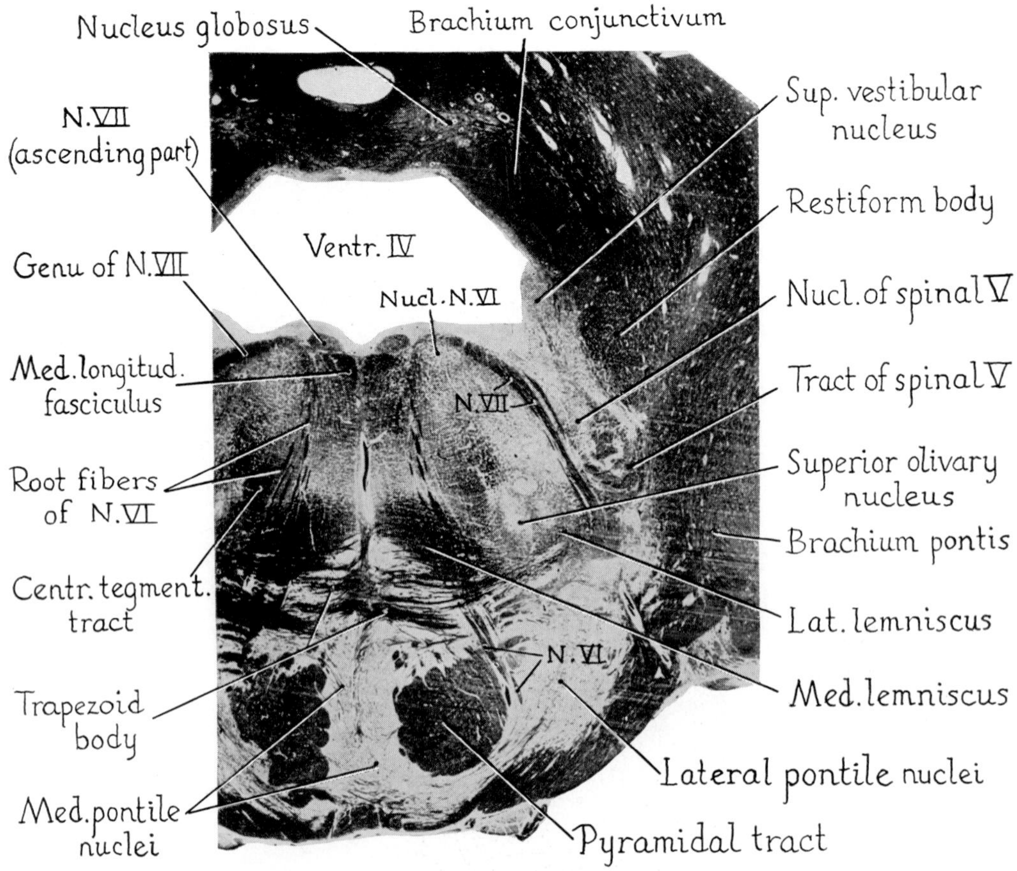

FIG. 255. Transverse section of adult pons, through nucleus and root fibers of N.VI. Weigert's myelin stain. Photograph, ×6.

cochlear nerve on entering the brain terminates in two nuclear masses, the *ventral* and the *dorsal cochlear nucleus,* placed on the external surface of the restiform body just caudal to the point where the latter turns to enter the cerebellum (Figs. 243, 247). The dorsal nucleus forms an elevation, the *tuberculum acusticum,* on the most lateral portion of the ventricular floor.

The *secondary cochlear* (auditory) pathways to the cerebral cortex are quite complex and there is still considerable uncertainty regarding their exact composition and course. From the ventral cochlear nucleus arises a strong bundle of fibers which course medially along the ventral border of the pontile tegmentum and form the *trapezoid body* (Fig. 258). Many of these pass through or ventral to the medial lemniscus, cross the raphé and reach the dorsolateral border of the opposite superior olive where they turn upward to form a longitudinal ascending bundle known as the *lateral lemniscus* or *lateral fillet.* Other trapezoid fibers terminate in the homolateral and contralateral nuclei of the superior olive and of the trapezoid body, two nuclear masses interposed in the secondary cochlear pathway. From these nuclei arise fibers which join the lateral lemniscus of the same and the opposite side.

From the dorsal cochlear nucleus and also from the dorsomedial part of the ventral nucleus fibers arise which pass medially, dorsal to the restiform body (Figs. 245, 258). Some run close to the floor of the

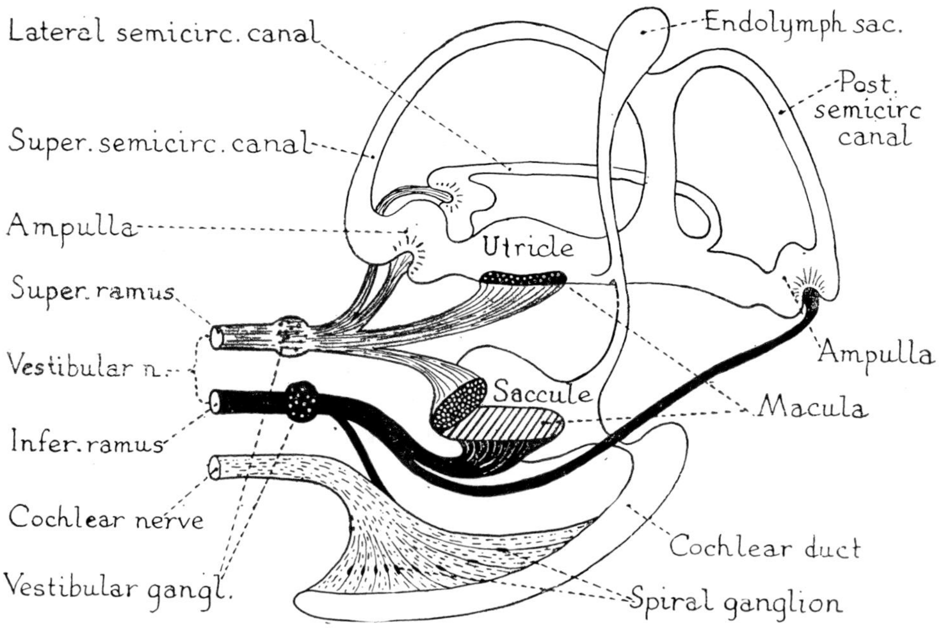

FIG. 256. Diagram showing innervation of the membranous labyrinth of the rabbit. (After de Burlet from Kolmer.)

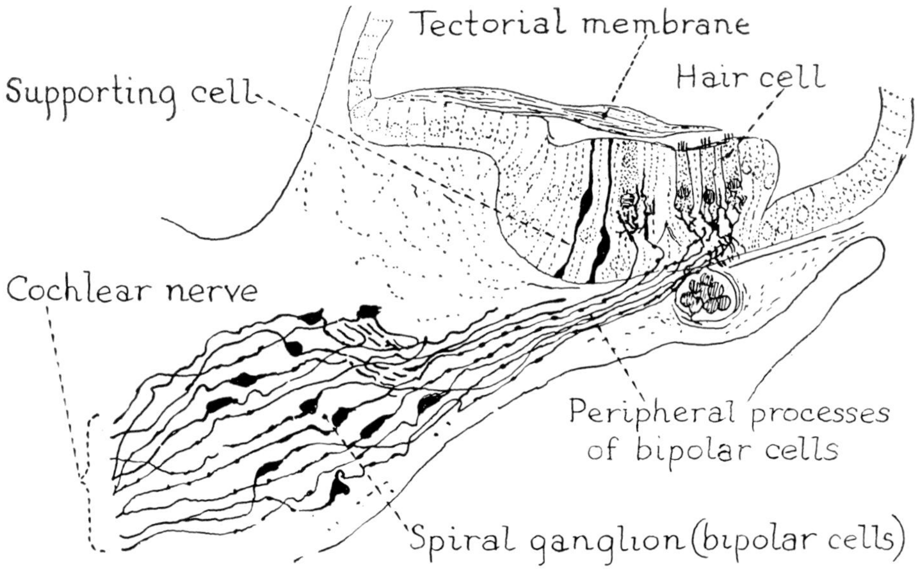

FIG. 257. Section through the spiral ganglion and organ of Corti of five day mouse. (After Cajal.)

fourth ventricle as dorsal trapezoid fibers (decussation of Monakow), cross the midline, and then dip ventrally to join the lateral lemniscus of the opposite side. Others dip more deeply into the reticular formation (intermediate trapezoid fibers, decussation of Held), then decussate and join the lateral lemniscus. Both dorsal and intermediate fibers may give off collaterals or terminals to the superior olivary and trapezoid nuclei.

A considerable number of these fibers ascend in the lateral lemniscus of the same side.

Interposed in the course of the lateral lemniscus in the upper portion of the pons, are other more diffuse cellular aggregations which constitute the *nucleus of the lateral lemniscus* (Fig. 258). To these the lemniscus contributes some terminals or at least collaterals, and probably receives additional fibers from them. The lateral lemniscus then reaches the midbrain where a considerable portion terminates either directly or by collaterals in the inferior colliculus, some fibers reaching the colliculus of the opposite side through the commissure of the inferior colliculi. The rest of the lateral lemniscus fibers continue to the medial geniculate nucleus of the thalamus from which fibers are projected to the transverse temporal gyri of the cerebral cortex (auditory cortex). From the inferior colliculus fibers likewise pass to the medial geniculate body, joining the fibers of the lateral lemniscus, and together with these constituting the *brachium of the inferior colliculus* (*inferior quadrigeminal brachium*, Fig. 258).

It is evident from the above that the hearing pathway has a more complex composition than the sensory systems heretofore studied, receiving contributions from a number of intercalated nuclear masses, and that it has a considerable ipsilateral representation. It is difficult to state the number of neurons involved in the auditory pathway from periphery to cortex, but the principal ones are: (1) spiral ganglion and cochlear nerve, (2) dorsal and ventral cochlear nuclei and lateral lemniscus, (3) superior olive and lateral lemniscus, (4) inferior colliculus and its brachium, and (5) medial geniculate nucleus and geniculocortical fibers (auditory radiations). Whether all these nuclei contribute fibers which carry impulses ultimately reaching the cortex is not fully settled. There is some evidence (Winkler) that the dorsal and intermediate trapezoid fibers which arise from the dorsal cochlear nucleus, and from the dorsomedial portion of the ventral nucleus pass directly to the medial geniculate body, and thence by a third neuron system to the cortex. This three-neuron path may be the path of hearing, the other nuclei of the cochlear pathway subserving reflex functions.

The *reflex* cochlear connections are likewise complex and many of them have not been fully determined. Probably all the nuclei intercalated in the auditory pathway, (superior olive, trapezoid nucleus, nucleus of the lateral lemniscus, inferior colliculus), are involved in these reflex circuits, sending fibers to the various motor nuclei for reflex movements in response to cochlear stimulation (sound). From the superior olive arises a fiber bundle known as the peduncle of the superior olive. Some of the fibers pass dorsomedially to the abducens nucleus for reflex turning of eyes. Others course in the reticular formation or enter the medial longitudinal fasciculus and go to the nucleus of the facial nerve, and to the nuclei innervating the muscles of the neck, eye, and ear (closing of the eye to loud noise, stapedius reflex, turning of head to sound, etc.). The nucleus of the lateral lemniscus gives rise to fibers which decussate and ascend in the lateral lemniscus to the inferior colliculus of the opposite side. Other fibers from this nucleus enter the reticular formation of the pons to be distributed to various motor nuclei. The inferior colliculus probably contributes fibers to the tectobulbar and tectospinal tracts, though according to some these tracts originate solely in the superior colliculus (Rasmussen). Since the inferior colliculus also sends fibers to the superior one, the latter may be concerned with auditory as well as optic reflexes.

Destruction of the cochlear nerve or of both cochlear nuclei will naturally cause complete deafness on the same side. Since the secondary cochlear pathways are both crossed and uncrossed, lesions of one lateral lemniscus or of the auditory cortex effect a bilateral diminution of hearing (partial

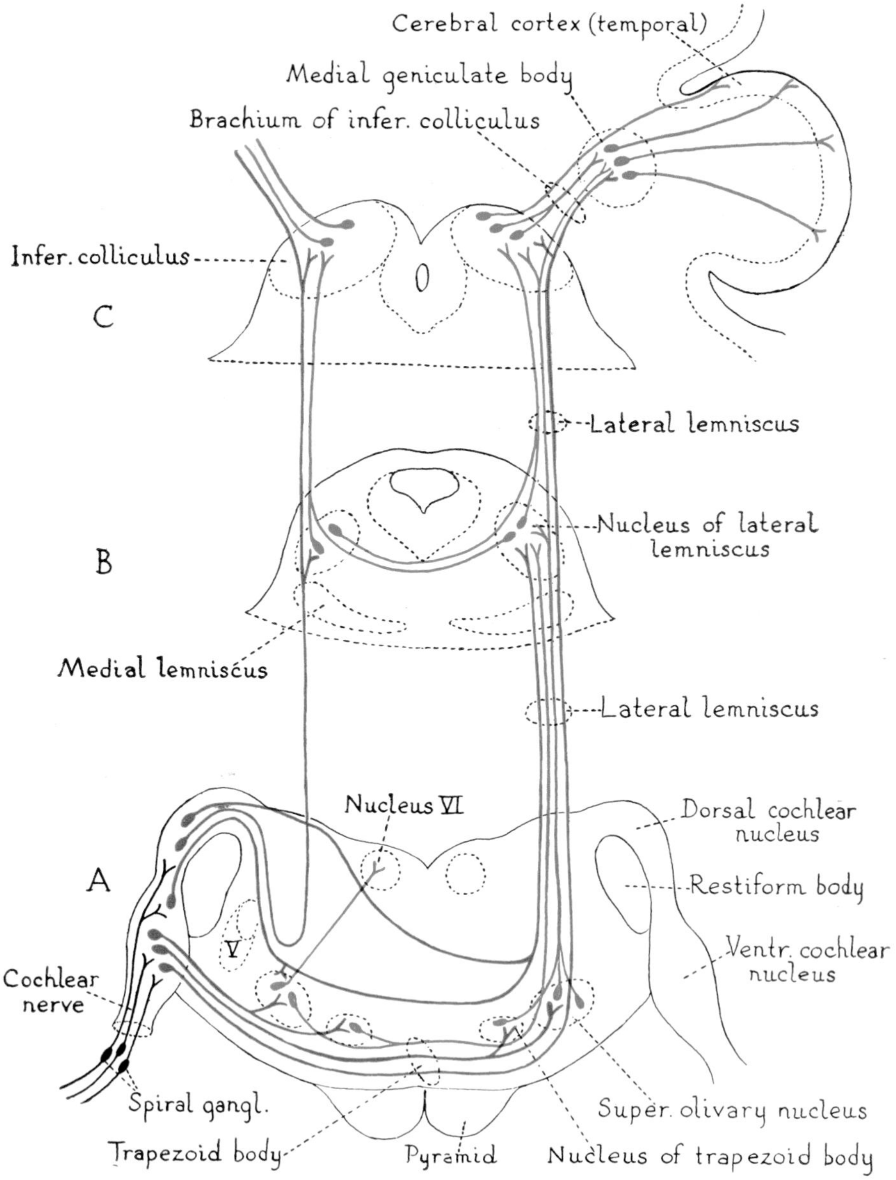

FIG. 258. Diagram of the auditory pathway. *A*, medulla; *B*, isthmus; *C*, midbrain.

deafness) usually more marked in the contralateral ear. Removal of one temporal lobe causes an impairment of sound localization on the opposite side, especially as regards judgment of the distance from which the sound is coming (Penfield and Evans, 1932).

The vestibular nerve and its central connections. The vestibular portion of the inner ear, concerned with equilibratory functions, consists of three semicircular canals, the utricle, and the saccule (Fig. 256). The semicircular canals are arranged at right angles to each other, representing approximately the three planes of space. At one end each canal has a dilatation, the *ampulla*, containing a patch of sensory epithelium, the *crista ampullaris*, char-

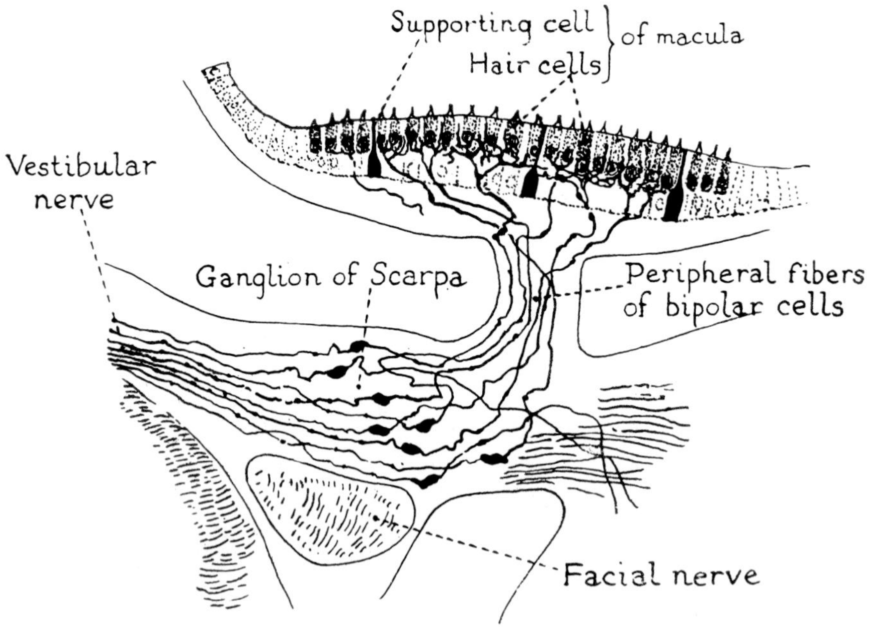

FIG. 259. The ganglion of Scarpa and terminations of the peripheral branches of its bipolar cells in a macula. Fetus of mouse near term. (After Cajal.)

acterized by the presence of special neuroepithelial cells, the *hair cells,* which constitute the vestibular receptors. The utricle and saccule each have a similar patch of sensory epithelium, the *macula utriculi* and *macula sacculi,* but here the hair cells are in contact with a gelatinous covering containing small calcareous crystals or particles, the *otoliths.* Hence utricle and saccule together constitute the so-called "otolith organ".

The cristae are stimulated by movement, and especially by rotatory (angular) movement, the pressure changes resulting from the displacement of the endolymph providing the adequate stimuli for the hair cells. The utricular macula is an organ of static sense, concerned mainly with the orientation of the individual with regard to gravity. Macular impulses convey information concerning the position of the head in space, the hair cells being stimulated by the otolithic particles whose position varies under the influence of gravity. The functions of the saccular macula is not fully understood. Destruction of both sacculae does not apparently produce any disturbance in equilibrium (De Kleijn and Versteegh), and it has been suggested that they might be concerned with cochlear rather than vestibular function, perhaps serving as an organ for registering bone vibration in the head (Tait).

The maculae and cristae are innervated by the vestibular ganglion (ganglion of Scarpa), an aggregation of bipolar cells located in the internal auditory meatus. The shorter peripheral processes of these cells go to the maculae and cristae (Figs. 256, 259), the longer central ones form the vestibular nerve which enters the medulla somewhat higher and medial to the cochlear nerve. The vestibular root fibers pass dorsally between the restiform body and the spinal trigeminal tract, and at some distance from the floor of the fourth ventricle most of them divide into short ascending and longer descending branches, the latter forming the descending vestibular tract broken up into a number of fascicles. Some of the root fibers continue without interruption to the cerebellum, terminating in the nucleus fastigii, the cortex of the flocculonodular lobe, and in other portions of the posterior vermis (uvula), constituting the direct vestibular tract to the cerebellum. The other vestibular fibers end in four terminal nuclei which can not all be seen in any one section: the *descending* or *spinal* vestibular nucleus, the *medial* or *principal* vestibular nucleus (nucleus triangularis, nucleus of Schwalbe), the *superior* vestibular nucleus (nucleus angularis, nucleus of von Bechterew), and the *lateral* vestibular nucleus of Deiters (Fig. 260). The ascending fibers terminate mainly in the superior and medial nuclei, the descending ones in the lateral and spinal nuclei.

The descending (spinal) vestibular nucleus is composed mainly of medium sized cells among which there are also many small ones. It extends from the zone of entry of the nerve caudally to about the upper limit of the nucleus gracilis. The lateral nucleus is a scattered mass of large multipolar cells (nucleus magnocellularis) resembling the large "motor" cells of the reticular formation and is by many considered as an aggregation of such cells. It is found in the lateral ventricular floor in the region of entry of the vestibular nerve and extends to the rostral level of the abducens nucleus. The superior nucleus lies somewhat dorsal to the lateral nucleus with which it is continuous, in the angle of the floor and lateral wall of the fourth ventricle. It extends from the level of the abducens nucleus to the principal sensory nucleus of the trigeminal nerve. The cells are of medium size and contain coarse chromofilic bodies. The medial nucleus is the largest and occupies most of the floor of the area vestibularis. Its rostral and caudal boundaries are difficult to delimit, appearing in lower levels than the lateral nucleus and becoming lost near the upper boundary of the abducens nucleus. It is composed mainly of small cells, hence it is also known as the *nucleus parvocellularis.*

The terminal vestibular nuclei give rise to secondary vestibular tracts which go primarily to the cerebellum and to the motor

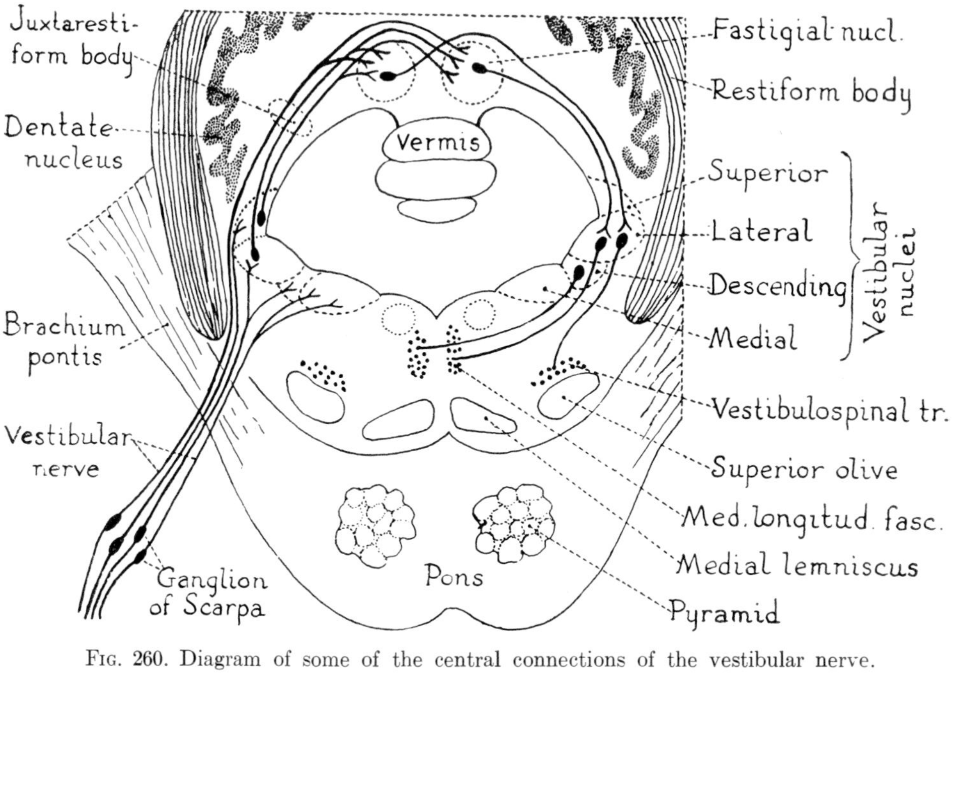

FIG. 260. Diagram of some of the central connections of the vestibular nerve.

nuclei of the cranial and spinal nerves. In addition to the root fibers which go directly to the cerebellum, vestibulocerebellar fibers (nucleocerebellar) pass to the same and opposite nucleus fastigii, and to the cortex of the flocculonodular lobe, uvula, and lingula. These fibers originate primarily in the superior, and to a lesser extent in the lateral vestibular nucleus, and it is possible that the other vestibular nuclei may likewise contribute similar fibers (Fig. 260). From the fastigial (and globose) nuclei of the cerebellum crossed and uncrossed fibers pass to the medulla and terminate mainly in the vestibular nuclei, some ending in the reticular formation or even descending to the cervical cord (fastigiobulbar or cerebellobulbar tract). The direct vestibular root fibers, the vestibulocerebellar and fastigiobulbar fibers course medial to the restiform body and collectively constitute the internal segment of the inferior cerebellar peduncle or *juxtarestiform body* (Fig. 260). Thus while the restiform body is composed primarily of afferent cerebellar fibers, the juxtarestiform portion contains both afferent and efferent ones, all of which are related to the vestibular mechanism. It is obvious that the vestibular nuclei are not only relay stations in vestibulobulbar and vestibulospinal reflexes, but serve also as parts of afferent and efferent cerebellar pathways.

The secondary vestibular fibers which go to the motor nuclei of the brain and spinal cord are organized into several bundles (Figs. 198, 260, 261). The uncrossed lateral vestibulospinal tract has already been discussed. It arises principally from the lateral vestibular nucleus, to a lesser extent from the descending nucleus. The fibers enter the reticular formation of the same side, pass downward along the dorsal surface of the inferior olive and enter the spinal cord where they descend throughout its whole length in the ventral funiculus. The tract mediates reflex responses of the trunk and limb muscles to vestibular stimulation.

From the superior, medial, and descending nucleus, and probably from the lateral as well, internal arcuate fibers pass to the medial longitudinal fasciculus of the same and the opposite side where many bifurcate into ascending and descending arms, while others turn up or down without bifurcation (Figs. 198, 261). The ascending fibers go primarily to the midbrain (vestibulomesencephalic), especially to the nuclei of N.VI, N.IV, and N.III which innervate the ocular muscles. Some terminate in the interstitial nucleus of Cajal and the nucleus of the posterior commissure (nucleus of Darkschewitsch). The descending fibers are distributed to the nuclei of N.XI and to the upper cervical cord innervating the neck musculature. These fibers bring the eye and neck muscles under reflex vestibular control. The exact contributions of the different vestibular nuclei to the medial longitudinal fasciculus are not fully ascertained for man, but appear to be as follows in some of the animals studied (Rasmussen, 1932; Buchanan, 1937). The superior nucleus furnishes ascending fibers to the fasciculus of the same side. Fibers from the medial nucleus, and from the lateral also, mainly cross to the opposite side where they bifurcate into ascending and descending arms. Most of the fibers from the descending nucleus apparently cross and descend in the opposite fasciculus as the medial vestibulospinal tract (Fig. 198).

From the medial (triangular) nucleus there also arise fibers which pass to the reticular formation of the same and opposite side (trianguloreticular bundle of Spitzer). These medium sized fibers reach the visceral motor nuclei of the cranial nerves such as the dorsal motor nucleus of N.X, the secretory nuclei, and other autonomic cell groups, mediating such reflexes as vomiting and pallor on excessive vestibular stimulation. Many of these fibers enter the dorsal longitudinal bundle of Schütz and are relayed in the nucleus intercalatus or nucleus interpositus before reaching the visceral nuclei.

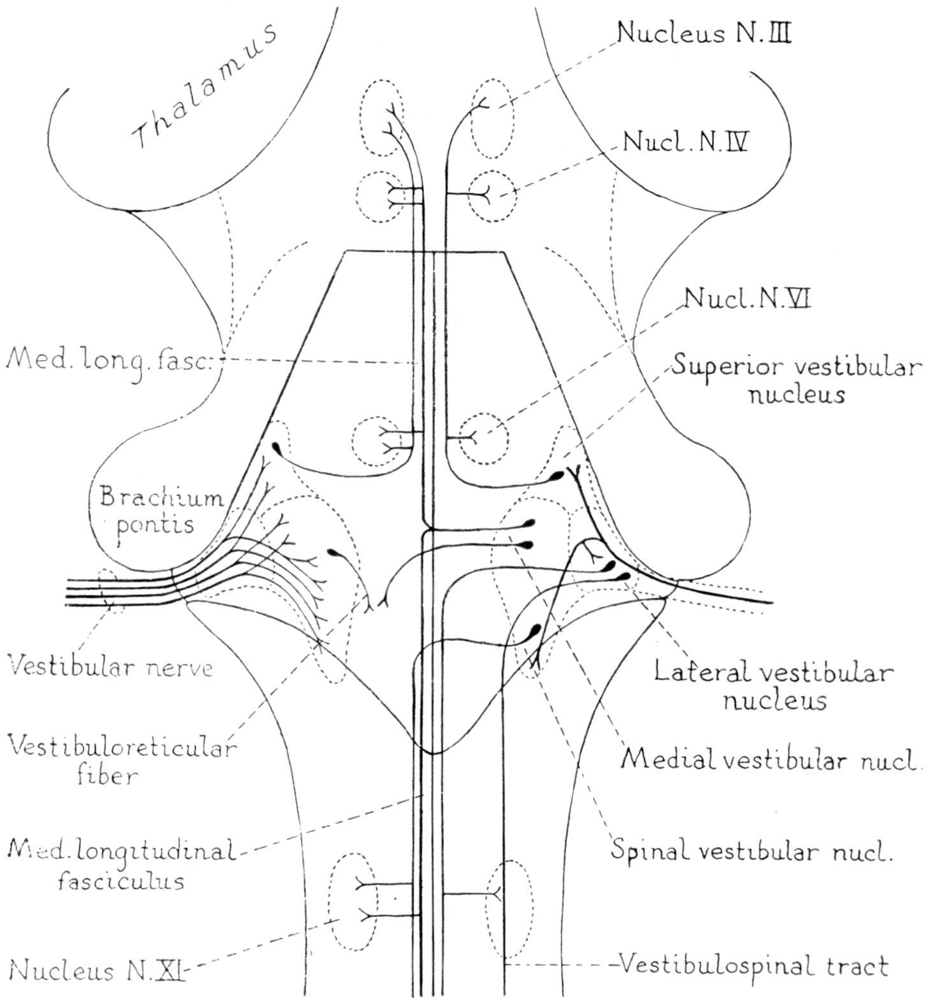

FIG. 261. Diagram of some of the principal connections of the vestibular nerve.

In a general way the superior, lateral, and descending nuclei composed of large and medium sized cells and constituting the lateral vestibular column are concerned with somatic vestibular control. The small-celled medial nucleus is in addition extensively associated with reflex visceral activities in response to vestibular stimulation.

Secondary vestibular pathways to the cortex of the temporal lobe undoubtedly exist, but their course and the exact location of the vestibular cortex are not fully ascertained. Such vestibulocortical connections would explain the dizziness or vertigo which in man is a frequent symptom of vestibular disease. In animals (cats and dogs) it has been experimentally shown that vestibular impulses reach the cortex. When the temporal convolutions are sensitized by painting with strychnine, stimulation of the labyrinth by rotation produces convulsive movements (Spiegel), but these movements fail to appear if the eighth nerve is destroyed (Aronson). Spiegel has also shown that the electrical action currents led off from the temporal lobe increased in strength during vestibular stimulation. The important researches of Winkler have suggested a probable cortical pathway. According to this investigator the fibers supplying the maculae of the utricle and saccule terminate only in part in the vestibular nuclei, another portion terminating in the ventral part of the ventral cochlear nucleus. From the latter nucleus secondary fibers (trapezoid fibers) proceed to end in part in the superior olivary and the trapezoid nuclei of the same and opposite side, and in part to form the ventrolateral portion of the lateral lemniscus where some of the fibers reach the inferior colliculus. From the inferior colliculus impulses are projected to the temporal cortex, either directly or after a relay in the medial geniculate body. The lateral lemniscus would thus be a link in both the auditory and vestibular cortical pathways.

The mechanisms governing equilibrium, i.e., the maintenance of appropriate positions of the body in space, are largely of a reflex character and are activated by afferent impulses from several sources. Among the more important of these are the general proprioceptive impulses from the muscles of the eyes, neck, trunk and lower limbs, and the special proprioceptive impulses from the vestibular sense organ of the ear (labyrinth). Impulses from the retina which reach the cerebral cortex and contribute to the conscious perception of visual space are likewise important aids in proper spatial orientation. In this equilibratory complex the labyrinth constitutes a highly specialized proprioceptor stimulated by the *position* or *changes in position* of the head. When the head is moved, either by contraction of the neck muscles or by the shifting of the body as a whole, the cristae are stimulated and through the central vestibular connections effect the reflex compensatory adjustments of the eyes and limbs needed for the particular movement (kinetostatic reflexes). The new attitude, as long as the position of the head remains unchanged, is then sustained by reflexes originating in the macula of the utricle. The sustaining (static) reflexes are initiated by the gravitational pull of the otolithic membrane on the macular hair cells.

The vestibulospinal tracts, and other descending fibers from the reticular formation of the medulla exert a strong excitatory influence on the tonus of the extensor (antigravity) muscles. Normally extensor tonus is kept within optimal limits by impulses from higher centers passing through the pyramidal and extrapyramidal tracts. The influence of these centers is removed by a transection of the brain stem anywhere above the level of the vestibular nuclei and below the superior colliculi of the midbrain. In such animals the extensor tonus of the limbs, neck, and tail is tremendously augmented, giving rise to the condition of "decerebrate rigidity". The rigidity is abolished by the destruction of the vestibular nuclei or the vestibulospinal tracts.

Abnormal stimulation or irritative lesions of the vestibular nerve or of its central connections produce forced movements of the body such as falling, and kinetic deviations expressed in *past-pointing* and the rhythmic oscillations of the eyeballs known as *nystagmus*. In severe cases there may be vertigo and such visceral disturbances as vomiting, nausea, sweating, and vasomotor changes.

THE FACIAL NERVE

The facial nerve is both afferent and efferent (Fig. 262). It contains (a) special visceral efferent (branchiomotor) fibers to the striped superficial muscles of the face and scalp (mimic musculature), the platysma, stylohyoid, posterior belly of digastric, and stapedius. (b) General visceral efferent (preganglionic) fibers which go to the submandibular and sphenopalatine ganglia and supply the submaxillary, sublingual, and lacrimal glands and the mucous membrane of the nose and roof of the mouth. (c) Special visceral afferent fibers of taste from the anterior two thirds of the tongue, which have their cell bodies in the *geniculate ganglion*. (d) There are probably a few general somatic afferent fibers from

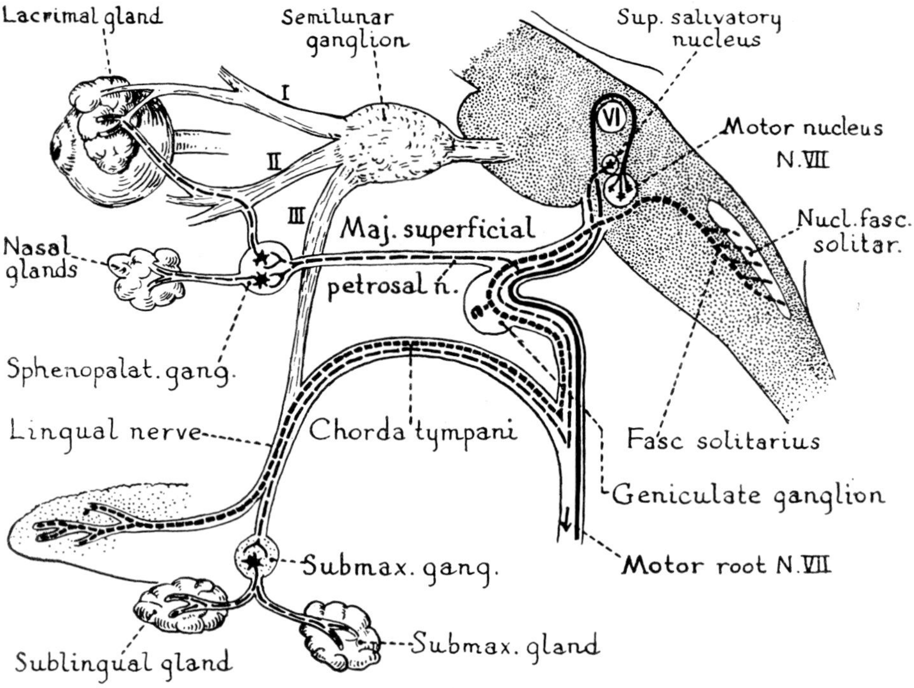

FIG. 262. Diagram showing components of facial nerve (intermediofacial). *I*, ophthalmic, *II*, maxillary, and *III*, mandibular ramus of trigeminal nerve. (After Villiger.)

cells in the geniculate ganglion which together with similar fibers from N.IX and N.X aid in the innervation of the external auditory meatus and the skin back of the ear.

The fibers supplying the facial muscles form the large motor root. The afferent and efferent visceral fibers constitute the intermediate nerve of Wrisberg which emerges between the facial motor root and the vestibular nerve (Fig. 249). According to some the intermediate nerve is entirely afferent, the efferent preganglionic fibers forming part of the motor root.

There are some observations which suggest that the facial nerve may carry impulses of deep pain and deep pressure from the face (Hunt). In some cases where the trigeminal nerve was cut for the relief of facial neuralgia, deep pain due to heavy pressure apparently persisted, and on the other hand such pain is sometimes diminished in lesions of the facial nerve (L. E. Davis). The question is not fully settled, but recent investigations indicate that both deep and superficial pain are probably mediated exclusively by the trigeminal nerve (Smyth).

The *motor* (*branchiomotor*) *nucleus* of N.VII is a column of typical multipolar motor cells, about 4 mm. long, occupying a lateral position similar to that of the nucleus ambiguus (Figs 220, 223, 249). The axons of the cells leave the nucleus on its dorsal surface, loop around the abducens nucleus as already described, and emerge on the lateral aspect of the pons as the motor root. The nucleus is composed of a number of distinct cell groups which probably innervate specific facial muscles but the exact distribution of their fibers has not been fully worked out. In a general way a dorsal and several ventral groups may be recognized. The dorsal furnishes fibers to the superior branch of the nerve supplying the frontalis, orbicularis oculi, and corrugator supercilii. The ventral groups, passing from the most medial to the most lateral, probably innervate respectively the stapedius, the platysma, the muscles of the ear, mouth, and face. A small group of similar motor cells found dorsomedial to the main nucleus is known as the *accessory facial nucleus.* It may send fibers to the phylogenetically older muscles innervated by N.VII, such as the stylohyoid, posterior belly of the digastric, and the stapedius.

The nucleus receives terminals from many sources. Among these are (1) secondary trigeminal fibers, also direct collaterals from the spinal V, for the corneal and other trigeminofacial reflexes. (2) Secondary and tertiary fibers from the superior olive and other acoustic nuclei for acousticofacial reflexes, such as closing of eyes to loud noise and the stapedius reflex. (3) Fibers from the superior colliculi (blinking reflex). (4) Corticobulbar (pyramidal) fibers for voluntary facial movement. These fibers detach themselves from the pyramidal tract at or above the level of the facial nucleus and stream fountain-like into the latter, going to both the same and the opposite side (Sand, 1903). (5) Terminals or collaterals from extrapyramidal systems, representing the emotional control of the facial musculature. These probably come from the corpus striatum, substantia nigra and thalamus, either directly or by way of the reticular formation (reticulobulbar) and the medial longitudinal fasciculus.

The *visceral motor nucleus* also known as the *superior salivatory nucleus* is difficult to distinguish and is apparently represented by a scattered group of cells in the lateral part of the reticular formation. The cells extend caudally to the upper tip of the nucleus ambiguus, the more caudal cells constituting the inferior salivatory nucleus of the glossopharyngeal nerve (Yagita). In Fig. 220 these two cell groups are indicated schematically as a single nuclear column. The superior salivatory nucleus and probably other accessory cells send out preganglionic fibers which leave the brain stem by way of the intermediate nerve. Some pass via the chorda tympani to the submandibular ganglion whence they are relayed to the submaxillary and sublingual glands. Others enter the greater superficial petrosal nerve and reach the sphenopalatine ganglion from which postganglionic secretory and vasomotor fibers go to the lacrimal gland, and to the mucous membrane of the nose and roof of the mouth. The terminals ending in the superior salivatory nucleus which elicit lacrimal and salivary reflexes are not well known on account of the obscurity and the diffuse character of the pons in the region of the salivatory nucleus (Figs. 262, 263).

The *afferent visceral fibers* of N.VII, conveying principally taste impulses from the anterior portion of the tongue, form the main component of the nervus intermedius. These fibers enter the fasciculus solitarius and terminate in the upper portion of the nucleus of that bundle (nucleus gustatorius).

Lesions of the facial nerve produce a total ipsilateral paralysis of facial movements, both reflex and voluntary, with atrophy and RD. Emotional expression is completely lost. There is inability to wrinkle the forehead, to close the eye, to show the teeth, puff out the cheek or whistle. The palpebral fissure is widened, the angle of the mouth droops. It is obvious that the corneal and blinking reflexes are lost since the motor arc of these reflexes is destroyed. If the stapedius is involved there is increased sensitivity of hearing (hyperacusis), especially toward deep tones. Lesion of the nervus intermedius will cause an ipsilateral loss of taste on the anterior two thirds of the tongue.

In pyramidal lesions involving one side of the face (upper motor neuron paralysis) the upper facial muscles concerned with wrinkling the forehead, frowning or closing of eyes, appear to be little affected, while there is marked weakness in the lower face, especially in the perioral region. The generally accepted explanation is that the cell

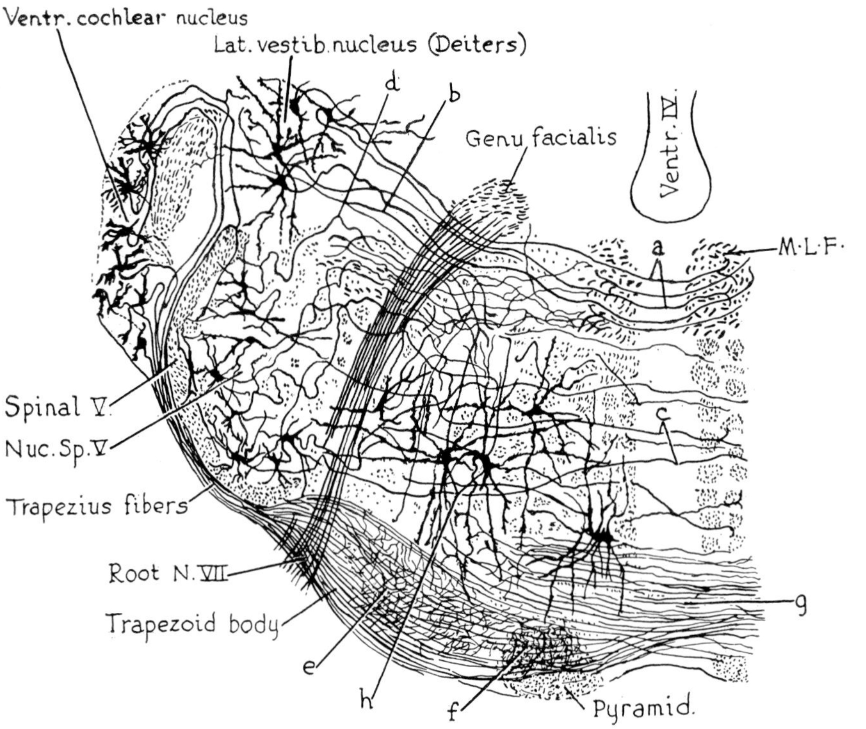

FIG. 263. Transverse section through medulla of new-born mouse at level of emergence of facial nerve. Golgi impregnation. *a*, decussating fibers of secondary vestibular tract (from Deiters' nucleus); *b*, uncrossed fiber of secondary vestibular tract; *c*, decussating secondary trigeminal fibers; *d*, uncrossed secondary trigeminal fiber in dorsal part of reticular formation; *e*, collaterals from trapezoid body terminating in superior olivary nucleus; *f*, collaterals from trapezoid body terminating in trapezoid nucleus; *g*, decussating trapezoid fibers, the more dorsal ones are from the opposite side; *h*, large (premotor) cells of the reticular formation; *M.L.F.*, medial longitudinal fasciculus. (After Cajal.)

groups of the motor nucleus supplying the upper face and forehead receive a bilateral pyramidal innervation, i.e., both crossed and uncrossed fibers, while the pyramidal innervation of that part of the nucleus supplying the lower face is predominantly crossed.

The mimetic or emotional innervation of the face is to a large extent involuntary. In purely pyramidal lesions involving one side of the face the patient has difficulty in showing his teeth or whistling. However, spontaneous laughing or crying and other emotional expression is unaffected. Expression may at times be actually accentuated on the paralyzed side. The innervation is probably by fibers from the globus pallidus and substantia nigra, which reach the facial nucleus directly or through intercalated neurons of the reticular formation. When these extrapyramidal connections are destroyed, as in lesions of the globus pallidus or substantia nigra, the emotional play of the facial muscles is reduced or lost and the face assumes a frozen or mask-like appearance.

THE ABDUCENS NERVE

The abducens is primarily a motor nerve innervating the external rectus muscle of the eyeball, but may possibly contain some afferent proprioceptive fibers from that muscle, from scattered ganglion cells found along the root (Tozer and Sherrington). The nucleus forms a column of typical somatic motor cells, about 3 mm. long, placed in the lateral part of the median eminence. The root fibers pass ventrally to emerge at the caudal border of the pons in close relation to the pyramidal tract. The nucleus receives crossed and uncrossed vestibular fibers through the medial longitudinal fasciculus for vestibular control of lateral eye movement; fibers from the superior olive for reflex lateral turning of eyes to sound; pyramidal (corticobulbar) fibers for voluntary movement; and probably fibers from the colliculi, globus pallidus and other extrapyramidal sources by way of the medial longitudinal and predorsal fasciculi.

All ocular movements, whether lateral, vertical or rotatory, require the reciprocal activity of both eyes. In movements of lateral gaze the external rectus of one eye and the internal rectus of the other must contract simultaneously. The central mechanism securing conjugate lateral movement has not been demonstrated with certainty but appears to be as follows. In the reticular formation close to the motor cells of the abducens nucleus, are small groups of cells which send fibers to the oculomotor nucleus by way of the medial longitudinal fasciculus (Fig. 264). The exact course of these *internuclear* or *interocular* fibers has not been fully determined. They ascend uncrossed to the ipsilateral oculomotor nucleus which then sends crossed root fibers to the opposite internal rectus. Any impulses effecting lateral eye movement, whether vestibular, auditory, pyramidal or extrapyramidal, first impinge on these intercalated cells and through the fibers of the latter are related to both the abducens and the oculomotor nucleus. These cell groups, sometimes termed the *parabducens nucleus*, and their fibers are often referred to as the pontile "center for lateral gaze".

Lesions of the sixth nerve cause an ipsilateral paralysis of the lateral rectus muscle with consequent *internal strabismus* (squint) due to the unopposed action of the medial rectus. The other eye is unaffected and is able to move in all directions. When the abducens nucleus itself is affected there may occur a paralysis of *lateral gaze* toward the side of the injury and both eyes are turned to the opposite side (conjugate deviation).

The explanation of this curious finding is that pontine lesions in the region of the abducens nucleus also destroy the adjacent neurons in the parabducens nucleus. Axons from the latter are thus injured before they enter the medial longitudinal fasciculus and ascend to terminate in the oculomotor nucleus. As a result the oculomotor nucleus fails to receive coordinating impulses and the contralateral medial rectus muscle does not participate in reflex lateral gaze, while the ipsilateral lateral rectus muscle is paralyzed. Since the lateral gaze mechanism of the opposite side is intact, both eyes will be pulled over to that side (Fig. 264).

Owing to the proximity of the emerging root fibers of N.VI and the pyramidal tract, lesions in the caudal third of the pons may result in a so-called middle alternating hemiplegia similar to that noted for N.XII. There is a lower motor neuron paralysis of the ipsilateral external rectus muscle with internal strabismus and inability to turn the eye outward, and a contralateral upper motor neuron (pyramidal) paralysis of the trunk and extremities.

THE MEDIAL LONGITUDINAL FASCICULUS (FIG. 264)

This fasciculus together with the predorsal bundle which is functionally related to it, represents a complex system of fibers which are among the earliest to myelinate during fetal development. It extends as a definite bundle from the most cranial portion of the midbrain to the lower portion of the medulla where the fibers become incorporated in the ventral funiculus of the spinal cord. How far they descend in the latter is not definitely determined. The majority undoubtedly end in the upper cervical segments supplying the neck muscles, but some may descend to lower levels, a few reaching the lumbar and perhaps even the sacral seg-

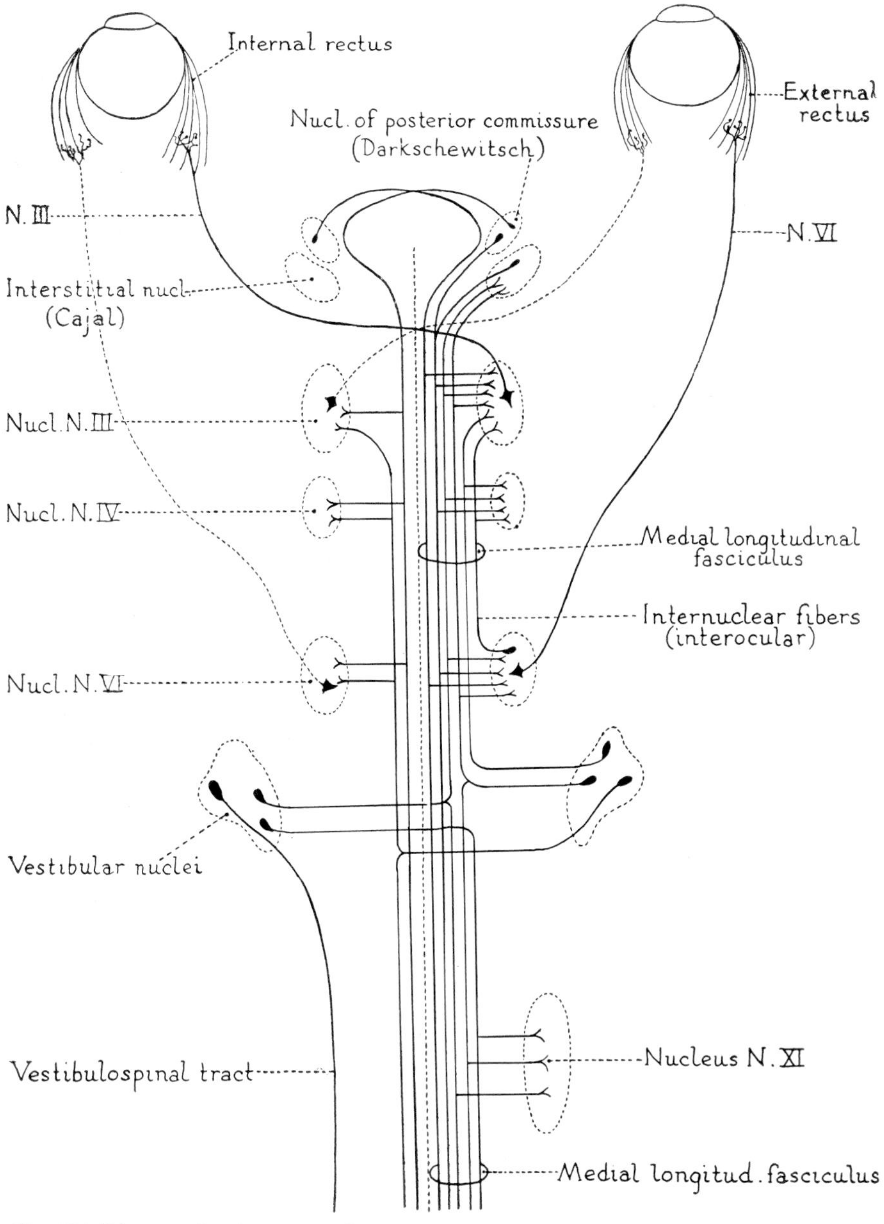

FIG. 264. Diagram showing some of the important components of the medial longitudinal fasciculus.

ments. Below the level of the vestibular nuclei the fibers are all descending, above that level the bundle contains both ascending and descending fibers.

Though of complex constitution the medial longitudinal fasciculus nevertheless constitutes a certain functional entity. It relates impulses from various sources to the motor nuclei of the cranial nerves and the upper cervical cord, especially to those of the eye and neck muscles concerned with oculogyric and cephalogyric movements. Among the more important components of the fasciculus are the following: (1) Descending fibers from the *interstitial nucleus* (interstitiospinal) and the *nucleus of the posterior commissure* or *nucleus of Darkschewitsch* (commissurospinal), two nuclei situated in the most cranial portion of the midbrain tegmentum. Since these nuclei receive fibers from the globus pallidus, superior colliculi, and probably from the substantia nigra, the interstitiospinal and commissurospinal fibers bring the eye and neck muscles under extrapyramidal control. (2) Secondary vestibular fibers, both crossed and uncrossed, which ascend to the nuclei of Nn. VI, IV, and III, and descend to the nucleus of N.XI and the ventral horn of the upper cervical cord, bringing the eye and neck muscles under reflex vestibular control. Some of the vestibular fibers terminate in the interstitial and commissural nuclei (Fig. 264). (3) Internuclear fibers connecting the abducens with the oculomotor nucleus, which form part of the central mechanism securing conjugate lateral eye movements. (4) Fibers from the superior olive to the abducens and the facial nuclei mediating reflex facial and lateral gaze movements in response to sound. (5) Tectobulbar and tectospinal fibers from the superior colliculi for optic reflexes (Fig. 199). These descend mainly in the more loosely arranged predorsal bundle but are functionally a part of the same system. Besides the above fibers there are others originating in the reticular formation (reticulobulbar and reticulospinal) which descend in or near the medial longitudinal fasciculus and are especially numerous in the predorsal bundle (Fig. 197). Finally, it is the belief of some authorities that the corticobulbar (pyramidal) fibers innervating the eye muscles join the medial longitudinal fasciculus to reach the nuclei supplying those muscles.

SECTION OF PONS AND PONTILE TEGMENTUM THROUGH ROOTS OF TRIGEMINAL NERVE (FIGS. 265, 266, 267)

The fourth ventricle is narrower, its roof still formed by the cerebellum in which may be distinguished the deep cerebellar nuclei. The right side is somewhat lower and still shows the restiform body and brachium pontis. Fibers of the juxtarestiform body connect the superior vestibular nucleus with the roof nuclei of the cerebellum. On the left side the section is above the restiform body, and the superior cerebellar peduncle (brachium conjunctivum) arising primarily from the dentate nucleus, is now a large fiber bundle forming the dorsolateral wall of the fourth ventricle.

The basilar portion is larger than the tegmentum and as before contains the transverse and longitudinal fibers and the pontile nuclei. The pyramidal and corticopontile tracts are broken up into numerous bundles, and a number of vertical or perpendicular fibers are seen passing from the pons to the tegmentum. Those within the raphé are probably continuations of transverse pontile fibers which connect the tegmentum with the cerebellum (tegmentocerebellar). The more laterally placed perpendicular bundles are aberrant pyramidal (corticobulbar) fibers going directly or indirectly to some of the cranial motor nuclei (Figs. 223, 266).

In the tegmentum the central tegmental tract is assuming a more central position. The medial lemniscus is traversed by numerous fibers of the now strongly developed trapezoid body, and the lateral lemniscus is a well formed bundle in the ventrolateral part of the tegmentum, in close relation to the superior olive which is still visible in the right (lower) half of the section. On that side the superior vestibular nucleus is also still present, connected to the roof nuclei of the cerebellum by fibers of the juxtarestiform body (Fig. 265). On the left side the superior olive and superior vestibular nucleus have practically disappeared. The spinothalamic and ventral spinocerebellar tracts are in their usual position, as are the large medial longitudinal and predorsal fasciculi. Dorsolateral to the medial longitudinal fasciculus are the longitudinally cut fibers of the facial genu (Fig. 266).

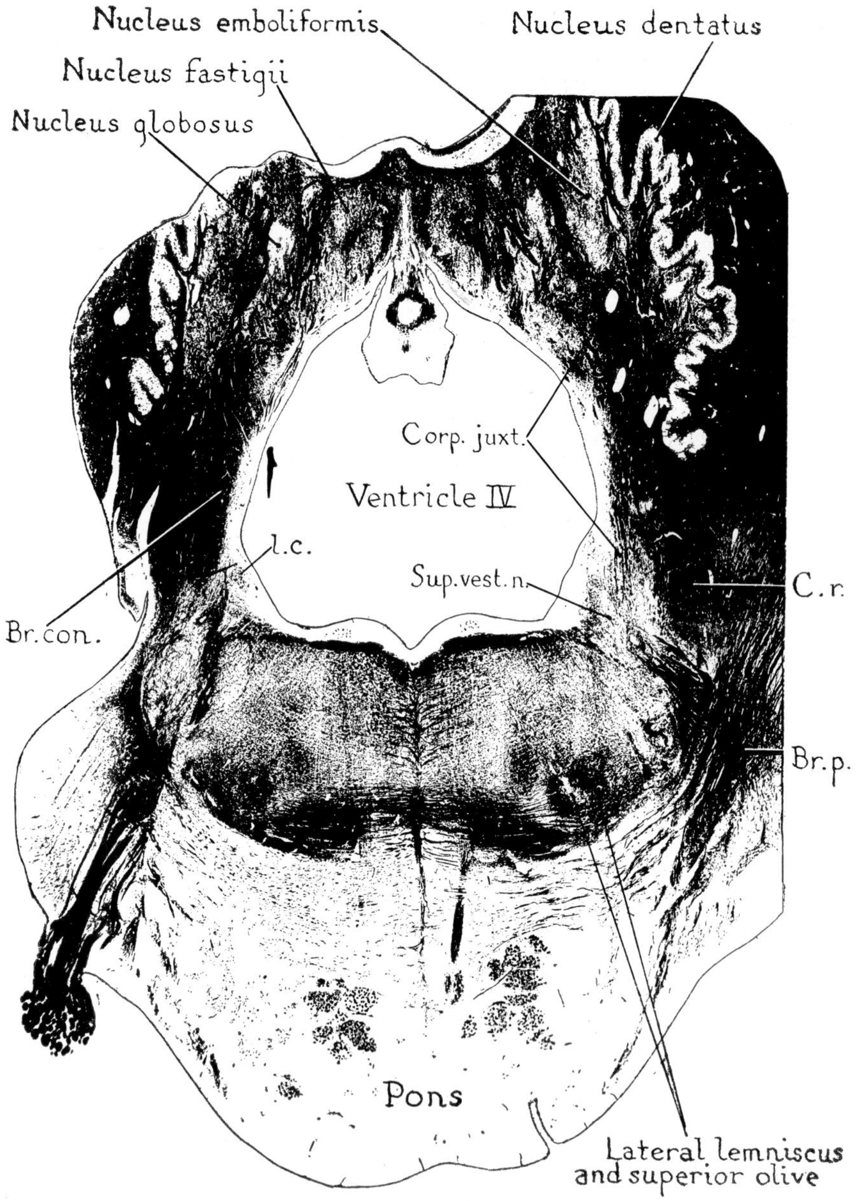

FIG. 265. Section of pons, pontile tegmentum and part of cerebellum, through root of trigeminal nerve. One month infant. Weigert's myelin stain. Photograph, ×6½. *Br.con.*, brachium conjunctivum; *Br.p.*, brachium pontis; *C.r.*, corpus restiforme; *l.c.*, locus ceruleus; *Sup. vest.n.*; superior vestibular nucleus.

The reticular formation is somewhat diminished. The nucleus of the medial eminence (eminentia teres) lies dorsal to the facial genu. In the region of the raphé are extensive cellular aggregations. In the ventral portion between and immediately above the medial lemnisci, is the *reticular tegmental nucleus* of the pons which is a continuation of the inferior central nucleus seen in lower levels. It is considered by some as a medial tegmental extension of the pontile nuclei which it resembles, but

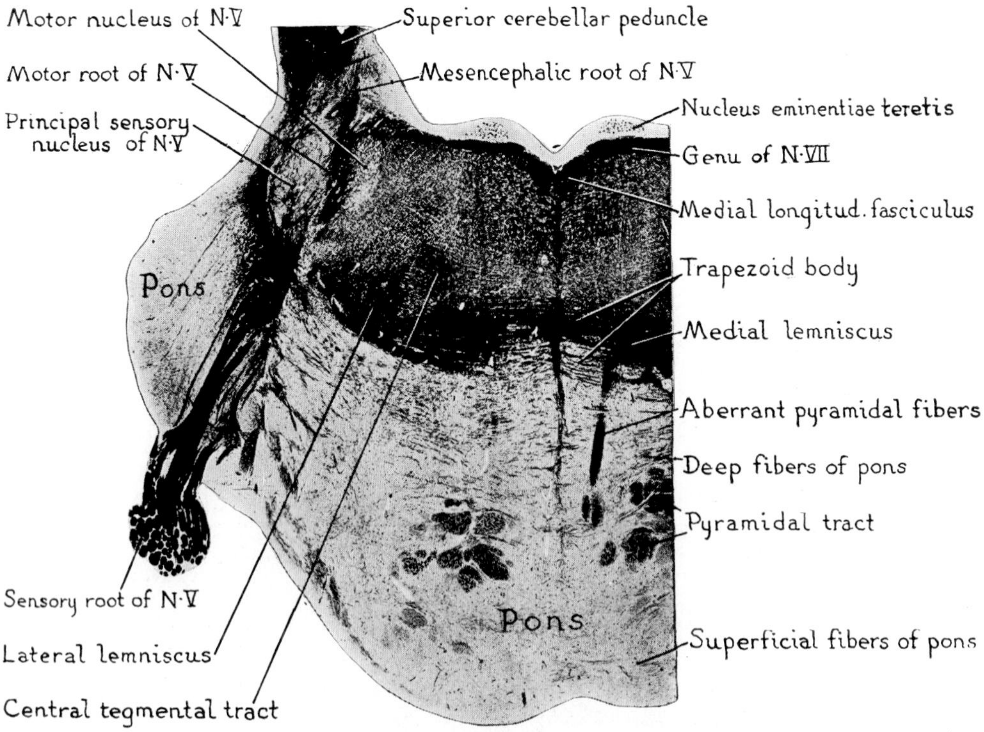

FIG. 266. Section of pons and pontile tegmentum of one month infant through entrance of trigeminal nerve. Weigert's myelin stain. Photograph, ×8.

contains also large multipolar cells not found in the pons. More dorsally in the raphéal region is the *superior central nucleus*, a closely packed aggregation of relatively small cells most prominent in the upper pontile levels (Figs. 270, 275). More laterally the reticular formation is rather poor in cells, but scattered among them are the large cells which form the motor reticular nucleus.

The afferent root fibers of the trigeminal nerve pass through the pons and reach the tegmentum where many are seen terminating in the cephalic end of the terminal nucleus of N.V (Figs. 266, 268). This is a large gray mass known as the "main" or "principal" sensory nucleus of N.V and is broken up into several cellular groups lying dorsolateral to the entering fibers (Fig. 270). Medial to this is the oval motor nucleus of N.V whose coarse efferent fibers are seen passing out internal to the afferent ones, between the motor and sensory nuclei. Another small bundle of root fibers is seen running dorsally from the motor root toward the angle of the ventricular floor where they turn upward and form a longitudinal bundle extending to the upper portion of the midbrain (Figs. 266, 273). This is the *mesencephalic tract* or *root of N.V* whose fibers arise from large unipolar cells placed in the lateral part of the central gray matter of the cerebral aqueduct, extending the whole length of the midbrain (Figs. 275, 276). In every section a few such cells may be seen lying medial to the mesencephalic tract. The significance of these cells and their fibers is discussed below.

THE TRIGEMINAL NERVE

The trigeminal contains both sensory and motor nerve fibers. The afferent fibers convey general somatic impulses of touch, pain, and temperature from the skin of the face

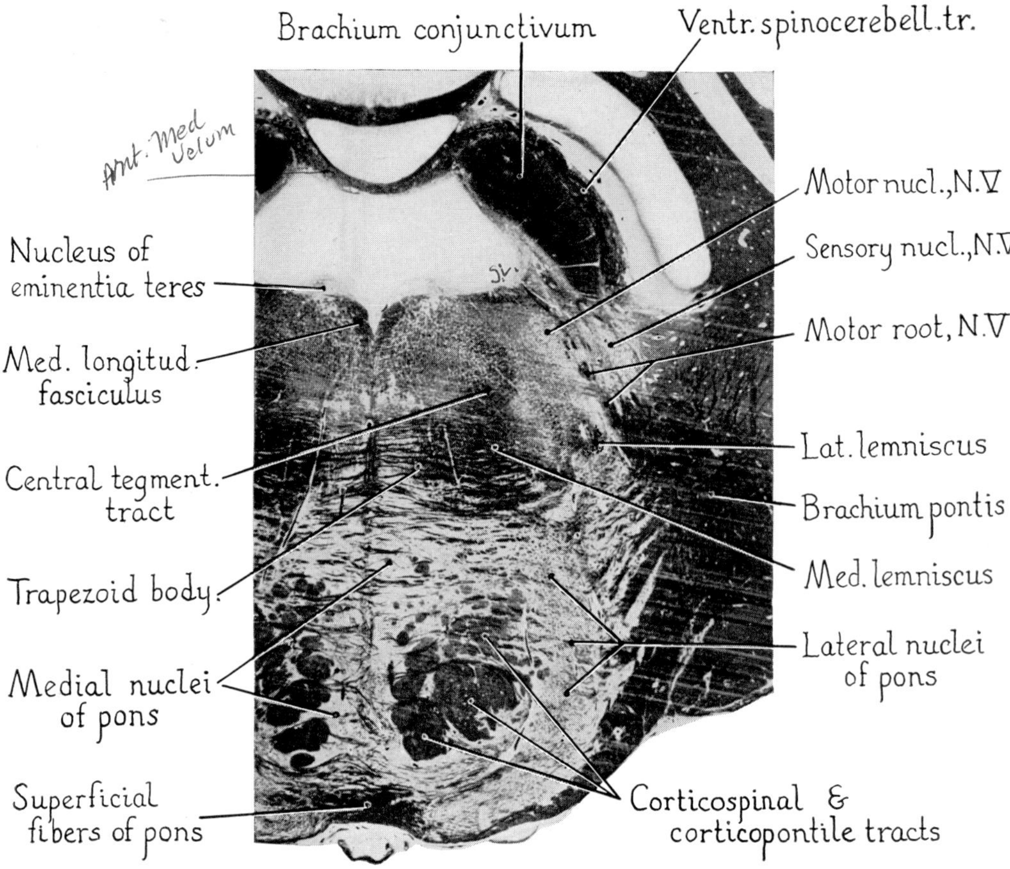

FIG. 267. Transverse section of adult pons, through motor trigeminal nucleus. Weigert's myelin stain. Photograph, ×6.

and forehead, from the ectodermal mucous membrane of the nose and oral cavity, from the meninges (dura mater), and proprioceptive fibers from the masticatory muscles. The efferent branchiomotor (special visceral) fibers supply the musculature of the jaw, the tensor tympani and tensor veli palatini. The afferent fibers constitute the large sensory root or portio major of the nerve. The efferent fibers form the smaller motor root or portio minor, also known as the masticator nerve.

The afferent fibers, with the exception of the proprioceptive ones, have their cell bodies in the large, flattened, crescent-shaped *semilunar* or *Gasserian ganglion* placed on the cerebral surface of the petrous bone in the middle cranial fossa and composed of typical unipolar ganglion cells (Fig. 268). The peripheral processes of these cells form the three main divisions of the trigeminal nerve: ophthalmic, maxillary, and mandibular. The first two are wholly sensory, but in the mandibular branch is also incorporated the entire motor root supplying the jaw muscles. The ophthalmic branch innervates the forehead, upper eyelid, cornea, conjunctiva, dorsum of nose, and the mucous membrane of the nasal vestibule and of the frontal sinus. The maxillary division supplies the upper lip, lateral and posterior portions of the nose, upper cheek, anterior portion of temple, and the mucous membrane of the nose, upper jaw, upper teeth, and roof of mouth to the palatopharyngeal arch. The sensory fibers of the man-

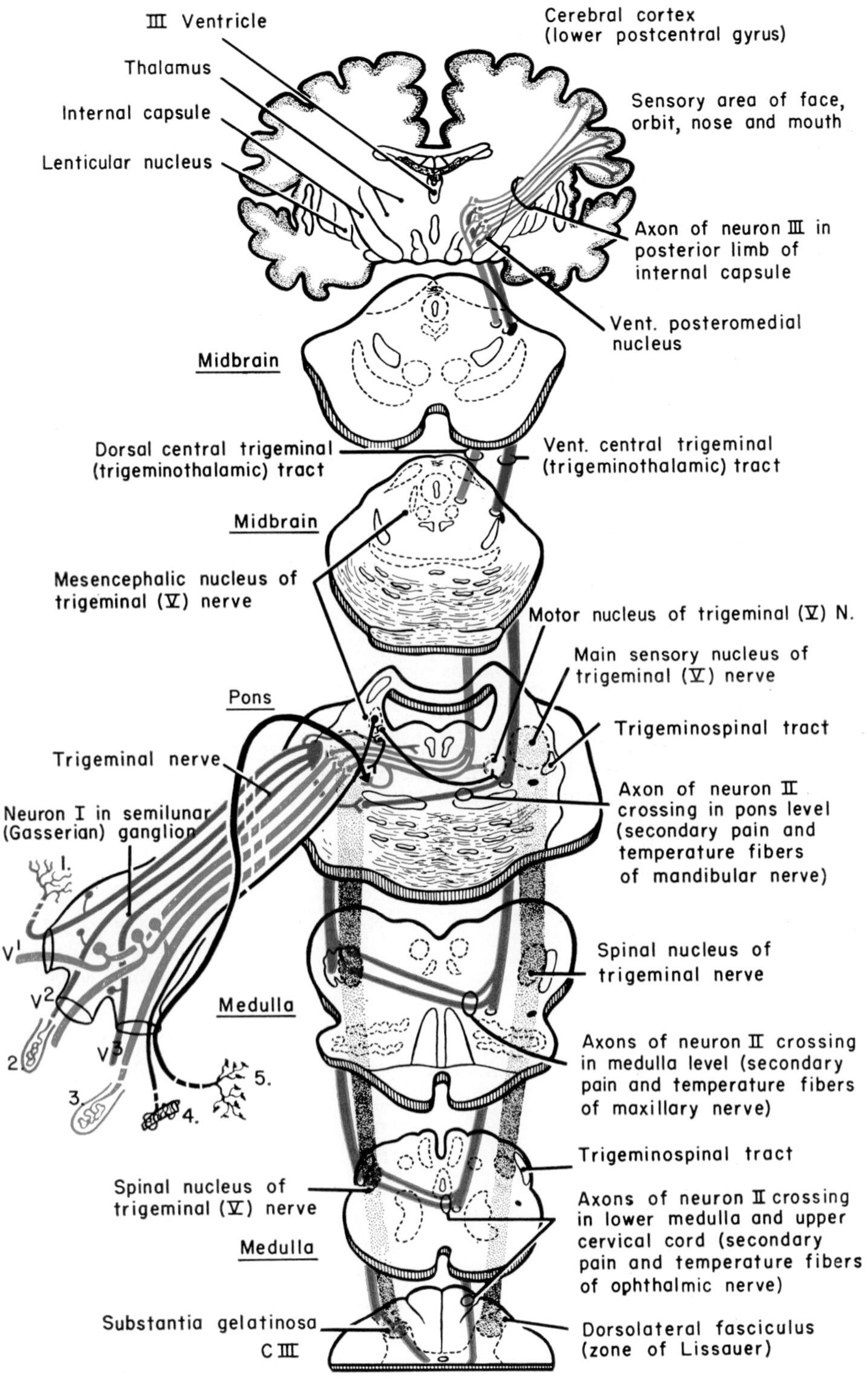

FIG. 268. Diagram of secondary trigeminal tracts. The ventral central trigeminal tract (red) conveys pain and temperature impulses; the dorsal central trigeminal tract (blue) is the pathway for touch and pressure. The brain stem location of the ascending lateral spinothalamic tract is indicated in black on the right side. The ophthalmic (V1), maxillary (V2), and mandibular (V3) divisions of the trigeminal nerve are identified. 1. Free nerve ending; 2. heat receptor; 3. Meissner's corpuscle; 4. neuromuscular spindle; 5. motor end plate in muscle of mastication.

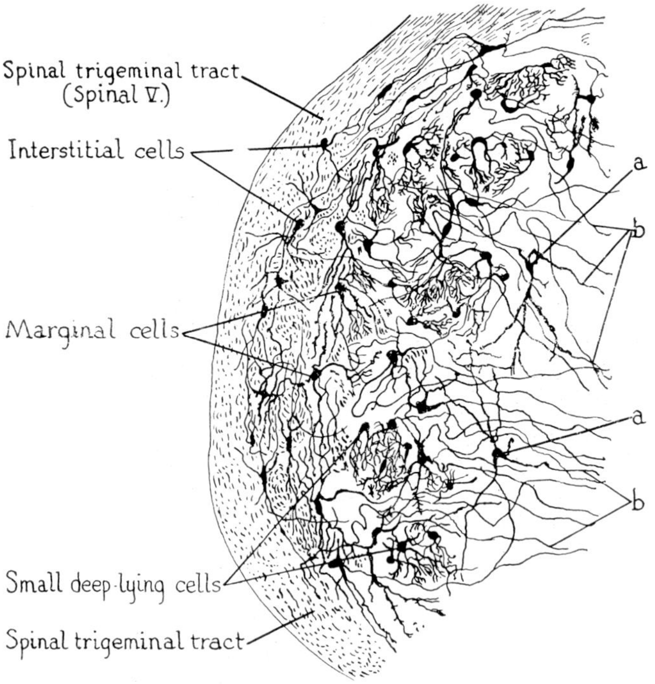

FIG. 269. Transverse section through spinal trigeminal tract and its terminal nucleus. Newborn rabbit. Golgi impregnation. *a*, large stellate cell; *b*, axons from cells of terminal nucleus forming crossed and uncrossed secondary trigeminal tracts. (After Cajal.)

dibular branch are distributed to the lower lip, chin, posterior portion of cheek and temple, external ear, and to the mucous membrane of the lower jaw, lower teeth, cheeks, anterior two-thirds of the tongue, and floor of the mouth. All three branches contribute sensory fibers to the dura which is also innervated by fibers from the tenth, ninth, and seventh nerves (posterior fossa, Penfield and McNaughton).

The central processes of the semilunar ganglion cells form the sensory root which passes through the pons and enters the tegmentum where many fibers divide into short ascending and long descending arms. Others descend or ascend without bifurcation (Windle). The short ascending fibers and their collaterals terminate in the main sensory nucleus lying dorsolateral to the entering fibers. The long descending arms form the spinal trigeminal tract whose longest fibers reach the uppermost segments of the cord, giving off terminals and collaterals to the nucleus of the spinal V en route (Fig. 269). The nucleus of the spinal V is thus a long column of cells, rostrally in contact with the main sensory nucleus, caudally merging with the substantia gelatinosa of the cord. The tract of the spinal V lies lateral to the nucleus and has a superficial position in the medulla, appearing as a continuation of the zone of Lissauer. In the pons it is separated from the surface by the transverse fibers of the brachium pontis.

Within the spinal tract there is a definite topographical grouping of fibers from the three main peripheral divisions. The ophthalmic fibers are most ventral and descend to the most caudal levels, some reaching the second or third cervical segments. The maxillary fibers are central in the tract and descend to near the caudal limit of the medulla. The mandibular fibers are most dorsally placed and do not reach below the uppermost level of the medulla (Fig. 268).

There is considerable clinical evidence

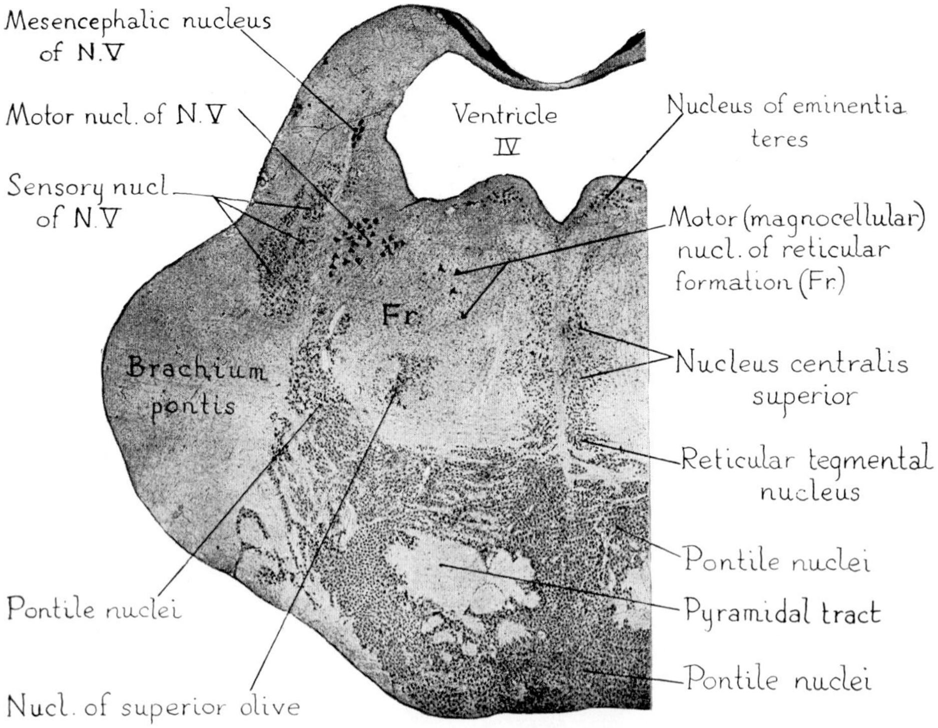

FIG. 270. Section through pons and pontile tegmentum of one month infant, about same level as Fig. 266. Cresyl Violet. Photograph, with cell groups schematically blocked in.

that lesions of the spinal tract result chiefly in loss or diminution of pain and temperature in the area innervated by the trigeminal, while tactile sensibility is apparently unaffected. It is probable that the non-bifurcating descending fibers mediate exclusively pain and temperature, while the bifurcating ones convey tactile sensibility. Hence in lesions of the spinal V many tactile fibers may be destroyed but the ascending arms of these fibers would still reach the main sensory nucleus, and touch remains intact. Clinically there is no doubt that pain and temperature are handled entirely by the spinal V, while touch and two-point discrimination are in large part related to the main sensory nucleus (Fig. 268).

Another source of afferent trigeminal fibers is a slender column of cells found in the lateral portion of the central gray of the upper fourth ventricle and cerebral aqueduct, and extending from the level of the trigeminal motor nucleus to the upper limit of the midbrain (Figs. 270, 275). This so-called *mesencephalic nucleus* of N.V is composed chiefly of large unipolar cells resembling those of the cerebrospinal ganglia. Their processes form a slender sickle-shaped bundle, the *mesencephalic tract of N.V.* These fibers descend to the level of the trigeminal motor nucleus where they give off collaterals to the motor cells and then emerge as part of the motor root (Figs. 268, 271). There is convincing evidence that the fibers of this nucleus convey proprioceptive impulses from the masticatory muscles, especially from the masseter, temporal, and pterygoid (Allen, 1919), and from the teeth and hard palate (Corbin and Harrison, 1940). The cells of the nucleus may be regarded as afferent peripheral neurons which have been "retained" within the central nervous system, i.e., have failed to migrate out to the root ganglia. Besides the mesencephalic nucleus, scattered ganglion cells found along the motor root likewise furnish proprioceptive fibers. Some of these apparently innervate the mylohyoid and digastric muscles. Pearson (1949) has established that the connections of the mesencephalic nucleus are more extensive than formerly supposed. Some fibers leave the mesencephalic tract and enter the white matter of the cerebellum, possibly connecting with the deep cerebellar nuclei. Others can be traced to the roof of the iter, especially to the region of the superior colliculi; while still others go to the nuclei of N.III and IV, either synapting there or continuing as root fibers to these nerves. Cells resembling those of the mesencephalic nucleus are also found scattered at the base of the cerebellum and to a smaller extent in the roof of the iter.

Some authorities believe that deep sensibility of the lingual, facial, and ocular muscles is likewise mediated by the fifth nerve, perhaps by fibers of the mesencephalic root. This can not be entirely the case with the tongue and eye muscles which in part receive proprioceptive fibers through their own nerves, from external ganglion cells found along the roots. It is possible, however, that additional fibers may be furnished by the mesencephalic nucleus, at least for the oculomotor and abducens nerves (Pearson, 1949). Deep sensibility of the face is largely handled by the trigeminal nerve (Smyth) but may be supplemented from other sources, perhaps from afferent fibers of the facial nerve. There is much that is still obscure about the afferent innervation of the muscles and other deep structures of the head.

The *motor nucleus of N.V* or *nucleus masticatorius* is an ovoid column of typical multipolar motor cells, lying medial to the main sensory nucleus. Its coarse efferent fibers emerge internal to the entering sensory root and pass underneath the semilunar ganglion to become incorporated in the mandibular branch (Figs. 268, 271). Among the terminals ending in the nucleus are collaterals from the mesencephalic root and other afferent fibers of N.V. These furnish a two-neuron arc for reflex proprioceptive control of the jaw muscles. Additional secondary trigeminal fibers, both crossed and uncrossed provide reflex control of the jaw muscles by superficial stimuli, especially from the lingual and oral mucous membrane. Terminals of descending crossed and uncrossed pyramidal fibers for voluntary movements such as mastication, participation in the act of speech, etc.; and fibers exercising extrapyramidal control also end in this motor nucleus. The locus caeruleus (Figs. 275, 276) gives origin to a fiber bundle which descends as far as the nucleus intercalatus of the medulla, and probably this mechanism furnishes a connection between the motor nucleus of N.V and the salivatory nuclei, relating mastication with salivary secretion.

SECONDARY TRIGEMINAL PATHWAYS

The secondary trigeminal pathways arise from neurons in the main sensory nucleus and the spinal nucleus of the trigeminal nerve (Fig. 268). Collaterals from incoming sensory fibers, as well as the axons of cells in these two nuclei, provide numerous largely uncrossed secondary reflex fibers to motor nuclei of the brain stem.

As illustrated in Fig. 268, the small incoming nerve fibers, conveying impulses for pain and temperature, divide and the descending limbs become incorporated into the trigeminospinal tract. The central processes of the ophthalmic nerve descend to the medulla and upper segments of the cervical spinal cord before terminating in the spinal nucleus of V. Descending pain and temperature fibers of the maxillary nerve descend to the mid-olivary level of the medulla, while similar fibers of the mandibular nerve terminate promptly within the spinal nucleus at pontine levels. The axons of nerve cells within the spinal nucleus cross to the opposite side, and turn rostrally as the *ventral central trigeminal tract* (trigeminothalamic tract). This tract terminates in the ventral posteromedial nucleus of the thalamus. The composition, location, and relations of this tract are of considerable diagnostic as well as surgical importance (Fig. 268). For example, it can be noted that the ophthalmic fibers have the longest descending course, are isolated in the trigeminospinal tract in the lowest levels of the medulla, and could be most easily interrupted surgically. However, the preservation of the sensory fibers from the orbit and eye is of the greatest importance. Fortunately these fibers are least often involved in trigeminal neuralgia. Unfortunately the pain and temperature fibers of the mandibular nerve are most frequently involved in neuralgia and cannot be differentially resected in the brain stem (intramedullary tractotomy) without interrupting similar fibers from the remaining two divisions of the trigeminal nerve.

The relations of the ventral central trigeminal tract to the lateral spinothalamic tract should be noted at different levels of the brain stem. The location of the latter tract is represented in solid black on the right side of each level in Fig. 268. Vascular lesions in the lower medulla often involve the lateral spinothalamic tract (at this level conveying pain and temperature from the controlateral side of the body), and the spinal nucleus and tract of V (descending pain and temperature fibers of the ipsilateral ophthalmic nerve). At higher levels of the medulla the ascending spinothalamic tract may be injured with descending uncrossed fibers of both the ophthalmic and maxillary nerves. Ascending fibers from the contralateral spinal nucleus of V also may be involved. In the upper pons and midbrain levels these two pain and temperature pathways lie adjacent to each other near the surface of the brain stem. Injury at this level usually involves both tracts which are now composed almost entirely of crossed fibers. Lesions of these tracts here and at all higher levels, below the cortex, result in a contralateral loss of pain and temperature in the trunk, extremities, neck, and head.

Fibers from the main sensory nucleus of the trigeminal nerve, and perhaps some from the spinal nucleus, mediate impulses of touch and pressure. The axons from cells of the main sensory nucleus stream across midline near the level of entry of the fifth nerve, and ascend as the *dorsal central trigeminal tract*. As shown in Fig. 268, this tract terminates in the ventral posteromedial nucleus of the thalamus. Although represented as a crossed tract (Fig. 268), many axons ascend to the thalamus in the ipsilateral tract. Degeneration experiments in the cat led Russell (1954) to conclude that a dorsal central trigeminal tract did not exist in this animal. He believed these fibers to be part of an ascending lateral reticulothalamic pathway. More recent experimental studies have presented evidence for the existence of a bilateral dorsal ascending pathway in the cat (Berry, Anderson, Brooks, 1956; Torvik, 1957). This crossed and uncrossed tract was located lateral to the medial longitudinal fasciculus and manifested rapid fiber conduction. This tract has also been identified and traced by degeneration experiments in the monkey (Carpenter, 1957). However, in the monkey the dorsal trigeminal tract appears to be an uncrossed ascending pathway.

The numerous secondary *reflex* fibers arising from the terminal nuclei of N.V ascend and descend in the dorsolateral part of the reticular formation giving off terminals or collaterals to various motor nuclei (Fig. 271). They are largely uncrossed. They supply the connections for the many reflexes initiated by stimulation of the skin of the face, the oral and nasal mucous membrane, and muscles, tendons, and bones of the jaw and face. Among the more important of these reflexes and the motor nuclei to which the secondary fibers go are (1) the *corneal reflex* to motor nucleus of N.VII. Impulses from the cornea connect with the facial nuclei of both sides through crossed and uncrossed secondary fibers, hence stimu-

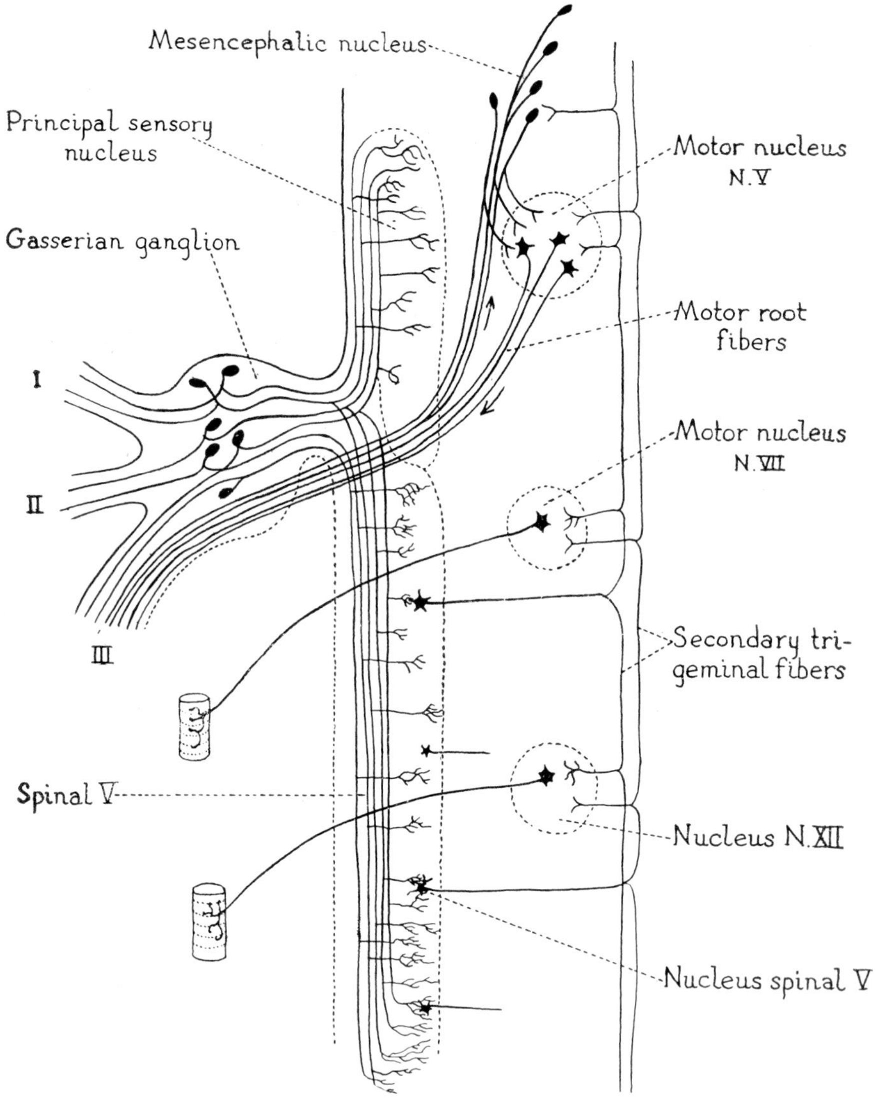

FIG. 271. Diagram of the trigeminal nuclei and some of the trigeminal reflex arcs. *I*, ophthalmic nerve; *II*, maxillary nerve; *III*, mandibular nerve. (Modified from Cajal.)

lation of one cornea will produce closure of both eyes (consensual reflex). In injury of the trigeminal nerve (ophthalmic branch) there will be an absence of reflex eye closure on both sides when the involved cornea is stimulated, while in lesions of the facial nerve only the direct (ipsilateral) reflex will be lost since the arc for the consensual (contralateral) reflex is still intact. (2) the *lacrimal* or *tearing* reflex, to "lacrimal" nucleus of N.VII; (3) *sneezing*, to nucleus of N.XII, nucleus ambiguus, and associated respiratory nuclei of the cord, i.e., phrenic, intercostal, and others; (4) *vomiting*, to dorsal motor nucleus of N.X, nucleus ambiguus, and other nuclei including motor nucleus of N.V; (5) *salivary reflexes*, to salivatory nuclei of Nn.VII and IX; (6) *ocullocardiac* reflex (slowing of the heart elicited by pressure on the eyeball), to dorsal motor nucleus of N.X. Secondary fibers also go to the hypoglossal nucleus for reflex tongue movement following stimulation of the tongue and oral mucous membrane, and possibly for reflex control of tongue movements during the act of eating. A few fibers probably enter the medial longitudinal fasciculus, and according to some authorities direct or secondary trigeminal fibers go to the cerebellum.

THE LOCUS CAERULEUS

The locus caeruleus or *nucleus pigmentosus pontis* is a considerable aggregation of closely packed pigmented cells appearing near the superior end of the main sensory trigeminal nucleus and extending some distance into the midbrain. It is composed of medium sized polygonal cells among which there often may be found some scattered large oval cells probably belonging to the mesenchephalic nucleus which lies immediately dorsal to the locus caeruleus (Figs. 275, 276). In spite of its large size the significance of the nucleus is not clear. It is believed by many investigators to be intimately related to the fifth nerve, either receiving afferent trigeminal fibers or contributing fibers to the motor root. Most of its axons combine to form a tract, the *bundle of Probst*, which descends in the dorsolateral part of the reticular formation and has been traced as far as the nucleus intercalatus and dorsal motor vagus nucleus. Some consider the locus caeruleus as an upper pontile reflex center for respiratory regulation (Hess and Pollack).

Similar pigmented cells extend from the locus caeruleus into the roof of the fourth ventricle toward the cerebellum. Others are found scattered diffusely throughout the pontile tegmentum.

SECTIONS THROUGH ISTHMUS OF HINDBRAIN AT LEVEL OF EXIT OF TROCHLEAR NERVE (N.IV) (FIGS. 273, 274)

The narrower portion of the hindbrain lying superior to the cerebellum and merging with the midbrain is often known as the *isthmus rhombencephali*. Sections shown in Figs. 273, 274 represent the most cephalic level of this region, i.e., the junction of isthmus and midbrain. As in previous sections three regions are distinguishable: a roof, tegmentum, and basilar pons.

The cerebellum has disappeared, the roof consisting now of a thin white membrane, the *anterior medullary velum*. The neural cavity is greatly reduced and forms the transition between the fourth ventricle and the *Sylvian aqueduct* or *iter* of the midbrain. The cavity is bounded ventrally and laterally by a broad band of central gray matter. The root fibers of the *trochlear nerve*

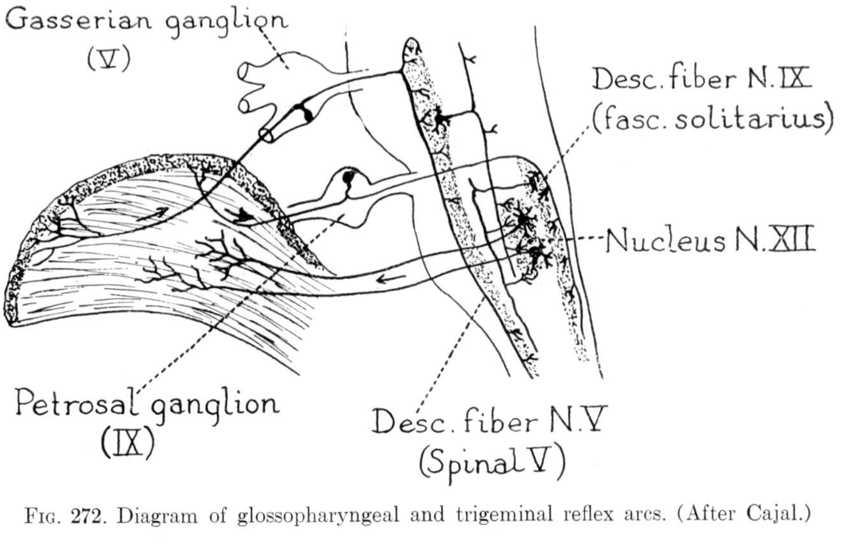

FIG. 272. Diagram of glossopharyngeal and trigeminal reflex arcs. (After Cajal.)

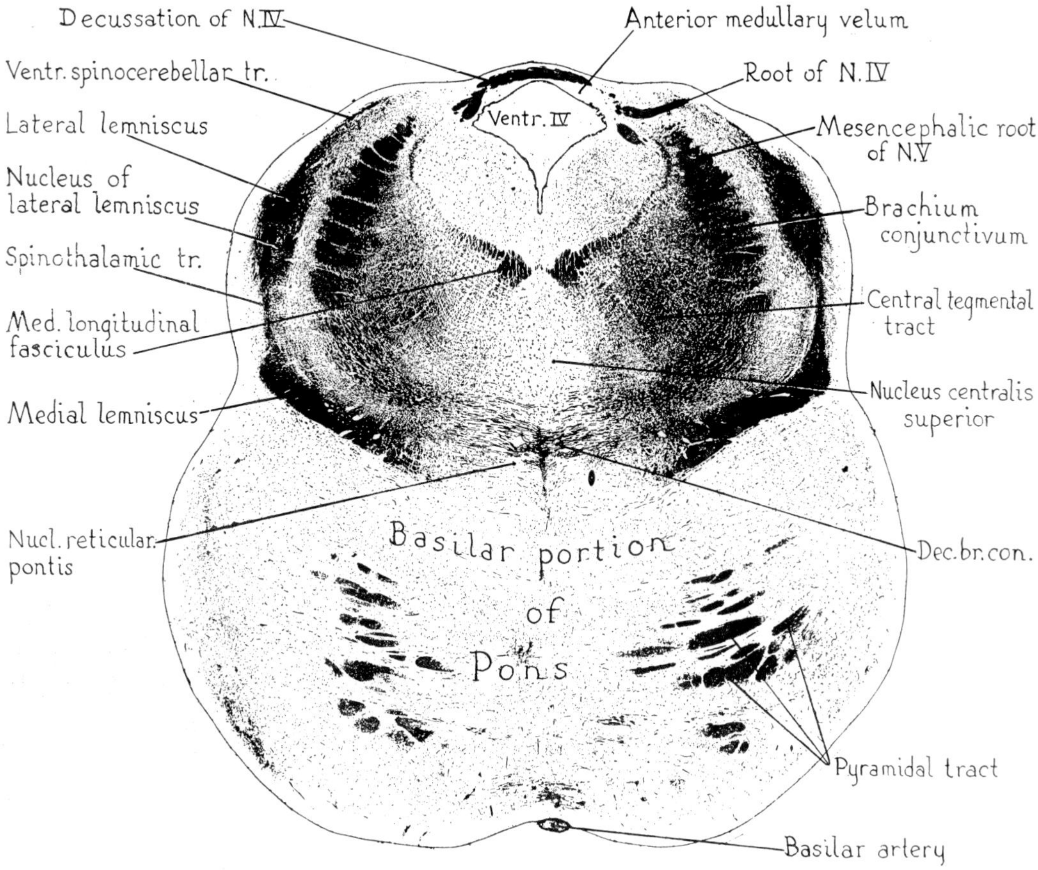

FIG. 273. Section of isthmus of one month infant, through exit of nerve IV. Weigert's myelin Stain. Photograph, ×7.

(N.IV) are seen in the anterior medullary velum. They originate from nuclei which lie more cephalad in the ventral part of the central gray. The fibers arch dorsally and somewhat caudally around the fourth ventricle or iter, then decussate in the roof and emerge (Fig. 199). Only the decussation is seen in this level. The nerve innervates the superior oblique muscle of the eyeball.

The basilar portion of the pons is considerably larger than the tegmental portion. The pontile nuclei are extensive, the pyramidal and corticopontile tracts are broken up into numerous bundles.

In the tegmentum the mesencephalic tract of N.V forms a slender sickle-shaped bundle in the lateral part of the central gray. Mingled with it may be seen the oval cells of the mesencephalic nucleus and ventral to this is the relatively large nucleus pigmentosus pontis or locus caeruleus characteristic of the uppermost pontile levels. The lateral lemniscus lies near the surface in the lateral part of the tegmentum, forming the major part of the external structure known as the *trigonum lemnisci.* Groups of cells among its fibers constitute the *nucleus of the lateral lemniscus,* one of several nuclei interpolated in the auditory pathway. The medial lemniscus is a flattened band extending transversely in the lateroventral part of the tegmentum, and the spinothalamic tract is in its usual position between the two lemnisci. Included in the medial lemniscus and spinothalamic tracts are the secondary ventral trigeminal, and vago-glossopharyngeal fibers. The secondary dorsal trigeminal

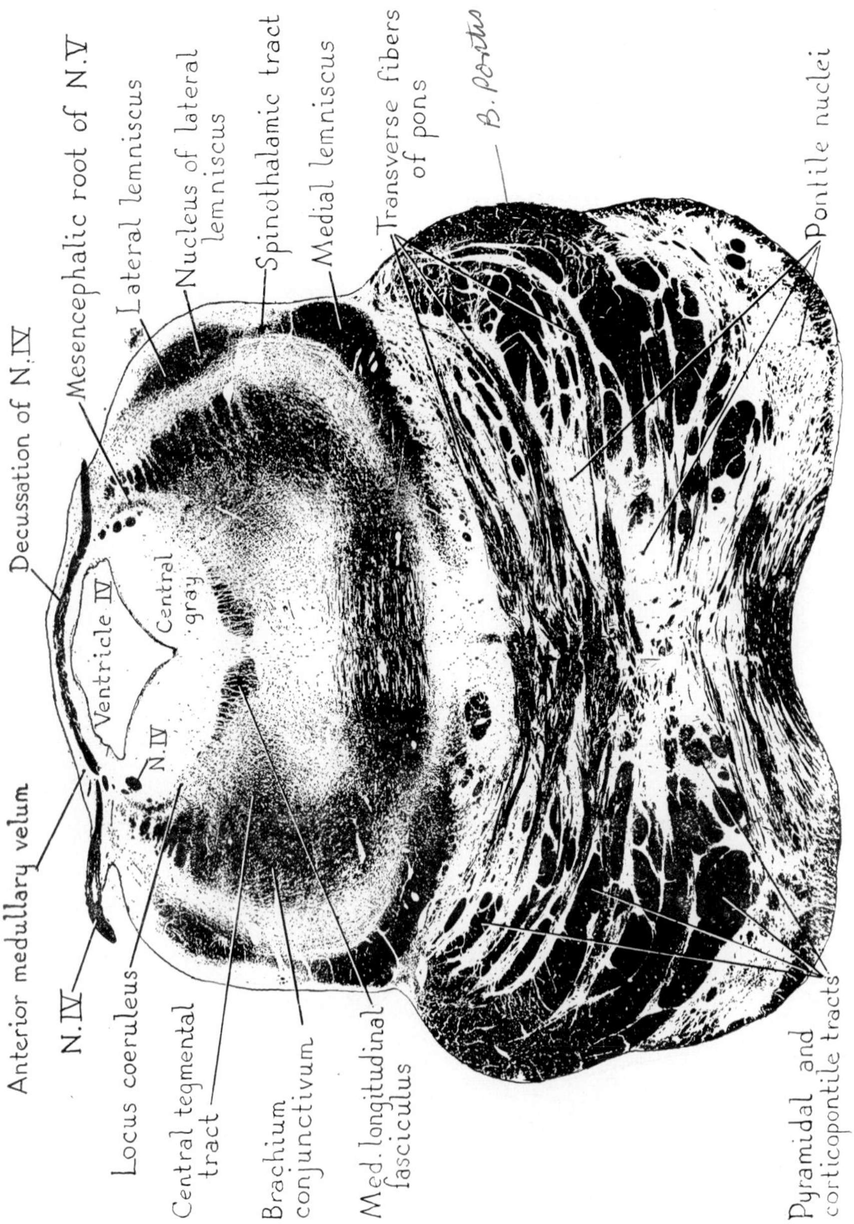

Fig. 274. Section of isthmus of adult through exit of nerve IV. Weigert's myelin stain. Photograph, ×7.

fibers ascend in the dorsal part of the reticular formation, lateral to the medial longitudinal fasciculus. All these secondary cranial nerve tracts carry tactile, proprioceptive, pain, and temperature sensations from the head and mouth, and possibly also visceral sensibility. Thus at this level the principal afferent suprasegmental paths form a peripheral shell of fibers enclosing the rest of the tegmentum and representing general body and head sensibility as well as hearing.

The superior cerebellar peduncle or *brachium conjunctivum* has entered the tegmentum where it forms a large crescentic bundle in the lateral part of the reticular formation. The brachium conjunctivum which arises from the dentate and emboliform nuclei forms the most important efferent fiber system of the cerebellum. Emerging from the latter it first forms the dorsolateral wall of the fourth ventricle, then dips into the pontile tegmentum, and in the caudal portion of the midbrain undergoes a complete decussation (Fig. 192). Many of its fibers end in the nucleus ruber, others continue directly to the ventral lateral nucleus of the thalamus. Some ascend and descend in the reticular formation where they make connections with the motor nuclei of the midbrain, pontile tegmentum, and medulla. Many of the fibers are already decussating at this level.

The central tegmental tract is large and occupies a truly central position. The ventral spinocerebellar tract now lies on the surface, external to the brachium conjunctivum, and its fibers appear to be cut longitudinally. This tract has an aberrant course to the cerebellum. It ascends in the lateral part of the reticular formation to the uppermost limit of the pons, and at this point turns caudally, forming a loop on the external surface of the brachium conjunctivum (Figs. 36, 192, 267). Then, accompanying the latter but in a reverse direction, it descends in the anterior medullary velum to terminate in the vermis of the anterior lobe

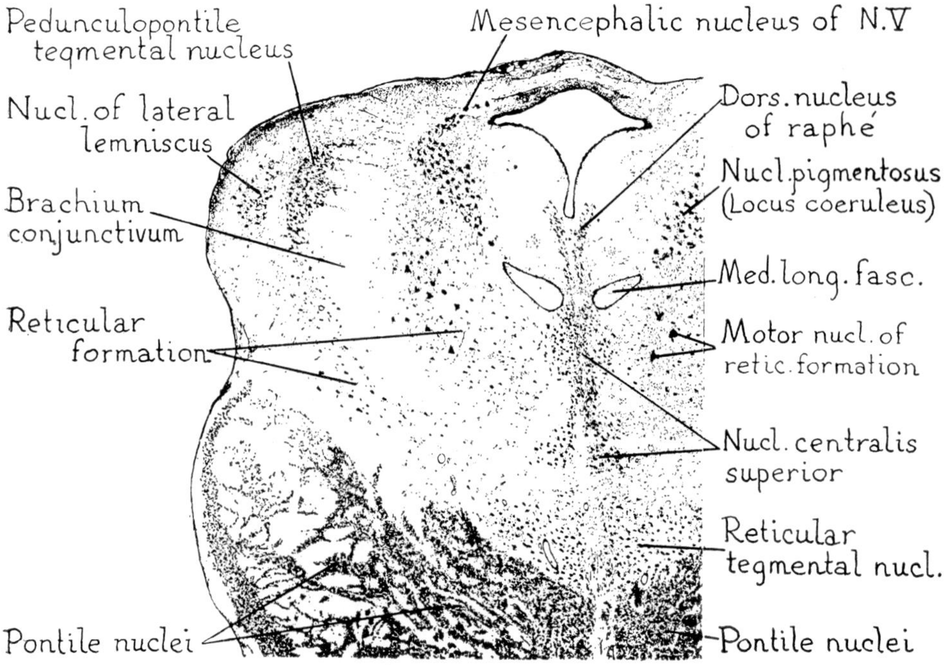

FIG. 275. Section through isthmus of three months infant. Cresyl Violet. Photograph, with cell groups schematically blocked in.

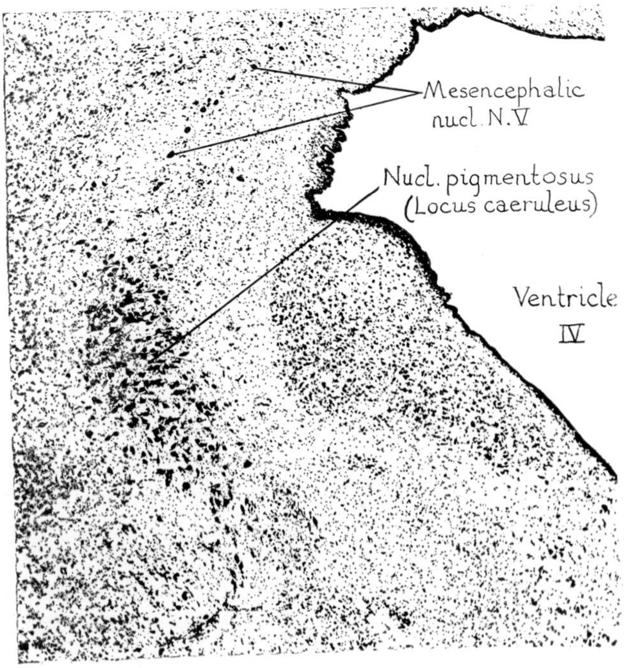

FIG. 276. Portion of pontile tegmentum in oral region of pons (isthmus). Twelve weeks baby. Nissl stain. Photograph.

of the cerebellum. Only the turn or bend of the fibers is seen at this level (Figs. 267, 273).

The medial longitudinal and predorsal fasciculi are in their usual positions. The rubrospinal tract has shifted to a more medial position, lying dorsal to the medial lemniscus. It is more easily distinguishable as a definite tract in the caudal portions of the midbrain, near its origin from the nucleus ruber (Figs. 199, 280).

The cell groups of the reticular formation are most extensive near the raphé (Fig. 275). Most ventrally in this region is the *reticular tegmental nucleus* already described, considered by some as a tegmental extension of the pontile nuclei (Jacobsohn). Dorsal to this is the *superior central nucleus* characteristic of the upper pons, a large closely packed aggregation of small and medium sized cells extending laterally into the reticular formation. On each side of the midline, dorsal to the medial longitudinal fasciculus, is the *dorsal nucleus of the raphé*, a narrow band of cells which merge above with the larger and more complex *dorsal tegmental nucleus* of the midbrain (Fig. 282).

The main body of the reticular formation is divided into a medial and a lateral portion by the superior cerebellar peduncle. In the lateral part a dense collection of medium sized cells constitutes the *pedunculopontile tegmental nucleus* closely applied to the external surface of the brachium conjunctivum and extending into the caudal portion of the midbrain. Elsewhere the reticular formation is diffusely organized, and scattered within it, especially in its medial portion, are the large multipolar cells belonging to the *motor reticular nucleus* (Fig. 275).

THE BLOOD SUPPLY OF THE MEDULLA AND PONS

The medulla and pons receive their arterial blood supply from the *anterior* and *posterior spinal arteries*, the *vertebral*, the *basilar* and the *posterior inferior cerebellar arteries* (Figs. 63, 64). Minor contributions of a negligible character may also be made by the *superior* and the *anterior inferior cerebellar arteries.* There is great variation in the extent of the areas supplied by each vessel, as well as considerable overlapping of adjacent fields, hence the normal distribution of the individual arteries is often difficult to determine. These variations are due in part to the fluctuating level of origin of the anterior spinal arteries and to the equally varying level of fusion of the two vertebrals into the basilar artery. Not uncommonly one or another artery may be missing altogether and its place taken by the vessel supplying the adjacent territory. Thus the area of the posterior spinal may be taken over by the posterior inferior cerebellar artery, or the latter be replaced by the vertebral. Since the vascular supply of this region has considerable clinical importance, the main structures normally supplied by the various arteries are briefly summarized (Figs. 277, 278).

The *anterior spinal* supplies the medial structures of the medulla including the pyramids and pyramidal decussation, medial lemniscus, medial longitudinal fasciculus, predorsal bundle, and the hypoglossal nucleus except its most cephalic portion. In addition the artery supplies the medial accessory olive, and the most caudal portion of the nucleus and fasciculus solitarius, and of the dorsal vagus nucleus. Towards the lower border of the pons the distribution of the artery is gradually reduced, to be replaced by branches of the vertebral and basilar arteries.

The bulbar branches of the *vertebral artery* normally supply the pyramids at the lower border of pons, the most cephalic part of the hypoglossal nucleus, and most of the olive including the dorsal accessory olive. It also supplies the olivocerebellar fibers traversing the reticular formation, and a portion of the dorsal vagus nucleus, and the nucleus and fasciculus solitarius in the region of the calamus scriptorius. At the level of the pyramidal decussation the most caudal branches are distributed to practically the whole lateral region of the medulla lying between the ventral horn and fasciculus cuneatus.

The *posteroir inferior cerebellar artery* supplies the retroolivary region containing the spinothalamic and rubrospinal tracts, the nucleus and tract of the spinal V, nucleus ambiguus, dorsal vagoglossopharyn-

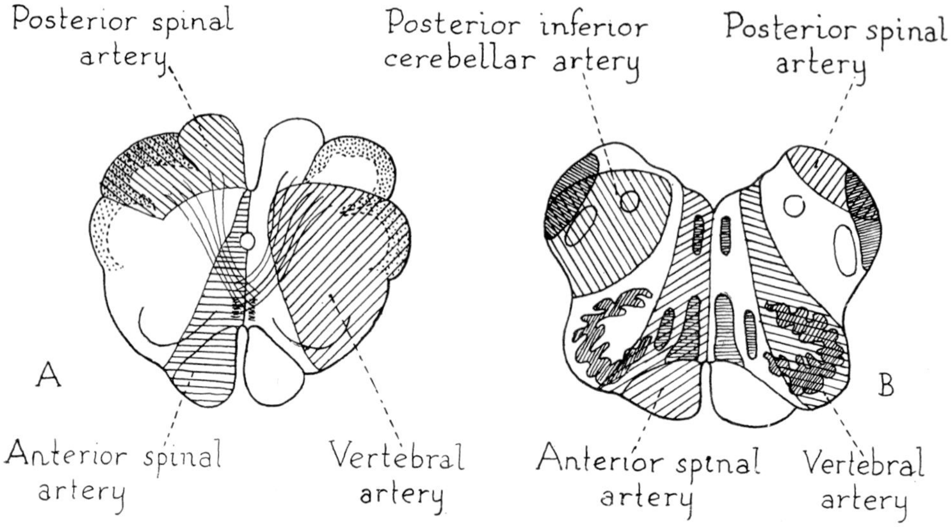

FIG. 277. Diagram showing arterial supply of medulla. *A,* level of clava; *B,* midolivary level. (From data by Stopford.)

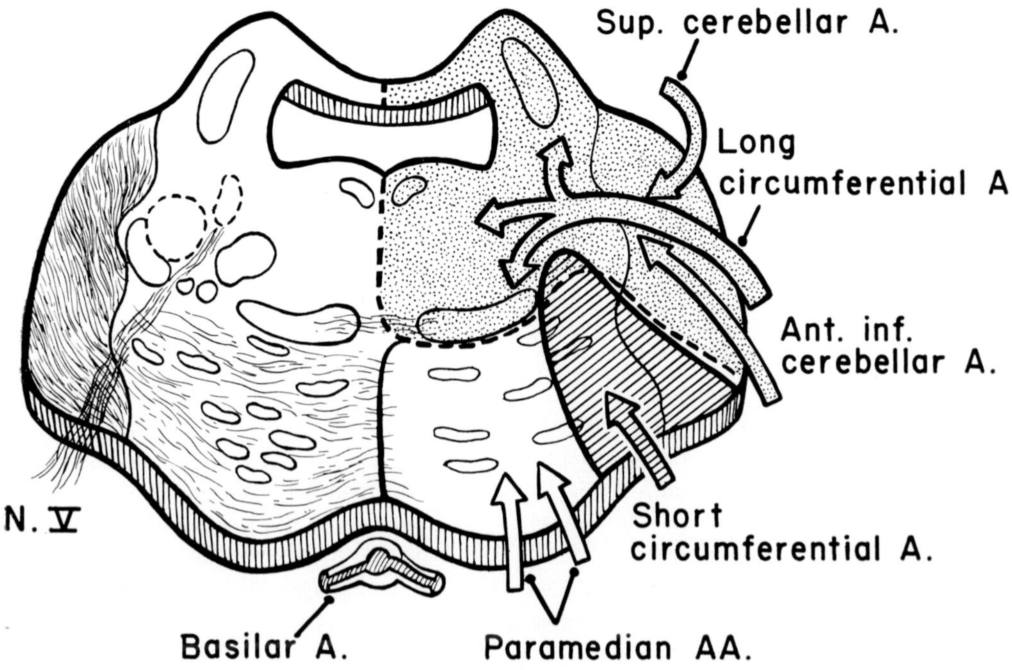

FIG. 278. Diagram of arterial supply of pons by paramedian and circumferential branches of the basilar artery. (Modified from Frantzen and Olivarius.)

geal nucleus and the emerging fibers of these nerves, and the ventral part of the restiform body. Descending central autonomic tracts are also found in this area.

The *posterior spinal* supplies the gracile and cuneate fascicles and their nuclei, and the caudal and more dorsal portion of the restiform body. When missing, its territory is taken over by the posterior inferior cerebellar artery.

The basilar portion of the pons receives arterial blood from three series of branches, all derived from the *basilar artery* (Fig. 278). The first series are the *paramedian arteries* which leave the dorsal surface of the parent vessel to supply the most medial pontine area including pontine nuclei, corticopontine, corticospinal, and corticobulbar tracts. Smaller arterial twigs also penetrate dorsally to supply the most ventral part of the pontine tegmentum including a portion of the medial lemniscus. Obstruction of the paramedian arteries is usually followed by: hemiplegia (at times a quadriplegia), pseudobulbar palsy including dysarthria and dysphagia; transitory hemianesthesia but otherwise unimpaired sensation; paresis of conjugate eye movements with deviation of the eyes to the side opposite the lesion (Frantzen and Olivarius, 1957). A second group of *short circumferential arteries* supply a wedge of tissue along the ventrolateral pontine surface. Neural structures in this intermediate area of the pons include a variable number of fibers of the corticospinal tract and medial lemniscus, pontine nuclei and pontocerebellar fibers, and part of the nuclei and fibers of the trigeminal and facial nerves. Some of the circumferential branches ascend to supply part of the cerebral peduncle. Obstruction of the short circumferential arteries may therefore result in ipsilateral cerebellar symptoms, contralateral hemianesthesia, and visceral disturbances of the sympathetic system including an ipsilateral Horner's syndrome.

The third series or *long circumferential arteries* pass laterally on the ventral surface of the pons to anastomose with smaller branches of the anterior inferior cerebellar and superior cerebellar arteries (Fig. 278). The long circumferential and anterior *inferior* cerebellar arteries supply most of the tegmentum in the caudal portion of the pons, whereas the long circumferential and *superior* cerebellar artery supply a similar area in the more cranial levels of the pons. Important nerve structures within this area of vascular distribution are the nuclei of cranial nerves III to VIII including the trigeminospinal nucleus and tract, the medial longitudinal fasciculus, medial lemniscus, spinothalamic and spinocerebellar tracts, brachium conjunctivum, and the reticular formation. Obstruction of these vessels may produce nuclear injury and paresis of one or more of the cranial nerves mentioned, paresis of conjugate eye movements, contralateral hemianesthesia, ipsilateral cerebellar symptoms, nystagmus, and sympathetic disturbances. Alterations in the individual's sensorium may increase until coma supervenes due to anoxia or hemorrhage into the pontine tegmentum.

Complete or partial thrombosis of the basilar artery may occur suddenly and is accompanied by severe headache, vomiting, and a precipitous loss of consciousness. Complete thrombosis is generally fatal although recoveries have been observed after partial occlusion (Haugsted, 1956). Thrombosis of the basilar artery was once considered of purely academic interest. Today it is of great practical importance as well, for it can be recognized during life and aids in the differential diagnosis and case prognosis. The symptoms of basilar artery occlusion are due to massive pontine damage and include a deep comatose state; generalized loss of muscular tone (flaccidity of limbs); dilated or pin point pupils that do not react to light, and loss of superficial abdominal reflexes. Increased muscular tone and the Babinski response may be present within a variable period of time after such vascular accidents. There is often an intermingling of symptoms depending upon the level, branches, and degree of arterial occlusion. For example, thrombosis of the cranial part of the basilar artery, near the bifurcation into the two posterior cerebral arteries, may result in only visual defects (bilateral homonymous hemianopsia, pp. 81, 403).

Invasive tumors within the substance of the pons may produce neurologic symptoms that resemble those that follow occlusion of one or more branches of the basilar artery. Multiple cavities within the brain stem (syringobulbia) and sclerosing diseases may also simulate vascular injury of the medulla and pons. However, the neural signs and symptoms gradually increase in number as tumors enlarge or more cavities and sclerotic foci are formed. Vascular occlusions, however, are usually sudden in onset.

The exact distribution of the veins of the medulla has not been fully ascertained. In general they run parallel to the arteries and drain the corresponding territories. They are gathered into larger branches on the surface and make connections caudally with the veins of the spinal cord. Cranially they join the pontile veins. The latter are usually gathered into two larger trunks lying on either side of the basilar groove, which empty into the superior petrosal sinus.

17

The Mesencephalon

It will be recalled from the gross inspection of the brain stem (Figs. 218, 219), that the midbrain presented two large *cerebral peduncles* ventrally, and the *quadrigeminal plate* or *tectum* dorsally. This small segment of the brain stem contains many important suprasegmental neural mechanisms, including ocular reflexes, eye movements, righting reactions, auditory and visual relay nuclei, and many essential pathways between higher and lower brain levels. The principal nuclear masses and fiber pathways are observed at two levels, namely the levels of the inferior and superior colliculi. The latter is shown diagrammatically in Fig. 279.

SECTION OF MIDBRAIN THROUGH INFERIOR COLLICULI (FIGS. 280, 281, 225)

Compared with sections of the isthmus the following are the most conspicuous changes: The roof of the fourth ventricle has expanded into the inferior colliculi, and a great part of the tegmentum is occupied by the decussating fibers of the superior cerebellar peduncle. The pyramidal and corticopontile fibers are being organized into the pes pedunculi, and dorsal to the pes a new gray mass has appeared, the substantia nigra.

The *nucleus of the trochlear nerve* (N.IV) which supplies the superior oblique muscle is located in the ventral part of the central gray, indenting the dorsal surface of the medial longitudinal fasciculus. This column of typical somatic motor cells is essentially a caudal appendage of the oculomotor nucleus. The root fibers emerge from the nucleus, curve dorsally and caudally around the cerebral aqueduct in the outer part of the central gray, and reach the superior medullary velum in which they decussate and make their exit (Figs. 199, 220).

The mesencephalic tract and nucleus of N.V, locus caeruleus, medial lemniscus, spinothalamic, and spinotectal tracts are in the same position as in the previous section. The fibers of the lateral lemniscus however have spread out and are apparently entering or enveloping the inferior colliculus whose capsule they form. Many of these fibers end in the colliculus, while others pass by laterally to reach the medial geniculate body. From the inferior colliculus arise fibers which likewise go to the medial geniculate body, joining the fibers of the lateral lemniscus, and together with these constituting the *inferior quadrigeminal brachium* which thus represents a continuation of the auditory pathway to the thalamus. In higher sections the brachium may be seen lying on the lateral aspect of the midbrain tegmentum (Figs. 284, 285).

The brachia conjunctiva now occupy a large part of the reticular formation and many of their fibers are crossing to the opposite side in the *decussation of the brachia conjunctiva*. Immediately ventral to the decussation and not far from the midline are the rubrospinal tracts now definitely organized into two small and compact fiber bundles. The central tegmental tract lying in its usual position is difficult to distinguish from the decussating fibers of the superior cerebellar peduncle.

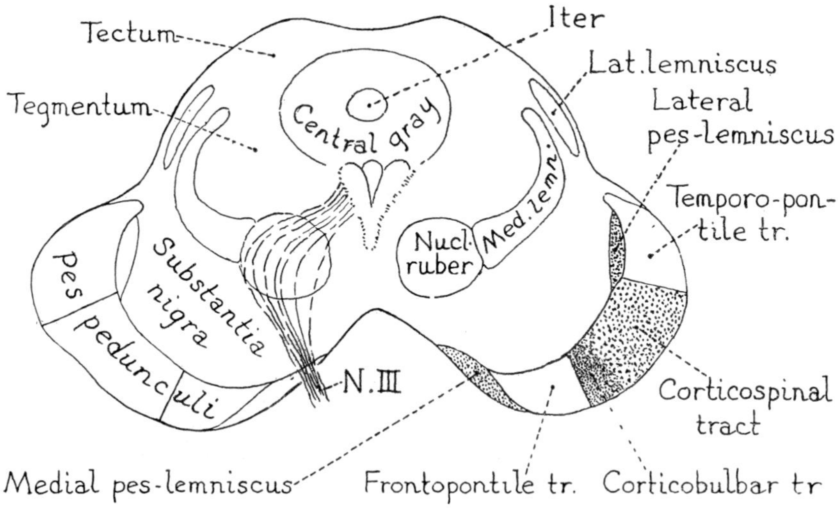

FIG. 279. Transverse section through upper portion of midbrain, schematic.

The narrow aqueduct, somewhat triangular in section, is surrounded by a broad layer of central gray substance poor in myelinated fibers and containing numerous diffusely grouped cells. In the raphéal region several new nuclei are present at this level (Fig. 282). The dorsal nucleus of the raphé has expanded into the *dorsal tegmental nucleus* composed of many small cells among which are scattered larger ones. It lies in the central gray dorsal to the trochlear nucleus. Immediately ventral to the medial longitudinal fasciculus the cells near the raphé are sometimes known as the *ventral tegmental nucleus* which appears to be a continuation of the superior central nucleus of the pons. Near the medial ventral surface of the tegmentum in the floor of the interpeduncular fossa is the *interpeduncular nucleus* composed of medium sized, multipolar, slightly pigmented cells. Prominent in most mammals it is greatly reduced in man. It receives fibers from the nucleus habenulae of the diencephalon (*habenulo-interpeduncular*) and sends fibers to the dorsal tegmental nucleus (Fig. 316). The latter also receives fibers from the mammillary bodies (*mammillotegmental*) and participates in the formation of the tract in the central gray known as the dorsal longitudinal bundle of Schütz which descends as far as the dorsal motor nucleus of N.X. The interpeduncular and the dorsal tegmental nucleus are thus relay stations in descending pathways from olfactory and other visceral centers.

The pyramidal tract and a large mass of corticopontile fibers are now gathered together to form the beginning of the *pes pedunculi*. At slightly higher levels these fibers are separated from the tegmentum by a mass of gray matter, the *substantia nigra*. In the lowest sections of the midbrain, both pes and substantia nigra are covered ventrally by the cephalic portion of the pons. (Fig. 281, 282).

The inferior colliculi. Each inferior colliculus consists of an ovoid cellular mass, the *nucleus of the inferior colliculus,* and a thin cellular layer or cortex on the surface external and medial to the nucleus. The nucleus is composed of small and medium sized cells, the latter sending their axons into the inferior quadrigeminal brachium. It receives afferent fibers from the lateral lemniscus, from the colliculus of the opposite side, and from the medial geniculate body via the inferior brachium (Fig. 258). Many fibers of the lateral lemniscus, coming mainly from the superior olive and the

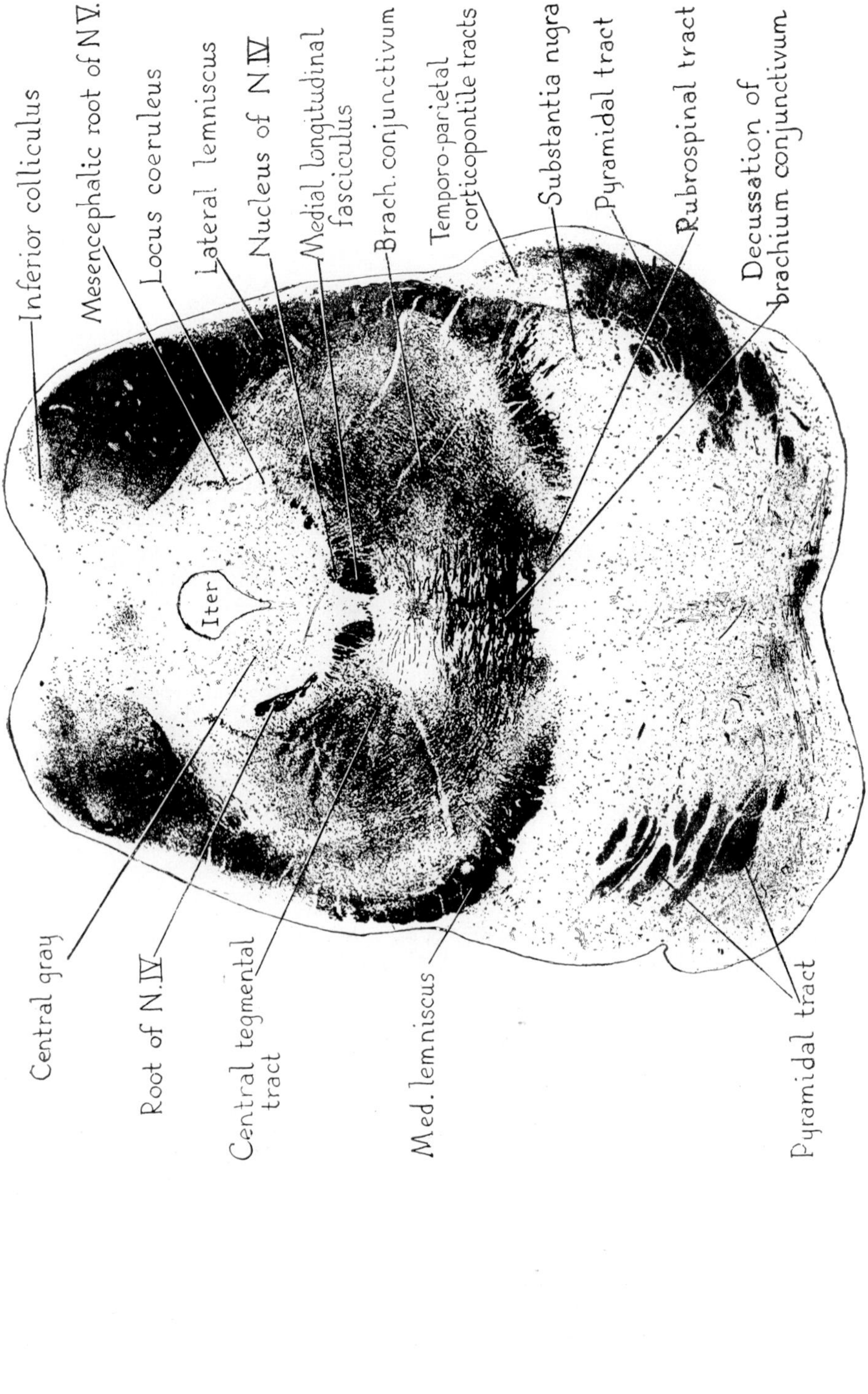

FIG. 280. Section of midbrain through inferior colliculi. One month infant. Weigert's myelin stain. Photograph, ×7.

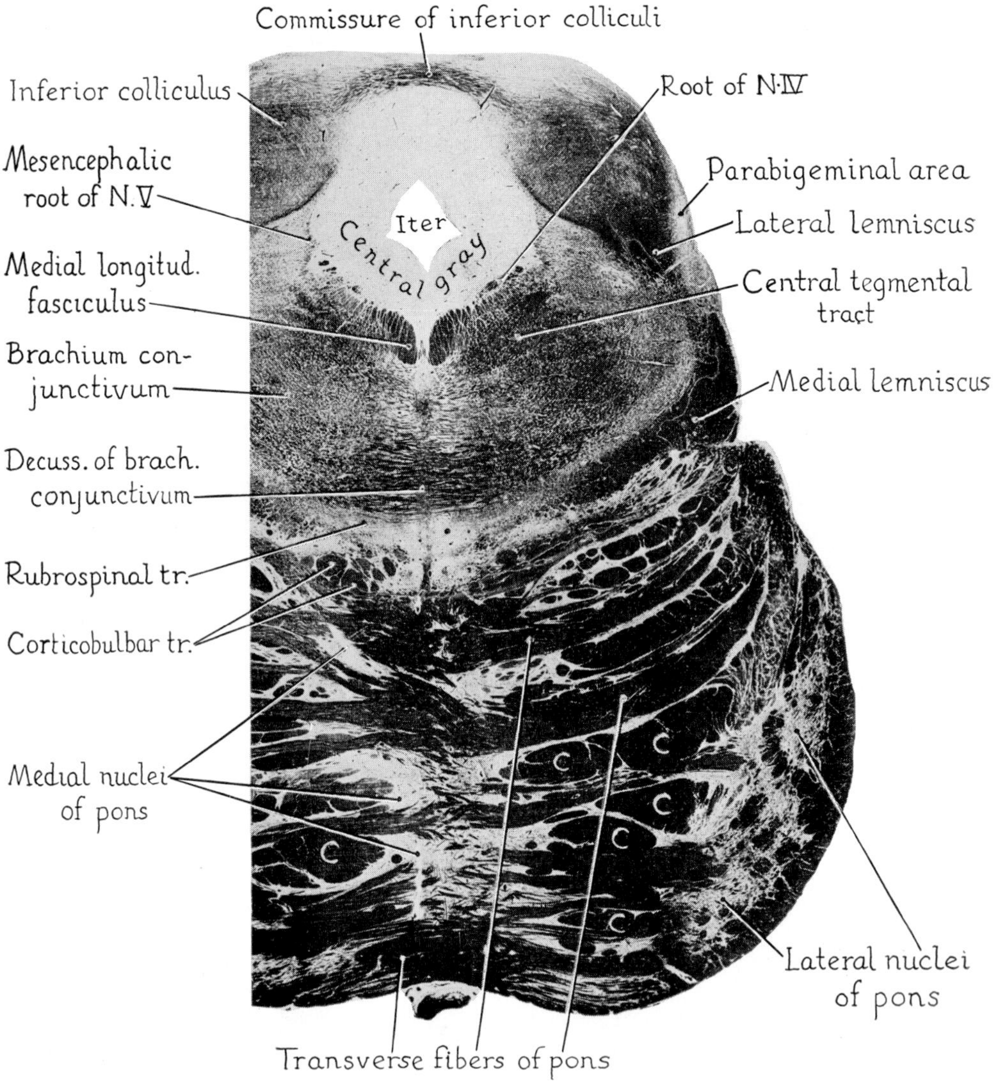

FIG. 281. Transverse section of adult midbrain, through inferior colliculi. Weigert's myelin stain. Photograph, ×7. C, corticospinal and corticopontile tracts.

nucleus of the lateral lemniscus, terminate directly in the colliculus, some crossing to the colliculus of the opposite side. Other lemniscal fibers, probably from the dorsal cochlear nucleus, send collaterals to the colliculus, the fibers themselves continuing to the medial geniculate body.

The efferent fibers arising from collicular cells go in considerable part to the medial geniculate body via the inferior quadrigeminal brachium. Others pass to the opposite inferior colliculus and to the superior colliculi or enter the tegmentum to form descending tracts which terminate in the nucleus of the lateral lemniscus, and other reticular nuclei. The exact location of these descending fibers is not fully ascertained. Some probably become incorporated in the predorsal bundle as tectobulbar and tectospinal fibers, though according to some authorities the latter fibers come entirely from the superior colliculi.

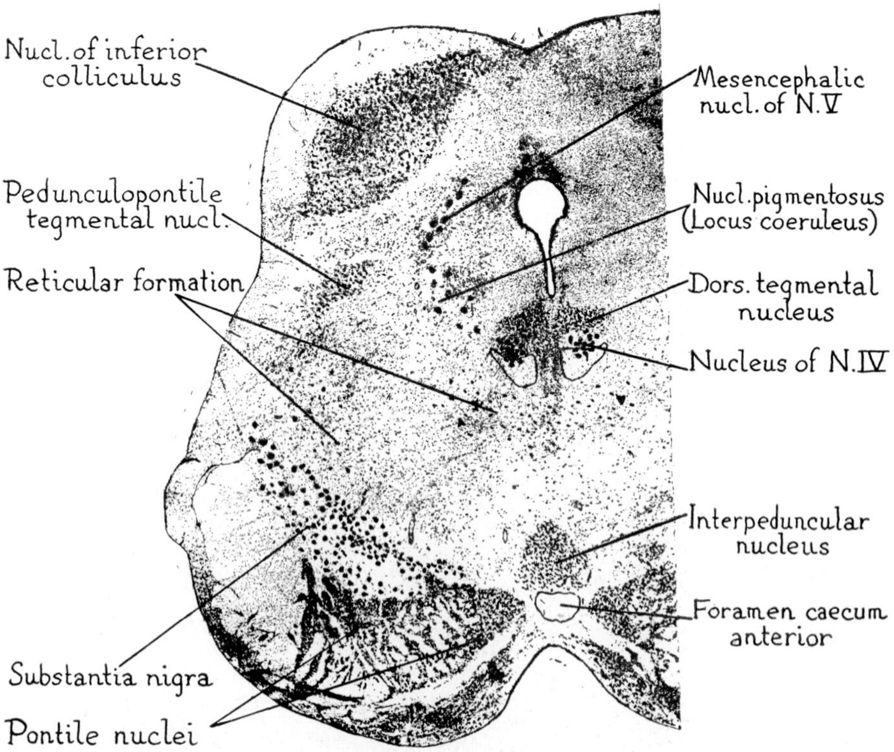

FIG. 282. Section through inferior colliculi of midbrain. Three months infant. Cresyl Violet. Photograph, with schematic representation of main cell groups.

The inferior colliculi are thus both relay stations in the hearing pathway, and reflex acoustic centers. They are newer parts of the brain related primarily to the cochlear apparatus and the projection of auditory stimuli upon the neopallial cortex.

Ventrolateral to the inferior colliculus is a fairly well defined zone known as the *parabigeminal area*, lying between the lateral lemniscus and the periphery (Fig. 281). It is composed mainly of obliquely or transversely running fibers among which are scattered cells or groups of cells constituting the *parabigeminal nucleus*. Its connections are obscure, but apparently some fibers from the nucleus go to the lateral nuclei of the pons. The more numerous fibers gathered at the lateral periphery of the area are regarded by some as corticopontile fibers from the occipital cortex.

SECTIONS OF THE MIDBRAIN THROUGH SUPERIOR COLLICULI (FIGS. 283–285, 287, 225)

The sections through the rostral half of the midbrain show the following main features. The roof is formed by the *superior colliculi*; the tegmentum contains the *nucleus ruber* (*red nucleus*) and the nuclei and roots of the oculomotor nerve (N.III); and instead of the pons, the ventral part of the brain now consists of the *pes pedunculi*, composed of a mass of efferent pallial fibers, and the *substantia nigra* (Fig. 279).

The aqueduct is surrounded by a broad band of central gray, poor in myelinated fibers and having a gelatinous appearance in Weigert preparations. The nuclear complex of the *oculomotor nerve* is located in the ventral part of the central gray in a V-shaped trough formed by the diverging medial longitudinal fasciculi. The complex is

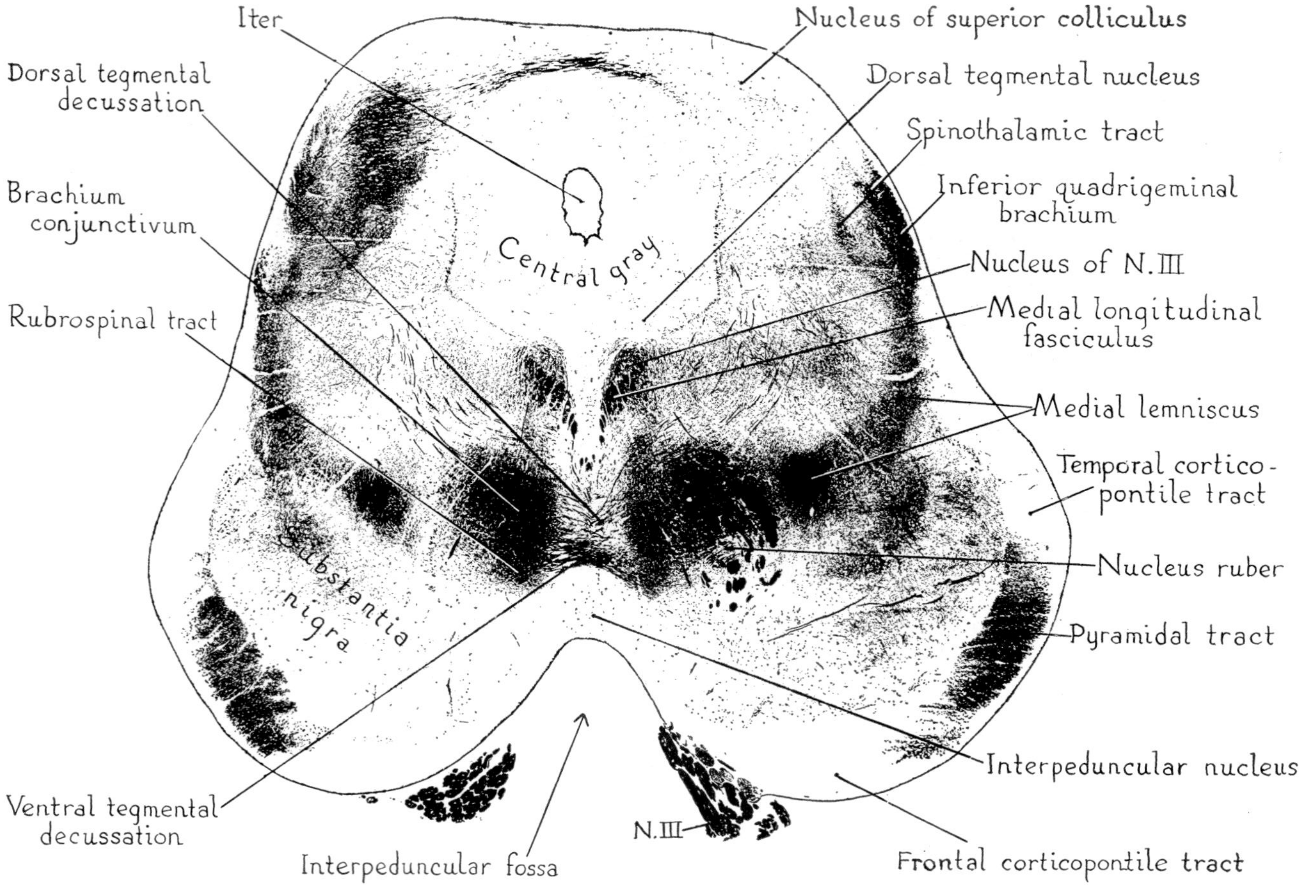

FIG 283. Section of midbrain through caudal border of superior colliculi. One month infant. Weigert's myelin stain. Photograph.

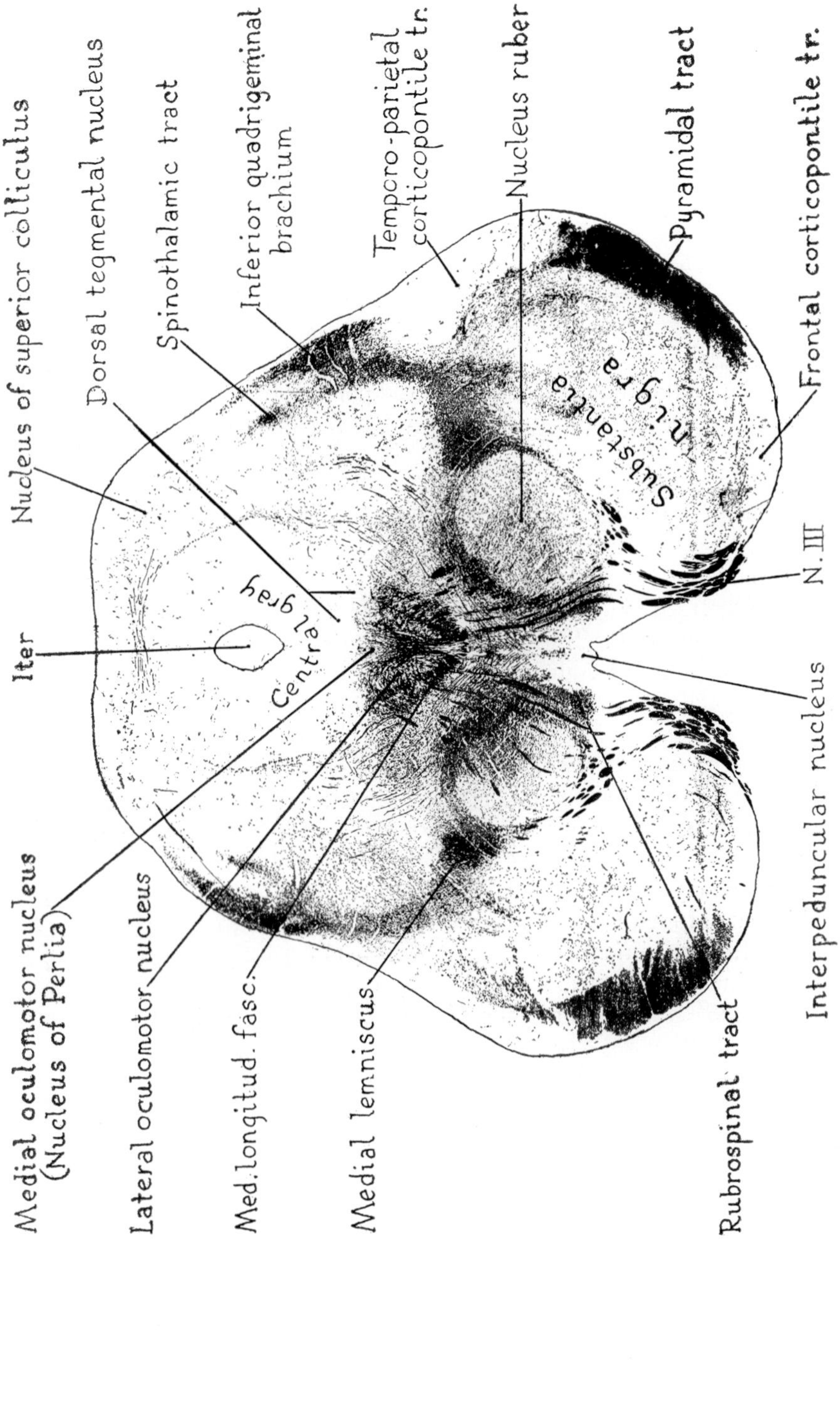

FIG. 284. Section of midbrain through exit of nerve III. One month infant. Weigert's myelin stain. Photograph, ×7.

composed of several nuclear groups which can not all be seen in any one section. In the most caudal level only the *lateral* or *chief* nuclei are seen (Fig. 283), but in the middle levels a medially placed cell group, the *central nucleus of Perlia,* is wedged in between the two lateral nuclei (Figs. 284–286). In the most oral portions the central nucleus disappears again, to be replaced by two small cell groups, the *nuclei of Edinger-Westphal,* lying dorsomedial to the lateral nuclei (Fig. 287). The root fibers emerge ventrally from the nucleus, pass through and around the nucleus ruber, then converge again and make their exit on the ventral surface of the midbrain. The oculomotor nerve and its connections are discussed more fully below.

The brachia conjunctiva have completed their decussation and in the most caudal levels each brachium forms a large oval fiber bundle about to make contact with the red nucleus (Fig. 283). In higher levels some of these fibers may be seen within the red nucleus which is one of their terminal nuclei. Other fibers continue without interruption to the thalamus.

The lateral lemniscus which had partly terminated in the inferior colliculus is now replaced by the inferior quadrigeminal brachium lying on the lateral surface of the tegmentum. As already stated the brachium is composed in part of long lemniscal fibers, in part of fibers from the inferior colliculus, all of which terminate in the medial geniculate body (Fig. 258). Axons from cells of this body constitute the last relay of the cochlear path to the temporal cortex.

The medial lemniscus is now a curved bundle displaced laterally by the red nucleus and brachium conjunctivum. The lateral spinothalamic tract is plainly distinguishable as a small bundle close to the dorsal tip of the medial lemniscus with which it practically fuses. At this level, therefore, the ascending sensory tracts from spinal cord and medulla are in close continuity (Figs. 190, 191, 268). Spinotectal fibers running in close proximity to the spinothalamic tracts, detach themselves in this region and enter the superior colliculus (Figs. 36, 190).

The medial longitudinal fasciculus is an elongated obliquely placed fiber bundle. In transverse sections the two fasciculi form a V-shaped trough in which the oculomotor nucleus is set. Progressing orally the bundle diminishes in size and disappears completely in the region of junction of the superior colliculi and thalamus.

The rubrospinal and tectospinal tracts arise from this region of the midbrain. The rubrospinal tract is emerging from the caudal portion of the nucleus ruber and is crossing as a compact bundle to the opposite side, forming the *ventral tegmental decussation of Forel* (Figs. 199, 283). After crossing, some of the descending fibers go to the motor nuclei of the pons and medulla (rubrobulbar), others reach the cord as rubrospinal fibers. The *dorsal tegmental decussation* or *fountain decussation of Meynert* is composed of more loosely arranged, obliquely crossing fibers (Figs. 199, 283). These arise from large cells of the superior colliculi, sweep fountain-like through the reticular formation, and after decussating in the dorsal part of the raphé, descend as tectobulbar and tectospinal fibers in the predorsal fasciculus (Fig. 199). Other fibers from the superior colliculi probably descend uncrossed in the reticular formation, in or near the medial longitudinal fasciculus. While the rubrospinal decussation is limited to the caudal region of the nucleus ruber, the dorsal tegmental decussation is more extensive and some of its crossing fibers may be seen in practically all sections of the superior collicular levels.

The central tegmental tract is displaced dorsally by the nucleus ruber and becomes less and less conspicuous in the more cephalic sections. Most of its fibers are believed to originate from the nucleus ruber, thalamus, striatum, and reticular cells

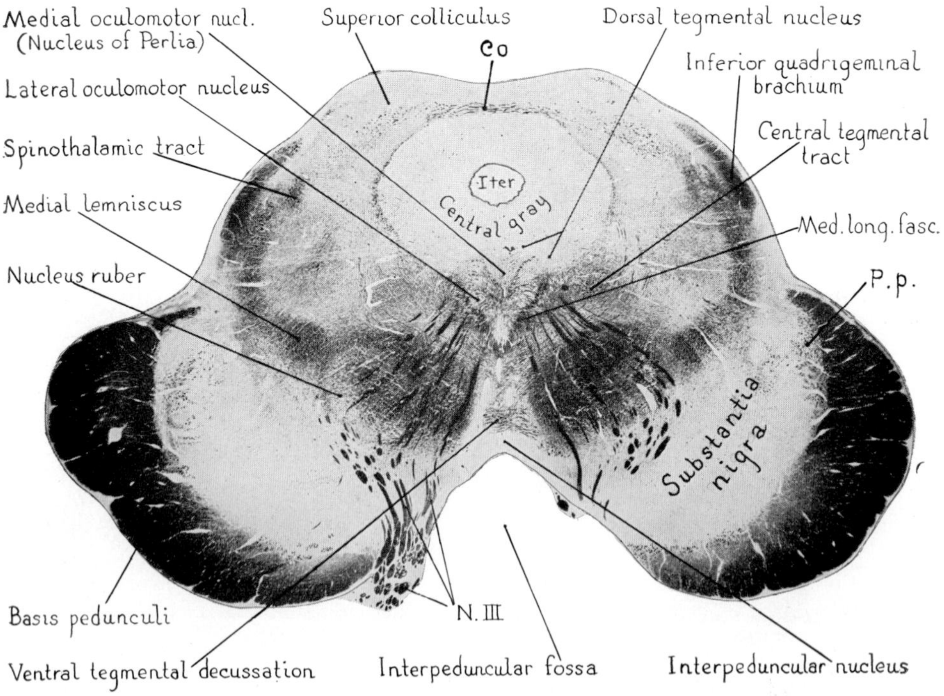

FIG. 285. Transverse section of adult midbrain through exit of nerve III. Weigert's myelin stain. Photograph, ×6. *Co*, commissure of superior colliculi; *P.p.*, strionigral and cortico-nigral fibers.

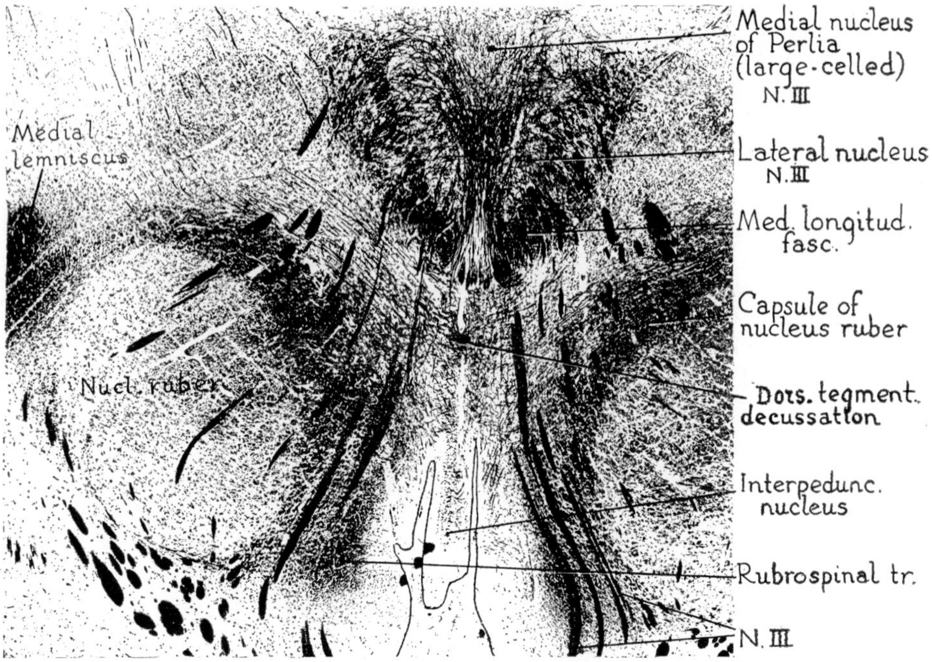

FIG. 286. Portion of midbrain tegmentum of one month infant. Weigert's myelin stain. Photograph.

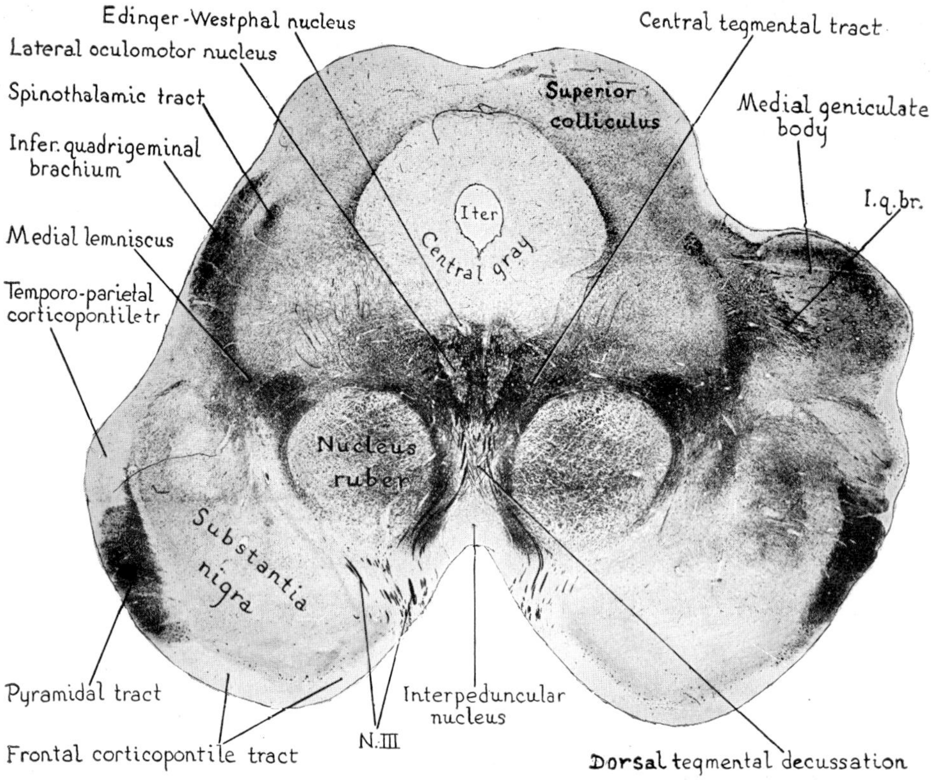

FIG. 287. Transverse section of midbrain through superior colliculi, somewhat higher level than FIG. 284. One month infant. Weigert's myelin stain. Photograph. *I.q.br.*, inferior quadrigeminal brachium.

within this region of the upper midbrain tegmentum.

Reticular cells and nuclei of the tegmentum. The reticular formation contains many scattered cells and several important nuclear masses which may be regarded as special condensations of such cells. The most conspicuous of these is the *nucleus ruber*; other smaller ones are the *interstitial nucleus of Cajal* and the *nucleus of the posterior commissure* (nucleus of Darkschewitsch) located in the region of the junction of midbrain and thalamus. In the raphéal area are still the dorsal tegmental and the interpeduncular nucleus which constitute relay stations in descending olfactory and other visceromotor pathways.

The diffuse cells may be roughly grouped into a lateral and a medial mesencephalic nucleus (Fig. 288). The cells are of large or medium size and generally belong to the so-called "motor reticular nucleus" whose cells, isolated or in groups, have been noted in practically all sections of the pontile tegmentum and reticular formation of the medulla. Their axons, largely uncrossed, usually bifurcate into *ascending* and *descending arms* of variable length. Some of these reach the motor nuclei of the brain stem and spinal cord as reticulobulbar or reticulospinal fibers, some go to the inferior olive as reticuloolivary fibers. The latter, together with similar fibers from the nucleus ruber, form a large part of the central tegmental tract. Other shorter fibers terminate in the reticular formation of lower levels (reticuloreticular) and reach the spinal cord by a series of short intercalated neurons. Within the cord these chains are probably continued downward by short spinospinal fibers of intersegmental neurons.

The reticular cells receive collaterals or terminals from secondary afferent neurons (medial lemniscus, lateral lemniscus, secondary trigeminal, vestibular, cerebellar). They also receive fibers from the nucleus ruber and tectum of the midbrain, from the corpus striatum hence indirectly from the thalamus, and from the cerebral cortex. Thus the reticular cells and their fibers form a diffuse but extensive system which constitutes the intrinsic associative mechanism of the brain stem. They mediate and coordinate bulbar and spinal reflexes, and form important links in the descending extrapyramidal pathways from cortex, thalamus, and striatum (Fig. 197).

Functional considerations of the reticular system. Recent electrophysiological investigations on animals including the monkey, have yielded new and important information regarding the organization and functional significance of the reticular system. Magoun and Rhines (1946) found an elongated region lying ventromedially in the reticular formation of the medulla, whose stimulation inhibited or reduced spinal cord reflexes. Stimulation of this area inhibited the patellar reflex and the flexion reflex of the foreleg; caused loss of extensor tonus in decerebrate rigidity, and inhibited responses from stimulation of the motor cortex or of descending fibers in the internal capsule. This medullary or bulbar "suppressor center" sends efferent fibers (medial reticulospinal) to the ventral funiculus of the cord (Fig. 197). There is evidence that it is activated by higher centers whose stimulation likewise causes inhibition of motor activity or of extensor tonus, such as the "suppressor" areas of the cortex, the striatum, and the anterior lobe of the cerebellum.

A far greater portion of the reticular formation when stimulated facilitates or augments reflexes of lower centers and cortically induced movements (Rhines and Magoun, 1946). In the medulla this "facilitatory" region lies lateral to the bulbar suppressor area. Rostrally it extends uninterruptedly through the pontile and mesencephalic tegmentum into the basal portion of the diencephalon (subthalamus and hypothalamus, Fig. 334). Here it receives contributions from the globus pallidus and certain nuclei of the thalamus (intralaminar and midline nuclei). The facilitatory effects can be elicited at any level of this long stretch of reticular formation, and appear to be mediated by a descending system of interconnected neurons, finally discharging into the spinal cord by the lateral reticulospinal tracts (Fig. 197). It is probable, therefore, that decerebrate rigidity is due not only to the excitatory action of the vestibular nuclei, but also to the action of the reticular facilitatory center, transmitted through the lateral reticulospinal fibers. Destruction of the cortical and striate suppressor areas, and especially of the bulbar suppressor center enhances spasticity. Lesions in the reticular facilitatory area greatly reduce spasticity and spasticity is completely abolished by additional destruction of the vestibular nuclei. Schreiner, Lindsley and Magoun (1949) conclude that in the cat at least, spasticity is maintained by "facilitatory influx to the cord, conducted by reticulospinal and vestibulospinal tracts coursing chiefly in the ventral half of the lateral and in the ventral funiculi".

More recently, Magoun (1950, 1952) has demonstrated that the facilitatory region of the reticular formation also acts in an *ascending direction* and influences the spontaneous electrical activity of the cerebral cortex. The cortical electroencephalogram of the cat is different in the waking and the sleeping state, and the change from the one to the other can be readily recorded. In sudden awakening, caused for instance by some auditory or tactile stimuli, the waking electroencephalogram appears at once with concomitant increase in behavioral alertness (arousal or recruiting reaction). The regions of stimulation that elicit the arousal reaction are distributed throughout the length of the brain stem, and contains two functionally distinct systems most easily recognized in the midbrain tegmentum. Near the lateral periphery are the long ascending sensory paths of the medial lemniscus, lateral lemniscus, and spinothalamic tracts, and their direct stimulation induces the same arousal reaction as that of peripheral nerve stimulation. Medially is the more extensive area of the reticular formation, apparently composed of ascending relays running uninterruptedly from the medulla through the midbrain tegmentum and basal diencephalon to the internal capsule. Stimulation of any level in this long stretch, and especially of the midbrain tegmentum and diencephalon, will likewise induce the cortical arousal reaction.

It is significant that bilateral interruption of the ascending afferent tracts still leaves the animal with the electrocortigram of the wakeful state. However, after lesions of the reticular system which spare the afferent tracts, the electroencephalogram changes to that of the sleeping state. Moreover, after lesions in the rostral part of the midbrain, which destroy the somatic and auditory tracts but leave the reticular system intact, tactile and auditory stimuli will still cause the arousal reaction, though the stimuli no longer reach the thalamus and cortex by their normal pathway. This strongly suggests that the afferent stimuli do not induce the wakeful state directly, but through excitation of the ascending reticular system to which they are related by collaterals. Such collaterals are given off by the afferent tracts at all levels of the reticular formation, and are especially numerous in the region of the midbrain and basal diencephalon (Starzl, Taylor and Magoun, 1951). The mesencephalic and the basal diencephalic portions of the reticular system are the sites whose stimulation most readily produces the electrocortical changes seen in awakening, and whose destruction most definitely results in impairment of wakefulness. As will be seen later, the most cephalic level of this reticular activating system is represented by the intralaminar and certain other nuclei of the thalamus which constitute the so-called "thalamic reticular system" (Jasper, 1949).

From the above it appears that a large part of the reticular formation constitutes an extensive brain stem center, composed of interconnected neurons that discharge by ascending relays into the cerebral cortex, and by descending relays into the motor centers of the bulb and spinal cord. Magoun (1950) suggests that the importance of this reticular system is in regulating the background activities of the rest of the nervous system. It is flanked by the long ascending fiber systems from which it receives numerous collaterals, and is connected by diffuse and overlapping projections with extensive areas of the cortex (Jasper et al., 1952). Its own influence is exerted at both caudal and cephalic levels. Caudally, it facilitates reflex and cortically induced movements and thus contributes to optimum motor performance. Its cephalic influence is to activate and regulate the cortical activities underlying the state of wakefulness or alertness on which the higher functions of the brain largely depend.

The nucleus ruber. The red nucleus, which in the fresh condition has a pinkish-yellow color, is a large ovoid or cylindrical column of cells extending from the caudal margin of the superior colliculi into the diencephalon. In transverse sections it appears as a circular area occupying a considerable portion of the tegmentum. The nucleus is composed of a caudal large-celled part (paleoruber) and a more extensive smaller-celled part (neoruber) especially prominent in man (Fig. 288). The magnocellular portion, extensive in lower mammals but greatly reduced in man, consists of large multipolar neurons which give rise to the rubrospinal and rubrobulbar fibers. The small-celled or parvocellular portion forms the bulk of the nucleus and is composed of smaller cells rather sparsely distributed. Between the cells run numerous

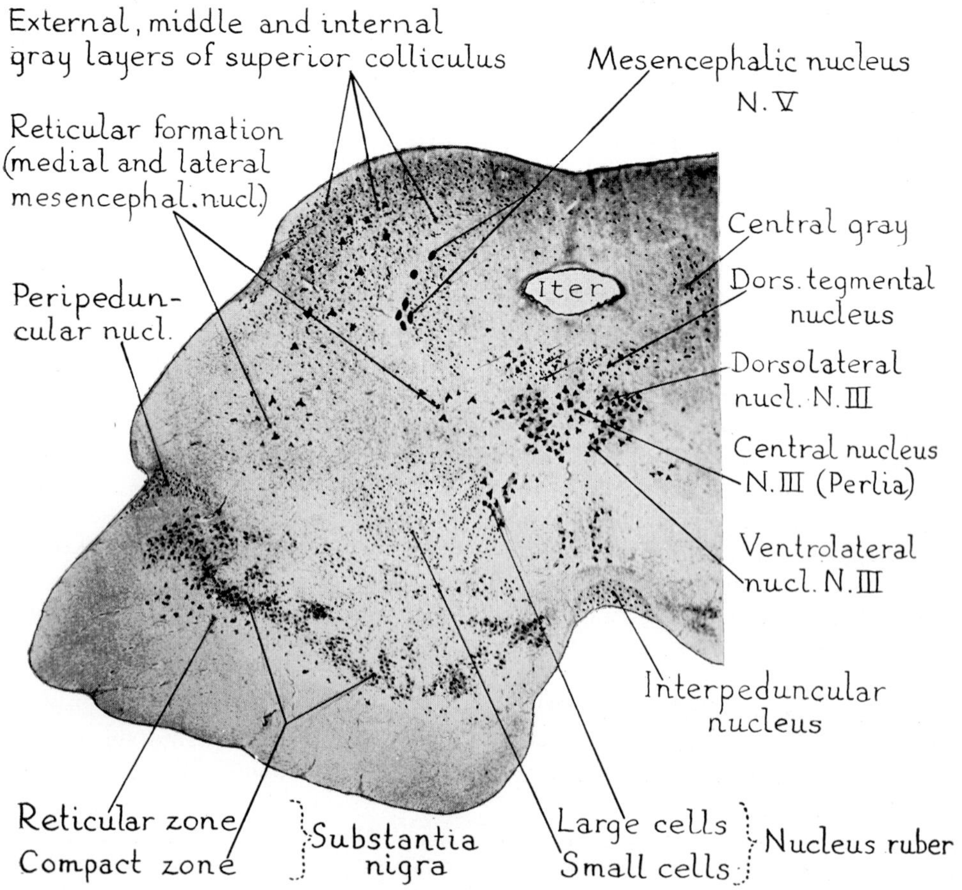

FIG. 288. Section through superior colliculi of midbrain. Three months infant. Cresyl Violet. Photograph in which the main cell groups have been schematically blocked in.

small bundles of myelinated fibers which give the nucleus a punctate appearance in transverse sections. These are primarily fibers from the superior cerebellar peduncle which terminate in the nucleus or traverse it on the way to the thalamus. The nucleus is surrounded by a capsule of fibers most abundant on the medial surface and representing afferent and efferent connections of the nucleus. In a general way the cephalic portion of the capsule represents connections with the thalamus, cortex, and corpus striatum, while the caudal portion is related to the cerebellum and to the brain stem structures lying caudal to the red nucleus.

The fiber systems of the nucleus ruber are extensive. The afferent fibers include (a) a strong contingent from the cerebellum (dentatorubral) by way of the brachium conjunctivum, a considerable part of which ends in the red nucleus (Fig. 192). Most of these fibers go to the neoruber, only a small portion terminating in the magnocellular part and reticular formation; (2) some *vestibulorubral* fibers ascending in or near the medial longitudinal fasciculus; (3) *pallidorubral* fibers from the globus pallidus of the corpus striatum, either directly or through intercalated cells (nucleus of the field of Forel) lying immediately oral to the red nucleus; (4) *corticorubral* fibers from the premotor frontal cortex; (5) *tectorubral* fibers from the superior colliculi by way of the dorsal tegmental decussation.

The efferent fibers include (1) the *rubrospinal* and *rubrobulbar* tracts arising from the magnocellular portion. Strongly developed in lower mammals where the magnocellular nucleus is large, they are greatly reduced in man, forming a small bundle which crosses completely in the ventral tegmental decussation and descends in the reticular formation. Some go to the motor nuclei of the cranial nerves, the rest enter the spinal cord where they continue downward in the lateral funiculus (Fig. 199). (2) *Rubroreticular* and *rubroolivary fibers.* This is a fairly extensive system and forms part of the complex central tegmental tract. Some go directly to the inferior olive, others end in the reticular formation whence new neurons send fibers to the olive (reticuloolivary), to the motor nuclei of the cranial and spinal nerves (reticulobulbar and reticulospinal), and to other levels of the reticular formation (reticuloreticular). The rubroolivary fibers are uncrossed, the rubroreticular are in part composed of crossed fibers. (3) A considerable bundle of *rubrothalamic* fibers goes mainly to the lateral ventral nucleus of the thalamus whence they are projected to the motor and premotor cortex (Areas 4 and 6, Figs. 334, 335). With these there may be direct *rubrocortical* fibers to the same areas and to the prefrontal cortex.

It is evident from the above that the red nucleus is a station interposed in many complex pathways. It relays cerebellar and vestibular impulses via the rubrospinal and rubroreticular tracts to the motor nuclei of the brain stem and cord, thus mediating postural reflex adjustments. This is perhaps more important in lower mammals than in man where many postural adjustments are to a large extent dominated by the cerebral cortex and the higher extrapyramidal centers. More significant is the great development of the small-celled portion (neoruber) as a link in the extensive and phylogenetically younger cerebellopallial pathway, connecting the cerebellar hemispheres with the motor and premotor areas of the cortex. Finally the nucleus ruber is one of the important relay stations through which extrapyramidal impulses from the cortex, thalamus, and corpus striatum may be related to the motor neurons of the brain stem and cord.

There is considerable evidence that in lower mammals (cats and dogs) the midbrain contains a center for the integration of those complex postural reflexes which enable an animal to change from an abnormal to a normal position (righting reactions). This center is probably located in the caudal magnocellular portion of the red nucleus and in the adjacent reticular formation of the same level. Destruction of the superior colliculi or of the substantia nigra does not interfere with these reactions, but they are abolished when the ventral tegmental decussation is severed. It is doubtful if the same conditions obtain in man where the magnocellular nucleus is greatly reduced. In man the righting reactions and postural orientation as a whole are to a large extent mediated by retinal impulses which are integrated in cortical centers. Clinically, large lesions of the nucleus ruber produce tremor and certain types of exaggerated involuntary movements known as choreo-athetoid movements. These symptoms are believed to be due to the interruption of the pathway running from the cerebellum through the red nucleus and thalamus, which influences the activities of the corpus striatum. According to others, these abnormal movements are due to interruption of the cerebellopallial pathway, the lack of cerebellar reinforcement producing defective or disorganized pyramidal movements. Since the brachium conjunctivum forms the initial outlet from the cerebellum for the two paths, it is quite possible that the activities of both cortex and striatum may be involved.

Other tegmental nuclei. The *interstitial nucleus of Cajal* is a small cell group located at the junction of the iter and third ventricle in the dorsomedial part of the tegmentum, immediately oral to the oculomotor nucleus (Figs. 291, 314). It is composed of relatively large cells resembling those of the red nucleus and reticular formation. It receives fibers from the vestibular nuclei, globus pallidus, superior colliculi, and probably from the substantia nigra. It contributes uncrossed descending interstitiospinal fibers to the medial longitudinal fasciculus, which go primarily to the nuclei innervating the eye and neck muscles (Fig. 264). It is probable that the extrapyramidal control of the mimetic musculature is in part mediated by fibers from the interstital nucleus and nucleus of Darkschewitsch.

Dorsal to the interstitial nucleus in the same region is another small cell group, the *nucleus of Darkschewitsch* or *nucleus of the posterior commissure,* set practically within the central gray substance. Its afferent connections are similar to those of the interstitial nucleus. Many of its efferent fibers cross through the posterior commissure and descend as commissurospinal fibers in the medial longitudinal fasciculus. Others descend uncrossed (Figs. 291, 264).

Substantia nigra. The substantia nigra is the most voluminous nuclear mass of the human mesencephalon, extending the whole length of the midbrain and projecting into the diencephalon. It is rudimentary in lower vertebrates, making its definite appearance in mammals and reaching its greatest development in man. In sections two zones are distinguishable: a dorsal compact or black zone and a ventral reticular zone which has a reddish-brown color in the fresh condition, similar to that of the globus pallidus (Fig. 288). The compact zone appears as an irregular band of closely packed large polygonal or pyramidal cells containing granules of melanin pigment. These pigmented cells do not appear until the fourth or fifth year and are apparently found only in man. The zone extends to the most caudal part of the midbrain where it is covered ventrally by the pontile nuclei. The reticular zone, also known as the stratum intermedium, lies close to the pes pedunculi and is composed of scattered cells of irregular shape, rich in iron content but containing no melanin pigment. Islands of such cells may be seen penetrating between the peduncular fibers. Within the stratum intermedium, especially in its lateral portion, are many bundles of descending myelinated fibers coming chiefly from the corpus striatum, the cortex, and the subthalamic nucleus (Fig. 285, P.p.). The zone extends upward into the diencephalon where it lies ventral to the subthalamic nucleus (Fig. 315).

Dorsal to the substantia nigra, between the latter and the nucleus ruber, is a region containing scattered cells of various sizes and shapes among which are large cells with melanin pigment. It is not quite certain whether some of these belong to the substantia nigra or the tegmentum, but many authorities regard the whole region as a diffusely organized extension of the compact zone. Lateral to the substantia nigra a layer of small cells, the *peripeduncular nucleus,* caps the dorsal surface of the pes (Fig. 288).

In spite of its prominence the fiber connections of the substantia nigra have not been fully worked out. It receives strionigral fibers from the putamen and caudate nucleus (Verhaart, 1950; Papez, 1942); corticonigral fibers from areas 4 and 6 of the frontal lobe and perhaps from other cortical areas; and a smaller contingent from the subthalamic nucleus (Woodburne et al., 1946). No fibers appear to come from the globus pallidus (Verhaart, 1950) though such fibers (pallidonigral) have been described by other investigators. The bundles of myelinated fibers seen in the stratum intermedium are largely composed of the above named descending tracts. Fewer fibers apparently reach the substantia nigra from the superior colliculi, medial lemniscus, lateral lemniscus, and basal olfactory areas, representing practically all the sensory modalities. However, the number of such fibers is slight compared to that from the corpus striatum and cortex.

The efferent fibers include nigrostriatal (Ranson and Ranson, 1942), nigrorubral, and nigroreticular fibers, and also fibers to the hypothalamus and globus pallidus. Some apparently cross in the posterior commissure and go to the interstitial and commissural nuclei. The course of many of the fibers is not fully determined. Some enter the pes pedunculi, descend for a short distance and terminate in the motor centers of the reticular formation. Others pass dorsally to reach the reticular formation and nucleus ruber by way of the midbrain tegmentum.

The substantia nigra is undoubtedly an important center of the extrapyramidal motor pathway, influenced primarily by the corpus striatum and thalamus, and by the pallium. Extensive lesions of the nucleus give symptoms similar to those of the globus pallidus, and occasionally even more accentuated. There is muscular rigidity and tremor interfering with the ease and rapidity of volitional activities. There is impairment or loss of those semi-automatic associative movements normally accompanying voluntary movements or postural changes, such as swinging the arms when walking. The emotional play of the mimetic musculature is likewise reduced or absent, the face appearing immobile or mask-like.

Pes pedunculi. The most ventral part of the midbrain which constitutes the pes pedunculi is composed of a massive band of descending cortical fibers. The middle three fifths are occupied by the corticospinal and corticobulbar tracts coming from the motor cortex (Fig. 193). Those for the legs are most laterally placed, the larger area for the arm is in the middle portion, while those for the face are located most medially. Medial to the pyramidal tracts are the frontal corticopontile fibers from the frontal lobe, while lateral to the pyramidal tracts are corticopontile fibers from the temporal, parietal and probably from the occipital cortex. Besides the above named tracts there are often found two fiber bundles which descend partly within the pes and partly in the region of the medial lemniscus and are hence known as *pes-lemniscus* bundles. The *medial* or *superficial pes-lemniscus* detaches itself from the lateral portion of the peduncles, winds ventrally around the pes and forms a semilunar fiber bundle lying medial to the frontal corticopontile tract (Fig. 279). In lower levels the fibers leave the peduncle, pass dorsally through the substantia nigra and descend in or near the ventromedial portion of the medial lemniscus. The *lateral* or *deep pes-lemniscus* detaches itself from the dorsal surface of the pes, runs for some distance in the lateral portion of the substantia nigra, then turns dorsally and likewise descends in the region of the medial lemniscus (Fig. 279). The significance of these bundles is not clear. According to Déjérine they represent aberrant pyramidal (corticobulbar) fibers which go to the motor nuclei of the eye muscles, and hence they are also known as the medial and lateral corticobulbar tracts. There is considerable evidence, however, that this interpretation is incorrect at least for the medial bundle whose fibers do not degenerate after lesions of the motor area. They are probably aberrant corticopontile fibers which terminate in the reticular tegmental nucleus of the pons (Poppi).

THE CORTICOBULBAR TRACT

The cortical fibers mediating volitional control of the muscles innervated by the cranial nerves constitute the corticobulbar or corticonuclear tract (Fig. 223). The fibers destined for the muscles of the larynx, pharynx, palate, jaw, tongue, face, and some of the neck muscles originate from cells in the ventral portion of the precentral and caudal part of the inferior frontal gyrus. Those for the eye muscles come from the caudal part of the middle frontal gyrus. The fibers descend through the corona radiata and genu of the internal capsule to enter the pes pedunculi. Within the pes many of them lie medial to the cotricospinal tract. During its further descent the tract gradually diminishes in size, constantly giving off fibers which pass to the tegmentum to reach the motor nuclei of the cranial nerves. The course of the fibers to the oculomotor nuclei is not well known. Some of them probably detach themselves in the most rostral part of the midbrain, perhaps even in the subthalamus, and reach the oculomotor nucleus in some as yet unknown way. Others appear to leave through the lateral corticopontile tract (lateral pes-lemniscus), descend in the region of the medial lemniscus to the upper pontile levels, and join the medial longitudinal fasciculus through which they are distributed to the nuclei of N.VI, N.IV, and N.III.

In the rostral part of the pons most of the corticobulbar fibers are still in contact with the pyramidal tract and form the most dorsal bundles of the latter. From about the level of the trochlear decussation and continuing downward, fibers constantly leave these dorsal bundles to enter the tegmentum. In the upper portion of the pons they appear as obliquely running fascicles (aberrant pyramidal bundles, Fig. 266), in the lower pons and medulla they leave as isolated fibers. Some fibers run dorsomedially and cross in the raphé to reach the contralateral motor nuclei, others terminate in the nuclei of the same side. Many of the fibers, especially the crossed ones, detach themselves some distance above the level of the nuclei supplied and hence have a short descending course in the region of the medial lemniscus, where they are easily recognized as lighter staining fiber bundles.

It is obvious from the above that the cranial muscle groups receive a far more extensive bilateral pyramidal innervation than do those of the extremities. This bilateral control is most marked in those muscle groups which can not as a rule be voluntarily contracted on one side only. Unilateral electrical stimulation of the motor area for these groups causes bilateral movements of the vocal cords, pharynx, palate, and upper facial muscles. The vertical and converging movements of the eyes, and the vertical movements of the jaw are likewise bilaterally controlled. On the other hand, there is conjugate lateral movement of the eyes to the opposite side, and contralateral contraction of the lower facial muscles when the respective cortical areas are unilaterally excited. Such results indicate that the pyramidal innervation for the external rectus and lower facial muscles is mainly crossed. The head is likewise deviated to the opposite side but here the reverse must be true. Since the sternocleidomastoid muscle normally turns the head to the opposite side, it is assumed that the lower motor neurons to this muscle are primarily controlled by ipsilateral cortical fibers (Fig. 223).

Due to this bilateral control, the symptoms in unilateral lesions of the corticobulbar tract (upper motor neuron paralysis) are comparatively mild. There is marked voluntary weakness of the lower facial movements such as showing the teeth, pursing the lips or puffing out the cheek, while movements of the upper face are little affected. There is usually also a slight weakness of the tongue (genioglossus) and jaw (pterygoid) movements on the opposite side, expressed by deviation of the tongue when protruded and of the jaw when the mouth is opened. Emotional facial movements such as spontaneous crying or laughing are not affected.

THE SUPERIOR COLLICULI AND PRETECTAL AREA

The superior colliculi are two flattened eminences which form the rostral half of the midbrain roof. In fish and amphibians they are massive bodies whose complex laminated structure resembles that of the cerebral cortex. They receive optic fibers as well as many fibers conveying general somatic sensibility and constitute a most important suprasegmental correlation center.

Beginning with the reptiles their significance progressively diminishes (Fig. 4). The optic fibers establish more and more extensive connections with the thalamus and cortex, as do also the fibers of general body sensibility. In man they have become greatly reduced optic reflex centers primarily concerned with the reflex adjustments of the eyes and head in response to optic stimuli.

Each colliculus still shows in a rudimentary form the complex laminated structure found in lower forms, consisting of several alternating layers of gray and white matter (Figs. 199, 289, 290). These layers proceeding from the external surface inward are: (1) An outer mainly fibrous layer, the *stratum zonale*, composed of fine nerve fibers coming mainly from the occipital cortex and entering the colliculus through the superior quadrigeminal brachium. Among the fibers are small mostly horizontal cells with tangentially or centrally directed axons. (2) The *stratum cinereum* or superficial gray layer consists of radially arranged cells whose dendrites pass peripherally and their axons inward. The larger cells lie deepest. The corticotectal fibers mentioned above and most of the optic fibers terminate in this layer. (3) The *stratum opticum* or superficial white layer is composed of optic fibers from the retina and lateral geniculate body. These enter through the superior brachium and terminate mainly in the stratum cinereum, some however going to the deeper layers of the colliculus. Among the fibers are scattered cells whose axons pass into the next layer. (4) The remaining layers are often collectively termed the *stratum lemnisci* which may be subdivided into a middle gray and white layer, and a deep gray and white layer (Figs. 289, 290). The stratum lemnisci receives the spinotectal fibers and also some fibers from the medial and the lateral lemniscus, and from the inferior colliculus. It contains many medium sized and large stellate cells, the latter sometimes known as the "motor" cells of the tectum. The axons of the smaller cells pass to the lateral portion of the reticular formation (tectoreticular) or cross to the opposite nucleus through the *commissure of the superior colliculi.* Among them are probably some tectorubral and tectonigral fibers. The axons of the large cells,

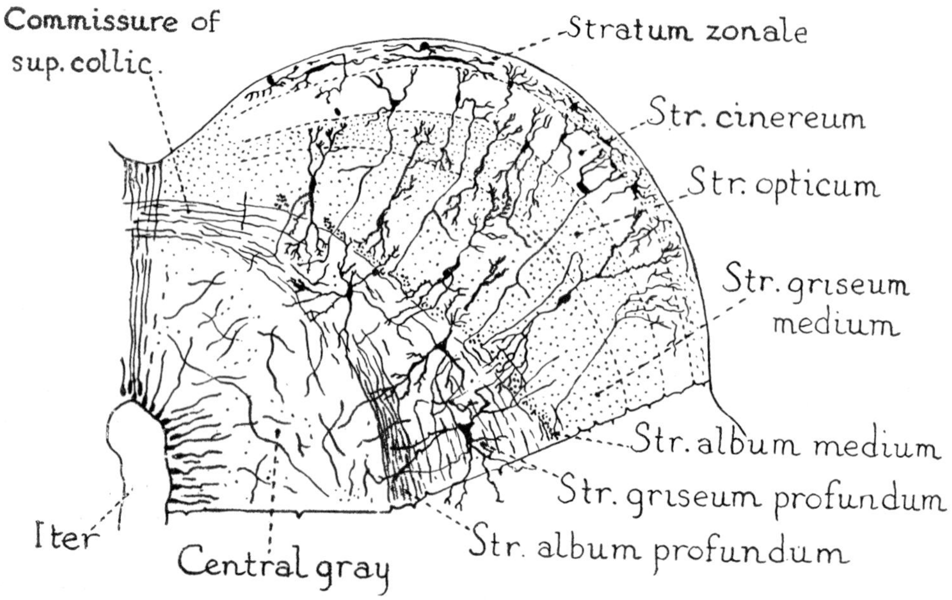

FIG. 289. Cells of superior colliculus reconstructed from Golgi preparations. Human fetus of eight months. (After Sterzi.)

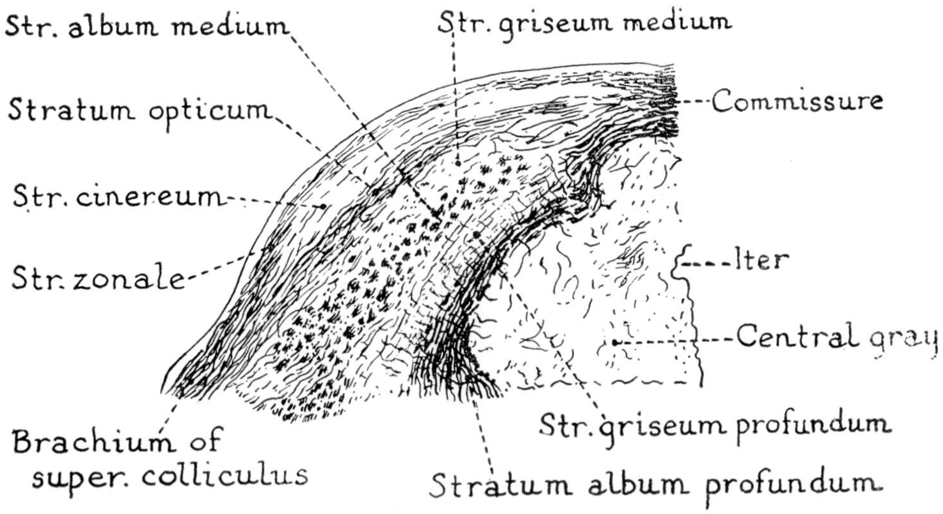

FIG. 290. Section through superior colliculus of adult. Weigert's myelin stain. (After Sterzi.)

which form the main part of the deep white layer, swing ventrally around the central gray and cross in the dorsal tegmental decussation. Some terminate in the oculomotor nucleus, the others descend as tectobulbar and tectospinal fibers in the predorsal bundle (Fig. 199). Some tectobulbar fibers are also believed to descend uncrossed near the medial longitudinal fasciculus.

The superior colliculus thus receives afferent fibers from the pallium, lateral geniculate body, and retina. These fibers terminate in the superficial layers of the colliculus. The spinotectal and other secondary afferent fibers end in the deeper layers. The efferent fibers are collected in the deep white layers and their most important connections are with the muscles of the eyes, neck, and face and possibly with the body. Between the afferent fibers and the efferent neurons are the smaller association cells whose axons do not leave the colliculus. The older optic connections are reduced, the pallial connections are phylogenetically new. It is quite possible that some of the optic "reflexes", such as turning of eyes and head with a moving object, have a cerebral arc in which the optic stimuli first reach the occipital cortex and are then referred to the colliculi by corticotectal fibers.

Immediately oral to the superior colliculus, in the region of junction of midbrain and thalamus is the *pretectal area*, usually considered a part of the mesencephalon (Figs. 199, 314). The area, which is composed of several indistinct groups of small and large cells, receives fibers from the optic tract, lateral geniculate body, and the posterior parietal cortex (Le Gros Clark), and sends fibers to the mesencephalic tegmentum and the substantia nigra. Ranson and his collaborators have demonstrated that the pretectal area, and not the superior colliculus, is the midbrain center for the pupillary light reflex.

In the zone of junction of the iter and third ventricle (pretectal area), the roof contains a considerable bundle of crossing fibers, known as the *posterior commissure.* The origin and termination of its component fibers are not altogether clear. Included are (1) Fibers from the globus pallidus, some of which go to the tegmentum and red nucleus, either directly or through intercalated cells lying within the commissure itself. Others go to the interstitial nucleus and nucleus of Darkschewitsch, and through these

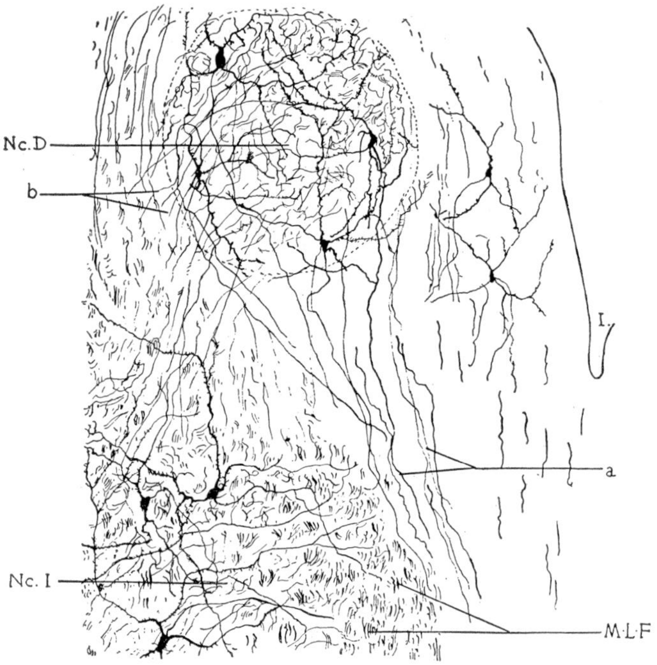

FIG. 291. Nucleus of Darkschewitsch (*NcD*) and portion of interstitial nucleus of Cajal (*NcI*) of cat several days old. Golgi impregnation. *I*, iter; *a*, axons entering the medial longitudinal fasciculus (MLF); *b*, collaterals terminating in Darkschewitsch's nucleus. (After Cajal.)

to the medial longitudinal fasciculus (Fig. 291). (2) Probably some fibers from the substantia nigra, but the course of these is undetermined. (3) Commissural fibers connecting the superior colliculi. (4) Corticotectal fibers entering the stratum zonale of the superior colliculus. (5) Fibers from cells of pretectal area going to the contralateral Edinger-Westphal nucleus. These form part of the pupillary reflex pathway.

THE OCULOMOTOR NERVE

The third nerve is primarily efferent but also contains some afferent proprioceptive fibers from the muscles supplied by N.III. These fibers are derived in part at least from ganglion cells found along the root and orbital portion of the nerve (Tozer and Sherrington), and possibly from the mesencephalic nucleus of N.V. The efferent portion contains (a) Somatic efferent fibers to the voluntary striped external muscles of the eyeball except the lateral rectus and superior oblique. These include the superior, inferior and internal recti, the inferior oblique, and the levator palpebrae superioris. (b) Visceral efferent preganglionic fibers to the ciliary ganglion whose postganglionic fibers, by way of the short ciliary nerves, supply the internal smooth muscle fibers of the eye, including the cilary body and the sphincter of the iris. The nerve thus elevates the eyelid, controls the vertical and converging movements of the eyeball, participates in the lateral movements, contracts the pupil, and alters the convexity of the lens (accommodation).

The oculomotor nuclear complex is located in the ventral part of the central gray in a V-shaped trough formed by the diverging fibers of the medial longitudinal fasciculi (Figs. 284, 285), and extends from the trochlear nucleus to about the rostral limit of the superior colliculi. It is divided into large-celled and small-celled groups. The

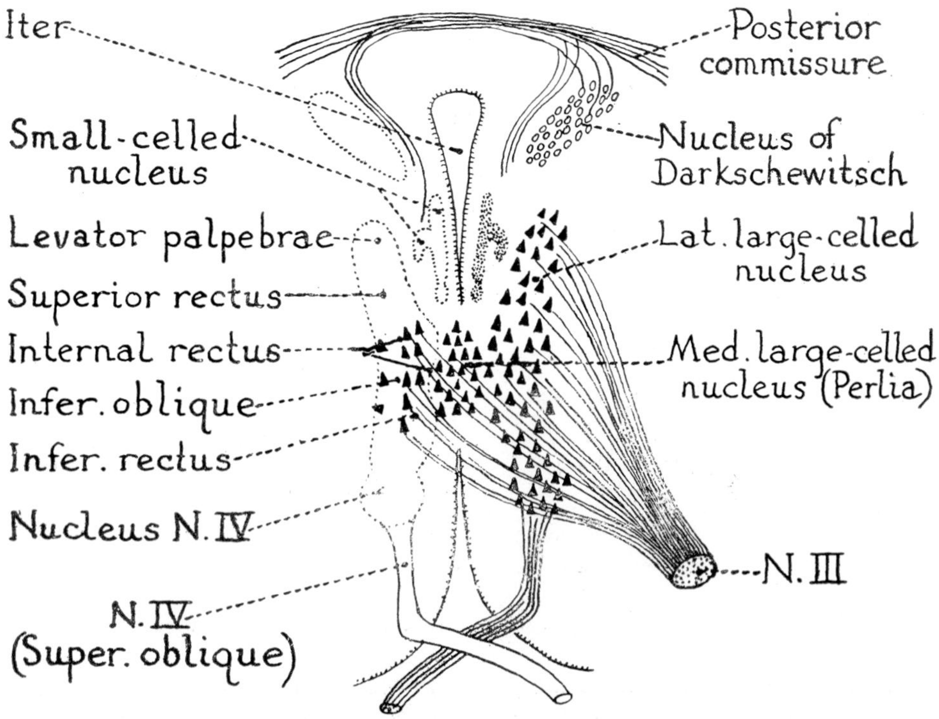

FIG. 292. The region of the Sylvian aqueduct viewed from above. Diagram showing the position of the nuclei of nerves III and IV and their subdivisions. The small-celled nucleus represented as one on each side, is subdivided into a lateral portion (Edinger-Westphal nucleus) and medial one (anterior-median nucleus). (Modified from Edinger.)

former constitute the somatic motor nuclei of N.III, composed of typical large motor cells which innervate the striped muscles and comprise the paired *lateral*, and the unpaired *central nucleus of Perlia*. The small-celled groups include the *nucleus of Edinger-Westphal* and the *anterior median nucleus*, composed of smaller spindle-shaped or ovoid cells resembling those of the lateral horn or dorsal motor nucleus cf the vagus. These are the visceral motor nuclei of N.III, believed to send preganglionic fibers to the ciliary body and sphincter iridis. Each lateral nucleus is an obliquely placed plate of cells, extending practically the whole length of the complex, closely applied to the dorsomedial surface of the medial longitudinal fasciculus. The cells actually infiltrate the fasciculus and may even extend to the external surface of the bundle. The nucleus is indistinctly divided into a smaller dorsolateral and a larger ventrolateral portion. The lateral nuclei are fused along their middle third with the centrally placed nucleus of Perlia (Figs. 286, 292). The Edinger-Westphal nucleus is located in the cephalic part of the nuclear complex lying dorsomedial to the lateral nucleus. It begins in the region of the nucleus of Perlia and extends beyond the rostral tip of the lateral nucleus. In front of, and ventral to, the Edinger-Westphal nucleus is the vertical plate of cells constituting the anterior median nucleus, regarded by many as the rostral continuation of the Edinger-Westphal nucleus (Fig. 293).

Attempts to determine the cell groups within the oculomotor nucleus which innervate specific muscles of the eyeball have yielded contradictory results. The most accepted view is that the lateral nucleus, be-

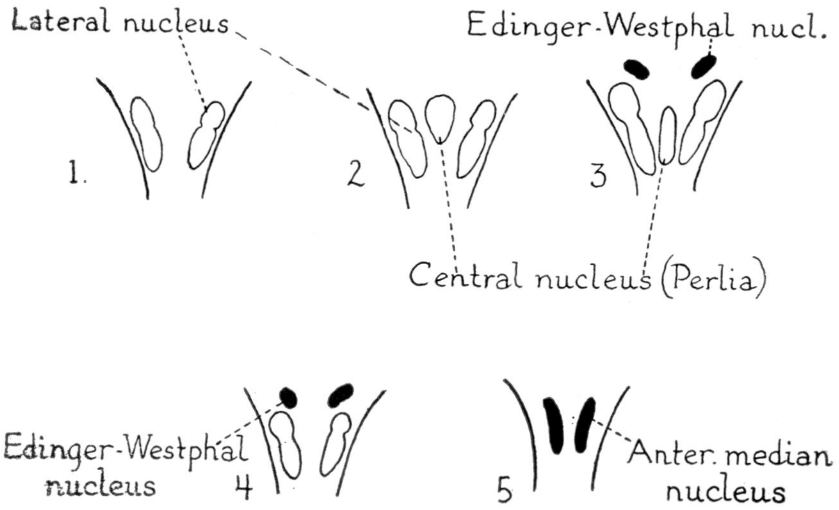

FIG. 293. Diagrams showing components of oculomotor nucleus in sections progressing from the caudal to the rostral end of the nucleus. (After Brouwer.)

ginning at its rostral end and proceeding caudally, supplies the extrinsic muscles in the following order (Bernheimer, Edinger, Brouwer): levator palpebrae, superior rectus, internal rectus, inferior oblique, inferior rectus. The fibers to the levator and superior rectus are uncrossed, those to the internal rectus and inferior oblique are both crossed and uncrossed, while those to the inferior rectus are entirely crossed. According to Warwick (1950) about one-sixth of the axons appear to be derived from the caudal two-thirds of the contralateral nuclear complex. The nucleus of Perlia is probably concerned with movements of convergence and sends fibers to the internal rectus of both eyes (Fig. 292).

The specific innervation of the intrinsic eye muscles is likewise not fully determined. The accepted belief is that the Edinger-Westphal nucleus controls the pupillary contraction to light, while the anterior median nucleus sends fibers to the ciliary body for accommodation. Comparative anatomical studies suggest that the reverse may be true. Thus the Edinger-Westphal nucleus is variably developed in many mammals, reaching its greatest extent in primates and man, while the anterior median nucleus is a constant feature of all mammals. This is correlated with the relatively constant occurrence of the pupillary reflex and the rather variable capacity for accommodation, which is most highly developed in man.

The root fibers arising from the oculomotor nucleus pass ventrally in a number of bundles, some coursing medial to, some traversing, and some passing lateral to the superior cerebellar peduncle and red nucleus. Ventral the fibers converge and emerge in the oculomotor sulcus on the ventral aspect of the midbrain. This spreading of the root fibers through and around the nucleus ruber is an expression of the intraradicular expansion of the red nucleus during embryological development.

The oculomotor nucleus receives terminals and collaterals from the medial longitudinal fasciculus, including ascending axons from the vestibular nuclei and from internuclear neurons lying near the nucleus of VI, and descending fibers from the interstitial and commissural nuclei. In addition it receives fibers from the superior colliculi, superior cerebellar peduncle, and reticular formation. The vestibular fibers reflexly correlate the positions of the eyes with those of the head; while the internuclear fibers in the medial longitudinal fasciculus associate the abducens and oculomotor nuclei in the performance of lateral eye movements. The collicular fibers put the eye movements under control of the collicular optic reflex center, and thereby under one of the eye-movement centers of the cerebral cortex which sends fibers to the superior colliculus. The fibers to the Edinger-Westphal nucleus, believed to effect pupillary contraction, do not come from the superior colliculi but from a region immediately above them, known as the pretectal area. The oculomotor nucleus also receives corticobulbar (pyramidal) fibers for voluntary movement. Some of them appear to detach themselves from the pes pedunculi in the caudal part of the midbrain and join the medial longitudinal fasciculus through which they are distributed to the motor nuclei of the eye nerves. The pyramidal fibers probably do not reach the nucleus directly but through the intermediation of intercalated cells in the adjacent reticular formation, which constitute intrinsic "centers" for the vertical and converging movements. The fact that the conjugate eye movements, lateral, vertical, and converging, can not be dissociated voluntarily or reflexly, suggests that the pyramidal and all other fibers act on internuncial cells. These in turn integrate the various motor neurons used in the eye movements. This would certainly seem to be the case with the conjugate lateral movements which are controlled by two widely separated nuclei, VI for external rectus, and III for internal rectus.

Lesion of the third nerve produces an ipsilateral lower motor neuron paralysis of the muscles supplied by the nerve. There is an external strabismus (squint) due to the unopposed action of the external rectus, inability to move the eye vertically or inward, drooping of the eyelid (ptosis), dilation of the pupil (mydriasis), loss of pupillary reflex to light and convergence, and loss of accommodation of the lens. The nearness of the emerging root fibers of N.III to the pyramidal tracts of the pes pedunculi may lead to the inclusion of both structures in a single lesion, causing an alternating hemiplegia similar to those already described for the sixth and twelfth nerves (Fig. **193**). In this case there would be an ipsilateral lower motor neuron paralysis of N.III showing the symptoms described above, combined with a contralateral spastic hemiplegia of the body and extremities. Since at this level the corticobulbar and corticospinal fibers are in close conjunction, there may also be contralateral paralysis or paresis (weakness) of the muscles innervated by the cranial nerves, especially those of the lower face and tongue. This constitutes the *superior* or *oculomotor alternating hemiplegia* clinically known as *Weber's syndrome.*

THE PUPILLARY REFLEXES

When a beam of light is thrown on the retina of one eye both pupils contract. The response of the eye stimulated is called the *direct reaction*, that of the opposite eye the *consensual reaction.* The pathway for this *pupillary* or *light reflex* consists of the following neurons: (1) Fibers from retinal cells which pass through the optic nerve and tract, and enter the superior brachium through which they reach the pretectal area; (2) axons of pretectal cells, partially crossing through the posterior commissure, sweep ventrally along the central gray matter and terminate in the Edinger-Westphal nucleus of the same and opposite side; (3) preganglionic fibers from the Edinger-Westphal nucleus go by way of N.III to the ciliary ganglion from which (4) postganglionic fibers pass to smooth muscle fibers known as the sphincter of the iris.

When the gaze is suddenly shifted from a distant to a near object the accommodation-convergence reaction occurs. Contraction of the internal recti muscles causes convergence of the eyes, contraction of the ciliary muscle effects a thickening of the lens (*accommodation*), and the pupils are likewise constricted as an aid to the sharper definition of the image. In this instance pupillary constriction is an associated part of a more elaborate reflex response that involves both smooth and skeletal muscle fibers, and the neural pathway includes cells of the cerebral cortex. The retinal impulses, or perhaps proprioceptive impulses from the contracting ocular muscles, reach the visual cortex. Descending cortical impulses are then sent directly or by way of the frontal eye centers to the "convergence center" of the oculomotor nuclei. Since the pupilloconstrictor pathways for light and accommodations are distinct, they may be involved separately in isolated lesions. This occurs in certain diseases such as tabes dorsalis, in which there is loss of pupillary constriction (miosis) to light but not to accommodation. As a result the pupil is small (less than 2.5 mm.), fails to constrict in even bright light, and dilates imperfectly to atropine—yet has a brisk response during convergence and accommodation. A small immobile pupil with these properties is known as an *Argyll-Robertson* pupil. Many contemporary authors place the responsible lesion in the afferent visual pathway after the retinal fibers leave the optic tract to enter the pretectal area (Fig. 199). However, a unilateral Argyll-Robertson pupil is not an infrequent clinical observation, and a single pathologic or experimental lesion in the brain stem can not satisfactorily explain this peculiar ophthomologic finding. Some believe the most plausible lesion is located in the efferent pathways for pupillary constriction (Naquin, 1954). Other workers attribute the fixed Argyll-Robertson pupil to abnormalities of the blood vessels, nerves, and smooth muscle within the iris (Langworthy and Ortega, 1943; Apter, 1954a, b). The fibers serving accommodation, which remain in the optic tract and go to the lateral geniculate body and cortex are, left intact.

In intense illumination contraction of the pupil may be accompanied by closure of the eyelids, lowering of the brows, and general contraction of the face, designed to shut out the maximal amount of light. In so far as they are not volitional, these are reflex movements mediated through the superior colliculi and the tectobulbar tracts.

The central pathway for pupillary dilation is not fully ascertained. Dilation occurs reflexly on shading the eye or scratching the side of the neck with a pin, and is a constant feature in severe pain and emotional states. Experimental evidence points to a path from the frontal cortex to the posterior region of the hypothalamus which is one of the highest autonomic centers of the brain stem. From the hypothalamus fibers descend through the reticular formation (and periventricular region) of the midbrain, pons, and medulla to terminate in the upper portion of the lateral sympathetic nucleus (intermediolateral column) of the spinal cord. The latter sends preganglionic fibers by way of the upper two or three rami communicantes and sympathetic trunk to the superior cervical ganglion, whence postganglionic fibers go to the dilator muscle of the iris (Fig. 204). The descending pathway from the hypothalamus probably contains intercalated neurons, and the dilator fibers run close to those which control the tonic elevation of the upper eyelid through the superior tarsal muscle. Hence central lesions usually affect both of these fibers and cause the diminished pupil (miosis) and slight drooping of the eyelid (ptosis) characteristic of Horner's syndrome.

Blood supply. The arterial supply of the midbrain is derived principally from the basilar system, to a lesser degree from branches of the internal carotid. The main vessels include the *posterior cerebral*, the *superior cerebellar*, the *posterior communicating*, and the *anterior chorioidal arteries* (Fig. 63). The branches from these arteries which supply the midbrain may be grouped, as in the case of the pons, into (a) *paramedian* or *central* arteries which enter medially in the region of the interpeduncular fossa, and (2) *peripheral* or *circumferential* arteries which wind laterally around the peduncle and supply its lateral and dorsal portions.

The paramedian branches are derived from the posterior communicating artery, from the basilar bifurcation and proximal portions of the posterior cerebral arteries. They form an extensive plexus in the interpeduncular fossa and enter the posterior perforated substance to supply the floor of the fossa, the raphéal region including the oculomotor nucleus and medial longitudinal fasciculus, the red nucleus, and the most medial part of the pes pedunculi. Branches from the anterior chorioidal artery supply similar vessels to the most oral portion of the interpeduncular fossa, medial to the optic tract.

The circumferential branches may be short or long ones. The short ones arise in part from the interpeduncular plexus, in part from the proximal portions of the posterior cerebral and superior cerebellar arteries. The short circumferential arteries supply the middle and lateral parts of the pes, the substantia nigra, and lateral part of the tegmentum. In the upper midbrain similar branches are contributed by the anterior chorioidal artery. The long circumferential arteries arise primarily from the posterior cerebral. The most important of these is the *quadrigeminal artery* which encircles the lateral periphery and furnishes the main blood supply to the superior and inferior colliculi. Other long branches contributing to the supply of the roof are furnished by the inferior chorioidal and superior cerebellar arteries.

The numerous veins which arise from the capillaries generally run parallel to the arteries but not directly with them. They form an extensive peripheral plexus in the pia and are collected by two larger channels, the basal veins, which drain into either the great cerebral vein of Galen or the internal cerebral veins.

18

Internal Structure of the Cerebellum

As noted in chapter IV the surface of the cerebellum is composed of numerous narrow lamina, the *cerebellar folia*, and these in turn possess secondary and tertiary infoldings. Deeper sulci subdivide the vermis and cerebellar hemispheres into lobes and lobules which can be identified in gross specimens, as well as in mid-sagittal section (Figs. 40, 41, 39).

The oldest portion of the cerebellum (*archicerebellum*) represents an elaborate expansion of the lateral vestibular area of the brain stem. It is prominent in lower animals (Fig. 4) while in the human the archicerebellum is represented by the flocculi and certain parts of the vermis (lingula, nodulus, and uvula). This ancient area of the cerebellum forms the greater part of the posterior lobe (Fig. 294).

The *paleocerebellum* was added to the existing archicerebellum to provide integrating centers for the reception of general proprioceptive stimuli from the muscles of the body and head. The paleocerebellum forms most of the cerebellum in lower animals (Fig. 4), while in man it is represented principally by the spinocerebellar areas of the vermis (lobulus centralis, culmen, pyramis, uvula, and simple lobule). The anterior lobe of the cerebellum (Fig. 294) and deeper lying nuclei (fastigii, emboliformis, and globosus) are paleocerebellar structures primarily related to equilibrium, muscle tone and the gross synergic movements used in locomotion. The paleocerebellum is intimately related to the spinal cord and reticular formation of the brain stem by many afferent and efferent fiber pathways.

Phylogenetically the newest and also the largest portion of the human cerebellum is designated the *neocerebellum*. It includes the cerebellar hemispheres, the more lateral areas of the anterior lobe, and the ventrolateral portions of the dentate nuclei. The neocerebellum of man comprises most of the middle cerebellar lobe (Fig. 294), and is primarily related to the fine movements of the extremity muscles whose movement is initiated by the motor cortex. By ascending and descending pathways the neocerebellum is intimately related to the other new portions of the central nervous system, e.g., the red nucleus, thalamus, and higher reticular nuclei of the brain stem. Through thalamic relay nuclei, the integrative neural activity of the neocerebellum also reaches and influences the basal ganglia and the cerebral cortex.

The dorsally placed cerebellum is attached to the medulla, pons, and midbrain by the three cerebellar peduncles. These three compact bridges are composed of the old and new fiber pathways that interconnect the archi-, paleo-, and neocerebellum with the spinal cord and brain stem. The origin, course, and termination of the fibers to and from the cerebellum reveals the true significance of this "great integrative center" for the reflex coordination of muscular activity. Before examining the afferent and efferent fibers of the cerebellum it will be profitable to consider the finer structures of the cerebellar cortex.

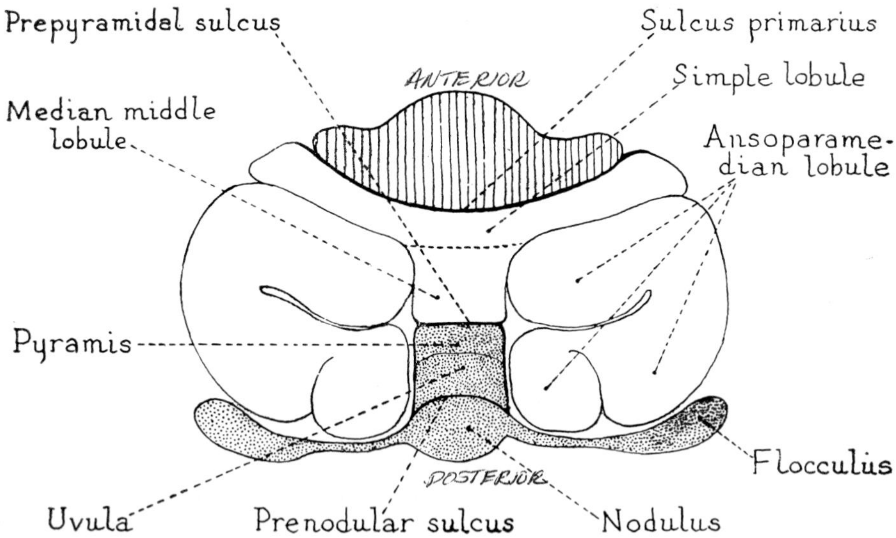

FIG. 294. Diagram of human cerebellum. Anterior lobe striped, middle lobe clear, posterior lobe stippled.

STRUCTURE OF THE CEREBELLAR CORTEX

The cerebellar cortex has a relatively similar structure in all parts of the cerebellum, and is composed of three layers: an outer *molecular* layer with relatively few cells and few myelinated fibers, an inner densely cellular *granular* layer, and between the two a single row of large flask-shaped cells, the *cells of Purkinje* (Figs. 295, 297, 298, 299). These cells have a clear vesicular nucleus with deeply staining nucleolus, and irregular Nissl bodies usually arranged concentrically. Each cell gives off two or three main dendrites which enter the molecular layer and form a remarkably rich arborization extending to the surface. The larger and medium sized branches are smooth, but the finer terminal ones are beset with numerous small excrescences or "gemmules". The dendritic arborization does not spread uniformly in all directions but is flattened fanlike in a plane at right angles to the long axis of the folium, hence its full extent can only be seen in transverse sections (Figs. 79, 299). The axon arises from the end of the cell opposite to the dendrites, acquires a myelin sheath, passes through the granular layer and enters the underlying white matter to go to one of the deep cerebellar nuclei or to some other part of the cortex. Not far from its origin, each axon gives off a number of collaterals which run horizontally and terminate on the bodies of adjacent Purkinje cells (Fig. 299). Occasionally somewhat smaller aberrantly placed Purkinje cells may be found in the granular or molecular layer. Since the axons of the Purkinje cells are the only ones to enter the white, it is evident that all impulses entering the cerebellum must converge on these cells to reach the efferent cerebellar paths.

The *granular layer* in ordinary stains presents the appearance of closely packed chromatic nuclei, not unlike those of lymphocytes, with irregular light spaces here and there which constitute the so-called "islands" or "glomeruli" (Figs. 295, 297). In silver preparations these nuclei are seen to belong to small multipolar cells, the *granule cells* about 4–8 micra in diameter (Fig. 78B). The cells have three or four rather short dendrites which arborize in peculiar claw-like endings within the "glomeruli". The unmyelinated axons ascend to the molecular layer where each bifurcates

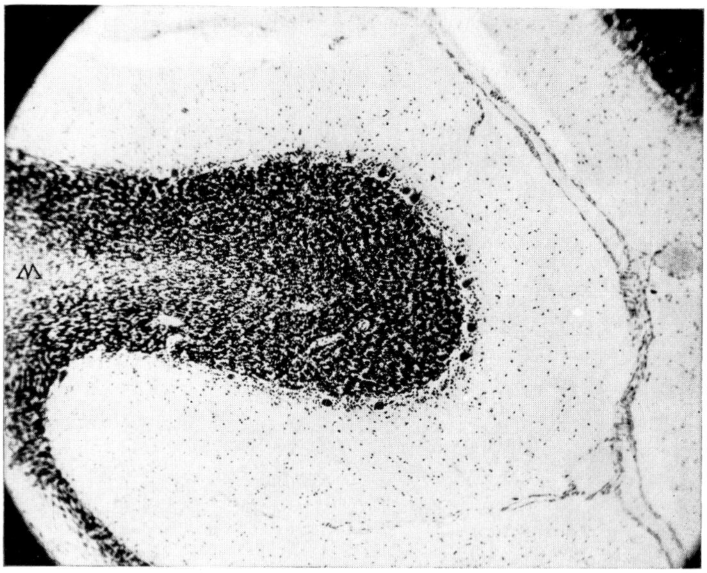

Fig. 295. Section through small folium of human cerebellum showing the dark staining granular layer with glomeruli (light spaces), the light staining molecular layer containing scattered nuclei, and between the two a single row of Purkinje cell nuclei. Cresyl Violet. Photograph. *M*, medullary core.

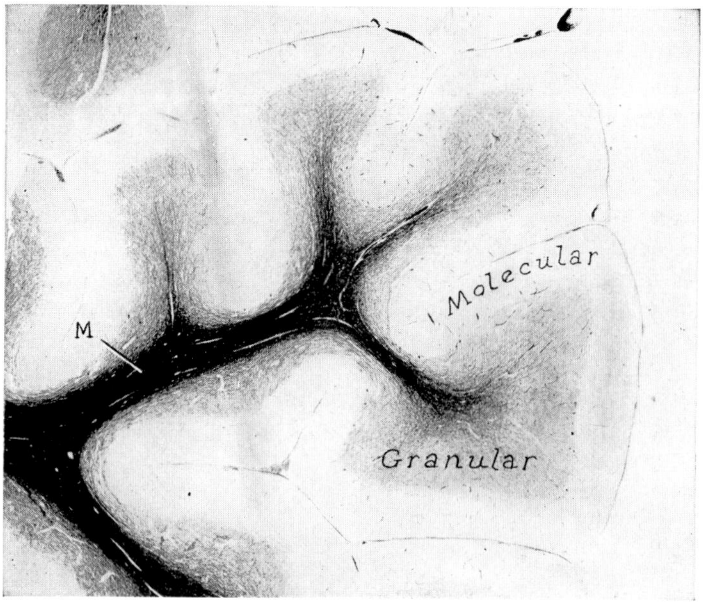

Fig. 296. Section through portion of adult cerebellum showing several secondary folia. Weigert's myelin stain. Photograph. *M*, medullary core.

into two branches which run parallel to the long axis of the folium. These parallel fibers practically fill the whole depth of the molecular layer and run transversely to the dendritic expansions of the Purkinje cells. They traverse layer after layer of these expansions, appearing like telegraph wires strung along the branches of a tree, and

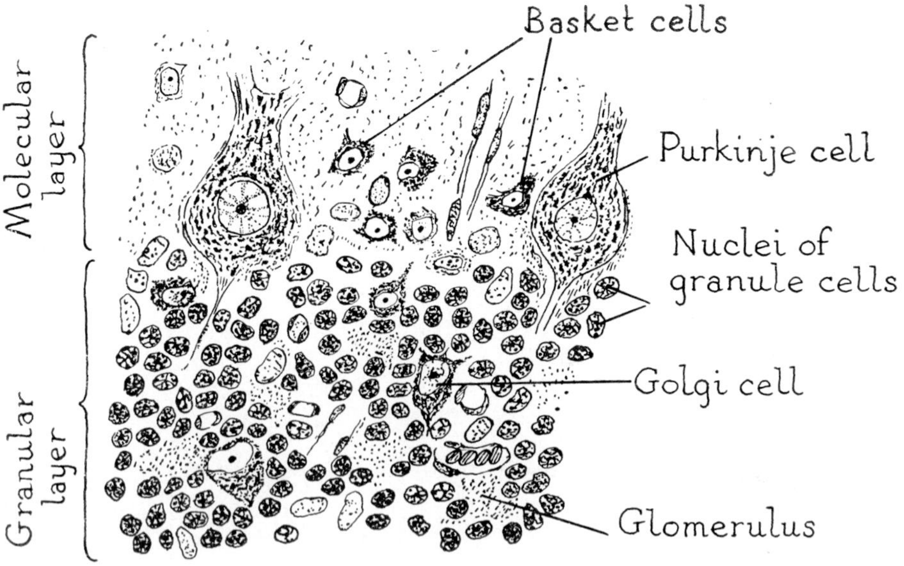

FIG. 297. Part of a section through human cerebellar cortex. Nissl stain. (After Cajal.)

extend the whole length of a folium, finally terminating in delicate button-shaped enlargements (Fig. 300).

Scattered through all parts of the granular layer are the *Golgi type II cells* or *cells of van Gehuchten*, with vesicular nuclei and definite chromofilic bodies (Figs. 297, 298). Many of their branching dendrites enter the molecular layer where they may extend to the surface. Their axon springs directly from the cell body and almost immediately splits into a complex arborization within the granular layer, the terminal fibrils being mainly concentrated in the glomeruli where they come in contact with the dendritic terminals of the granule cells. Larger cells found occasionally in the superficial portion of the granular layer, which have long axons entering the white, are believed to be aberrantly placed Purkinje cells (Cajal, Jakob).

The *molecular layer* contains relatively few cells of a stellate or triangular shape. The superficial stellate cells are small, with short thin dendrites, and fine unmyelinated often horizontally running axons. The larger deeper stellate cells situated in the vicinity of the Purkinje cell bodies are also known as *basket cells*. Many of their numerous branching dendrites ascend in the molecular layer. The unmyelinated axons spring from one side of the cell body and run as horizontal fibers transversely to the folium, i.e., in the same plane as the dendritic arborizations of the Purkinje cells. These horizontal axons pass a number of Purkinje cells, to each of which they give off one or more descending collaterals which form an intricate end arborization or "basket" around the Purkinje cell bodies (Fig. 103). A single collateral may furnish terminals for two Purkinje cells or the latter may receive terminals from several basket cells. Thus a single basket cell may come in synaptic relations with many Purkinje cells situated in a transverse plane of the folium, its axon even extending to a neighboring folium. It is evident from the above that besides the relatively few cells the molecular layer is composed primarily of unmyelinated dendritic and axonal processes which include the dendrites of the Purkinje cells, the longitudinally running axons of the granule cells, the transversely running axons of the basket cells, and also the dendrites of the basket and Golgi type II cells.

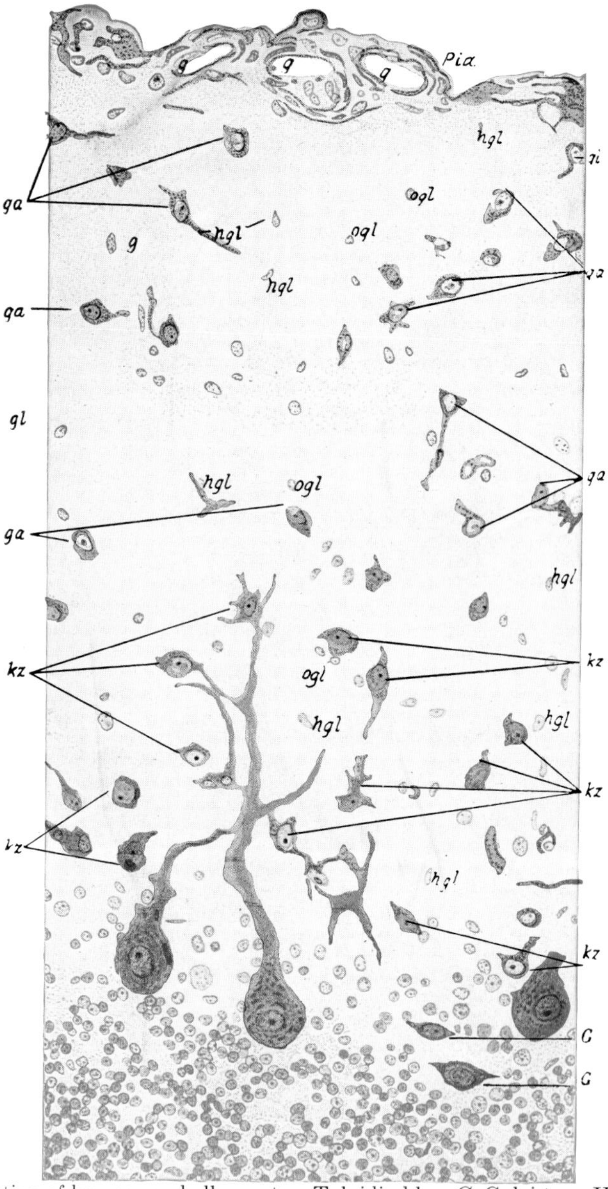

FIG. 298. Section of human cerebellar cortex. Toluidin blue. *G*, Golgi type II cell; *g*, blood vessel; *ga*, stellate cell; *gl*, macroglia; *hgl*, microglia; *ogl*, oligodendroglia; *kz*, basket cells. (Jakob.)

Section of all these processes gives to the molecular layer its finely punctate appearance. Only in its deepest portion is there found a narrow horizontal plexus of myelinated fibers composed of collaterals from the axons of Purkinje cells (Fig. 299).

Nerve fibers. The efferent fibers of the cerebellar cortex are all axons of Purkinje cells which go mainly to the deep cerebellar nuclei, though a few may leave the cerebellum without relaying in those nuclei. Such fibers have been found in the flocculi and nodule and may also be present in other portions of the vermis. Some of the Purkinje cell axons are undoubtedly associative in character, connecting different parts of the cerebellum on the same side or crossing through the white of the vermis to terminate on the opposite side (Clarke and Horsley, Brouwer and Coenen, Saito). These association fibers are found in the most superficial portion of the medullary substance and as short, arcuate fibers may connect adjacent folia or lobules, or may extend a distance of two or three lobules.

The afferent fibers to the cerebellar cortex are furnished by the tracts entering the cerebellum through the inferior and middle peduncles, including the vestibulo-, spino-, olivo-, and pontocerebellar fibers. To a smaller extent, there are also association fibers coming from other parts of the cerebellum. Structurally two types of afferent terminals are found in the cerebellar cortex, *mossy fibers* and *climbing fibers*. The mossy fibers, so-called from the appearance of their terminations in the embryo, are the coarsest fibers in the white matter. While still in the white they bifurcate repeatedly into numerous branches which then enter the granular layer, the branches of a single fiber often going to adjacent folia. They course through the granular layer and give off many fine collaterals, each of which enters a "glomerulus", loses its myelin sheath, and forms an arborization related to the claw-like dendritic endings of the granule cells (Fig. 300). The fiber itself ends in a similar termination in the superficial portion of the granular layer. Thus the "islands" or "glomeruli" contain the endings of the mossy fibers, the dendritic endings of the granule cells, and the axonal terminals of the Golgi type II cells.

The climbing fibers pass from the white matter through the granular layer and past the Purkinje cell bodies to reach the main dendrites of the latter. There they lose their myelin sheath and split into a number of terminal fibrils which climb ivy-like along the dendritic arborization whose branchings they closely imitate (Fig. 104). According to Cajal, each climbing fiber is related to only one Purkinje cell.

The respective sources of the climbing and mossy fibers have not been fully determined. Cajal suggested that the pontocerebellar and vestibulocerebellar tracts terminated in climbing fibers, while the spino- and olivocerebellar have mossy endings. This view has not been substantiated by the findings of other investigators. It seems certain that many of the mossy fibers are furnished by the spinocerebellar, olivocerebellar, and pontocerebellar tracts, since section of these tracts causes extensive degeneration of the mossy endings but leaves the climbing fibers intact (Miscolczy, 1931, 1934; Snider, 1936; Mettler and Lubin, 1942). The sources of the climbing fibers are still somewhat obscure. It is unlikely that they are endings of the vestibulocerebellar tracts since these tracts terminate primarily in the flocculi and certain restricted portions of the vermis, while both climbing and mossy fibers are found in all parts of the cerebellar cortex. Moreover there is considerable evidence that the climbing fibers may not be afferent cerebellar fibers at all, but may form part of an intracerebellar association system. Thus Lorente de Nó (1924) regards them as recurrent axonal collaterals of Purkinje cells, while Carrea, Reissig and Mettler (1947) conclude they are chiefly, if not entirely, axons or recurrent axonal collaterals of cells in the deep cerebellar nuclei.

The structural mechanism of the cerebellar cortex furnishes a number of intracortical paths for entering cerebellar impulses; some direct and limited, others intricate and diffuse. Thus impulses may pass through (a) Climbing fiber, Purkinje cell and out again by the axon of the latter, the shortest circuit possible. (b) Mossy fiber, granule cell and Purkinje cell, permitting extensive diffusion in the longitudinal axis of the folium. (c) Mossy fiber, granule cell, basket cell, and Purkinje cell. Such a circuit would produce transverse diffusion along the axons of the basket cells. (d) Mossy fiber, granule cell, Golgi type II cell, and back again to granule cell, an exceedingly involved pathway in which the impulse would pass to and from the granular and molecular layer, involving progressively

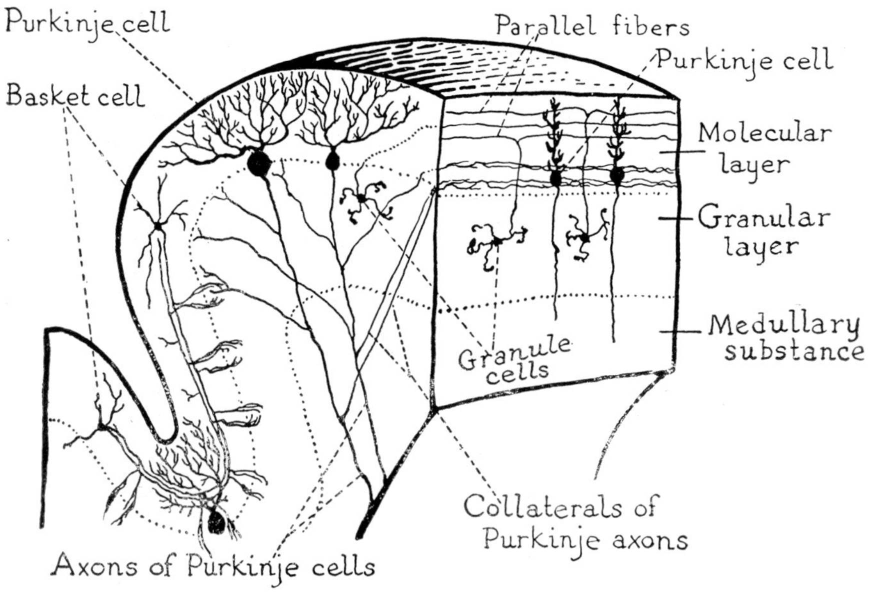

FIG. 299. Schematic representation of neuronal arrangement in a transverse and longitudinal section of a cerebellar folium. (Jakob, after Villiger.)

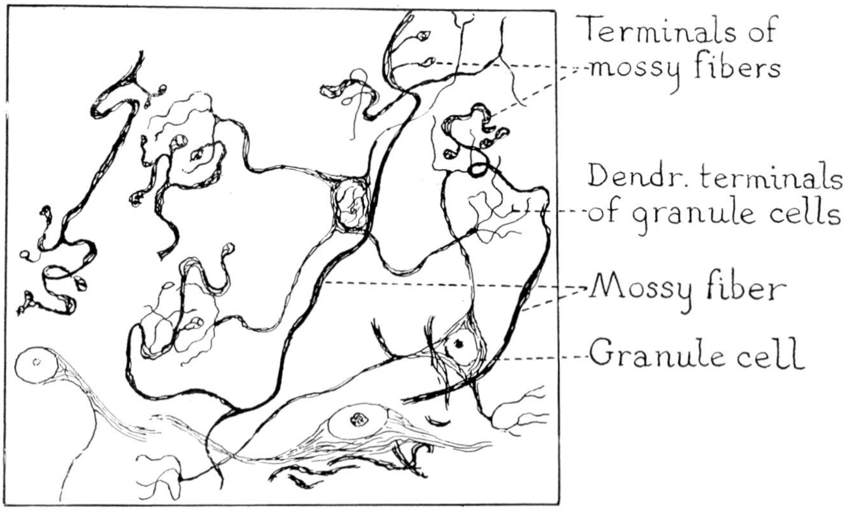

FIG. 300. Granule cells and mossy fibers in cerebellum of cat. (After Cajal.)

new granule and Golgi cells. In addition, impulses may be transmitted directly from one Purkinje cell to adjacent ones by means of its axon collaterals. The cerebellar cortex thus constitutes a mechanism for tremendous radiation and reverberation of impulses which ultimately must be concentrated on the efferent Purkinje cells. In a recent study it was estimated that the human cerebellar cortex contained 15 million Purkinje cells (Braitenberg and Atwood, 1958). It has also been determined that the combined surface area of the dendritic branchlets and spines of one monkey Purkinje cell was 220,000 square microns (Fox and Barnard, 1957). A synaptic

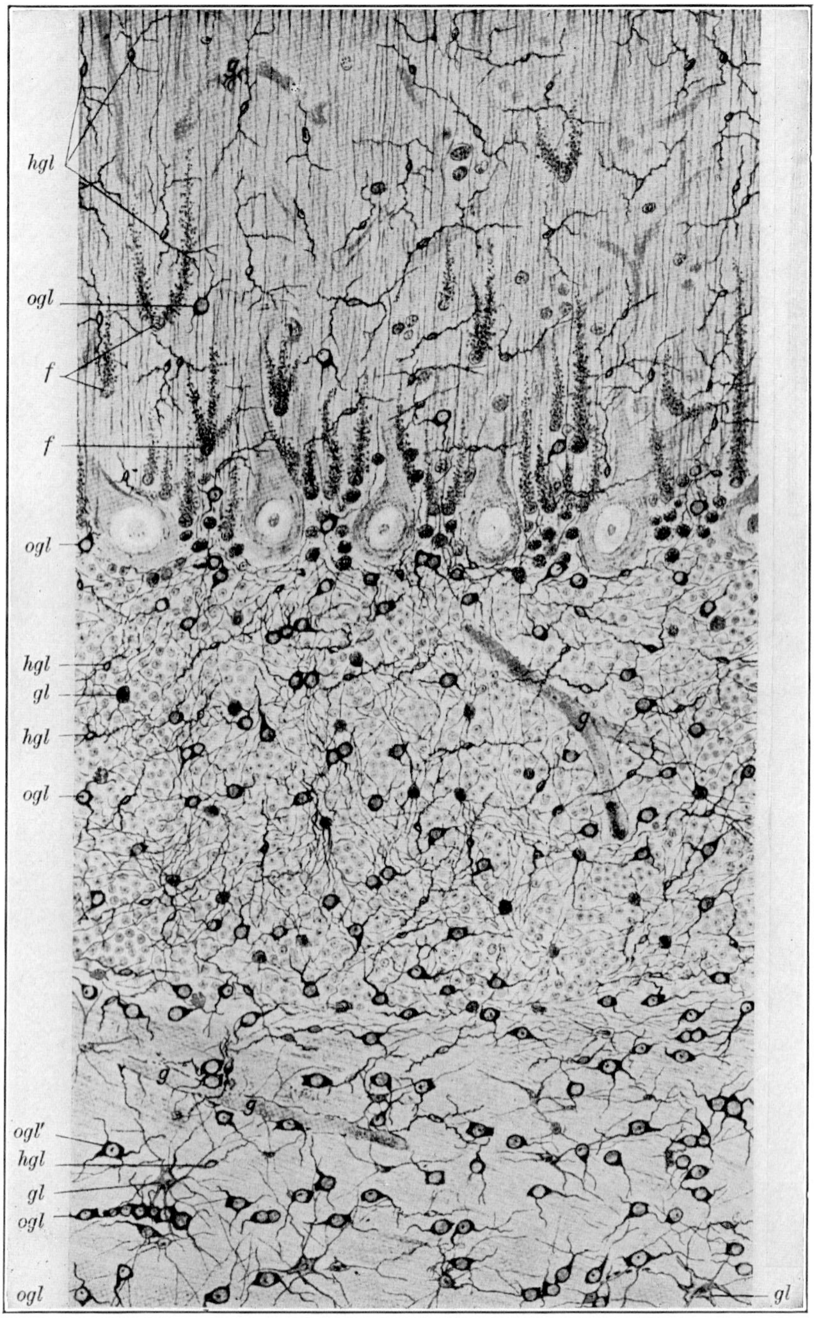

FIG. 301. Arrangement of neuroglia cells in human cerebellar cortex. *f*, cells of Fañanas; *gl*, astroglia; *hgl*, microglia; *ogl*, *ogl'*, oligodendroglia. (Jackob, after A. H. Schröder.)

area of such magnitude on each of 15 million cells provides a rather diffuse and elaborate substrate in the cerebellar cortex. Such an elaborate substrate, and also the fact that all parts of the cerebellar cortex have a similar structure, would argue against any precise localization of cerebellar function.

Neuroglia. While most of the neuroglia cells in the cerebellum are of the same general types seen elsewhere, there are found in the Purkinje layer modified astrocytes known as the epithelial cells of Cajal (cells of Bergmann). They are small rounded cells, lying in several rows between the Purkinje cell bodies, which give off a number of vertical processes beset with short leaf-like branches. These processes reach the surface and terminate in small end feet which fuse to form the external limiting glial membrane. They probably support the dendritic processes of the Purkinje cells. Related to these cells are the feathered cells of Fañanas, found in the deeper portion of the molecular layer, with fewer, and shorter vertical processes (Fig. 301).

THE DEEP CEREBELLAR NUCLEI

Imbedded in the white matter of each half of the cerebellum are four nuclear masses (Figs. 302, 303). The most medial of these, and phylogenetically the oldest,

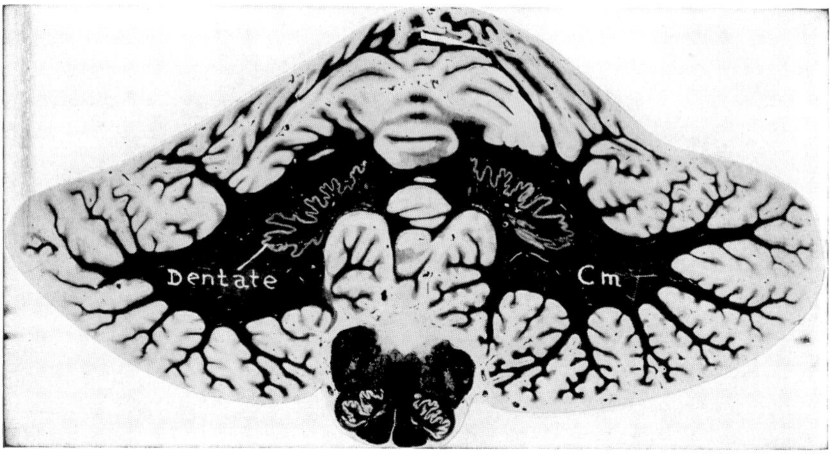

Fig. 302. Transverse section through adult cerebellum and medulla. Weigert's myelin stain. Photograph. *Cm*, corpus medullare.

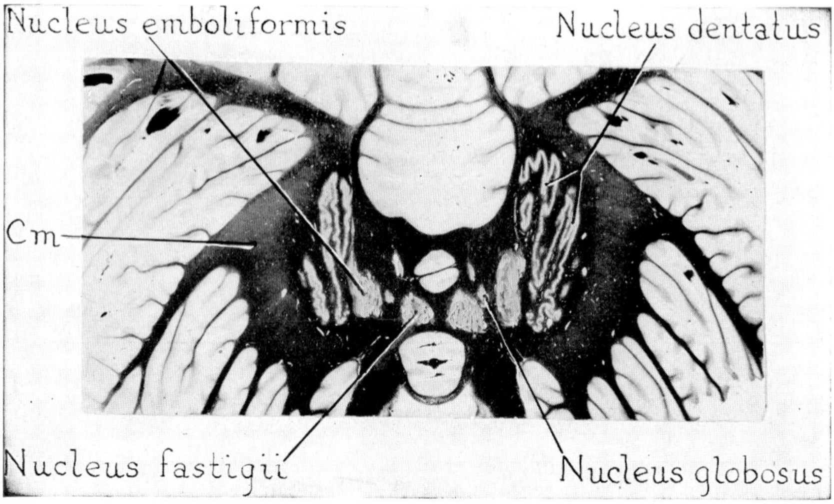

Fig. 303. Horizontal section through adult cerebellum showing corpus medullare and deep nuclei. Weigert's myelin stain. Photograph, slightly retouched. *Cm*, corpus medullare.

is the *nucleus fastigii* placed near the midline in the roof of the fourth ventricle, close and ventral to the lingula and lobulus centralis. It consists of a lateral older portion containing large multipolar cells and a medial newer portion of smaller cells.

The *nucleus dentatus* is the largest of the nuclei and lies in the white matter of the cerebellar hemisphere close to the vermis. It is a convoluted band of gray having the shape of a much-folded bag with the opening or hilus directed mesially and dorsally. In transverse section it has a characteristic denticulate appearance similar to that of the inferior olivary nucleus. It is found as a definite nucleus only in the mammals and becomes greatly enlarged in man and the anthropoid apes. A dorsomedial older portion may be distinguished from a newer, larger, ventrolateral portion. The nucleus is composed mainly of large multipolar cells with branching dendrites and high iron content. Their axons acquire a myelin sheath while still in the nucleus and pass out as fibers of the superior cerebellar peduncle. Between these cells are small stellate ones whose axons apparently arborize within the nucleus. Afferent fibers from the Purkinje cells enter on the lateral side and form a dense fiber plexus, the amiculum, around the nucleus.

The *nucleus emboliformis* is a wedge-shaped gray mass placed close to the hilus of the dentate nucleus and often difficult to delimit from the latter. It is composed of clumps of cells resembling those of the dentate nucleus (Fig. 303).

The *nucleus globosus* consists of one or several rounded gray masses lying between the fastigial and emboliform nuclei. It likewise contains large and small multipolar-cells.

The fastigial, globose, and emboliform nuclei, and the dorsomedial part of the dentate nucleus, may be considered paleocerebellar, related to the older cerebellar pathways. They project to the vestibular nuclei and reticular formation of the medulla (fastigial, globose), to the large-celled portion of the red nucleus, and to the tegmentum of midbrain and pons (globose, emboliform, dentate). The large ventrolateral neocerebellar portion of the dentate nucleus sends fibers to the small-celled part of the red nucleus, and to the thalamus from which impulses are projected into the frontal cortex and corpus striatum.

CORPUS MEDULLARE AND FIBER CONNECTIONS

The corpus medullare is a compact mass of white matter continuous from hemisphere to hemisphere and covered everywhere by the cerebellar cortex. It consists of afferent projection fibers to the cerebellar cortex, efferent projection fibers from the cerebellar cortex and to a lesser extent, of association fibers connecting the various portions of the cerebellum. Many fibers, afferent, efferent and associative, cross to the other side, the commissural fibers being concentrated in two cerebellar commissures: a posterior commissure in the region of the fastigial nuclei; and an anterior in front of the dentate nuclei.

The corpus medullare is continuous with the three peduncles which connect the cerebellum with the brain stem: the inferior cerebellar peduncle or *corpus restiforme* with the medulla; the middle peduncle or *branchium pontis* with the pons; and the superior cerebellar peduncle or *brachium conjunctivum* with the midbrain. Medially and ventrally, near the roof of the ventricle, the corpus medullare splits into two white lamina, inferior and superior, which separate at an acute angle to form the tent-like roof recess (fastigium) of the fourth ventricle. The inferior lamina is a thin white plate which passes backward over the nodulus as the inferior medullary velum. It becomes continuous with the tela chorioidea and chorioid plexus of the fourth ventricle, with which it forms the roof of the lower half of that ventricle (Fig. 39). Laterally the inferior medullary velum extends to the flocculi and actually forms the narrow bridge connecting these structures with the nodulus (Fig. 41).

The largest part of the medullary substance is continued into the superior lamina which consists of the three cerebellar peduncles and the superior medullary velum (Fig. 41). The latter is a thin white plate joining the two brachia conjunctiva, and together these structures form the roof and dorsolateral walls of the upper part of the fourth ventricle.

Afferent fibers. The fiber connections of the cerebellum have been investigated in recent years by electrophysiological (oscillographic) methods which have largely confirmed the known anatomical findings and, in addition, have indicated some connections for which the exact anatomical pathways are still poorly known. The heightened activity of a group of neurons, resulting from faradic stimulation or strychnine application, can be recorded electrically by the appearance of potential changes or "spikes". More important, this activity is transmitted by the axons of the cells to the nuclear groups in which the axons terminate. As a result, these nuclear groups are likewise thrown into greater activity and similar potential changes appear in their electrical record. If the pathway is more complex and involves a number of neurons, the activity will be transmitted through successive nuclei to the terminal cell groups of the pathway. Thus if the stimulation of a certain region in the cerebral cortex evokes potentials in a definite area of the cerebellar cortex it is logical to conclude the existence of anatomical connections between the two areas. Similarly, stimulation of afferent peripheral fibers or their endings will evoke potentials in those parts of the brain which form the terminal stations of the afferent peripheral pathway. Naturally these methods do not disclose the exact anatomical location of the fiber systems and nuclei, nor the number of neurons involved in a pathway. However, a suggestion of the number of synapses traversed may be given by the latency of the response, i.e., the time elapsed between the stimulus and the appearance of the electrical waves. The various neural connections determined by "physiological neuronography", as this method is called, are based almost wholly on animal experimentation, and may not always represent conditions in the human nervous system.

The afferent cerebellar fibers are nearly three times more numerous than the efferent ones (Snider, 1950). They convey impulses from the periphery and from various levels of the central nervous system, medullary, mesencephalic, diencephalic, and cortical. Most of the fibers enter the cerebellum through the inferior and middle peduncles, a smaller amount by way of the brachium conjunctivum. The inferior peduncle consists of a larger entirely afferent portion, the restiform body, and a smaller medial juxtarestiform portion containing both afferent and efferent fibers primarily concerned with vestibulocerebellar and cerebellovestibular connections. With the exception of some vestibulocerebellar and olivocerebellar fibers which go to the deep cerebellar nuclei, all the afferent fibers terminate in the cerebellar cortex.

The afferent fibers which connect the cerebellum with the periphery, directly or indirectly, convey mainly special proprioceptive impulses from the vestibular sense organ, and general proprioceptive impulses from the muscles, tendons, and joints. However, electrophysiological experiments on several animals including the monkey, have definitely shown that exteroceptive impulses, such as tactile, auditory, and visual, likewise reach the cerebellum, though the fiber tracts conveying them are not fully known (Snider, 1950). Moreover, the projection of the exteroceptive impulses to the cerebellar cortex is more definitely localized than is the case with the proprioceptive ones. Tactile stimulation evokes potential changes in the anterior lobe and simple lobule of the same side, and in the paramedian lobules of both sides. The leg is represented in the central lobule, the arm in the culmen, and the head in the simple lobule. The orientation is reversed in the paramedian lobules, the leg area lying most caudally and the head area most rostrally (Fig. 304). Similarly auditory and visual stimulation evokes potentials in limited areas of the cerebellar cortex, comprising the simple lobule, folium and tuber, and their immediately adjacent portions of the hemispheres. The meaning of this localized projection is not altogether clear.

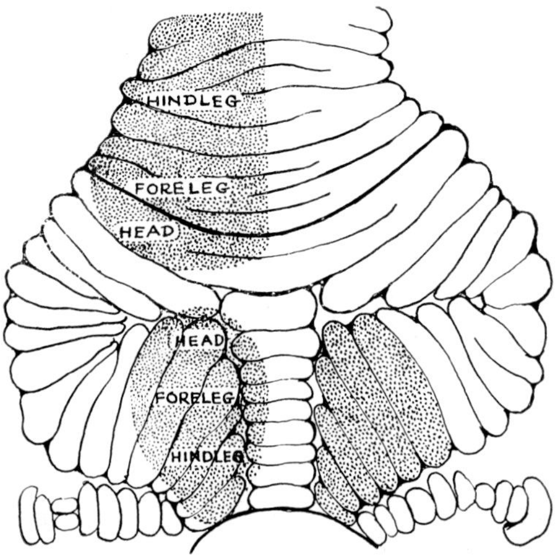

FIG. 304. Tactile areas of the cerebellum of the monkey, as mapped out by discrete movement of hairs on the left side of the animal. (Snider.)

The *vestibulocerebellar fibers* enter largely through the juxtarestiform body and include: (1) Direct vestibular root fibers to the nodulus, flocculi, and fastigial nuclei, some fibers also going to the lingula and posterior portion of the uvula. (2) Vestibulocerebellar (nucleocerebellar) fibers from the lateral and superior vestibular nuclei. These go to the same cerebellar areas which receive the direct fibers, though according to Winkler a few may terminate in the emboliform and the dentate nucleus. Both direct and nuclear fibers cross to a considerable extent to the opposite side of the cerebellum, the decussation passing through and dorsal to the fastigial nuclei.

The *dorsal spinocerebellar tract* passes through the restiform body and goes to the cortex of the anterior and posterior vermis (lingula, lobulus centralis, culmen, pyramis, and uvula) and in part also to the simple lobule.

The *ventral spinocerebellar tract* has an aberrant course. It ascends in the brain stem to the rostral levels of the pons, then arches dorsally, and enters the cerebellum alongside the superior cerebellar peduncle (Figs. 36, 192). Its fibers are distributed to the vermis of the entire anterior lobe terminating more medially than the dorsal spinocerebellar tract.

The *cuneatocerebellar fibers* (dorsal external arcuate fibers) from the external cuneate nucleus pass through the restiform body to the anterior and posterior vermis, terminating in the same areas which receive the spinocerebellar tracts. The external cuneate nucleus may be regarded as the medullary equivalent of Clarke's column, whose fibers supplement the dorsal spinocerebellar tract, conveying uncrossed impulses to the cerebellum from the muscles of the upper extremity and neck (Fig. 192).

The spinocerebellar and cuneatocerebellar tracts carry general proprioceptive impulses from the muscles, tendons, and joints. There is some evidence, however, that exteroceptive impulses may be conveyed by some of these fibers, especially those of the ventral spinocerebellar tract (Adrian, 1943).

Reticulocerebellar fibers from the lateral reticular nucleus likewise reach the homolateral cerebellum through the restiform body and are distributed predominantly to the vermis, but probably also to other parts of the cerebellar cortex. The lateral reticular nucleus is in part the terminus of a group of fibers from the spinal cord, which ascend in the ventrolateral funiculus. Hence this may be a possible path to the cerebellum for the conduction of tactile impulses (Brodal, 1949). However, it is probable that the reticular nucleus also receives impulses from higher levels of the nervous system.

Trigeminocerebellar fibers from the main sensory nucleus of N.V have been described, but their course and distribution is difficult to follow in man. Electrophysiological studies on animals indicate their termination in the posterior portion of the culmen and in the simple lobule. They are believed to convey exteroceptive impulses from the face.

More certain anatomically are the cerebellar connections with the mesencephalic nucleus of N.V. Pearson (1949) has traced axons from cells of this nucleus to the deep cerebellar white matter but their exact termination was not ascertained. He believes that some fibers end in the deep cerebellar nuclei. This fiber system conducts proprioceptive impulses from the jaw muscles and possibly also from the ocular and facial muscles. Some *vagocerebellar fibers* relaying similar impulses from the larynx may also reach the cerebellum, or may be represented by fibers of the mesencephalic nucleus.

Some *tectocerebellar fibers* from the roof of the midbrain reach the cerebellum by way of the brachium conjunctivum. Their anatomical distribution has not been ascertained, but physiological experiments on animals indicate that the fibers terminate primarily in the tuber, folium, and posterior part of the simple lobule and in the hemispheral portions immediately adjacent to these structures (Snider and Stowell, 1944). They are believed to carry visual and auditory impulses.

Afferent fibers conveying impulses to the cerebellum from upper levels of the central nervous system are represented by the olivocerebellar and pontocerebellar tracts. The reticulocerebellar fibers may in part belong to this category.

The *olivocerebellar fibers* form the largest component of the restiform body. They arise from the contralateral inferior olivary nucleus and are distributed to all parts of the cerebellar cortex in a very orderly pattern. In man, fibers from the medial portion of the olive and the accessory olives go to all portions of the vermis. A much stronger component from the larger lateral portion is distributed to the hemisphere. The dorsal part of the olive projects to the superior surface, the ventral to the inferior surface of the cerebellum (Holmes and Stuart, 1908). The olivocerebellar projection in young cats and rabbits has been worked out in detail by Brodal (1940). The intracerebellar nuclei as well as all parts of the cortex receive olivary fibers, and the distribution is exquisitely localized, each portion of the olive projecting to a specific cerebellar area.

The inferior olivary complex is highly developed in man, but its functions are not clear. Besides sending fibers to the upper cervical cord by the tract of Helweg (Fig. 192), it receives a strong fiber bundle, the central tegmental tract, from the nucleus ruber and tegmentum of the midbrain. Since both of these structures are connected directly or indirectly with the globus pallidus, the olivocerebellar tract may constitute the last relay of a pallidocerebellar pathway (Fig. 307).

The massive *pontocerebellar tract* or brachium pontis conveys to the cerebellum impulses from the cerebral cortex. The pontile nuclei receive cortical fibers mainly from the frontal and temporal lobes, and to a lesser extent from the parietal and occipital lobes. The fibers from the temporal cortex terminate in the caudal, those from the frontal cortex in the cranial portion of the pons. In man the pontocerebellar fibers are almost entirely crossed (Fig. 308B), and are distributed primarily to the ansa-paramedian lobe and probably to the lobus medium medianus of the middle lobe (folium, tuber). According to Winkler, both uncrossed and crossed pontile fibers also go to all parts of the vermis except the nodulus, and this has been confirmed by the experimental investigations of Brodal and

Jansen (1946). Thus while the neocerebellum receives the bulk of the pontocerebellar fibers, a considerable number of fibers go to the paleocerebellum as well.

Anatomically, the pontocerebellar projection does not show a definite pattern of localization. Electrical stimulation of the cerebral cortex in cats and monkeys evokes potentials in extensive cerebellar areas. They are more definite and widespread from the motor and sensory cortex but may be also elicited from parietal, temporal, and occipital regions (Dow, 1942). More recently several investigators have obtained remarkably localized cerebellar projections at least from certain cortical areas. The various results have been summarized by Snider (1950). Thus the motor area (area 4) and the somatic sensory area (3, 1, 2) project to the anterior lobe and the simple lobule. Within the cerebellum the cortical leg area goes to the central lobule, the arm area to the culmen, and face area to the simple lobule (Fig. 305). These are the same cerebellar regions which respectively receive tactile impulses from the leg, arm, and face. Similarly the auditory and visual areas of the cortex project to the simple lobule, folium and tuber. These again are the cerebellar regions receiving auditory and visual impulses from the periphery. The probable meaning of these projections will be discussed in the section on cerebellar function.

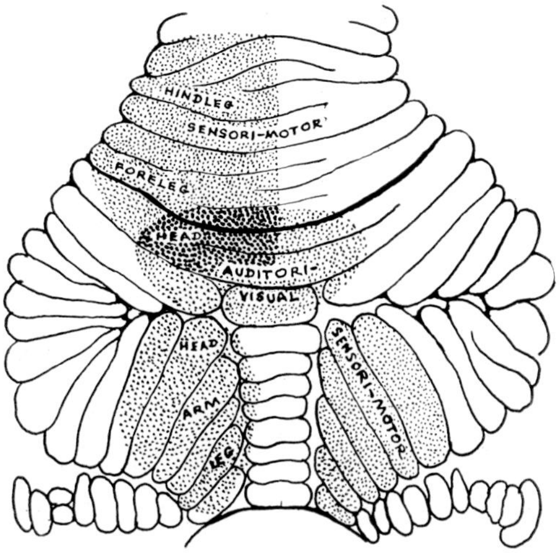

Fig. 305. Corticocerebellar projections in the monkey (Macaca mulatta). Note the head, arm, and leg areas receiving projections from the sensorimotor cortex. Note also the overlap of the head area with the area receiving projections from the audiovisual cortex. (Snider.)

Efferent fibers. The axons of the Purkinje cells which constitute the efferent fibers from the cerebellar cortex, terminate almost entirely in the deep nuclei. Only the flocculus sends a phylogenetically old fiber bundle to the vestibular nuclei (flocculovestibular tract), and some fibers also go to the vestibular nuclei and reticular formation of the medulla from the nodulus, uvula, and rostral portion of the anterior lobe. The fiber projection from the cerebellar cortex to the deep nuclei is not fully known in man, but in the monkey and some other animals it shows a remarkably definite topographical arrangement, each part of the cortex projecting to a definite region of the deep nuclei (Jansen and Brodal, 1942). The vermis sends fibers to the fastigial nucleus, perhaps a few also to the globose. The anterior vermis projects to the rostral portion; the simple lobule, folium, and tuber to the middle portion; and the pyramis, uvula, and nodulus to the caudal portion of the fastigial nucleus. The fibers from the cerebellar hemispheres show a similar rostrocaudal orientation. The lateral parts of the anterior lobe and the medial portions of the hemispheres behind the primary fissure project to the emboliform, globose, and the older medial portion of the dentate nucleus. The fibers from the rest of the ansiform lobe go to the newer, larger ventrolateral part of the dentate nucleus.

The main efferent tracts arise from the deep nuclei. From the nucleus fastigii (and globosus) arise the *fastigiobulbar fibers* which go to the vestibular nuclei, especially the lateral, and to the reticular formation of the medulla. Many of them cross in the roof of the fourth ventricle. The fastigiobulbar fibers form part of the

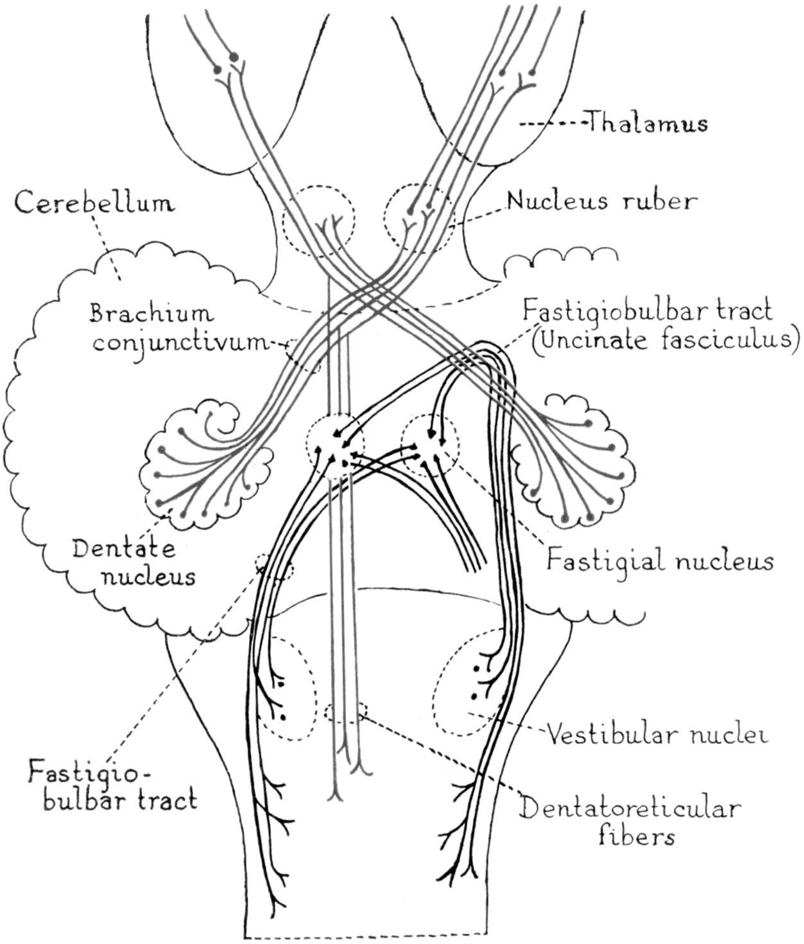

FIG. 306. Diagram of some efferent cerebellar tracts.

juxtarestiform body. Some of them pass close to the ventricle and medial to the dentate nucleus. Others curve around the superior cerebellar peduncle as the *uncinate bundle of Russell* (Fig. 306). The whole system carries cerebellar impulses by way of the vestibular nuclei and reticular formation to the muscles, especially those of the eyes, neck, and body (Figs. 197, 198, 261). Fibers in the ascending limb of the uncinate fasciculus of the cat have been traced as far rostrally as the parafascicular and centromedian nuclei of the thalamus. It has been suggested that such ascending paleocerebellar fibers may relay vestibular impulses to the thalamus and other suprasegmental levels (Carpenter, Brittin, and Pines, 1958).

The *brachium conjunctivum* which arises from the dentate, emboliform, and also the globose nuclei, constitutes the most important efferent fiber system of the cerebellum. Emerging from the hilus of the dentate nucleus, it forms the dorsolateral wall of the upper part of the fourth ventricle, then dips into the pontile tegmentum, and in the region of the inferior colliculi undergoes a practically complete decussation (Figs. 281, 307). A considerable number of fibers terminate in the contralateral red nucleus (*dentatorubral*) and are related primarily to the small-celled newer portion, to a lesser extent with the older large-celled portion which gives origin to the rubrospinal tract. The largest component goes directly to the

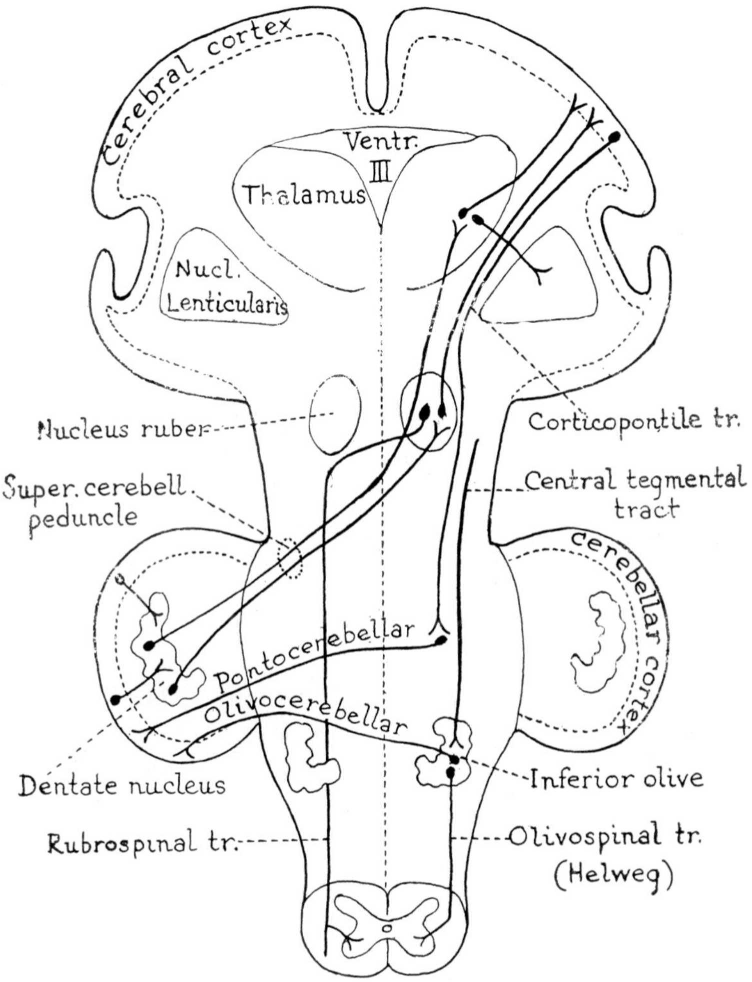

FIG. 307. Diagram of principal afferent and efferent cerebellar connections (largely neocerebellar) with midbrain and forebrain.

thalamus. Most of these *dentatothalamic fibers* come from the larger, newer ventrolateral part of the dentate nucleus (neodentatum) and end in the ventral lateral thalamic nucleus, whence they are projected to the cerebral cortex, mainly to areas 4 and 6 (Figs. 334, 335). A much smaller number arise from the emboliform nucleus and terminate in the central (centromedian) nucleus of the thalamus, possibly constituting a link in a pathway from cerebellum to corpus striatum (Hassler, 1950). Fibers which go to the subthalamic nucleus have also been described (André-Thomas).

Dentatoreticular fibers from the caudomedial portion of the dentate nucleus detach themselves from the brachium just before, and beyond the decussation, and descend as crossed and uncrossed fibers in the reticular formation (Fig. 192). Most of them apparently terminate near or in the pterygoid nucleus of the pontile tegmentum. A few fibers go directly to the oculomotor and trochlear nuclei, and to the nuclei of the posterior commissure. Some may enter the medial longitudinal fasciculus.

The efferent projection to the nucleus ruber and the reticular formation, probably represents an older pathway transmitting

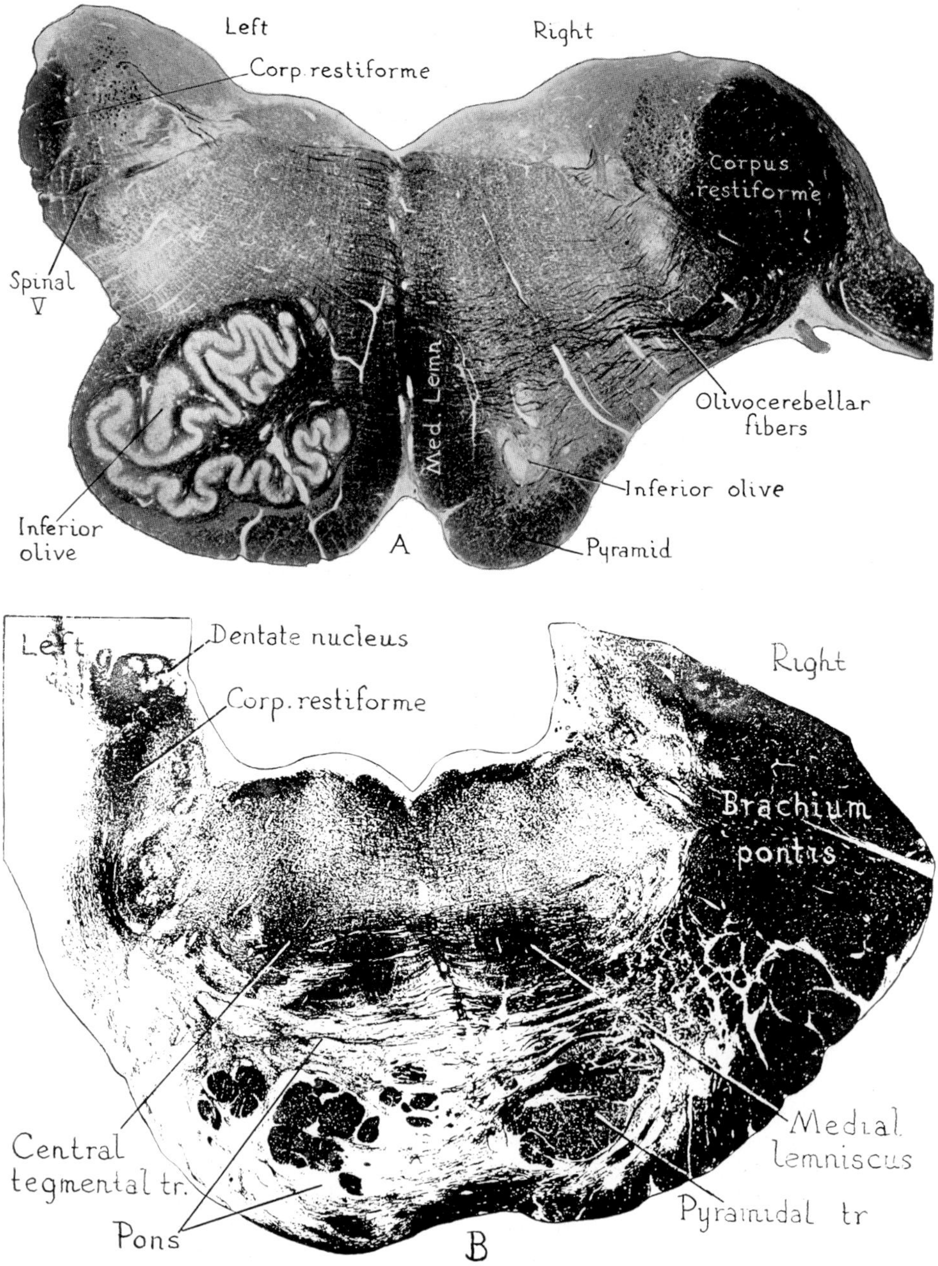

FIG. 308. Transverse section through medulla (*A*) and pons (*B*), from a case in which the left cerebellar hemisphere had failed to develop. Myelin stain. Photograph. See text for discussion.

cerebellar impulses to the muscles of the head and body by way of the rubroreticular and reticulospinal tracts, and to a lesser extent by the rubrospinal tract which is greatly reduced in man (Fig. 199). The bulk of the superior peduncle, coming mainly from the larger ventrolateral part of the dentate nucleus, constitutes an extensive newer pathway linking the cerebellum with the cerebral cortex and also with the striatum (Fig. 307).

Some of the neocerebellar connections in

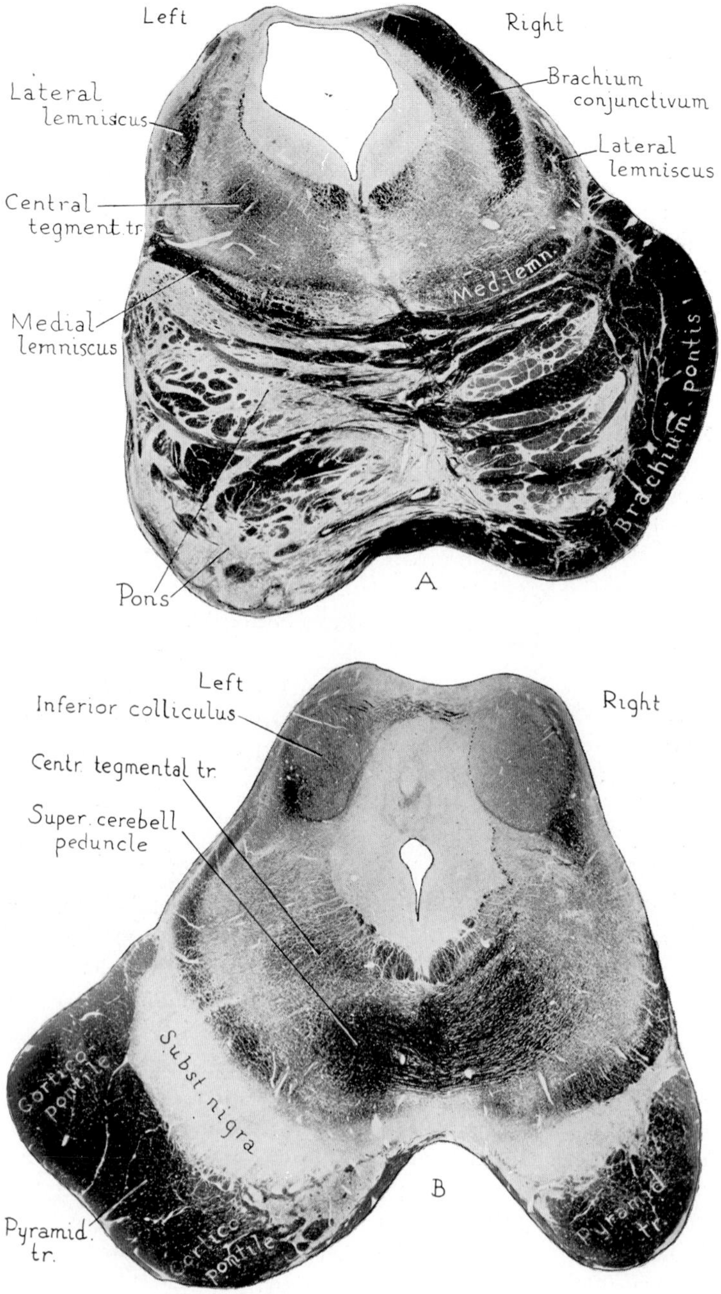

FIG. 309. Transverse section through isthmus (*A*) and midbrain (*B*), from same case as Fig. 308. Myelin stain. Photograph.

man are especially brought out in Figs. 308, 309. These show sections through the medulla, pons, isthmus, and midbrain from a case in which the left cerebellar hemisphere, except the flocculus, had failed to develop (agenesia). With this there was a correlated agenesia of all the afferent and efferent pathways to and from the left cerebellar hemisphere. The spinocerebellar and the vestibular connections were normal, since the vermis and flocculi were intact. On the other hand, the left dentate nucleus was represented by a minute structure (paleodentatum), the right inferior olive greatly reduced (paleo-olive), the right nucleus ruber (not shown) and right pontile nuclei practically absent. As a result, the left restiform body was greatly reduced by absence of olivocerebellar fibers. The left brachium conjunctivum was represented by a few scattered fibers, and the left brachium pontis was entirely absent. Similarly lacking were the right central tegmental and the corticopontile tracts. As a result the right pes pedunculi was composed only of pyramidal fibers. A survey of these preparations shows that in man the superior and middle cerebellar peduncles and the olivocerebellar fibers are practically all crossed.

FUNCTIONAL CONSIDERATIONS

It is generally agreed that the cerebellum is primarily concerned with the coordination of muscular activity. Special emphasis is placed on the afferent cerebellar connections with the proprioceptor endings in the muscles, tendons, and joints and in the vestibular sense organ. Sherrington in fact has called the cerebellum the "head ganglion of the proprioceptive system." However, the cerebellum is not concerned with sensation and even in severe cerebellar lesions there is no impairment of the sense of position and movement. Nor does it send motor impulses for the initiation of movements comparable to those of the cerebral motor cortex. The cerebellum is primarily a neural mechanism regulating and graduating muscular tension states for the proper maintenance of equilibrium and posture, and the smooth performance of voluntary movements. Each movement requires the coordinated action (synergy) of a group of muscles. There are the agonists which actually move the part and the antagonists which must give or relax to permit the movement. Associated with these are other synergic or fixating muscles which fix neighboring or even distant joints to the extent needed for the desired movement. The maintenance or changes of posture similarly involve the cooperation of synergically acting muscle groups.

Such synergic units must obviously have a complex reciprocal innervation, receiving both inhibitory and excitatory impulses which effect the alterations in muscular tension needed for any specific movement. While other neural centers are probably involved in this reciprocal innervation, the cerebellum may be regarded as the highest center for its finest automatic regulation. Its function is to furnish optimum tension states for all the muscles both during rest and during activity. It plays an integral though masked role in all simple and complex skeletal muscle actions. The entire cerebellum normally works efficiently behind the scenes in the maintenance of posture, walking, standing, sitting, running, or the performance of discrete and often complex movements of the limbs or digits. Small or large lesions of the cerebellum result in marked deficits and musculary incoordination. Such deficits provide one with a greater appreciation of the "normal activity" of the cerebellum.

In man injury to the cerebellum or its fiber systems causes hypotonia and certain abnormalities of movement collectively termed *cerebellar asynergia* or *ataxia*. Sensation is normal. In unilateral lesions the symptoms appear on the same side as the injury.

Lesions involving only the posterior vermis and flocculi (paleocerebellum), mainly affect the axial musculature and the bilaterally linked movements used for locomotion and for the maintenance of equilibrium. The patient sways and is generally unsteady when standing, he walks staggeringly or "drunkenly" on a broad base, and has a tendency to fall backward. The speech muscles may be affected, resulting in jerky and slurring articulation, the words often shot out with unnecessary force.

Nystagmus and abnormal attitudes if present are usually ascribed to injury of the vestibular tracts. Muscle tone is little affected, there is usually no tremor, and there is no incoordination of arm and leg movements when the patient is resting in bed.

Lesions of the hemispheres (neocerebellum) primarily affect the isolated finer movements of the extremities, i.e., pyramidally induced movements. The muscles are flabby (*hypotonia*) and tire easily. There are severe disorders of movement (asynergia) expressed in faulty range, direction, and force of muscular contraction. Most striking is the inability to gauge distance properly (*dysmetria*), the movements overshooting or falling short of the mark, or erring in direction and passing it by (*past-pointing*). The cerebellar asynergia may be brought out in many tests. When the elbow of a normal man is made to flex against resistance and the arm is suddenly released, overflexion is arrested by the contraction of the triceps. In cerebellar disease the contraction of the triceps is delayed with resulting uncontrolled flexion so that the patient may hit himself in the face or chest (*rebound phenomenon*). There is inability to execute rapid alternating movements such as pronation and supination of the hand (*adiadochokinesis*), and movements which require simultaneous action at several joints may be broken up into series of successive movements each involving a single joint (*decomposition of movement*). Thus when asked to touch his nose with a finger raised above his head, the patient will first lower his arm and then flex the elbow to reach his nose.

The hypotonia and irregularities of muscular contraction are responsible for the coarse tremor in voluntary movements often demonstrable in cerebellar disease (Holmes). It is especially conspicuous and enduring when the dentate nucleus or the superior peduncle is destroyed. Nystagmus, occurring when the eyes are moved laterally, is likewise present in many cases and is similarly explained by the asynergy of the ocular muscles (Holmes).

The maintenance of equilibrium does not depend on vestibular impulses alone but also on general proprioceptive stimuli, and the vestibular and spinocerebellar components are closely interrelated and difficult to dissociate. On the efferent side the paleocerebellum exerts its influence through the fastigiobulbar (vestibular) fibers of the juxtarestiform body and the older portion of the brachium conjunctivum. The fibers of the latter originate in the globose, emboliform, and dorsomedial parts of the dentate nuclei. These paleocerebellar fibers go to the red nucleus, the reticular formation, and motor nuclei of the midbrain, pons, and medulla. It has been shown experimentally that stimulation of the anterior lobe inhibits the extensor tonus of the antigravity muscles, and its removal increases the rigidity of decerebrate animals. The flocculi and nodulus are similarly believed to exert an inhibitory influence on vestibular tonus.

With the development of the pallium and the appearance of isolated pyramidal movements, the cerebellum increased in importance. It now received the massive corticopontocerebellar connections related mainly to the cerebellar hemispheres and the median portion of the middle lobe. Along with this there was increased development of the dentate nuclei, superior peduncles, and red nuclei representing new cerebello-thalamo-cortical pathways. Thus the neocerebellum is characterized by its massive afferent and efferent cortical connections, and functionally it is primarily concerned with the regulation of pyramidal movements. Hence the dysmetric symptoms of cerebellar disease are well marked only when volitional movement is intact, and are greatly diminished or disappear altogether with destruction of the motor area or pyramidal tract.

How far there is topographical bodily representation in the cerebellum is still a controversial question. Historically there have been two opposing concepts of cerebellar function. Bolk (1906), after a detailed comparative study of the mammalian cerebellum, concluded that there was a discrete somatotopic localization in the cerebellum, each cerebellar lobule controlling specific muscle groups. A similar though more restricted view was held by Rijnberk (1926) who found that the head and neck muscles had their center in the simple lobule, the arm in the superior, and the leg in the inferior portion of the ansaparamedian lobule. On the other hand, Luciani (1891) and Sherrington (1906) maintained that the cerebellum functioned as a whole in the service of muscular coordination, and that its various parts did not control individual muscles. Sherrington pointed out that the cerebellum is a "mechanism that deals with the innervation, not of this or that piece of musculature, but with the innervation of the musculature of the body as a whole" (Fulton, 1949). This "unitarian" concept of cerebellar function, still dominant in clinical neurology, found strong support in the histological work of Golgi and Cajal. They demonstrated histologically that unlike the cerebral cortex, the cerebellar cortex has a remarkably uniform structure throughout its whole extent. Clinically there is little evidence of functional localization as far as the extremities are concerned, neocerebellar lesions producing ipsilateral symptoms in both arm and leg (Holmes).

However, more recent experimental investigations on animals, including the monkey and chimpanzee, indicate that the cerebellum possesses a remarkable degree of functional localization, especially in the anterior lobe, simple lobule, and tuber. The investigations also suggest that cerebellar influence is not solely related to the control of muscular coordination, but is exerted in practically all neural functions, sensory and motor. The results of these investigations have been critically reviewed by Snider (1950).

The afferent impulses reaching the cerebellum through the cortico-ponto-cerebellar pathway are in part likewise projected from specific cortical to specific cerebellar areas. The motor area and the somatic sensory area of the cortex project to the anterior lobe and simple lobule in such a manner that the cortical leg area goes to the central lobule, the cortical arm area to the culmen, and the cortical face area to the simple lobule (Fig. 305). These are the same areas which respectively receive tactile impulses from the leg, arm, and face. The auditory and visual areas of the cortex project to the simple lobule, folium and tuber, and these again are the cerebellar regions which receive auditory and optic impulses from the periphery.

Impulses from the corpus striatum, nucelus ruber, and the reticular formation reach the cerebellum mainly by way of the central tegmental tract and the olivocerebellar fibers, and perhaps to a lesser extent by the reticulocerebellar fibers. The topographical organization of the central tegmental tract is still obscure, but the olivocerebellar fibers are distributed in a very orderly pattern, each portion of the olive projecting to a specific cerebellar area (Brodal, 1940). This localization suggests that the extrapyramidal projection to the cerebellum may have a more definite functional organization than was hitherto supposed.

On the efferent side the cerebellum likewise projects impulses to all the neural centers which in turn project to the cerebellum. Here too a remarkable degree of somatotopic and functional localization is evident, especially in the cerebellar projections to the periphery and to the cerebral cortex. It has been known for some time that stimulation of the anterior lobe will inhibit, or at times facilitate, the reflex movement of decrebrate animals. Snider and associates demonstrated that both reflex and cortically induced movements can be suppressed, or facilitated, by cerebellar stimulation, and most definitely by stimulation of the anterior lobe—simple lobule complex and the paramedian lobules. They were able to map out localized areas for the control of leg, arm, and facial movements, and found that these were identical with the tactile receiving areas. The leg was represented in the central lobule, the arm in the culmen, and the face in the simple lobule. In the paramedian lobule the orientation was reversed, the face area lying most rostrally and the leg area most caudally. Comparable results were obtained by Nulsen et al. (1948) who studied the inhibitory effects of anterior lobe stimulation on cortically induced movements in several animals including the monkey and chimpanzee. They found that when a specific muscle is activated from a discrete point of the motor area (area 4), inhibition of this muscle can be evoked from only one discrete focus of the anterior lobe, and from no other. The localized areas mapped out by this procedure were identical with those of the previous investigators. They also found that stimulation of the same cerebellar focus can produce either suppression or facilitation, the result depending on the frequency of the stimulating current. Evidence was adduced that inhibition and facilitation were mediated by separate anatomical pathways. The inhibitory impulses passed by way of the dentate nucleus to the bulboreticular suppressor center, the facilitatory impulses went by way of the fastigial nucleus to the facilitatory centers of the reticular formation.

Recent studies by Sprague and Chambers (1954) indicate that stimulation of either paleocerebellar structures or the medial reticular formation of the cat can induce reciprocal postural responses. Stimulation of vermian areas and the cortex of the anterior lobe, resulted in ipsilateral facilitation of foreleg flexor muscles and inhibition of the extensor muscles. In the opposite limb, stimulation produced facilitation of the extensor muscles and inhibition of the flexor muscles. These changes in the limb muscles were accompanied by turning of the head and body to the side of stimulation. They observed more variable postural effects following stimulation of the lateral areas of the cerebellar cortex and lateral reticular formation. These postural adjustments included facilitation of both ipsilateral extension and contralateral flexion. They succeeded in initiating, and also inhibiting, a variety of muscle movements by stimulating different cortical points on the vermis and cerebellar hemispheres. The above experimental results provide strong evidence that the cerebellum influences posture in a reciprocal manner by one and not two separate pathways.

The cerebellar projections which pass by way of the thalamus to the motor and premotor areas of the cerebral cortex have been known for a long time. The experimental studies of Henneman et al. (1948), and Hampson (1949) on cats and monkeys have demonstrated that the cerebellum also projects to the various sensory areas of the cortex. Electrical stimulation of the anterior lobe, simple lobule, and paramedian lobules evokes responses in both the motor and the somatic sensory areas. In a similar way the central lobule projected to the cortical leg area, the culmen to the cortical arm area, and the simple lobule to the cortical face area. Similarly, stimulation of the cerebellar "audiovisual" area (simple lobule and tuber) evokes responses in the cortical auditory area and part of the cortical visual area.

From the experimental evidence cited above, the following conclusions may be drawn:

1. The cerebellum receives exteroceptive as well as proprioceptive impulses from the periphery.

2. There are localized areas in the cerebellum for the reception of tactile, cochlear, and optic impulses. These areas are reciprocally connected with the corresponding tactile, auditory, visual, and motor areas of the cerebral cortex.

3. There are specific areas in the cerebellum whose stimulation produces localized suppression or facilitation of reflex and cortically induced movements. Even lo-

calized overt movements have been produced by stimulation of these areas (Hampson et al., 1946).

4. The cerebellum projects to sensory as well as motor cortical areas, and to practically all levels of the brain stem. Most, if not all, of the centers which receive projections from the cerebellum, in turn send projections back to the cerebellum, though all the anatomical pathways of these reciprocal connections have not been fully established.

5. It is certain that the cerebellum exerts a profound influence on the coordination of muscular activity, and that defects of muscular coordination are the most obvious symptoms of cerebellar injury. However, Snider maintains that the concept of cerebellar function must be broadened to include cerebellar influence on both "sensory and motor centers of the cerebrum, as well as related influences on diencephalic, mesencephalic, and medullary centers." It is probable "that this influence is exerted in such a way as to alter the threshold of excitability of these centers," thereby augmenting or diminishing their activity, depending on the physiological need of the moment. Thus the cerebellum can modify the activity of all neural centers, and should be regarded as "the great modulator of neurologic function" (Snider, 1950).

19

The Diencephalon and Corpus Striatum

The expanded rostral end of the brain stem is composed of the diencephalon, and its component subdivisions. The adjacent basal ganglia, though part of the telencephalon, will be discussed with the diencephalic structures. The topography of these large nuclear masses and the internal capsule can be reviewed in Figs. 44–48, 310. Portions of the epithalamus, hypothalamus and metathalamus can be recognized in gross specimens and are not difficult to orient. However, the components of the subthalamus (Fig. 48) and thalamus are less obvious and best seen in microscopic preparations.

Before attempting a complete discussion of these structures it is essential to become acquainted with their actual location, extent, and relationship. This will be done by a number of microphotographs representing a graded series of transverse sections extending from the uppermost portion of the midbrain through the entire extent of the diencephalon and corpus striatum. The level and plane of each section are given in Fig. 312.

SECTION THROUGH ROSTRAL PORTION OF MIDBRAIN NEAR ITS JUNCTION WITH THE THALAMUS (FIGS. 312, 313)

To the midbrain structures are now added several nuclei of the thalamus including the *medial* and *lateral geniculate bodies*, the *pulvinar*, and the posterior (retrolenticular) portion of the *internal capsule.* The caudal tip of the pineal gland is lying between the superior colliculi, while in the interpeduncular space are seen the caudal portions of the mammillary bodies. From the thalamic nuclei fibers are passing laterally to the internal capsule through which they are distributed to various portions of the pallium (cerebral cortex). Many of these arise in the thalamus and go to the cortex, others arise in the cortex and end in the thalamus. These thalamocortical and corticothalamic fibers constitute the *thalamic radiations.* Lateral to the pulvinar is the tail of the caudate nucleus separated from the former by the *semicircular sulcus* (terminal sulcus).

The fibers of the optic tract are entering the ventral surface of the lateral geniculate body, in which most of them terminate (Fig. 313). Some optic fibers, however, continue beyond the lateral geniculate body to form the *superior quadrigeminal brachium* which terminates in the optic stratum of the superior colliculi and in the pretectal area. These fibers mediate reflex adjustment of eye, neck, and body muscles to optic stimulation (Fig. 199). From the lateral geniculate body fibers pass laterally into the internal capsule, representing the beginning of the geniculocalcarine tract (optic radiation) to the occipital cortex, thereby completing the visual pathway.

Internal to the lateral geniculate body is the medial geniculate body in which terminate the fibers of the inferior quadrigeminal brachium. From its lateral surface fibers gather to form the geniculotemporal tract (auditory radiation) which enters the internal capsule and is projected to the temporal cortex, thus completing the auditory pathway (Fig. 258).

The pulvinar is a large nuclear mass lying dorsal to the medial geniculate body. Its

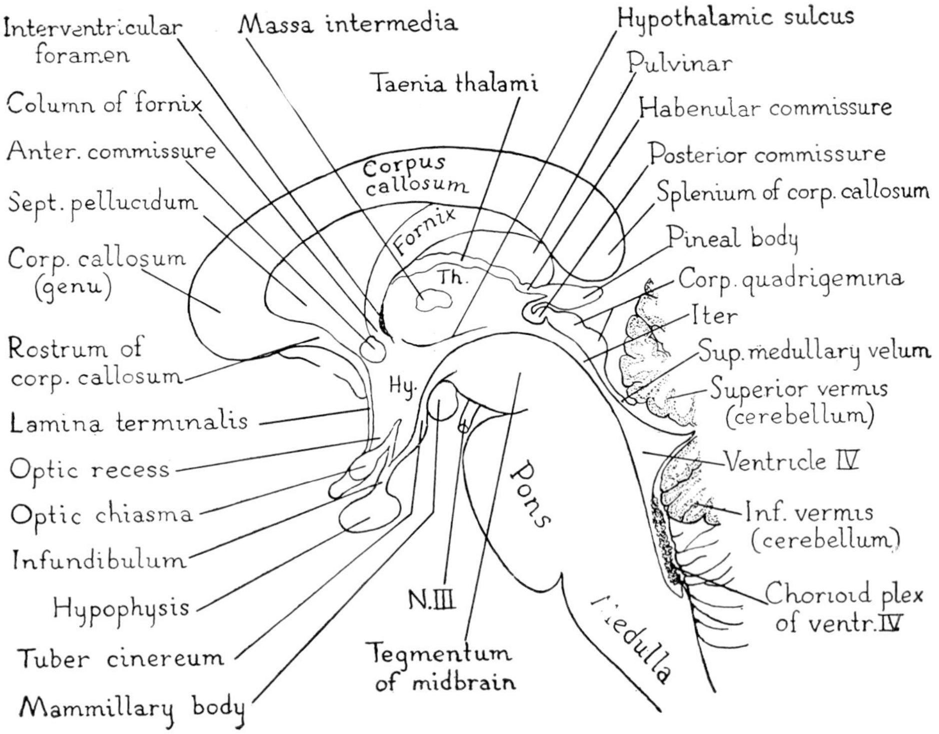

FIG. 310. Median sagittal section of brain stem. *Hy*, hypothalamus; *Th*, thalamus.

dorsal surface is covered by a thin plate of fibers, the *stratum zonale.* Fibers passing laterally from the nucleus contribute to the retrolenticular portion of the internal capsule and are distributed to the posterior parietal and occipitotemporal cortex. The innermost portion of the internal capsule wedging in between the pulvinar and lateral geniculate body, forms a triangular area, the *zone of Wernicke,* in which there is a mixture of transverse and longitudinal fibers (Fig. 313). The field is composed mainly of fibers of the optic radiation which, after leaving the lateral geniculate body, run forward for a distance and then loop backward to reach the occipital cortex (Fig. 329). Intermingled with these are fibers from the pulvinar and also from the medial geniculate bodies.

In the midbrain portion the fibers of the third nerve have practically disappeared, but the rostral portions of the oculomotor nucleus are still present, mainly the small celled Edinger-Westphal nucleus. The large nucleus ruber is surrounded by a fibrous capsule. Within the nucleus are seen fibers of the superior cerebellar peduncle, while the capsular fibers mainly represent connections of the nucleus ruber with the thalamus and pallium. Lateral to the nucleus ruber are the medial lemniscus and the spinothalamic tract, while the inferior quadrigeminal brachium is terminating in the medial geniculate body. The reticular formation is greatly reduced, as is also the central tegmental tract. The small medial longitudinal and predorsal fasciculi are difficult to distinguish from the medial capsule of the red nucleus.

The pes pedunculi occupies the same position and dorsal to it is the diminished substantia nigra containing many myelinated fiber bundles. These include strionigral fibers from the corpus striatum, and subthalamonigral from the subthalamus.

SECTION THROUGH JUNCTION OF MIDBRAIN AND THALAMUS PASSING THROUGH POSTERIOR COMMISSURE (FIG. 314)

The plane of the section is such in Fig. 313 that ventrally the same structures are seen as in Fig. 314, while dorsally the section passes through a more rostral level. The iter is expanding into the deeper third ventricle whose roof is here formed by the posterior commissure, which marks the boundary between midbrain and interbrain. Above the commissure is the stalk of the pineal body enclosing the pineal recess of the third ventricle. The superior colliculi have disappeared as have the oculomotor nuclei and fibers, though possibly the anterior median nucleus may still be present in the light staining area below the ventricle. In close contact with the dorsomedial surface of the red nucleus is the small *interstitial nucleus*, and dorsal to this the *nucleus of the posterior commissure* (nucleus of Darkschewitsch), almost within the central gray substance. Since these are the most rostral nuclei contributing to the medial longitudinal fasciculus, that already greatly diminished bundle will no longer be present above this level.

Lateral to the posterior commissure is the pretectal area, transitional between the superior colliculus and pulvinar of the thalamus. It is believed to be the center for the pupillary light reflex, receiving fibers from the optic tract and lateral geniculate body, and sending fibers to the Edinger-Westphal nuclei of both sides. The structure and connections of the pretectal area and posterior commissure have been discussed in a previous chapter (p. 351).

The medial portion of the nucleus ruber is traversed by a vertical fiber bundle known as the *fasciculus retroflexus* or *habenulopeduncular tract*. The fibers arise from the *habenular nucleus* situated at a somewhat more rostral level and pass backward and downward to end in the interpeduncular nucleus of the midbrain. The tract is a link in a reflex pathway connecting the olfactory areas of the brain with some of the motor nuclei of the brain stem (Fig. 316).

The medial lemniscus, spinothalamic, and secondary trigeminal tracts are spreading out diffusely, about to terminate in the ventral thalamic nuclei from which they are projected to the cerebral cortex. The capsular fibers of the red nucleus are likewise changing from a longitudinal to a transverse direction, and now form a radiating bundle extending from the dorsolateral surface of the nucleus ruber toward the ventral portion of the thalamus. This is the beginning of the *tegmental field of Forel* or *prerubral field* (field H) mainly composed at this level of rubrothalamic, dentatothalamic, and perhaps some rubrocortical fibers. Cells scattered among the fibers and especially along the dorsal surface of the field, constitute the *nucleus of the tegmental field of Forel* (*nucleus of prerubral field*) which may be regarded as a continuation of the mesencephalic reticular formation (Fig. 332).

The pulvinar is larger, the medial geniculate body somewhat reduced. From both of these nuclei and from the lateral geniculate as well, fibers stream as thalamic radiations into the internal capsule. In the groove between the ventricular surfaces of the caudate nucleus and the thalamus, lies a bundle of fibers known as the *stria semicircularis* (stria terminalis, stria cornea). It represents an olfactory connection to be discussed later.

SECTION OF INTERBRAIN THROUGH HABENULAR GANGLION AND INFUNDIBULUM (FIGS. 315, 312)

The region of the interpeduncular space is now occupied by two rounded nuclear masses, the *mammillary bodies*, below which is seen the tuber cinereum, infundibular recess of the third ventricle, and infundibulum. All these structures belong to the hypothalamus. Each mammillary body consists of a larger *medial nucleus* and a smaller

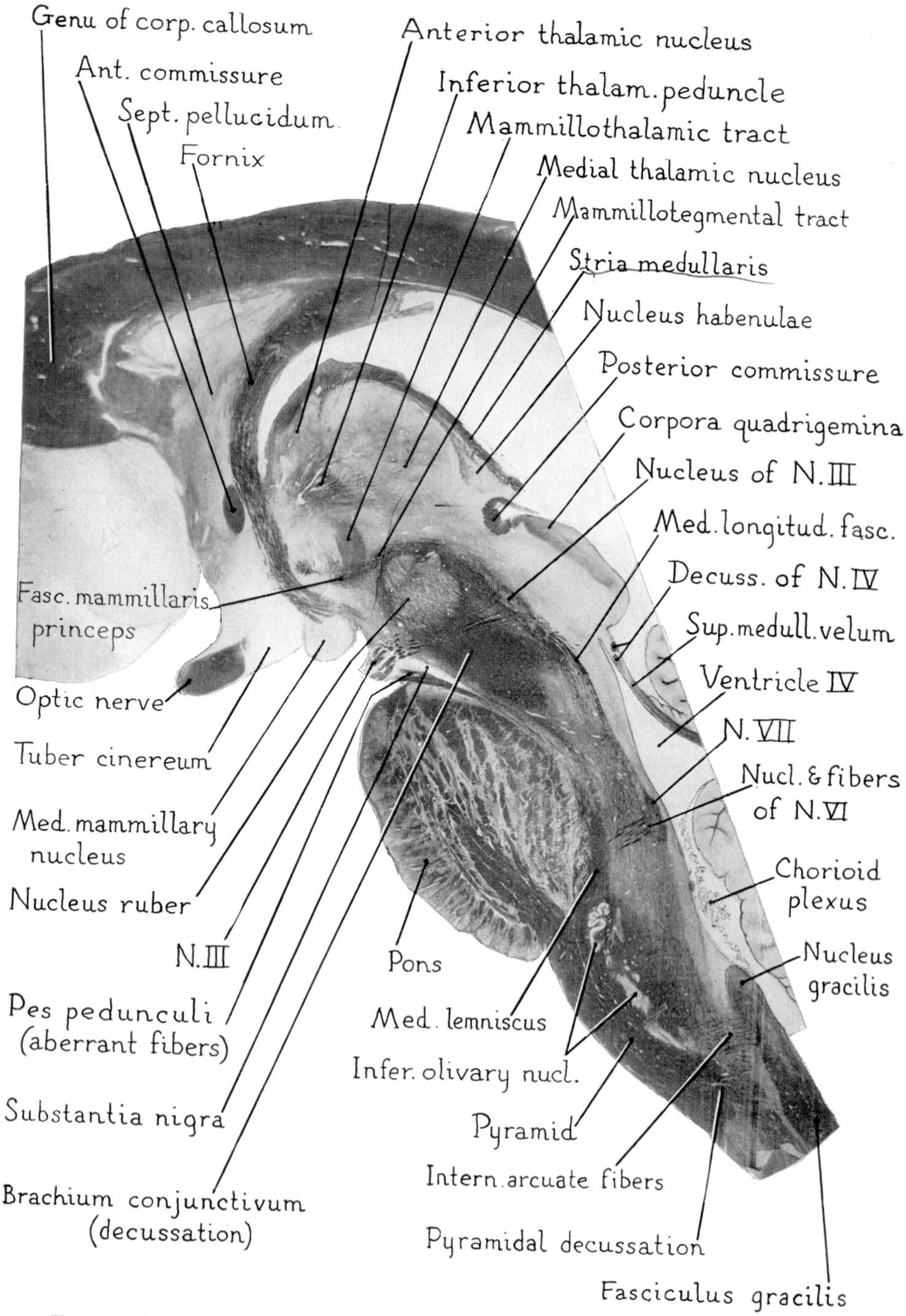

FIG. 311. Sagittal section of brain stem through pillar of fornix and root of third nerve. Weigert's myelin stain. Photograph.

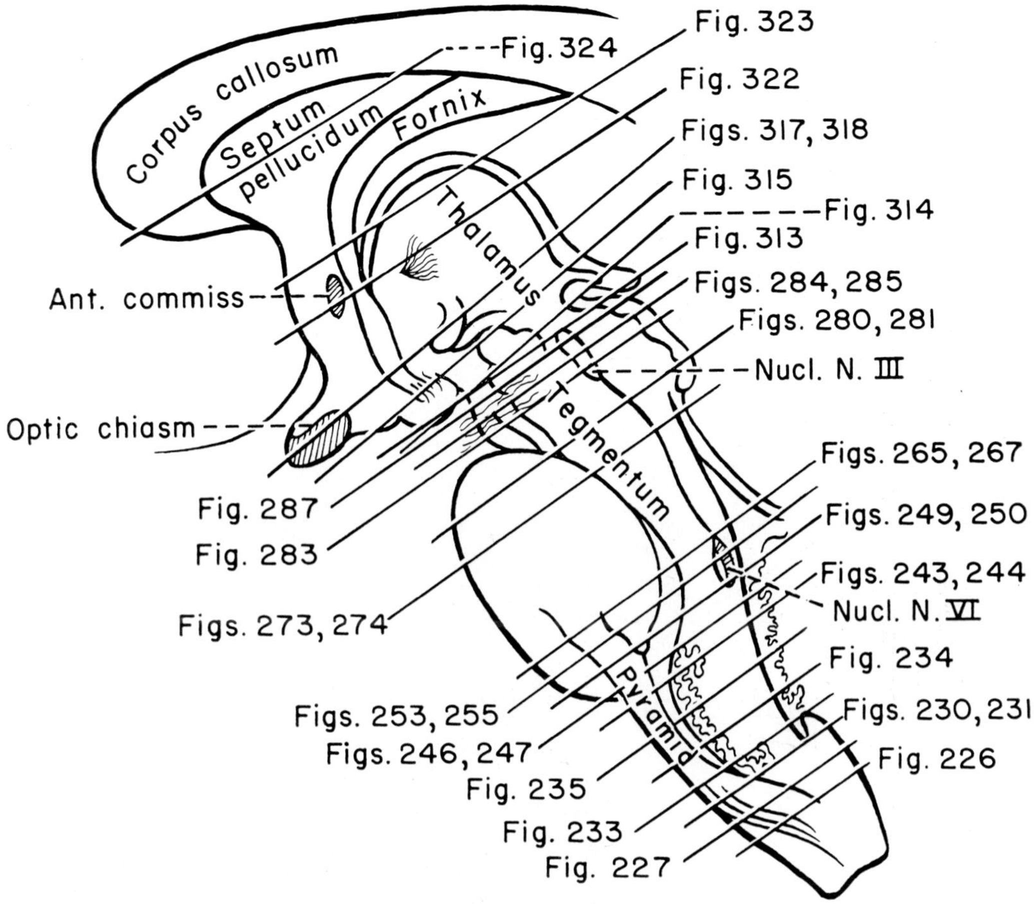

FIG. 312. Outline of paramedian sagittal section of brain stem, showing level and plane of the transverse sections of the figures indicated. For identification of structures see Fig. 311.

lateral portion known as the *nucleus intercalatus* (lateral nucleus of Le Gros Clark, intermediate nucleus). The mammillary body receives olfactomammillary fibers from the basal olfactory areas of the brain and corticomammillary fibers by way of the fornix from the hippocampal cortex (Figs. 316, 311). It also receives collaterals or terminals from the medial lemniscus and other ascending sensory tracts, these fibers forming the *peduncle* of the mammillary body (Fig. 316). From the mammillary body arises a considerable bundle of fibers, the *fasciculus mammillaris princeps*, which splits into two tracts. The larger *mammillothalamic tract* or *bundle of Vicq d'Azyr* passes diagonally upward and forward to terminate in the anterior nucleus of the thalamus. The smaller *mammillotegmental tract* curves caudally and goes to the tegmental nuclei of the midbrain (Fig. 316).

The third ventricle has deepened. The habenular ganglia or nuclei are two small gray masses forming triangular eminences on the medial surface of the thalamus. The thin roof of the ventricle extending between the habenulae has been removed, its torn margin of attachment on each side constituting the *taenia thalami* within which may be seen a transversely cut fiber bundle, the

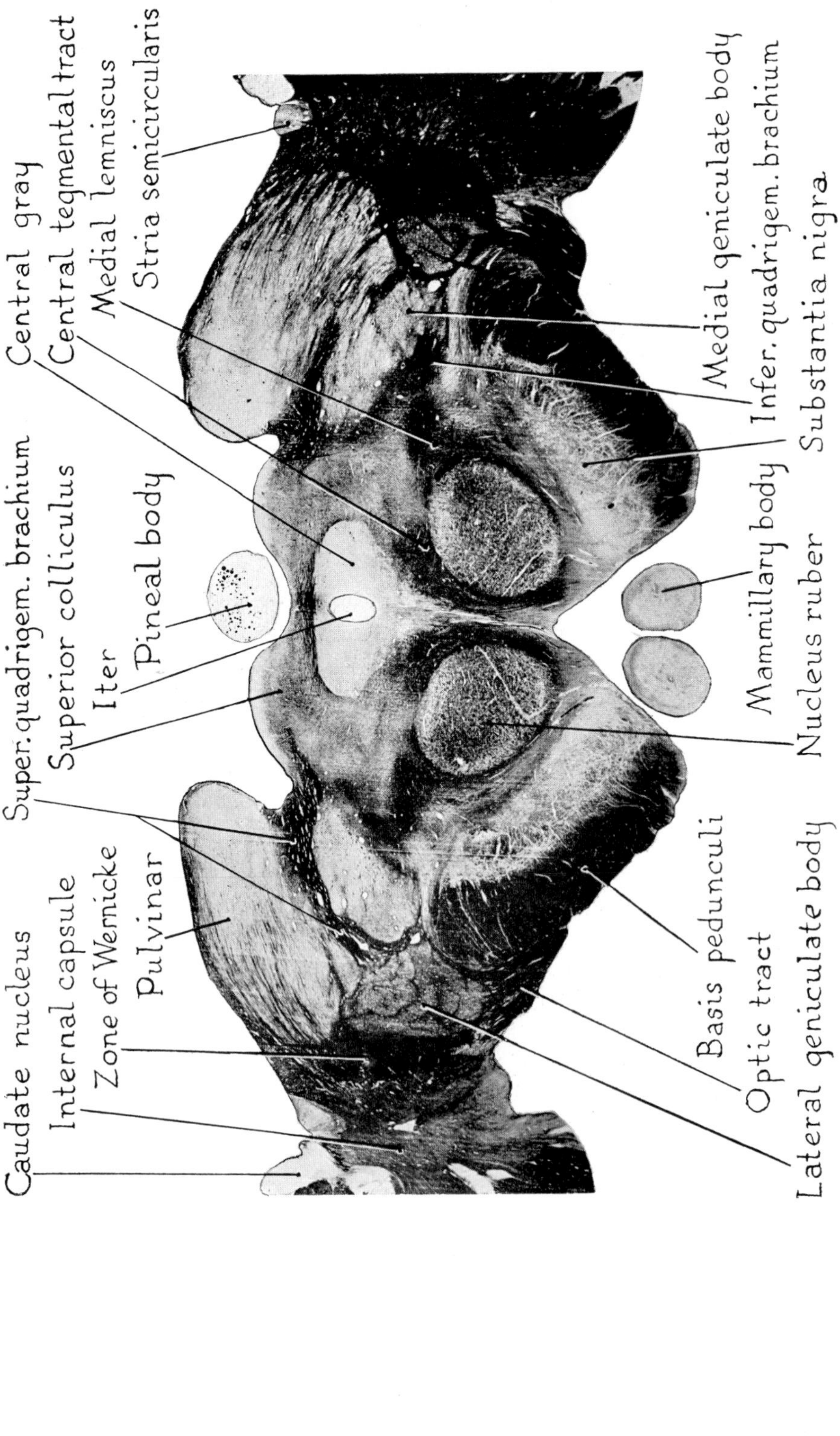

Fig. 313. Transverse section through junction of midbrain and thalamus. Weigert's myelin stain. Photograph.

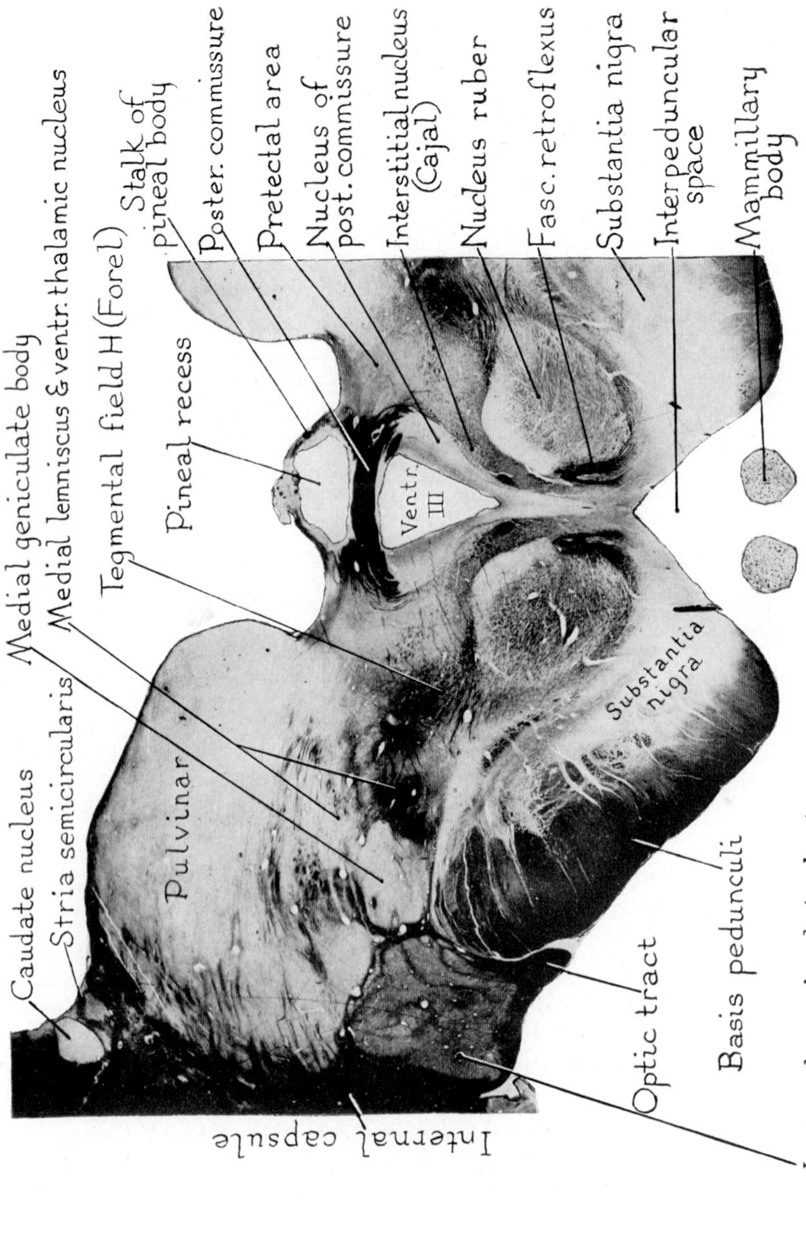

FIG. 314. Transverse section through caudal border of diencephalon at level of posterior commissure. Weigert's myelin stain. Photograph.

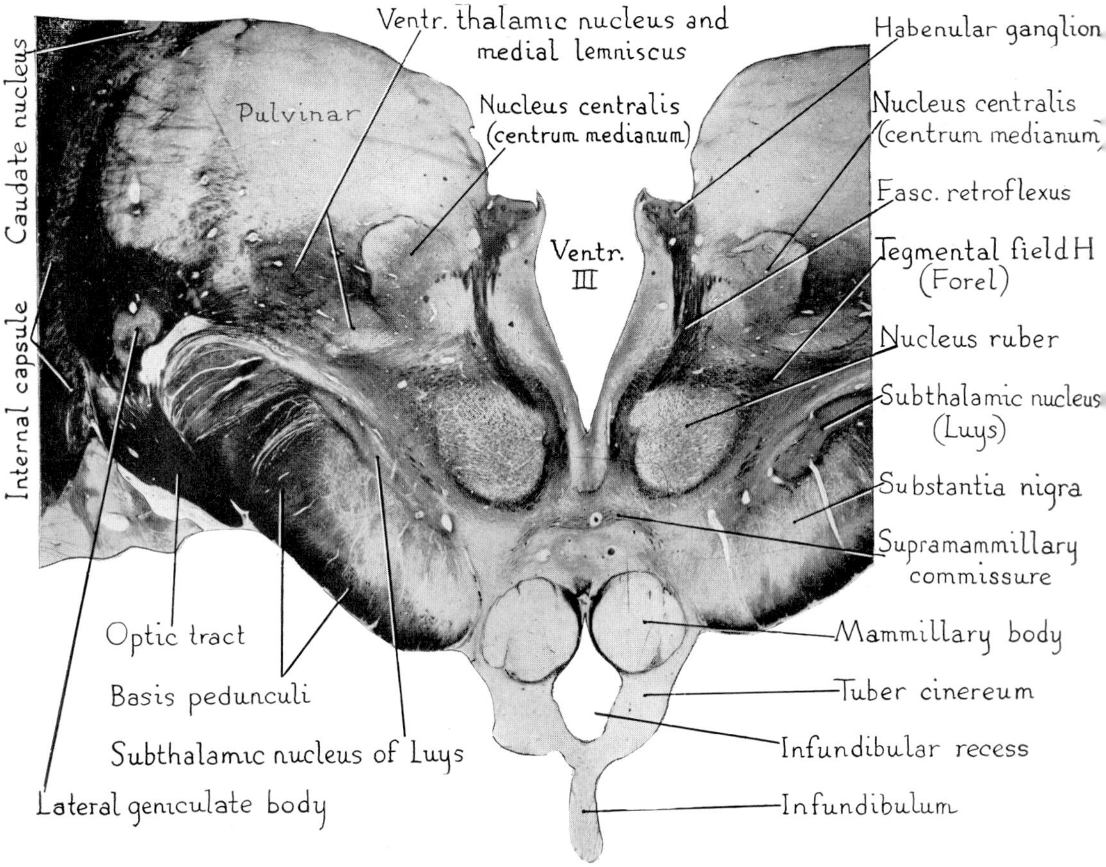

FIG. 315. Transverse section of diencephalon through habenular ganglion and infundibulum. Weigert's myelin stain. Photograph.

stria medullaris. The habenular ganglion receives fibers from the basal olfactory nuclei and from the hippocampal cortex by way of this bundle, some fibers crossing to the opposite ganglion in the slender *habenular commissure* (not shown in the section). The axons of the habenular cells form the fasciculus retroflexus which passes ventrally and caudally, perforates the medial portion of the red nucleus, and as already stated, terminates in the interpeduncular nucleus.

The diminished substantia nigra is diffusely infiltrating the medial portion of the pes pedunculi. The area is now occupied by an elliptic or lens-shaped gray mass, the *subthalamic nucleus* (*corpus subthalamicum*), closely applied to the inner surface of the pes. Many fibers are related to this nucleus. They arise primarily from the globus pallidus of the corpus striatum situated at a somewhat higher level, traverse the pes pedunculi as perforating fibers, and in part terminate directly in the subthalamic nucleus (pallidosubthalamic). Others continue over the nucleus, forming its dorsal capsule, and together with fibers arising within the nucleus itself pass medially to terminate in the substantia nigra, nucleus ruber, and reticular formation of the midbrain. Some cross to the opposite side through the slender *supramammillary* or *posterior hypothalamic* decussation and end in the contralateral subthalamic nucleus or reach the reticular formation of the opposite side.

The nucleus ruber is smaller and flanked

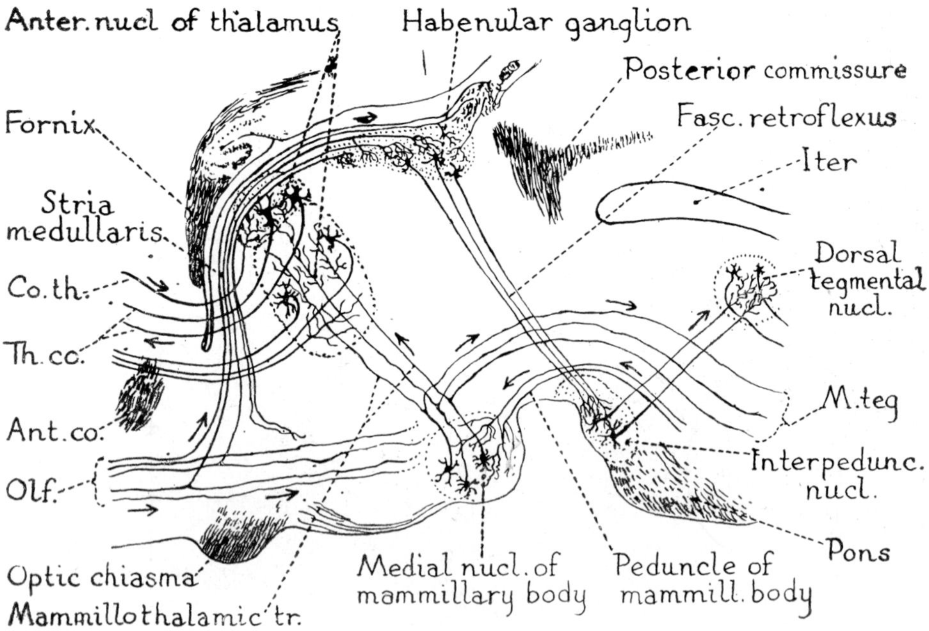

FIG. 316. Some of the important afferent and efferent connections of the mammillary body, habenular ganglion, and anterior nucleus of the thalamus. *Ant.co.*, anterior commissure; *Co.th.*, corticothalamic fiber; *M.teg.*, mammillotegmental tract (tegmental tract of Gudden); *Olf.*, fibers from basal olfactory area (olfactohabenular, olfactohypothalamic). (After Cajal.)

dorsolaterally by the tegmental field of Forel. Between the dorsal capsule of the subthalamic nucleus and the tegmental field is a narrow band of gray matter known as the *zona incerta*. Like the nucleus of the field of Forel it may be regarded as a continuation of the reticular formation (Figs. 317, 318).

The thalamus is large. The pulvinar has reached its greatest extent and may include part of the lateral thalamic nucleus with which the pulvinar is rostrally continuous. Ventral to this are the ventral thalamic nuclei and the round *central* or *centromedian nucleus*, the latter sharply delimited by a thin fibrous capsule. Within the ventral posterior nucleus are terminating the fibers of the medial lemniscus, spinothalamic, and secondary trigeminal tracts (Fig. 334). The medial geniculate body has disappeared and the lateral geniculate is greatly reduced. From the now isolated optic tract a detached slender bundle, the transverse peduncular tract, curves around the lateral margin of the pes to become lost in the subthalamic area.

SECTIONS THROUGH INTERBRAIN AND BASAL GANGLIA AT LEVEL OF OPTIC CHIASMA (FIGS. 317, 318, 312)

These sections pass through the deepest part of the diencephalon, showing all its main portions: thalamus, hypothalamus, and subthalamus. The third ventricle cuts into the optic chiasma, forming its optic recess (Fig. 318), and on each side a groove on the ventricular surface, the *hypothalamic sulcus*, separates the dorsal thalamus from the hypothalamus. The internal capsule is now represented by its lenticulothalamic portion, being flanked medially by the thalamus, and laterally by the large lenticular nucleus. The lenticular nucleus shows an outer, lighter staining portion, the *putamen*, in which there are few myelinated

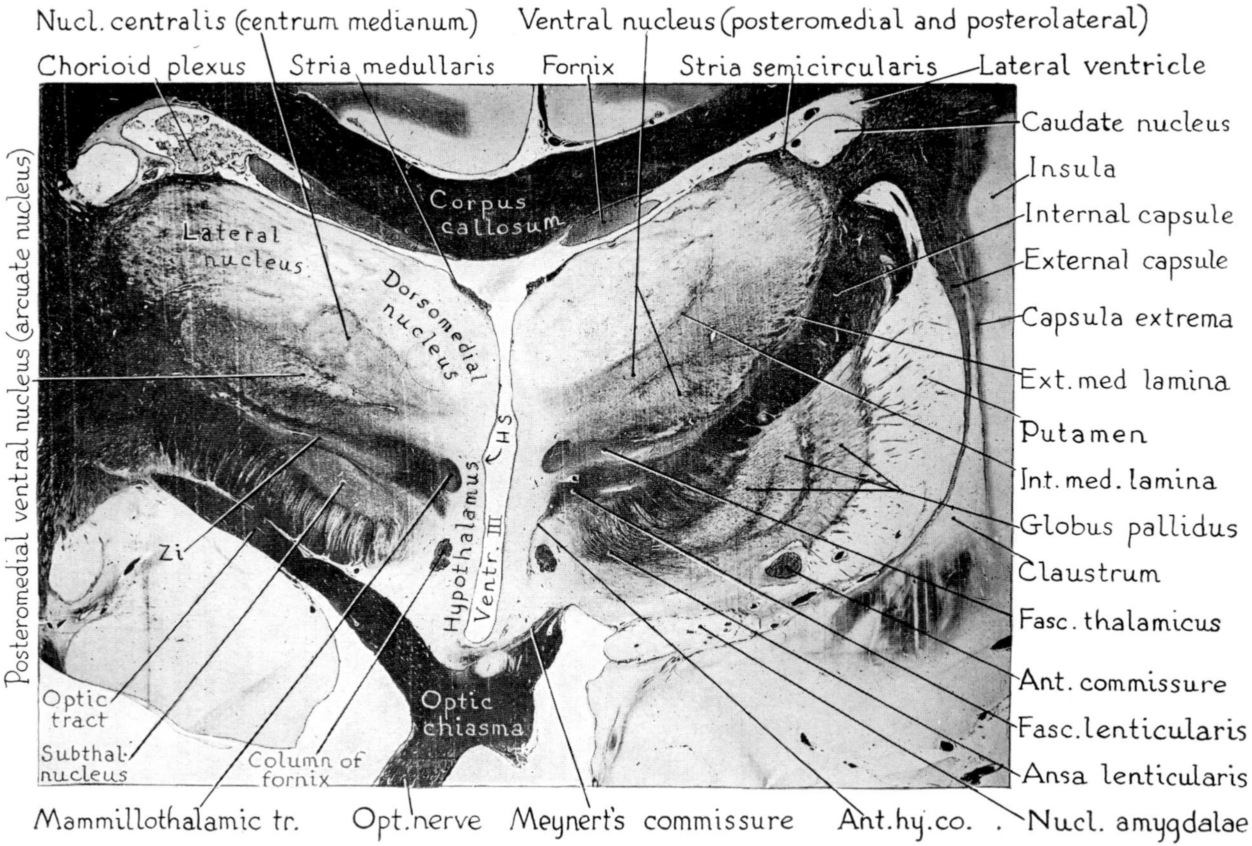

FIG. 317. Transverse section through diencephalon and basal ganglia at level of optic chiasma. The right side is cut at a higher level than the left. Weigert's myelin stain. Photograph. *Ant.hy.co.*, anterior hypothalamic commissure; *Hs*, hypothalamic sulcus; *Zi*, zona incerta. The gray stripe separating the external medullary lamina from the internal capsule constitutes the reticular nucleus which ventrally becomes continuous with zona incerta.

fibers, and an inner hemispherical portion rich in myelinated fibers and known as the *globus pallidus*. The two are separated by a sheath of fibers constituting the external medullary lamina, and the globus pallidus is itself broken up into several segments by the internal medullary laminae (Fig. 317). From the dorsal surface of the putamen incomplete gray bridges extend across the internal capsule toward the caudate nucleus and in more rostral sections the two actually become continuous with each other (Figs. 322, 323). The putamen and caudate nucleus are similar in structure and represent the phylogenetically newer part or *neostriatum*. The globus pallidus is the *paleostriatum* and more nearly equivalent to the structure found in lower vertebrates. There is a tendency to call the globus pallidus the *pallidum*, and reserve the term *striatum* for the putamen and caudate nucleus. The latter is composed mainly of small spindle-shaped or rounded cells among which are scattered relatively few larger multipolar ones. The axons of the small cells either terminate within the striatum itself or enter the globus pallidus. The myelinated fibers of the larger cells go in part to the pallidum, in part to the substantia nigra. The globus pallidus is composed almost entirely of large multipolar cells of the "motor" type whose axons form the efferent fiber systems of the corpus striatum (Fig. 78L).

The fibers of the optic nerve are partially decussating in the optic chiasma beyond which the continuation of the optic fibers is known as the optic tract. Dorsal to the optic chiasma are usually seen several fine bundles of crossing fibers constituting the hypothalamic decussations. The stoutest of these is the *dorsal supraoptic decussation* or *commissure of Meynert* composed mainly of fibers from the globus pallidus to the subthalamic nucleus and zona incerta. Dorsal to this, and somewhat more rostrally, is the slender *anterior hypothalamic decussation* (Ganser's commissure) whose composition is not fully known (Fig. 319). In part it consists of pallidohypothalamic fibers to several hypothalamic nuclei, in part it probably connects the hypothalamic regions of the two sides. A third bundle, insignificant in man, is the *ventral supraoptic decussation* or *Gudden's commissure* which lies closely applied to the dorsal surface of the optic chiasma and optic tract and is difficult to distinguish from these structures. Some maintain that this bundle is absent in man. It apparently belongs to the auditory pathway since it can be traced on each side to the medial geniculate body.

The thalamus is large, its dorsal surface covered by the stratum zonale, and at the junction of the dorsal and medial thalamic surfaces are the transversely cut striae medullares (taeniae thalami) which terminate caudally in the habenular ganglia. The thalamus is now divided into a medial and a lateral portion by a delicate band of obliquely cut fibers, the *internal medullary lamina* (Figs. 317, 48, 334). In the lateral portion may be distinguished a ventral and a lateral (dorsal) nuclear mass. The ventral nuclear mass extends the whole length of the thalamus and is usually subdivided into three nuclei: a caudal or *ventral posterior*, an intermediate or *ventral lateral*, and a rostral or *ventral anterior*. The ventral posterior which is cut in these sections shows an external segment, the *ventral posterolateral nucleus*, and an internal one, the *ventral posteromedial nucleus*, also known as the *arcuate* or *semilunar nucleus* (Fig. 317). These two portions of the ventral posterior nucleus form the thalamic end station for the medial lemniscus, spinothalamic, and secondary trigeminal tracts (Fig. 334B). The central (centromedian) nucleus if still present lies wedged between the medial and ventral nuclei.

Along the outer border of the thalamus fibers accumulate to form the *external medullary lamina* which separates the thalamus from the internal capsule. Cells lying between and external to these fibers form a thin and frequently broken gray stripe, the

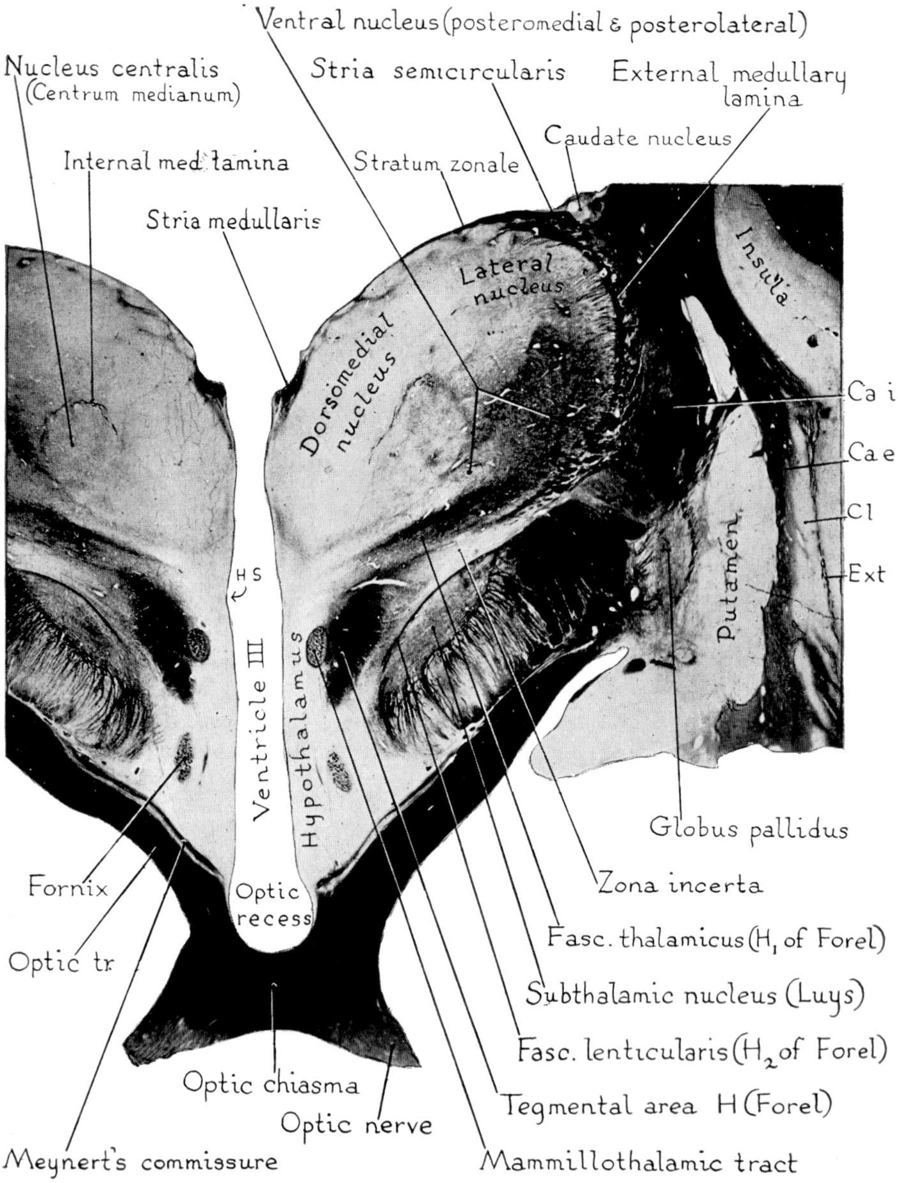

FIG. 318. Transverse section through diencephalon and basal ganglia at level of optic chiasma. Weigert's myelin stain. Photograph. *Ca e,* external capsule; *Ca i,* internal capsule; *Cl,* claustrum; *Ext,* capsula extrema; *Hs,* hypothalamic sulcus.

reticular nucleus, which ventrally becomes continuous with the zona incerta (Figs. 317, 333, 334). Most of these fibers represent thalamic radiations which enter the internal capsule and are distributed to the cortex. Some go to the caudate nucleus or traverse the internal capsule to terminate in the putamen of the lenticular nucleus, representing thalamostriate connections. From the caudate nucleus also fibers cross the internal capsule in a dorsoventral direction and enter the lenticular nucleus. Most of them pass medial to the putamen in the outer medullary lamina to terminate in the

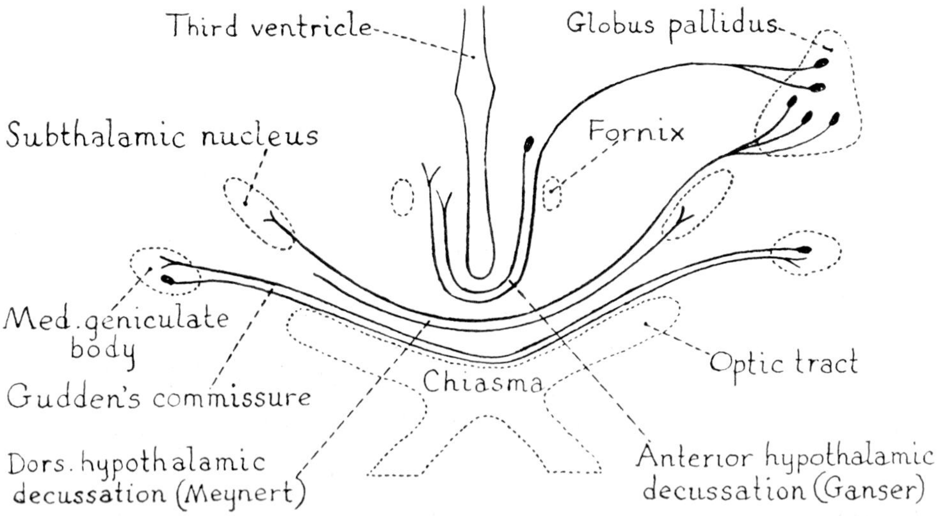

FIG. 319. Diagram of hypothalamic decussations, showing origin and termination of some of their fibers.

globus pallidus. The latter receives numerous fibers directly from the putamen. The external medullary layer of the lenticular nucleus thus represents essentially striatopallidal connections. In addition to the fibers from the thalamus, the striatum and pallidum both receive fibers from the substantia nigra and from the frontal cortex by direct corticostriate and corticopallidal tracts. These nuclei may receive collaterals from the pyramidal tract (Cajal). Thus the afferent connections of the striatum are from the cortex, thalamus, and substantia nigra, while its efferent fibers discharge mainly into the globus pallidus (Fig. 321).

With the disappearance of the lateral geniculate body the pes pedunculi has become incorporated in the internal capsule, forming its peduncular or subthalamic portion. The red nucleus has disappeared and in its place is seen the tegmental field of Forel (prerubral field, field H), composed of fibers and scattered cells which constitute the nucleus of the tegmental field (nucleus of prerubral field). The field now contains several fiber components. Some are rubrothalamic and dentatothalamic fibers, derived from the capsule of the red nucleus and going to the ventral lateral nucleus of the thalamus. Others are fibers from the globus pallidus, terminating mainly in the nucleus of the prerubral field. The cells of this nucleus give rise to a short fiber bundle, the *prerubral tract,* which enters the rostral pole of the red nucleus (Fig. 321). Lateral to the tegmental field are two transversely running fiber bundles enclosing between them a strip of gray matter, the *zona incerta* (Fig. 318). The dorsal bundle or *thalamic fasciculus* (field H1) is closely applied to the ventral surface of the thalamus; the *lenticular fasciculus* (H2) is in contact with the subthalamic nucleus or with the internal capsule in levels above that nucleus. The composition of these bundles is best understood by an analysis of the efferent pallidal connections. Subthalamic nucleus, tegmental field, zona incerta, lenticular and thalamic fasciculi, and peduncular portion of the internal capsule together constitute the *subthalamus.*

The efferent fibers of the corpus striatum arise almost entirely from the globus pallidus. Many of these fibers perforate the peduncular portion of the internal capsule and on reaching the inner surface of the latter, are gathered into a bundle which runs medially and constitutes the lenticular fas-

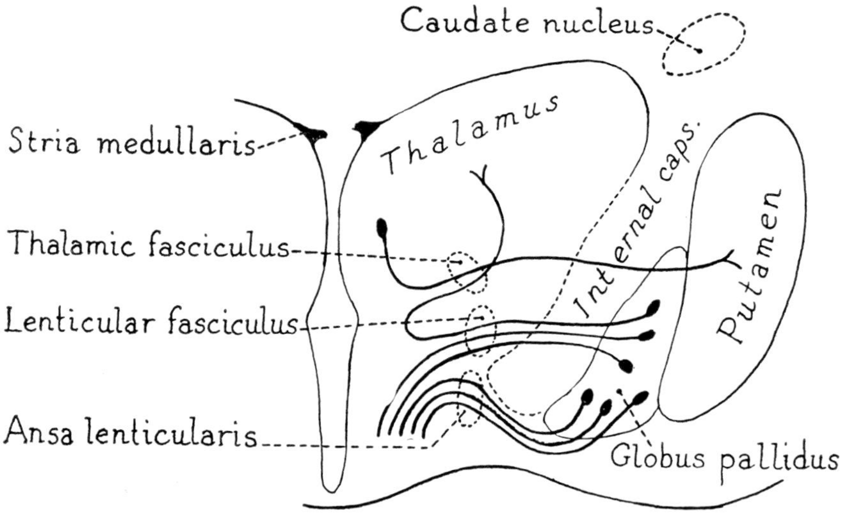

FIG. 320. Diagram showing composition of the ansa lenticularis and the lenticular and thalamic fasciculi. In the thalamic bundle only the connections of the thalamus with the corpus striatum are shown.

ciculus mentioned above. Other fibers, especially from the ventral part of the pallidum, sweep around the medial border of the internal capsule, forming a looped bundle, the *ansa lenticularis*, which curves dorsally to join the lenticular fasciculus (Fig. 320). These two bundles, ansa lenticularis and fasciculus lenticularis, constitute the whole system of efferent fibers from the globus pallidus, terminating in numerous and widely distributed nuclei which are relay or end stations in the extrapyramidal outflow from the corpus striatum (Fig. 321). Many of the fibers make homolateral connections, others cross in the several hypothalamic decussations. Included are: (1) Pallidothalamic fibers to the ventral anterior nucleus and perhaps to some of the medial thalamic nuclei. (2) Pallidohypothalamic fibers to the tuber cinereum and other hypothalamic regions. (3) Fibers to the subthalamic nucleus and zona incerta. (4) Fibers to the nucleus of the prerubral field and thence to the nucleus ruber; perhaps some direct pallidorubral fibers. Pallidal impulses can also reach the nucleus ruber through the subthalamic nucleus and zona incerta. (5) The substantia nigra receives direct fibers from the large cells of the putamen and the caudate nucleus (strionigral) and sends nigrostriatal fibers to these nuclei. The presence of pallidonigral fibers has been denied by Verhaart (1950). (6) Fibers to the interstitial nucleus and nucleus of Darkschewitsch by way of the posterior commissure. (7) Pallidoreticular fibers to the reticular formation of the midbrain, pons, and medulla. It appears that some of the pallidal fibers may go directly to the motor nuclei innervating the ocular, facial, masticatory, and other muscles of the head (Morgan). From the above it is evident that efferent impulses from the globus pallidus do not reach the lower motor neurons by long fibers as is the case with the pyramidal tract, but are interrupted in many nuclei widely scattered throughout the brain stem.

The *thalamic fasciculus* has several components. In part it is a continuation of the tegmental field connecting the red nucleus and cerebellum with the thalamus and cortex (Figs. 334, 335). The rubrothalamic and dentatothalamic fibers terminate in the intermediate portion of the ventral thalamic nucleus rostral to the termination of the medial lemniscus and spino-

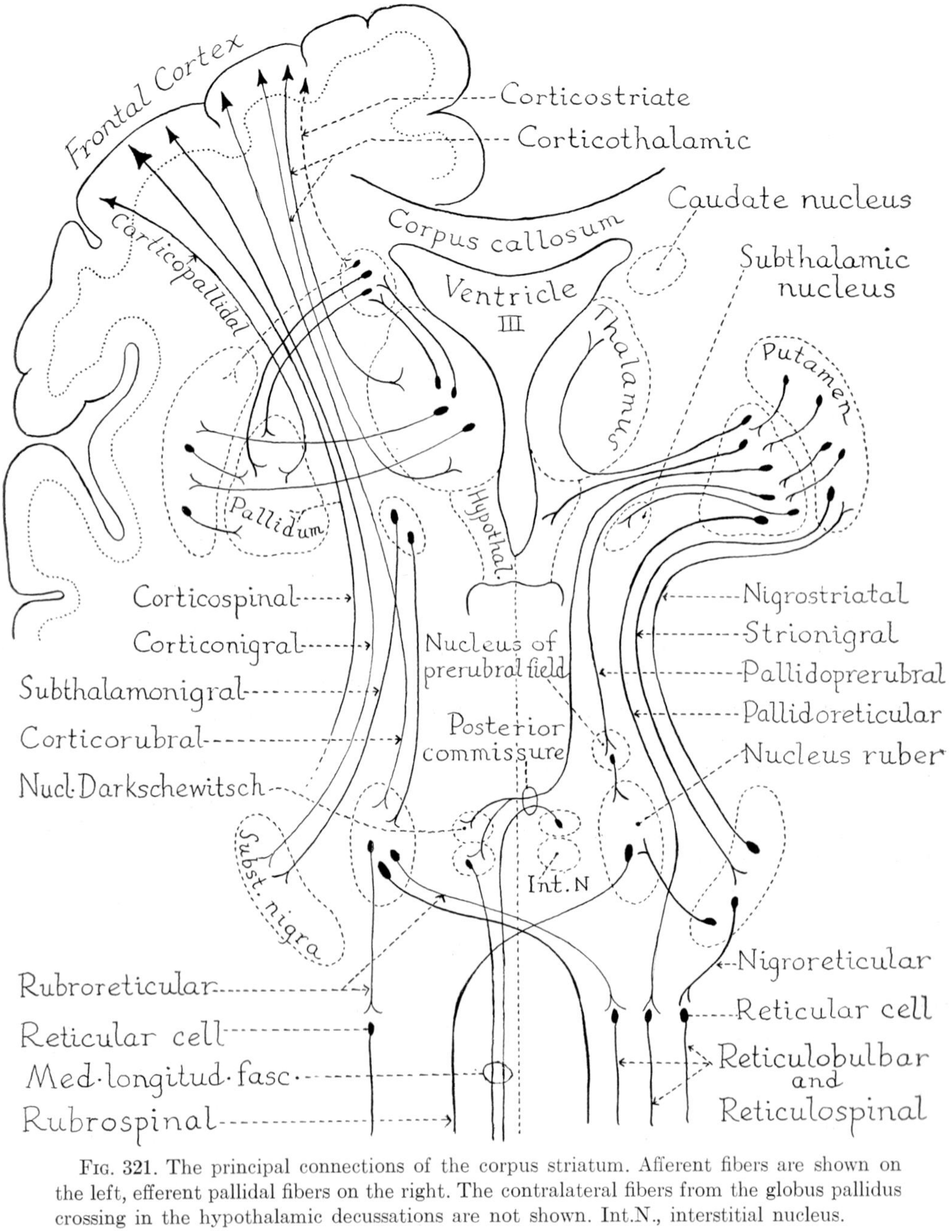

FIG. 321. The principal connections of the corpus striatum. Afferent fibers are shown on the left, efferent pallidal fibers on the right. The contralateral fibers from the globus pallidus crossing in the hypothalamic decussations are not shown. Int.N., interstitial nucleus.

thalamic tracts. More important fibers within the thalamic fasciculus are from the globus pallidus. These emerge with the lenticular fasciculus, then loop laterally and enter the thalamic bundle through which they reach the anterior portion of the ventral thalamic nucleus (Fig. 320). Thus the ventral nucleus receives sensory fibers in its posterior segment (ventral posterior nucleus), cerebellar fibers in its intermediate portion (ventral lateral nucleus), and pallidal fibers in its anterior portion (ventral anterior nucleus). Intermingled with these fibers are thalamopallidal and thalamostriate fibers from thalamic nuclei to the corpus striatum.

External to the putamen is a band of mainly longitudinally running fibers, the *external capsule*, flanked laterally by a plate of gray matter, the *claustrum*, whose function and connections are not fully understood. It is regarded by some as a detached portion of the putamen, by others as belonging to the cortex of the insula (island of Reil). The latter is separated from the claustrum by a layer of subcortical white matter known as the *capsula extrema* (Fig. 193). A transversely cut fiber bundle indenting the ventral surface of the lenticular nucleus is the beginning of the anterior commissure (Fig. 317).

In the hypothalamic region, which lies below the hypothalamic sulcus and merges laterally with the subthalamus, are seen two conspicuous transversely cut fiber bundles: the *fornix* and the *mammillothalamic tract*. The fornix, to be studied more fully with the olfactory system, arises in the hippocampal cortex of the temporal lobe, and passes dorsally over the thalamus. Then it curves ventrally, enters the hypothalamus and runs caudally to end in the mammillary body (Fig. 311). The mammillothalamic tract originates in the mammillary body and runs diagonally upward and forward to terminate in the anterior thalamic nucleus (Figs. 316, 334B).

SECTION THROUGH THALAMUS AND CORPUS STRIATUM AT LEVEL OF ANTERIOR COMMISSURE (FIGS. 322, 312)

The section passes rostral to the hypothalamus. The somewhat smaller thalamus shows clearly a division into an inner and an outer portion, the two separated by the internal medullary lamina. In the inner portion are the large *dorsomedial nucleus* and the central (ventricular) gray substance in which there are a number of poorly defined cell clusters known as the *midline nuclei* (Fig. 334). The outer portion comprises the lateral nucleus and the *ventral lateral nucleus* which receives the cerebellar fibers from the red and the dentate nuclei. The medial lemniscus and other sensory tracts have already terminated at a lower level in the ventral posterior nucleus. Dorsally another gray mass, the *anterior thalamic nucleus*, has made its appearance and is spread out equally above the medial and lateral nucleus, separated from these by a fork of the internal medullary lamina. The striae medullares are still present and in the ventricular floor are seen the anterior commissure, and dorsal to it the columns of the fornix. The anterior commissure belongs to the rhinencephalon. It connects the olfactory portions of the two temporal lobes and to a lesser extent the two olfactory bulbs.

Fibers from the lateral thalamic nuclei and apparently from the anterior as well, gather along the outer border of the thalamus in the external medullary lamina. The fibers soon enter the internal capsule and form a part of the superior or middle thalamic radiation related to the frontal and parietal cortex. In the medial nuclei are also seen longitudinally or obliquely cut fibers which run ventrally toward the most medial portion of the internal capsule. This bundle, known as the *ansa peduncularis*, is composed in part of fibers which connect the thalamus with the basal temporal cortex and the insula, in part of fibers of the ansa lenticularis representing efferent outflows from the globus pallidus. At the boundary between the medial and lateral nucleus is the mammillothalamic tract.

The lenticular nucleus is large, especially the putamen which now is medially continuous with the head of the caudate nucleus whose caudal portion is cut at this level. The boundary zone between the two is marked by a bundle of longitudinally cut fibers which represent the beginning of the anterior limb of the internal capsule (caudatolenticular portion). The tail of the caudate nucleus is still present and occupies

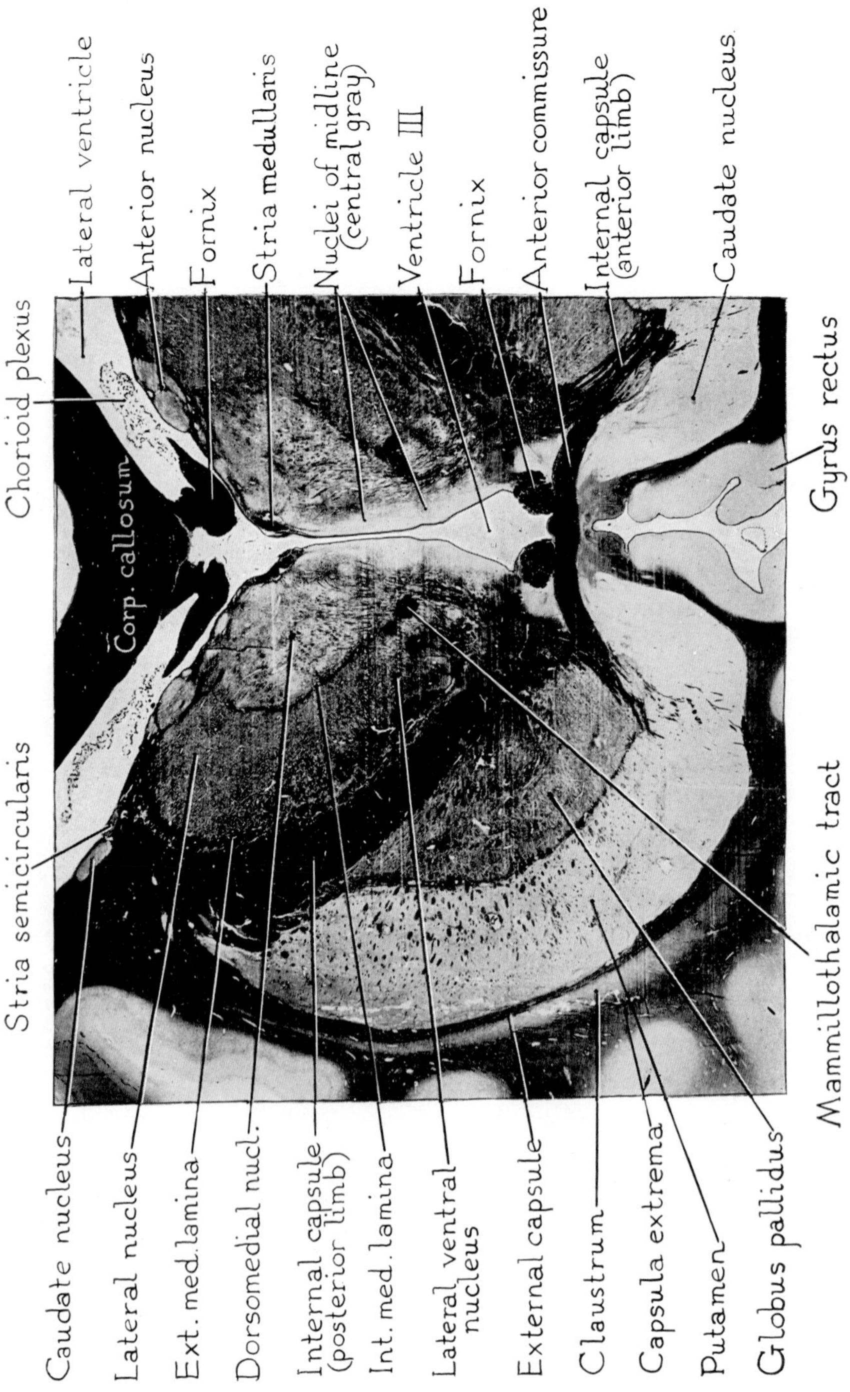

FIG. 322. Transverse section through diencephalon and basal ganglia at level of anterior commissure. Weigert's myelin stain. Photograph.

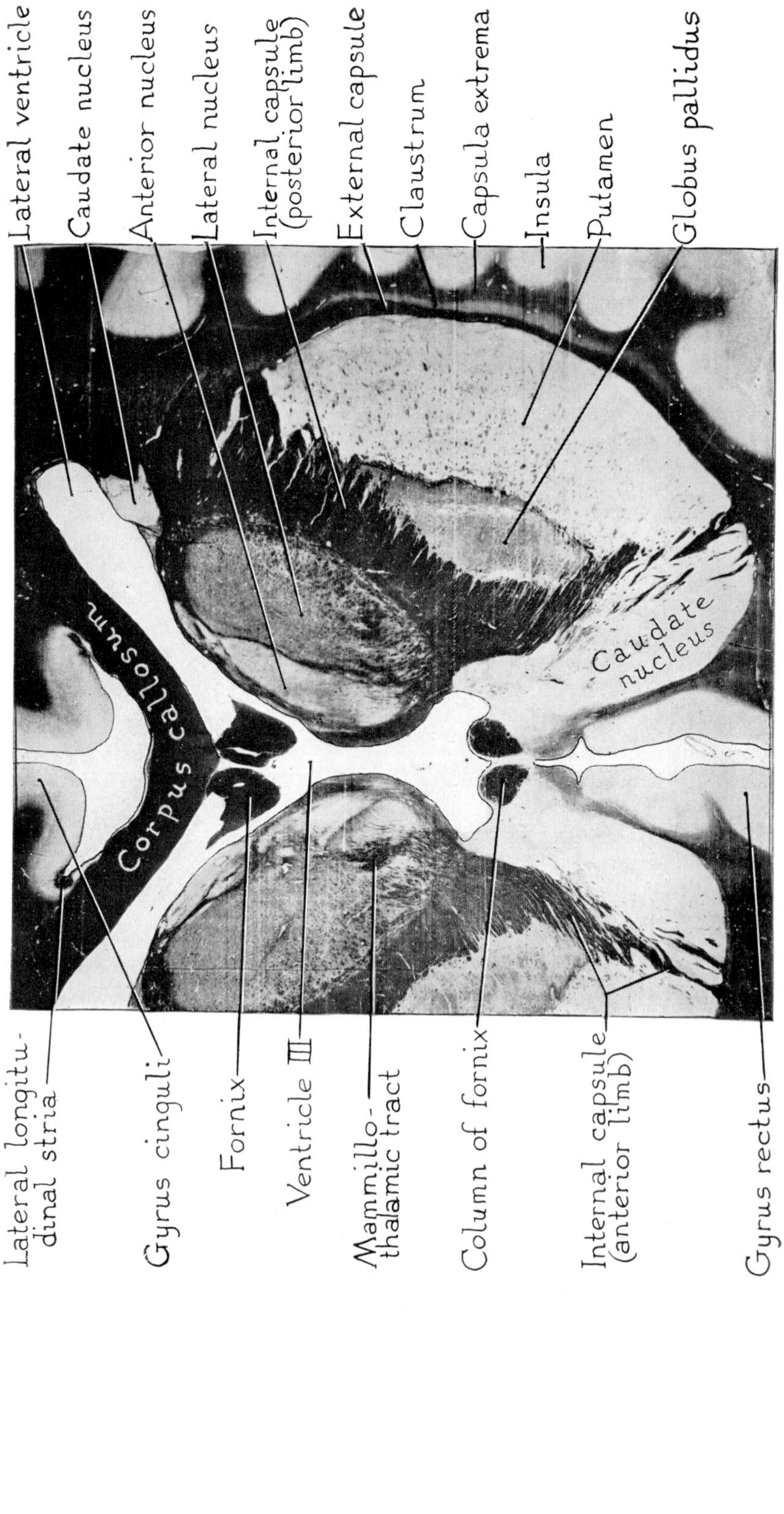

FIG. 323. Transverse section through basal ganglia and rostral portion of thalamus. Weigert's myelin stain. Photograph.

its previous position, immedately lateral to the stria semicircularis.

SECTION THROUGH CORPUS STRIATUM AND ROSTRAL PORTION OF THALAMUS (FIGS. 323, 312)

The medial thalamic nucleus has disappeared and the much diminished thalamus now consists of the anterior nucleus and the most rostral portion of the lateral nuclear mass, the two are separated by the internal medullary lamina. The lateral mass is mainly made up of the ventral anterior nucleus, the most dorsal portion perhaps still belonging to the lateral dorsal nucleus. The mammillothalamic tract is about to enter the anterior nucleus in which its fibers terminate.

The putamen is large, the globus pallidus considerably smaller. Ventrally the putamen is practically fused with the head of the caudate nucleus. The junctional zone between the two is perforated by fibers of the internal capsule (anterior limb). The internal capsule has the form of a shallow V whose apex is directed medially. The dorsal stouter portion between thalamus and lenticular nucleus belongs to the posterior limb; the ventral portion between the caudate and lenticular nuclei constitutes the anterior limb or lenticulo-caudate portion. External capsule, claustrum, and extreme capsule are in the same position.

SECTION THROUGH SEPTUM PELLUCIDUM AND HEAD OF CAUDATE NUCLEUS (FIGS. 324, 312)

The section passes rostral to the thalamus. The anterior limb of the internal capsule is bounded medially by the large head of the caudate nucleus, laterally by the much

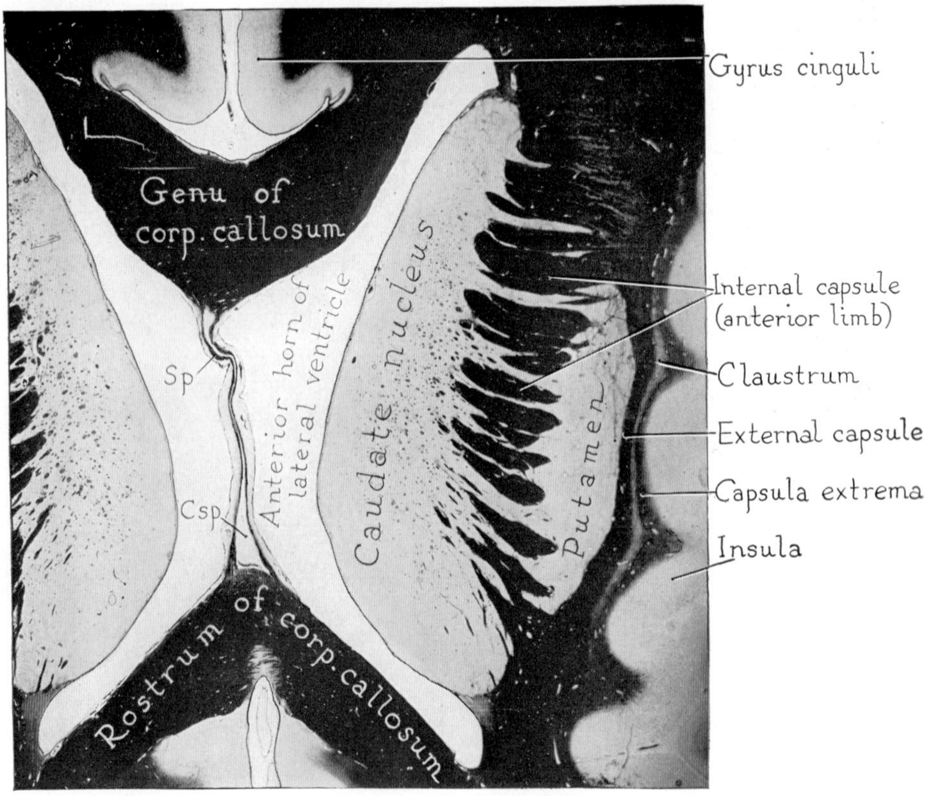

FIG. 324. Transverse section of basal ganglia, through head of caudate nucleus and anterior limb of internal capsule. Weigert's myelin stain. Photograph. *Sp*, septum pellucidum; *Csp*, cavum of septum pellucidum.

diminished putamen. The globus pallidus has disappeared. Putamen and caudate nucleus are connected by numerous gray bridges which extend across the internal capsule and produce the striped appearance responsible for the term corpus striatum.

The third ventricle has disappeared and the lateral ventricles are now represented by their most rostral portions, the anterior or frontal horns. The lateral wall of the anterior horn of each ventricle is formed by the caudate nucleus, the roof and floor respectively by the body and rostrum of the corpus callosum. The thin medial wall separating the two ventricles is the *septum pellucidum* composed of two thin plates of neural tissue, the *laminae of the septum pellucidum*. Between the two laminae there is a space of variable extent, the *cavum of the septum pellucidum*. Each lamina consists of fibers covered superficially by a layer of gray matter.

THE THALAMIC RADIATIONS AND INTERNAL CAPSULE

The fibers which connect the thalamus and cortex in both directions constitute the thalamic radiations. These thalamocortical and corticothalamic fibers form a continuous fan emerging along the whole lateral extent of the caudate nucleus. The fibers radiate forward, upward, backward and downward, and pass obliquely through the various portions of the internal capsule of which they form a large part (Figs. 325, 326, 327). Though the radiations connect with practically all parts of the cortex, the richness of connections varies considerably for specific cortical areas. Most abundant are the projections to the frontal granular cortex, the precentral and postcentral gyri, the calcarine area, and the gyrus of Heschl. The posterior parietal region and adjacent portions of the temporal lobe also have rich thalamic connections, but relatively

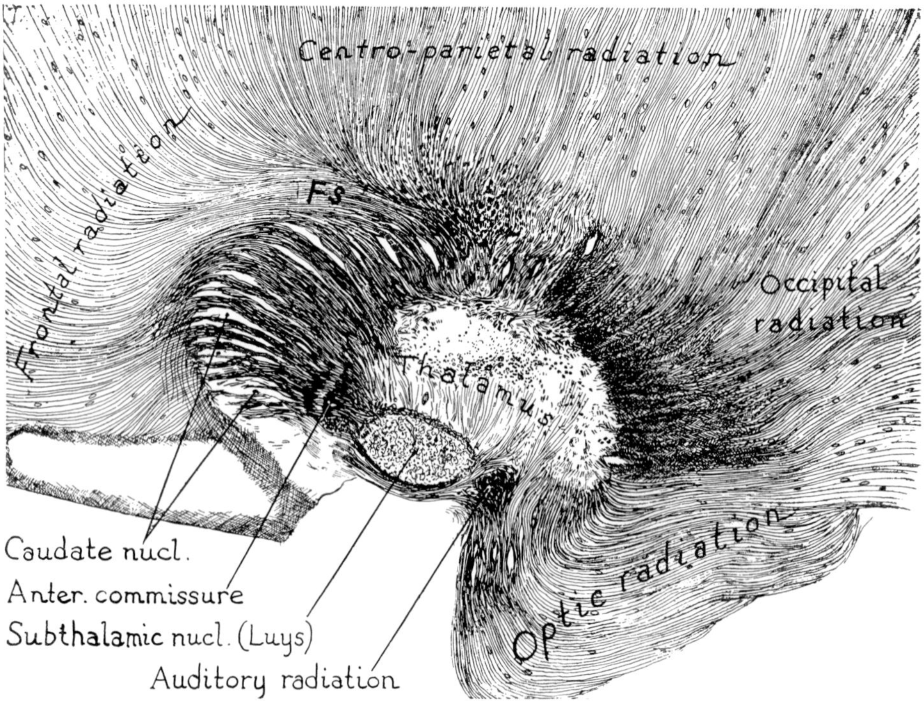

FIG. 325. The thalamic radiations. Composite picture drawn from photographs of serial sections and dissections. *Fs*, fasciculus subcallosus of frontal radiation. (After J. Rosett.)

scanty radiations go to other cortical areas, especially the temporal lobe (Walker) (Fig. 335).

The thalamic radiations are usually grouped into four subradiations, often known as the thalamic *peduncles* or *stalks* (Figs. 325, 330). The *anterior* or *frontal peduncle* connects the frontal lobe with the medial and anterior thalamic nuclei, and with the anterior portion of the lateral nuclei. The *superior* or *centroparietal peduncle* connects the Rolandic area, and adjacent portions of the frontal and parietal lobes with the lateral and ventral thalamic nuclei. The fibers carrying general sensory impulses from the body and head form part of this radiation and terminate in the postcentral gyrus (Figs. 327, 334, 335). The *posterior* or *occipital peduncle* connects the occipital and posterior parietal convolutions with the caudal portions of the thalamus, especially the pulvinar. It includes the optic radiation (geniculocalcarine) from the lateral geniculate body to the calcarine occipital cortex (striate area). The *inferior* or *temporal* peduncle is relatively small and includes the scanty connections of the thalamus with the temporal lobe and the insula. In this may be included the stronger auditory radiation (geniculotemporal) from the medial geniculate body to the temporal gyrus of Heschl.

The cerebral hemisphere is connected with the brain stem and spinal cord by an extensive system of projection fibers, some afferent, others efferent. They arise from the whole extent of the cortex and enter the white substance of the hemisphere where they appear as a radiating mass of fibers, the *corona radiata*, converging toward the brain stem (Fig. 56). On reaching the latter they form a broad compact fiber band, the *internal capsule*, flanked medially by the thalamus and caudate nucleus, laterally by the lenticular nucleus (Fig. 327). The internal capsule is thus composed of all the fibers, afferent and efferent, which go to, or come from the cerebral cortex. A large part of the capsule is obviously composed of the thalamic radiations described above. The rest is mainly composed of efferent cortical fiber systems which descend to lower portions of the brain stem and to the spinal cord. These include the corticospinal, corticobulbar, and corticopontile tracts, and the smaller bundles to the hypothalamus, substantia nigra, nucleus ruber, subthalamic nucleus, and to certain other gray masses of the brain stem. Below the level of the thalamus these descending systems constitute the pes pedunculi of the midbrain (Fig. 193).

The internal capsule, as seen in a horizontal section, is composed of a shorter *anterior* and a longer *posterior limb* which meet at an obtuse angle, the junctional zone being known as the *genu* (Figs. 326, 327). The anterior limb lies between the lenticular and caudate nuclei. The posterior limb consists of the large *lenticulothalamic* portion lying between the lenticular nucleus and the thalamus, and a caudal *retrolenticular portion* extending a short distance behind the lenticular nucleus. In this caudal region a number of fibers pass beneath the lenticular nucleus to reach the temporal lobe and collectively form the *sublenticular* portion of the internal capsule.

(1) The *anterior limb* contains the anterior thalamic radiation or peduncle, the prefrontal corticopontile tract, and also fibers from the orbital cortex to the hypothalamus. (2) The *genu* contains the corticobulbar fibers to the motor cranial nuclei, those for the eye muscles being placed most anteriorly, those for the tongue and face extending a short distance into the posterior limb. (3) The *posterior limb* includes the corticospinal tract, the superior thalamic radiation, the frontal corticopontile tract from areas 4 and 6, smaller fiber bundles from areas 6, 8, and the caudal portion of 9 to the nucleus ruber, subthalamus, hypothalamus, substantia nigra, and globus pallidus (Meyer, 1949). In the pyramidal tract the fibers

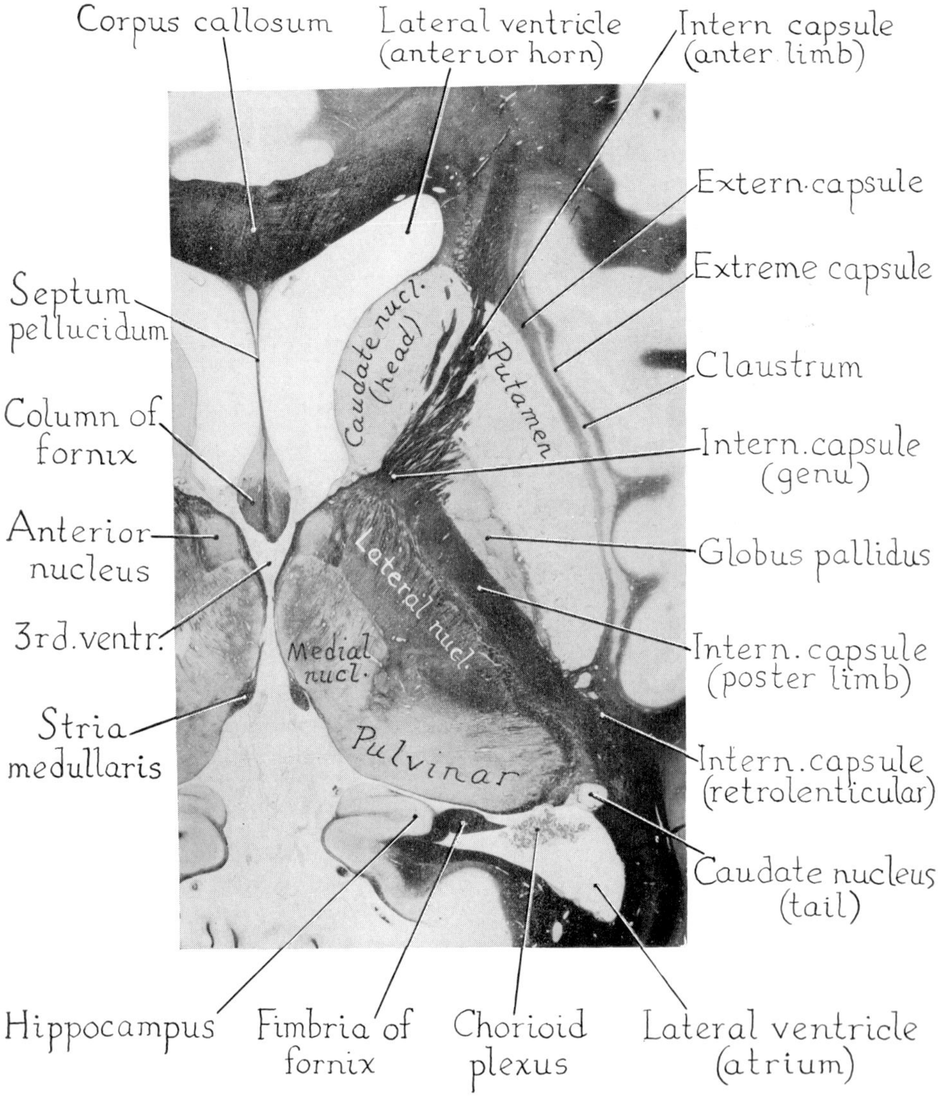

FIG. 326. Horizontal section through thalamus and basal ganglia. Weigert's myelin stain. Photograph.

for the neck are closest to the genu, followed respectively by those of the upper extremity, trunk, and lower extremity. The fibers of the superior thalamic radiation which project general body sense to the post-central gyrus are located in the caudal portion, immediately behind the pyramidal tract. (4) The *retrolenticular portion* of the posterior limb contains the posterior thalamic radiation including among others the geniculocalcarine (optic) radiation, parietal and occipital corticopontile fibers, and fibers from the occipital cortex to the superior colliculi and pretectal region. The *sublenticular portion*, difficult to separate from the retrolenticular, contains the inferior thalamic peduncle including the geniculotemporal (auditory) radiation, and corticopontile fibers from the temporal, and also from the parietooccipital areas.

All of the thalamocortical and corticofugal fibers within the internal capsule

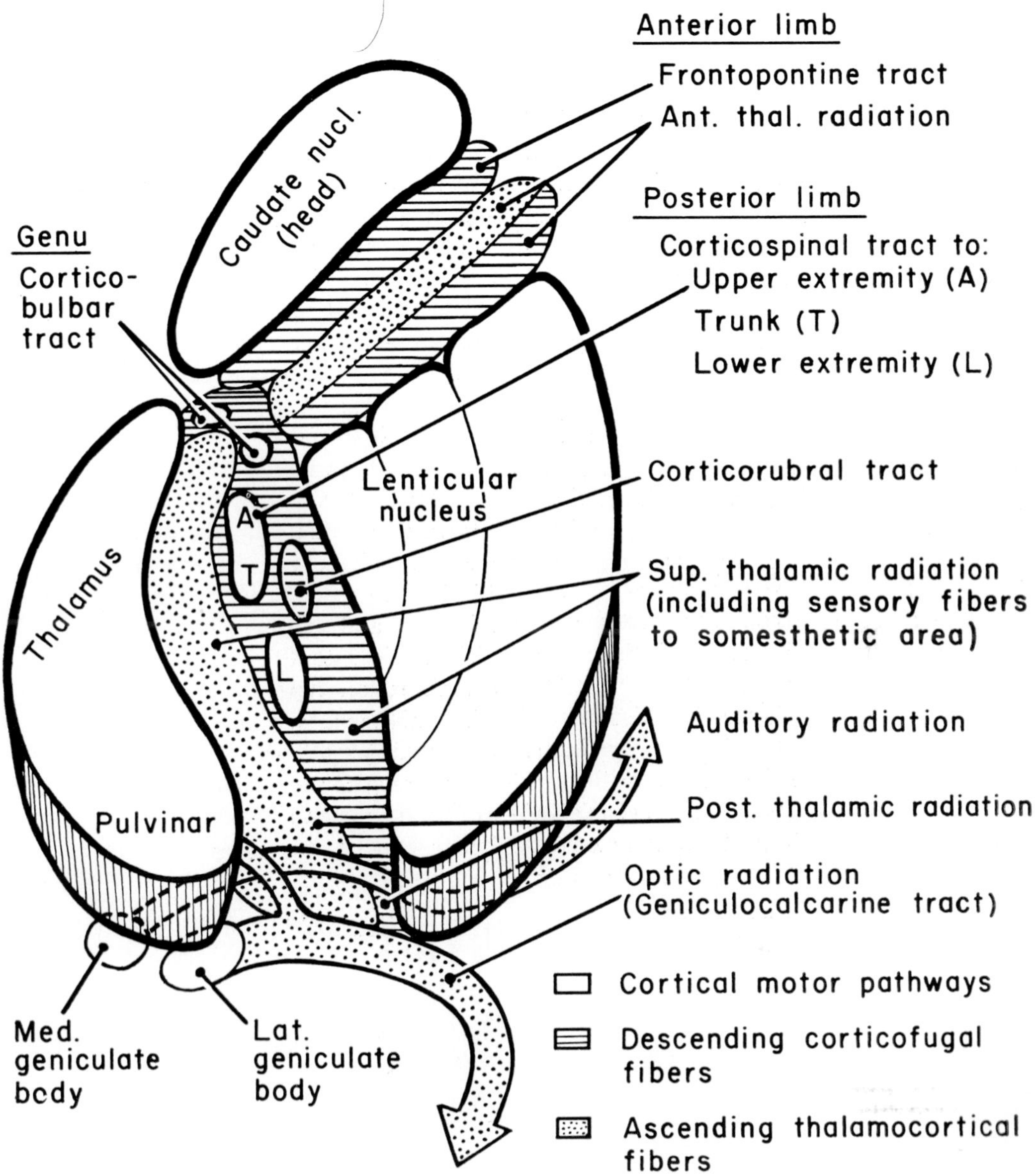

FIG. 327. Components of the right internal capsule. This diagram has same orientation as Figure 326. Blood supply of the internal capsule is shown in Figure 71.

occupy a comparatively small, compact area (Fig. 327). Lesions in this area produce more widespread disability than lesions in any other region of the nervous system. Thrombosis or hemorrhage of the anterior choroid, striate, or capsular branches of the middle cerebral arteries (Fig. 71) are responsible for most injuries to the internal capsule. Vascular accidents in the posterior limb of the internal capsule result in contralateral hemianesthesia (or hemihypesthesia) of the head, trunk, and limbs due to injury of thalamocortical fibers enroute to the sensory cortex. There is also a contralateral hemiplegia (hemiparesis) due to injury of the corticospinal tracts. If the genu of the internal capsule is included in the injury, the corticobulbar tract is also destroyed (see p. 344). Lesions in the posterior one-third of the posterior limb may include the optic and auditory radiations. In such instances there may be a contralateral triad consisting of hemianesthesia, hemianopsia, and hemihypacusis. The more posterior corticospinal fibers to the lower extremity may also be injured with resulting spasticity in only the lower limb (monoplegia). More extensive vascular lesions may include the thalamus or corpus striatum, so that affective changes and extrapyramidal symptoms may be added to those indicative of injury to the internal capsule.

THE VISUAL PATHWAY

The *retina* arises as an evaginated portion of the brain, the optic pouch, which secondarily is invaginated to form the two-layered optic cup. The outer layer gives rise to pigmented epithelium. The inner layer forms the neural portion of the retina in which are differentiated the bipolar rod and cone cells, the bipolar and horizontal neurons confined within the retina itself, and the multipolar ganglionic neurons whose axons form the optic nerve (Fig. 328). The latter thus really constitutes a fiber tract connecting two parts of the brain. Its fibers possess no neurilemma sheaths, and its connective tissue investments represent continuations of the meningeal sheaths of the brain: pia, arachnoid and dura.

The rod and cone cells are the visual receptors which react specifically to physical light. The cones, numbering some 7,000,000 in the human eye, have a higher threshold of excitability and are stimulated by light of relatively high intensity. They are responsible for sharp vision and for color discrimination in adequate illumination. The rods whose number has been estimated at over 100,000,000 react to low intensities of illumination and subserve twilight and night vision. Close to the posterior pole of the eye, the retina shows a small circular yellowish area, the *macula lutea*, in direct line with the visual axis. The macula represents the retinal area for central vision, and the eyes are fixed in such a manner that the retinal image of any object is always focused on

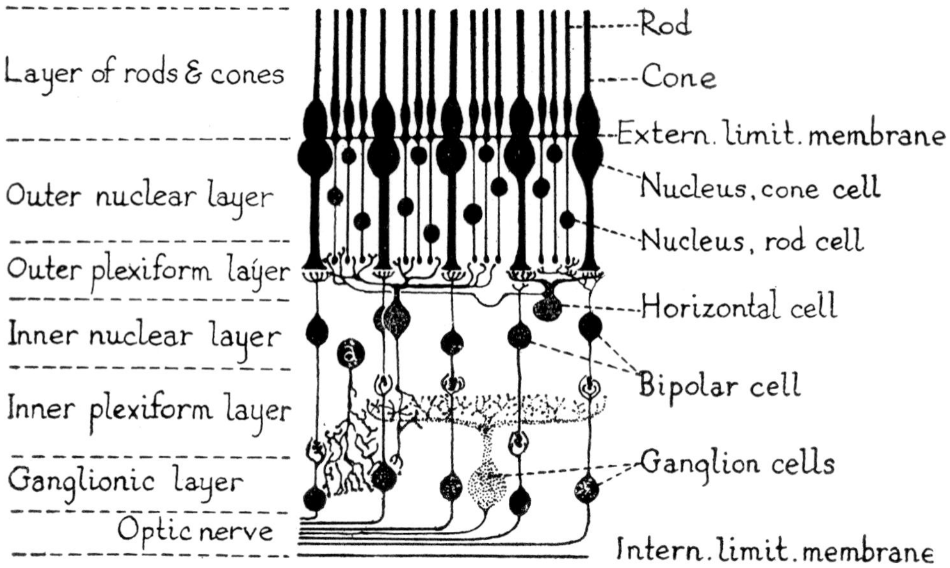

FIG. 328. The neural elements of the human retina as seen in Golgi preparations. *a*, amacrine cell. (Modified from Walls.)

the macula. The rest of the retina is concerned with pericentral (paracentral) and peripheral vision. In the macular region the inner layers of the retina are pushed apart, forming a small central pit, the *fovea centralis*, which constitutes the point of sharpest vision and most acute color discrimination. Here the retina is composed entirely of closely packed slender cones.

The nerve impulses from the rod and cone cells are transmitted to the bipolar neurons which in turn establish synaptic relations with the dendrites or bodies of the multipolar ganglionic cells. The axons of the latter, at first unmyelinated, are arranged in fine radiating bundles which run parallel to the retinal surface and converge at the optic disc to form the optic nerve. On emerging from the eyeball the fibers at once acquire a myelin sheath with consequent increase in the size of the optic nerve.

The optic nerves enter the cranial cavity through the optic foramen and unite to form the optic chiasma, beyond which they are continued as the optic tracts. Within the chiasma a partial decussation occurs, the fibers from the nasal halves of the retina crossing to the opposite side, those from the temporal halves of the retina remaining uncrossed (Fig. 329). It must be remembered that in binocular vision each visual field, right and left, is not projected upon the retina of only one side, but upon portions of both retinae. Thus the images of objects in the right field of vision (red in Fig. 329) are projected on the right nasal and the left temporal half of the retina. In the chiasma the fibers from these two retinal portions are combined to form the left optic tract, which now represents the complete right field of vision. By this arrangement the whole right field of vision is projected upon the left hemisphere, and the left visual field upon the right hemisphere.

Each optic tract sweeps outward and backward, encircling the hypothalamus and rostral portion of the pes pedunculi. Most of its fibers terminate in the lateral geniculate body, and a smaller portion continues as the superior quadrigeminal brachium to the superior colliculi and pretectal area (Fig. 329). Some of the optic fibers also enter the hypothalamus to terminate in the supraoptic nucleus and in the medial nuclei of the tuber cinereum (Marburg). Of all these terminal nuclei only the lateral geniculate body appears to receive fibers concerned with visual perception and gives rise to the geniculocalcarine tract which forms the last relay of the visual path. The other nuclei subserve various optic reflexes. The pretectal area is concerned with the light reflex (p. 351), the superior colliculi with reflex movement of the eyes and head in response to optic stimuli. The retinohypothalamic fibers probably mediate the retinal reflex control of the hypophysis, since the latter receives fibers from the supraoptic hypothalamic nucleus. In lower vertebrates this fiber pathway may regulate the distribution of pigment in the melanophores (pigment cells) of the skin in response to different light intensities. In man the significance of these fibers is obscure.

The *geniculocalcarine* tract arises from the lateral geniculate body, passes through the retrolenticular portion of the internal capsule, and forms the optic radiation which ends in the striate area (area 17) located on the medial surface of the occipital lobe on either side of the calcarine fissure (Fig. 335). The fibers of this radiation do not all reach the cortex by the shortest route (Figs. 329, 330). The most dorsal fibers pass almost directly backward to the striate area. Those placed more ventrally first turn forward and downward into the temporal lobe, spread out over the tip of the inferior horn, then loop backward, and running close to the outer wall of the lateral ventricle (external sagittal stratum) reach the occipital cortex. The more ventral the fiber, the longer is the loop, the most ventral ones extending to the uncus region of the temporal lobe before turning back.

The retinal areas have a precise point-to-

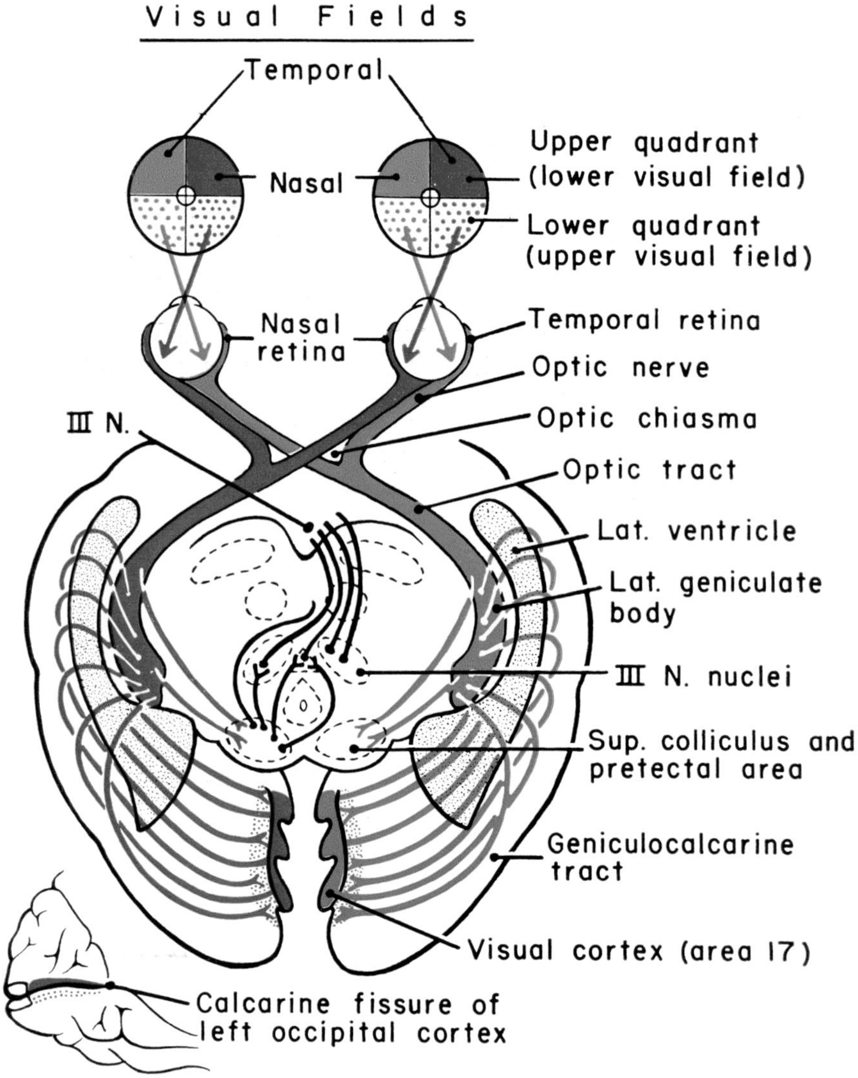

FIG. 329. Diagram of visual pathways. Note projection of visual fields upon retina and cortex. Fibers of pupillary light reflex are indicated on left side of midbrain. Insert shows quadrants of right visual field projected schematically on left visual (calcarine) cortex. Macular vision (uncolored) is most posterior on cortex. (Modified from Haymaker.)

point relationship with the lateral geniculate body, each retinal portion projecting on a specific and topographically limited portion of the geniculate. The fibers from the upper retinal quadrants (representing the lower visual field) terminate in the medial half; those from the lower quadrants in the lateral half of the geniculate body. The macular fibers occupy the central portion, flanked medially and laterally by fibers from the paracentral and peripheral retinal areas. A similar point-to-point relation exists between the geniculate body and the striate cortex. The medial half of the lateral geniculate body representing the upper quadrants (lower visual field) projects to the dorsal lip of the calcarine fissure, the fibers forming the dorsal portion of the optic radiation (Fig. 329). The lateral half of the lateral geniculate body, representing

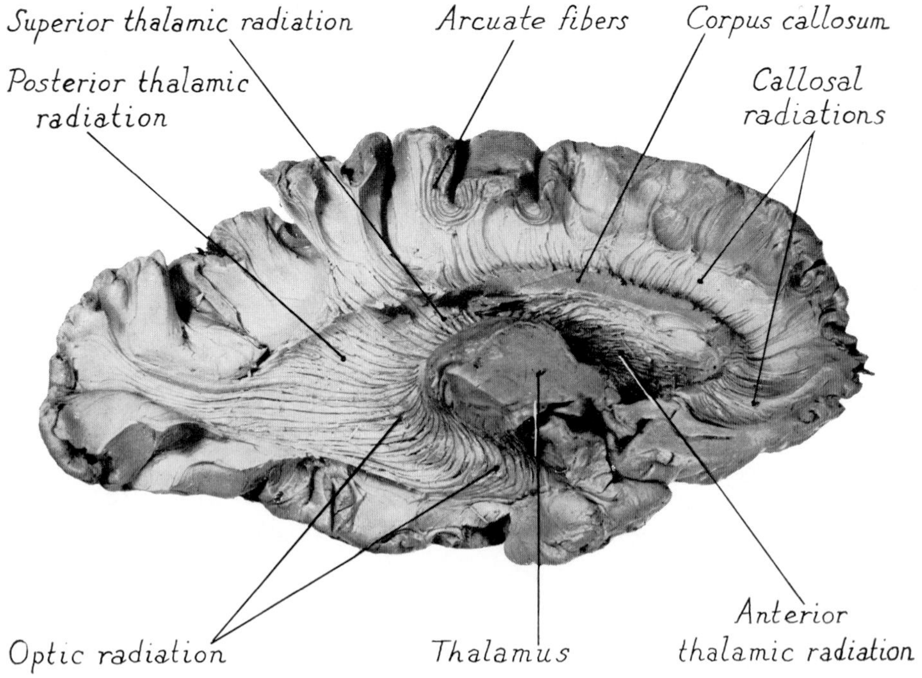

FIG. 330. Dissection of brain from medial surface, showing internal capsule (thalamic radiations) and portion of callosal radiation. Photograph.

the lower retinal quadrants (upper visual field) projects to the ventral lip of the calcarine fissure. These fibers occupy the ventral portion of the optic radiation. The macular fibers which constitute the intermediate half of the optic radiation, terminate in the caudal third of the calcarine cortex, those from the paracentral and peripheral retinal areas end in respectively more rostral portions.

Clinical considerations. Injury to any part of the optic pathway produces visual defects whose nature depends on the location and extent of the injury. During examination each eye is covered in turn as the retinal quadrants of the opposite eye are tested. Visual defects are said to be *homonymous* when restricted to a single visual field, right or left; *heteronymous* when parts of both fields are involved. It is evident that homonymous defects will be caused by lesions on one side placed anywhere behind the chiasma, i.e., optic tract, geniculate body, optic radiation, and visual cortex. Complete destruction of any of these structures results in a loss of the whole opposite field of vision (*homonymous hemianopsia* (Fig. 331C)), partial injury produces *quadrantic homonymous* defects. Lesions of the temporal lobe by compressing or destroying the looping fibers in the lower portion of the optic radiation are likely to produce such quadrantic defects in the upper visual field. Injury to the parietal lobe may involve the more dorsally placed fibers of the radiation and cause similar defects in the lower field of vision.

Lesions of the chiasma may cause several kinds of heteronymous defects. Most commonly the crossing fibers from the nasal portions of the retina are involved, with consequent loss of the two temporal fields of vision (*bitemporal hemianopsia* (Fig. 331D)). In rare cases both lateral angles of the chiasma may be compressed, affecting the non-decussating fibers from the temporal retinae and resulting in a loss of the nasal visual fields (*binasal hemianopsia*). Injury

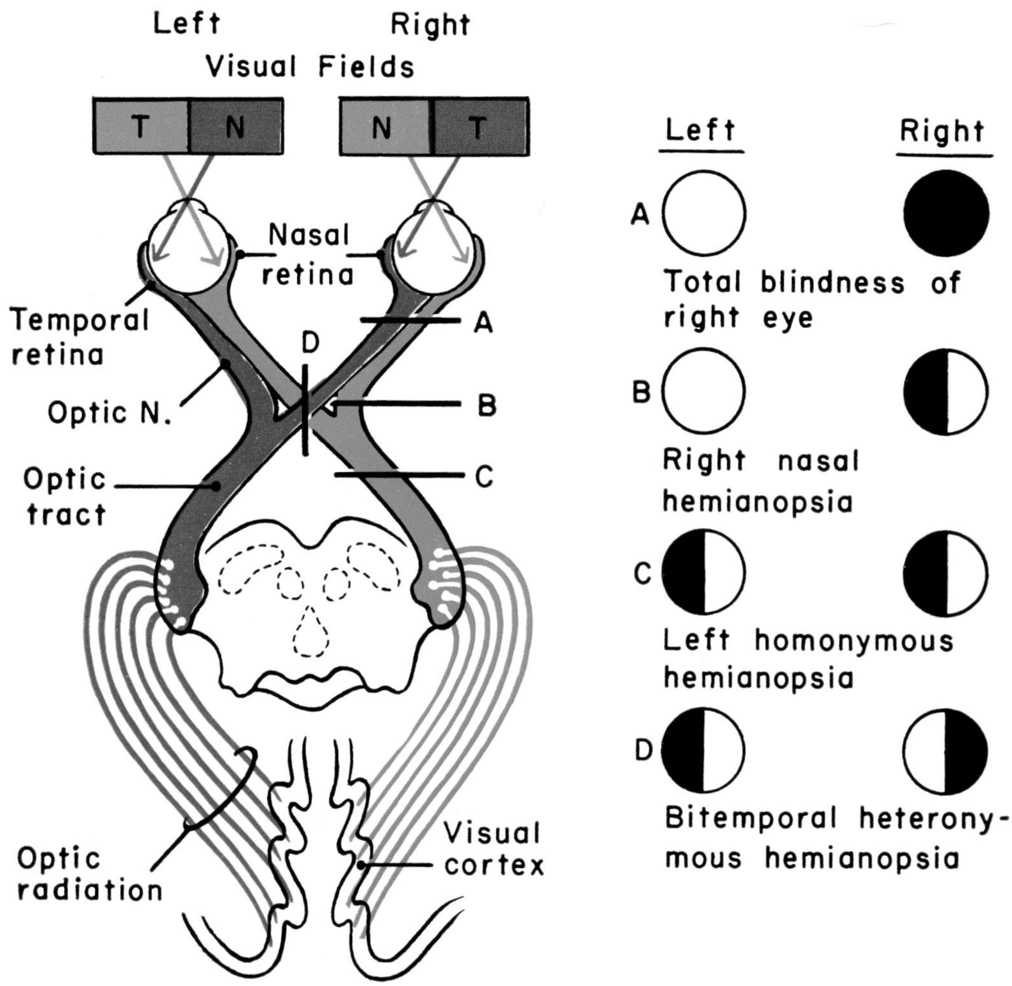

FIG. 331. Diagram of common lesions within the visual pathway. On the left A-D indicates lesions. Corresponding visual field defects are shown on the right (Modified from Haymaker).

of one optic nerve naturally produces blindness in the corresponding eye with loss of the pupillary reflex to light entering that eye (Fig. 331A). The pupil will, however, contract consensually to light entering the other eye, since the pretectal reflex center is related to both Edinger-Westphal nuclei. The pupillary reflex will not be affected by lesions of the visual pathway placed above the superior quadrigeminal brachium (Fig. 329).

THE THALAMUS

The thalamic nuclei and their connections. The thalamus is divided by a vertical plate of fibers, the internal medullary lamina, into a medial and a lateral portion each containing several nuclear masses.

The nuclei are particularly difficult to visualize in three dimensions. In addition, the nomenclature is complex, and in some instances the fiber connections and significance of the smaller thalamic nuclei remain unknown. In a general way, depending upon their fiber connections, the thalamic nuclei may be classified functionally as either specific relay (R) or specific association (A) centers. Additional scattered nuclei have diffuse cortical and subcortical connections (D), while other small cell groups with unknown connections still remain unclassified (?). Russell (1955), in an attempt to simplify the thalamus for the student, employed the following combined functional and morphological classification:

A. Anterior Nuclear Group
   1. **Nucleus anterior (R)**
   2. Nucleus anterodorsalis (R)
B. Medial Nuclear Group
   1. **Nucleus medialis dorsalis**
      a. para parvocellularis (A)
      b. pars magnocellularis (?)
C. Midline Nuclear Group
   1. Nucleus parataenialis (?D)
   2. Nucleus paraventricularis (?D)
   3. Nucleus reuniens (?D)
   4. Nucleus rhomboideus (?D)
D. Intralaminar Nuclear Group
   1. Nucleus centrum medianum (D)
   2. Nucleus parafascicularis (D)
   3. Nucleus paracentralis (D)
   4. Nucleus centralis lateralis (D)
   5. Nucleus centralis medialis (D)
E. Lateral Nuclear Group
   Pars Dorsalis
   1. **Nucleus lateralis posterior (A)**
   2. **Nucleus lateralis dorsalis (A)**
   3. **Pulvinar (A)**
   Pars ventralis
   4. **Nucleus ventralis anterior (R and D?)**
   5. **Nucleus ventralis lateralis (R)**
   6. Nucleus ventralis ventralis (R)
   7. **Nucleus ventralis posterior (R)**
      a. **Posterolateralis** (pars lateralis)
      b. **Posteromedialis** (pars medialis, arcuatus)
F. Metathalamus
   1. **Corpus geniculatus laterale (R)**
   2. **Corpus geniculatus mediale (R)**
G. Miscellaneous unclassified nuclei
   1. Nucleus submedius (?)
   2. Nucleus suprageniculatus (?)
   3. Nucleus limitans (?)
   4. **Nucleus reticularis thalami (D?)**

The most important nuclei which are considered in the instruction of the functional systems are set in bold face type while less prominent nuclei are set in regular type. The nucleus reticularis thalami (G4) is properly a nucleus of the subthalamus and reticular formation rather than of the thalamus, but is included here by tradition and general usage.

The major thalamic nuclei are presented schematically and identified in Fig. 334. In this same figure the major afferent and efferent fiber connections of each nucleus are included. For example, the ascending medial lemniscus and spinothalamic tracts (Figs. 185, 190, 191) are shown terminating in the ventral posterior nucleus (posterolateral nucleus) of Fig. 334B. The efferent thalamic impulses of this nucleus are then relayed to the sensory area of the cerebral cortex as shown in Fig. 335. The cortical areas are indicated in this simplified manner for the other important nuclei of the thalamus. Such incoming and outgoing nerve fibers of the thalamus form conspicuous diencephalic pathways. Some of the fiber bundles can be identified macroscopically (e.g., brachium conjunctivum, internal capsule). Others can only be observed in stained microscopic sections.

The medial portion comprises the *anterior* and the *dorsomedial* (*medial*) *thalamic nucleus*. The lateral portion, lying between the internal and external medullary lamina, is divided into two tiers or étages, the ventral tier composed of the *ventral nucleus*, the dorsal tier comprising the *lateral nucleus* which does not extend rostrally as far as the ventral one. Caudally these become continuous with the *pulvinar* and the *geniculate bodies* which form the hindmost nuclei of the lateral portion, the pulvinar belonging to the dorsal tier, the geniculates to the ventral tier (Fig. 334A).

The *anterior nucleus* lies beneath the dorsal surface of the most rostral part of the thalamus where it forms a distinct swelling, the anterior tubercle. It consists of a large main nucleus (anteroventral) and several clumps of cells consituting the accessory anterior nucleus (anterodorsal). The rounded or polygonal cells composing the nucleus are of medium or small size, with

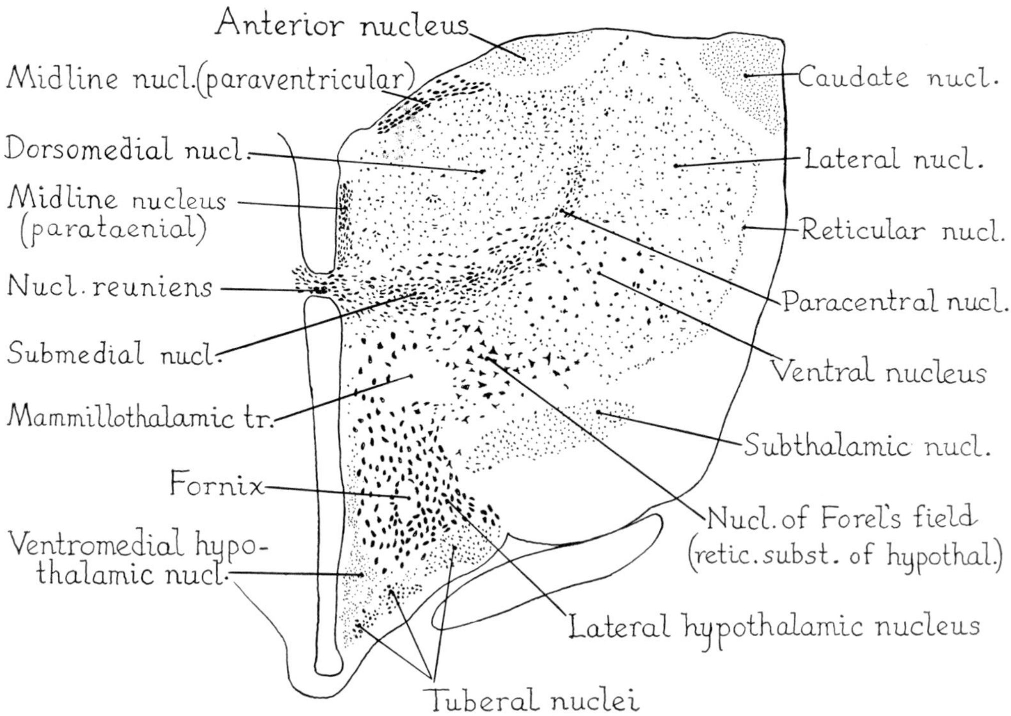

FIG. 332. Transverse section through interbrain at level of tuber cinereum. Nissl stain. (Modified from Malone.)

little chromophilic substance and a moderate amount of yellow pigment. The anterior nucleus receives the stout mammillothalamic tract and sends fibers to the mammillary body by the same bundle (thalamomammillary Fig. 334B). It sends a strong projection through the anterior limb of the internal capsule to the gyrus cinguli (areas 23, 24, 32) and probably receives fibers from the same areas (Meyer et al., 1947; Freeman and Watts, 1948). Fibers to the habenular ganglion via the stria medullaris, and to the caudate nucleus have also been described by some investigators.

The large *dorsomedial* (*medial*) *nucleus* occupies most of the space between the internal medullary lamina and the periventricular gray (Figs. 48, 332, 334A). It is composed of a small ventromedial magnocellular portion containing fairly large polygonal deeply staining cells, and a larger dorsolateral portion of smaller, paler staining cells. The nucleus has extensive connections with the centromedian and other intralaminar nuclei and with the lateral nuclear groups. The magnocellular portion is related reciprocally to the hypothalamus and the periventricular gray, and sends fibers to the orbital cortex. The much larger parvocellular portion is connected by a massive projection with practically the entire frontal cortex rostral to areas 6 and 32 (Meyer et al., 1947; Freeman and Watts, 1948).

The *midline nuclei* are more or less distinct cell clusters which lie in the periventricular gray matter of the dorsal half of the ventricular wall and in the massa intermedia (Figs. 332, 333, 334). They are small and difficult to delimit in man but in the lower vertebrates they, together with some of the intralaminar nuclei, form the largest part of the thalamus (paleothalamus). They consist of small fusiform, rather darkly

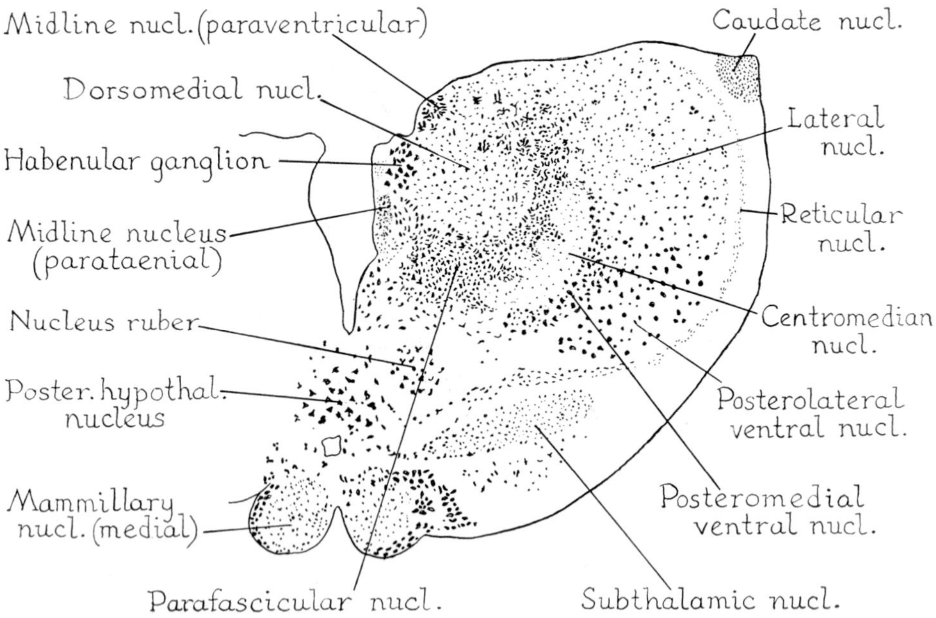

FIG. 333. Transverse section through interbrain at level of habenulae and mammillary bodies. Nissl stain. (Modified from Malone.)

staining cells resembling preganglionic autonomic neurons (Malone), and hence are believed to be concerned with visceral activities. Their scanty connections are mainly with the hypothalamic region by finely myelinated and unmyelinated fibers which run in the periventricular gray substance. They are also related to the magnocellular portion of the dorsomedial nucleus and to the intralaminar nuclei. The more distinct of the midline cell groups include the *parataenial nucleus* near the stria medullaris, and the *paraventricular nucleus* in the dorsal ventricular wall. In an attempt to homologize these ill defined nuclei with the more strongly developed nuclei of lower mammals, some authorities recognize several cell groups in this periventricular gray: the *nucleus reuniens*, the *rhomboidal nucleus*, and the *median central nucleus*. They are difficult to distinguish in man.

The *intralaminar nuclei* (Figs. 332, 333) are diffuse cell groups of variable extent infiltrating the internal medullary lamina, which separates the medial from the lateral thalamic mass. Their cells, though varying in size in the different nuclei, are usually fusiform and darkly staining, and resemble those of the midline nuclei. Their fiber connections are diffuse and difficult to work out (Fig. 334B).

While most of the intralaminar nuclei are small and their boundaries indistinct, the *centromedian* or *central nucleus* is a large and sharply defined cell group. This prominent nucleus is located in the middle third of the thalamus between the dorsomedial nucleus above and the ventral nucleus below (Figs. 48, 333). It is almost completely surrounded by fibers of the internal medullary lamina, except at its medial border where it merges by interdigitations with the parafascicular nucleus (Fig. 333). It is composed of small, loosely arranged ovoid or rounded cells containing a considerable amount of yellow pigment. The nucleus has extensive connections with adjacent thalamic nuclei, receives a fiber contingent from the brachium conjunctivum (Hassler, 1950), and sends a strong projection to the putamen

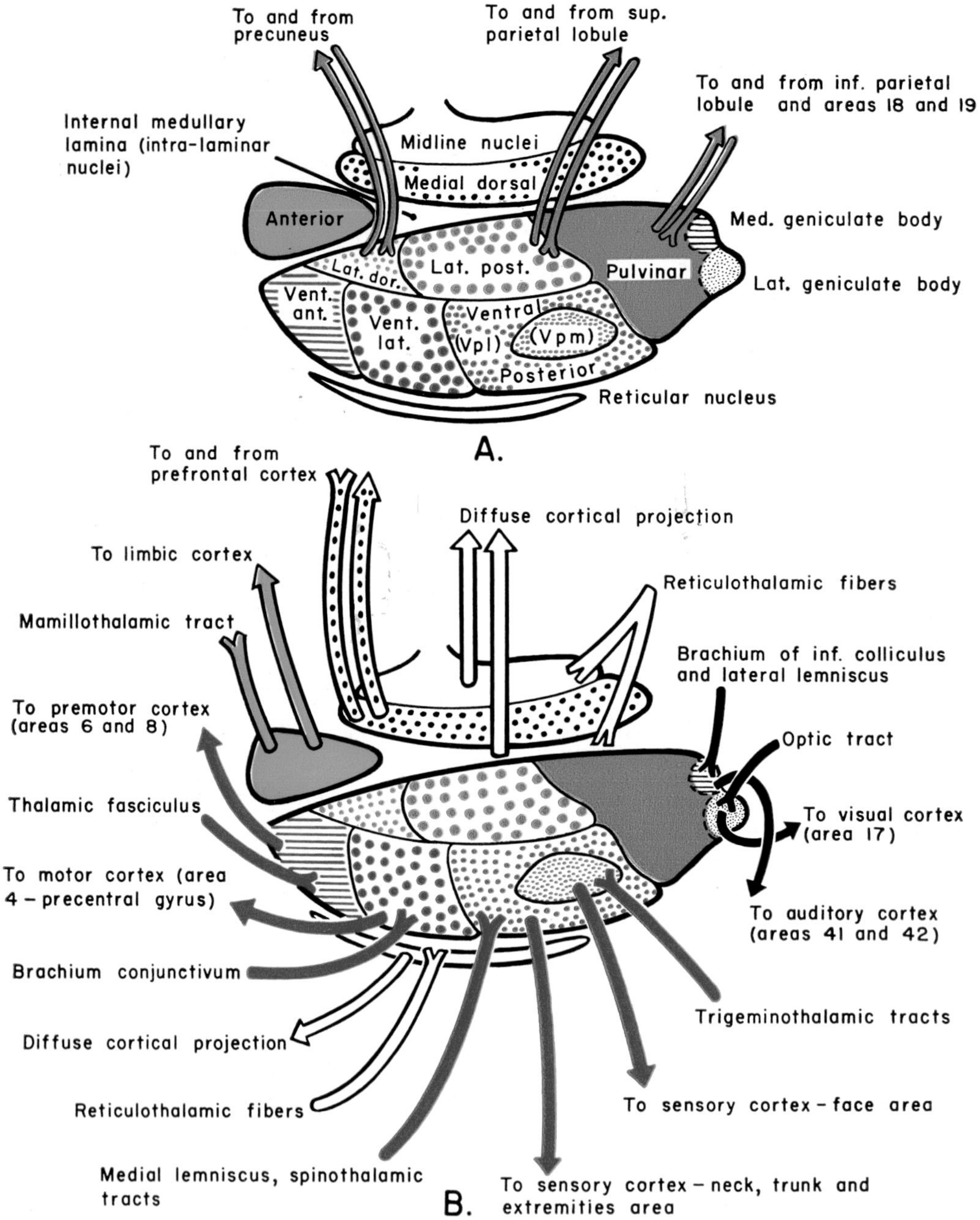

Fig. 334. Diagram of major thalamic nuclei. Dorsolateral view. A. identification of nuclei of left thalamus; B. principal afferent and efferent fiber connections of thalamic nuclei. The ventral posteromedial (vpm) and larger ventral posterolateral (vpl) nuclear subdivisions of the ventral posterior nucleus are indicated. Medial and lateral geniculate bodies (metathalamus), and reticular nuclei are included. Schema and colors correspond to those of Fig. 335.

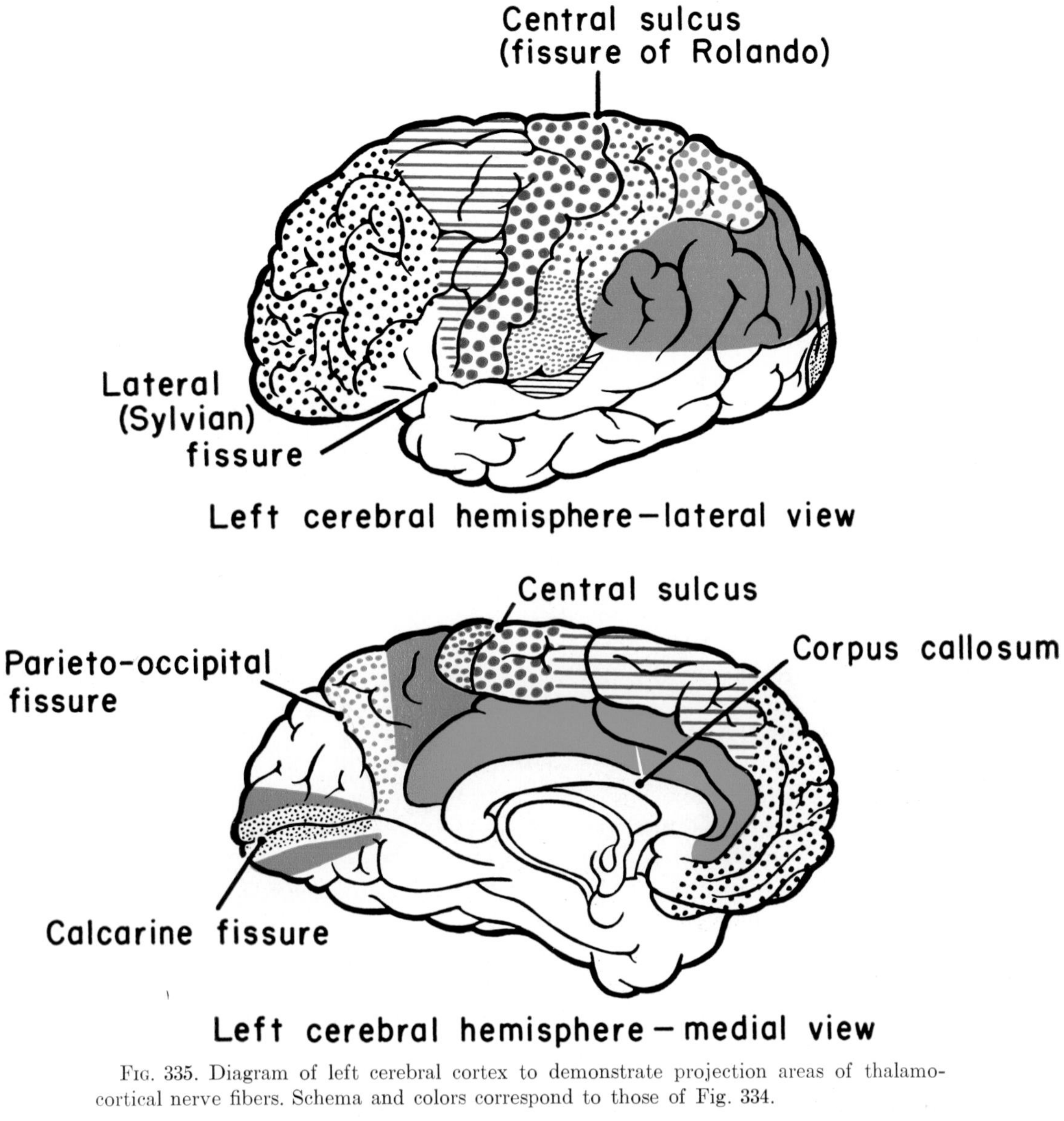

FIG. 335. Diagram of left cerebral cortex to demonstrate projection areas of thalamo-cortical nerve fibers. Schema and colors correspond to those of Fig. 334.

and caudate nucleus (McLardy, 1948; Freeman and Watts, 1947). It also receives collaterals of sensory fibers from the secondary trigeminal tracts and medial lemniscus. Le Gros Clark (1932) regards the centromedian nucleus as an expanded intralaminar cell group, prominent in primates and man, and constituting a complex intrathalamic integrating mechanism.

Functionally related to the intralaminar cell groups is the *reticular nucleus*, a thin sheet of rather large dark staining polygonal cells lying between the external medullary lamina and the internal capsule (Figs. 333, 334B). It envelops the entire lateral periphery of the thalamus, and also extends over the rostral surface where it apparently fuses with the most oral tip of the ventral anterior nucleus. Ventrally it becomes continuous with the zona incerta. It is believed to be a derivative of the subthalamus (Kuhlenbeck, 1948).

The intralaminar and midline nuclei have constituted for a long time a rather unexplored region of the thalamus. In man and primates especially, many of these nuclei are small and indistinct, and their fiber systems difficult to work out. They were regarded as having no cortical connections, their associations being primarily with other thalamic nuclei, with the corpus striatum, the subthalamus, the hypothalamus, and the mesencephalic reticular formation. Recent intensive electrophysiological studies in the cat and monkey have demonstrated that these cell groups have widespread though diffuse cortical projections. These same cortical areas receive specific projections as well from the larger thalamic nuclei. (Jasper, 1949; Jasper et al., 1952; Starzl and Magoun, 1951). These diffuse or non-specific cortical afferents have the remarkable property of regulating the rhythmic electrical activity of the cortex, and their stimulation evokes the so-called recruiting or activating response in extensive cortical areas (Fig. 334B). Jasper and his associates have obtained this activating effect upon cortical activity from the reticular nucleus, especially its rostral portion; from the rostral pole of the anterior ventral nucleus; from all the intralaminar nuclei including the centromedian; from the suprageniculate nucleus and from the more indistinct cell groups of the midline. Similar results have been reported by Starzl and Magoun (1951). These diffuse projections are quite independent of the more concentrated projections from the specific thalamic nuclei, and the recruiting responses can still be obtained after destruction of the dorsomedial, the ventral, and the lateral nuclear groups. On the other hand, relatively small destruction of the diffuse projection system in the rostral thalamus will abolish the generalized responses, even though the specific projection nuclei are not affected (Hanberry and Jasper, 1952).

All these interconnected thalamic cell groups with their diffuse cortical projections have been designated as the *"thalamic reticular system"* (Jasper, 1949) which constitutes the most rostral portion of the ascending reticular system. Caudally it is in intimate relation with the reticular centers of the midbrain and basal diencephalon, and like the latter it receives overlapping projections from extensive cortical areas (Jasper et al., 1952). The reticular complexes of the subthalamus and midbrain affect the electrical activities of the cortex in a generalized manner. However, the thalamic reticular system appears to be a more differentiated portion which exerts its activating influence on more restricted cortical areas. In general, though not in all instances, the medial and rostral cell groups project to the frontal regions, the caudal and lateral to the parietal, occipital, and temporal regions.

The lateral nucleus begins as a narrow strip some distance from the anterior limit of the thalamus, enlarges posteriorly and merges caudally with the pulvinar. It consists of two smaller gray masses, the lateral dorsal and lateral posterior nuclei (Fig. 334A). The boundaries between the two nuclei are indistinct. These nuclei receive few ascending sensory fibers, but they do possess reciprocal connections with a rather extensive area of the cortex. The lateral dorsal nucleus sends and receives fibers from the precuneal cortex, while the lateral posterior nucleus is intimately connected with the superior parietal lobule (areas 5 and 7) and supramarginal gyrus (Figs. 334A, 335). A few fibers may go to the postcentral and precentral region. Its internuclear connections are primarily with the ventral and medial thalamic nuclei.

The pulvinar is a large nuclear mass forming the posterior portion of the thalamus. Caudally it overhangs the geniculate bodies and dorsolateral surface of the midbrain. It is usually divided into a narrower lateral portion lying above the lateral geniculate body and containing clumps of rather large deeply staining cells, and a larger medial portion composed of more compactly arranged small polygonal cells. The pulvinar does not receive any ascending sensory fibers but has internuclear relations with other thalamic nuclei, especially the medial and lateral geniculate bodies and the dorsomedial nucleus. It is connected in both directions with the supramarginal and angular convolutions, with the superior parietal lobule and with the occipital and posterior temporal portions of the cortex (areas 18, 19 and 7, Figs. 334A, 335).

The *ventral nuclear mass* consists of a most rostral portion, the *ventral anterior nucleus*; a larger middle portion, the *ventral lateral nucleus*; and a caudal portion, the *ventral posterior nucleus.* The *ventral anterior nucleus* receives fibers from the globus pallidus by way of the lenticular and thalamic fasciculi. It was formerly believed to have no cortical connections, but recent investigations indicate that it sends a fiber projection to the frontal cortex and perhaps also to other cortical areas (Figs. 334B, 335). It is part of the so-called "thalamic reticular system" (Jasper et al., 1952; Starzl and Magoun, 1951).

The *ventral lateral nucleus* receives the fibers from the cerebellum, i.e., the dentatothalamic and rubrothalamic fibers, and is connected with the motor area (area 4) of the cortex and to a lesser extent with the premotor (area 6). There appears to be a definite topographical representation within the nucleus, the most medial portion projecting to the cortical face area, the next to the arm area, and the most lateral part to the leg area.

The *ventral posterior nucleus* whose cells are among the largest in the thalamus is composed of two portions, *posteromedial* and *posterolateral* (Fig. 333). The former, also known as the arcuate or semilunar nucleus, receives the secondary trigeminal tracts. The posterolateral is the end station for the medial lemniscus and spinothalamic tracts (Figs. 334B, 335). These nuclei project to the postcentral gyrus (areas 3, 2, 1). The face area of the cortex receives fibers from the posteromedial nucleus; the arm area from the medial portion, and the leg area from the lateral portion of the posterolateral nucleus.

The medial and lateral geniculate bodies may be considered as the caudal continuations of the ventral nuclear mass and like the latter receive terminals of sensory tracts. The *medial geniculate body* consists of a ventral nucleus of large closely packed polygonal cells, and a dorsal nucleus of more loosely arranged smaller cells (Malone). The nucleus, especially its dorsal portion, receives the auditory fibers from the cochlear nuclei and inferior colliculus. The main connection is with the superior temporal convolution (transverse gyrus of Heschl) by the geniculotemporal or auditory radiation (Figs. 334B, 335). It also appears to be related by fibers to the ventral and lateral thalamic nuclei, and to the pulvinar. The ventral portion of the nucleus sends fibers to the subthalamic region and by way of Gudden's commissure to the opposite medial geniculate and perhaps to lower portions of the brain stem (Rioch). Embryologically it appears to be a derivative of the subthalamus.

The lateral geniculate body, intimately associated with the optic tract, consists in most mammals of a dorsal and a ventral nucleus. The former is connected with the ventral thalamic nucleus, pulvinar, and area striata of the cortex. The ventral nucleus apparently represents a subthalamic structure related to the zona incerta. In man the ventral nucleus is represented by scattered cells lying medial to the main nucleus among the entering fibers of the optic tract. The principal nucleus is a lamellated mass the shape of a horseshoe whose hilus is directed ventromedially (Fig. 336). It is composed of six concentrically arranged cell layers separated by intervening fiber bands. The four outer layers consist of small and me-

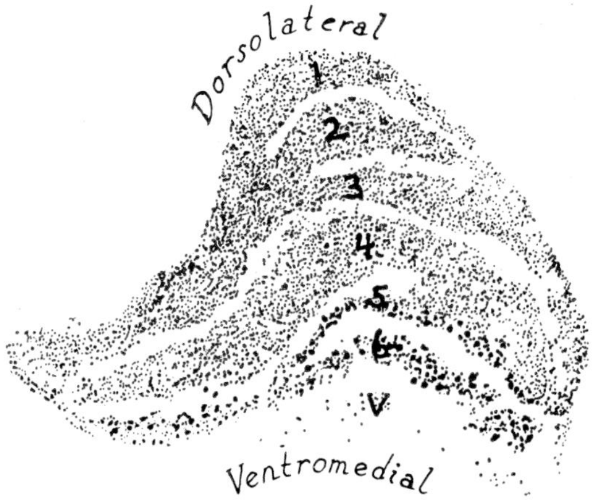

Fig. 336. The cellular laminae of the lateral geniculate body. *v*, scattered cells ("ventral" nucleus) in basal medullary layer. (After Rose.)

dium sized cells; in the two narrower, innermost layers the cells are large and more loosely arranged (magnocellular nucleus of Malone). Phylogenetically, the nucleus first differentiates into three cell layers, and becomes six-layered in forms where the optic tracts show only a partial decussation, the uncrossed and crossed portions each using three alternate lamina (Minkowski, Le Gros Clark).

The lateral geniculate nucleus is the main end station of the optic tract and sends a strong projection to the calcarine cortex (area 17) by the geniculocalcarine or visual radiation, also receiving corticogeniculate fibers from the same area. Its internuclear connections are with the pulvinar, and with the ventral and lateral thalamic nuclei. It also sends fibers to the superior colliculi and pretectal area by way of the superior quadrigeminal brachium.

Functional considerations. All sensory impulses, with the sole exception of the olfactory ones, terminate in the gray masses of the thalamus from which they are projected to specific cortical areas by the thalamocortical radiations. Even the olfactory impulses which go directly to the older olfactory cortex are secondarily brought in relation with the anterior thalamic nuclei. Yet a consideration of its structure and connections strongly suggests that the thalamus is far more than a mere relay station for the various sensory paths to the pallium. Such stations appear to be adequately provided for by the ventral thalamic nuclei and by the geniculate bodies. There still remain the bulk of the thalamic nuclei, a large part of the thalamocortical fibers, all the corticothalamic fibers, and the intrathalamic association fibers. It seems certain therefore that the thalamus is itself a sensory integrating organ of great complexity. The relatively simple impulses from the periphery do not pass through it unchanged, but are associated and synthesized on a "thalamic" level of greater or lesser complexity before being projected to the pallium. It has been pointed out by Head and Holmes, Foerster and others that crude sensory modalities such as touch, temperature, and pain may be separately injured below the thalamic level. Above that level these sensory impulses become intimately fused and can no longer be individually segregated. If this is true, the sensory cortex has no direct association with the peripheral sense organs and must depend for its activities on sensory material already modified and integrated in the thalamus. In animals which have no pallium, or but a poorly developed one, the thalamus undoubtedly constitutes the highest sensory correlation center in which somatic and visceral impulses are blended and integrated into more complex entities. Such impulses are then referred to visceral and somatic effectors by way of the hypothalamus and the forebrain basal ganglia.

There is moreover considerable clinical evidence verified by post mortem studies (Head and others) that the activities of the thalamus are related to consciousness. The thalamus represents the neurological substratum of a crude sort of awareness such as the recognition of touch (mere contact), temperature and pain, and of the affective quality of sensation, i.e., its pleasantness or unpleasantness. In certain lesions of the thalamus or of the thalamocortical connections, after a brief initial stage of complete contralateral anesthesia, pain, crude touch, and much of temperature sense return. However, tactile localization, two-point discrimination, and the sense of position and movement are lost or severely impaired. The sensations recovered are poorly localized and are accompanied by a great increase in "feeling tone", most commonly of an unpleasant character. Though the threshold of excitability is raised on the affected side, tactile and thermal stimuli previously not unpleasant, now evoke the most disagreeable sensations (dysesthesias) not easily characterized by the patient. He can not endure innocuous cutaneous stimulation, yet can not tell the nature of the exciting stimulus. Occasionally the reverse occurs, a previously indifferent stimulus evoking a most pleasant feeling. These feeling states may even be induced by other sensations as for instance auditory ones (Head). Thus one patient could not go to church because listening to the hymns produced the most disagreeable sensations on his affected side. The dysesthesias may become intensified into spontaneous intractable pains which appear spasmodically, often without any apparent peripheral irritation. The pains are difficult to localize and do not respond even to powerful narcotic drugs.

It has already been stated that there are two aspects to sensation: the discriminative and the affective. In the former, stimuli are compared as to intensity, locality and relative position in space and time, i.e., they are localized, discriminated, and integrated into perceptions of form, size, and texture; movements are judged as to extent, direction, and sequence. It is this aspect which is primarily related to cortical function and is affected by cortical lesions, and by lesions of certain sensory paths and their particular thalamic nuclei. On the other hand there is the "affective" side of sensation: pain, agreeableness and disagreeableness. Pain is naturally nearly all "affect" except perhaps its localization and intensity, temperature and many tactile sensations likewise have a marked affective tone. This is especially true for all visceral sensations in which the discriminative element is practically absent. This affective quality which forms the basis of general bodily well being or of *malaise*, and of the more intense emotional states is believed to be "appreciated" by the thalamus rather than the cortex, though profoundly modified and controlled by the latter. The appreciation of pain, crude touch and much of temperature is retained even after complete destruction of the sensory cortical areas of both sides.

The thalamus is played upon by two great streams of afferent fibers: the peripheral and the cortical. The former bring sensory impulses from all parts of the body informing the thalamus of any changes in the external and internal environment of the individual. The cortical connections link the thalamus to the associative memory mechanism of the pallium and bring it under cortical control. The thalamus has efferent subcortical connections with the hypothalamus and corpus striatum through which thalamic influence may be referred to visceral and somatic effectors. The reactions mediated by this efferent thalamic pathway are primarily affective ones, characterized by immediate and excessive movements, secretory, vasomotor and other visceral changes, in contrast to discriminative ones which are precise, not excessive, and often delayed. It is evident that this pathway, like the thalamus itself, is under the control of the cerebral cortex.

The significance of the corticothalamic fibers has been variously interpreted. They are considered as inhibiting thalamic activity and their interruption causes a thalamic release evidenced by the dysesthesias described above (Head and Holmes). According to Foerster the whole thalamostriate mechanism is involved in this release from cortical inhibition. It would seem however that in addition a more positive function should be assigned to the corticothalamic fibers. For example, the perception of emotion-arousing objects exerts a strong influence on visceral structures. It is very probable that the efferent pathway for this involves corticothalamic neurons. Some believe that the sensory changes are due to injury of the thalamus itself, either by irritation of the thalamic cells or interference with the intrathalamic associations. Brouwer and others have suggested that the corticothalamic fibers constitute a mechanism for the selective regulation of thalamic sensibility, permitting the more efficient functioning of one center while inhibiting the activity of others.

The significance of the individual thalamic nuclei can only be surmised from a consideration of their fiber connections. In a general way the lateral part of the thalamus is related to somatic, the medial part to visceral functions. In the lateral mass the ventral nucleus and the geniculate bodies which receive the ascending sensory fibers probably send crude integrations to the primary sensory and motor areas. The lateral dorsal and posterior nuclei which receive fibers from the ventral nuclei are apparently concerned with more complex somesthetic associations relating the various parts of the body, which are then projected to the parietal association areas. The pulvinar which receives geniculate fibers as well, integrates body sense with the special senses of vision and hearing and projects to the posterior parietal and occipitotemporal region. Thus the lateral thalamic mass is primarily concerned with simple or more complex integrations of somatic sensory impulses, to be used for the discriminative activities of the pallium.

In the medial half, the midline and most of the intralaminar nuclei are phylogenetically the oldest nuclei which practically make up the thalamus of lower vertebrates. They form an interconnected group, the thalamic reticular system, which through diffuse projections influences the basic electrical activities of the cortex. It has access to a variety of afferent impulses, many of them coming from visceral structures and representing the more elementary and affective forms of sensations. It is related to the corpus striatum, to the subthalamic and mesencephalic reticular formation, and to the autonomic centers of the hypothalamus. It is possible that this diffuse thalamic system represents the neurological substrate of affective sensibility or consciousness which energizes, and gives incentive and direction to, the complex discriminative activities of the cortex.

There has been much conjecture regarding the significance of the dorsomedial nucleus, the most prominent gray mass of the medial thalamus, which is highly developed in primates and especially in man (Fig. 334). It is connected with the lateral thalamus, the hypothalamus and the corpus striatum, and has moreover a strong reciprocal connection with the frontal granular cortex (Fig. 334B). Head and Holmes believe that through its connections with the lateral thalamus, the nucleus abstracts and is able to appreciate the affective qualities of somatic sensations and to integrate them with the visceral. It has been suggested (Le Gros Clark) that in this nucleus the somatic impulses forming the basis for discriminative cortical sensibility are blended with the feeling tone engendered by visceral activities. These somatovisceral entities are then projected to the prefrontal cortex. The latter constitutes a large phylogenetically new cortical area highly developed only in man. While its significance is not fully understood, it may be regarded as the place where the discriminative cortical activities attain their highest elaboration. Here they are blended with the activities of the hypothalamus and medial thalamus, representing the more primitive affective components of consciousness. Large injuries to the frontal lobes of both hemispheres are likely to cause defects in complex association as well as certain changes in behavior, expressed by loss of acquired inhibitions and more direct and excessive emotional responses. There is evidence that similar alterations in emotional behavior are produced when the pathways between the dorsomedial nucleus and frontal cortex are severed (e.g., in frontal lobotomy).

THE SUBTHALAMUS

The subthalamus, also known as the ventral thalamus, is bounded dorsally by the thalamus, ventrally and laterally by the pes pedunculi and adjacent portion of the internal capsule, medially and rostrally by the hypothalamus (Figs. 48, 318). Caudally it is continuous with the tegmentum and basilar portion of the midbrain, and actually contains the rostral portions of the nucleus ruber and substantia nigra. The more prominent fiber bundles of the subthalamus, many of them fibers of passage, are the tegmental field of Forel (prerubral field, field H), the ansa lenticularis, the fasciculus lenticularis (field H_2), and the fasciculus thalamicus (field H_1) (Fig. 320). The intrinsic gray masses include the subthalamic nucleus, the zona incerta, and the subthalamic reticular nucleus composed of the nucleus of the tegmental field.

The *subthalamic nucleus* or *corpus Luysi* is an ovoid or lense-shaped gray mass composed of fairly large multipolar cells. It is situated at the junction of the subthalamus and midbrain, closely applied to the inner surface of the pes pedunculi or the peduncular portion of the internal capsule (Figs. 317, 333). Poorly defined in lower mammals and even in the monkey, the nucleus is large and distinct in man. It receives fibers from the globus pallidus and the premotor frontal cortex (Meyer, 1949), and sends fibers to the substantia nigra, nucleus ruber, and midbrain tegmentum (Fig. 321). It is related functionally to the corpus striatum, especially the globus pallidus. In man, large isolated lesions of this nucleus may give rise to coarse involuntary movements, especially of the upper extremities, expressed as continuous uncontrollable flinging movements of an arm, a condition known as "hemiballismus".

The *fasciculus lenticularis* and *ansa lenticularis* constitute the whole system of efferent fibers from the globus pallidus (Fig. 320). Many of the efferent pallidal fibers perforate the peduncular portion of the internal capsule and form the lenticular fasciculus. This fasciculus runs medially, in close contact with the inner surface of the internal capsule and with the subthalamic nucleus. Other efferent fibers from the inner segment of the globus pallidus sweep around the medial border of the internal capsule, forming a looped bundle, the ansa lenticularis, which curves dorsally to join the lenticular fasciculus. Some of the fibers from the ansa and the lenticular bundle terminate in the subthalamic nucleus and nucleus of the tegmental field. Others merely pass through the subthalamus to reach the thalamus, hypothalamus, and other nuclear masses of the brain stem (Fig. 321). Scattered along and between the fiber bundles of the ansa are strands of cells which constitute the *nucleus of the ansa lenticularis* or *entopeduncular nucleus*. The cells resemble those of the globus pallidus and are believed to be detached cells of the latter (Fig. 78L). They apparently receive fibers from the putamen and caudate nucleus, and contribute fibers to the ansa lenticularis.

The *fasciculus thalamicus*, closely applied to the ventral surface of the thalamus, has several fiber components. Some are fibers from the lenticular fasciculus which loop laterally, enter the thalamic fascicle and go to the ventral anterior nucleus of the thalamus (Figs. 320, 334B). Others are dentatothalamic and rubrothalamic fibers derived from the capsule of the nucleus ruber, which pass through the tegmental field and thalamic fascicle to the ventral lateral nucleus of the thalamus. Intermingled with these are thalamostriate (and thalamopallidal) fibers from the centromedian and other thalamic nuclei en route to the corpus striatum.

The *tegmental* or *prerubral* field (Fig. 318) is composed of fibers and scattered cells which constitute the *nucleus of the tegmental* or *prerubral field.* Some of the fibers are dentatothalamic and rubrothalamic fibers which continue into the thalamic fasciculus to reach the ventral lateral nucleus of the thalamus. Others are fibers from the lenticular fasciculus which terminate directly or by collaterals in the nucleus of the prerubral field. From this nucleus arise fibers which in part enter the rostral portion of the nucleus ruber, in part go to the reticular formation of the midbrain. The nucleus of the prerubral field together with similar cells scattered along the thalamic and lenticular fasiculi are often referred to as the *subthalamic reticular nucleus.*

The *zona incerta* is a strip of gray matter lying between the thalamic and the lenticular fasciculi. It is composed of diffuse cell groups which laterally become continuous with the reticular nucleus of the thalamus (Figs. 317, 318). The zone receives fibers from the globus pallidus and from the premotor cortex, and is intimately associated with the intralaminar thalamic nuclei, the nucleus ruber, and the midbrain tegmentum. The subthalamic reticular nucleus and the zona incerta have a common origin, and may be regarded as the subthalamic continuation of the mesencephalic reticular formation.

Electrophysiological studies on cats and monkeys have demonstrated that the gray masses of the subthalamus, including the subthalamic nucleus, are important functional components of the brain stem reticular system. They are continuous caudally with the reticular complex of the midbrain, dorsorostrally with the reticular thalamic system. Stimulation of the subthalamus enhances muscular tone, facilitates reflex and cortically induced movements, and induces the electrical recruiting response over widespread cortical areas (Rhines and Magoun, 1946; Magoun, 1952). The subthalamus, together with the adjacent portions of the hypothalamus whose stimulation causes similar responses, have been referred to by some investigators as the "basal diencephalic" portion of the reticular system. A more detailed account of the organization and function of the reticular system is given on pp. 338 and 428.

THE EPITHALAMUS

The epithalamus comprises the pineal body, the habenular trigones, the striae medullares, and the epithelial roof of the third ventricle. The habenular ganglion in man consists of a smaller medial and a larger lateral nucleus. The medial nucleus consists of small, closely packed deeply staining round cells; in the lateral the cells are larger, paler, and more loosely arranged. The ganglion receives the terminals of the stria medullaris and gives origin to the habenulopeduncular tract or fasciculus retroflexus which terminates in the interpeduncular nucleus. The stria medullaris is a complex bundle composed of (1) fibers from the septal and basal olfactory nuclei which receive impulses from the olfactory bulb. (2) Fibers from the hippocampal formation which constitutes a higher cortical olfactory center. These fibers detach themselves from the fornix and join the stria medullaris. (3) Fibers from the anterior thalamic nucleus and also from the globus pallidus (Ranson). Some of the strial fibers cross to the opposite side in the habenular commissure. Thus the stria medullaris, habenula, and fasciculus retroflexus form segments of efferent olfactory pathways, both reflex and cortical (Fig. 316).

The pineal body or epiphysis is a small cone-shaped body attached to the roof of the third ventricle in the region of the posterior commissure. It appears to be a rudimentary gland whose function in the adult is not fully ascertained. It consists of a network of richly vascular connective tissue trabeculae in the meshes of which are found glia cells and cells of a peculiar type, the *pineal* or *epiphysial cells.* These are cells of variable size with a pale nucleus, granular argentophile cytoplasm, and relatively few branching processes. They may represent modified nerve cells since they are not stained by glia stains. True nerve cells do not appear to be present though occasional cells with typical Nissl bodies have been observed by some investigators. The gland is said to receive fibers from the stria medullaris, habenular ganglion, and posterior commissure, the fibers terminating in a plexus between the epiphysial cells.

THE HYPOTHALAMUS

The hypothalamus comprises the ventral wall of the third ventricle below the hypothalamic sulcus, and the structures of the ventricular floor including the optic chiasma, tuber cinereum with infundibulum, and the mammillary bodies. Anteriorly it passes without any definite demarcation into the basal olfactory area (diagonal gyrus of the anterior perforated substance), caudally it is similarly continuous with the central gray matter and tegmentum of the midbrain. It may be conveniently described as extending from the region of the optic chiasma to the caudal tip of the mammillary body (Fig. 337). The region immediately in front of the chiasma, extending to the lamina terminalis and anterior commissure, is known as the *preoptic area* and

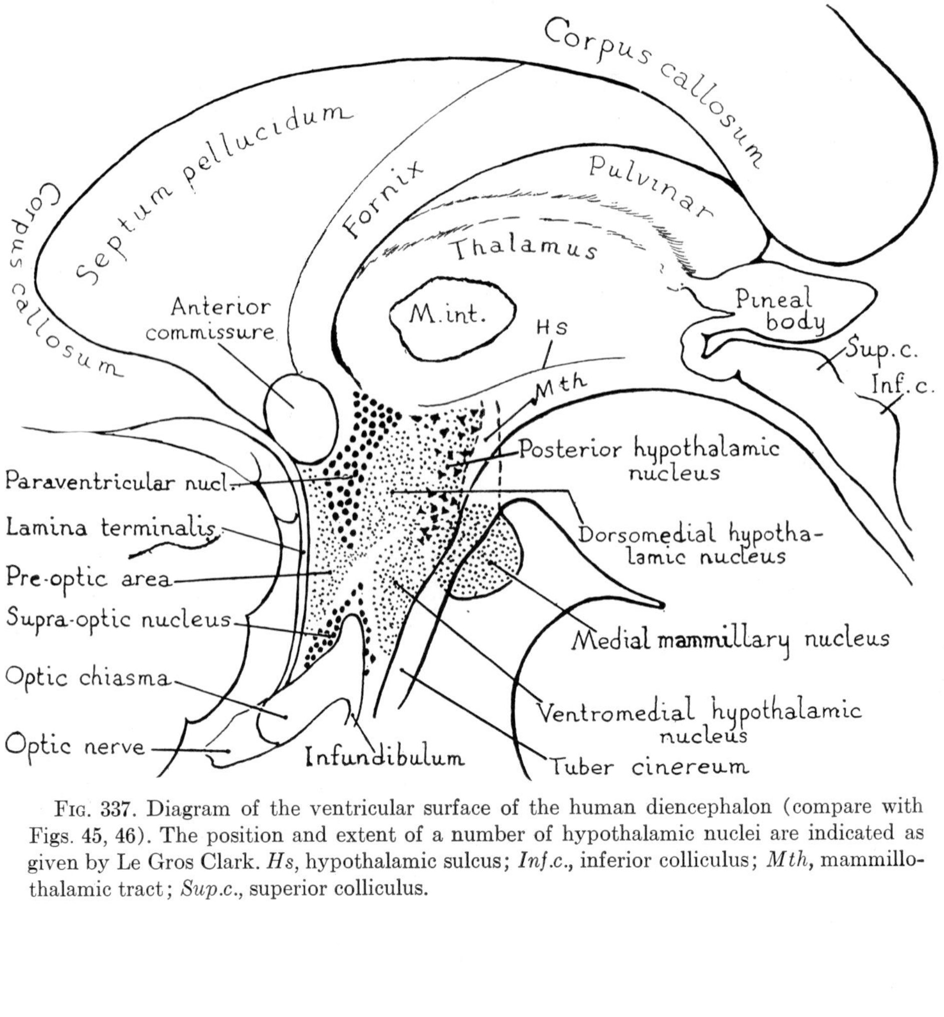

FIG. 337. Diagram of the ventricular surface of the human diencephalon (compare with Figs. 45, 46). The position and extent of a number of hypothalamic nuclei are indicated as given by Le Gros Clark. *Hs*, hypothalamic sulcus; *Inf.c.*, inferior colliculus; *Mth*, mammillothalamic tract; *Sup.c.*, superior colliculus.

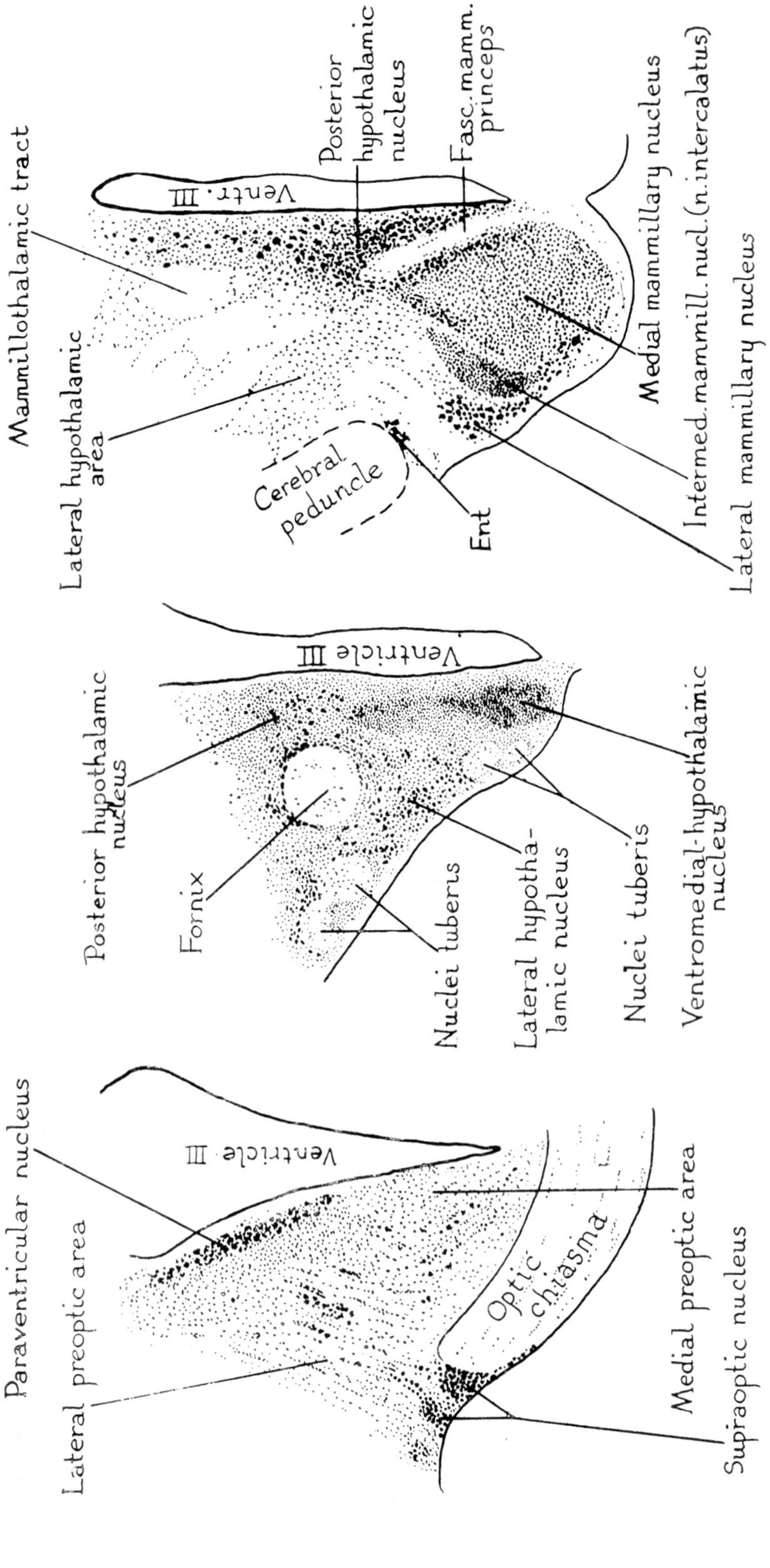

FIG. 338. Transverse sections through supraoptic (*A*), infundibular (*B*), and mammillary (*C*) portions of human hypothalamus. *Ent*, entopeduncular nucleus. (After Le Gros Clark).

though belonging to the endbrain is usually included with the hypothalamic structures. Dorsally the hypothalamus is covered by the thalamus, laterally it is directly continuous with the subthalamic region (Fig. 48).

The hypothalamic nuclei. Pervading the whole area is a diffuse matrix of cells constituting the central gray substance in which are found a number of more or less definitely organized nuclear masses. A sagittal plane passing through the anterior pillar of the fornix roughly separates a medial from a lateral hypothalamic area. The lateral area, which abuts upon the subthalamus and pes pedunculi, is narrow in its rostral and caudal portion, but in the region of the tuber it expands considerably (Fig. 338). It contains scattered groups of large darkly staining cells, the *lateral hypothalamic nucleus*, and two or three sharply delimited circular cell groups known as the *nuclei tuberis*, which often produce small visible eminences on the basal surface of the hypothalamus. They consist of small pale multipolar cells surrounded by a delicate fiber capsule about which are found the large cells of the lateral hypothalamic nucleus (Figs. 337, 338).

In a cephalocaudal direction three hypothalamic regions may be conveniently recognized: (1) an anterior or *supraoptic*, lying above the chiasma and continuous in front with the preoptic area, (2) a middle or *tuberal*, and (3) a caudal or *mammillary* region, continuous behind with the central gray of the iter.

The poorly differentiated preoptic area forms the central gray of the most rostral part of the third ventricle. Le Gros Clark distinguishes a medial preoptic nucleus of rather densely grouped small cells, and a lateral nucleus in which the medium sized cells are more diffusely arranged (Fig. 337).

The supraoptic region contains two of the most striking and sharply defined hypothalamic nuclei, the *paraventricular* and the *supraoptic nucleus*, which have certain common features as to cell structure and fiber connections (Figs. 337, 338). They are both composed of large, often bipolar, deeply staining cells. These neurons frequently possess several nuclei. The Nissl substance is peripherally distributed, and in the cytoplasm are found inclusions of colloidal material regarded by some as evidence of secretory activity. Both nuclei send fibers to the posterior lobe of the hypophysis. The paraventricular nucleus is a fairly broad, flat vertical plate of densely packed cells occupying a considerable portion of the dorsal hypothalamic wall. Ventrally it extends almost to the optic chiasma, dorsally to the hypothalamic sulcus where it comes in relation with the midline nuclei of the thalamus. The supraoptic nucleus is ventrally placed and straddles the lateral portion of the optic chiasma. Scattered isolated cells or small cell groups appear to form an incomplete bridge between the two nuclei. The less differentiated central gray of this region is also known as the *anterior hypothalamic nucleus* which merges imperceptibly with the preoptic area.

In the tuberal region the hypothalamus reaches its widest extent, the fornix separating a medial from the lateral hypothalamic area already described. The medial portion forms the central gray substance of the ventricular wall in which there may be distinguished a *ventromedial* and a *dorsomedial nucleus* poorly delimited from each other (Le Gros Clark, Fig. 337). They are composed of uniformly small ovoid cells. In the caudal part of this region are found many large oval or rounded cells scattered in a matrix of smaller ones, which constitute the *posterior hypothalamic nucleus*. The large cells are especially numerous in man, and extend caudally over the mammillary body to become continuous with the ventricular gray and tegmentum of the midbrain. The cells resemble those of the lateral hypothalamic area, and are often included with the latter in a single and more extensive nuclear mass, the *mammilloinfundibular nucleus* (Malone). These large cells are believed to furnish most of the efferent hypothalamic fibers to the lower portions of the brain stem.

The mammillary portion consists of the mammillary bodies covered dorsally by the caudal cells of the posterior hypothalamic nucleus. In man the mammillary body consists almost entirely of the large spherical *medial mammillary nucleus* composed of relatively small cells invested by a medullary capsule. Lateral to this is the small intermediate or *intercalated mammillary nucleus* (lateral nucleus of Le Gros Clark) composed of even smaller cells. Ventral and more laterally is a well defined group of large cells, the *lateral mammillary nucleus* (intercalated nucleus of Le Gros Clark), which probably represents a condensation of cells from the posterior hypothalamic nucleus (Figs. 338C, 339).

The most characteristic features of the human hypothalamus are the sharply circumscribed tuberal nuclei, the large size of the medial mammillary nuclei, and the extensive distribution of the large cells in the posterior and lateral hypothalamic areas.

Connections of the hypothalamus. The hypothalamus, in spite of its small size, has remarkably extensive and complex fiber connections, some organized into definite and conspicuous bundles, others diffuse and difficult to trace. It receives fibers from the secondary olfactory and general sensory tracts, from the hippocampal cortex, from the globus pallidus and subthalamic nucleus, from the thalamus, and from several regions of the frontal cortex. It sends fibers to the preganglionic autonomic centers of the brain stem and cord, to the dorsomedial nucleus of the thalamus, to the posterior lobe of the hypophysis, and an especially strong fiber bundle to the anterior thalamic nucleus.

The afferent systems include (1) *Olfactohypothalamic fibers* from the basal olfactory regions including among others the area olfactoria, amygdaloid nucleus, and the gray masses of the septum pellucidum. These nuclei receive impulses from the olfactory bulb and give rise in lower vertebrates to the medial forebrain bundle, a tract of considerable size whose fibers terminate in the hypothalamus and tegmentum of the midbrain (Fig. 316). In man the medial forebrain bundle is considerably reduced and inconspicuous. Its diffusely spread fibers also end in the hypothalamus and midbrain tegmentum. (2) *Corticomammillary fibers* from the hippocampal cortex and dentate gyrus forming the conspicuous tract known as the fornix (Figs. 347, 349). This tract goes mainly to the hypothalamus, most of the fibers terminating in the mammillary nuclei. Some, however, appear to end in the tuberal and other hypothalamic nuclei and in the preoptic area. In addition to fibers from the hippocampus, direct corticohypothalamic fibers are also projected from several regions of the frontal lobe. The premotor cortex (area 6 and 8) sends fibers to the mammillary body and also to the ventromedial thalamic nucleus. There is evidence that a considerable projection from the posterior orbital cortex is distributed to several hypothalamic nuclei (Meyer, 1949; Le Gros Clark and Meyer, 1950). These connections are in part bilateral, many of the fibers crossing through the rostrum of the corpus callosum, and passing through the preoptic region in association with the descending columns of the fornix. (3) *Fibers from the medial thalamic nuclei*, chiefly from the magnocellular portion of the dorsomedial nucleus and from the midline nuclei. These form part of the periventricular fiber system to be described below. (4) Fibers from the *globus pallidus*, *subthalamic nucleus* and *zona incerta*, some of the fibers crossing in the anterior hypothalamic commissure. (5) Ascending sensory fibers which detach themselves from the medial lemniscus and secondary trigeminal tracts in the midbrain region and, as the *peduncle of the mammillary body*, terminate mainly in the lateral portion of that nuclear mass

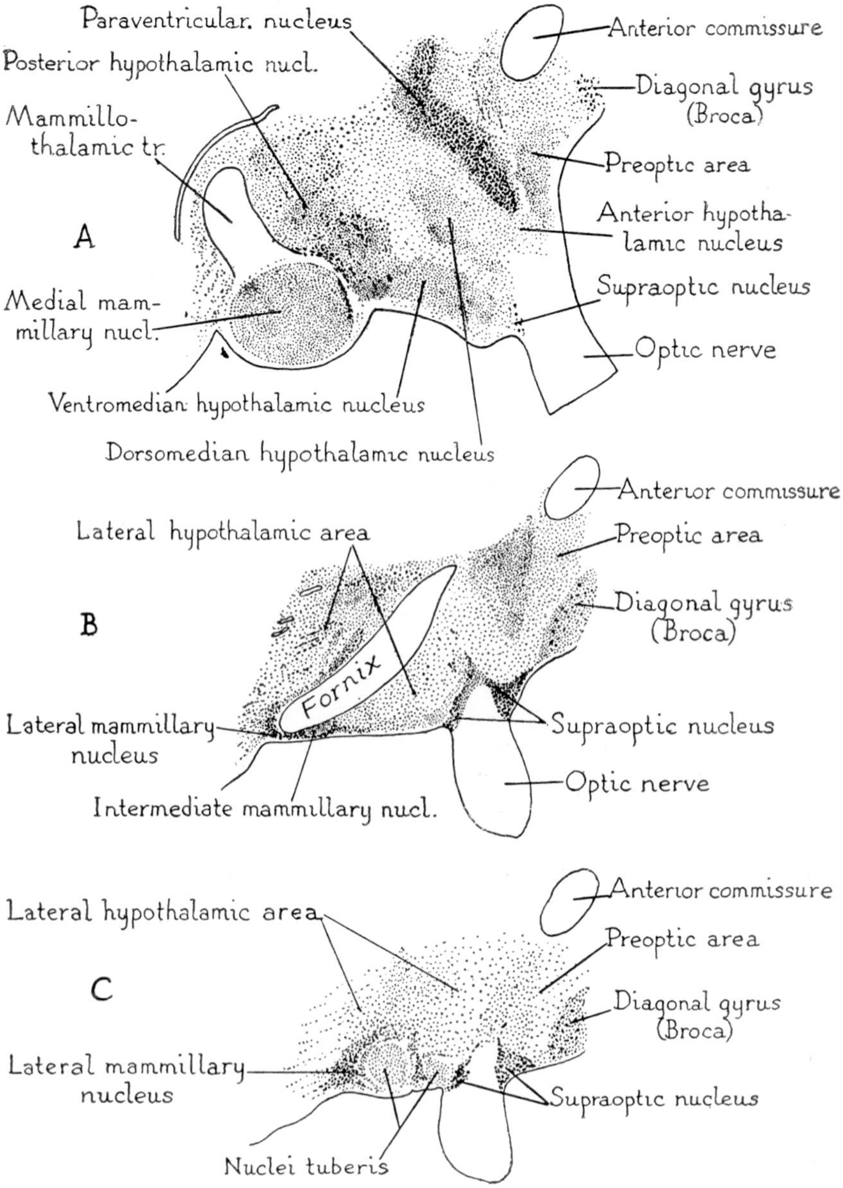

FIG. 339. Sagittal sections of human hypothalamus. *A*, near median (ventricular) surface; *B*, through anterior column of fornix; *C*, near lateral border of hypothalamus. (After Le Gros Clark.)

(Papez, Tello). They are believed to conduct gustatory and other visceral sensory impulses, and perhaps sensory impulses from the oral and nasal mucous membranes. (6) The hypothalamus also receives fibers from the retina which detach themselves from the optic tract and terminate in the supraoptic and the ventromedial hypothalamic nucleus (Marburg). Since both of these nuclei send fibers to the posterior lobe of the hypophysis, the latter is brought under retinal control by a two-neuron pathway, i.e., retino-supraoptic and supraopticohypophysial.

The efferent hypothalamic fibers com-

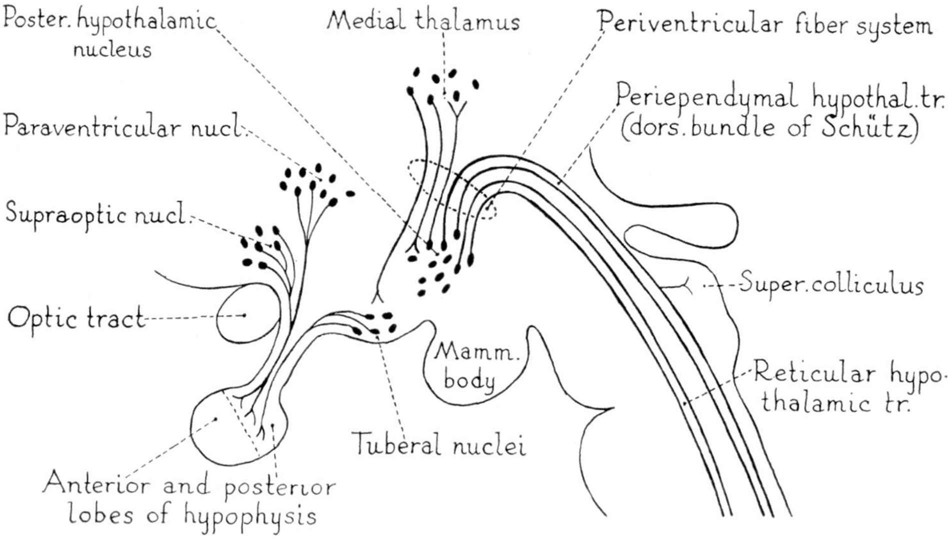

FIG. 340. Diagram showing some of the efferent fiber tracts from the hypothalamus.

prise the conspicuous fiber bundles emerging from the mammillary bodies, the periventricular fibers, and the hypophysial connections (Fig. 340). From the medial mammillary nucleus and perhaps from the lateral and intercalated as well, arises a well defined fiber bundle, the *fasciculus mammillaris princeps,* which passes dorsally for a short distance and then separates into two bundles: the *mammillothalamic* and the *mammillotegmental tract* (Fig. 350). The former passes upward and forward and terminates in the anterior thalamic nucleus. Some fibers of the tract apparently run in the reverse direction, i.e., from the anterior nucleus to the mammillary body. Since the anterior nucleus is reciprocally connected with the gyrus cinguli, the mammillary body is brought indirectly under the control of that cortical area (Figs. 334B, 335). The mammillotegmental tract curves in a caudal direction to terminate in some of the tegmental nuclei of the midbrain.

The periventricular fibers arise primarily from the large cells of the posterior hypothalamic nucleus, to some extent also from the nuclei of the tuberal and supraoptic regions. These finely myelinated and unmyelinated fibers at first pass dorsally in the periventricular gray. Some terminate in the dorsomedial thalamic nucleus and in some of the midline nuclei, intermingled with fibers which pass from these thalamic nuclei to the hypothalamus (Figs. 334B, 340). This two-way connection brings the hypothalamus in relation with the frontal granular cortex since the latter is reciprocally connected with the dorsomedial thalamic nucleus.

The majority of the periventricular fibers turn caudally and descend to lower portions of the brain stem. Their exact course is not fully understood. A few run dorsal to the iter and terminate in the midbrain tectum. A larger number descends ventral to the iter in the subependymal portion of the central gray and forms the dorsal bundle of Schütz (periependymal tract) which has been traced as far caudally as the vestibular nuclei and dorsal nucleus of the vagus (Fig. 340). Other fibers descend in the reticular formation of the midbrain and medulla. Those which reach the cord descend in the ventrolateral white and are believed to terminate in the intermediolateral cell column. The fibers appear to be largely uncrossed.

The connections of the hypothalamus with the posterior lobe of the hypophysis have been well established for man (Pines, Greving, Stengel). They are unmyelinated fibers which arise principally from the supraoptic and paraventricular nuclei and form a well defined bundle, the *supraoptico-hypophysical tract* (Fig. 340). A smaller bundle, the *tuberohypophysial tract*, is contributed by the medial cells of the tuber cinereum.

It is evident from the above that the efferent descending hypothalamic fibers represent essentially connections with lower autonomic centers innervating visceral structures. The hypothalamus is itself under control of thalamic and pallial mechanisms, and in turn influences the activity of these centers. Pallial control is in part mediated by direct corticohypothalamic fibers. Greater pallial control is mediated by way of the dorsomedial and anterior thalamic nuclei which connect the frontal and cingulate cortex with the hypothalamus. Since the dorsomedial and the anterior nucleus are reciprocally connected with both cortex and hypothalamus, these pathways are also important channels through which hypothalamic influence can be transmitted to the cortex. Other connections are through the zona incerta, globus pallidus and the gray matter of the septum pellucidum, all of which apparently receive fibers from the frontal cortex and send fibers to the hypothalamus.

In addition to the connections mentioned above, there is physiological evidence that certain regions of the hypothalamus are intimately related to, and integrated with, the reticular system of the brain stem. Stimulation of the lateral and posterior hypothalamus facilitates reflex and cortically induced movements. It evokes the same activating effects on the electrical activities of the cortex which are obtained from stimulation of the mesencephalic and subthalamic reticular centers.

Functional considerations. A large accumulation of experimental evidence and clinical observations have demonstrated beyond doubt that the hypothalamus and immediately adjoining region are intimately related to all kinds of visceral activities. The most diverse disturbances of autonomic functions such as water balance, internal secretion, sugar and fat metabolism, and temperature regulation can all be produced by stimulation or destruction of hypothalamic areas. Even the mechanism for normal sleep may be profoundly altered by such lesions. It is now definitely established that the hypothalamus is the chief subcortical center for the regulation of both sympathetic and parasympathetic activities. These dual activities are integrated into coordinated responses which maintain adequate internal conditions in the body. Whether each of the autonomic activities has its own discrete center, is highly improbable in view of the small size of the hypothalamus and the complex nature of these activities. However, a specific and limited function has apparently been established for the supraoptic nucleus. There is a fairly definite topographical orientation as regards the two main divisions of the autonomic system. The control of parasympathetic activities is related to the anterior and medial hypothalamic regions (supraoptic and preoptic areas) and the ventricular portion of the tuber cinereum. Stimulation of this region result in increased vagal and sacral autonomic activities characterized by reduced heart rate, peripheral vasodilation, and increased tonus and motility of the alimentary and vesical walls. Of the several nuclei found in this region, the supraoptic nucleus is definitely concerned with the maintenance of a proper water balance in the body (Figs. 338A, 339B). Destruction of the two supraoptic nuclei or their hypophysial connections is invariably followed by the condition known as *diabetes insipidus* in which there is increased secretion of urine (polyuria) without increase in the sugar content of the urine. It was believed that the nuclei stimulated the production of an antidiuretic hormone in the posterior lobe of the hypophysis. Destruction of these neurons caused the degeneration of the cells that secrete the hormone. From recent investigations it seems more probable that the hormone is secreted directly by the cells of the supraoptic and also of the paraventricular nucleus. The secretion is then conducted to the posterior lobe along the unmyelinated axons of these cells (Bargmann et al., 1950). There is some evidence that the ventromedial hypothalamic nucleus and the paraventricular are related to sugar metabolism.

The lateral and posterior hypothalamic regions are concerned with the control of sympathetic responses. Stimulation of this area, especially of the posterior portion from which most of the descending efferent fibers arise, activates the thoracicolumbar outflow and results in the heightened metabolic and somatic activities characteristic of states of emotional stress, of combat, or of flight. They are expressed in dilation of the pupil, erection of the hair, acceleration of the heart, elevation of blood pressure, increase in the rate and amplitude of respiration, somatic struggling movements, with concomitant inhibition of the gut and bladder. All these signs of emotional excitement are also readily elicited when the hypothalamus is released from cortical control. Thus removal of the cortex or interruption of the cortical connections with the hypothalamus, induces many of the above visceral symptoms collectively designated as "sham rage" (Bard; Fulton and Ingraham). On the other hand, destruction of the posterior hypothalamus produces emotional lethargy, abnormal sleepiness, and a fall in temperature due to the reduction of general visceral (and somatic) activities.

The coordination of sympathetic and parasympathetic responses is strikingly shown in the regulation of body temperature. This complex function involving widely spread physical and chemical processes is apparently mediated by two hypothalamic mechanisms, one concerned with the dissipation of heat, the other with its production and conservation. There is considerable experimental evidence that the anterior hypothalamus, especially the preoptic area, is sensitive to increases in temperature and sets in motion the machinery for getting rid of the excess heat. In man this consists mainly in profuse sweating and vasodilation of the cutaneous blood vessels. These actions permit the rapid elimination of heat by convection and radiation from the surface of the engorged blood vessels and by the evaporation of sweat. In animals with fur this is supplemented to a considerable degree by rapid respiratory movements of shallow amplitude (panting), the heat loss being effected mainly by the warming of rapidly successive streams of inspired air.

The posterior hypothalamus, on the other hand, is sensitive to conditions of decreased body temperature and institutes measures for the conservation and increased production of heat. The cutaneous blood vessels are constricted and sweat secretion shut off, reducing to a minimum the heat loss through radiation and evaporation. Simultaneously there is augmentation of visceral activities and the somatic muscles stiffen and are thrown into the involuntary movements of shivering. All these activities tremendously increase the processes of oxidation with consequent production of heat.

These two intrinsically antagonistic mechanisms do not function independently but are continually interrelated and balanced against each other to meet the changing needs of the body, the coordinated responses always directed to the maintenance of a constant optimum temperature.

THE BASAL GANGLIA

In close relation to the diencephalon are a number of gray masses belonging to the endbrain, more or less completely buried in the medullary substance of the hemisphere. These *basal ganglia* comprise the *lenticular* and *caudate nuclei*, the *amygdaloid nucleus* and the *claustrum*. The caudate

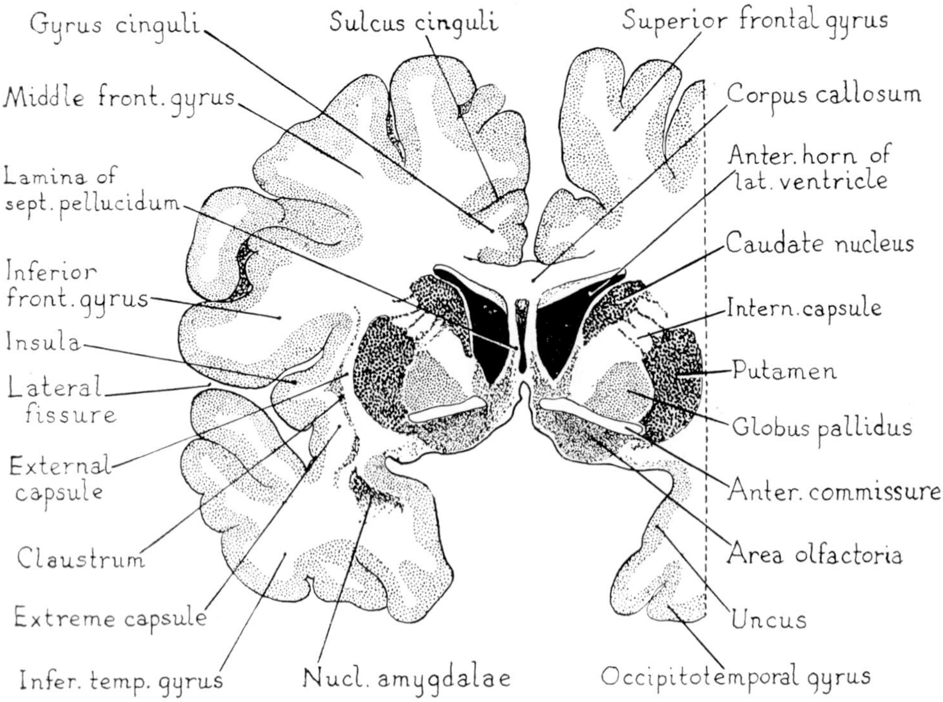

FIG. 341. Frontal section of brain passing through anterior commissure.

and lenticular nuclei together with the internal capsule which separates them, constitutes the *corpus striatum.*

The **amygdaloid nucleus** is a complex gray mass situated in the dorsomedial portion of the temporal lobe, in front and partly above the tip of the inferior horn. It is covered by a layer of rudimentary cortex and is caudally continuous with the uncus of the hippocampal gyrus (Figs. 341, 342). It is related medially to the area olfactoria, laterally to the claustrum, while dorsally it is hidden in part by the lenticular nucleus. The connections of the amygdaloid nucleus, mainly olfactory ones, have not been fully worked out. It receives fibers from the lateral olfactory stria, and gives rise to a fiber bundle known as the *stria terminalis* or *stria semicircularis* (Figs. 44, 47) which arches along the entire medial border of the caudate nucleus and terminates mainly in the area olfactoria, septal region, and anterior portion of the hypothalamus. Some of the fibers cross in the anterior commissure, connecting the two amygdalae, and it is probable that many fibers of the stria terminalis run in a reverse direction, i.e., from the basal olfactory regions to the amygdaloid nucleus. The nucleus is believed to receive fibers from the thalamus and from the anterior portion of the gyrus cinguli. The amygdaloid nucleus sends fibers to the habenular ganglion by way of the stria medullaris, and to the uncus and hippocampal formation. The amygdaloid complex is found in all mammals and has been homologized with the olfactory striatum (archistriatum) of submammalian forms.

Striking changes in emotional and sexual behavior have been observed in animals and man after extensive bilateral lesions of the temporal lobes, uncus, hippocampus, and amygdaloid nuclei (Klüver and Bucy, 1939; Bard and Mountcastle, 1948; Terzian and Ore, 1955; Green, Clemente and De-

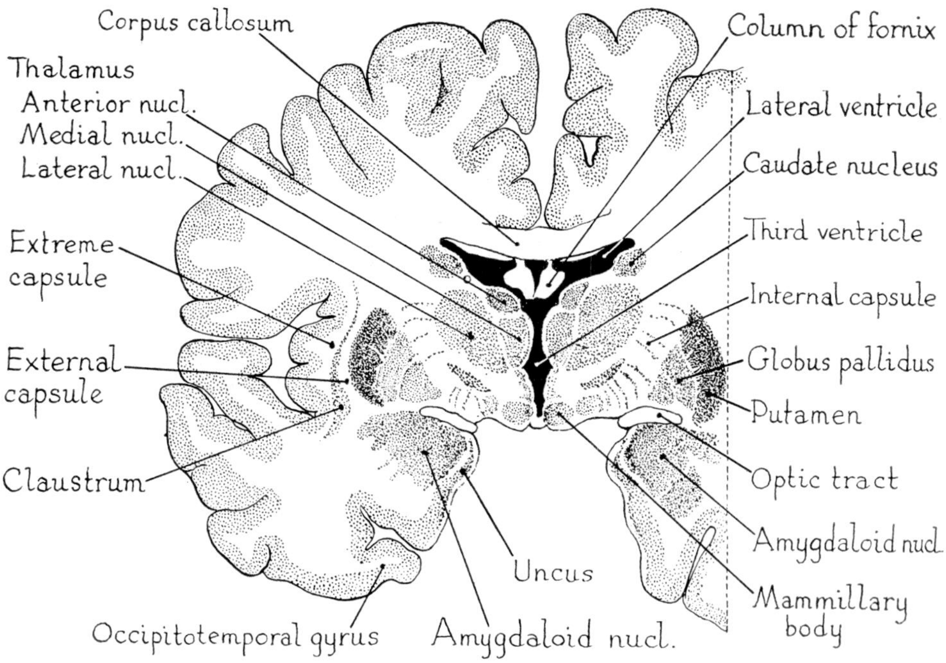

FIG. 342. Frontal section of brain passing through mammillary bodies.

Groot, 1957; Green, 1958). These studies suggest that the amygdalae and adjacent rhinencephalic structures are related to brain stem mechanisms that regulate visceral activity and emotional behavior. Destruction of these visceral centers in man presumably result in a loss of fear and rage reactions, increased sexual activity and homosexual tendencies, excessive eating, and severe deficiencies in memory (Klüver-Bucy syndrome). The deficits in memory are probably due in large part to destruction of the temporal cortices (Penfield and Jasper, 1954).

The **claustrum** is a thin plate of gray matter lying in the medullary substance of the hemisphere between the lenticular nucleus and the cortex of the insula, separated from these structures by two white lamina: the external capsule medially, and the extreme capsule laterally (Figs. 193, 341). Some consider it a part of the striatum, but there is considerable evidence that it originates from the deep layers of the insular cortex from which it secondarily splits off. Its functions and connections are obscure.

The corpus striatum. Arising as a single gray mass during early development the corpus striatum becomes secondarily divided by the fibers of the internal capsule into two cellular masses, the *lenticular* and the *caudate nucleus*. This separation, however, is not complete. In its most rostral portion the head of the caudate is ventrally continuous with the lenticular nucleus, and more dorsally the two nuclei are connected by a number of slender gray bridges extending across the internal capsule (Figs. 341, 343, 324). These bridges give the striped appearance which has led to the designation of corpus striatum.

The *caudate nucleus* is an elongated arched gray mass related throughout its extent to the ventricular surface of the lateral ventricle (Figs. 47, 343). Its enlarged anterior portion or *head* lies rostral to the thalamus and bulges into the anterior horn. Its long attenuated caudal portion or *tail* extends along the dorsolateral border of the thalamus, separated from the latter by the terminal sulcus in which are lodged the stria terminalis and terminal

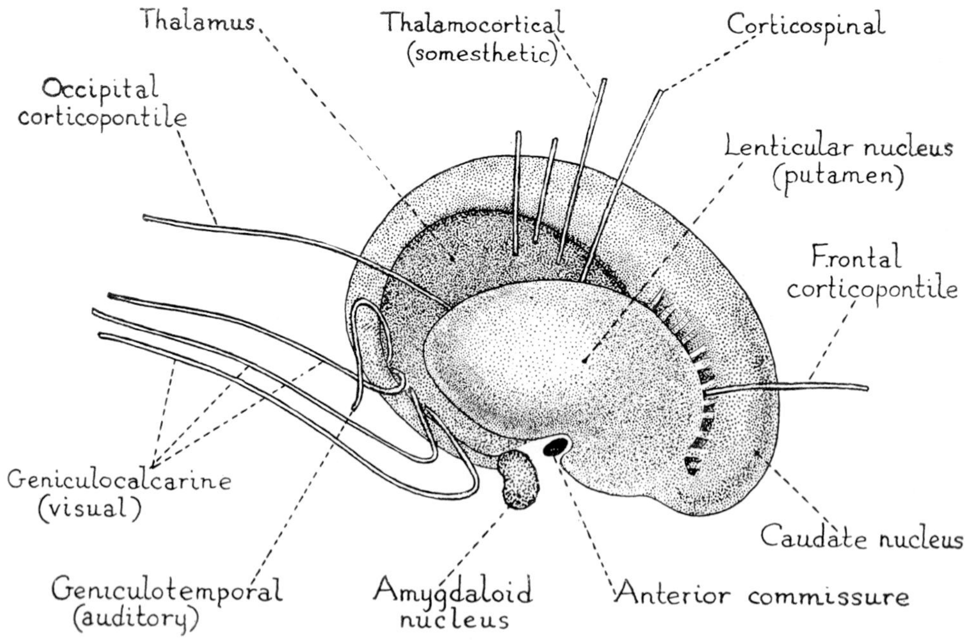

FIG. 343. Lateral view of corpus striatum, thalamus, and amygdaloid nucleus, semischematic. Some of the fibers in the anterior, superior, posterior and retrolenticular portions of the internal capsule are indicated. (Modified from Elze.)

vein. On reaching the caudal limit of the thalamus the tail arches ventrally and runs forward in the roof of the inferior horn to reach the amygdaloid nucleus (Fig. 343).

The lenticular nucleus has the size and form of a Brazil nut. In frontal sections this nucleus appears as a stout wedge whose broad somewhat convex base is directed laterally and its blade medially. It has no ventricular surface but lies deeply buried in the white matter of the hemisphere, closely applied to the lateral surface of the internal capsule, which separates it from the caudate nucleus and the thalamus (Figs. 342, 343). A vertical plate of white matter, the external medullary lamina divides the nucleus into an outer larger portion, the *putamen*, and an inner portion known as the *globus pallidus*. The latter is broken up into several segments by the internal medullary laminae (Figs. 342, 317). The globus pallidus is traversed by many myelinated fibers, hence in the fresh condition appears paler than the putamen or caudate nucleus. Only the putamen is continuous with the caudate nucleus by the gray bridges mentioned above.

The putamen and caudate nucleus constitute the phylogenetically newer part of the striate complex (*neostriatum*) and are often designated as just the *striatum*. They are composed of small and medium sized cells with a sprinkling of larger ones, and represent primarily the receptive portion of the corpus striatum. The phylogenetically older globus pallidus (*paleostriatum* or *pallidum*) is composed almost entirely of large cells of a "motor" character whose axons form the efferent fiber systems.

The connections of the corpus striatum, more fully discussed on pp. 389, may be briefly summarized. The afferent fibers which terminate principally in the putamen and caudate nucleus come from the motor and premotor frontal cortex, from the substantia nigra, from the centromedian thalamic nucleus, and from the other thalamic nuclei. The efferent fibers from the putamen and caudate nucleus discharge mainly into the globus pallidus, though a smaller contingent goes to the substantia nigra. The globus pallidus receives *corticopallidal* fibers from the premotor cortex (Meyer, 1949), and some fibers from the thalamus and substantia nigra. The principal afferents are from the putamen and caudate nucleus (striopallidal). The efferent fibers from the globus pallidus, constituting the ansa lenticularis and lenticular fasciculus, project to a number of nuclei (Fig. 321). They go to the subthalamus, hypothalamus, and the ventral anterior nucleus of the thalamus; to the nucleus ruber, probably being first relayed in the nucleus of the tegmental field; to the interstitial and commissural nuclei, and to the more diffuse cell groups of the reticular formation. Some may go directly to the motor nuclei of certain cranial nerves. It is evident that on the whole, the efferent pallidal impulses do not reach the lower motor neurons by long fibers as is the case with the pyramidal pathways, but are first interrupted in many gray masses widely scattered throughout the brain stem.

THE EXTRAPYRAMIDAL MOTOR SYSTEM

It is now generally accepted that movements of a volitional or semivolitional character may be mediated through other than pyramidal channels. In lesions of the motor area or pyramidal tract, it is primarily the finer isolated movements of the distal parts of the extremities which are severely and permanently affected. Gross synergic movements of locomotion, expression, and postural adjustment, and those semiautomatic movements which are normally associated with voluntary activities, such as swinging the arms in walking, persist to a considerable extent or reappear shortly after an initial period of paralysis. There is considerable clinical evidence to suggest that the corpus striatum and associated nuclei, such as the globus pallidus, substantia nigra, nucleus ruber, and subthalamic nucleus, play an important part in this extrapyramidal motor control. These nuclei constitute an older or *extrapyramidal motor system,* in existence long before the advent of the motor cortex and pyramidal tract.

This older system is, however, under the dominance of the cerebral cortex. It has been demonstrated that stimulation of the premotor cortex (area 6), and certain other cortical areas in the parietal and temporal lobes, produce complex synergic movements on the opposite side even after complete destruction of the motor area (area 4). Such areas have been designated as extrapyramidal ones whose impulses do not pass uninterruptedly to the lower motor neurons, but are relayed in the corpus striatum or other nuclei of the old motor system. Direct corticostriate fibers from the frontal lobe have been reported for the monkey by a number of investigators (Hirasawa and Kato, 1935; Mettler, 1947), and a corticopallidal projection from the premotor cortex has been demonstrated in the human brain (Meyer, 1949). According to Cajal, collaterals from the pyramidal tract also terminate in the corpus striatum. Even if the direct connections are rather scanty, there are more extensive routes from cortex to striatum by way of the thalamus and substantia nigra. These pathways are undoubtedly important channels through which cortical influence is transmitted to the basal ganglia. Through the thalamus the corpus striatum may also receive impulses from the ascending sensory tracts and the cerebellum.

The neopallium is phylogenetically a late acquisition, appearing first in the higher reptiles, but in both reptiles and birds it remains on a rudimentary plane and the descending fibers from the cortex are few in number. It is only in the mammals that the motor area and its massive pyramidal projection become a constant and striking feature of the nervous system. The corpus striatum on the other hand is an old part of the endbrain, found in all vertebrates. The paleostriatum, comparable to the globus pallidus, is already well developed in fish. It receives mainly olfactory impulses and gives rise to the "basal forebrain bundle" which discharges into the thalamus, hypothalamus, and midbrain, whence impulses are ultimately relayed to the motor nuclei of the cranial and spinal nerves. This bundle is probably homologous in mammals with the ansa lenticularis from the globus pallidus. In reptiles and birds a neostriatum is added, the caudate and putamen of higher vertebrates, now receives impulses mainly from the thalamus. In birds the whole striatal complex becomes highly differentiated and enlarged to form the most massive portion of the cerebrum (Fig. 4). It seems certain that in animals without a cortex, or with a poorly developed one, the corpus striatum is a most important center. Upon the integrity of the striatum depends the normal, largely instinctive activities of these forms, such as locomotion, defense, feeding, courting, etc. In birds these activities are practically unaffected after ablation of the primitive cortex, but they are severely impaired in lesions of the corpus striatum (Rogers). Thus in submammalian forms the diencephalon and corpus striatum together constitute the highest sensory-motor integrating mechanism of the forebrain. The thalamus of such animals represents the receptive center, the corpus striatum and hypothalamus are related to motor control. The corpus striatum discharges through intercalated nuclei to the somatic muscles, the hypothalamus is similarly connected with the visceral effectors. These reactions are determined on the afferent side by sensory stimuli of an affective rather than discriminative nature, and are expressed in movements which are gross, postural, and stereotyped.

With the evolution of the neopallium in mammals the functions of the corpus striatum becomes subordinated to those of the cerebral cortex and are brought in balance with the activities of the motor area. Dominated now by extrapyramidal cortical centers, the old motor system is still utilized for the production of many of the more or less automatic movements concerned with postural adjustments, reactions of defense, feeding, etc. Many mammals are able to perform their normal activities after destruction of both pyramidal tracts. Even chimpanzees recover sufficiently to feed themselves and execute movements of walking and climbing. Whether the human striatum has similar if reduced functions is still a disputed question. It is possible that in man the basal ganglia have a different significance than in lower mammals. Destruction of the pyramidal tract causes a far more complete and lasting paralysis, but even in man the grosser movements are less severely affected and recover to a considerable extent. According to Kinnier Wilson, the corpus striatum maintains a postural background for voluntary activities, reinforcing and steadying movements, and postures of cortical origin, but is incapable of initiating such movements. Others maintain that even in man the grosser, more automatic volitional movements, as well as postural adjustments, are mediated through the extrapyramidal system, and that these movements are most severely affected in diseases of the corpus striatum.

The cerebral cortex thus projects to the lower motor centers through two main channels. The motor area discharging in part through the long fibers of the pyramidal tract is primarily concerned with the finer nonpostural, isolated, and modifiable movements which form the basis for the acquisition of skill. The extrapyramidal centers of the premotor, motor, and perhaps other cortical areas, are largely concerned with postural adjustments and the grosser volitional movement patterns. Through hypothalamic connections the cortex is also related to the regulation of autonomic functions. These areas do not discharge directly to the lower motor neurons but utilize the existing, though modified, machinery of the old motor system. The two systems do not function independently but are in constant balance with each other, the smooth execution of nonpostural pyramidal movements implying a concomitant regulation and modification of the postural mechanisms.

Clinically, the chief manifestations of striatal disease are muscular rigidity and involuntary movements such as tremor, chorea, and athetosis. *Chorea* is expressed in spontaneous, abrupt and rapidly successive movements of considerable complexity, resembling aimless fragments of voluntary or emotional activities. They involve the extremities and face, resulting in constant gesticulation and facial grimacing, and the tongue, pharynx, and larynx may likewise be affected. Muscle tone is as a rule reduced. In *athetosis* there are slow writhing or twisting movements of the extremities, especially of the fingers and hand, the movements blending with each other to give the appearance of a continuous mobile spasm. Similar, but more rare, spasms may involve large portions of the body and lead to severe torsion of the neck, hip, and shoulder girdle (torsion spasms). Between the spasms the muscles are apparently hypotonic.

Many clinicians recognize two symptom complexes of striatal disease, one hypokinetic, the other hyperkinetic. The former is best exemplified in the condition known as paralysis agitans (Parkinsonism). It is characterized by muscular rigidity and tremor resulting in disturbances of posture and the ease and rapidity of voluntary movements. The augmentation of muscle tone is not selective as in hemiplegia, but is present to the same extent in antagonistic muscle groups, i.e., in both flexors and extensors of the same joint. In addition to muscular rigidity there is impairment or loss of associated movements such as extension of the wrist on flexing the fingers, swinging the arms in walking, and of normal emotional expression, the face appearing immobile or mask-like. The poverty of associated movements and facial expression is ascribed to a loss of pallidal function, the rigidity and tremor to the release of medullary and spinal centers from pallidal control. The site of the destructive lesion is believed to be in the globus pallidus, substantia nigra, or both areas.

The hyperkinetic manifestations of chorea and athetosis are more difficult to explain. These symptoms are the reverse of those present in paralysis agitans. Moreover, choreoathetoid movements may appear in lesions of the superior cerebellar peduncle, nucleus ruber, thalamus, and extrapyramidal cortex. When present in striatal disease the lesion is said to involve the neostriatum (caudate and putamen) which is believed to inhibit the activities of the globus pallidus. The exaggerated movements are hence ascribed to a release of the pallidum from striatal and cortical inhibition. Impulses from the extrapyramidal cortex and cerebellum both reach the striatum by way of the thalamus. Hence lesions of the cortico-thalamo-striate and cerebello-rubro-thalamo-striate pathways will effect a loss or impairment of striatal inhibition upon the globus pallidus.

The significance of the afferent pallidal fibers from the cerebellum, thalamus, cortex, and striatum has been long recognized. However, the role of efferent pallidal fibers in the normal facilitation and inhibition of other brain stem nuclei has not been determined. Thus partial destruction of the globus pallidus and substantia nigra may alter, secondarily, the normal neural activities of the nucleus ruber, subthalamus, thalamus, cerebral cortex, and reticular formation throughout the brain stem. At present it is not known which nuclei or fiber paths are primarily responsible for the clinical symptoms of Parkinsonism.

Dramatic and often gratifying relief of Parkinsonian rigidity and tremor has been reported, in selected patients, after neurolytic lesions have been placed in both the globus pallidus and ventrolateral nucleus of the thalamus (Cooper, et al., 1958). Destruction of the globus pallidus most effectively relieved contralateral rigidity, whereas thalamic lesions were most successful in the alleviation of contralateral tremor. Small electrolytic lesions within the globus pallidus and its efferent pathways have also yielded beneficial results in patients with this incapacitating neurological affliction (Spiegel and Wycis, 1954). Long term postoperative evaluations, as well as postmortem neuropathologic studies of such patients, may eventually provide more concrete neuroanatomic information on this baffling disorder of the central nervous system.

Kinnier Wilson maintains that the influence of the corpus striatum is in the control of tone and steadiness of innervation, and not in the initiation of movement. He believes that the poverty of movement in paralysis agitans may be fully explained by the rigidity which makes all movements difficult and requires a greater effort on the part of the patient. On the other hand, chorea and athetosis are regarded as being primarily due to lesions of the afferent pathway going from the cerebellum, by way of the nucleus ruber and thalamus, to the motor and premotor cortex. These cortical areas, especially the premotor area which is considered as a higher center of volitional control, suffer an impairment of function with the result that normal voluntary movements are displaced by disordered involuntary ones. Chorea and athetosis are thus considered as involuntary cortical activities mediated through the pyramidal tract. These involuntary activities disappear when the pyramidal tract is destroyed by disease or surgical section. The loss of cerebellar impulses may also account for the hypotonia and incoordination of choreic movements.

20

The Rhinencephalon and Olfactory Pathways

THE BASAL OLFACTORY STRUCTURES

The rhinencephalon comprises all those portions of the brain primarily concerned with the reception and integration of olfactory impulses, and with the regulation of motor activities in response to such stimuli. It consists of the basally placed *olfactory lobe* sometimes designated as the paleocortex, and the *archipallium* represented by the hippocampal formation. Large and conspicuous in lower vertebrates, and even in many macrosmatic mammals, the human rhinencephalon is considerably reduced in size. The archipallium has become pushed to the medial surface and is largely hidden from view by the tremendous expansion of the neopallium.

The *olfactory lobe* makes its appearance in the second month as a narrow longitudinal bulge on the basal surface of the developing cerebral hemisphere, ventral and medial to the basal ganglia (Figs. 14, 16). It is distinctly demarcated from the lateral surface of the pallium by the *external rhinal fissure*, and soon differentiates into an anterior and posterior portion. The anterior, at first containing an extension of the lateral ventricle, elongates into a tubular stalk which becomes solid by the end of the third month and forms the rudiment of the olfactory tract and bulb. The posterior portion differentiates into the olfactory area (anterior perforated substance) and certain other olfactory structures closely related to the anteromedial portion of the temporal lobe and collectively known as the *piriform area*.

During the second month, a longitudinal thickening, the *hippocampal ridge*, appears on the medial wall of the hemisphere, a short distance from the dorsal margin (Fig. 21). This ridge soon folds into the hemisphere producing the *hippocampal fissure* on the medial surface and a corresponding elevation in the ventricular wall. When the pallium curves ventrally and forward to form the temporal lobe, the hippocampal fissure and associated structures likewise increase in length and finally extend from the region of the interventricular foramen to the tip of the inferior horn. The hippocampal ridge develops into the *hippocampal formation* (Fig. 348). It is the most ancient olfactory portion of the pallium and is present in amphibians. Hence it is known as the *archipallium*, as distiguished from the more recently acquired non-olfactory *neopallium* which is highly developed only in mammals.

The structures of the olfactory lobe are practically limited to the basal surface of the cerebral hemisphere. The *olfactory bulb* is a flattened ovoid body resting on the cribriform plate of the ethmoid bone, its dorsal surface pressed into the anterior portion of the olfactory sulcus (Figs. 54, 344). Delicate fascicles of fine unmyelinated fibers, the *fila olfactoria*, pass from the nasal fossa through the apertures of the cribriform plate and enter the ventral surface of the bulb. These fila are the central processes of the bipolar receptor cells in the olfactory mucous membrane, and collectively they constitute the *olfactory nerve* (N.I.). The olfactory bulb is thus the terminal "nucleus" of the olfactory nerve.

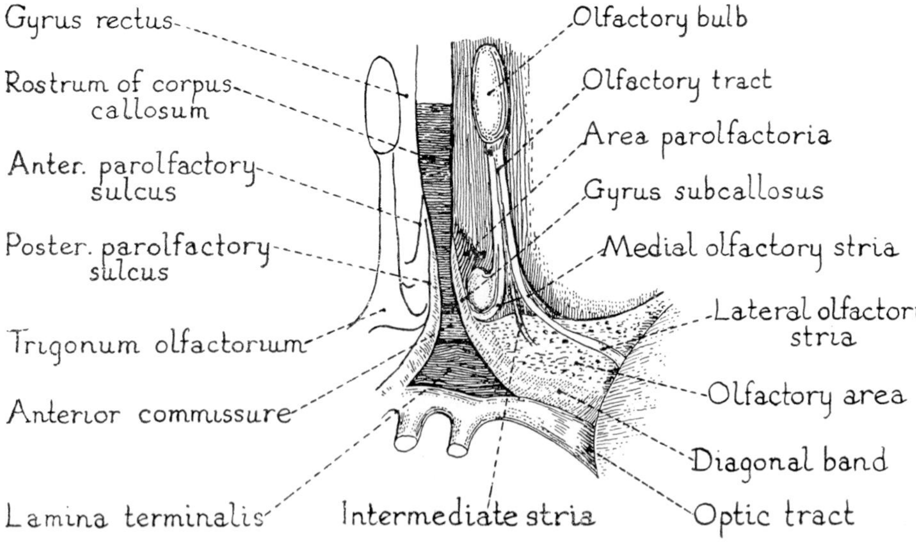

FIG. 344. Olfactory lobe as seen on the basal surface of the human brain. The optic nerves and chiasma have been folded backward. (Modified from His.)

The *olfactory tract* is a narrow white band lying in the olfactory sulcus. It extends from the olfactory bulb to the anterior perforated substance where it enlarges to form the *olfactory trigone* and divides into two roots, the *lateral* and *medial olfactory striae* (Fig. 344). A less definite intermediate stria often dips directly into the anterior perforated substance. The olfactory tract consists principally of secondary olfactory fibers from cells of the bulb, covered dorsally by a layer of primitive cortex greatly reduced in man. The cells of this gray layer receive collaterals from the secondary olfactory fibers and in turn contribute fibers to the olfactory tract (Fig. 345). The latter

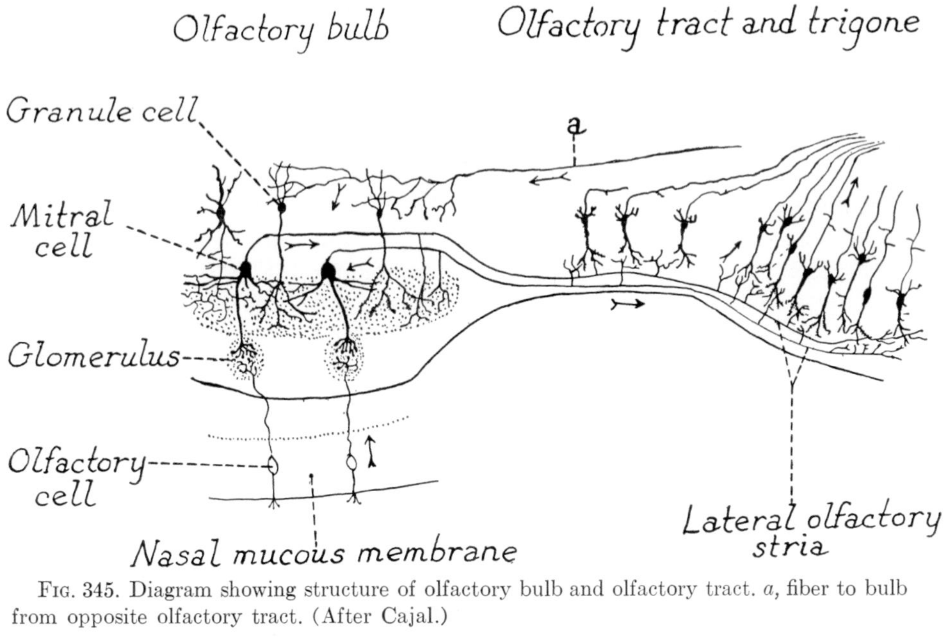

FIG. 345. Diagram showing structure of olfactory bulb and olfactory tract. *a*, fiber to bulb from opposite olfactory tract. (After Cajal.)

thus contains both secondary and tertiary myelinated fibers which are continued into the olfactory striae mentioned above. The olfactory striae are likewise covered by a thin coating of gray substance greatly reduced in man, and are hence also known as the *lateral* and *medial olfactory gyri.*

The medial olfactory gyrus is prolonged to the medial hemispheric surface and there becomes continuous with a small field known as the *parolfactory area* placed beneath the rostrum of the corpus callosum (Figs. 344, 347). This area is limited in front by the anterior parolfactory sulcus, while behind it is separated by the posterior parolfactory sulcus from another strip of cortex, the *subcallosal gyrus,* closely applied to the rostral lamina of the corpus callosum. Parolfactory area and subcallosal gyrus together constitute the *paraterminal body* or *septal area.* The parolfactory area connects the medial olfactory gyrus with the cortex of the gyrus cinguli, hypothalamus, and tegmental nuclei of the brain stem.

The lateral olfactory gyrus passes outward across the anterior perforated substance towards the Sylvian fissure and reaches the inferior apex of the insula (Fig. 51). There it loops sharply backward, the loop forming the limen of the insula, and passes medially in the floor of the fissure to terminate in the uncus and anterior portion of the hippocampal gyrus. Some fibers also end in the amygdaloid nucleus which lies buried beneath the uncus, above and in front of, the tip of the inferior horn. Lateral olfactory gyrus, uncus and anterior part of the hippocampal gyrus constitute the so-called *piriform area* which is more highly developed in macrosmatic mammals. In man the caudal limits of this area are indistinct, and it is uncertain how much of the hippocampal area should be included.

The *area olfactoria* or *anterior perforated substance* is a quadrilateral or rhomboid region bounded rostrally by the olfactory trigone and caudally by the optic tract. Its surface especially in the anterior region is studded with numerous apertures serving for the passage of blood vessels. The posterior region which borders on the optic tract is smoother in appearance and forms an oblique band, the *diagonal band* (Fig. 344). The functions of the olfactory area are not wholly olfactory ones. In macrosmatic animals, especially in those with well developed snouts or muzzles, the rostral portion of the area is marked by a prominent elevation, the *olfactory tubercle,* of which only rudiments are present in man. This tubercle receives not only olfactory fibers, but also a strong ascending bundle of secondary trigeminal fibers from the oral and nasal mucous membranes. It has been suggested that the olfactory tubercle constitutes a center for "oral sense" concerned with the feeding reflexes of the snout (Edinger). Olfactory area, diagonal band and subcallosal gyrus constitute the posterior portion of the olfactory lobe, while the anterior portion comprises the olfactory bulb, trigone, lateral and medial olfactory gyri, and the parolfactory area.

THE HIPPOCAMPAL FORMATION

The hippocampal formation, which represents the cortical part of the olfactory system, is laid down in the embryo on the medial wall of the hemisphere along the hippocampal fissure, immediately above and parallel to the chorioidal fissure which marks the invagination into the ventricle of the chorioid plexus. With the formation of the temporal lobe both these fissures are carried downward and forward, each now forming an arch extending from the region of the interventricular foramen to the tip of the inferior horn. The various parts of the hippocampal arch do not develop to the same extent. The upper, or anterior portion of the hippocampal fissure, becomes invaded by the crossing fibers of the corpus callosum and ultimately becomes the callosal fissure separating the massive commissure from the overlying pallium. The corresponding part of the hippocampal formation which

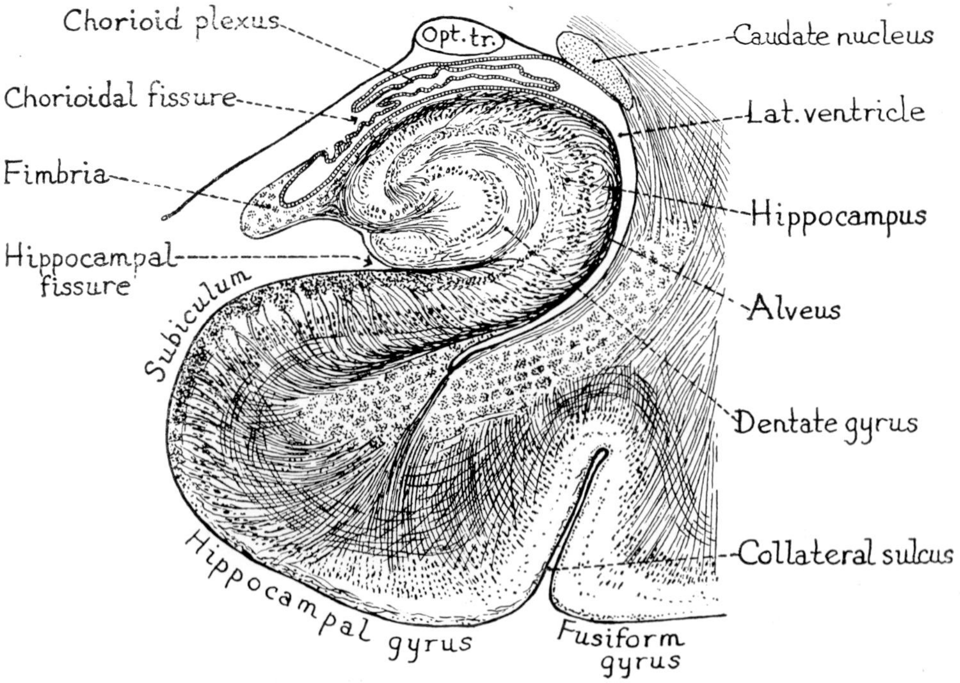

FIG. 346. Transverse section through human hippocampus and hippocampal gyrus. (After Edinger.)

now lies above the corpus callosum differentiates but little, forming in the adult a vestigial convolution, the supracallosal gyrus or indusium griseum (Fig. 347). The lower temporal portion of the arch which is not affected by the corpus callosum differentiates into the main structures of the hippocampal formation. The hippocampal fissure deepens, the invaginated portion which bulges deeply into the inferior horn becomes the *hippocampus*, while the lips of the fissure give rise to the *dentate* and the *hippocampal gyrus*. The relation of these structures are best illustrated in a frontal section through this area (Fig. 346). Proceeding from the collateral sulcus, the *hippocampal gyrus* extends to the hippocampal fissure whose dorsal lip it forms, and there dips into the ventricle to form the *hippocampus*. The latter curves dorsally and medially and on reaching the medial surface curves inward again to form a semilunar convolution, the *dentate gyrus* or *fascia dentata*. The whole ventricular surface of the hippocampus is covered by a layer of white substance, the *alveus*, composed primarily of axons from cells of the hippocampus and dentate gyrus. These fibers converge on the medial surface of the hippocampus to form a flattened band, the *fimbria*, lying between the hippocampus and the dentate gyrus and constituting the beginning of the fornix system (Figs. 347, 348). The free thin border of the fimbria is directly continuous with the epithelium of the chorioidal fissure which lies immediately above it. The chorioid plexus, invaginated into the ventricle along this fissure, partly covers the hippocampus (Fig. 346). The dorsal portion of the hippocampal gyrus adjoining the hippocampal fissure is known as the *subiculum*, and the area of transition between it and the hippocampus proper as the *presubiculum*. Subiculum, presubiculum, hippocampus

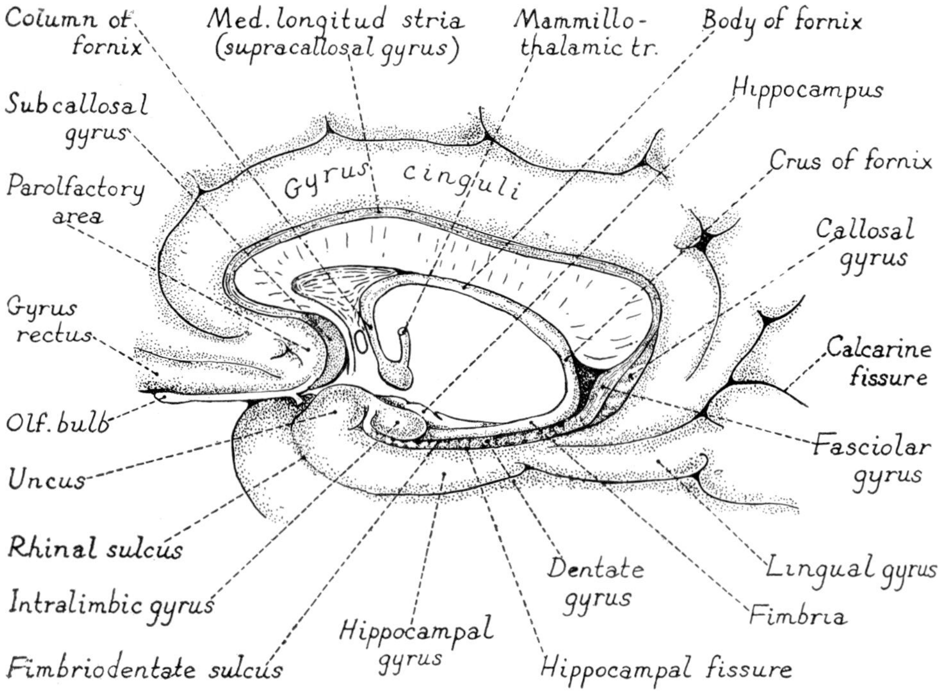

FIG. 347. Portion of medial surface of hemisphere. The thalamus has been removed and the hippocampal gyrus pulled downward to expose the structures related to the hippocampal fissure.

and dentate gyrus, all belong to the archipallium which has an allocortical structure. The larger ventral portion of the hippocampal gyrus bounded by the collateral fissure is neopallial and has the general structure of the isocortex.

When the hippocampal fissure is opened up the *dentate gyrus* is seen as a narrow notched band of cortex between the hippocampal fissure below and the fimbria above (Fig. 347). Traced backward the gyrus accompanies the fimbria almost to the splenium. Then it separates from the fimbria, loses its notched appearance and as the delicate *fasciolar gyrus* (fasciola cinerea) passes to the dorsal surface of the corpus callosum. Here it spreads out into a thin gray sheet representing a vestigial convolution, the *supracallosal gyrus* or *indusium griseum* (Fig. 347). Imbedded in the indusium are two slender bands of myelinated fibers which appear as narrow longitudinal ridges on the dorsal surface of the corpus callosum. These are known as the *medial* and *lateral longitudinal striae* or *striae Lancisii*, and constitute the white matter of the vestigial convolution. Indusium griseum and longitudinal striae extend the whole length of the callosum, pass over the genu and become continuous with the subcallosal gyrus, which is in turn prolonged into the diagonal band of Broca (Fig. 344). Traced forward the dentate gyrus extends into the notch between the uncus and hippocampal gyrus. Here it makes a sharp dorsal bend and passes as a smooth band across the inferior surface of the uncus. This terminal portion is known as the *band of Giacomini*, and the part of the uncus lying posterior to it is often designated as the *intralimbic gyrus*.

THE FORNIX

The fornix constitutes the main efferent fiber system of the hippocampal formation, including both projection and commissural fibers (Figs. 347, 348). It is composed of axons from the large cells of the hippocampus and dentate gyrus, which spread over the ventricular surface as the *alveus* and then converge to form the *fimbria*. Proceeding backward the fimbriae of the two sides increase in thickness. On reaching the posterior end of the hippocampus, they arch under the splenium as the *crura* or *posterior columns* of the fornix, at the same time converging toward each other. In this region a number of fibers pass to the opposite side, forming a thin sheet of crossing fibers, the *hippocampal commissure* or *psalterium*, rather poorly developed in man. The two crura then join to form the *body of the fornix* which runs under the corpus callosum to the rostral margin of the thalamus. Here the bundles separate again and as the *anterior columns of the fornix*, arch ventrally in front of the interventricular foramina and enter the substance of the hypothalamus to reach the mammillary bodies.

THE ANTERIOR COMMISSURE

The anterior commissure crosses the median plane as a compact fiber bundle placed in the lamina terminalis, immediately in front of the anterior columns of the fornix (Fig. 348). Proceeding laterally it splits into two portions. The small anterior or olfactory portion, greatly reduced in man, loops rostrally and connects the gray substance of the olfactory tract with the olfactory bulb of the opposite side. The larger posterior portion forms the bulk of the anterior commissure. It passes laterally beneath the lenticular nucleus, arches backward and downward, and streams into the anterior portion of the hippocampal gyrus and adjacent area of the temporal lobe. The archipallial portions of the two hemispheres are thus interrelated by two commissural systems. The reduced hippocampal commissure connects the two hippocampi and dentate gyri, the larger part of the anterior commissure connects the hippocampal gyri and probably the adjacent neopallial portions of the temporal lobe.

THE OLFACTORY PATHWAYS

The olfactory receptors are spindle-shaped bipolar cells situated in the epithelium of the nasal mucous membrane. Their short peripheral processes extend to

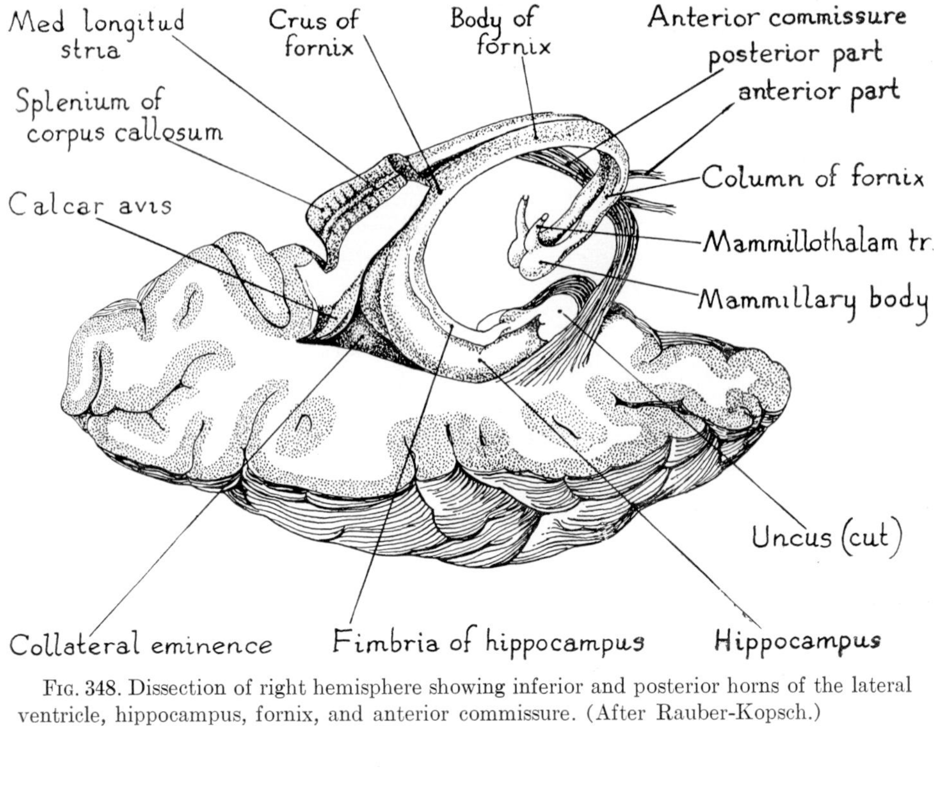

FIG. 348. Dissection of right hemisphere showing inferior and posterior horns of the lateral ventricle, hippocampus, fornix, and anterior commissure. (After Rauber-Kopsch.)

the nasal surface, their long fine central processes form the unmyelinated fibers of the olfactory nerve. Arranged in delicate bundles, the *fila olfactoria,* they pass through the apertures of the cribriform plate and enter the olfactory bulb where they form synaptic relations with certain cells of the latter (Fig. 345). The olfactory bulb is thus the terminal "nucleus" of the olfactory nerve. Within the gray matter of the bulb are several types of nerve cells, the most striking of which are the large triangular or pyramidal *mitral cells,* so named because of their resemblance to a bishop's mitre (Fig. 345). Each of these cells gives off a number of peripherally directed dendrites, one of which passes vertically downward and suddenly breaks up into a brushlike mass of short terminals. These interlace with similar terminals from one or more olfactory fibers, the two together forming circumscribed spherical structures, the *olfactory glomeruli.* Smaller cells of the olfactory bulb, known as *tufted cells,* similarly have a number of dendrites one of which participates in the formation of a glomerulus. The axons of the mitral and tufted cells enter the olfactory tract as secondary olfactory fibers.

The secondary olfactory pathways are numerous and complicated and many of them have become greatly reduced in man. As in the case of other sensory systems they may be grouped into *reflex* and *cortical paths.* The former reach the lower motor neurons, especially the motor nuclei of the cranial nerves, through a series of intercalated subcortical centers. The cortical connections involve the hippocampal formation.

Reflex connections. The secondary fibers from the mitral and tufted cells of the olfactory bulb end directly or by collaterals in the gray substance of the olfactory tract, the olfactory trigone, the olfactory area, and the septal region (subcallosal gyrus and parolfactory area). From these centers which constitute the basal olfactory nuclei, arises a diffuse system of fibers known as the medial or *basal olfactory bundle* (Edinger-Wallenberg, Fig. 349). The fibers pass beneath the head of the caudate nucleus, through the hypothalamic region where it sends terminals or collaterals to the tuber cinereum and mammillary body (*olfacto-hypothalamic*). The basal bundle continues to the tegmentum of the midbrain (*olfacto-tegmental*), some fibers possibly reaching

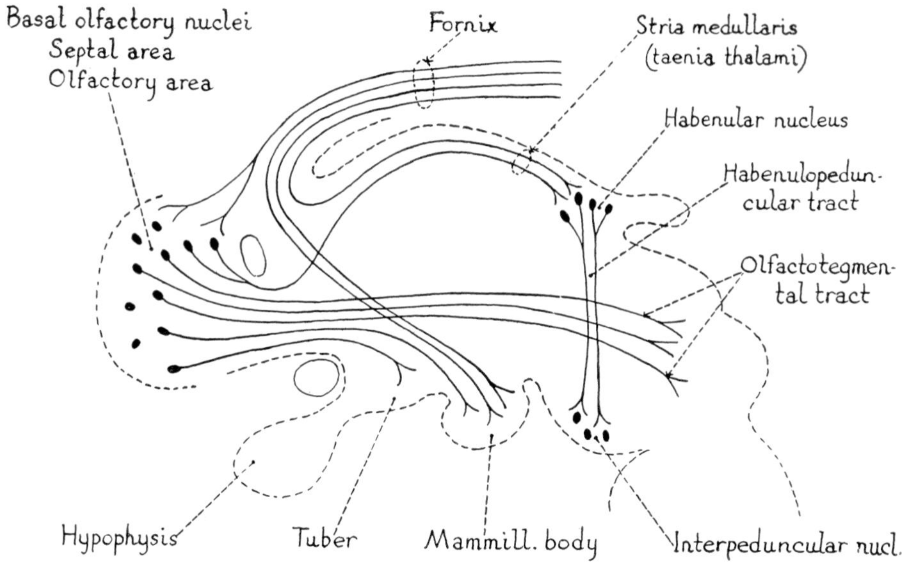

FIG. 349. Diagram showing some of the olfactory connections.

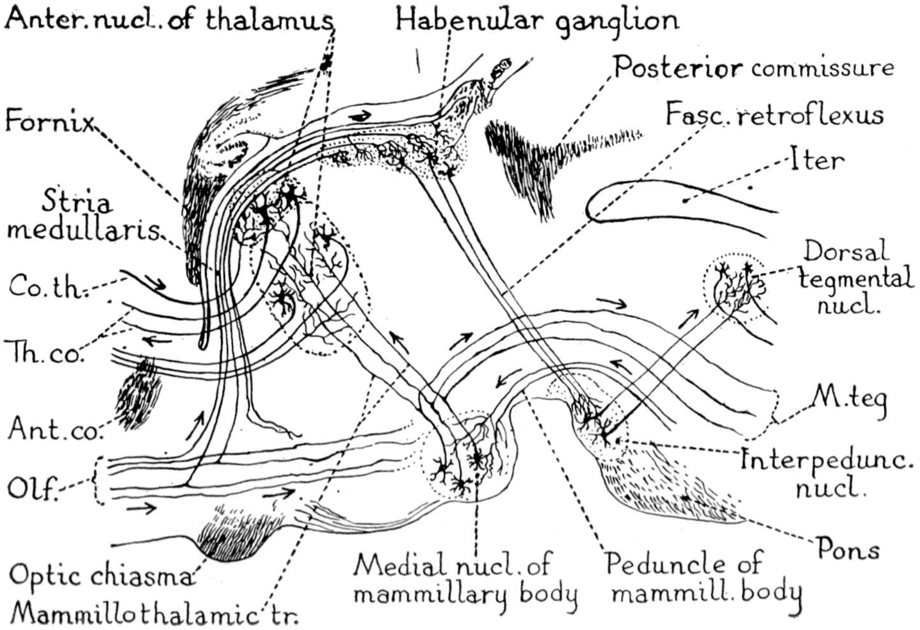

FIG. 350. Some of the important olfactory connections. *Ant.co.*, anterior commissure; *Co.th.*, corticothalamic fiber; *M.teg.*, mammillotegmental tract; *Olf.*, fibers from basal olfactory nuclei (olfactohabenular, olfactohypothalamic); *Th.co.*, thalamocortical fibers. (After Cajal.)

the medulla and even the spinal cord. Other fibers curve dorsally and entering the medullary stria of the thalamus go to the habenular nucleus of the same and opposite side (*olfactohabenular*). The further course of this pathway may be briefly summarized. The habenular nucleus gives origin to the *habenulopeduncular tract* (fasciculus retroflexus) which goes to the interpeduncular nucleus, and is thence relayed to the dorsal tegmental nucleus of the midbrain (Fig. 350). From this nucleus fibers descend to the pons and medulla, forming part of the *dorsal longitudinal bundle of Schütz*.

The hypothalamus likewise gives origin to a number of descending fiber tracts. The *periventricular fiber system* arising from the posterior and tuberal hypothalamic regions, descends through the entire length of the brain stem, many of its fibers entering the spinal cord. Some run with the dorsal longitudinal bundle, others run more diffusely through the reticular formation. From the mammillary body a *mammillotegmental tract* reaches the midbrain tegmentum, and is thence relayed to the lower motor neurons. By this diffuse system, involving a number of intercalated nuclei, the somatic and visceral effectors of the body, especially of the head, are brought under reflex olfactory and hypothalamic control.

Cortical connections. The main connection of the olfactory bulb with the cortical centers is through the lateral olfactory stria. These arise from the mitral cells and pass directly to the uncus and adjacent anterior portions of the hippocampal gyrus. These regions may therefore be regarded as the olfactory projection areas of the archipallium, just as the calcarine region represents the visual projection area of the neopallium. From the uncus a diffuse system of fibers reaches the hippocampus and dentate gyrus which represent higher olfactory cortical centers, including also the dorsal (subicular) portion of the hippocampal gyrus. To a much smaller extent the hippocampal formation receives afferent fibers through the medial olfactory striae and diagonal band.

The *amygdaloid nucleus* likewise receives

fibers from the lateral olfactory stria and gives rise to a fiber bundle known as the *stria terminalis.* This bundle arches along the entire medial border of the caudate nucleus (Fig. 47) and terminates mainly in the olfactory area, septal region, and anterior portion of the hypothalamus. Some of its fibers cross in the anterior commissure, connecting the two amygdalae, and it is probable that many fibers of the stria terminalis run in a reverse direction, i.e., from basal olfactory regions to the amygdaloid nucleus.

The main efferent system from the hippocampal formation is the *fornix* whose anatomical relations have been previously described (Figs. 347, 348). The majority of the fibers form the large *corticomammillary tract* which terminates in the mammillary body. However, some fibers go to the septal and preoptic areas, while others pass through the medullary stria of the thalamus to end in the habenular nucleus (*corticohabenular,* Fig. 349). A few efferent fibers from the dentate gyrus and hippocampus are continued over the splenium into the longitudinal striae where they run a variable distance and then perforate the corpus callosum to join the fornix. Some of these perforating fibers are believed to come from the gyrus cinguli. The further course of the efferent cortical impulses to the motor nuclei of the cranial and spinal nerves is the same as that described for the reflex pathways.

Besides its connections with lower brain stem nuclei, the mammillary body provides a strong bundle of fibers, the *mammillothalamic* tract to the anterior nucleus of the thalamus. This tract is of special interest since the anterior thalamic nucleus is reciprocally connected with practically all parts of the gyrus cinguli (Figs. 334, 335). The significance of the gyrus cinguli is largely obscure, but this thalamic connection suggests that it may represent a higher, newer neopallial center related to olfactory and hypothalamic activities.

21

The Cerebral Cortex

STRUCTURE OF THE CORTEX

The early stages in the histogenesis of the pallium resemble those of other parts of the neural tube. During the first two months the wall of the pallium remains relatively thin and is composed of an ependymal, a mantle, and a marginal layer. At the end of the second month, however, cells begin to wander from the mantle layer into the marginal zone where they form a superficial gray layer, the *cerebral cortex*. As the cerebral cortex gradually thickens by the addition and differentiation of the migrating cells, it assumes a laminated appearance. The cells become organized into a number of horizontal layers, and between the sixth and eighth months six such layers may be distinguished (Brodmann). This sesquilaminated condition is characteristic of the whole neopallium. Hence the neopallial cortex has been called the *isocortex* (Vogt) or *homogenetic cortex* (Brodmann). The rhinencephalon alone seems to be built on a different plan, either showing no lamination at all, or only an incomplete one. Hence the olfactory cortex is known as the *allocortex* or *heterogenetic cortex.*

The cerebral cortex has an area of some 2200 square centimeters or nearly 2½ square feet. Only about one third is found on the free surface of the cortex, the other two thirds lines the walls and floors of the fissures. The average thickness of the cortex is 2.5 mm. but varies considerably in different regions, from a maximal thickness of about 4.5 mm. in the motor area of the precentral gyrus, to a minimal one of 1.5 mm. in the floor of the calcarine fissure. In any portion of the hemisphere the cortex is always thickest on the crown of a convolution and gradually diminishes towards the floor of the sulcus. It has been estimated that besides nerve fibers, neuroglia and blood vessels, the cerebral cortex contains the cell bodies of nearly fourteen billion neurons (Economo).

The cerebral cortex obviously contains (1) the endings of afferent fibers from other parts of the nervous system, such as the thalamocortical fibers; (2) association neurons whose axons interrelate near and distant parts of the same hemisphere, or as commissural fibers pass to the cortex of the opposite side; and (3) projection neurons whose axons conduct the integrated cortical impulses to other portions of the nervous system. These latter axons pass through the corona radiata and form the corticospinal, corticopontile, corticothalamic, and other descending cortical tracts previously studied. Which neurons furnish the projection fibers is still largely an unsettled question, except for the neurons of the precentral motor cortex. In this case it has been definitely determined that the pyramidal tract arises in part at least from the giant pyramidal cells of Betz (Fig. 193). There is considerable evidence for the belief that most of the projection fibers arise from the deeper layers of the cortex, while the association fibers come mainly, though not exclusively, from the more superficial ones. A striking feature of pallial structure is the relatively small number of efferent projection fibers as compared with the enormous number of cortical neurons, indicating that

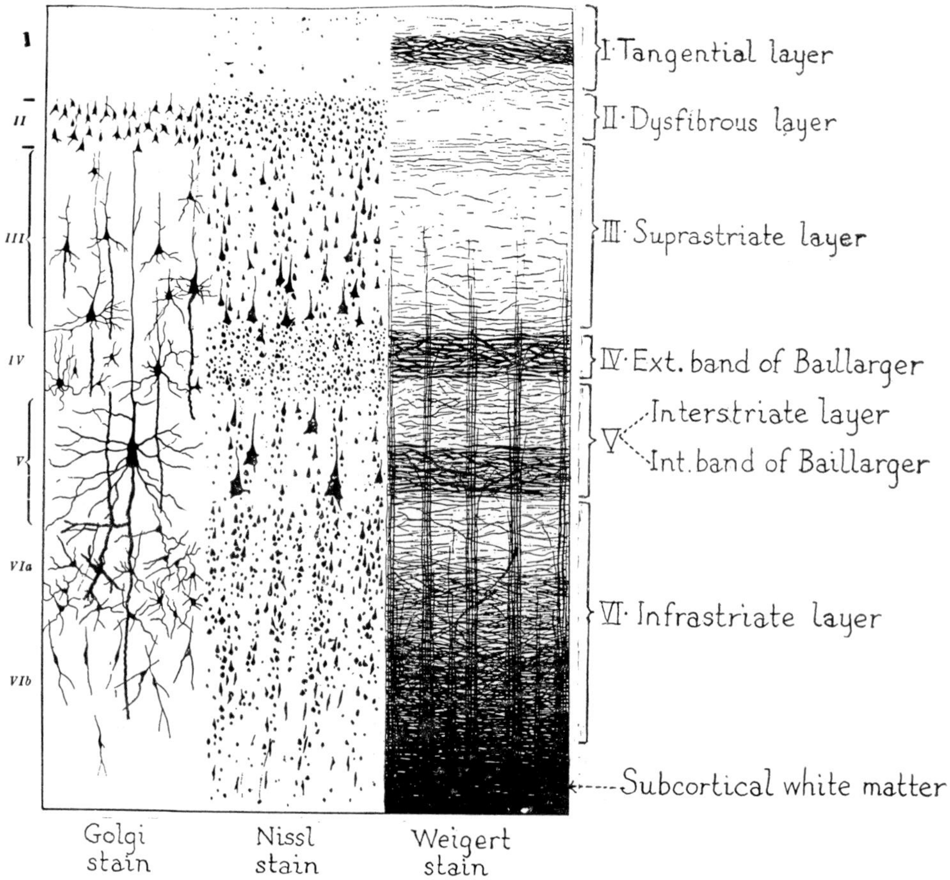

FIG. 351. The cell layers and fiber arrangement of the human cerebral cortex. Semi-schematic. (After Brodmann.)

by far the great majority of the cortical cells are concerned with associative functions.

The cortical cells and fibers. The principal types of cells found in the cortex are the pyramidal, stellate, and fusiform neurons (Figs. 79, 351, 352). The *pyramidal cells,* most characteristic of the cortex, have the form of a pyramid or isosceles triangle whose upper pointed end is continued toward the surface of the brain as the *apical dendrite.* Besides the apical dendrite a number of more or less horizontally running *basal dendrites* spring from the cell body and arborize in the vicinity of the cell. The axon emerges from the base of the cell and descends toward the medullary substance, either terminating in the deeper layers of the cortex or entering the white matter as a projection or association fiber. The pyramidal cells have a large vesicular nucleus and well marked Nissl bodies. They are usually classified as small, medium, and large neurons. The height of the cell body varies from 10 or 12 micra for the smaller neurons to 45 or 50 micra for the larger ones. Unusually large pyramidal cells, the giant pyramidal cells of Betz, whose body may be more than 100 micra in height, and found in the motor area of the precentral gyrus.

The *stellate* or *granule cells* are as a rule small with a polygonal or triangular shape. They have dark-staining nuclei and scanty cytoplasm, varying in size from 4–8 micra. They have a number of dendrites passing in all directions and a short axon which ramifies close to the cell body (Golgi type

II). Other larger stellate cells have longer axons which may enter the medullary substance, and some resemble pyramidal cells by having an apical dendrite which extends to the surface and are hence known as *stellate pyramidal cells* or *star pyramids* (Lorente de Nó). Stellate cells are found throughout the whole depth of the cortex but are especially numerous in layer IV.

The *fusiform* or *spindle cells* are mainly found in the deepest layer, their long axis usually placed vertical to the surface. The two poles of the cell are continued into dendrites, the lower one arborizing within the layer, the upper ascending toward the surface and often reaching the superficial layer. The axon arises from the middle or lower part of the cell body and enters the white matter as a projection or association fiber.

Other cell types found in the cortex are the *horizontal cells of Cajal*, and the *cells with ascending axons* also known as the *cells of Martinotti* (Fig. 353). The former are small fusiform or pear-shaped cells found in the most peripheral layer, their long axons running horizontally for considerable distances and arborizing within that layer. The Martinotti cells, present in practically all the layers, are small triangular or polygonal cells whose axons are directed toward the surface and extend a variable distance. Some arborize in the same layer, others send collaterals to a number of layers. It is evident from the above that the projection and subcortical association fibers are continuations of descending axons from the pyramidal, fusiform, and larger stellate cells. The Golgi type II granule cells, the horizontal and Martinotti cells are wholly concerned with intracortical connections.

The *fibers* of the cortex, as far as their direction is concerned, are disposed either radially or tangentially. The former are arranged in delicate radiating bundles running vertically from the medullary substance toward the cortical periphery (Fig. 351). They obviously include the axons of pyramidal, fusiform, and stellate cells which leave the cortex as projection or association fibers, and the entering afferent projection and association fibers which terminate within the cortex. The ascending axons of the Martinotti cell likewise have a vertical course. The tangential fibers run horizontal to the surface and are composed principally of the terminal branches of the afferent projection and association fibers, the axons of the horizontal and granule cells, and the terminal branches of collaterals from the pyramidal and fusiform cells. The horizontal fibers represent in large part the terminal portions of the radial fibers, which bend horizontally to come in synaptic relation with cortical cells. The tangential fibers are not distributed evenly throughout the thickness of the cortex but are concentrated at varying depths into denser horizontal bands or plexuses, separated by layers in which such fibers are relatively few (Fig. 351). The two most prominent bands are known as the *bands of Baillarger*, visible even to the naked eye as delicate white stripes in sections of the fresh cortex.

The cortical layers. A striking feature of cortical structure is its laminated character. In sections stained by the Nissl method it is seen that the cell bodies are not uniformly distributed, but are arranged in horizontal superimposed layers. Each layer is distinguished by the types, density, and arrangement of its cells. In preparations stained for myelin, a similar lamination is visible, in this case determined primarily by the disposition of the horizontal fibers which differ in amount and density for each corresponding cellular layer (Fig. 351). In the neopallial cortex or isocortex which forms over 90% of the hemispheric surface, six fundamental layers are usually recognized (Brodmann), some of them being subdivided into two or more sub-layers. Proceeding from the surface of the cortex toward the medullary substance these layers include (I) the molecular layer, (II) the external granular layer, (III) the layer of pyramidal cells, (IV) the internal granular layer, (V)

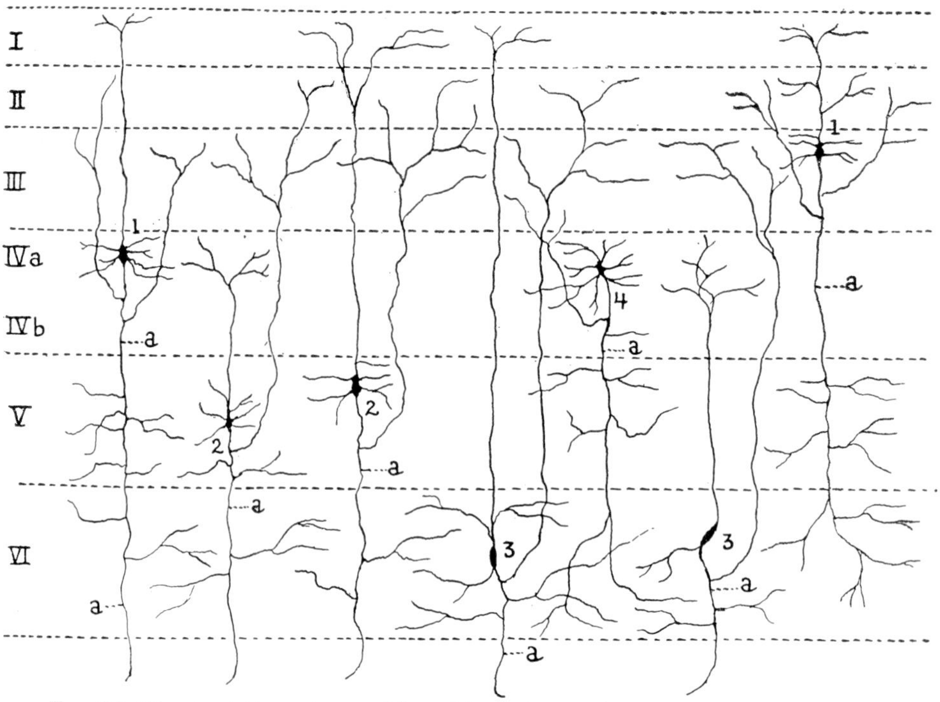

FIG. 352. The dendritic and axonal branchings of several types of cortical neurons with descending axons. Semischematic. *1,* pyramidal cells of superficial layers; *2,* pyramidal cells from ganglionic layer; *3,* spindle cells; *4,* stellate cells; *a,* axon. Based on data by Cajal and de Nó.

the ganglionic layer, and (VI) the multiform layer.

I. The *molecular* or *plexiform layer* contains relatively few cells of two kinds, cells with horizontal axons and Golgi type II cells. Within it are found the terminal dendritic ramifications of the pyramidal and fusiform cells from the deeper layers and the axonal endings of Martinotti cells. All these dendritic and axonal branches form a fairly dense tangential fiber plexus, hence the name of plexiform layer.

II. The *external granular layer* or *layer of small pyramids* consists of numerous closely packed small cells of triangular or pyramidal shape, whose apical dendrites terminate in the molecular layer. Their axons descend to the deeper layers, many terminating in the cortex, some entering the white as association fibers. The layer is rather poor in myelinated fibers, containing the basal dendrites of its own cells and the terminals of axon collaterals from more deeply lying cells. The dendritic shafts of pyramidal and fusiform cells naturally pass through it to reach the molecular layer.

III. The *layer of pyramidal cells* (external pyramidal layer) is composed mainly of typical well formed pyramidal neurons. Two sublayers are usually recognized: a superficial layer of medium pyramids and a deeper layer of larger ones. Their apical dendrites go to the first layer, while most of their axons enter the white matter, chiefly as association or commissural fibers. Some may end within the cortex. Intermingled with the pyramidal neurons are many granule cells and cells of Martinotti. In the most superficial part of the layer there is a greater number of horizontal myelinated fibers constituting the band of Kaes-Bechterew.

Lorente de Nó places the larger, deeper pyramids into layer IV where they are designated as the sublayer of stellate pyramidal cells. According to him these cells, in addition to their numerous shorter dendrites which give them a stellate appearance, possess an apical dendrite which gives off branches to layer IV and then ascends unbranched to the molecular layer.

IV. The *internal granular layer* is composed chiefly of closely packed stellate cells (granules). Many of these are very small, with short axons ramifying within the layer. Others are larger and have descending axons which terminate in the deeper layers or may enter the white substance. The whole layer is permeated by a dense horizontal plexus of myelinated fibers forming the external band of Baillarger, composed in considerable part of the terminal ramifications of thalamocortical and other afferent fibers. According to de Nó the large stellate pyramidal neurons of layer III should be included in this layer.

V. The *ganglionic* or *internal pyramidal layer* consists principally of medium-sized and large pyramidal neurons intermingled with granule and Martinotti cells. The apical dendrites of the larger pyramids ascend to the molecular layer, those of the smaller ones ascend only to layer IV or may even arborize within the ganglionic layer (de Nó). The axons enter the white matter chiefly as projection fibers and to a lesser extent as association fibers. According to de Nó a considerable number of callosal fibers are furnished by the smaller pyramidal cells. The rich horizontal fiber plexus in the deeper portion of this layer constitutes the internal band of Baillarger.

VI. The *multiform layer* or *layer of fusiform cells* contains predominantly spindle-shaped cells whose long axis is perpendicular to the cortical surface, also granule, Martinotti, and stellate cells. Like the pyramidal neurons of layer V, the spindle cells also vary in size, the larger ones sending a dendrite to the molecular layer. The dendrites of the smaller ones ascend only to layer IV or arborize within the fusiform layer itself. Thus the dendrites of many pyramidal and spindle cells from layers V and VI come in direct relation with the endings of sensory thalamocortical fibers which ramify chiefly in the internal granular layer. The axons of the spindle cells enter the white substance both as projection and association fibers. It is maintained that many of the short arcuate association fibers connecting adjacent convolutions are furnished by the deep stellate cells of layer VI (de Nó). The multiform layer may be subdivided into an upper sublayer of more densely packed larger cells, and a lower one in which the smaller cells are more loosely arranged. The whole layer is pervaded by fiber bundles which enter or leave the medullary substance.

Besides the horizontal cellular lamination the cortex also exhibits a vertical radiate arrangement of the cells, giving the appearance of slender vertical cell columns passing through the whole thickness of the cortex (Fig. 358). This vertical lamination is quite distinct in the parietal, occipital, and temporal lobes, but is practically absent in the frontal lobe. The arrangement into vertical cell columns is produced by the radial fibers of the cortex, just as the horizontal lamination is largely determined by the distribution of the tangential fibers.

Many authorities believe that a distinction should be made between the *supragranular* and *infragranular layers* of the cortex. The former which includes layers II and III are the latest to arise, are most highly differentiated, and most extensive in man ((Kaes, '07). The fibers which they receive, or send out, are chiefly associative in character, hence they are believed to be concerned with the more purely cortical associative mnemonic functions. The infragranular layers, composed of layers V and VI, are well developed in other mammals and are directly connected with subcortical structures by descending projection systems. It has been shown by Nissl that when the cortex of newborn rabbits is isolated from the rest of the nervous system, the infragranular layers fail to increase during subsequent development while the growth of the supragranular cortex remains unaffected. The older layers appear to be concerned with the more fundamental cortical activities primarily of a motor character. The internal granular layer, which intervenes between the supragranular and infragranular cortex, receives chiefly the afferent projection fibers. The supragranular layers are lacking in the archipallium.

The interrelation of cortical neurons. The pictures of cortical structure seen in preparations treated with the Nissl or myelin methods, are of necessity incomplete. They show only the types and arrangement of the cell bodies or the course and distribution of the myelinated fibers. These methods give no information regarding the dendritic and axonal end arborizations which constitute the synaptic junctions through which nerve impulses are transmitted. An understanding of the neuronal relationships, and hence of the intracortical conduction circuits, can only be obtained by impregnation methods which give a total picture of the cell body and all its processes. By the use of such methods, the distribution of the dendritic and axonal terminals has been worked out by a number of investigators, notably by Cajal. More recently Lorente de Nó has given a detailed account of the elementary pattern of cortical organization applicable for the parietal, temporal, and occipital isocortex. According to this investigator the arrangement of the axonal and dendritic branchings forms the most constant feature of cortical structure. The following paragraphs are largely based on de Nó's account.

The afferent fibers to the cortex include projection fibers from the thalamus and association fibers from other cortical areas of the same and opposite side. The thalamo-cortical fibers, especially the specific afferent ones from the ventral thalamic nuclei and the geniculate bodies, pass unbranched to layer IV (Figs. 185, 190, 191, 268). Here the axons arborize into a dense terminal plexus, some of the fibers extend to layer III and arborize there (Fig. 353B). The association and callosal fibers on the other hand, give off some collaterals to layers V and VI, ramify mainly in layers II and III, and to a lesser extent in layer IV. The further course of the entering impulses will naturally depend on the axonal branching of the cells which have synaptic relations with the afferent fibers.

The cortical neurons, as regards the direction and extent of their fiber processes, may be grouped into cells with descending, ascending, horizontal, and short axons. The last three types serve wholly for intracortical connections (Fig. 353). The cells with descending axons (pyramidal, fusiform and larger stellate cells) furnish all the efferent projection and association fibers, but in addition their axonal collaterals form an extensive system of intracortical connections. Naturally, the descending axons which do not reach the medullary substance have only intracortical branches.

The pyramidal cells of layers II, III, and IV have a similar pattern of dendritic and axonal branchings (Fig. 352). They have a number of basilar dendrites which arborize in the same layer and an apical dendrite which ends in the molecular layer. Their descending axons in part terminate in the deeper layers of the cortex, in part are continued as association or callosal fibers. During their descent they give off a few recurrent collaterals to their own layers, chiefly II and III, and numerous horizontal collaterals to V and VI where they contribute to the horizontal plexuses of these layers. These axonal ramifications thus chiefly connect layers II and III with V and VI.

The pyramidal and fusiform cells of layers V and VI have a very characteristic pattern of dendritic and axonal branchings. All the pyramidal cells of V give off basilar dendrites to their own layer, and an apical dendrite which in most cases extends to the molecular layer. There are, however, medium-pyramid sized pyramidal neurons

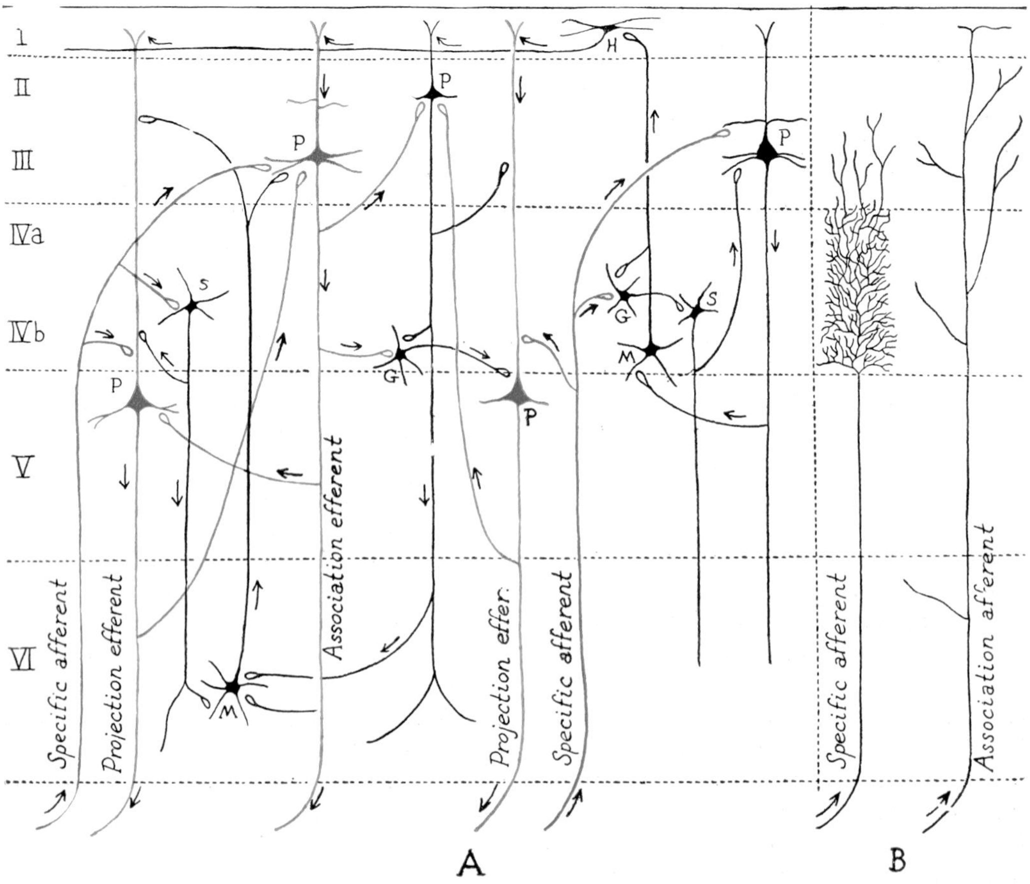

FIG. 353. *A*, Diagram showing some of the intracortical circuits. Synaptic junctions are indicated by loops. *Red*, afferent thalamocortical fibers; *blue*, efferent cortical neurons; *black*, intracortical neurons. *G*, granule cell; *H*, horizontal cell; *M*, Martinotti cell; *P*, pyramidal cell; *S*, stellate cell. *B*, mode of termination of afferent cortical fibers. Based on data by de Nó.

whose apical dendrites terminate in IV, and short pyramidal cells whose dendrites all ramify in V (Fig. 352). The spindle cells of layer VI have similar branches, the ascending dendritic shafts that terminate respectively in I and IV while other dendrites arborize in VI. The dendritic terminals of the medium pyramids and spindles thus come in direct contact with the endings of specific afferent fibers in layer IV. The axons of the pyramidal and spindle neurons, and of many deep stellate cells are continued as projection, association or callosal fibers, and have collateral branchings of a definite character. All these axons send horizontal collaterals to V and VI, contributing largely to the horizontal plexuses of these layers especially V (internal band of Baillarger). Many have in addition one or more recurrent collaterals which ascend unbranched through layer IV and arborize in II and III, some even extending to the molecular layer (Fig. 352). The horizontal plexus of III and II is in considerable part formed by these recurrent collaterals. Thus the impulses reaching the efferent cells of the deeper layers may spread horizontally within these layers, or be returned by the recurrent collaterals to the superficial layers, especially II and III.

Added to this extensive system of intracortical connections furnished by the cells with descending axons, are the still more intricate arborizations of the cells with short, ascending, and horizontal axons. These small cells, less numerous in lower mammals, have become tremendously increased in man where their number has been estimated at six billion (Economo). These are small stellate cells with numerous short dendrites, whose axon breaks up close to the cell body into a dense end arborization. Synaptically their short axons are related to the bodies of many pyramidal cells with descending axons. The cell and all its processes are confined to one layer, though the axon may extend horizontally for a short distance before ramifying. The short axon cells are most concentrated in layer IV, but are found in large numbers in all the layers. The cells with horizontal axons are chiefly found in the molecular layer, their long axons often running for considerable distances and making contact with the dendritic terminals of many pyramidal and fusiform cells (Fig. 353). The cells of Martinotti are also present in every layer except the most superficial one. Their dendrites are usually but not always confined to a single layer, their ascending axons have a variable length and distribution. Some from layers V and VI arborize chiefly in III and II. Others extend to the surface and may send collaterals to all the layers through which they pass. Thus while the horizontal and short axon cells have intralaminar connections, the Martinotti cells interconnect the various lamina. Through these cortical circuits nerve impulses reaching the cells of the deeper layers can be returned again and again to the more superficial ones.

From the arrangement of the cell processes described above it is evident that any vertical strip of cortex may be regarded as an elementary functional unit, or aggregation of such units, in which are present all the necessary elements (afferent, internuncial, and efferent) for the formation of complete cortical circuits. The simplest vertical chain of such a unit involves a single synapse, such as the synaptic junction of an afferent fiber with the apical dendrite of an efferent pyramidal cell (Fig. 353). Superimposed upon this fundamental cortical arc, are vertical chains of varying complexity involving a progressively larger number of synaptic junctions. The character of the axonal branchings indicates that in such complex circuits the entering impulses are repeatedly switched from the more peripheral to the deeper layers and vice versa. The impulses return again and again to the same cells and ultimately leave the cortex through efferent fibers. All these vertical chains are interconnected by short neuronal links, represented primarily by the short axon granule cells whose processes arborize within a single layer. Through these short links cortical excitation may spread along the horizontal plane and involve a progressively larger number of vertical chains (Fig. 353). Thus a specific afferent fiber may not only fire off the vertical chains in its immediate vicinity, but may reach more distant chains through the shorter communicating links of the Golgi type II cells. The vertical chains are fundamentally similar in all mammals, but the chains with short links increase in complexity in the higher forms and especially in man whose brain contains enormous numbers of short axon cells. According to Cajal, the intricacy and delicacy of functioning of the human brain is anatomically expressed by the large number of its small cells.

THE CORTICAL AREAS

The cerebral cortex does not have a uniform structure throughout. However, it may be mapped out into a number of areas which differ from each other in the thickness of the cortex as a whole, the thickness and density of the individual layers, and the arrangement and amount of their cells and fibers. In certain areas the structural devia-

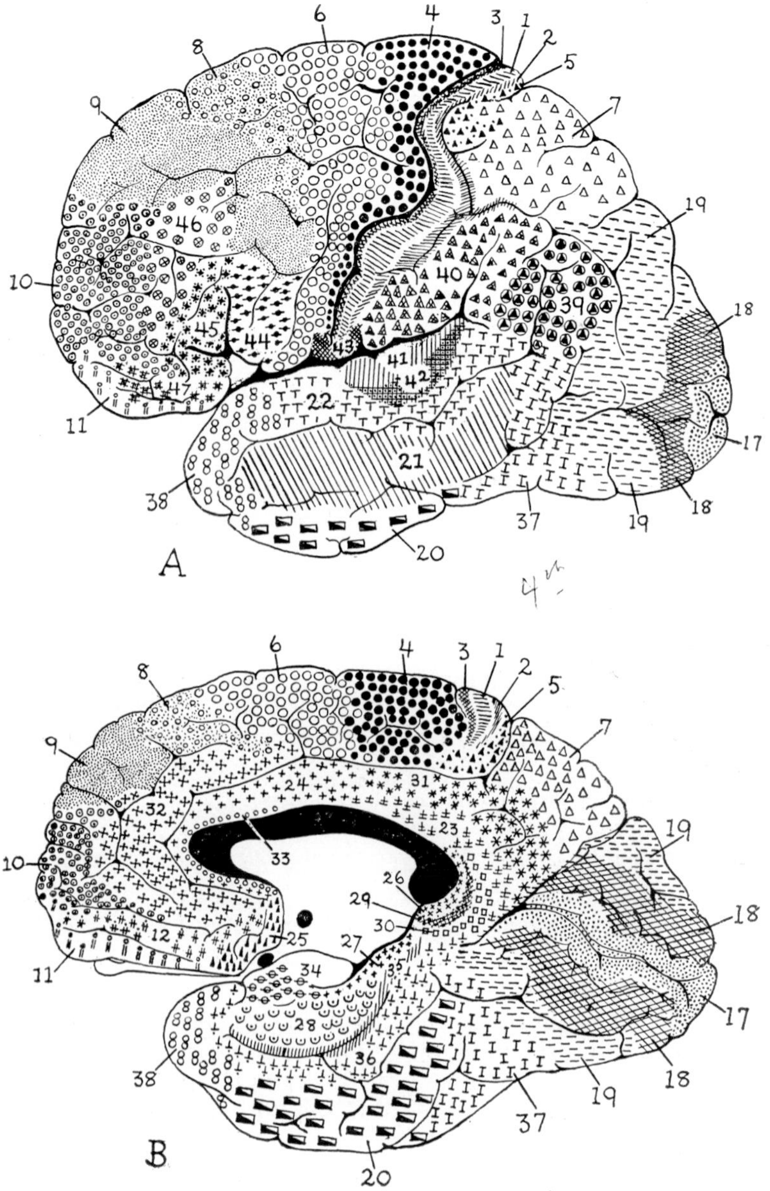

FIG. 354. Cytoarchitectural map of human cortex. *A*, convex surface; *B*, medial surface. (After Brodmann.)

tions are so extreme that the basic sesquilaminated pattern is practically obscured and individual cortical layers can no longer be made out. Such areas are termed *heterotypical* as opposed to the *homotypical* cortex in which the six layers are easily distinguished (Brodmann). Histological surveys based on differences in the arrangement and types of the cells and in the pattern of the myelinated fibers, have furnished several fundamentally similar cortical maps in which the number of areas has been variously estimated. Thus Campbell (1905) described some 20 cortical fields which were increased by Brodmann (1909) to 47, and by von Economo (1929) to 109, while the Vogts

(1919) parcelled the human brain into more than 200 areas. Even this number is apparently insufficient, since recent investigators have found a number of cyto-architectural fields in regions previously considered homogeneous (Rose, Beck). Brodmann's chart which is most widely used for purposes of reference, is shown in Fig. 354.

According to von Economo, all cortical structure is reducible to five fundamental types, based primarily on the relative development of the granule and pyramidal cells. Types 2, 3 and 4, known respectively as the frontal, parietal and polar types are homotypical and constitute by far the largest part of the cortex. The agranular (1) and granulous (5) types are heterotypical and are limited to relatively small regions (Figs. 355, 356).

The *frontal type* is thick and shows the six layers distinctly (Fig. 357C). The pyramidal cells of layers III and V are large and well formed, as are the spindles of layer VI. The granular layers though distinct are rather narrow and composed chiefly of loosely arranged small triangular cells. In the *parietal type* the layers are even more distinct due to the greater depth and density of the granular layers (Fig. 358A and B). The pyramidal layers are thinner, and their cells smaller and more irregularly arranged. The *polar type* found near the frontal and occipital poles is characterized by its thinness and its comparative wealth of cells which are especially numerous in the narrow but well defined granular layers. At the frontal pole the ganglionic layer contains many large pyramidal cells, while at the occipital pole these are as a rule smaller and fewer. The *agranular type* is distinguished by its great thickness and the absence of granule cells (Fig. 357A and B). The pyramidal cells of layers III and V and

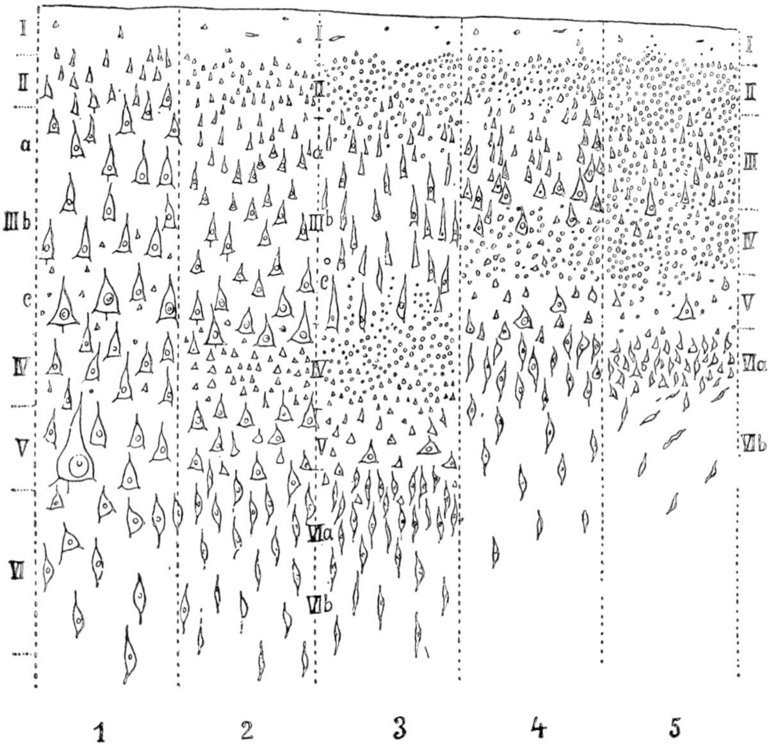

FIG. 355. The five fundamental types of cortical structure. *1*, agranular; *2*, frontal; *3*, parietal; *4*, polar; *5*, granulous (koniocortex). (von Economo.)

well formed and large, but even the smaller cells of layers II and IV are mostly pyramidal in shape, hence the individual layers are difficult to distinguish. This type is best represented by the cortex of the precentral gyrus. The *granulous type* or *koniocortex* is the reverse of type I. It is even thinner than the polar cortex and is composed mainly of densely packed granule cells. These are not only found in layers II and IV, but the other layers also, especially III, show large numbers of such small cells with a consequent reduction of the pyramidal cells. The most striking example of this type is the calcarine cortex, in which there is even a duplication of the internal granular layer (Fig. 358, C).

The general distribution of these five structural types is shown in Fig. 356. The agranular cortex covers the caudal part of the frontal lobe in front of the central sulcus,

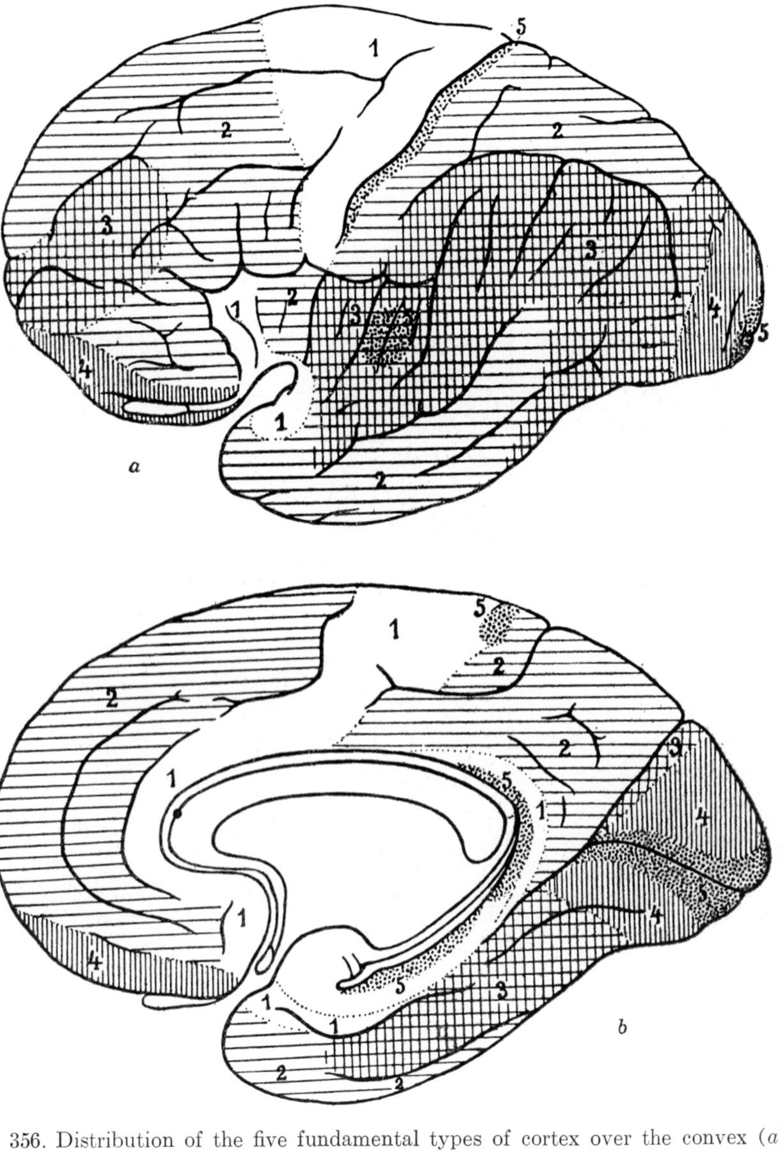

Fig. 356. Distribution of the five fundamental types of cortex over the convex (*a*) and the medial (*b*) surface of the hemisphere. *1*, agranular; *2*, frontal; *3*, parietal; *4*, polar; *5*, granulous (koniocortex). (von Economo.)

the anterior half of the gyrus cinguli, and the anterior portion of the insula. A narrow strip is also found in the retrosplenial region of the gyrus cinguli, and is continued along the hippocampal gyrus and uncus, the latter regions belonging to the allocortex. Since the chief efferent fiber systems arise from these regions, especially from the precentral gyrus, this may be considered as the efferent or motor type of cortex (Figs. 193, 223). Similarly the koniocortex may be regarded as primarily sensory in character, since it is found only in the areas receiving the specific sensory thalamocortical projections. These include the anterior wall of the postcentral gyrus, the walls and lips of the calcarine fissure, and the transverse temporal gyrus of Heschl. Again there is a narrow strip of koniocortex in the retrosplenial region and along the dorsal wall of the hippocampal fissure.

By far the largest part of the hemispheric

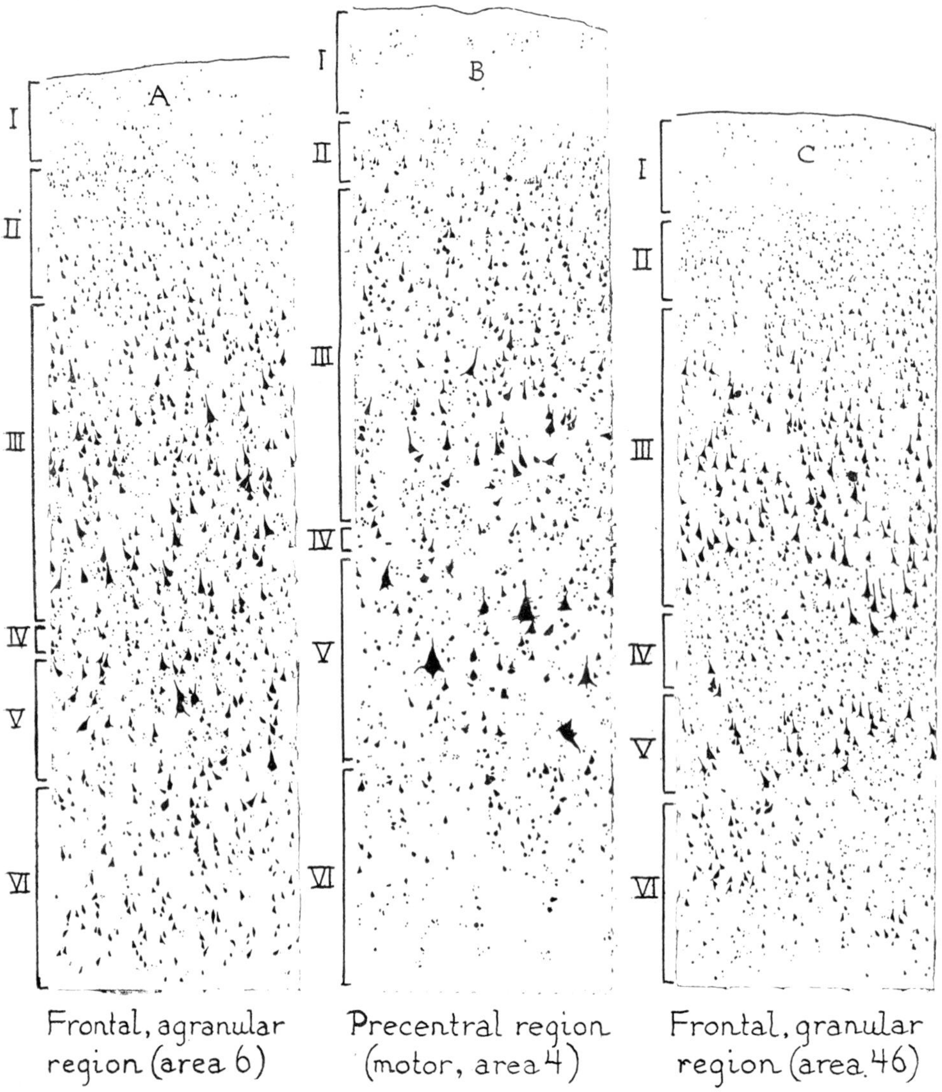

Fig. 357. Cytoarchitectural pictures of several representative cortical areas. (After Campbell.)

surface is covered by homotypical cortex. The frontal type is spread over the larger anterior part of the frontal lobe, the superior parietal lobule, precuneus, and most of the middle and inferior temporal gyri. The parietal type includes chiefly the inferior parietal lobule, the superior temporal gyrus, the fusiform gyrus, and the anterior convex parts of the occipital lobe. The polar type as already stated covers the areas near the frontal and occipital poles. These extensive cortical areas are probably concerned with the higher mnemonic associative functions. Their thalamic connections are chiefly with the association nuclei, such as the medial and lateral thalamic nuclei and the pulvinar. The areas lying behind the central sulcus are primarily related to receptive or psychosensory activities, segregating and recombining the primary afferent impulses into more complex unisensory and multisensory entities. Similarly the frontal areas may form the substratum of the more complex psychomotor activities ultimately expressed through the efferent projection systems of the agranular cortex, especially the pyramidal tract.

Practically every part of the cerebral cortex is connected with subcortical centers by afferent and efferent projection fibers. Strictly speaking there are no circumscribed cortical areas which are purely associative or projective in character. In a general way, however, there are regions from which

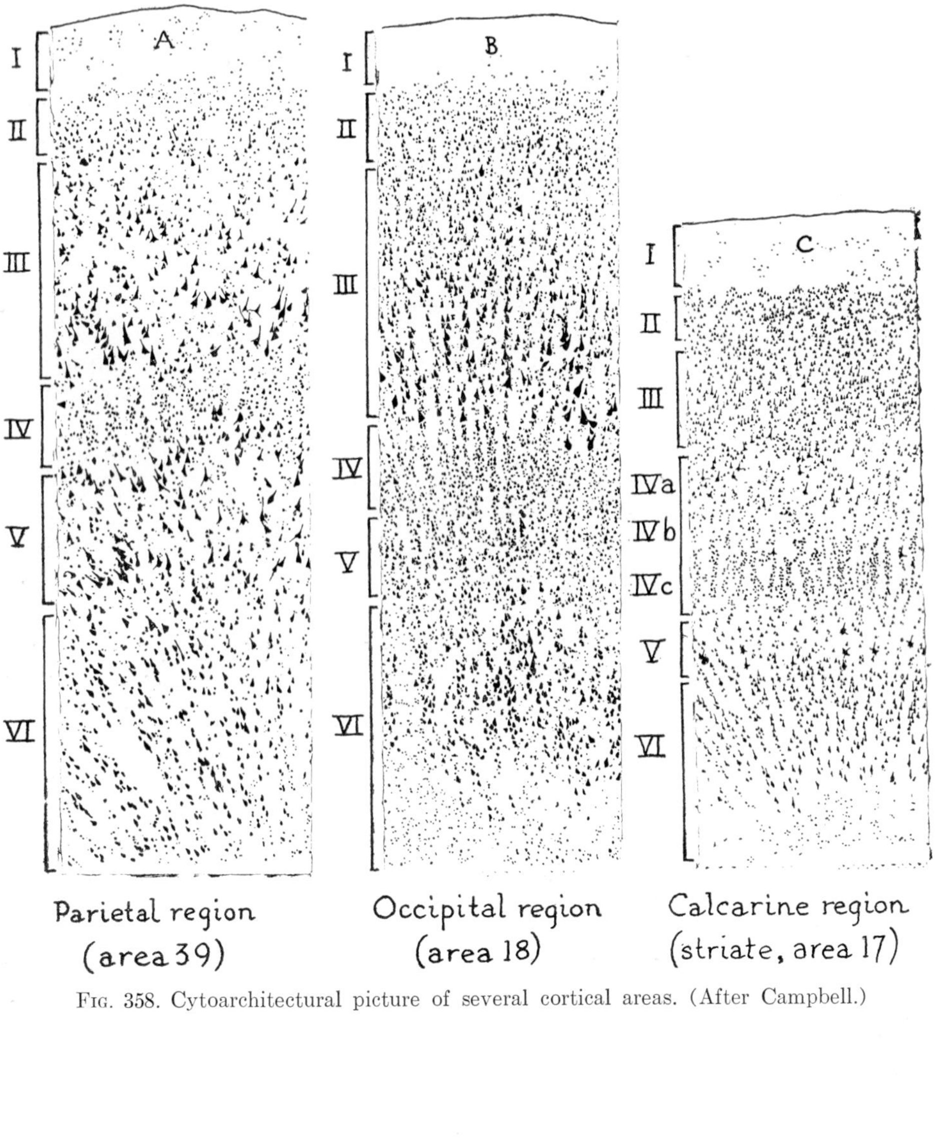

FIG. 358. Cytoarchitectural picture of several cortical areas. (After Campbell.)

the more important descending tracts arise. Directly or through intercalated centers these tracts reach the lower motor neurons for the initiation and control of both somatic and visceral activities (Penfield and Jasper, 1954). These primarily efferent or motor areas from which muscular movements can be elicited by electrical stimulation, are chiefly concentrated in the precentral part of the frontal lobe, but to a lesser extent are also found in widely distributed areas of the parietal, occipital, and temporal lobes. Similarly those more specific regions which receive the direct thalamocortical sensory fibers from the ventral thalamic nuclei and from the geniculate bodies, represent the primary receptive or sensory areas. The remaining portions of the cortex are less directly related to the sensory and motor periphery. They receive their afferent impulses from the association nuclei of the thalamus and more especially from the primary receptive cortical areas. These areas discharge in turn into the efferent centers of the precentral and other regions of the cortex. Such "association areas" are characterized by the wealth of their intracortical connections and constitute by far the largest part of the cerebral cortex.

THE EFFERENT CORTICAL AREAS

The motor area. Area 4 of Brodmann, commonly designated as the motor area, is located on the anterior wall of the central sulcus and adjacent portions of the precentral gyrus (Fig. 354). Broad at the dorsal border of the hemisphere, where it spreads over a considerable part of the precentral gyrus, it constantly narrows in a ventral direction, and at the level of the inferior frontal gyrus is practically limited to the anterior wall of the Rolandic fissure. On the medial surface it comprises the anterior portion of the paracentral lobule, extending as far as the sulcus cinguli. The unusually thick cortex of the motor area (3.5–4.5 mm.) is agranular in structure and its ganglionic layer contains the giant pyramidal cells of Betz whose cell bodies may reach a height of 60–120 micra (Figs. 79, 357B). They are largest in the paracentral lobule near the dorsal border, and smallest in the ventral opercular portion.

The pyramidal tract which transmits impulses for volitional movements from the cortex to the lower motor neurons arises principally from this area. The larger corticobulbar and corticospinal fibers are undoubtedly axons of the giant pyramidal cells (Figs. 193, 223). The more numerous finer fibers probably come from other cells of this region, such as the premotor area (area 6) and possibly from other cortical areas. Due to the crossing of the pyramidal fibers the motor cortex of one side controls the muscular activities of the opposite side, but this crossing is incomplete and all muscles are represented to some extent in the ipsilateral motor area. In muscles, which as a rule can not be voluntarily contracted on one side alone, such as the vocal cords, pharynx, upper face, and trunk the bilateral pyramidal control is most marked and unilateral lesions of the motor cortex produce negligible symptoms.

Electrical stimulation of the motor area evokes discrete isolated movements on the opposite side of the body. Usually the contractions involve the functional muscle groups concerned with a specific movement, but individual muscles, even a single interosseus, may be separately contracted. While the pattern of excitable foci is the same for all mammals, the number of such foci and hence the number of discrete movements is greatly increased in man. Thus flexion or extension at a single finger joint, twitchings at the corners of the mouth, elevation of the palate, protrusion of the tongue, and even vocalization expressed in involuntary cries or exclamations, may all be evoked by careful stimulation of the proper areas. Charts of motor representation, which are in substantial agreement, have been furnished by a number of investigators, notably by Foerster (1936), Penfield and Boldrey

(1937), and by Penfield and Jasper (1954). At the time of surgery they stimulated a large number of human brains under local anesthesia. The location of centers for specific movements may vary from individual to individual, but the sequence of motor representation appears to be constant, e.g., the point which on stimulation produces a movement of the pharynx will always lie nearer to the Sylvian fissure than that producing a movement of the lips, and so on. Ipsilateral movements have not been observed in man, but bilateral responses occur in the eyes, face, tongue, jaw, larynx, and pharynx. According to Penfield and Boldrey, the center for the pharynx (swallowing) lies in the most ventral opercular portion of the precentral gyrus, followed above by those for the tongue, jaw, lips, larynx (vocalization), eyelid, and brow in the order named. Next come the extensive areas for finger movements, the thumb being lowest and the little finger highest, and this is followed by the hand, wrist, elbow, and shoulder. Finally in the most dorsal part are the centers for the hip, knee, ankle, and toes. The last named are situated at the medial border and extend into the paracentral lobule which also contains the centers for the anal and vesicle sphincters (Fig. 359).

There is still considerable controversy regarding the location of the centers for the lower extremity, due in part to the difficulty of stimulating the medial surface. The paracentral lobule undoubtedly "contains the foci of the foot, of the toes, of the bladder and of the rectum" (Foerster). Yet there must be a wide overlapping of motor foci, since Penfield and Boldrey obtained leg movements in twenty-three cases by stimulating the dorsal portion of the precentral gyrus. More recently Scarff (1940) was unable to elicit any leg movements by

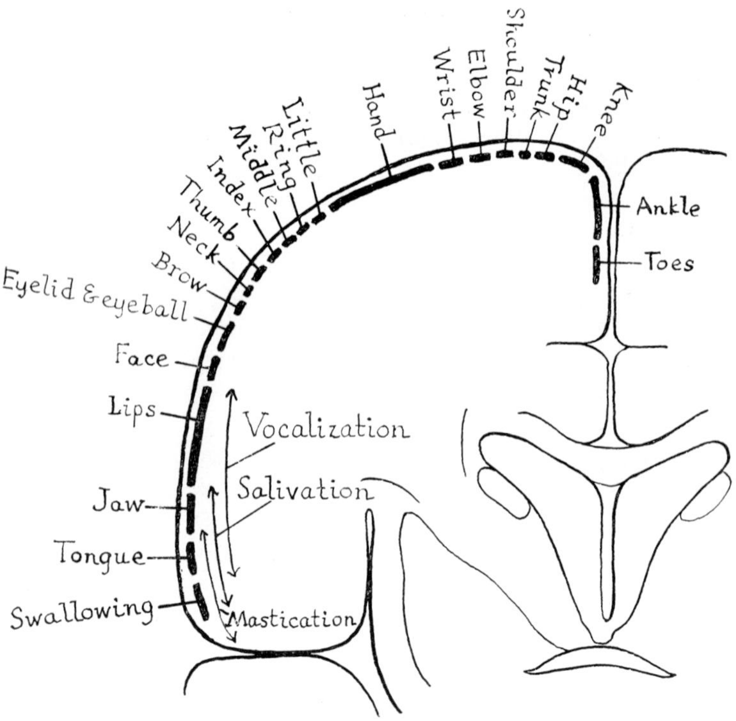

FIG. 359. Diagram of motor sequences in the plane of the central sulcus, as mapped out by threshold stimulation of the human cortex. (Modified from Rasmussen and Penfield, 1947.)

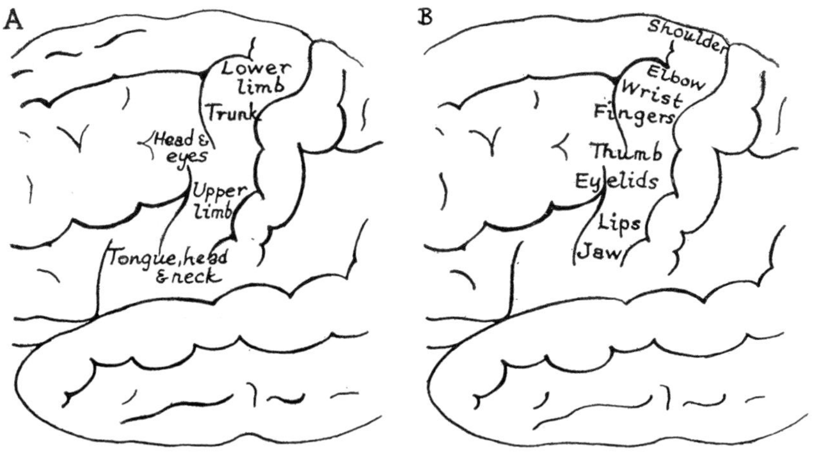

Fig. 360. The representation of the body in the motor area of the human brain (*A*) according to a diagram from Gray's Anatomy and (*B*) according to the observations of J. E. Scarff.

stimulating the lateral surface of the hemisphere in fourteen patients, though he did get such movements in one case when the medial surface was stimulated (Fig. 360). He concludes "that the primary motor area for the upper extremity commonly extends upward on the lateral surface to the superior mesial border, while the leg as a rule is represented only on the mesial surface", i.e., in the paracentral lobule. He believes that this upward shift of the motor area, unique in man, is due to the release of the upper extremity from the burden of locomotion and its consequent elaboration into a more complex motor organ. These new acquisitions have led to an expansion of the motor areas representing the tongue, mouth, lips, and upper extremity, so that the leg areas have been crowded upward and finally pushed over to the medial surface. Focal contractions of the rectal sphincter by stimulating the paracentral lobule, were likewise reported for the first time by this investigator.

Lesions of the motor cortex produce a contralateral paralysis of volitional movements, of the type already described. Since the pyramidal tract is widely spread out in this region, cortical lesions are likely to involve only part of the fibers and produce a paralysis of a single limb (monoplegia) or of the face (Figs. 193, 223). In time there may be considerable restitution, especially for the grosser movements, while the finer isolated movements are permanently lost.

Fulton and his co-workers (Kennard, Jacobsen, Viets) found that ablation of the motor area (area 4) in primates produced a paralysis of the flaccid type, and that spasticity only appeared when the premotor area (area 6) was involved. Fulton believes that the same is applicable to man, and several clinical cases supporting this view have been reported (Shmidt, 1946). More recently, however, in a series of experiments on the monkey, Denny-Brown and Botterell (1948) have found that spasticity accompanied the paralytic manifestations of all area 4 lesions, and was most enduring in total ablations. These authors regard hemiplegic spasticity as a sign of pyramidal or motor area involvement. In extensive lesions of the human pyramidal tract below the cortical level, especially in the internal capsule and pes pedunculi, spasticity is a common feature, but the pyramidal tract receives contributions from both the motor and premotor areas, and perhaps from other cortical areas as well. A full discussion of the structure and significance of the motor area may

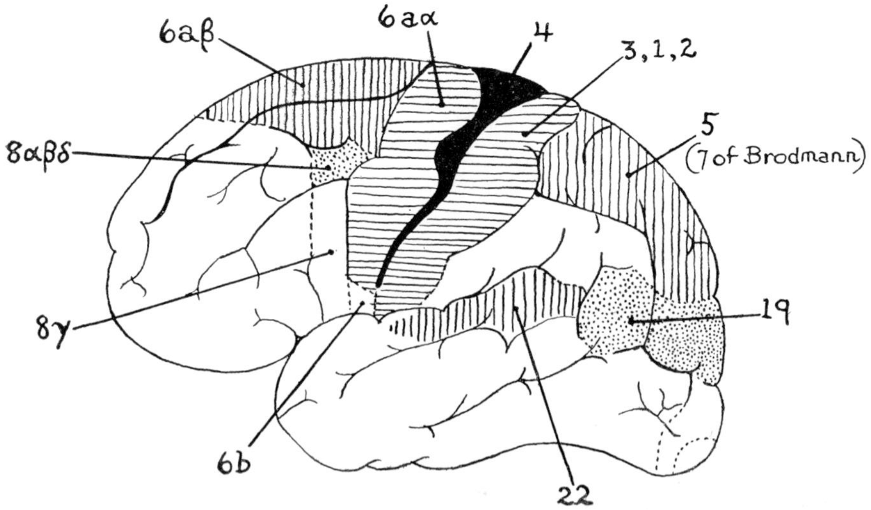

FIG. 361. The areas of electrically excitable cortex on the lateral surface of the human brain. The motor area is shown in black, the extrapyramidal areas are hatched except for the eye fields which are stippled. (After Foerster.)

be found in the *"Precentral Motor Cortex"* edited by P. C. Bucy (1949).

Extrapyramidal motor areas. The premotor area (area 6) lies immediately in front of the motor area. It likewise runs dorsoventrally along the whole lateral aspect of the frontal lobe and is continued on the medial surface to the sulcus cinguli (Fig. 354). Near the dorsal border it is quite broad and includes the caudal portion of the superior frontal gyrus. Proceeding ventrally it narrows rapidly and at the operculum is completely limited to the precentral gyrus. Its histological structure resembles that of the motor area, being principally composed of large well-formed pyramidal cells, but the giant cells of Betz are altogether lacking (Fig. 357A). This region also responds to electrical stimulation but stronger currents are required to evoke movements than are necessary in the case of area 4. Area 6 is usually divided into a large upper portion (6aα) lying in front of the leg and arm area of the motor cortex, and a small narrower portion (6aβ) in front of the face area (Fig. 361).

Foerster and others have shown that faradic stimulation of area 6 gives rise to two kinds of contralateral movements: isolated movements of individual muscles resembling those of the motor area, and more complex synergic movements such as flexion of the contralateral extremities or turning of head and eyes to the opposite side. Similar complex movements involving the facial, masticatory, laryngeal, and pharyngeal muscles are evoked by stimulating the lower portion of this area (6b). The isolated movements are apparently due to a transmission of the stimulation to area 4, for they are no longer elicitable when area 6 is isolated from the motor area by a cortical incision or when the motor area or pyramidal tract are destroyed. The more complex mass movements remain. These must be mediated by extrapyramidal fibers which pass by way of the thalamus, basal ganglia and other subcortical centers to the lower motor neurons. In man such fibers have been traced from areas 6 and 8 to the thalamus, hypothalamus, globus pallidus, subthalamic nucleus, zona incerta, nucleus of Forel's field, and nucleus ruber (Meyer, 1949). Thus the premotor area relays cortical impulses to area 4 for the execution of the finer isolated movements. It is also capable of mediating grosser volitional synergies related to postural adjustments and the more instinctive activities of locomotion and defense.

Immediately in front of the premotor area is a narrow strip of cortex which is likewise motor in function and responds to strong faradic stimulation. This area 8 differs cytoarchitecturally from the motor and premotor cortex by having distinct granular layers, and thus belongs to the sesquilaminated frontal type. Its dorsal portion is usually included as part of the premotor area. Its middle segment, which forms the caudal portion of the middle frontal gyrus, constitutes the frontal eye field designated in Foerster's map as $8\alpha\beta\delta$ (Fig. 361). Stimulation of this area causes strong conjugate deviation of the eyes, and occasional vertical movements have been described (Foerster). It is believed to be the cortical center for the voluntary scanning and spying movements of the eyes. Recent investigations indicate, however, that the frontal eye center is represented by a more extensive area, including not only the caudal part of the middle frontal gyrus (area 8) but also the contiguous portion of areas 6 and 4 (Rasmussen and Penfield, 1948). The lower part of area 8 and adjacent portion of area 6 which together form the opercular part of the inferior frontal gyrus, have become considerably modified in man and form the area of Broca, believed to be concerned with the motor formulation of speech (areas 44 and 45 of Brodmann).

The extrapyramidal areas are not limited to the frontal lobe, but are also found behind the central fissure in regions which otherwise must be considered as receptive or sensory in character (Fig. 361). Strong faradic stimulation of the postcentral gyrus (areas 3, 1, 2) likewise produces both isolated and complex movements, the former again depending on the integrity of the motor area. Similar mass movements are elicited by stimulation of the superior parietal lobule (area 7 of Brodmann) and the superior temporal gyrus, while conjugate deviation of the eyes to the opposite side may be evoked from area 19 of the occipital lobe (occipital eye field).

Summarizing the results of stimulating the various cortical areas it may be said that the motor cortex represents the specific area for the production of isolated movements. Any such movements evoked from other regions depend on the integrity of the motor area. There are a number of areas capable of responding to stimulation with complex synergic movements of the head, eyes, trunk and extremities, even when the motor area and the pyramidal tract are destroyed. These extrapyramidal areas (Foerster), especially those of the frontal lobe, constitute the cortical centers of the extrapyramidal motor pathway whose fibers are relayed in the thalamus and other subcortical nuclei before reaching the motor cells of the cranial and spinal nerves. Their significance in the control of postural adjustments and of the grosser volitional movements of instinctive behavior have been discussed in connection with the corpus striatum and diencephalon (p. 428).

We know from daily experience that the cortex exerts a strong influence on autonomic activies, both sympathetic and parasympathetic, as shown in the cardiovascular, digestive and other visceral changes that accompany different mental states. The cortical connections with the hypothalamus may be briefly mentioned. One important channel is undoubtedly furnished by the corticothalamic fibers from the prefrontal cortex to the dorsomedial thalamic nucleus, from which impulses may be relayed to the hypothalamus by the periventricular fiber system. In addition, direct corticohypothalamic fibers are projected from the premotor region (areas 6 and 8) and the posterior orbital cortex (area 47), and there is evidence that some fibers or collaterals of the pyramidal tract may terminate in the hypothalamus (Spiegel and Hunsicker, 1936).

While cortical control of autonomic activities is of great functional importance in emotional states, the cortex is probably not concerned with the finer regulation of vegetative activities, which is mediated at the hypothalamic level. In decorticate animals autonomic regulation is not disturbed to any considerable extent (Hess, 1949).

Another important system of efferent cortical fibers is represented by the extensive corticopontile tracts which arise from the frontal, temporal, parietal, and occipital regions of the cortex. These tracts have been recently reinvestigated in man and the monkey (Meyer et al., 1947; Beck, 1950; Nyby and Jansen, 1951). The massive *frontopontile tract* (bundle of Arnold) arises mainly from the lateral and dorsal convexity of the whole prefrontal cortex (areas 10, 9, 8, 45, 46) with the exception of the orbital region and the extreme frontal pole. A smaller contingent comes from the precentral region (areas 4 and 6). The prefrontal fibers pass through the anterior limb of the internal capsule, the precentral ones through the posterior limb. On reaching the midbrain the frontopontile tract forms the medial one-fifth of the pes pedunculi, and is distributed to the medial pontile nuclei (Fig. 307). Other corticopontile tracts arise from the superior, middle, and inferior temporal gyri (*temporopontile*), and from the superior and inferior parietal lobules (*parietopontile*). A smaller *occipitopontile* bundle comes chiefly from area 18 of the occipital lobe (Nyby and Jansen, 1951). The temporal, parietal, and occipital fibers, collectively known as the *bundle of Türck*, descend through the retrolenticular and sublenticular portions of the internal capsule. These fibers occupy the lateral fifth of the pes pedunculi, and are distributed mainly to the lateral and dorsolateral cell groups of the pons. Through these tracts the cerebral cortex is brought into intimate association with the synergic regulating mechanism of the cerebellum. The ataxia and hypotonia sometimes observed in frontal and temporal lesions may be due to injury of these corticocerebellar connections.

A survey of the various descending fibers described above suggests that at least three main streams of efferent impulses emerge from the cerebral cortex. One is primarily concerned with the finer nonpostural discrete movements of skilled activity. Another regulates the somatic and visceral reactions of affective or instinctive behavior, while the third acts on the synergic regulating cerebellar mechanism. The first is mediated largely through the corticospinal and corticobulbar tracts, the second through the corticothalamic and other extrapyramidal fibers, the third through the cortico-ponto-cerebellar system. The coöperation of all three is essential to the production of properly balanced and properly executed pallial reactions.

Suppressor areas. There are certain special areas in the cerebral cortex whose stimulation suppresses the spontaneous electrical activity of area 4, inhibits responses elicited from the motor area, and causes relaxation of contracted muscles. The first suppressor area was reported by Hines (1936) in the monkey as a narrow strip lying between areas 4 and 6, to which the name *strip area* (4s) was given. A similar area was found in the chimpanzee (Dusser de Barenne et al., 1941) and there is evidence that such an area also exists in man (Garol and Bucy, 1944). Other suppressor zones in the monkey and chimpanzee have been located in area 8 of the frontal lobe, area 2 of the parietal lobe, area 19 of the occipital lobe, and more recently in area 24 of the cingular gyrus (Smith, 1945; Fig. 362). Stimulation of area 24 in addition causes marked autonomic changes, such as alterations in blood pressure, heart rate, and respiration. It is of interest that the only efferent cortical connections of the suppressor strips are with areas 32 and 31 on the medial surface of the hemisphere. These areas apparently receive cortical afferents only from the suppressor strips. Areas 32

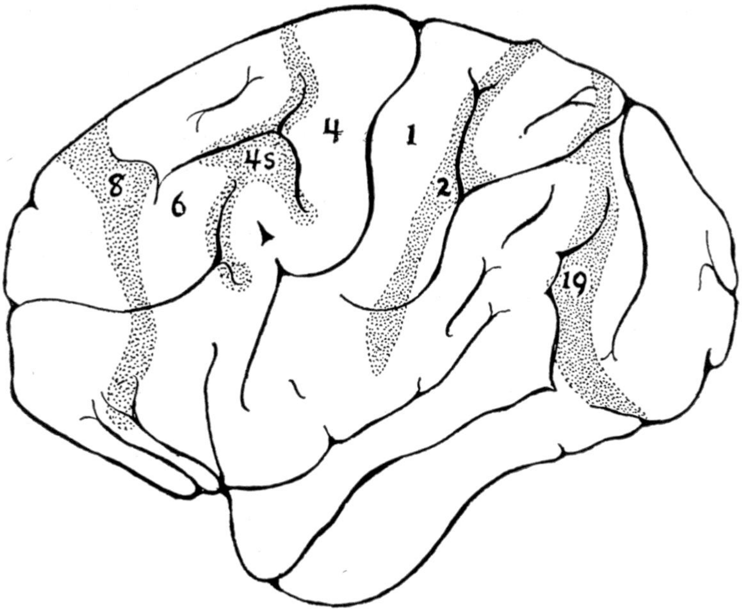

FIG. 362. Diagram of suppressor areas in the chimpanzee. (Modified from McCulloch, in Bucy's *Precentral Motor Cortex.*)

and 31 are not themselves suppressor areas, but constitute an important focal region concerned with the activities of the cortex as a whole (Le Gros Clark, 1948). It must be emphasized that with the possible exception of 4s, suppressor areas have not been definitely identified in the human brain, nor is there any clear understanding of the role which these suppressor areas play in the normal functioning of the cortex.

The pathway through which the suppressor strips inhibit the spontaneous electrical activity of the motor area probably involves the caudate nucleus, globus pallidus, and thalamus. The presence of direct corticocaudate projections from all the suppressor areas has been physiologically demonstrated in the monkey and chimpanzee (Dusser de Barenne et al., 1942). These cortical projections were corroborated anatomically by Glees (1944) who was able to trace fine degenerating fibers from several suppressor areas to the caudate nucleus in the cat. It is believed that activation of the suppressor areas in some way interrupts or reduces the interplay between thalamus and cortex, perhaps by preventing impulses which reach the thalamus from being relayed to the cortex (Ward, 1948). In addition to the corticocaudate fibers, there is physiological evidence that the suppressor areas also give origin to fibers which descend through the internal capsule, midbrain, and pons, and terminate in the bulbar "suppressor center" of the reticular formation, whence impulses are relayed to the motor cells of the cord by reticulospinal fibers (McCulloch et al., 1946). It is probable that suppression of motor activities is largely mediated through this descending pathway (Fig. 197). As in the case of the cortical suppressor areas, stimulation of the bulbar suppressor center likewise causes relaxation of contracted muscles, and inhibition of reflex and cortically induced responses (Magoun and Rhines, 1946).

THE PRIMARY RECEPTIVE AREAS

The **somesthetic sensory area** which subserves general somatic sensibility, superficial as well as deep, is principally located on the postcentral gyrus and its medial extension in the paracentral lobule (Fig. 354). Histologically the gyrus is composed of three narrow strips of cortex (3, 1, 2) which differ in their architectural structure. The most anterior strip (area 3), facing the central sulcus, is very thin (2 mm. or less). It is composed principally of granular elements, hence belongs to the granulous type of Economo. Areas 1 and 2, forming respectively the crown and posterior wall of the postcentral gyrus, have the sesquilaminated structure of the frontal type (type 2).

The postcentral gyrus receives the thalamic projections from the posterior ventral nuclei, which relay impulses from the medial lemniscus and secondary trigeminal tracts. The various regions of the body are represented in specific portions of the postcentral gyrus, the pattern corresponding to that of the motor area (Fig. 359). Thus the face area lies in the most ventral part, while above this are placed the sensory areas for the hand, arm, trunk, leg, and foot in the order named, the lower extremity probably extending into the paracentral lobule. There are many observations which suggest that the somesthetic area is not limited to the postcentral gyrus, but may extend caudally into the superior and inferior parietal lobule, and frontally into the precentral gyrus (de Barenne, Head). Dusser de Barrene has found that application of strychnine to the postcentral gyrus in monkeys induced cutaneous sensory hyperesthesias, most marked on the opposite side but present to some extent on the same side. Deep sensibility appeared to have a contralateral representation only. Whether the discriminative aspects of tactile sensibility are bilaterally represented in the human cortex is not definitely known. Clinically the sensory defects caused by cortical lesions of this area are noticeable only on the opposite side.

The sensory cortex is not primarily concerned with the recognition of crude sensory modalities, such as pain, temperature, and mere contact. These apparently enter consciousness at the level of the thalamus, and their appreciation is retained even after complete destruction of the sensory area. "The sensory activity of the cortex . . . endows sensation with three discriminative faculties. These are: (a) recognition of spatial relations; (b) a graduated response to stimuli of different intensity; (c) appreciation of similarity and difference in external objects brought into contact with the surface of the body" (Head). Hence in lesions of the sensory area there is loss of appreciation of passive movement, of two point discrimination, and of ability to differentiate various intensities of stimuli. These faculties have a definite spatial orientation in the sensory area and may correspondingly be disturbed to an unequal degree, depending on the location and extent of the injury. Spatial relationship is most severely affected when the lesion is in the most anterior portion of the postcentral gyrus. The appreciation of similarities and differences are related to the middle portion of this gyrus. Lesions of the posterior wall of the gyrus and adjacent portions of the supramarginal convolution and superior parietal lobule, disturb the faculty of discriminating between stimuli of different intensities. In severe lesions the patient, though aware of the stimulus and its sensory modality is, unable to locate accurately the point touched; to gauge the direction and extent of passive movement; to distinguish between different weights, textures, or degrees of temperature; and as a result is unable to identify objects by merely feeling them (astereognosis). The more complicated the test, the more evident becomes the sensory defect. With all this there is a variability of response so that a definite threshold for a given sensation can not be established.

Penfield (1949) has found a second sensory area in man, located in the upper lip of the Sylvian fissure. Its position varies somewhat in different individuals. It may be just anterior, or just posterior, to the lower end of the Rolandic motor and sensory strips. Stimulation of this area produces sensations resembling those obtained from the postcentral gyrus, such as tingling, numbness, and a sense of movement. However, the area for hand representation lies dorsal to that for the foot. The function of this area is not clear, and its extirpation produces no discernible sensory deficit.

The **visual receptive area** (area 17) is located in the walls of the calcarine fissure and adjacent portion of the cuneus and lingual gyrus. It occasionally extends around the occipital pole to the lateral surface of the hemisphere (Figs. 335, 354). The exceedingly thin cortex of this area (1.5–2.5 mm.) is the most striking example of the heterotypical granulous cortex (type 5). Layers II and III are narrow and contain numerous small pyramidal cells, hardly larger than the typical granule cells (Fig. 358C). Layer IV is very thick and subdivided by a light band into three sublayers. The upper and lower sublayers are packed with small granule cells. In the middle lighter layer, the small cells are fewer, and scattered between them are large stellate cells (giant stellate cells of Meynert). The light layer is occupied by the greatly thickened outer band of Baillarger, here known as the band of Gennari, which is visible to the naked eye in sections of the fresh cortex and has given this region the name of *area striata* (Fig. 363). Layer V is relatively narrow and poor in cells, but scattered among them are isolated large pyramidal cells which may reach a height of 60 micra (Fig. 358C).

The visual cortex receives the geniculocalcarine tract whose course and exact projection have been discussed in an earlier chapter (Fig. 329, p. 402). The macular fibers terminate in the caudal third of the calcarine area, those from the paracentral and peripheral retinal areas end in respectively more rostral portions. In man, complete destruction of the visual cortex on one side produces a crossed homonymous hemianopia, i.e., loss of the contralateral visual field. Destruction of both striate areas causes total blindness. Other mammals, such as dogs and monkeys, are still able to distinguish between light intensities after ablation of the visual cortex.

The **auditory receptive area** (areas 41,

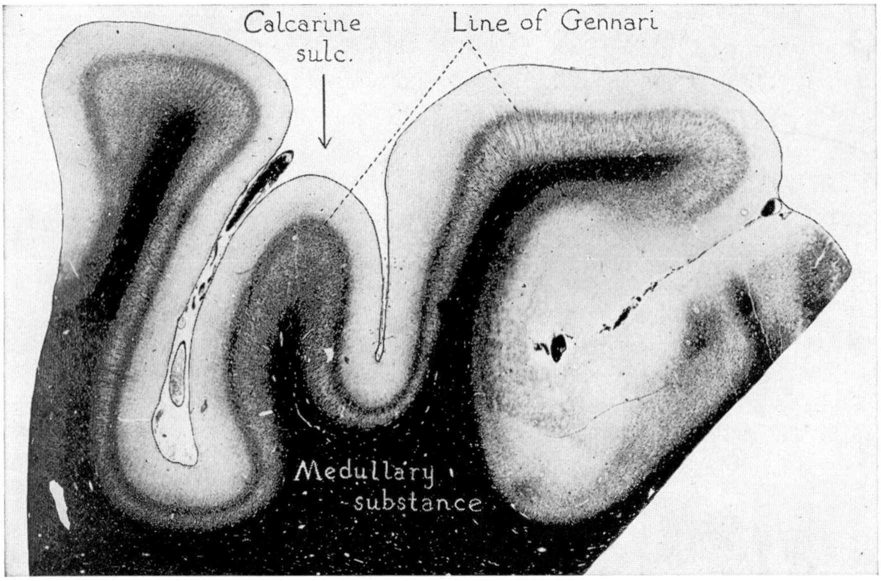

Fig. 363. Frontal section through calcarine cortex (area striata) showing extent of line of Gennari. Weigert's myelin stain. Photograph.

42) is located on the two transverse gyri of Heschl which lie on the dorsal surface of the superior temporal convolution, buried in the floor of the Sylvian fissure (Figs. 335, 354). Area 41 occupies the middle of the anterior transverse gyrus and a portion of the posterior, and is surrounded by area 42 which extends somewhat on the lateral surface in the middle region of the superior temporal convolution. The two areas are cytoarchitecturally different. Area 41, though relatively thick (3 mm.), is composed of koniocortex resembling that of areas 3 and 17. Area 42 has the sesquilaminated cortex of the parietal type (type 3, Fig. 355). A distinctive feature of the latter is the presence of a number of large pyramidal cells in layer III.

The auditory area receives the geniculotemporal fibers (auditory radiation) from the medial geniculate body. Since these fibers conduct impulses from both ears, hearing is bilaterally represented, hence unilateral lesions cause only partial deafness (Fig. 258). According to Penfield and Evans, removal of one temporal lobe produces an impairment of sound localization on the opposite side, especially as regards judgment of the distance from which the sounds are coming. The integration and interpretation of auditory impulses is highly elaborated in the cortex of man. However, it is still uncertain whether the fundamental auditory sensations, such as the pitch and quality of sound, may not also be appreciated to some extent by subcortical structures. In animals, ablation of both temporal lobes does not apparently cause total deafness.

The temporal cortex probably also contains a primary receptive center for vestibular impulses, though its exact location has not been fully ascertained. When the temporal convolutions are sensitized with strychnine, stimulation of the labyrinth produces convulsive movements (Spiegel), but these movements fail to appear when the eighth nerve is destroyed. In man, sensations of dizziness or vertigo occur not only in vestibular disease, but may accompany irritative lesions of the temporal lobes. The work of Winkler suggests that vestibular fibers in part terminate in the cochlear nuclei and reach the cortex by way of the lateral lemniscus and auditory radiation. If this is the case, areas 41 and 42 would constitute receptive centers for both auditory and vestibular impulses.

The **gustatory and olfactory receptive areas** have not been determined with certainty. The work of Börnstein suggests that taste is located in the most ventral (opercular) portion of the postcentral gyrus, and this view has been strengthened by more recent experimental work (Patton, Ruch and Walker). The primary centers for smell are probably located in the uncus and anterior portion of the hippocampal gyrus, since the lateral olfactory stria terminates in these areas (Fig. 344).

THE GENERAL NATURE OF CORTICAL FUNCTIONING

One of the most striking features of the human brain is its elaborate neural mechanism for the more complex correlation and discrimination of sensory impulses, and the greater utilization of former reactions. The principal function of this mechanism may be termed *associative memory* and such reactions *mnemonic* (memory) reactions. In man, the acquired changes which occur in the cortex after birth permit the neurons to alter subsequent stimuli reaching the cortex. This ability to retain, modify, and reuse neuronal chains provides the basis of conscious and unconscious memory, of personal experience, and of individually acquired neural mechanisms. Other animals utilize individual experience and thus "learn". However, it is very doubtful if any other animal than man summates experience by transmitting it to other individuals and generations in ever varying amounts. The symbolization necessary for this summation undoubtedly requires a great complexity of the pallial mechanism for associative memory. It has been estimated that the cerebral cortex contains nearly 14 billion nerve cells, and by far the greater number of these are utilized for the above activities.

In a general way, the central sulcus of Rolando divides the brain into a posterior receptive portion and an anterior portion related more closely to efferent or motor functions. In the posterior part are located all the primary receptive areas which receive specific sensory impulses from the lower centers of the brain, and hence indirectly from the sensory periphery. The stimuli entering these primary areas produce sensations of a sharply defined character such as distinct vision and hearing, sharply localized touch, and accurate sensations of position and movements. However, these sensations have not attained the perceptual level necessary for the recognition of an object. This requires the association of primary stimuli into progressively more complicated sensory entities. The regions in immediate contact with the receptive centers, known as *parasensory areas*, serve for the combination and elaboration of the primary impulses into more complex unisensory perceptions, capable of recall under appropriate conditions. In the more distant association areas the various sensory fields are overlapping, e.g., the inferior parietal lobule and adjacent portions of the occipital and temporal lobes. In these areas the combinations are still more complicated and are expressed as multisensory perceptions of a progressively higher order. Thus tactile and kinesthetic stimuli are built up into perceptions of form, size, and texture (stereognosis). Visual impulses are similarly compounded into perceptions of visual object recognition. Hence any object comes to be ultimately represented by a constellation of memories, compounded from several sensory channels, as a result of previous experience. When sensory impulses initiated by feeling or seeing an object are capable of exciting these memory constellations, the object is "recognized," i.e., is remembered as having been seen or felt before. This arousal of the associative mnemonic complexes by afferent cortical impulses may be termed "gnosis" and forms the basis of understanding and knowledge. Disorders of this mechanism caused by lesions in the association areas are usually known as gnostic disturbances or *agnosias*. The tactile, visual, or auditory stimuli evoked by an object no longer arouse the appropriate memories, hence the object and its uses appear unfamiliar and strange. When such gnostic disturbances involve the far more complicated associative mechanisms underlying the comprehension of language, they are known as *aphasias*. The symbolic meanings of spoken or written words and of their interrelationships in phrases and sentences are no longer understood, and as a result there is also impairment of appropriate and purposeful behavior. In extensive lesions of certain association areas, such as the inferior parietal lobule and adjacent regions, the gnostic disturbances may have the character of a severe intellectual deterioration. In such patients the understanding, the importance, and the relationships of things in the external world are wholly disrupted, a condition which Head has designated as *semantic aphasia*.

In the frontal lobe there is a similar superimposition of more complex associative areas upon the primary ones, but here they are more closely related to the expressive phases of cortical activity. Immediately in front of the Rolandic sulcus are the primary motor centers of the precentral gyrus, concerned with the contraction of individual muscles or muscle groups for specific movements of the limbs or face. Destruction of these centers produces a motor paralysis, just as destruction of the primary sensory areas causes blindness, deafness or loss of touch and movement sensations. In front of the motor area lie the centers for progressively higher types of motor expression. The premotor area is concerned with the more complex purposful skilled movements related to locomotion, manual manipulation, mastication and swallowing, and the more complicated acts of motor speech formulation. The execution of these pallial acts may be termed *"praxis"* and is based on memory constellations of similar acts previously performed. Lesions of this area do not cause paralysis of muscular movement, but there is difficulty or inability to carry out complex purposive movements, a condition usually known as *apraxia.* When such disturbances affect the motor formulation of speech, they are known as *motor aphasias,* but in this case it is the expressive phases of speech which are most severely affected. The patient has difficulty in forming words both in speaking and writing, and his memory for the proper sequence of letters in a word, or of words in a sentence is likewise impaired. The misspelled and mispronounced words are used in the correct sense, and his appreciation of the meaning of words in complex relations is apparently unimpaired. It is the formulation rather than the comprehension of speech which is primarily disturbed.

Still more forward are the extensive prefrontal areas, of relatively late phylogenetic acquisition, which are strongly developed only in primates and especially in man. These areas receive a strong projection from the dorsomedial thalamic nucleus and are thus brought into relation with the autonomic centers of the hypothalamus. They are connected by the cingulum and uncinate fasciculus with the anterior portions of the temporal lobes which are believed to be concerned with the storage of specific memories (Penfield and Jasper, 1954). Directly or indirectly they are also connected with the parietal and adjacent occipitotemporal association areas. It is the opinion of some that the complex memory patterns formed in the post-Rolandic brain are transmitted to the prefrontal area, to be synthesized into mnemonic constellations of a still more complex type, which perhaps form the basis of abstract thinking and of the higher creative activities. In the prefrontal region these highly discriminative cortical activities are blended with the activities of the hypothalamus and medial thalamus, representing the more primitive affective components of consciousness, which energize and give initiative and direction to conscious mental processes. Russell (1948) believes that the prefrontal areas are not primarily concerned with memory or general intelligence, but with the establishment and conditioning of emotional reactions. Hence they are of great importance during childhood and the growing years when behavioral patterns are being impressed on the brain. Such emotional reactions become less important after maturity when behavior patterns have already become firmly crystallized.

Considerable information regarding the functions of the prefrontal cortex in man has been obtained from cases where a prefrontal *leucotomy* or *lobotomy* has been performed for the relief of morbid anxiety and of obsessive-compulsive states in psychotic patients. The operation is usually performed bilaterally, and has as its purpose the cutting of the fiber connections of the frontal association areas. Introduced by Moniz in 1936, lobotomies with varied and greatly improved techniques have now been carried out on thousands of human subjects with considerable success.This neurosurgical procedure permitted many institutionalized patients to return home and even to resume their former activities. Moreover, a considerable number of lobotomies have now been performed for the relief of chronic intractable pain of organic origin, when other drastic measures, such as massive doses of narcotics and even cordotomy have proved of no avail (Falconer, 1948; Watts and Freeman, 1948; Scarff, 1949). After the operation the patient no longer complains of spontaneous pain nor does he appear to be in any distress, though he acknowledges when asked that pain is still present. Apparently relief is due to the absence of anxiety and fear usually associated with the pain. Since these operations are performed on patients of normal mentality, it is naturally of great importance to know the possible intellectual and behavioral defects that might be incurred in such a drastic procedure.

The results of numerous lobotomies have been critically discussed in a number of recent publications (Freeman and Watts, 1949; Partridge, 1950; Denny-Brown, 1951). The data are often difficult to interpret, but it seems fairly certain that the above operations are followed by a varying degree of intellectual deterioration, and more especially by changes in emotional behavior indicative of a lowered ethical standard. Intellectual damage is difficult to evaluate. General memory returns rapidly and ordinary intelligence tests are accurately performed. However, tests which require familiarity with abstract concepts are poorly answered. There is great distractibility, judgment is poor, initiative is reduced. Mental concentration and the capacity for sustained intellectual effort are impaired, with consequent difficulty or inability to solve complicated problems, especially those of an abstract nature. Rylander (1948) believes that the intellectual damage may be severe, and cautions against operating on nonpsychotic patients of a high intelligence level.

More striking are the alterations in emotional behavior, characterized by Freeman and Watts as a lessening of "consciousness of the self", a narrowing of the patient's mental horizon to the immediate present and to his own person. The patient is easily amused, careless in personal habits, unconcerned in social relations, little affected by criticism. His emotional reactions are abrupt, transient and superficial, and often accompanied by outspoken tactlessness. Pain and hardship are not associated with anxiety, nor is there much concern about financial or domestic difficulties. There is inability to gauge or appreciate the gravity of a situation, and to maintain a responsible attitude towards it. These are the most enduring changes which can be attributed to the operation, and they are probably responsible for the successful abolition of morbid anxiety and obsessional states (Freeman and Watts, 1949). In summary, it may be stated that large bilateral lesions of the prefrontal cortex not only cause defects of the intellect, especially as regards judgment and the capacity for solving abstract problems, but also produce disturbances of initiative, of the will, and of emotional behavior with resulting regressive changes in conduct and ethical standards. All these belong to the expressive aspect of the personality, and may be regarded as motor defects of a high psychic order.

Anatomical studies of lobotomized brains indicate that section of the central portion of the prefrontal white matter is most effective in securing improvement of mental states, and that the more ventral fibers which serve the orbital surface are of special importance (Meyer and McLardy, 1948). The specific fiber systems responsible for the effects have not been definitely ascertained. There is evidence that the results of lobotomy depend primarily on the interruption of the thalamofrontal projections, yet improvement has been found in cases where these fiber bundles were left intact (Meyer and Beck, 1945). Moreover, the operation severs connections between the prefrontal cortex and the anterior portions of the temporal lobes, and the fiber systems of the anterior cingulate gyrus may also be involved. In monkeys, experimental ablation of these areas likewise causes marked changes in emotional behavior. It is possible therefore that the relaxation of anxiety and tension, may be attributable to section of several prefrontal fiber systems.

The above discussion does not imply that there are two distinct divisions to cortical functioning: receptive-apperceptive and expressive. On the contrary, they are two integrated aspects of a continuous process, and every mnemonic reaction probably requires the cooperation of the entire brain. A lesion in any part of the mnemonic apparatus will cause an impairment of cortical functioning as a whole, the severity of the symptoms corresponding to the amount of brain substance destroyed. However, the organization of the cortex and its relation to the sensory and motor periphery are such, that disturbances of understanding will be more marked in lesions of the caudal half. In extensive lesions of the frontal lobe the expressive functions will be most severely affected.

It is an interesting, but unexplained, fact that in man most of the higher cortical functions are vested principally in one cerebral hemisphere, the left one in right-handed individuals, a phenomenon known as "cerebral dominance". The various agnosias and apraxias discussed above, occur only when the dominant hemisphere is damaged, lesions of the other hemisphere producing as a rule no recognizable disturbances.

The structure and function of the basic levels of the human nervous system have been presented in the foregoing pages. The reader should have acquired a familiarity with the major ascending and descending pathways that connect and integrate these important levels. The executive suites are located on the uppermost levels. All essential information must be relayed upward to these central agencies within the cerebral cortex. Memory reactions and evaluating processes are thus set in motion. Ultimate decisions and orders are then issued to lower levels and carried to final completion by subordinate nerves and muscles in the periphery. Normally this intricate system functions smoothly. Short circuits, physical and chemical accidents, or death to key neurons can suddenly interrupt or alter the lines of communication. The subordinate cells and fibers of lower levels can, at such times, assume command. However, the orders they give are often faulty, incoordinated, and lack refinement. Systematic appraisal of all these poorly integrated or absent neuro-muscular responses usually provide a clue to the location of an injury.

A thorough appreciation of the nervous system is essential in twentieth century medicine. Review and augmentation of neuroanatomy is necessary if one desires to use this knowledge with diagnostic acumen and confidence.

BIBLIOGRAPHY

Comprehensive Texts and Atlases

Bumke, O., and Foerster, O. *Handbuch der Neurologie.* Vol. 1, Julius Springer, Berlin, 1935.

Déjérine, J. *Anatomie des centres nerveux.* 2 vols., Rueff et Cie., Paris, I, 1895; II, 1901.

Jelgersma, G. *Atlas anatomicum cerebri humani.* Scheltema & Holkema, Amsterdam, 1931.

Kappers, C. U. A., Huber, G. C., and Crosby, E. C. *The comparative anatomy of the nervous system of vertebrates, including man.* 2. vols., The Macmillan Co., New York, 1936.

Ramón y Cajal, S. *Histologie du système nerveux de l'homme et des vertébrés.* 2 vols., A. Maloine, Paris, I, 1909; II, 1911.

Olszewski, J., and Baxter, D. Cytoarchitecture of the human brain stem. J. B. Lippincott Co., Philadelphia, 1954.

Riley, H. A. *An atlas of the basal ganglia, brain stem and spinal cord, based on myelin-stained material.* The Williams & Wilkins Co., Baltimore, 1943.

Truex, R. C., and Kellner, C. E. Detailed atlas of the head and neck. Oxford University Press, New York, 1948.

Winkler, C. *Opera omnia.* Vols. 1–10. E. F. Bohn, Haarlem, 1918–1933.

Ziehen, T. *Anatomie des Zentralnervensystems.* Vol. 4 in K. von Bardeleben's *Handbuch der Anatomie des Menschen.* G. Fischer, Jena, 1896–1934.

General and Special References Including Those Quoted in Text

Abbie, A. A. The morphology of the forebrain arteries, with especial reference to the evolution of the basal ganglia. J. Anat., 1934, **68:** 433–470.

Abd-El-Malek, S. On the presence of sensory fibers in the ocular nerves. J. Anat., 1938, **72:** 524–530.

Abercrombie, M., and Johnson, M. L. The effect of reinnervation on collagen formation in degenerating sciatic nerves of rabbits. J. Neurol., Neurosurg. & Psychiat., 1947, **10:** 89–92.

Adrian, E. D. Mechanism of sense organs. Physiol. Rev., 1930, **10:** 336–347.

Adrian, E. D. Localization in cerebrum and cerebellum. Brit. Med. J., 1944, **2:** 137–140.

Adrian, E. D. Afferent areas of the cerebellum connected with the limbs. Brain, 1943, **66:** 289–315.

Aitken, J. The effect of peripheral connection on the maturation of regenerating nerve fibers. J. Anat., 1949, **83:** 32–43.

Alexander, L. The vascular supply of the striopallidum. Assoc. Res. Nerv. & Ment. Dis., 1942, **21:** 77–132.

Allen, W. F. Application of the Marchi method to the study of the radix mesencephalica trigemini in the guinea pig. J. Comp. Neurol., 1919, **30:** 169–216.

Allen, W. F. Experimental-anatomical studies on the visceral bulbospinal pathway in the cat and guinea pig. J. Comp. Neurol., 1927, **42:** 393–456.

Allison, A. C., and Feindel, W. H. Nodes in the central nervous system. Nature, 1949, **163:** 449–450.

Apter, J. T. The significance of the unilateral Argyll Robertson Pupil. Part I. A report of 13 cases. Am. J. Ophth., 1954, **38:** 34–43.

Apter, J. T. The significance of the unilateral Argyll Robertson Pupil. Part II. A critical review of the theories of its pathogenesis. Am. J. Ophth., 1954, **38:** 209–222.

Aronson, L. The conduction of labyrinthine impulses to the cortex. J. Nerv. & Ment. Dis., 1933, **78:** 250–259.

Asang, E. Zur radiculären Innervation (Myotome, Sklerotome, Dermatome) der unteren Extremität an Hand eines Sympus monopus. Zeitsch. f. Anat. u. Entwicklungsgesch., 1952, **116:** 219–275.

Aubert, M. Vascularization des pédoncules cérébraux chez l'homme. Acta Anat., 1949, **8:** 251–263.

Bailey, P., and Bonin, G. v. *Isocortex of man.* University Illinois Press, 1951.

Balado, M., and Franke, E. Das Corpus geniculatum externum. Monogr. u. Gesammtgebiete der Neur. u. Psychiat., 1937, **62:** 1–116.

Baló, J. The dural venous sinuses. Anat. Rec., 1950, **106:** 319–325.

Bard, P. Central nervous mechanisms for emotional behavior patterns in animals. Assoc. Res. Nerv. & Ment. Dis., 1939, **19:** 190–218.

Bard, P., and Mountcastle, V. B. Some forebrain mechanism involved in expression of rage with special reference to suppression of angry behavior. Assoc. Res. Nerv. & Ment. Dis., 1948, **27**: 362–404.

BARGMANN, W., HILD, W., ORTHMANN, R., AND SCHIEBLER, TH. H. Morphologische und experimentelle Untersuchungen über das hypothalamischhypophysäre System. Acta Neuroveg., 1950, **1**: 233–275.

BARNARD, J. W. A phylogenetic study of the visceral afferent areas associated with the facial, glossopharyngeal, and vagus nerves, and their fiber connections. The efferent facial nucleus. J. Comp. Neurol., 1936, **65**: 503–603.

BARNARD, J. W. The hypoglossal complex of vertebrates. J. Comp. Neurol., 1940, **72**: 489–524.

BARNES, S. Degenerations in hemiplegia: with special reference to a ventrolateral pyramidal tract, the accessory fillet and Pick's bundle. Brain, 1901, **24**: 463–501.

BARR, M. L. Observations on the foramen of Magendie in a series of human brains. Brain, 1948, **71**: 281–289.

BARR, M. L., AND BERTRAM, E. G. The behavior of nuclear structures during depletion and restoration of Nissl material in motor neurons. J. Anat., 1951, **85**: 171–181.

BARR, M. L., BERTRAM, L. F., AND LINDSAY, H. A. The morphology of the nerve cell nucleus according to sex. Anat. Rec., 1950, **107**: 283–297.

BARTELMEZ, G. W., AND HOERR, N. L. The vestibular club endings in Ameiurus. Further evidence on the morphology of the synapse. J. Comp. Neurol., 1933, **57**: 401–428.

BEAMS, H. W., AND KING, R. L. The effect of ultracentrifuging the spinal ganglia cells of the rat, with special reference to Nissl bodies. J. Comp. Neurol., 1935, **61**: 175–184.

BECK, E. Die myeloarchitektonische Felderung des in der Sylvischen Furche gelegenen Teiles des menschlichen Schläfenlappens. J. f. Psychol. u. Neurol., 1929, **36**: 1–21.

BECK, E. The origin, course and termination of the prefronto-pontine tract in the human brain. Brain, 1950, **73**: 368–391.

BENJAMIN, J. W. Nucleus of the oculomotor nerve, with special reference to innervation of pupil and fibers from pretectal region. J. Nerv. & Ment. Dis., 1939, **89**: 294–310.

BENSLEY, R. R., AND GERSH, I. Studies on cell structure by the freezing-drying method. III. The distribution in cells of the basophil substances in particular the Nissl substance of the nerve cell. Anat. Rec., 1933, **57**: 369–385.

BERNHEIMER, S. Über Ursprung und Verlauf des Nervus oculomotorius im Mittelhirn. Monatschr. f. Psych. u. Neurol., 1904, **15**: 151–153.

BERRY, C. M., ANDERSON, F. D., AND BROOKS, D. C. Ascending pathways of the trigeminal nerve in cat. J. Neurophysiol., 1956, **19**: 144–153.

BERRY, C. M., KARL, R. C., AND HINSEY, J. C. Course of spinothalamic and medial lemniscus pathways in cat and rhesus monkey. J. Neurophysiol., 1950, **13**: 149–156.

BIELSCHOWSKY, M. Morphologie der Ganglienzelle. In von Möllendorff's *Handb. d. mikr. Anat. d. Menschen.* Berlin, 1928, **4**: 8–96.

BISHOP, G. H. Neural mechanism of cutaneous sense. Physiol. Rev., 1946, **26**: 77–102.

BISHOP, G. H , HEINBECKER, P., AND O'LEARY, J. L. The function of the non-myelinated fibers of the dorsal roots. Am. J. Physiol., 1933, **106**: 647–669.

BODIAN, D. The structure of the vertebrate synapse. A study of the axon endings on Mauthner's cell and neighboring centers in the goldfish. J. Comp. Neurol., 1937, **68**: 117–159.

BODIAN, D. Further notes on the vertebrate synapse. J. Comp. Neurol., 1940, **73**: 323–335.

BODIAN, D. Nucleic acid in nerve-cell regeneration. Symp. Soc. Exp. Biol., 1947, **1**: 163–178.

BOEKE, J. Nerve endings, motor and sensory. In Penfield's *Cytology & Cellular Pathology of the Nervous System.* New York, 1932, **1**: 243–315.

BOK, S. T. Das Rückenmark. In von Möllendorff's *Handb. d. mikr. Anat. d. Menschen.* Berlin, 1928, **4**: 478–578.

BOLK, L. *Das Cerebellum der Säugethiere.* Bohn, Haarlem, 1906.

BOLTON, B. The blood supply of the human spinal cord. J. Neurol. and Psychiat., 1939, **2**: 137–148.

VON BONIN, G. Architecture of the precentral motor cortex and some adjacent areas. In Bucy's *The precentral motor cortex*, 1949, pp. 7–82.

BÖRNSTEIN, W. S. Localization of cortical taste area in man and method of measuring impairment of taste in man. Yale J. Biol. & Med., 1940, **13**: 133–156.

BOTTERELL, E. H., AND FULTON, J. F. Functional localization in the cerebellum of primates. II. Lesions of midline structures (vermis and deep nuclei). J. Comp. Neurol., 1938, **69**: 47–62.

BOWDEN, R. E. M., AND GUTMANN, E. Denervation and re-innervation of human voluntary muscle. Brain, 1944, **67**: 273–313.

Bowden, R. E. M., and Sholl, D. A. The advance of functional recovery after radial nerve lesions in man. Brain, 1950, **73:** 251–266.

Bozler, E. Über die Struktur der Ganglienzellen. Zeitschr. vergl. Physiol., 1927, **6:** 255–263.

Brain, W. R. *Diseases of the nervous system.* Oxford Med. Publications, London, 4th Ed., 1951.

Brain, W. R. The cerebral basis of consciousness. Brain, 1950, **73:** 465–479.

Braitenberg, V., and Atwood, R. P. Morphological observations on the cerebellar cortex. J. Comp. Neurol., 1958, **109:** 1–27.

Brickner, R. M. *The intellectual function of the frontal lobes.* The Macmillan Co., New York, 1936.

Brock, S. *The basis of clinical neurology.* Williams & Wilkins Co., 1952.

Brodal, A. *Neurological anatomy.* Oxford University Press, London, 1948.

Brodal, A. Spinal afferents to the lateral reticular nucleus of the medulla oblongata in the cat. J. Comp. Neurol., 1949, **91:** 259–295.

Brodal, A. The reticular formation of the brain stem. Anatomical aspects and functional correlations. Chas. C Thomas, Springfield Illinois, 1958.

Brodal, A., and Jansen, J. The ponto-cerebellar projection in the rabbit and cat. J. Comp. Neurol., 1946, **84:** 31–118.

Brodmann, K. *Vergleichende Lokalisationslehre der Grosshirnrinde in ihren Prinzipien dargestellt auf Grund des Zellenbaues.* J. A. Barth, Leipzig, 1909.

Brouwer, B. Klinisch-anatomische Untersuchung über den Oculomotoriuskern. Ztschr. f. d. ges. Neurol. & Psychiat., Berlin, 1918, **40:** 152–193.

Brouwer, B. Projection of the retina on the cortex in man. Assoc. Res. Nerv. & Ment. Dis. 1934, **13:** 529–534.

Brouwer, B., and Zeeman, W. P. C. The projection of the retina in the primary optic neuron in monkeys. Brain, 1926, **49:** 1–35.

Brown, J. O., and McCouch, G. P. Abortive regeneration of the transected spinal cord. J. Comp. Neurol., 1947, **87:** 131–138.

Buchanan, A. R. The course of the secondary vestibular fibers in the cat. J. Comp. Neurol., 1937, **67:** 183–204.

Bucy, P. C. *The precentral motor cortex.* University Illinois Press, 2nd Ed., 1949.

Bueker, E., and Meyers, C. The maturity of peripheral nerves at the time of injury as a factor in nerve regeneration. Anat. Rec., 1951, **109:** 723–743.

Campbell, A. W. *Histological studies on the localisation of cerebral function.* Cambridge University Press, 1905.

Campbell, J. B., Bassett, C. A. L., Husby, J., and Noback, C. R. Regeneration of adult mammalian spinal cord. Science, 1957, **126:** 929.

Campbell, J. B., Bassett, C. A. L., Husby, J., and Noback, C. R. Axonal regeneration in the transected adult feline spinal cord. Surgical Forum, 1958, **8:** 528–532.

van Campenhout, E. Contribution to the problem of the development of the sympathetic nervous system. J. Exp. Zoöl., 1930, **56:** 295–320.

Cannon, W. B. *Bodily changes in pain, hunger, fear and rage. An account of recent researches into the function of emotional excitement.* D. Appleton & Co., New York, 1929.

Cannon, W. B., and Rosenblueth, A. *Autonomic neuro-effector systems.* The Macmillan Co., New York, 1937.

Carpenter, M. B. The dorsal trigeminal tract in the Rhesus monkey. J. Anat., 1957, **91:** 82–90.

Carpenter, M. B., Brittin, G. M., and Pines, J. Isolated lesions of the fastigial nuclei in the cat. J. Comp. Neurol., 1958, **109:** 65–89.

Carrea, R. M. E., and Grundfest, H. Electrophysiological studies of cerebellar inflow. I. Origin, conduction and termination of ventral spino-cerebellar tract in monkey and cat. J. Neurophysiol., 1954, **17:** 208–238.

Carrea, R. M. E., and Mettler, F. A. Physiologic consequences following extensive removals of the cerebellar cortex and deep cerebellar nuclei and effect of secondary cerebral ablations in the primate. J. Comp. Neurol., 1947, **87:** 169–288.

Carrea, M. E., Reissig, M., and Mettler, F. A. The climbing fibers of the simian and feline cerebellum. J. Comp. Neurol., 1947, **87:** 321–365.

Caspersson, T. The relationship between nucleic acid and protein synthesis. Symp. Soc. Exp. Biol., 1947, **1:** 127–151.

Caspersson, T. *Cell growth and cell function.* W. W. Norton & Co., New York, 1950.

Cauna, N., and Mannan, G. The structure of human digital pacinian corpuscles (Corpuscula Lamellosa) and its functional significance J. Anat., 1958, Part 1, **92:** 1–20.

de Castro, F. Sensory ganglia of the cranial and spinal nerves, normal and pathological. In Penfield's *Cytology & cellular pathology of the nervous system.* New York, 1932, **1:** 93–143.

de Castro, F. Sympathetic ganglia, normal and pathological. In Penfield's *Cytology & cellu-*

lar pathology of the nervous system. New York, 1932, **1:** 319–379.

CHAPMAN, W. P., LIVINGSTON, R. B., AND LIVINGSTON, K. E. Frontal lobotomy and electrical stimulation of orbital surface of frontal lobes. Arch. Neurol. and Psychiat., 1949, **62:** 701–716.

CHAPMAN, E. M., KINSEY, D., CHAPMAN, W. P., AND SMITHWICK, R. H. Sympathetic innervation of the heart in man. Preliminary observations of the effect of thoracic sympathectomy on heart rate. J. Am. Med. Assoc., 1948, **137:** 579–584.

CLARK, D. A. Muscle counts of motor units: a study in innervation ratios. Am. J. Physiol., 1931, **96:** 296–304.

CLARK, W. E. L. The structure and connections of the thalamus. Brain, 1932, **55:** 406–470.

CLARK, W. E. L. Functional localization in the thalamus and hypothalamus. J. Ment. Sci., 1936, **82:** 99–118.

CLARK, W. E. L. The connections of the frontal lobes of the brain. Lancet, 1948, **I:** 353–356.

CLARK, W. E. L., BEATTIE, J., RIDDOCH, G., AND DOTT, N. M. *The hypothalamus.* Oliver & Boyd. Edinburgh, 1938.

CLARK, W. E. L. AND MEYER, M. Anatomical relationships between the cerebral cortex and the hypothalamus. Brit. Med. Bull., 1950, **6:** 341–345.

CLAUDE, A. Studies on cell morphology and functions. Ann. N. Y. Acad. Sci., 1950, **50:** 854–860.

COGHILL, G. E. Correlated anatomical and physiological studies of the growth of the nervous system of amphibia. I. J. Comp. Neurol., 1914, **24:** 161–223.

COGHILL, G. E. *Anatomy and the problem of behavior.* Oxford University Press, London, 1929.

COIDAN, R. S. The paranucleolar bodies in spinal neurons of mammals. J. Comp. Neurol., 1952, **97:** 61–71.

COLLIER, J., AND BUZZARD, F. The degenerations resulting from lesions of posterior nerve roots and from transverse lesions of the spinal cord in man. A study of twenty cases. Brain, 1903, **26:** 559–591.

COMBS, C. M. Bulbar regions related to localized cerebellar afferent impulses. J. Neurolphysiol., 1956, **19:** 285–300.

COOPER, E. R. A. The development of the substantia nigra. Brain, 1946, **69:** 22–33.

COOPER, E. R. A. The development of the human red nucleus and corpus striatum. Brain, 1946, **69:** 34–44.

COOPER, I. S., BRAVO, G. J., RIKLAN, M., DAVIDSON, N. W., AND GOREK, E. A. Chemopallidectomy and chemothalamectomy for parkinsonism. Geriatrics, 1958, **13:** 127–147.

COOPER, S., AND DANIEL, P. M. Muscle spindles in human extrinsic eye muscles. Brain, 1949, **72:** 1–24.

CORBIN, K. B. Observations on the peripheral distribution of fibers arising in the mesencephalic nucleus of the fifth cranial nerve. J. Comp. Neurol., 1940, **73:** 153–177.

CORBIN, K. B., AND HARRISON, F. Function of the mesencephalic root of the fifth cranial nerve. J. Neurophysiol., 1940, **3:** 423–435.

COWDRY, E. V. The Neurone. General character. In Penfield's *Cytology & cellular pathology of the nervous system.* New York, 1932, **1:** 1–41.

CRITCHLEY, M. The anterior cerebral artery and its syndromes. Brain, 1930, **53:** 120–165.

CROSBY, E. C., AND WOODBURNE, R. T. The comparative anatomy of the preoptic area and the hypothalamus. Assoc. Res. Nerv. & Ment. Dis., 1940, **20:** 52–169.

CROSBY, E. C., AND HUMPHREY, T. Studies of the vertebrate telencephalon. II. The nuclear pattern of the anterior olfactory nucleus, tuberculum olfactorum and the amygdaloid complex in adult man. J. Comp. Neurol., 1941, **74:** 309–352.

CROUCH, R. L. The efferent fibers of the Edinger-Westphal nucleus. J. Comp. Neurol., 1936, **64:** 365–373.

DALE, H. H., AND FELDBERG, W. The chemical transmitter of effects of the gastric vagus. J. Physiol., 1933, **80:** 16P–17P.

DAVISON, C., AND DEMUTH, D. L. Disturbance in sleep mechanism. Arch. Neurol. & Psychiat., 1945, **54:** 241–255; 1946, **55:** 111–133, 364–381.

DEL RIO-HORTEGA, P. Microglia. In Penfield's *Cytology & cellular pathology of the nervous system.* New York, 1932, **2:** 483–534.

DENNY-BROWN, D. Importance of neural fibroblasts in the regeneration of nerve. Arch. Neurol. and Psychiat., 1946, **55:** 171–215.

DENNY-BROWN, D. The frontal lobes and their functions. In A. FEILING'S *Modern Trends in Neurology.* Paul B. Hoeber, New York, 1951, pp. 13–89.

DENNY-BROWN, D., AND BOTTERELL, E. H. The motor functions of the agranular frontal cortex. Assoc. Res. Nerv. and Ment. Dis., 1948, **27:** 235–345.

DETWILER, S. R. *Neuroembryology: an experimental study.* The Macmillan Co., New York, 1936.

DETWILER, S. R. Observations upon the migration of neural crest cells, and upon the development of the spinal ganglia and vertebral arches in Amblystoma. Am. J. Anat., 1937, **61:** 63–94.

DETWILER, S. R., AND KEHOE, K. Further observations on the origin of the sheath cells of Schwann. J. Exper. Zoöl., 1939, **81:** 415–435.

DOGIEL, A. S. *Der Bau der Spinalganglien des Menschen und der Säugetiere.* G. Fischer, Jena, 1908.

DOW, R. S. Efferent connections of the flocculonodular lobe in Macaca mulatta. J. Comp. Neurol., 1938, **68:** 297–305.

DOW, R. S. Cerebellar action potentials in response to stimulation of the cerebral cortex in monkeys and cats. J. Neurophysiol., 1942, **5:** 121–136.

DOW, R. S. The evolution and anatomy of the cerebellum. Biol. Rev., 1942, **17:** 179–220.

DOW, R. S., AND ANDERSON, R. Cerebellar action potentials in response to stimulation of proprioceptors and exteroceptors in the rat. J. Neurophysiol., 1942, **5:** 363–371.

DUSSER DE BARENNE, J. G. Experimental researches on sensory localization in the cerebral cortex of the monkey. Proc. Roy. Soc., 1924, **96B:** 272–291.

DUSSER DE BARENNE, J. G. Some aspects of the problem of "corticalization" of function and of functional localization in the cerebral cortex. Assoc. Res. Nerv. & Ment. Dis., 1934, **13:** 85–106.

DUSSER DE BARENNE, J. G., AND SAGER, O. Sensory functions of the optic thalamus of the monkey (Macacus rhesus): symptomatology and functional localization investigated with the method of local strychninization. Arch. Neurol. & Psychiat., 1937, **38:** 913–926.

DUSSER DE BARENNE, J. G., GAROL, H. W., AND McCULLOCH, W. S. Physiological neuronography of the cortico-striatal connections. Assoc. Res. Nerv. and Ment. Dis., 1942, **21:** 246–266.

DUSSER DE BARENNE, J. G., GAROL, H. W., AND McCULLOCH, W. S. The "motor" cortex of the chimpanzee. J. Neurophysiol., 1941, **4:** 287–303.

DUSSER DE BARENNE, J. G., AND McCULLOCH, W. S. Suppression of motor response obtained from area 4 by stimulation of area 4s. J. Neurophysiol., 1941, **4:** 311–323.

ECCLES, J. C. An electrical hypothesis of synaptic and neuro-muscular transmission. Ann. N. Y. Acad. Sci., 1946, **47:** 429–455.

VON ECONOMO, C. F. *The cytoarchitectonics of the human cerebral cortex.* Oxford Med. Publications, London, 1929.

ECTORS, L. The function of the cerebellum. In Confinia neurologica. Basel, 1942, **4:** 181–212.

EDINGER, L. *Vorlesungen über den Bau der nervösen Zentralorgane des Menschen und der Tiere.* F. C. W. Vogel, Leipzig, 1911.

EDDS, M. V., JR. Collateral regeneration of residual motor axons in partially denervated muscles. J. Exp. Zoöl., 1950, **113:** 517–551.

ELWYN, A. The structure and development of the proprioceptors. Assoc. Res. Nerv. & Ment. Dis., 1929, **6:** 244–280.

ELZE, C. Zentrales Nervensystem. Vol. 3 in Braus' *Anatomie des Menschen.* Julius Springer, Berlin, 1932.

ERLANGER, J., AND GASSER, H. S. *Electrical signs of nervous activity.* University of Pennsylvania Press. Philadelphia, 1937.

FERRARO, A., AND BARRERA, S. E. Posterior column fibers and their termination in Macacus rhesus. J. Comp. Neurol., 1935, **62:** 507–530.

FITZGERALD, J. E., AND WINDLE, W. F. Some observations on early human fetal movements. J. Comp. Neurol., 1942, **76:** 156–167.

FOERSTER, O. *Die Leitungsbahnen des Schmerzgefühls und die chirurgische Behandlung der Schmerzzustände.* Urban & Schwarzenberg, Berlin, 1927.

FOERSTER, O. Über die Vasodilatoren in den peripheren Nerven und hintern Rückenmarkswurzeln beim Menschen. Dtsch. Z. Nervenheilk., 1928, **107:** 41–56.

FOERSTER, O. Spezielle Anatomie und Physiologie der peripheren Nerven. In Lewandowsky's *Handbuch der Neurologie,* 1929, Suppl. Pt. **2:** 815–974.

FOERSTER, O. The dermatomes in man. Brain, 1933, **56:** 1–39.

FOERSTER, O. Motor cortex in man in the light of Hughlings Jackson's doctrines. Brain, 1936, **59:** 135–159.

FOERSTER, O. Symptomatologie der Erkrankungen des Rückenmarks und seiner Wurzeln. In Bumke and Foerster's *Handbuch der Neurologie,* 1936, **5:** 1–400.

FOERSTER, O. Symptomatologie der Erkrankungen des Grosshirns. Motorische Felder und Bahnen. In Bumke and Foerster's *Handbuch der Neurologie,* 1936, **6:** 1–357.

FOERSTER, O., AND GAGEL, O. Die Vorderseitenstrangdurchschneidung beim Menschen. Eine klinischpathophysiologisch-anatomische Studie. Ztschr. f. d. ges. Neurol. u. Psychiat., 1932, **138:** 1–92.

FOERSTER, O., AND GAGEL, O. Über afferente Nervenfasern in den vorderen Wurzeln. Ztschr. f. d. ges. Neurol. u. Psychiat., 1933, **144:** 313–324.

FOERSTER, O., GAGEL, O., AND SHEEHAN, D. Veränderungen an den Endösen im Rückenmark des Affen nach Hinterwurzeldurchschneidung. Ztschr. Anat. Entwgesch., 1933, **101:** 553–565.

Foley, J. M., Kinney, T. D., and Alexander, L. The vascular supply of the hypothalamus in man. J. Neuropath. & Exp. Neurol., 1942, **1:** 265–296.

Foley J. O. and Schnitzlein, H. N. The contributions of individual thoracic spinal nerves to the upper cervical sympathetic trunk. J. Comp. Neurol., 1957, 109–120.

Fox, C. A., and Barnard, J. W. A quantitative study of the Purkinje cell, dendritic branchlets and their relationship to afferent fibres. J. of Anat., 1957, **91:** 299–313.

Frantzen, E., and Olivarius, B. I. F. On thrombosis of the basilar artery. Acta Psych. and Neurol. Scandinav., 1957, **32:** 431–439.

Freeman, L. W. Return of function after complete transection of the spinal cord of the rat, cat and dog. Am. Surg., 1952, **136:** 193–205.

Freeman, W., and Watts, J. W. Retrograde degeneration of the thalamus following prefrontal lobotomy. J. Comp. Neurol., 1947, **86:** 65–93.

Freeman, W., and Watts, J. W. The thalamic projection to the frontal lobe. Assoc. Res. Nerv. and Ment. Dis., 1948, **27:** 200–209.

Freeman, W., and Watts, J. W. *Psychosurgery, intelligence, emotion and social behavior following prefrontal lobotomy for mental disorders.* Charles C. Thomas, Springfield, Illinois, 2nd Ed., 1949.

French, J. D., and Magoun, H. W. Effects of chronic lesions in central cephalic brain stem of monkeys. Arch. Neurol. & Psychiat., 1952, **68:** 591–604.

Fulton, J. F. *Functional localization in the frontal lobes and cerebellum.* Clarendon Press, Oxford, 1949.

Fulton, J. F. Note on the definition of "motor" and "premotor" areas. Brain, 1935, **58:** 311–316.

Fulton, J. F. *Physiology of the nervous system.* Oxford Med. Publications, New York, 3rd Ed., 1949.

Fulton, J. F. Levels of autonomic function with particular reference to the cortex. Assoc. Res. Nerv. & Ment. Dis., 1939, **19:** 219–236.

Fulton, J. F., and Ingraham, F. D. Emotional disturbances following experimental lesions of the base of the brain (pre-chiasmal). J. Physiol., 1929, **67:** 27–28.

Fulton, J. F., and Kennard, M. A. A study of flaccid and spastic paralysis produced by lesions of the cerebral cortex in primates. Assoc. Res. Nerv. & Ment. Dis., 1934, **13:** 158–210.

Garol, H. W., and Bucy, P. C. Suppression of motor response in man. Arch. Neurol. and Psychiat., 1944, **51:** 528–532.

Gaskell, W. H. *The involuntary nervous system.* Longmans, Green & Co., London, 1916.

Gasser, H. S. Conduction in nerves in relation to fiber types. Assoc. Res. Nerv. & Ment. Dis., 1935, **15:** 35–59.

Gasser, H. S., and Erlanger, J. The rôle of fiber size in the establishment of a nerve block by pressure or cocaine. Am. J. Physiol., 1929, **88:** 581–591.

Gasser, H. S., and Grundfest, H. Axon diameters in relation to the spike dimensions and the conduction velocity in mammalian A fibers. Am. J. Physiol., 1939, **127:** 393–414.

Gerard, M. W. Afferent impulses of the trigeminal nerve: The intramedullary course of the painful, thermal and tactile impulses. Arch. Neurol. & Psychiat., 1923, **9:** 306–338.

Gerebtzoff, M. A. Les voies centrales de la sensibilité et du goût et leurs terminaisons thalamiques. Cellule, 1939, **48:** 91–146.

Gerebtzoff, M. A. Les bases anatomiques de la physiologie du cervelet. La Cellule, 1941, **49:** 71–166.

Gerebtzoff, M. A. Recherches sur la projection corticale du labyrinthe; des effets de la stimulation labyrinthique sur l'activité électrique de l'écorce cérébrale. Arch. internat. de physiol., 1940, **50:** 59–99.

Gersh, I., and Bodian, D. Some chemical mechanisms in chromatolysis. J. Cell. Comp. Physiol., 1943, **21:** 253–279.

Getz, B., and Sirnes, T. The localization within the dorsal motor vagal nucleus. J. Comp. Neurol., 1949, **90:** 95–110.

Gibson, W. C. Degeneration of the boutons terminaux in the spinal cord: an experimental study. Arch. Neurol. & Psychiat., 1937, **38:** 1145–1157.

Glees, P. The anatomical basis of corticostriate connections. J. Anat., 1944, **78:** 47–51.

Glees, P., and Nauta, W. J. H. A critical review of studies on axonal and terminal degeneration. Mschr. Psychiat. Neurol., 1955, **129:** 74–91.

Golgi. C. *Untersuchungen über den feineren Bau des centralen und peripherischen Nervensystems.* Gustav Fischer, Jena, 1894.

Green, J. D., Clemente, C. D., and DeGroot, J. Rhinencephalic lesions and behavior in cats. J. Comp. Neurol., 1957, **108:** 505–545.

Green, J. D. The rhinencephalon: aspects of its relation to behavior and the reticular activating system, pp. 607–619. Reticular formation of the brain. Henry Ford Hospital International Symposium. Little, Brown & Co., Boston, 1958.

Greving, R. Makroskopische Anatomie und Histologie des vegetativen Nervensystems.

In Bumke and Foerster's *Handb. d. Neurologie.* 1935, **1:** 811–886.

Grinker, R. R. *Neurology.* Charles C. Thomas, Springfield, Illinois, 4th Ed., 1949.

Grundfest, H. Bioelectric potentials. Ann. Rev. Physiol., 1940, **2:** 213–242.

Grundfest, H. The properties of mammalian B fibers. Am. J. Physiol., 1939, **127:** 252–262.

Gutmann, E., Guttmann, L., Medawar, P. B., and Young, J. Z. Rate of regeneration of nerve. J. Exp. Biol., 1942, **19:** 14–44.

Gutmann, E., and Young, J. Z. The re-innervation of muscle after various periods of atrophy. J. Anat., 1944, **78:** 15–43.

Guttmann, L. Rehabilitation after injuries to spinal cord and cauda equina. Brit. J. Phys. Med., 1946, **9:** 162–171.

Guttmann, L. Studies on reflex activity of the isolated cord in the spinal man. J. Nerv. & Ment. Dis., 1952, **116:** 957–972.

Häggquist, G. Analysis of fibers of the pyramidal tract. Acta Psychiat. et Neurol., 1937, **12:** 457–466.

Hammond, W. S. Formation of the sympathetic nervous system in the trunk of the chick embryo following the removal of the thoracic neural tube. J. Comp. Neurol., 1949, **91:** 67–85.

Hampson, J. L. Relationships between cat cerebral and cerebellar cortices. J. Neurophysiol., 1949, **12:** 37–50.

Hampson, J. L., Harrison, C. R., and Woolsey, C. N. Somatotopic localization in the cerebellum. Federation Proc., 1946, **5:** 41.

Hanberry, J., and Jasper, H. Independence of the diffuse thalamo-cortical projection system shown by specific nuclear destruction. Fed. Proc., 1952, **11:** 64.

Harrison, R. G. The outgrowth of the nerve fiber as a mode of protoplasmic movement. Jour. Exp. Zoöl., 1910, **9:** 787–847.

Harrison, R. G. On the origin and development of the nervous system studied by the methods of experimental embryology. (Croonian Lecture.) Proc. Roy. Soc., 1935, **118B:** 155–196.

Hassin, G. B. Cerebrospinal fluid. J. Neuropath. and Exper. Neurol., 1948, **7:** 172–181.

Hassler, R. Über Kleinhirnprojektionen zum Mittelhirn und Thalamus beim Menschen. Dtsch. Z. Nervenheilk., 1950, **163:** 629–671.

Haugsted, H. Occlusion of the basilar artery. Diagnosis by vertebral angiography during life. Neurol., 1956, **6:** 823–828.

Haymaker, W. Bing's local diagnosis in neurological diseases. C. V. Mosby Co., St. Louis, pp. 57–62; 105–112, 1956.

Haymaker, W., and Woodhall, B. *Peripheral nerve injuries.* W. B. Saunders Co., Philadelphia, 1945.

Head, H. *Studies in neurology.* 2 vols. Oxford University Press, London, 1920.

Head, H. *Aphasia and kindred disorders of speech.* Cambridge University Press, 1926.

Heath, R. G., and Pool, J. L. Bilateral resections of frontal cortex for the treatment of psychoses. J. Nerv. & Ment. Dis., 1948, **107:** 411–429.

Heinbecker, P., Bishop, G. H., and O'Leary, J. L. Functional and histologic studies of somatic and autonomic nerves of man. Arch. Neurol. & Psychiat., 1936, **35:** 1233–1255.

Henneman, E., Cooke, P., and Snider, R. S. Cerebellar projections to the cerebral cortex in cat and monkey. Am. J. Physiol., 1948, **155:** 443.

Herren, R. Y., and Alexander, L. Sulcal and intrinsic blood vessels of human spinal cord. Arch. Neurol. & Psychiat., 1939, **41:** 678–687.

Herrick, C. J. *Introduction to neurology.* W. B. Saunders Co., Philadelphia, 1931.

Herrick, C. J. *The brains of rats and men.* University of Chicago Press, Chicago, 1926.

Herrick, C. J. Morphogenesis of the brain. J. Morphol., 1933, **54:** 233–258.

Herrick, C. J., and Coghill, G. E. The development of reflex mechanisms in Amblystoma. J. Comp. Neurol., 1915, **25:** 65–85.

Hess, W. R. *Die funktionelle Organisation des vegetativen Nervensystems.* Benno Schwabe & Co., Basel, 1948.

Hess, W. R. *Das Zwischenhirn.* Benno Schwabe & Co., Basel, 1949.

Hess, W. R. Die Stellung des Hypothalamus im vegetativen Regulationsystem. Schweiz. Arch. f. Neurol. und Psychiat., 1950, **65:** 425–426.

Hines, M. The anterior border of the monkey's (Macaca mulatta) motor cortex and the production of spasticity. Am. J. Physiol., 1936, **116:** 76.

Hines, M. On cerebral localization. Physiol. Rev., 1929, **9:** 462–574.

Hines, M. The motor cortex. Bull. Johns Hopkins Hosp., 1937, **60:** 313–336.

Hinsey, J. C. The innervation of skeletal muscle. Physiol. Rev., 1934, **14:** 514–585.

Hinsey, J. C. Are there efferent fibers in the dorsal roots? J. Comp. Neurol., 1934, **59:** 117–137.

Hinsey, J. C. The hypothalamus and somatic responses. Assoc. Res. Nerv. & Ment. Dis., 1940, **20:** 657–685.

Hirasawa, K., and Kato, K. Fasern, insbesondere die corticalen extrapyramidalen aus den Areae 8 (α, β, τ, δ.) and 9(c, d,) der Grosshirnrinde beim Affen. Folia anat. japon., 1935, **13:** 189–217.

Hirt, A. Über den Aufbau des Spinalganglions und seine Beziehungen zum Sympathicus. Ztschr. f. d. ges. Anat., 1928, **87:** 275–318.

Hochstetter, F. *Beiträge zur Entwicklungsgeschichte des Gehirns.* Franz Deuticke, Wien, I, 1919; II, 1929.

Hoff, E. C. Central nerve terminals in the mammalian spinal cord and their examination by experimental degeneration. Proc. Roy. Soc., 1932, **111B:** 175–188.

Hoff, E. C. The distribution of the spinal terminals (boutons) of the pyramidal tract, determined by experimental degeneration. Proc. Roy. Soc., 1932, **111B:** 226–237.

Hoff, E. C., and Hoff, H. E. Spinal terminations of the projection fibers from the motor cortex of primates. Brain, 1934, **57:** 454–474.

Holmes, G. The cerebellum of man. Brain, 1939, **62:** 1–30.

Holmes, G., and May, W. P. On the exact origin of the pyramidal tracts in man and other mammals. Brain, 1909, **32:** 1–43.

Holmes, G., and Stewart, T. G. On the connections of the inferior olive with the cerebellum in man. Brain, 1908, **31:** 125–137.

Holmes, W., and Young, J. Z. Nerve regeneration after immediate and delayed suture. J. Anat., 1942, **77:** 63–96.

Hooker, D. *The origin of overt behavior.* University Michigan, Ann Arbor, 1944.

Horsley, V., and Clarke, R. H. The structure and functions of the cerebellum examined by a new method. Brain, 1908, **31:** 45–124.

Huber, G. C., and Crosby, E. C. Somatic and visceral connections of the diencephalon. Assoc. Res. Nerv. & Ment. Dis., 1930, **9:** 199–248.

Hunt, J. R. The sensory field of the facial nerve. Brain, 1915, **38:** 418–446.

Hunt, J. R. Progressive atrophy of the globus pallidus (primary atrophy of the pallidal system). A system disease of the paralysis agitans type, characterized by atrophy of the motor cells of the corpus striatum. A contribution of the functions of the corpus striatum. Brain, 1917, **40:** 58–148.

Hursh, J. B. Conduction velocity and diameter of nerve fibers. Am. J. Physiol., 1939, **127:** 131–139.

Hydén, H. Protein metabolism of the nerve cell during growth and function. Acta Physiol. Scand., 1943, Suppl. 6, 136 pp.

Hydén, H. Protein and nucleotide metabolism in the nerve cell under different functional conditions. Symp. Soc. Exp. Biol., 1947, **1:** 152–162.

Hydén, H., and Hartelius, H. Stimulation of the nucleoprotein-production in the nerve cells by malononitrile and its effect on psychic function in mental disorder. Acta Psychiat. et Neurol., 1948, Suppl. **48:** 5–117.

Hyndman, O. R. Physiology of the spinal cord. II. The influence of chordotomy on existing motor disturbances. J. Nerv. & Ment. Dis., 1943, **98:** 343–358.

Ingram, W. R. The hypothalamus: A review of the experimental data. Psychosomat. Med., 1939, **1:** 48–91.

Ingram, W. R., and Ranson, S. W. The nucleus of Darkschewitsch and nucleus interstitialis in the brain of man. J. Nerv. & Ment. Dis., 1935, **81:** 125–237.

Ingvar, S. Zur Phylo- und Ontogenese des Kleinhirns. Folia neuro-biol., 1918, **11:** 205–495.

Jacobsen, C. F. The effect of extirpations on higher brain processes. Physiol. Rev., 1939, **19:** 303–322.

Jacobsohn, L. Über die Kerne des menschlichen Rückenmarks. Aus dem Anhang zu den Abhandlungen der koenigl. preuss. Akademie der Wissenschaften vom Jahre 1908.

Jacobsohn, L. Über die Kerne des menschlichen Hirnstamms. Aus dem Anhang zu den Abhandlungen der koenigl. preuss. Akademie der Wissenschaften vom Jahre 1909.

Jakob, A. The anatomy, clinical syndromes and physiology of the extrapyramidal system. Arch. Neurol. & Psychiat., 1925, **13:** 596–620.

Jakob, A. Das Kleinhirn. In von Möllendorf's *Handb. d. mikr. Anat. d. Menschen.* Berlin, 1928, **4:** 674–916.

Jansen, J., and Brodal, A. Experimental studies on the intrinsic fibers of the cerebellum. II. The cortico-nuclear projection. J. Comp. Neurol., 1940, **73:** 267–321.

Jasper, H. Diffuse projection systems: The integrative action of the thalamic reticular system. Electroencephalog. & Clin. Neurophysiol., 1949, **1:** 405–420.

Jasper, H., Ajmone-Marsan, C., and Stoll, J. Corticofugal projections to the brain stem. Arch. Neurol. & Psychiat., 1952, **67:** 155–171.

Jefferson, M. Altered consciousness associated with brain-stem lesions. Brain, 1952, **75:** 55–67.

Kaes, T. Die Grosshirnrinde des Menschen in ihren Massen und in ihrem Fasergehalt. Gustav Fischer, Jena, 1907, 2 parts in 1 Vol., 64 pages, 92 plates.

Kahr, S., and Sheehan, D. The presence of

efferent fibers in posterior spinal roots. Brain, 1933, **56**: 265–281.

KAPPERS, C. U. A. The development of the cortex and the functions of its different layers. Acta Psychiat. Neurol., 1928, **3**: 115–132.

KAPPERS, C. U. A. Principles of development of the nervous system. (Neurobiotaxis.) In Penfield's *Cytology & cellular pathology of the nervous system*. New York, 1932, **1**: 45–89.

KARPLUS, J. P. Die Physiologie der vegetativen Zentren. In Bumke and Foerster's *Handb. d. Neurologie*, 1937, **2**: 402–475.

KEEGAN, J. J., AND GARRETT, F. D. The segmental distribution of the cutaneous nerves of the limbs of man. Anat. Rec., 1948, **102**: 409–437.

KENNARD, M. A. Corticospinal fibers arising in the premotor area of the monkey as demonstrated by the Marchi method. Arch. Neurol. & Psychiat., 1935, **33**: 698–711.

KENNARD, M. A., VIETS, H. R., AND FULTON, J. F. The syndrome of the premotor cortex in man: Impairment of skilled movement, forced grasping, spasticity and vasomotor disturbances. Brain, 1934, **57**: 69–84.

KENNARD, M. Autonomic function. In Bucy's *The precentral motor cortex*. University Illinois Press, 2nd Ed., 1949, pp. 293–306.

KINGSBURY, B. F. The fundamental plan of the vertebrate brain. J. Comp. Neurol., 1922, **34**: 461–491.

DE KLEIJN, A., AND VERSTEEGH, C. Some remarks upon the present position of the physiology of the labyrinth. J. Laryng. Otol., 1927, **42**: 649–655.

KLÜVER, H., AND BARRERA, E. A method for the combined staining of cells and fibers in the nervous system. J. Neuropath. & Exp. Neurol., 1953, **12**: 400–403.

KLÜVER, H., AND BUCY, P. C. Preliminary analysis of functions of the temporal lobes in monkeys. A.M.A. Arch. Neurol. and Psychiat., 1939, **42**: 979–1000.

KOELLIKER, A. Nervensystem des Menschen und der Tiere. Vol. 2 of *Handb. der Gewebelehre des Menschen*. Engelmann, Leipzig, 1896.

KOHNSTAMM, O. Der Nucleus salivatorius chordae tympani (nervi intermedii). Anat. Anz., 1902, **21**: 362–363.

KOHNSTAMM, O. Der Nucleus salivatorius inferior und das cranio-viscerale System. Neurol. Centralbl., 1903, **22**: 699.

KUBIK, C., AND ADAMS, R. D. Occlusion of the basilar artery. A clinical and pathological study. Brain, 1946, **69**: 73–121.

KUHLENBECK, H. The derivatives of the thalamus ventralis in the human brain and their relation to the so-called subthalamus. Military Surgeon, 1948, **102**: 433–447.

KUHN, R. A. Functional capacity of the isolated human spinal cord. Brain, 1950, **75**: 1–51.

KUNTZ, A. The development of the sympathetic nervous system in mammals. J. Comp. Neurol., 1910, **20**: 211.

KUNTZ, A. *The autonomic nervous system*. Lea & Febiger, Philadelphia, 3rd Ed., 1945.

KUNTZ, A., AND RICHINS, C. A. Reflex pupillodilator mechanisms. J. Neurophysiol., 1946, **9**: 1–7.

LANDACRE, F. L. The origin of the sensory components of the cranial ganglia. Anat. Rec., 1910, **4**: 71–79.

LANGLEY, J. N. *The autonomic nervous system*. Vol. I. W. Heffer & Sons, Cambridge, 1921.

LANGWORTHY, O. R. A study of the innervation of the tongue musculature with particular reference to the proprioceptive mechanism. J. Comp. Neurol., 1924, **36**: 273–293.

LANGWORTHY, O. R., AND ORTEGA, L. The iris. Medicine, 1943, V. **22**: 287–361.

LANGWORTHY, O. R., AND TAUBER, E. S. The control of the pupillary reaction by the central nervous system: a review. J. Nerv. & Ment. Dis., 1937, **86**: 462–475.

LARSELL, O. The cerebellum: A review and interpretation. Arch. Neurol. & Psychiat., 1937, **38**: 580–607.

LARSELL, O., AND DOW, R. S. Innervation of the human lung. Am. J. Anat., 1933, **52**: 125–146.

LARSELL, O. The nervus terminalis. Ann. Otol., Rhinol. & Laryngol., 1950, **59**: 414–438.

LARSELL, O. The development of the cerebellum in man in relation to its comparative anatomy. J. Comp. Neurol., 1947, **87**: 85–130.

LASHLEY, K. S. *Brain mechanisms and intelligence*. University of Chicago Press, Chicago, 1929.

LASSEK, A. M. The human pyramidal tract. II. A numerical investigation of the Betz cells of the motor area. Arch. Neurol. & Psychiat., 1940, **44**: 718–724.

LASSEK, A. M. The human pyramidal tract. IV. A study of the mature, myelinated fibers of the pyramid. J. Comp. Neurol., 1942, **76**: 217–225.

LASSEK, A. M. The human pyramidal tract VII. A critical review of its origin. J. Nerv. & Ment. Dis., 1944, **9**: 22–28.

LASSEK, A. M. The pyramidal tract: Basic considerations of corticospinal neurons. Assoc. Res. Nerv. & Ment. Dis., 1948, **27**: 106–128.

LASSEK, A. M. The human pyramidal tract. XVIII. An analysis of its pathophysiological status. Brain, 1950, **73**: 95–102.

LASSEK, A. M. The pyramidal tract. Charles C. Thomas, Springfield, Illinois, 1954.

LASSEK, A. M., AND EVANS, J. P. The human pyramidal tract. XII. The effect of hemispherectomies on the fiber components of the pyramids. J. Comp. Neurol., 1945, **83**: 113–119.

LASSEK, A. M., AND RASMUSSEN, G. L. The human pyramidal tract. A fiber and numerical analysis. Arch. Neurol. & Psychiat., 1939, **42**: 872–876.

LAVRENTIEV, B. J. The innervation of the heart. Am. Rev. Soviet Medicine, 1946, **3**: 229–235.

LEVIN, P. M. The efferent fibers of the frontal lobe of the monkey, Macaca mulatta. J. Comp. Neurol., 1936, **63**: 369–419.

LINDSLEY, D. B., SCHREINER, L. H., AND MAGOUN, H. W. An electromyographic study of spasticity. J. Neurophysiol., 1949, **12**: 197–205.

LOEWI, O. Chemical transmission of nerve impulses. Science in Progress, 1945, **4**: 98–119.

LOEWI, O. Über die humorale Übertragbarkeit der Herzenwirkung. Pflüg. Arch. ges. Physiol , 1921, **189**: 239–242.

LORENTE DE Nó, R. Etudes sur le cerveau posterieur. Trav. du Lab. de recherches biol. de l'Universitie de Madrid, 1924, **22**: 51–65.

LORENTE DE Nó. The structure of the cerebral cortex. In Fulton's *Physiology of the nervous system*. 1949, 291–325.

LUCIANI, L. *Il cervelleto: nuovi studi di fisiologia normale e patologica*. Le Monnier, Florence, 1891.

MADONICK, M. J. Statistical control studies in neurology. 8. The cutaneous abdominal reflex. Neurology, 1957, **7**: 459–465.

MAGNUS, R. *Körperstellung*. Julius Springer, Berlin, 1924.

MAGNUS, R., AND DE KLEIJN, A. Die Abhängigkeit des Tonus der Extremitätenmuskeln von der Kopfstellung. Pflüg. Arch., 1912, **145**: 455–548.

MAGOUN, H. W. Descending connections from the hypothalamus. Assoc. Res. Nerv. & Ment. Dis., 1940, **20**: 270–285.

MAGOUN, H. W., ATLAS, D., HARE, W. K., AND RANSON, S. W. The afferent path of the pupillary light reflex in the monkey. Brain, 1936, **59**: 234–249.

MAGOUN, H. W., AND RHINES, R. An inhibitory mechanism in the bulbar reticular formation. J. Neurophysiol., 1946, **9**: 165–171.

MAGOUN, H. W. An ascending reticular activating system in the brain stem. Arch. Neurol. & Psychiat., 1952, **67**: 145–154.

MAGOUN, H. W. *Spasticity, the stretch reflex and extrapyramidal systems*. Charles C. Thomas, Springfield, Illinois, 1948.

MAGOUN, H. W. Caudal and cephalic influences of the brain stem reticular formation. Physiol. Rev., 1950, **30**: 459–474.

MALONE, E. F. Über die Kerne des menschlichen Diencephalon. Aus dem Anhang zu den Abhandlungen der koenigl. preuss. Akademie der Wissenschaften vom Jahre 1910.

MARBURG, O. *Mikroskopisch-topographischer Atlas des menschlichen Zentralnervensystems*. Franz Deuticke, Leipzig, 1927.

MARBURG, O. Das dorsale Längsbündel von Schütz. Arb. a. d. Neur. Inst. d. Wiener Universität, 1931, **33**: 135–164.

MARBURG, O. Modern views regarding anatomy and physiology of the vestibular tracts. Laryngoscope, 1939, **49**: 631–652.

MARBURG, O. Primary endings of the optic nerve in man and in animals. Arch. of Ophthalm., 1942, **28**: 61–78.

MARQUIS, D. G. Phylogenetic interpretation of functions of the visual cortex. Arch. Neurol. & Psychiat., 1935, **33**: 807–815.

MARQUIS, D. G., AND HILGARD, E. R. Conditioned responses to light in monkeys after removal of occipital lobes. Brain, 1937, **60**: 1–13.

MASSAZZA, A. La citoarchitettonica del midollo spinale umano. Riv. di Patol. nerv. e. ment., 1922, **28**: 22.

McCULLOCH, W. S. Cortico-cortical connections. In Bucy's *The precentral motor cortex*. University Illinois Press, 2nd Ed., 1949, pp. 211–242.

McCULLOCH, W. S. The functional organization of the cerebral cortex. Physiol. Rev., 1944, **24**: 390–407.

McCULLOCH, W. S., GRAF, C., AND MAGOUN, H. W. Cortico-bulbo-reticular pathway from area 4s. J. Neurophysiol., 1946, **9**: 127–132.

McLARDY, T. Projection of the centromedian nucleus of the human thalamus. Brain, 1948, **71**: 290–303.

MERRILLEES, N., SUNDERLAND, S., AND HAYHOW, W. Neuromuscular spindles in the extraocular muscles in man. Anat. Rec., 1950, **108**: 23-30.

MERRITT, H. H., AND FREMONT-SMITH, F. *The cerebrospinal fluid*. W. B. Saunders Co., Philadelphia, 1938.

METTLER, F. A. Corticifugal fiber connections of the cortex of Macaca mulatta. J. Comp. Neurol., 1935, **61**: 221–256; 509–542; **62**: 263–291; **63**: 23–47.

METTLER, F. A. Relation between pyramidal and

extrapyramidal function. Assoc. Res. Nerv. & Ment. Dis., 1942, **21**: 150–227.

METTLER, F. A. Fiber connections of the corpus striatum of the monkey and the baboon. J. Comp. Neurol., 1945, **82**: 169–204.

METTLER, F. A. Extracortical connections of the primate frontal cerebral cortex. II. Corticofugal connections. J. Comp. Neurol., 1947, **86**: 119–166.

METTLER, F. A., COOPER, I., LISS, H., CARPENTER, M., AND NOBACK, C. Patterns of vascular failure in the central nervous sytem. J. Neuropath. and Exper. Neurol., 1954, **13**: 528–539.

METTLER, F. A., AND LUBIN, A. J. Termination of the brachium pontis. J. Comp. Neurol., 1942, **77**: 391–397.

MEYER, A., AND BECK, E. Neuropathological problems arising from prefrontal leucotomy. J. Ment. Sci., 1945, **91**: 411–422.

MEYER, A., BECK, E., AND MCLARDY, T. Prefrontal leucotomy: A neuroanatomical report. Brain, 1947, **70**: 18–49.

MEYER, A., AND MCLARDY, T. Posterior cuts in prefrontal leucotomy. A clinico-pathological study. J. Ment. Sci., 1948, **94**: 555–564.

MEYER, M. Study of efferent connections of the frontal lobe in the human brain after leucotomy. Brain, 1949, **72**: 265–296.

MINGAZZINI, G. Medulla oblongata und Brücke. In von Möllendorff's *Handb. d. mikr. Anat. d. Menschen*, Berlin, 1928, **4**: 579–643.

MINGAZZINI, G. Mittelhirn. In von Möllendorff's *Handb. d. mik. Anat. d. Menschen.* Berlin, 1928, **4**: 644–673.

MINCKLER, J., KLEMME, R. M., AND MINCKLER, D The course of efferent fibers from the human premotor cortex. J. Comp. Neurol., 1944, **81**: 259–277.

MINKOWSKI, M. Experimentelle Untersuchungen über die Beziehungen der Grosshirnrinde und der Netzhaut zu den primären optischen Zentren, besonders zum Corpus geniculatum externum. Arb. a. d. Hirnanat. Inst. Zürich, 1913 **7**: 255–362.

MISCOLCZY, D. Über die Endigungsweise der spinocerebellaren Bahnen. Ztschr. Anat. u. Entw., 1931, **96**: 537–542.

MISCOLCZY, D. Die Endigungsweise der olivocerebellaren Faserung. Arch. f. Psychiatrie, 1934, **102**: 197–201.

MORGAN, L. O. The corpus striatum. Arch. Neurol. & Psychiat., 1927, **18**: 495–549.

MORISON, R. S., AND DEMPSEY, E. W. A study of thalamocortical relations. Am. J. Physiol., 1942, **135**: 281–292.

MORUZI, AL., AND LECHINTSKI. Quelques observations au sujet des voies de transmission des sensations gustatives chez l'homme. Rev. Neurol., 1938, **70**: 478–483.

MORUZZI, G. Meccanismi e localizazioni delle azione inibitrici e dinamogene del cervelletto. Arch. di fisiol., 1941, **41**: 183–205.

MORUZZI, G., AND MAGOUN, H. W. Brain stem reticular formation and activation of the EEG. Electroencephalog. & Clin. Neurophysiol., 1949, **1**: 455–473.

MÜLLER, L. R. *Lebensnerven und Lebenstriebe.* Julius Springer, Berlin, 1931.

MURALT, A. V. *Die Signalübermittlung im Nerven.* Verlag Birkhäuser, Basel, 1946.

NACHMANSOHN, D. Chemical mechanism of nerve activity. Ann. N. Y. Acad. Sci., 1946, **47**: 395–428

NAQUIN, H. A. Argyll Robertson pupil following herpes zoster ophthalmicus with remarks on the efferent pupillary pathways. Am. J. Ophth., 1954, **38**: 23–33.

NATHAN, P. W., AND SMITH, M. C. The centripetal pathway from the bladder and urethra within the spinal cord. J. Neurol., Neurosurg. & Psychiat., 1951, **14**: 262–280.

NATHAN, P. W., AND SMITH, M. C. Long descending tracts in man. I. Review of present knowledge. Brain, 1955, Part II, **78**: 248–303.

NATHAN, P. W., AND SMITH, M. C. Spino-cortical fibres in man. J. Neurol., Neurosurg. & Psychiat., 1955, **18**: 181–190.

NAUTA, W. J. H., AND GYGAX, P. A. Silver impregnation of degenerating axon terminals in the central nervous system: (1) technic (2) chemical notes. Stain Tech., 1951, **26**: 5–11.

NAUTA, W. J. H., AND GYGAX, P. A. Silver impregnation of degenerating axons in the central nervous system: A modified technic. Stain Tech., 1954., **29**: 91–93.

NAUTA, W. J. H., AND KUYPERS, H. G. J. M. Reticular formation of the brain. Henry Ford Hospital International Symposium. Little, Brown & Co., Boston, pp. 3–30, 1958.

NIELSEN, J. M. *Agnosia, apraxia, aphasia.* Paul B. Hoeber, Inc., New York, 1946.

NONIDEZ, J. F. Studies on the innervation of the heart. 1. Distribution of the cardiac nerves with special reference to the identification of the sympathetic and parasympathetic postganglionics. Am. J. Anat., 1939, **65**: 361–413.

NULSEN, F. E., BLACK, S. P. W., AND DRAKE, C. G. Inhibition and facilitation of motor activity by the anterior cerebellum. Fed. Proc., 1948, **7**: 86–87.

NYBY, O., AND JANSEN, J. An experimental investigation of the corticopontine projection in Macaca mulatta. Norske Vid.-Akad. Avh. Math.-Naturv. Kl., 1951, **3**: 1–47.

OSTERTAG, B. *Einteilung und Charakteristik der Hirngewächse.* Fischer, Berlin, 1936.

PAPEZ, J. W. Reticulospinal tracts in the cat. J. Comp. Neurol., 1926, **41:** 345–399.

PAPEZ, J. W. Subdivisions of facial nucleus. J. Comp. Neurol., 1927, **43:** 159–191.

PAPEZ, J. W. A proposed mechanism of emotion. Arch. Neurol. & Psychiat., 1937, **38:** 725–743.

PAPEZ, J. W. Reciprocal connections of the striatum and pallium in the brain of Pithecus (Macacus) rhesus. J. Comp. Neurol., 1938, **69:** 329–349.

PAPEZ, J. W. A summary of fiber connections of the basal ganglia with each other and with other portions of the brain. Assoc. Res. Nerv. & Ment. Dis., 1940, **21:** 21–68.

PAPEZ, J. W., AND STOTLER, W. A. Connections of the red nucleus. Arch. Neurol. & Psychiat., 1940, **44:** 776–791.

PARKER, G. H. *The elementary nervous system.* J. B. Lippincott Co., Philadelphia, 1919.

PARTRIDGE, M. *Pre-frontal leucotomy: A survey of* **300** *cases personally followed over 1½–3 years.* Oxford, Blackwell, 1950.

PATTON, H. D., RUCH, T. C., AND WALKER, A. E. Experimental hypogeusia from Horsley-Clarke lesions of the thalamus in Macaca mulatta. J. Neurophysiol., 1944, **7:** 171–184.

PEARSON, A. A. The spinal accessory nerve in human embryos. J. Comp. Neurol., 1938, **68:** 243–266.

PEARSON, A. A. The hypoglossal nerve in human embryos. J. Comp. Neurol., 1939, **71:** 21–39.

PEARSON, A. A. Further observations on the intramedullary sensory type neurons along the hypoglossal nerve. J. Comp. Neurol., 1945, **82:** 93–100.

PEARSON, A. A. Further observations on the mesencephalic root of the trigeminal nerve. J. Comp. Neurol., 1949, **91:** 147–194.

PEARSON, A. A. Role of gelatinous substance of spinal cord in conduction of pain. Arch. Neurol. & Psychiat., 1952, **68:** 515–529.

PENFIELD, W. G. Alterations of the Golgi apparatus in nerve cells. Brain, 1920, **43:** 290–305.

PENFIELD, W. G. *Cytology and cellular pathology of the nervous system.* Paul B. Hoeber, Inc., New York, 1932.

PENFIELD, W. G. Neuroglia, normal and pathological. In Penfield's *Cytology & cellular pathology of the nervous system.* New York, 1932, **2:** 423–479.

PENFIELD, W. G. Memory mechanisms. Arch. Neurol. & Psychiat., 1952, **67:** 178–198.

PENFIELD, W. G. A secondary somatic sensory area in the cerebral cortex of man. Trans. Am. Neurol. Assoc., 1949, **74:** 184–186.

PENFIELD, W. G., AND BOLDREY, E. Somatic motor and sensory representation in the cerebral cortex of man as studied by electrical stimulation. Brain, 1937, **60:** 389–443.

PENFIELD, W. G., AND EVANS, J. Functional defects produced by cerebral lobectomies. Assoc. Res. Nerv. & Ment. Dis., 1932, **13:** 352–377.

PENFIELD, W., AND JASPER, H. Epilepsy and the functional anatomy of the human brain. Little, Brown & Co., Boston, pp. 145–147; 412–467, 1954.

PENFIELD, W. G., AND MCNAUGHTON, F. Dural headache and innervation of the dura mater. Arch. Neurol. & Psychiat., 1940, **44:** 43–75.

PENFIELD, W. G., AND RASMUSSEN, T. *The cerebral cortex of man.* The Macmillan Co., New York, 1950.

PFEIL, E. T. Hemiballismus: hemichorea following a lesion of the corpus Luysi. J. Nerv. & Ment. Dis., 1952, **116:** 36–47.

PICK, J., AND SHEEHAN, D. Sympathetic rami in man. J. Anat., 1946, **80:** 12–20.

PINES, I. L. Über die Innervation der Hypophysis cerebri. II. Mitteilung: Über die Innervation des Mittel- und Hinterlappens der Hypophyse. Ztschr. f. d. ges. Neurol. u. Psychiat., 1925, **100:** 123.

PITTS, R. F. Organization of the respiratory center. Physiol. Rev., 1946, **26:** 609–630.

POLIAK, S. *The main afferent fiber systems of the cerebral cortex in primates.* University California Publication in Anat., 1932.

POPPI, U. Über die Fasersysteme der Substantia nigra. Arb. a. d. Neurol. Inst. Wien. 1927, **29:** 8–49.

POTTS, T. K. The main peripheral connections of the human sympathetic nervous system. J. Anat., 1924–5, **59:** 129–135.

PUTNAM, T. J. Studies on the central visual system. IV. The details of the organization of the geniculostriate system of man. Arch. Neurol. & Psychiat., 1926, **16:** 683–707.

PUTNAM, T. J. The cerebral circulation. J. Neurol. & Psychopath., 1937, **17:** 193–212.

PUTNAM, T. J., AND LIEBMAN, S. Cortical representation of the macula lutea with special reference to the theory of bilateral representation. Arch. Ophth., 1942, **28:** 415–443.

QUENSEL, W. Über die Faserspezifität im sensiblen Hautnerven. Pflüger's Arch., 1944, **248:** 1–20.

RADEMAKER, G. G. J. *Die Bedeutung der roten Kerne und des übrigen Mittelhirns für Muskeltonus, Körperstellung, und Labyrinth-reflexe.* Julius Springer, Berlin, 1926.

RAMÓN Y CAJAL, S. *Studien über die Hirnrinde des Menschen.* 5 Hefte, J. A. Barth, Leipzig, 1900–1906.

RAMÓN Y CAJAL, S. *Degeneration and regeneration of the nervous system.* Oxford University Press, London, 1928.

RAMÓN Y CAJAL, S. Die Neuronenlehre. In Bumke and Foerster's *Handb. d. Neurologie,* Berlin, 1935, **1:** 887–994.

RANSON, S. W. The structure of the spinal ganglia and of the spinal nerves. J. Comp. Neurol., 1912, **22:** 159–175.

RANSON, S. W. The course within the spinal cord of the non-medullated fibers of the dorsal roots: a study of Lissauer's tract in the cat. J. Comp. Neurol., 1913, **23:** 259–281.

RANSON, S. W. Some functions of the hypothalamus. In *The Harvey Lectures,* Baltimore, 1936–1937, Series 32, 92–121.

RANSON, S. W., AND BILLINGSLEY, P. R. The conduction of painful afferent impulses in the spinal nerves. Am. J. Physiol., 1916, **40:** 571–584.

RANSON, S. W., AND BILLINGSLEY, P. R. The superior cervical ganglion and the cervical portion of the sympathetic trunk. J. Comp. Neurol., 1918, **29:** 313–358.

RANSON, S. W., AND DAVENPORT, H. K. Sensory unmyelinated fibers in the spinal nerves. Am. J. Anat., 1931, **48:** 331–353.

RANSON, S. W., DROEGMUELLER, W. H., DAVENPORT, H. K., AND FISHER, C. Number, size, and myelination of the sensory fibers in the cerebrospinal nerves. Assoc. Res. Nerv. & Ment. Dis., 1935, **15:** 3–34.

RANSON, S. W., AND MAGOUN, H. W. The central path of the pupillo-constrictor reflex in response to light. Arch. Neurol. & Psychiat., 1933, **30:** 1193–1204.

RANSON, S. W., RANSON, S. W., JR., AND RANSON, M. Fiber connections of corpus striatum as seen in Marchi preparations. Arch. Neurol. & Psychiat., 1941, **46:** 230–249.

RANSON, S. W., AND RANSON, S. W., JR. Efferent fibers of the striatum. Assoc. Res. Nerv. & Ment. Dis., 1942, **21:** 69–76.

RASMUSSEN, A. T. Secondary vestibular tracts in the cat. J. Comp. Neurol., 1932, **54:** 43–159.

RASMUSSEN, A. T. *The principal nervous pathways.* The Macmillan Co., New York, 1952.

RASMUSSEN, A. T., AND PENFIELD, W. Movement of head and eyes from stimulation of human frontal cortex. Assoc. Res. Nerv. & Ment. Dis., 1948, **27:** 346–361.

RASMUSSEN, A. T., AND PEYTON, W. T. The course and termination of the medial lemniscus in man. J. Comp. Neurol., 1948, **88:** 411–424.

DE RÉNYI, G. S. The structure of cells in tissues as revealed by microdissection. J. Comp. Neurol., 1929, **48:** 441–457.

RHINES, R., AND MAGOUN, H. W. Brain stem facilitation of cortical motor response. J. Neurophysiol., 1946, **9:** 219–229.

RIDDOCH, G. The reflex functions of the completely divided spinal cord in man, compared with those associated with less severe lesions. Brain, 1917, **40:** 264–402.

VAN RIJNBERK, G. Das Kleinhirn. Ergebn. d. Physiol., 1931, **31:** 592–843.

VAN RIJNBERK, G. Les dernières recherches relatives à la question de la localisation dans le cervelet: anatomie, physiologie, clinique. Arch. néerl. de physiol., 1926, **10:** 183–301.

RILEY, H. A. The mammalian cerebellum. A comparative study of the arbor vitae and folial pattern. Assoc. Res. Nerv. & Ment. Dis., 1929, **6:** 37–192.

RILEY, H. A. The central nervous system control of the ocular movements and the disturbances of this mechanism. Arch. of Ophth., 1930, **4:** 640–661, 885–910.

ROGERS, F. T. Studies of the brain stem. VI. An experimental study of the corpus striatum of the pigeon as related to various instinctive types of behavior. J. Comp. Neurol., 1922, **35:** 21–59.

ROSE, M. Cytoarchitektonik und Myeloarchitektonik der Grosshirnrinde. In Bumke and Foerster's *Handb. d. Neurologie.* 1935, **1:** 588–778.

ROSE, J. E., AND WOOLSEY, C. N. Organization of the mammalian thalamus and its relationships to the cerebral cortex. Electroencephalog. & Clin. Neurophysiol., 1949, **1:** 391–403.

ROSENBLUETH, A. *The transmission of nerve impulses at neuroeffector junctions and peripheral synapses.* Technology Press. John Wiley & Sons, Inc., New York, 1950.

RUNDLES, R. W., AND PAPEZ, J. W. Connections between the striatum and the substantia nigra in a human brain. Arch. Neurol. & Psychiat., 1937, **38:** 550–563.

RUSSELL, G. V. The dorsal trigemino-thalamic tract in the cat reconsidered as a lateral reticulo-thalamic system of connections. J. Comp. Neurol., 1954, **101:** 237–263.

RUSSELL, G. V. A schematic presentation of thalamic morphology and connections. Texas

Reports on Biology & Medicine, 1955, **13:** 989–992.

Russell, W. R. Functions of the frontal lobes. Lancet, 1948, **254:** 356–360.

Rylander, G. Personality analysis before and after frontal lobotomy. Assoc. Res. Nerv. and Ment. Dis., 1948, **27:** 691–705.

Sachs, E., Jr., Brendler, S. J., and Fulton, J. F. The orbital gyri. Brain, 1949, **72:** 227–240.

Saito, M. Experimentelle Untersuchungen über die inneren Verbindungen der Kleinhirnrinde und deren Beziehungen zu Pons und Medulla oblongata. Arb. a. d. Neurol. Inst. Wien. 1922, **23:** 74–106; 1923, **24:** 77–84.

Sand, R. Beitrag zur Kenntnis der corticobulbären und corticopontinen Pyramidenfasern beim Menschen. Arb. a. d. Neurol. Inst. Wien., 1903, **10:** 185–222.

De Saussure, R. L. Lateral spinothalamic tractotomy for relief of pain in cauda equina injury. Arch. Neurol. & Psychiat., 1950, **64:** 708–714.

Scarff, J. E. Primary cortical centers for movements of upper and lower limbs in man. Arch. Neurol. & Psychiat., 1940, **44:** 243–299.

Scarff, J. E. Unilateral prefrontal lobotomy for the relief of intractable pain and termination of the narcotic addiction. Surg., Gynec., Obstet., 1949, **89:** 385–392.

Scharrer, E., and Scharrer, B. Neurosecretion. Physiol. Rev., 1945, **25:** 171–181.

Scheibel, M. E., and Scheibel, A. B. Structural substrates for integrative patterns in the brain stem reticular core. Reticular Formation of the Brain, Henry Ford Hospital International Symposium. Little, Brown & Co., Boston, 1958, pp. 31–55.

Schlesinger, B. Venous drainage of the brain, with special reference to Galenic system. Brain, 1939, **62:** 274–291.

Schmitt, F. O., Bear, R. S., and Palmer, K. J. X-ray diffraction studies on the structure of the nerve myelin sheath. J. Cell. Comp. Physiol., 1941, **18:** 31–42.

Schneider, R. Ein Beitrag zur Ontogenese der Basalganglien des Menschen. Anat. Nachr., 1950, **1:** 116–137.

Schreiner, L. H., Lindsley, D. B., and Magoun, H. W. Role of brain stem facilitatory systems in the maintenance of spasticity. J. Neurophysiol., 1949, **12:** 207–216.

Scott, D., and Clemente, C. D. Mechanism of spinal cord regeneration in the cat. Fed. Proc., 1952, **11:** 143–144.

Schulte, H. von W., and Tilney, F. Development of the neuraxis in the domestic cat to the stage of twenty-one somites. Ann. New York Acad. Sci., 1915, **24:** 319–346.

Schwartz, H. G. Reflex activity within the sympathetic nervous system. Am. J. Physiol., 1934, **109:** 593–604.

Schwartz, H. G., and O'Leary, J. L. Section of spinothalamic tract in medulla. Surgery, 1941, **9:** 183–193.

Schwartz, H. G., and Weddell, G. Observations on the pathways transmitting the sensation of taste. Brain, 1938, **61:** 99–115.

Schwartz, Ph., und Fink, L. Morphologie und Entstehung der geburtstraumatischen Blutungen im Gehirn und Schädel des Neugeborenen. Zeitschr. f. Kinderheilkunde, 1926, **40:** 427–474.

Seddon, H. J. Three types of nerve injury. Brain, 1943, **66:** 237–288.

Sheehan, D. The autonomic nervous system. Ann. Rev. Physiol., 1941, **3:** 399–448.

Sheehan, D. Spinal autonomic outflows in man and monkey. J. Comp. Neurol., 1941, **75:** 341–370.

Shellshear, J. L. A contribution to our knowledge of the arterial supply of cerebral cortex in man. Brain, 1927, **50:** 236–253.

Sheps, J. G. The nuclear configuration and cortical connections of the human thalamus. J. Comp. Neurol., 1945, **83:** 1–56.

Sherrington, C. S. Experiments in examination of the peripheral distribution of the fibers of the posterior roots of some spinal nerves. Philos. Trans., 1893, **184B:** 641–763.

Sherrington, C. S. *The integrative action of the nervous system.* Scribner's Sons, N. Y., 1906; new ed., Yale University Press, New Haven, 1947.

Sherrington, C. S. *The brain and its mechanisms.* Cambridge University Press. Cambridge, 1933.

Shmidt, E. V. The pyramidal syndrome. Am. Rev. Soviet Medicine, 1946, **4:** 30–36.

Sinclair, D. C., Weddell, G., and Feindel, W. H. Referred pain and associated phenomena. Brain, 1948, **71:** 184–211.

Sjöqvist, O. Studies on pain conduction in the trigeminal nerve: contribution to surgical treatment of facial pain. Acta Psychiat. et Neurol., Suppl., 1938, **17:** 1–139.

Smith, M. C. The use of Marchi staining in the later stages of human tract degeneration. J. Neurol., Neurosurg. & Psychiat., 1951, **14:** 222–225.

Smith, M. C. The recognition and prevention of artefacts of the Marchi method. J. Neurol., Neurosurg. & Psychiat., 1956, **19:** 74–83.

Smith, M. C. The anatomy of the spino-cerebellar fibers in man. I. The course of the fibers in the spinal cord and brain stem. J. Comp. Neurol., 1957, **108:** 285–352.

SMITH, W. K. The functional significance of the rostral cingular cortex as revealed by its responses to electrical stimulation. J. Neurophysiol., 1945, **8:** 241–255.

SMYTH, G. E. The systemization and central connections of the spinal tract and nucleus of the trigeminal nerve. Brain, 1939, **62:** 41–87.

SNIDER, R. S. Recent contributions to the anatomy and physiology of the cerebellum. Arch. Neurol. & Psychiat., 1950, **64:** 196–219.

SNIDER, R. S., AND MAGOUN, H. W. Facilitation produced by cerebellar stimulation. J. Neurophysiol., 1949, **12:** 335–345.

SNIDER, R. S., MCCULLOCH, W. S., AND MAGOUN, H. W. A cerebello-bulbo-reticular pathway for suppression. J. Neurophysiol., 1949, **12:** 325–334.

SNIDER, R. S., AND ELDRED, E. Cerebro-cerebellar relationships in the monkey. J. Neurophysiol., 1952, **15:** 27–40.

SNIDER, R. S., AND STOWELL, A. Receiving areas of the tactile, auditory and visual systems in the cerebellum. J. Neurophysiol., 1944, **7:** 331–357.

SPATZ, H. Anatomie des Mittelhirns. In Bumke and Foerster's *Handb. der Neurologie*, 1935, **1:** 474–540.

SPEIDEL, C. C. Adjustments of nerve endings. The Harvey Lectures, Science Press, Lancaster, Pa. 1940, **36:** 126–158.

SPIEGEL, E. A. Labyrinth and cortex. The electroencephalogram of the cortex in the stimulation of the labyrinth. Arch. Neurol. & Psychiat., 1934, **31:** 469–482.

SPIEGEL, E. A., AND HUNSICKER, W. C., JR. The conduction of cortical impulses to the autonomic system. J. Nerv. & Ment. Dis., 1936, **83:** 252–274.

SPIEGEL, E. A., AND WYCIS, H. T. Ansotomy in paralysis agitans. A.M.A. Arch. of Neurol. & Psychiat., 1954, **71:** 598–614.

SPRAGUE, J. M., AND CHAMBERS, W. W. Control of posture by reticular formation and cerebellum in the intact, anesthetized, unanesthetized and in the decerebrated cat. Am. J. Physiol., 1954, **176:** 52–64.

STARZL, T. E., AND MAGOUN, H. W. Organization of the diffuse thalamic projection system. J. Neurophysiol., 1951, **14:** 133–146.

STARZL, T. E., TAYLOR, C. W., AND MAGOUN, H. W. Collateral afferent excitation of the reticular formation of the brain stem. J. Neurophysiol., 1951, **14:** 479–496.

STENGEL, E. Über den Ursprung der Nervenfasern der Neurohypophyse im Zwischenhirn. Arb. a. d. Neurol. Inst. Wien., 1926, **28:** 25–37.

STERN, K. Note on the nucleus ruber magnocellularis and its efferent pathway in man. Brain, 1936, **61:** 284–289.

STERN, K. Der Zellaufbau des menschlichen Mittelhirns. Ztschr. f. d. ges. Neurol. u. Psychiat., 1936, **154:** 521–598.

STERN, K. Thalamo-frontal projection in man. J. Anat., 1942, **76:** 302–307.

STÖHR, P., JR. Das peripherische Nervensystem. In von Möllendorff's *Handb. d. mik. Anat. d. Menschen.* Berlin, 1928, **4:** 202–447.

STOPFORD, J. S. B. The arteries of the pons and medulla oblongata. J. Anat. & Physiol., 1915, **50:** 131–164, 1916, **50:** 255–280.

STOPFORD, J. S. B. *Sensation and the sensory pathway.* Longmans, Green & Co., London, 1930.

STOOKEY, B. *Surgical and mechanical treatment of peripheral nerves.* W. B. Saunders Co., Philadelphia, 1922.

STOOKEY, B., AND SCARFF, J. Injuries of peripheral nerves. In *Neurosurgery and thoracic surgery.* W. B. Saunders Co., Philadelphia, 1943, pp. 81–184.

STOTLER, W. A., AND MCMAHON, R. A. The innervation and structure of the conductive system of the human heart. J. Comp. Neurol., 1947, **87:** 57–83.

STRAUS, W. L., JR., AND HOWELL, A. B. The spinal accessory nerve and its musculature. Quart. Rev. Biol., 1936, **11:** 387–405.

STRONG, O. S. The cranial nerves of amphibia: a contribution to the morphology of the vertebrate nervous system. J. Morph., 1895, **10:** 101–230.

STRONG, O. S. A case of unilateral cerebellar agenesia. J. Comp. Neurol., 1915, **25:** 361–391.

STRONG, O. S. Some observations on the course of the fibers from Clarke's column in the normal human spinal cord. Bull. Neurol. Inst. New York, 1936, **5:** 378–386.

SUGAR, O., AND GERARD, R. W. Spinal cord regeneration in the rat. J. Neurophysiol., 1940, **3:** 1–19.

SUH, T. H., AND ALEXANDER, L. Vascular system of the human spinal cord. Arch. Neurol. & Psychiat., 1939, **41:** 659–677.

SUNDERLAND, S. Course and rate of regeneration of motor fibers following lesions of the radial nerve. Arch. Neurol. & Psychiat., 1946, **56:** 133–157.

SUNDERLAND, S. A preliminary note on the presence of neuro-muscular spindles in the extrinsic ocular muscles in man. Anat. Rec. 1949, **103:** 561–562.

SUNDERLAND, S. Capacity of reinnervated muscles to function efficiently after prolonged denervation. Arch. Neurol. & Psychiat., 1950, **64:** 755–771.

SUNDERLAND, S. Factors influencing the course of regeneration and the quality of the recovery after nerve suture. Brain, 1952, **75:** 19–54.

SUNDERLAND, S., AND BRADLEY, K. C. Endoneurial tube shrinkage in the distal segment of a severed nerve. J. Comp. Neurol., 1950, **93:** 411–420.

SZENTAGOTHAI, J. Anatomical considerations of monosynaptic reflex arcs. J. Neurophysiol., 1948, **11:** 445–454.

SZENTAGOTHAI, J. The representation of facial and scalp muscles in the facial nucleus. J. Comp. Neurol., 1948, **88:** 207–220.

SZENTAGOTHAI, J. Functional representation in the motor trigeminal nucleus. J. Comp. Neurol., 1949, **90:** 111–120.

TAIT, J. Is all hearing cochlear? Ann. Otol. Rhinol. Laryngol., 1932, **41:** 681-704.

TARKHAN, A. A., AND ABD EL-MALEK, S. On the presence of sensory nerve cells on the hypoglossal nerve. J. Comp. Neurol., 1950, **93:** 219–228.

TERZIAN, H., AND ORE, G. D. Syndrome of Klüver and Bucy. Reproduced in man by bilateral removal of the temporal lobes. Neurol., 1955, **5:** 373–380.

TILNEY, F., AND RILEY, H. A. *The form and function of the central nervous system.* Paul B. Hoeber, Inc., New York, 1938.

TOENNIES, J. F. Reflex discharges over dorsal roots. J. Neurophysiol., 1938, **1:** 378–390.

TONCRAY, J. E., AND KRIEG, W. J. S. The nuclei of the human thalamus: A comparative approach. J. Comp. Neurol., 1946, **85:** 421–459.

TORVIK, A. The ascending fibers from the main trigeminal sensory nucleus. An experimental study in the cat. Am. J. Anat., 1957, **100:** 1–15.

TOWER, S. S. The pyramidal tract. In Bucy's *The precentral motor cortex.* University Illinois Press, 1949, pp. 149–172.

TOZER, F. M., AND SHERRINGTON, C. S. Receptors and afferents of the third, fourth and sixth cranial nerves. Proc. Roy. Soc., London, 1910, Ser. B, **82:** 450–457.

TRUEX, R. C. Morphological alterations in the gasserian ganglion cells and their association with senescence in man. Am. J. Path., 1940, **16:** 255–268.

TRUEX, R. C., SCOTT, J. C., LONG, D. M., AND SMYTHE, M. Q. Effect of vagus nerves on heart rate of young dogs: An anatomic-physiologic study. Anat. Rec., 1955, **123:** 201–226.

VAN BEUSEKOM, G. T. Fibre analysis of the anterior and lateral funiculi of the cord in the cat. 1955, Eduard Ijdo N.V.-Leiden, pp. 1–136.

VAN BUSKIRK, C. The seventh nerve complex. J. Comp. Neurol., 1945, **82:** 303–333.

VAN HARREVELD, A. Re-innervation of paretic muscle by collateral branching of the residual motor innervation. J. Comp. Neurol., 1952, **97:** 385–405.

VERHAART, W. J. C. Fiber analysis of the basal ganglia. J. Comp. Neurol., 1950, **93:** 425–440.

VERHAART, W. J. C. The central tegmental tract. J. Comp. Neurol., 1949, **90:** 173–192.

VERHAART, W. J. C., AND KENNARD, M. A. Corticofugal degeneration following thermocoagulation of areas 4, 6, and 4–s in Macaca mulatta. J. Anat., 1940, **74:** 239–254.

VIZOSO, A. D., AND YOUNG, J. Z. Internode length and fibre diameter in developing and regenerating nerves. J. Anat., 1948, **82:** 110–134.

VOGT, C., AND VOGT, O. Ergebnisse unserer Hirnforschung. J. f. Psychol. u. Neurol., 1919, **25:** 273–462.

VOGT, C., AND VOGT, O. Zur Lehre der Erkrankungen der striären Systeme. J. f. Psychol. u. Neurol., 1919–1920, **25:** 627–846.

VONDERAHE, A. R. The anatomic basis of emotion. Ohio State Med. J., 1943, **39:** 325–330.

WALKER, A. E. The thalamus of the chimpanzee. IV. Thalamic projections to the cerebral cortex. J. Anat., 1938, **73:** 37–93.

WALKER, A. E. *The primate thalamus.* University of Chicago Press, Chicago, 1938.

WALSHE, F. M. R. The mode of representation of movement in the motor cortex. Brain, 1943, **66:** 104–139.

WALSHE, F. M. R. On the "syndrome of the premotor cortex". Brain, 1935, **58:** 49–80.

WALSHE, F. M. R. The anatomy and physiology of cutaneous sensibility: a critical review. Brain, 1942, **65:** 48–112.

WALSHE, F. M. R. The giant cells of Betz, the motor cortex and the pyramidal tract: A critical review. Brain, 1942, **65:** 409–461.

WALSHE, F. M. R. *On the contribution of clinical study to the cerebral motor cortex.* E. & S. Livingstone, Edinburgh, 1947.

WANG, S. C. Localization of the salivatory center in the medulla of the cat. J. Neurophysiol., 1943. **6:** 195–202.

WANG, S. C., AND BORISON, H. L. The vomiting center. Arch. Neurol. & Psychiat., 1950. **63:** 928–941.

WARD, A. A., JR. The cingular gyrus: area 24. J. Neurophysiol., 1948, **11:** 13–23.

WARD, A. A., JR. The anterior cingular gyrus and personality. Res. Publ. Assoc. Res. Nerv. & Ment. Dis., 1948, **27:** 438–445.

WARD, A. A., JR., AND MCCULLOCH, W. S. The projection of the frontal lobe on the hypothalamus. J. Neurophysiol., 1947, **10:** 309–314.

WARD, A. A. Jr., AND REED, H. L. Mechanism of pupillary dilatation elicited by cortical stimulation. J. Neurophysiol., 1946, **9**· 329–335.

WARRINGTON, W. B., AND GRIFFITH, F. On the cells of the spinal ganglia and on the relationship of their histological structure to axonal distribution. Brain, 1904, **27:** 297–326.

WARWICK, R. A study of retrograde degeneration in the oculomotor nucleus of the rhesus monkey, with a note on a method of recording its distribution. Brain, 1950, **73:** 532–543.

WATTS, J., AND FREEMAN, W. Frontal lobotomy in the treatment of unbearable pain. Assoc. Res. Nerv. & Ment. Dis., 1948, **27:** 714–722.

WEDDELL, G. The pattern of cutaneous innervation in relation to cutaneous sensibility. J. Anat., 1941, **75:** 346–367.

WATERSTON, D. Observations on sensation. The sensory functions of the skin for touch and pain. J. Physiol., 1933, **77:** 251–275.

WEED, L. H. The cerebrospinal fluid. Physiol. Rev., 1922. **2:** 171–203.

WEED, L. H. The meninges, with special reference to the cell coverings of the leptomeninges. In Penfield's *Cytology & cellular pathology of the nervous system.* New York, 1932, **2:** 613–634.

WEIL, A., AND LASSEK, A. The quantitative distribution of the pyramidal tract in man. Arch. Neurol. & Psychiat., 1929, **22:** 495–510.

WEISENBURG, T. H. A study of aphasia. Arch. Neurol. & Psychiat., 1934, **31:** 1–33.

WEISS, P., AND WANG, H. Neurofibrils in living ganglion cells of the chick, cultivated in vitro. Anat. Rec., 1936, **67:** 105–117.

WEISS, P., AND HISCOE, H. B. Experiments on the mechanism of nerve growth. J. Exper. Zoöl., 1948, **107:** 315–396.

WEISSCHEDEL, E. Die zentrale Haubenbahn und ihre Bedeutung für das extrapyramidal-motorische System. Arch. f. Psychiat., 1938, **107:** 443–579.

WESTBROOK, W. H. L., AND TOWER, S. S. An analysis of the problem of emergent fibers in posterior spinal roots, dealing with the rate of growth and extraneous fibers into the roots after ganglionectomy. J. Comp. Neurol., 1940, **72:** 383–398.

WHITE, J. C., AND SMITHWICK, R. H. *The autonomic nervous system.* The Macmillan Co., New York, third ed., 1952.

WHITE, J., SWEET, W., HAWKINS, R., AND NILGES, R. Anterolateral cordotomy: results, complications and causes of failure. Brain, 1950, **73:** 346–367.

WILSON, S. A. K. *Modern problems in neurology.* Edward Arnold & Co., London, 1928.

WILSON, W. C., AND MAGOUN, H. W. The functional significance of the inferior olive in the cat. J. Comp. Neurol., 1945, **83:** 69–77.

WINDLE, W. F. Non-bifurcating nerve fibers of the trigeminal nerve. J. Comp. Neurol., 1926, **40:** 229–240.

WINDLE, W. F. *Physiology of the fetus.* W. B. Saunders Co., Philadelphia, 1940.

WINDLE, W. F. (Ed.) Regeneration in the central nervous system. Charles C. Thomas, Springfield, Illinois, 311 pp., 1955.

WINDLE, W. F., AND CHAMBERS, W. W. Regeneration in the spinal cord of the cat and dog. J. Comp. Neurol., 1950, **93:** 241–257.

WINDLE, W. F., AND FITZGERALD, J. E. Development of the human mesencephalic trigeminal root and related neurons. J. Comp. Neurol., 1942, **77:** 597–608.

WOLF, G. A., JR. The ratio of preganglionic neurons to postganglionic neurons in the visceral nervous system. J. Comp. Neurol., 1941, **75:** 235–243.

WOODBURNE, R. T., CROSBY, E. C., AND MCCOTTER, R. E. The mammalian midbrain and isthmus regions. Part II. The fiber connections. J. Comp. Neurol., 1946, **85:** 67–92.

WOOLLARD, H. H. Observations on the terminations of cutaneous nerves. Brain, 1935, **58:** 352–367.

WORLEY, L. G. The Golgi apparatus. An interpretation of its structure and significance. Ann. N. Y. Acad. Sci., 1946, **47:** 1–56.

YAKOVLEV, P. J., HAMLIN, H., AND SWEET, W. H. Frontal lobotomy. J. Neuropath. & Exper. Neurol., 1950, **9:** 250–285.

YOUNG, J. Z. The functional repair of nervous tissue. Physiol. Rev., 1942, **22:** 318–374.

YOUNG, J. Z. Factors influencing the regeneration in nerves. Adv. in Surg., 1949, **1:** 165–220.

YOUNG, J. Z., AND ZUCKERMAN, S. The course of fibers in the dorsal nerve roots of Macaca mulatta, the rhesus monkey. J. Anat., 1937, **71:** 447–457.

YNTEMA, C. L., AND HAMMOND, W. S. The origin

of intrinsic ganglia of trunk viscera from vagal neural crest in the chick embryo. J. Comp. Neurol., 1954, **101:** 515–542.

ZANDER, E., AND WEDDELL, G. Observations on the innervation of the cornea. J. Anat., 1951, **85:** 68–99.

ZIMMERMANN, A. A. The diencephalon: The neurological work and concepts of W. R. Hess. J. Neuropath. & Clin. Neurol., 1951, **1:** 26–36.

ZÜLCH, K. J. Mangeldurchblutung an der Grenzzone zweier Gefässgebiete als Ursache bisher ungeklärter Rückenmarksschädigungen. Deutsche Ztschr. Nervenh. 1954, **172:** 81–101, (Pp. 29, 31, 57).

Index